CHAMOIS

HARMSWORTH NATURAL HISTORY

A COMPLETE SURVEY OF THE ANIMAL KINGDOM

WITH PHOTOGRAPHS AND SKETCHES FROM LIFE,
AND AN UNRIVALLED SERIES OF COLOUR PLATES

CHIEF CONTRIBUTORS

RICHARD LYDEKKER, F.R.S.
SIR HARRY JOHNSTON
PROFESSOR J. R. AINSWORTH-DAVIS, M.A.

SECOND VOLUME

PUBLISHED AT
CARMELITE HOUSE, LONDON, E.C.
1910

ORDER VI. UNGULATA—CONTINUED
TAHR

THE Himalayan goat known as the tahr (*Hemitragus jemlaicus*), an allied species from Arabia, and a third from the Nilgiri Hills of Southern India differ so markedly from the true goats that they are classed in a genus by themselves. They are devoid of a beard, and also distinguished by having the extremity of the muzzle naked. The skull is longer and narrower than in the true goats, with the sockets of the eyes less prominent ; and the horns are relatively short, and little smaller in the does than in the bucks. In form the horns are compressed and angulated in front, with their bases quite close together ; and they curve backwards from the plane of the forehead. None of the species has glands in the fore feet.

The Himalayan tahr is distinguished by the form of the black horns, which have their lateral surfaces flattened and shelving regularly up to the sharp and beaded keel on the inner front border ; they diverge regularly from their bases, at the same time curving sharply backwards, with a slight inward inclination at the tips. On the head the hair is short, but it becomes longer on the body, and in old bucks is so lengthened on the neck, chest, and shoulders as to form a long, shaggy mane reaching below the knees.

There is considerable variation in colour, but the tint of the hair is dark or reddish brown, old males being generally very dark, although pale-coloured individuals of both sexes are not infrequently met with. The face and the front of the limbs are very dark, in some instances almost black, and old males have an indistinct dark line down the middle of the back. In young animals the colour is uniform greyish brown, and kids are reported to be very pale-coloured. The female tahr differs from all other goats, as well as from sheep, in having four teats.

In height the male tahr varies from 3 feet to 3 feet 4 inches at the shoulder, the does being much smaller. Good specimens of the horns vary from 12 to 15 inches in length, measured along the curve, but a pair has been recorded with a length of 16½ and a basal girth of 10½ inches. In the does the length of the horns is seldom more than 10 inches.

Tahr are found throughout the higher forest regions of the Himalaya, from the Pir Panjal range on the outer side of the valley of Kashmir in the north-west to Sikhim in the south-east, but are unknown in the arid Tibetan districts of the interior. Tahr is the native name by which they are known in the Western Himalaya, but in Kashmir they are termed kras ; while in Nepal they go by the name of jharal. A smaller species (*Hemitragus jayakeri*), with only two teats, inhabits Arabia ; and remains of a fossil tahr occur in the rocks of the Siwalik Hills at the foot of the Himalaya.

In spite of the small size of its horns, the tahr is decidedly a fine-looking animal, and is plentifully distributed over many parts of the Himalaya. Although in the Pir Panjal range tahr are often found on the same ground as markhor, in other districts they frequent almost worse ground, and I have known many instances where specimens have been completely smashed by falling down precipices after they were killed. After mentioning that the tahr resembles the markhor in its forest-loving habits, General A. A. Kinloch observes that "although it sometimes resorts to the rocky summits of the hills, it generally prefers the steep slopes which are more or less clothed with trees. Female tahr may frequently be found on open ground, but old males hide a great deal in the thickest jungle, lying during the heat of the day under the shade of trees or overhanging rocks. Nearly perpendicular hills with dangerous precipices, where the forest consists of oak and ringal-cane, are the favourite haunts of the old tahr, who climb with ease over ground where one

HEAD OF THE MUSK-OX

would hardly imagine that any animal could find a footing."

Old male tahr generally herd separately from the females during the summer, but about October the two sexes come together ; and it is believed that the kids are born in June and July, only a single one being produced at a birth.

The Nilgiri tahr, or wild goat (*H. hylocrius*)—the warri-atu of the Tamils, and the Nilgiri ibex of English sportsmen—is a southern species inhabiting the Nilgiri and Anamalai Hills, and the Western Ghats as far south as Cape Comorin. It is found at elevations of from 4,000 to 6,000 feet above the sea. but occasionally somewhat lower down. This species may be distinguished from the Himalayan tahr by the form of the horns, and the absence of the shaggy mane which forms such a conspicuous feature of the fore quarters of the males of the latter. Instead of being flattened externally. the horns of this goat have their outer

A

THE MUSK-OX

The desolate regions of the far north of the Western Hemisphere, where even in summer the surface of the ground scarcely thaws, are the home of the so-called musk-ox (*Ovibos moschatus*), which, although formerly placed next the cattle and sheep, is probably more nearly related to the takin. The species derives its name from the peculiar musky flavour with which the flesh is tainted, and forms the single living representative of its genus.

The musk-ox (page 141) is about two-thirds the size of the American bison, but from its long coat of hair looks larger than it really is. In appearance it has been compared to a large hairy ram, and it resembles sheep in the marked convexity of the profile of the face and the hairy muzzle. The head is broad, with the small and pointed ears almost concealed by the hair; the latter being long and thick, and generally of a dark brown colour, with a light saddle-patch, although paler in spring. Though matted and curling on the back, the hair on the throat and flanks is straight and reaches down to the middle of the legs, and hides the very short tail. Beneath the hair is a coat of fine, soft wool of a light brown colour. The long winter coat is shed in spring in large blanket-like masses.

In the bulls the horns have very wide and flattened bases, covering a large portion of the forehead, and meeting one another in the middle line; at first they curve sharply downwards, becoming at the same time gradually narrower and less expanded, and then curving sharply upwards and forwards, terminating in front of the eyes. At the bases the horns are very rough, and yellowish white in colour, but they gradually become less rough, and at the same time darker, till at the tips, where their section is cylindrical, they are smooth and black. In young bulls and cows the horns are much smaller, and separated from one another by a considerable interval in the middle line. The limbs are short and massive, and the feet peculiar in that, while the outer hoof of each is rounded, the inner one is pointed; there is a considerable growth of hair between the hoofs, which aids in obtaining a sure foothold on the ice. The molar teeth of the musk-ox are very like those of sheep, and thus quite different from those of cattle. Average-sized horns are about 24 or 25 inches in length, but they may reach 27¼ inches. The skeleton is remarkable for the extreme shortness of the cannon-bones of the legs, a feature shared by the takin and the white goat of the Rocky Mountains.

The range of the musk-oxen in Arctic America is limited to the south by the 60th degree of latitude, but extends northwards to the 83rd degree in Grinnell Land. In former years the range reached considerably farther south, examples having been found in 1770 near Fort Churchill, on the west coast of Hudson Bay, in latitude 58° 44′. The western boundary of the species at the present day is formed by the Mackenzie River. In 1908 Dr. R. Kowarzik pointed out that the living representatives of the species are divisable into two main groups—an eastern and a western—distinguished by skull characters. The line of division between the two types is formed by the Atlantic watershed and its continuation in the islands of the Arctic Ocean. The western type, *Ovibos m. mackenzianus* (of which *O. yukonensis* is a synonym), now inhabits the Mackenzie Valley, but appears to have been originally a native of Europe and Northern Asia, whence it reached America by way of Bering Strait. The skull is characterised by the nearly quadrangular outline of the basioccipital, the flattened but large horn-bases, the close approximation of the stout sheaths of the horn-sheaths to the forehead, the presence of distinct lachrymal pits, the marked curvature of the tooth-line and the long interval between the sphenoh-maxillary fossa and the last molar.

The Greenland musk-ox forms another race, *O. m. wardi*, while the one from the country north of Hudson Bay has been described as distinct under the name of *O. m. niphœcus*. This race is described as to a considerable extent intermediate between the typical Barren Ground musk-ox and the Greenland *O. m. wardi*, although in other respects peculiar. The jet-black colour of the coat differs markedly from the brown of the other two races, the narrow whitish

THE TAKIN

ORDER VI. UNGULATA—CONTINUED

TAHR

THE Himalayan goat known as the tahr (*Hemitragus jemlaicus*), an allied species from Arabia, and a third from the Nilgiri Hills of Southern India differ so markedly from the true goats that they are classed in a genus by themselves. They are devoid of a beard, and also distinguished by having the extremity of the muzzle naked. The skull is longer and narrower than in the true goats, with the sockets of the eyes less prominent ; and the horns are relatively short, and little smaller in the does than in the bucks. In form the horns are compressed and angulated in front, with their bases quite close together ; and they curve backwards from the plane of the forehead. None of the species has glands in the fore feet.

The Himalayan tahr is distinguished by the form of the black horns, which have their lateral surfaces flattened and shelving regularly up to the sharp and beaded keel on the inner front border ; they diverge regularly from their bases, at the same time curving sharply backwards, with a slight inward inclination at the tips. On the head the hair is short, but it becomes longer on the body, and in old bucks is so lengthened on the neck, chest, and shoulders as to form a long, shaggy mane reaching below the knees.

There is considerable variation in colour, but the tint of the hair is dark or reddish brown, old males being generally very dark, although pale-coloured individuals of both sexes are not infrequently met with. The face and the front of the limbs are very dark, in some instances almost black, and old males have an indistinct dark line down the middle of the back. In young animals the colour is uniform greyish brown, and kids are reported to be very pale-coloured. The female tahr differs from all other goats, as well as from sheep, in having four teats.

In height the male tahr varies from 3 feet to 3 feet 4 inches at the shoulder, the does being much smaller. Good specimens of the horns vary from 12 to 15 inches in length, measured along the curve, but a pair has been recorded with a length of $16\frac{1}{2}$ and a basal girth of $10\frac{1}{2}$ inches. In the does the length of the horns is seldom more than 10 inches.

Tahr are found throughout the higher forest regions of the Himalaya, from the Pir Panjal range on the outer side of the valley of Kashmir in the north-west to Sikhim in the south-east, but are unknown in the arid Tibetan districts of the interior. Tahr is the native name by which they are known in the Western Himalaya, but in Kashmir they are termed kras ; while in Nepal they go by the name of jharal. A smaller species (*Hemitragus jayakeri*), with only two teats, inhabits Arabia ; and remains of a fossil tahr occur in the rocks of the Siwalik Hills at the foot of the Himalaya.

In spite of the small size of its horns, the tahr is decidedly a fine-looking animal, and is plentifully distributed over many parts of the Himalaya. Although in the Pir Panjal range tahr are often found on the same ground as markhor, in other districts they frequent almost worse ground, and I have known many instances where specimens have been completely smashed by falling down precipices after they were killed. After mentioning that the tahr resembles the markhor in its forest-loving habits, General A. A. Kinloch observes that "although it sometimes resorts to the rocky summits of the hills, it generally prefers the steep slopes which are more or less clothed with trees. Female tahr may frequently be found on open ground, but old males hide a great deal in the thickest jungle, lying during the heat of the day under the shade of trees or overhanging rocks. Nearly perpendicular hills with dangerous precipices, where the forest consists of oak and ringal-cane, are the favourite haunts of the old tahr, who climb with ease over ground where one

HEAD OF THE MUSK-OX

would hardly imagine that any animal could find a footing."

Old male tahr generally herd separately from the females during the summer, but about October the two sexes come together ; and it is believed that the kids are born in June and July, only a single one being produced at a birth.

The Nilgiri tahr, or wild goat (*H. hylocrius*)—the warri-atu of the Tamils, and the Nilgiri ibex of English sportsmen—is a southern species inhabiting the Nilgiri and Anamalai Hills, and the Western Ghats as far south as Cape Comorin. It is found at elevations of from 4,000 to 6,000 feet above the sea, but occasionally somewhat lower down. This species may be distinguished from the Himalayan tahr by the form of the horns, and the absence of the shaggy mane which forms such a conspicuous feature of the fore quarters of the males of the latter. Instead of being flattened externally, the horns of this goat have their outer sides highly convex, and thus present a distinct front surface, internally to which is a slight ridge ; for some distance the two horns run parallel to one another, after which they diverge gradually.

The hair is short, thick, and coarse, the males having a short, stiff mane on the back of the neck and withers. The general colour is dark yellowish brown above, with a darker stripe down the back, but the under parts are paler. The females and young show a more or less decided grey tinge. In height old males of the Nilgiri tahr stand from $3\frac{1}{4}$ feet to $3\frac{1}{2}$ feet at the shoulder, the horns measuring from 12 to 16 inches in length along the curve, although in one instance a length of 17 inches has been recorded.

These tahr associate usually in herds of from five or six to fifty or sixty among the crags and rocky precipices that border the Nilgiris and other high ranges in the extreme south of India. They keep above the forest and rarely enter woods. Although they have been seen feeding on the grassy hills at the top of the Kundas west of the Nilgiris, their usual haunts are the grassy slopes and precipitous crags on the edges of the plateau ; they feed on the former in the mornings and evenings, and rest on ledges amongst the cliffs during the day. They are quite as wary and sharp-sighted as are Himalayan tahr or markhor, and just as nimble and alert on precipitous ground. An old doe, as in the case of other goats, usually acts as sentinel to the herd, and they always appear to suspect danger from below and not from above. The young may apparently be born almost at any season of the year, and there are generally two at a birth.

How this species originally reached its present habitat, so remote from that of its allies, is not easy to understand, but the occurrence of a fossil goat apparently allied to this group in Perim Island, in the Gulf of Cambay, may aid in solving the problem.

GORAL

The goral (*Urotragus*, or *Cemas*, *goral*) of the Himalaya is the representative of an assemblage of mountain-haunting ruminants which to a certain extent connect the goats with the antelopes. Most of these ruminants have a more

THE GORAL

or less goat-like build, goat-like teeth, short tails, relatively small cylindrical horns, and no beards. The goral is a relatively small animal standing only 27 inches at the shoulder, and having somewhat stout limbs, and rather coarse, short hair, which becomes elongated into a slight crest along the back of the neck. The general colour is brown, with a more or less rufous or grey tinge, but there is a dark

stripe from the nape of the neck to the black tail, and another down the front of each leg, while a patch on the throat is white. The muzzle is naked, and the face, as in goats, has no gland below the eye, while the skull lacks any depression in the same region. The short, black, and conical horns curve regularly backwards, and are marked, except at the tip, by a number of small and irregular rings. In the bucks they may vary from 6 to 8 inches in length, but a pair has been recorded of upwards of $9\frac{3}{4}$ inches. The horns of does are only slightly smaller than those of the bucks.

Goral are found throughout the outer ridges of the Himalaya, from Kashmir to Bhutan, at elevations of from 3,000 to 8,000 feet. There are two species of these Himalayan goral, the brown *U. goral* and the grey *U. bedfordi*, while a third species, the ashy goral (*U. cinereus*) ranges from the Sze-chuen province of China into Burma. In Amurland the group is represented by the long-tailed goral (*U. caudatus*), distinguished by its longer tail.

Himalayan goral are generally found in small parties of from four to eight, but sometimes associate only in pairs, and old bucks are generally solitary. They frequent rugged grassy hills or rocky forest-clad ground, and during cloudy weather feed throughout the day, but, when fine, only in the morning and evening. Where one goral is seen, others will almost certainly be found in the neighbourhood, and these ruminants rarely forsake their feeding grounds.

SEROWS

Nearly allied to the goral is the more shaggy ruminant known as the serow, which is the typical representative of a group peculiar to South-Eastern and Eastern Asia. Although resembling goral in their general build, naked muzzles, short tails, and the presence of four teats in the females, serows are distinguished by having a gland beneath the eye, and a corresponding shallow depression in the skull for its reception. Moreover, the plane of the forehead passes imperceptibly into that of the region behind the horns, whereas in the goral the two are separated by a distinct angle.

The serow (*Nemorhædus sumatrensis*) is typically a Sumatran ruminant, but it is best known by its Himalayan representatives, which range from Kashmir to the Mishmi Hills, where they are found at elevations of from 6,000 to 12,000 feet. These serow are much larger than goral, standing about 37 inches at the shoulders, and the horns of bucks generally measuring from 9 to 10 inches in length, although they may reach as much as $13\frac{1}{2}$ inches. Serows are rather ugly-looking ruminants, with large ears, and coarse and somewhat thin hair of moderate length, forming a kind of crest along the neck. In the Himalayan races, of which it will suffice to mention the Nepalese *N. sumatrensis bubalinus*, the head and neck are black, while the rest of the hair of the upper parts is black or dark grey, with a more or less distinct grizzle ; the muzzle, chin, and inside of the ears are white, and the under parts are also whitish, the flanks, chest, etc., being rusty red, and the lower parts of the limbs white, or white and rufous. The black horns curve regularly backwards, and, in addition to numerous rings, are marked by a number of longitudinal striæ. The two sexes are very similar.

In Arakan the species is represented by a red phase (*N. s. rubidus*), while there is a wholly black serow (*N. s. swettenhami*) in the Malay Peninsula. Another black race (*N. s. milne-edwardsi*) inhabits the Sze-chuen, which is also the home of the white-maned *N. argyrochætes*, a large species, characterised by much white in the mane and the red upper portion of the limbs.

The habits of all the serows are probably very similar. Writing of one of the Himalayan races, General A. A. Kinloch observes that it " has an awkward gait, but, in spite of this, it can go over the worst ground; and it has, perhaps, no superior in going down steep hills It is a solitary animal, and nowhere numerous; two or three may be found on one hill, four or five on another and so on. It delights in the steepest and most rocky hillsides, and its favourite resting-places are in caves, under the shelter of overhanging rocks, or at the foot of shady trees. Although very shy and difficult to find, the serow is a fierce and dangerous animal when brought to bay. I have even heard of an unwounded male charging when his mate has been shot. It is said that a serow will sometimes beat off a pack of wild dogs, and I believe that serows and dogs have been found lying dead together. When disturbed, the serow utters a most singular sound, something between a snort and a screaming whistle, and I have heard them screaming loudly when they had apparently not been alarmed." General Macintyre relates that on one occasion " a female serow had been shot by a sportsman, when, on his native follower approaching to secure it, a male companion rushed out from the dense covert hard by, and, going for the man, sent him rolling downhill with a butt from its horns."

TAKIN

One of the most remarkable members of this group is the takin (*Budorcas taxicolor*) of the Mishmi Hills, north of Assam, which is allied to the serows, although with very differently shaped horns. The takin is a heavily built and comparatively large ruminant, standing 3½ feet at the shoulder, with stout limbs, large lateral hoofs, and a small goat-like tail. The muzzle is covered with hair, except a small spot at the extremity, and the profile of the face is convex. The horns are black and thick in the bulls, rising close together, and at first curving outwards, after which they make a sharp turn and are directed straight backwards. Those of the cows are of the same type, but smaller. Male horns vary in length from 20 to 24 inches, with a basal girth of 9 or 10 inches. The head and limbs of the takin are black, but the colour of the coarse hair of the body is reddish brown mingled with black, and there is a light-coloured saddle-like patch on the back. In Bhutan occurs a smaller race of the species (*B. taxicolor whitei*); but in Sze-chuen and Kansu, North-Western China, the genus is represented by a distinct species (*B. tibetanus*) in which immature animals may be either golden yellow on the upper parts, or grey, passing into white on the neck. The horns are also of somewhat different form.

According to Mr. J. W. Brooke, in Sze-chuen takin inhabit dense bamboo and rhododendron jungle on precipitous hillsides, where it is nearly always raining. The elevation of these jungles is from 8,000 to 10,000 feet above sea-level, and here the males are found from October to May, except when driven down by inclement weather. The females, on the other hand, descend to the valleys during March, April, and May to feed and rear their young. These are suckled for a fortnight after birth, and soon become as

THE TAHR

active as their parents, as is evident from their tracks, which may be seen in the most precipitous situations.

Takin go about in herds of from five to about fifty head, and, according to the native hunters, when a herd takes to headlong flight, all its members follow the line of their leader, who may even leap over a precipice. Old males attain a large size, some of the tracks of their clumsy hoofs being six inches square. For a considerable part of the year the males separate themselves from the main herds, which consist of females and young males.

The best season to shoot takin is in winter, when heavy snow compels them to come down to the valleys; but as the snow is soon melted by warm winds from the plains, they are only to be found low down during long and heavy snowfalls. Throughout the winter they wander incessantly, as if never contented with a single grazing ground, and, if not found low down in the valleys, are almost impossible to hunt successfully. Except for the temporary descents, takin apparently haunt the elevated bamboo and rhododendron jungle throughout the year, unless they go still higher in summer.

Nearly related to the takin is the extinct *Bucapra daviesi*, of the Siwalik Hills of Northern India.

THE MUSK-OX

The desolate regions of the far north of the Western Hemisphere, where even in summer the surface of the ground scarcely thaws, are the home of the so-called musk-ox (*Ovibos moschatus*), which, although formerly placed next the cattle and sheep, is probably more nearly related to the takin. The species derives its name from the peculiar musky flavour with which the flesh is tainted, and forms the single living representative of its genus.

The musk-ox (page 141) is about two-thirds the size of the American bison, but from its long coat of hair looks larger than it really is. In appearance it has been compared to a large hairy ram, and it resembles sheep in the marked convexity of the profile of the face and the hairy muzzle. The head is broad, with the small and pointed ears almost concealed by the hair; the latter being long and thick, and generally of a dark brown colour, with a light saddle-patch, although paler in spring. Though matted and curling on the back, the hair on the throat and flanks is straight and reaches down to the middle of the legs, and hides the very short tail. Beneath the hair is a coat of fine, soft wool of a light brown colour. The long winter coat is shed in spring in large blanket-like masses.

In the bulls the horns have very wide and flattened bases, covering a large portion of the forehead, and meeting one another in the middle line; at first they curve sharply downwards, becoming at the same time gradually narrower and less expanded, and then curving sharply upwards and forwards, terminating in front of the eyes. At the bases the horns are very rough, and yellowish white in colour, but they gradually become less rough, and at the same time darker, till at the tips, where their section is cylindrical, they are smooth and black. In young bulls and cows the horns are much smaller, and separated from one another by a considerable interval in the middle line. The limbs are short and massive, and the feet peculiar in that, while the outer hoof of each is rounded, the inner one is pointed; there is a considerable growth of hair between the hoofs, which aids in obtaining a sure foothold on the ice. The molar teeth of the musk-ox are very like those of sheep, and thus quite different from those of cattle. Average-sized horns are about 24 or 25 inches in length, but they may reach $27\frac{1}{4}$ inches. The skeleton is remarkable for the extreme shortness of the cannon-bones of the legs, a feature shared by the takin and the white goat of the Rocky Mountains.

The range of the musk-oxen in Arctic America is limited to the south by the 60th degree of latitude, but extends northwards to the 83rd degree in Grinnell Land. In former years the range reached considerably farther south, examples having been found in 1770 near Fort Churchill, on the west coast of Hudson Bay, in latitude 58° 44'. The western boundary of the species at the present day is formed by the Mackenzie River. In 1908 Dr. R. Kowarzik pointed out that the living representatives of the species are divisable into two main groups—an eastern and a western—distinguished by skull characters. The line of division between the two types is formed by the Atlantic watershed and its continuation in the islands of the Arctic Ocean. The western type, *Ovibos m. mackenzianus* (of which *O. yukonensis* is a synonym), now inhabits the Mackenzie Valley, but appears to have been originally a native of Europe and Northern Asia, whence it reached America by way of Bering Strait. The skull is characterised by the nearly quadrangular outline of the basioccipital, the flattened but large horn-bases, the close approximation of the stout sheaths of the horn-sheaths to the forehead, the presence of distinct lachrymal pits, the marked curvature of the tooth-line and the long interval between the sphenoh-maxillary fossa and the last molar.

The Greenland musk-ox forms another race, *O. m. wardi*, while the one from the country north of Hudson Bay has been described as distinct under the name of *O. m. niphæcus*. This race is described as to a considerable extent intermediate between the typical Barren Ground musk-ox and the Greenland *O. m. wardi*, although in other respects peculiar. The jet-black colour of the coat differs markedly from the brown of the other two races, the narrow whitish

THE TAKIN

band on the crown of the head indicates relationship with *O. m. wardi*, but the dark legs recall the typical form. The horns are intermediate in character between those of the other two, as they spread farther from the head than in the typical race, but have less span than in *O. m. wardi*.

In Prehistoric and Pleistocene times the musk-ox ranged to the north-west into Alaska, its fossilised remains having been found in the frozen soil of Kotzebue Sound in Bering Strait, and also in the upper part of the Porcupine River in Canada. At a still earlier period—probably when North America was colder than at present—musk-oxen ranged as far south as Kansas and Kentucky, where their remains have been found between the 35th and 40th parallels of latitude; some of these representing extinct species, and, in the opinion of American naturalists, even genera, for which the names *Boötherium* and *Scaphoceros* have been proposed.

Passing eastwards from Alaska across Bering Strait into Asia, musk-ox bones are found in the frozen soil of Siberia as far eastwards as the Obi River; and these ruminants once ranged right across Russia, as there is evidence of their former existence in Germany so far south as Würtemberg. Thence they extended into France, but the Pyrenees and Alps seem to have marked the southern limits of their range. In England remains have been found in superficial deposits, and skulls have been dredged from the Dogger Bank. Although the alteration in climatic conditions affords a sufficient reason for the northward retreat of the musk-ox, we are at present in the dark why it has disappeared from the Eastern Hemisphere, while the reindeer still has a circumpolar distribution.

The regions inhabited by the musk-ox are of the most barren and inhospitable nature. It has been stated that these animals migrate southwards during the coldest part of the year, but this is denied by Mr. H. Biederbeck, who met with them in Grinnell Land in March, when the snow is deepest and the temperature lowest, and states that they inhabit that country and North Greenland throughout the year. Young musk-oxen have been imported into Europe, where some have survived for a few years.

In spite of its coarse grain, the meat of the musk-ox is described as being juicy and tender, that of the young animals being especially so, but in order to obviate the musky flavour it is essential that the carcase should be dressed as soon as killed.

A sheep-like ruminant of which remains have been discovered in a cave in California has been described under the name of *Preptoceras sinclairi*. It has doubly curved horns and sheep-like teeth, and, in common with an allied ruminant from the same district described as *Euceratherium*, seems related on the one hand to the musk-ox and on the other to the takin, while it is also supposed to have affinities with sheep. If these extinct ruminants really connect the takin

with the musk-ox, their systematic importance is great. From a geographical point of view nothing is more likely, for it is quite reasonable to expect that, like so many other peculiar forms from the same region, takin should at one period have had more or less nearly allied representatives on the American side of the Pacific.

ROCKY MOUNTAIN GOAT

The so-called white goat of the Rocky Mountains (*Oreamnus*, or *Haploceros*, *montanus*), which may be related both to serows and takin, is about the size of a large sheep, and averages 100 pounds in weight. It has very short and stout legs, terminating in broad and blunted hoofs, pointed ears, and jet-black horns, curving backwards, and ringed for about half their length, but smooth above. The body is covered in winter with a long coat of white hair, which is nearly straight, and falls on the sides of the body and limbs, but is erect along

ROCKY MOUNTAIN GOATS

the middle of the back, and it as becomes longer over the withers and haunches the animal looks as though it had two humps. Beneath the hair is a thick coat of wool. In the Selkirk Range of Southern British Columbia the white goats show a dark brown line running down the middle line of the back, to terminate in an almost black tail; this being common to both the summer and the winter dress. In summer the coat is comparatively short and close. There are no glands below the eyes. In length the horns vary from 6 to $10\frac{1}{2}$ inches. The skeleton, in common with that of the takin and musk-ox, is remarkable for the extreme shortness of the cannon-bones.

The range of the white goat extends through the Rocky Mountains from about lat. 36° in California at least so far north as lat. 62°, but may reach as far north as the mountains run. Although chiefly a

CHAMOIS
GLISADING

tains, the white goat does not appear to be a very wary species, and is perhaps the most stupid animal in the mountains, and needs little or no skill in hunting. The great difficulty is in reaching the almost inaccessible places which it usually inhabits. The best time for hunting is in September and October, before the rainy season sets in, although skins are not in the best condition till later.

CHAMOIS

The last representative of the goat-like ruminants is the well-known chamois, or gemse (*Rupicapra tragus*), of the mountains of Europe and Asia Minor, distinguished from all the rest by the short and cylindrical black horns rising for a considerable distance vertically from the forehead, and then bending sharply backwards and downwards in a hook-like manner. Chamois are strongly built ruminants, with relatively long and stout limbs and very short stumpy tails, the height being about two feet at the withers. The hair is close and rather long, with a thick woolly under fur. In the typical Alpine race the general colour in winter is chestnut brown, paler on the face and under parts, with a well-marked brown streak extending from below the eye nearly to the corner of the mouth; the tail being black. In summer the coat is lighter-coloured, having in spring a more or less marked grey hue.

The erect ears are sharply pointed; and the horns, except at their tips, are marked both by slight transverse rings and longitudinal striæ. Fair-sized horns are about 7 inches in length, but some specimens measure as much as 9 inches, or rather more, while a few reach 11 or 12 inches. The weight of a buck chamois may vary from 50 to 70 pounds. Light-coloured, or even white, specimens are occasionally met with. The face has a small gland below the eye, with a corresponding shallow depression in the skull for its reception, and the muzzle is completely covered with hair. The hoofs have their outer edges higher than the central portion, and are thus adapted for securing a firm foothold on rocks.

The chamois has a wide distribution in the mountains of Europe, occurring in the Pyrenees—where it is known as the izard—the mountains of the coast of Spain, in Dalmatia and Greece, in the Carpathians, the Swiss and Transylvanian Alps, the Apennines, Caucasus, the Taurus Range, in Asia Minor, and the mountains of Georgia. The Pyrenean izard (*R. tragus pyrenaica*) is a smaller form, with shorter horns and a more foxy-red' colour than the typical Alpine gemse; and the race inhabiting the Caucasus, where it is known as the atchi, as well as the one from the Apennines and that from the Taurus, also show distinctive features.

mountain animal, the white goat has occasionally been observed close to the sea-level, and even swimming salt-water estuaries or rivers. Such occurrences are, however, rare, and, as a rule, it lives above or close to the upper limit of forests. But when driven by hunger these ruminants sometimes descend to lower levels in the forest, while they not infrequently traverse the lowlands separating one mountain or range from another. During the pairing season, in November, and in the middle of winter they are gregarious, although not markedly so at other seasons of the year.

As might be inferred from their short and clumsy limbs, these ruminants have little speed, and when disturbed move leisurely off, trusting rather to concealment behind sheltering rocks than to rapidity of pace. Formerly the Rocky Mountain goat was much hunted by the Indians for the sake of its fleece, but now that the demand for blankets made from its wool has well-nigh ceased, their pursuit has been abandoned in many districts.

Although extremely agile among its native moun-

At the present day, chamois are rare in the Swiss Alps, but in the Eastern Alps, in the districts of Bavaria, Salzburg, Styria, and Carinthia, are far more common, while they are abundant on the precipitous summits of the Central Carpathians, and in the Taurus range.

Fossil remains of chamois are found in caverns at low elevations in several parts of Europe, indicating climatic conditions different from those now prevailing.

As regards habits, the general notion is that the chamois is an essentially Alpine animal—that is to say, one frequenting the glaciers and snowy peaks above the forest-level. This, however, is a mistaken idea ; the truth being that chamois are really forest-dwelling animals, and that most of them live from year's end to year's end within the limits of the forest. During summer, however, a certain number leave the main flock to take up their abode for a period of weeks or months among the glaciers and snowfields above the upper limit of forests ; these adventurous individuals being known to the hunters as glacier-chamois, in contradistinction to wood-chamois. A short spell of severe weather, however, is sufficient to drive even these back to the shelter of the forest. The favourite haunts of chamois are the western and north-western slopes of the Alps in summer, but in winter they prefer spots with an easterly or southerly aspect.

Chamois are essentially gregarious, usually associating in herds of fifteen or twenty. They repose during the night, but with the first glimmer of dawn begin feeding ; towards the middle of the day they again seek the shelter of rocks or trees, where they lie in the shade till evening, when they once more issue forth to feed. Their chief nutriment consists of lichens and the scanty mountain herbage. During the greater part of the year the old males live a solitary life apart from the flocks ; but during the pairing season, in October and November, they join the flocks of females, from which they drive away the young bucks. At this period the old bucks engage in fierce contests among themselves, which occasionally terminate fatally.

The fawns, one or occasionally two in number, are born in May or June, and are clothed with a thick woolly coat of a reddish colour. When but a day old they are able to follow their dams almost anywhere ; and in three months first show their horns. In three years they attain their full size ; and it is stated that the span of life of a chamois may extend from twenty to twenty-five years.

All who have seen chamois in their native haunts are agreed as to their extreme agility and wariness ; and their sure-footedness has become proverbial. When alarmed, they utter a shrill whistling sound, which at once sets the whole flock in rapid motion. A chamois is able to stand on the summit of a pinnacle of rock with all four feet gathered into a space of the size of a crown piece ; and as its senses of sight, smell, and hearing are of the acutest, its pursuit taxes the utmost powers of the hunter.

ELAND

Although chamois are often included under the same general title, eland, or impofo, may be considered as the first representatives of that large group of ruminants commonly known as antelopes ; a group which includes the remaining members of the bovine family. Despite the fact that the name antelope is in common use, and most of the members of the group are easily recognised, yet, owing to the number of types and the diversity of their structure, it is difficult to define antelopes as a whole from cattle on the one hand, and from goats on the other ; the transition to the former group being effected by means of the anoas (page 652), and to the latter by the serows and chamois,

In fact, the term, which seems to belong of right to the Indian blackbuck, is indefinable, including as it does a number of groups, each equivalent in value to the cattle or the sheep and goats. Antelope is thus merely a convenient general term to comprise most of such ruminants as cannot be called cattle, sheep, or goats. In this sense antelopes include the most generalised members of the family, and since they are also its oldest known representatives, it is probable that from them have been derived the more specialised cattle and goats.

As a whole, antelopes are characterised by their graceful build, and by the head being carried considerably above the level of the back. The horns, which may not be present in the females, are long, more or less cylindrical, and often lyrate in shape ; while they are frequently marked with prominent rings, and have an upright direction. Their bony internal cores, instead of being honeycombed, as in cattle, sheep, and goats, are nearly solid throughout. Very generally these ruminants possess glands beneath the eyes by which they are distinguished from cattle and goats ; but as regards their teeth, some of them resemble cattle, while others approximate to sheep and goats.

Antelopes, in the proper sense of the word, are

A PAIR OF ELAND

strictly confined to the Old World, and the great majority are restricted to Africa and the adjacent regions of Syria and Arabia. Indeed, with the exception of the widely spread group of gazelles, the only antelopes found beyond these regions are the blackbuck, four-horned antelope, the nilgai of India, the saiga of Tatary, and the chiru of Tibet. It was not, however, always so, since in Tertiary times antelopes of African types were distributed over a large portion of India and Southern Europe, and it is still a problem to account satisfactorily for the disappearance of these animals from the latter regions. The introduction of antelopes into Africa appears to have been compara-tively recent, but having once made good their footing on that continent they multiplied, both as regards individuals and species, in a manner unparalleled in any other region. Unfortunately, this profusion and exuberance of ruminant life which only a few decades back characterised the great southern conti-nent of the Old World is rapidly disappearing before the advance of civilisation, and at least one species is extinct, while others are on the verge of extermination.

The eland (*Taurotragus oryx*, or *Orias canna*) belongs to a group of large and almost exclusively African antelopes known as the *Tragelaphinæ*, and characterised by the frequent absence of horns in the females, and by those of the males being devoid of rings, angulated in front, and usually spirally twisted. There is a small gland below the eye, the muzzle is naked, the tail is long, and the upper molar teeth generally have short crowns (page 709).

Eland are the largest of all antelopes, and differ from most other members of the present group in having horns in both sexes, which are spirally twisted on their own axis and directed upwards and outwards, rising in the plane of the face, and bearing a sharp ridge in front and behind. The naked muzzle is broad, the gland below the eye small, the tufted tail reaches below the hocks, and both sexes have large dewlaps. The crowns of the upper molar teeth are low and broad. The horns of the cows are longer and thinner than those of the bulls, and sometimes more or less completely lose the spiral twist.

In the more typical southern races the bulls have a tuft, or "bush," of long, dark brown hair covering the forehead, but the colour of the rest of the head and body varies from pale fawn to bluish grey, the blue tint being most marked in old individuals—more especially bulls, in which, owing to the scantiness of the hair, the colour of the skin shows through. In the southern part of its range the eland is uniformly coloured, but farther north there is a race, *T. oryx livingstonei*, in which the body is marked with a number of vertical white stripes, and a dark patch on the inner side of the knee, which seems to disappear at a certain age. Still farther north elands show an im-perfect white chevron on the face, like that of a kudu, and a smaller and lighter-coloured "bush" on the forehead. For this Uganda race, which grades into the last, the name *T. o. pattersonianus* has been proposed.

Considerable variation, partly due to differences of age, occur among eland of the same herd, and in Nyasaland among a single troop individuals may be seen varying from light tawny yellow to slaty blue in very old age, while in some the stripes are clearly defined, in others faintly, and in others are not distinguishable at all. An average-sized bull eland

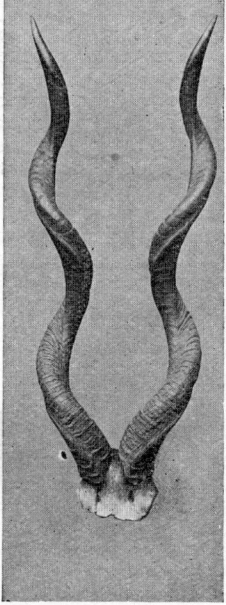

HORNS OF THE LESSER KUDU

stands about 5 feet 9 inches at the withers, but some specimens are doubtless taller. The average weight varies from 800 to 1,100 pounds, but in old bulls it may reach 1,400 or even 1,500 pounds. The average length of the horns may be set down at 25 inches for bulls and 26 inches for cows; but a length of 35 inches in the former and 32 inches in the latter has been recorded. In old bulls the horns may be worn down to less than a foot in length.

Eland were formerly distributed over all Southern and Eastern Africa, but have now disappeared from Cape Colony, Natal, the Orange River State, Griqua-land West, and the Transvaal. Some years ago these antelopes, however, were abundant in the districts between the Chobi and Zambezi, as well as in the country to the north of the latter, while they are still plentiful in parts of Nyasaland, and not uncommon in the Kilimanjaro district.

Eland are found in the desert country and in wooded districts, both hilly and flat. In Nyasaland their favourite haunts are un-dulating, well-timbered country, where the grass is not too long, and where there are intervening open plains; as a rule, they visit the plains at night or in the early morning to drink, and then wander back long distances to the forest, where they spend the hot hours of the day. In the Kalahari Desert eland go a long period without drinking water, except that which they obtain by eating water-melons and other plants. Eland are found in large herds, numbering from fifty to upwards of a hundred head, but solitary bulls or small parties of bulls are not infrequently observed. They are accompanied by "rhinoceros birds," which, in addition to their natural timidity, make the ruminants difficult to approach on foot. Consequently eland are generally hunted on horseback. The bulls, when fat, can be ridden down by a good horse, but the cows have greater speed and staying power. When pursued, eland frequently leap high in the air. The calves are born in July and August, but as the females do not breed oftener than once in every two years the rate of increase is slow. When they have calves with them, the cows will attack and impale dogs on their horns, but at other seasons both sexes are harmless.

In Senegambia, and also in the Bahr-el-Ghazal district of the Egyptian Sudan, the ordinary eland is replaced by a much finer and handsomer species known as Lord Derby's eland (*T. derbianus*), which attains a very large size and has enormous horns, and is a much broader and bigger animal than its relative. The body is of a rich mahogany colour, with a large number of narrow white vertical stripes, while part of the neck in old bulls is black; both sexes showing a chevron mark on the face. The large size of the ears indicates that this eland is to some extent at least a forest-dwelling animal.

BONGO

Large, broad ears and many narrow white stripes on a mahogany ground also characterise that handsome considerable antelope the bongo (*Boöcercus euryceros*), originally known from the West Coast of Africa, where it was seen by Paul du Chaillu, but afterwards ascertained to range right across the forest zone to the east side of the continent in Uganda. Nearly as large as a cow of that species, the bongo agrees with the eland in having horns in both sexes, and also in its tufted tail, but in the form of its horns and in its type of colouring it comes nearer to the nyala and situtunga.

The mahogany, or orange, red of the body passes into brown, or even blackish, on the forehead, and the white markings, in addition to the body stripes, comprise a crescent on the chest, a chevron on the forehead, and a pair of spots on each side of the face. There is no throat fringe, and apparently no dewlap. Old bulls stand nearly 4 feet at the shoulder. In this sex the horns are very massive, and form rather more than one complete turn, their length being from 30 to 35 inches in a straight line. Those of the cows are thinner. In both sexes the tips of the horns wear yellow. Bongo are essentially forest antelopes, their large ears and vertical white stripes being adaptations to such a life, the former being essential in order to catch every sound possible, while the white stripes on a red ground appear to be protective.

KUDU

The graceful and beautifully marked antelope known as the kudu (*Strepsiceros capensis*) is distinguished from the eland and the bongo by the absence of horns in the female, and by the shorter and untufted tail, which does not reach the hocks. The horns, which form an open, corkscrew-like spiral, and are characterised by the great development of the front ridge, rise from the skull at an obtuse angle to the plane of the face. The neck is maned, and the throat furnished with a fringe of long hair. The body is marked with narrow vertical white stripes descending from a white line on the back, and there is also a white chevron on the face, with white spots on the cheek, and white splashes on the throat and limbs (page 710). The hoofs are short.

The ground colour of females and young males is reddish or greyish brown, marked with eight or nine white stripes; but in old males it becomes bluish grey, apparently owing to the skin showing through the scanty hair. The kudu is only inferior in size to the eland, a full-grown bull standing about 4 feet 4 inches at the shoulder. The horns may occasionally attain a length of 4 feet in a straight line, although even good specimens seldom exceed 3 feet 9 inches or 3 feet 6 inches in a straight line. In a pair measuring 3 feet 5 inches in a straight line, the length along the curve was 5 feet 4 inches.

The range of the kudu extends from the Cape to the Abyssinian highlands and Somaliland, embracing all Eastern Africa and extending westwards to Angola. In the Kilimanjaro district kudu appear to be rare. They are usually partial to hilly country covered with dense thickets, but hills are by no means necessary to their existence, as they are common in the thick bush along both banks of the Chobi, where there are no hills, and are also plentiful in the w a i t - a - b i t thorn-jungles on the Lower Molapo, on the edge of the Kalahari Desert. Kudu are

fond of browsing on the young and tender shoots of trees and shrubs, especially in the dry season, when the grass has been burnt off. When alarmed, they sometimes give vent to a low bark, audible only at close quarters.

Kudu are found in pairs or in small parties. Their speed is not great; but owing to the fact that when disturbed they make for the roughest ground, while the districts they haunt are frequently infested with the tsetse fly, they are seldom hunted on horseback. With dogs, however, they afford excellent sport.

The lesser kudu (*S. imberbis*) is a much smaller antelope, restricted to Somaliland and Eastern Africa as far south as Kilimanjaro. In addition to its inferior dimensions, it is distinguished by the absence of a fringe of long hair on the throat, and the more compressed spiral of the horns. Measured in a straight line, the horns vary from about 17 to 25 inches in length. The lesser kudu, although very common about Kilimanjaro, is seldom seen, as it rarely leaves the bush. In Somaliland, while the large kudu frequents the mountain ranges, the present species inhabits the thicket-clad slopes at their feet.

An imperfect skull appears to indicate the occurrence of a kudu in India during the Pliocene period; and the European Tertiary genus *Palæorcas*, although nearer to the eland, is stated to have some characters of the kudu.

HARNESSED ANTELOPES

The group of antelopes represented by the nyala, the situtunga, and the bushbuck, often referred to collectively as harnessed antelopes, are some of the

SOUTH AFRICAN BUSHBUCKS

THE ADDAX

The addax (*Addax nasomaculatus*) is the first of a group of African and Arabian antelopes of large size, collectively forming the subfamily *Hippotraginæ*, and presenting the following distinctive characteristics. They have long, cylindrical horns in both sexes, which are placed over or above the eyes, and are either subspiral, straight, or recurved. The muzzle is covered with hair, and there is no gland below the eye, while the skull has no depression below the socket of the eye, and only a very narrow unossified space in the same region. The tail is long and tufted, and the upper molar teeth resemble those of cattle, having very tall and broad crowns, with a large additional column on the inner side.

The addax is an inhabitant of Northern Africa, and is characterised by the horns being ringed for the greater part of their length, and ascending in an open spiral nearly in the plane of the face. In height it stands a little over 3 feet, and the greater part of the body is covered with short and thick hair, but there is a tuft of long hair on the forehead, and in winter a mane extending down the neck to the shoulders, and also a fringe of long hair on the throat. The colour is yellowish white, or drab, in marked contrast to which is the brown of the head, neck, and mane. There is a transverse white band below the eyes, while the lips and a spot on the outer surface of the ears are also white.

In the males the long hair is more abundant and darker in colour than in the other sex, and in winter the yellowish white of the body tends to become darker and greyer. The horns attain a length of from 20 to 30 inches in a straight line, and from 26 to 38 inches along the spiral.

The range of the addax lies to the north of the 18th parallel of north latitude, this antelope inhabiting barren, sandy deserts, where water is scarce ; it is a shy and wary creature, doubtless able to go for long periods without slaking its thirst. Its mode of life is probably very similar to that of the gemsbok, and its pale drab colouring is admirably adapted to accord with the shimmer of the desert sand.

ORYX

Under the common title of oryx may be included five species of antelopes, distinguished from the addax by the straight or recurved horns, longer and more bushy tail, the small size of the mane on the neck, and by the throat being either short-haired or furnished with a single tuft of long hair. The horns, which are of great length, slope backwards more or less nearly in the plane of the face. Oryx are found throughout the desert regions of Africa, and also range into Arabia and Syria.

THE GEMSBOK

In South Africa the group is represented by the gemsbok (*Oryx gazella*), characterised by its long, straight horns, ringed for about half their length, the tuft of hair on the throat, and the black markings on the head, body, and limbs. The gemsbok stands about 4 feet in height, and its general colour is greyish, passing into white beneath. A black stripe on the flanks divides the grey of the sides from the white below, and there is also a black area on the haunches extending as a line on the back, and continued over the whole of the tail. In addition to this, there is black on the upper parts of the limbs, on the front of the legs above the fetlocks, and along the throat ; the throat-stripe dividing and running up the sides of the head nearly to the ears. On the face a black stripe runs from each horn through the eye nearly to the muzzle, which is connected by a narrow stripe with a broad black patch on the centre of the forehead, thus completely isolating the white of the muzzle from that of the upper part of the face. Male horns of from 45 to 47 inches in length are

A CHOUSINGHA LEAPING

known, while those of the females may reach 45½ inches.

Gemsbok inhabit the desert regions of South-Western Africa, and are fairly common in the Kalahari Desert, while in Damaraland they are reported to occur in large herds ; north of the Chobi they appear to be unknown. On the west coast they occur in Senegambia, Timbuctu, and Nigeria. They are generally met with where the country is either completely open or covered with stunted scrub. Gemsbok are by no means fleet, and can be ridden to a standstill. According to Boer reports, the gemsbok is enabled to beat off the lion with its spear-like horns, and instances are recorded where the skeletons of the two animals have been found together, the body of the lion transfixed by the horns of the antelope, which were too firmly planted in the flesh to admit of their withdrawal.

The name gemsbok (pronounced " hemsbok ") is derived from *gems*, or *gemse*, the German-Swiss title of the chamois.

THE BEISA ORYX

In Abyssinia, Somaliland, the Red Sea littoral, and Eastern Africa, the gemsbok is replaced by the beisa (*Oryx beisa*), distinguished by the absence of the tuft of hair on the throat, and by the black patch on the front of the face being separated from the stripe running through the eye. There is no black on the haunches and thighs, and the horns also are shorter and less divergent, their maximum recorded length being 37 inches in the male and 39 inches in the female. The beisa is probably the true oryx of the ancients, and has been thought to be the animal which gave rise to the legend of the unicorn, although this position is now claimed for the white rhinoceros. In Abyssinia these

the form of its horns and in its type of colouring it comes nearer to the nyala and situtunga.

The mahogany, or orange, red of the body passes into brown, or even blackish, on the forehead, and the white markings, in addition to the body stripes, comprise a crescent on the chest, a chevron on the forehead, and a pair of spots on each side of the face. There is no throat fringe, and apparently no dewlap. Old bulls stand nearly 4 feet at the shoulder. In this sex the horns are very massive, and form rather more than one complete turn, their length being from 30 to 35 inches in a straight line. Those of the cows are thinner. In both sexes the tips of the horns wear yellow. Bongo are essentially forest antelopes, their large ears and vertical white stripes being adaptations to such a life, the former being essential in order to catch every sound possible, while the white stripes on a red ground appear to be protective.

KUDU

The graceful and beautifully marked antelope known as the kudu (*Strepsiceros capensis*) is distinguished from the eland and the bongo by the absence of horns in the female, and by the shorter and untufted tail, which does not reach the hocks. The horns, which form an open, corkscrew-like spiral, and are characterised by the great development of the front ridge, rise from the skull at an obtuse angle to the plane of the face. The neck is maned, and the throat furnished with a fringe of long hair. The body is marked with narrow vertical white stripes descending from a white line on the back, and there is also a white chevron on the face, with white spots on the cheek, and white splashes on the throat and limbs (page 710). The hoofs are short.

The ground colour of females and young males is reddish or greyish brown, marked with eight or nine white stripes; but in old males it becomes bluish grey, apparently owing to the skin showing through the scanty hair. The kudu is only inferior in size to the eland, a full-grown bull standing about 4 feet 4 inches at the shoulder. The horns may occasionally attain a length of 4 feet in a straight line, although even good specimens seldom exceed 3 feet 9 inches or 3 feet 6 inches in a straight line. In a pair measuring 3 feet 5 inches in a straight line, the length along the curve was 5 feet 4 inches.

The range of the kudu extends from the Cape to the Abyssinian highlands and Somaliland, embracing all Eastern Africa and extending westwards to Angola. In the Kilimanjaro district kudu appear to be rare. They are usually partial to hilly country covered with dense thickets, but hills are by no means necessary to their existence, as they are common in the thick bush along both banks of the Chobi, where there are no hills, and are also plentiful in the wait-a-bit thorn-jungles on the Lower Molapo, on the edge of the Kalahari Desert. Kudu are fond of browsing on the young and tender shoots of trees and shrubs, especially in the dry season, when the grass has been burnt off. When alarmed, they sometimes give vent to a low bark, audible only at close quarters.

Kudu are found in pairs or in small parties. Their speed is not great; but owing to the fact that when disturbed they make for the roughest ground, while the districts they haunt are frequently infested with the tsetse fly, they are seldom hunted on horseback. With dogs, however, they afford excellent sport.

The lesser kudu (*S. imberbis*) is a much smaller antelope, restricted to Somaliland and Eastern Africa as far south as Kilimanjaro. In addition to its inferior dimensions, it is distinguished by the absence of a fringe of long hair on the throat, and the more compressed spiral of the horns. Measured in a straight line, the horns vary from about 17 to 25 inches in length. The lesser kudu, although very common about Kilimanjaro, is seldom seen, as it rarely leaves the bush. In Somaliland, while the large kudu frequents the mountain ranges, the present species inhabits the thicket-clad slopes at their feet.

An imperfect skull appears to indicate the occurrence of a kudu in India during the Pliocene period; and the European Tertiary genus *Palæorcas*, although nearer to the eland, is stated to have some characters of the kudu.

HARNESSED ANTELOPES

The group of antelopes represented by the nyala, the situtunga, and the bushbuck, often referred to collectively as harnessed antelopes, are some of the

SOUTH AFRICAN BUSHBUCKS

handsomest of the whole group, being, in many cases, ornamented with vertical white stripes like the bongo, while in some cases the ground colour is most brilliant. These antelopes resemble kudu in the females being hornless, but they differ in that the horns, which are placed behind the eyes, have but one or two turns to the spiral, while the ridge on their front surface is less strongly marked. Moreover, the skull generally lacks the deep depression in the middle of the forehead characteristic of kudu, and the vacuity below the eye is smaller. The throat may be either fringed or smooth, and in one species the hoofs are extraordinarily elongated. The colouring in the two sexes is usually very different. The group is confined to Africa. Two of the species are of large size, the third not exceeding the dimensions of an ordinary goat.

THE NYALA

The nyala (*Tragelaphus angasi*) is a native of South-Eastern Africa, extending from Zululand to Nyasaland, and also reported to occur in Angola. The males stand about 3 feet 4 inches at the withers, and have horns varying from 22 to 31 inches in length. The hair is long, and the colour of the males dark greyish brown, with the white stripes faintly marked and few in number, and a fringe of long hair on the neck and under parts of the body. The horns are characterised by their rough surface. Females are much more brilliant, being marked with numerous distinct white stripes on a reddish chestnut ground. These antelopes are only to be found in low-lying, fever-stricken swamps, where they frequent the densest jungle. They are shy and difficult to stalk, and from this fact, coupled with the feverish nature of their haunts, comparatively few are killed by Europeans.

THE BUSHBUCK

The smallest representative of the group is the bushbuck (*Tragelaphus scriptus*), or guib, as it is often called, which is about equal in dimensions to an ordinary goat, the average length of the horns being about 12 inches, although specimens varying from 16 to 19 inches have been recorded. This species has a wide distribution, ranging from Abyssinia to the Cape, and exhibits such diversity in colour, and in the presence or absence of a bare glandular collar on the neck, that it is divisible into a large number of local races. In the Abyssinian race, which is shorter and stouter than the others, the general colour is yellowish, and the stripes are nearly obsolete, but there is one distinct longitudinal band, sometimes broken into spots, and the haunches are spotted, while the back has a dark crest of long hair. In the typical West African race the colour is bright rufous brilliantly marked all over the body with white spots and longitudinal and vertical stripes. In the males the crest of long hair down the middle of the back is white and the chest has a fringe of blackish hair.

In East Africa occurs a race in which the colour of the bucks is dark brown, with two or three obscure vertical stripes on the hind quarters, and even these occasionally absent; the spots being variable, although less numerous than in the preceding race. In the ordinary bushbuck of the Cape the colour is a uniform dark brown in the males with no trace of stripes, and the spots reduced to a few indistinct ones on the haunches. In all cases there are spots on the sides of the face.

Numerous other races have, like those already mentioned, received distinct names, but do not call for detailed notice.

Guib are very common in most parts of Africa, but in the south are never met with except in places where dense bush comes down to the water's edge. On the Chobi they are seldom seen at a distance of more than a few hundred yards from the river.

THE SITUTUNGA

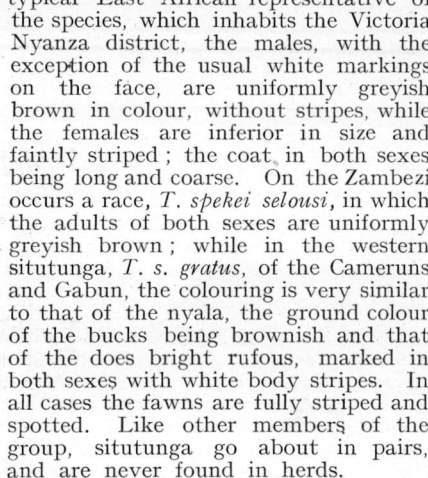

From all the other members of the harnessed group the situtunga, or nakong (*Tragelaphus spekei*), differs in the great elongation of its main hoofs and the relatively large size of the lateral pair; this being a special adaptation to enable these marsh-bucks, as they are sometimes called, to wade in lakes and swamps without sinking too deeply into the yielding mud. The bucks are handsome antelopes, standing about $3\frac{1}{2}$ feet at the shoulder, with the strongly wrinkled horns—which usually measure about 18 or 19 inches in a straight line—forming one complete turn, and thus approximating to those of the kudu.

In the typical East African representative of the species, which inhabits the Victoria Nyanza district, the males, with the exception of the usual white markings on the face, are uniformly greyish brown in colour, without stripes, while the females are inferior in size and faintly striped; the coat, in both sexes being long and coarse. On the Zambezi occurs a race, *T. spekei selousi*, in which the adults of both sexes are uniformly greyish brown; while in the western situtunga, *T. s. gratus*, of the Cameruns and Gabun, the colouring is very similar to that of the nyala, the ground colour of the bucks being brownish and that of the does bright rufous, marked in both sexes with white body stripes. In all cases the fawns are fully striped and spotted. Like other members of the group, situtunga go about in pairs, and are never found in herds.

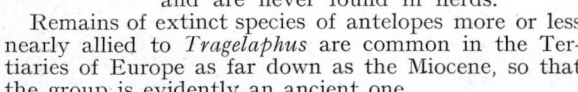
HEAD OF WESTERN SITUTUNGA

Remains of extinct species of antelopes more or less nearly allied to *Tragelaphus* are common in the Tertiaries of Europe as far down as the Miocene, so that the group is evidently an ancient one.

NILGAI

The nilgai (*Boselaphus tragocamelus*), the largest of the Indian antelopes, is the Oriental representative of the harnessed group, although it differs in several important structural features. The males only are horned, and the horns themselves are short, smooth, nearly straight, and directed upwards and backwards, with a triangular section at the base, but becoming cylindrical at the tip. In front the horns have a distinct ridge, comparable to the one in those of the eland, and in very old animals this ridge extends forwards and inwards till the horns almost touch at their bases. The nilgai is peculiar in having the fore limbs longer than the hind pair, and the withers very high, in consequence of which its whole appearance is somewhat ungainly. The tail is tufted and reaches the hocks; and in both sexes the neck is maned, while the throat of the male has a small tuft of hair. The gland below the eye is very small and the muzzle naked.

The upper molar teeth differ from those of the harnessed antelopes in their tall crowns, with a large additional column on the inner side. In colour the adult bull nilgai is dark grey, with either a brownish or bluish tinge; and is accordingly known to English sportsmen as the blue bull, an exact translation of the Indian name "nilgai." The long hairs on the neck, throat, and tail, and some portions of the ears are, however, black, and there are white markings on the face, ears, and throat, while the lower surface of the tail, the under parts of the body, and a ring above and below each fetlock are likewise white. In young males and females the colour is brown. A bull nilgai usually stands from 4 feet 4 inches to 4 feet 8 inches at the withers, but it is stated that 4 feet 10 inches has been measured. The cows are much smaller. The black horns average 8 or 9 inches in length, with a basal girth of 8 inches; but one pair has been recorded with a length of 11¾ and a girth of 9½ inches.

The nilgai is exclusively an Indian antelope, being unknown in Ceylon, while even in India its distribution is restricted, as it does not occur in Eastern Bengal, Assam, or near the Malabar coast. Fossil species occur in the river-gravels of Central India, and also in the Pliocene sandstones of the Siwalik Hills.

Nilgai may be found either on the plains or in low hills, preferring ground covered with thin bush, among which are scattered low trees, or alternations of scrub-jungle with open grassy plains. They are seldom met with in thick forest, although far from infrequent on cultivated grounds. The bulls are generally solitary, but occasionally assemble in small parties, which may include as many as a dozen head. The females and calves are found in parties of from four to ten, but sometimes in herds of from fifteen to twenty or more, and on some occasions are accompanied by one or more full-grown bulls. Nilgai both graze and browse, and will feed at any time of the day, although they resort sometimes to the shade for repose; in the cold season they probably drink but once in two or three days. They can be readily tamed, but the bulls are apt to be savage. Either one or two calves are produced at a birth.

THE FOUR-HORNED ANTELOPE

The chousingha, or four-horned antelope, (*Tetraceros quadricornis*) may be associated with the present group, although very different from all the rest, and differs from all other living ruminants in that the male generally has two pairs of horns, of which the larger is placed far back, while the smaller pair is situated immediately over the eyes. The gland below the eye has an elongated aperture, and the upper molar teeth have no additional column on the inner side. All the horns of the male are short, conical, and smooth; the front pair often being reduced to mere knobs, and not infrequently absent. In height the male chousingha stands 25½ inches at the withers, but an inch and a half higher over the haunches. The coat is thin, harsh, and short, and longer on the upper surface of the tail than elsewhere.

The colour is dull pale brown, with a more or less marked rufous tinge above, passing gradually into white on the under parts and the inner sides and lower portions of the limbs. There is a dark streak down the front of each leg, larger in the fore than in the hind limbs. The second pair of horns usually varies from 3½ to 4 inches in length, and does not appear to exceed 4½ inches. The front pair is generally not more than 1½ inches in length, but may reach 2½ inches; they are frequently absent in specimens from Madras.

The chousingha is found along the foot of the Himalaya from the Punjab to Nepal, and over the greater part of peninsular India in wooded and hilly country, although it avoids dense jungle. It is unknown in the plain of the Ganges, on the Malabar coast in Madras, and in Ceylon.

Dr. W. T. Blanford observes that the chousingha "differs from all other Indian antelopes in habits as much as in structure. It is not gregarious, very rarely are more than two seen together; it haunts thin forest and bush, and keeps chiefly to undulating or hilly ground. It drinks daily, and is never seen far from water. It is a shy animal, and moves with a peculiar jerky action whether walking or running. The rutting season is in the rains, and the young, one or two in number, are born about January or February."

Fossil remains of the existing species have been discovered in a cave in Madras, and it is believed that the genus is represented in the Pliocene deposits of the Siwalik Hills at the foot of the Himalaya.

A NILGAI BULL

THE ADDAX

The addax (*Addax nasomaculatus*) is the first of a group of African and Arabian antelopes of large size, collectively forming the subfamily *Hippotraginæ*, and presenting the following distinctive characteristics. They have long, cylindrical horns in both sexes, which are placed over or above the eyes, and are either sub-spiral, straight, or recurved. The muzzle is covered with hair, and there is no gland below the eye, while the skull has no depression below the socket of the eye, and only a very narrow unossified space in the same region. The tail is long and tufted, and the upper molar teeth resemble those of cattle, having very tall and broad crowns, with a large additional column on the inner side.

The addax is an inhabitant of Northern Africa, and is characterised by the horns being ringed for the greater part of their length, and ascending in an open spiral nearly in the plane of the face. In height it stands a little over 3 feet, and the greater part of the body is covered with short and thick hair, but there is a tuft of long hair on the forehead, and in winter a mane extending down the neck to the shoulders, and also a fringe of long hair on the throat. The colour is yellowish white, or drab, in marked contrast to which is the brown of the head, neck, and mane. There is a transverse white band below the eyes, while the lips and a spot on the outer surface of the ears are also white.

In the males the long hair is more abundant and darker in colour than in the other sex, and in winter the yellowish white of the body tends to become darker and greyer. The horns attain a length of from 20 to 30 inches in a straight line, and from 26 to 38 inches along the spiral.

The range of the addax lies to the north of the 18th parallel of north latitude, this antelope inhabiting barren, sandy deserts, where water is scarce; it is a shy and wary creature, doubtless able to go for long periods without slaking its thirst. Its mode of life is probably very similar to that of the gemsbok, and its pale drab colouring is admirably adapted to accord with the shimmer of the desert sand.

ORYX

Under the common title of oryx may be included five species of antelopes, distinguished from the addax by the straight or recurved horns, longer and more bushy tail, the small size of the mane on the neck, and by the throat being either short-haired or furnished with a single tuft of long hair. The horns, which are of great length, slope backwards more or less nearly in the plane of the face. Oryx are found throughout the desert regions of Africa, and also range into Arabia and Syria.

THE GEMSBOK

In South Africa the group is represented by the gemsbok (*Oryx gazella*), characterised by its long, straight horns, ringed for about half their length, the tuft of hair on the throat, and the black markings on the head, body, and limbs. The gemsbok stands about 4 feet in height, and its general colour is greyish, passing into white beneath. A black stripe on the flanks divides the grey of the sides from the white below, and there is also a black area on the haunches extending as a line on the back, and continued over the whole of the tail. In addition to this, there is black on the upper parts of the limbs, on the front of the legs above the fetlocks, and along the throat; the throat-stripe dividing and running up the sides of the head nearly to the ears. On the face a black stripe runs from each horn through the eye nearly to the muzzle, which is connected by a narrow stripe with a broad black patch on the centre of the forehead, thus completely isolating the white of the muzzle from that of the upper part of the face. Male horns of from 45 to 47 inches in length are

A CHOUSINGHA LEAPING

known, while those of the females may reach 45½ inches.

Gemsbok inhabit the desert regions of South-Western Africa, and are fairly common in the Kalahari Desert, while in Damaraland they are reported to occur in large herds; north of the Chobi they appear to be unknown. On the west coast they occur in Senegambia, Timbuctu, and Nigeria. They are generally met with where the country is either completely open or covered with stunted scrub. Gemsbok are by no means fleet, and can be ridden to a standstill. According to Boer reports, the gemsbok is enabled to beat off the lion with its spear-like horns, and instances are recorded where the skeletons of the two animals have been found together, the body of the lion transfixed by the horns of the antelope, which were too firmly planted in the flesh to admit of their withdrawal.

The name gemsbok (pronounced "hemsbok") is derived from *gems*, or *gemse*, the German-Swiss title of the chamois.

THE BEISA ORYX

In Abyssinia, Somaliland, the Red Sea littoral, and Eastern Africa, the gemsbok is replaced by the beisa (*Oryx beisa*), distinguished by the absence of the tuft of hair on the throat, and by the black patch on the front of the face being separated from the stripe running through the eye. There is no black on the haunches and thighs, and the horns also are shorter and less divergent, their maximum recorded length being 37 inches in the male and 39 inches in the female. The beisa is probably the true oryx of the ancients, and has been thought to be the animal which gave rise to the legend of the unicorn, although this position is now claimed for the white rhinoceros. In Abyssinia these antelopes are found in herds of considerable size, when they present an imposing appearance. Their favourite pace is a quick walk or trot, and they only break into a gallop when frightened. On such occasions they dash off with lowered heads and upraised tails, at the same time puffing and snorting. In Somaliland beisa chiefly frequent open stony ground or grassy plains, but may be found in any kind of country except thick jungle or cedar forests. The herds are chiefly composed of cows, the bulls wandering about by themselves. The Midgans of Somaliland hunt the beisa with packs of yellow pariah dogs.

In the Kilimanjaro district the species is represented by the fringe-eared beisa (*O. beisa callotis*), distinguished by the ground colour of the upper part of the face being rich fawn, and the sharply pointed ears terminating in tufts of long, black hair. This race is common in the plains and the tracts of thin, thorny bush.

THE ARABIAN ORYX

Compared with the gemsbok and beisa, the Arabian oryx (*Oryx beatrix*) is a much smaller animal, standing about 2 feet 8 inches in height, and is whitish in colour, with a dark spot on the face, and a large dark patch on each cheek meeting beneath the throat; there is a more or less distinct dark flank-band, and the knees and lower part of both legs are also blackish brown, and the end of the tail is black. The horns range from about 20 to 27 inches in length. This species inhabits the interior of Southern Arabia, where its exact range is still unknown, but it probably extends round the borders of the Roba-el-Khali, from east of the Yemen highlands to Oman, and as far north as Nejd. In Central Arabia (Nejd) it is not found, nor does it occur in Mesopotamia or Northern Arabia, but it reappears in the north-west, where it inhabits a comparatively small area between the oases of Jauf, Hail, Teima, and Tebuk. It does not range west of the Hedjaz railway nor go north of the 30th parallel of latitude. It is said to occur also in Southern Persia, but this requires confirmation.

"The Arabian oryx," writes Mr. D. Carruthers, "lives in very dry, barren, desert regions, either in the neighbourhood of sandstone hills or on the open sandy desert. I found it most numerous on the western edge of the Great Nafud, which is an entirely waterless region of sand-hills. Its food, found in the wadis and depressions, consists chiefly of a fine grass (*Aristida forskalii*), called nusi, or sebat, by the Bedouin, which grows to a height of 18 inches. It also feeds on the ghada bush, which grows on the sand-dunes, and is fond of digging in the sand to get at the long, juicy spadix of the parasites (*Cynomonium coccineum*) that grow on the roots of the ghada and tamarisk. Their broad, flat hoofs are no doubt a great advantage on the soft sand."

THE ARABIAN ORYX

THE WHITE ORYX

The last representative of the genus is the white oryx (*Oryx leucoryx*), which, while agreeing nearly in size with the beisa, differs from the other four species in its recurved, scimitar-like horns, and uniform whitish coloration, which frequently shows a reddish tinge. The reddish tinge is most pronounced on the under parts, the upper portions of the limbs, and the neck. The head is marked by six chestnut patches, one between the horns, two between the ears, and two between the horns and eyes, while the sixth forms a streak on the nose. The horns vary from 34 to 44 inches in length. The white oryx is confined to northern Central Africa, ranging from Nigeria to Sennar, Kordofan, and Nubia. It is common in Sennar and Kordofan.

Among the animals mummified in Egypt is the white oryx, now found on this side of Africa only in the Sudan, although in the time of the Pharaohs common in the Delta. The ancient Egyptian name of this signified the "white animal of the desert," and apparently was the same word as *beisa*, the native name of the beisa oryx of East Africa.

In the Pliocene deposits of various parts of Europe occur remains of antelopes closely allied to the oryx, some of which have been generically separated under the name of *Palæoryx*, and are believed to show signs of affinity with the sable antelope and its kindred.

ROAN AND SABLE ANTELOPES

The roan and sable antelopes, together with an extinct species, constitute an exclusively African genus nearly allied to oryx, and distinguished by the stout horns, ringed nearly to their tips, and rising vertically from a ridge on the skull immediately over the eyes at an obtuse angle to the plane of the lower part of the face, and then curving in a bold sweep backwards.

The neck is clothed with a distinct, erect, and often recurving mane; the tail is rather short and distinctly tufted; and the ears are enormous. The horns of females are shorter than those of males.

The roan, or equine, antelope (*Hippotragus equinus*), the bastard gemsbok of the Boers, is the largest representative of the genus, standing rather over $4\frac{1}{2}$ feet at the withers, and is defined by its roan, or reddish brown, colour, large white eye-tufts, and enormous, heavily tufted ears. There is considerable variation in colour, some specimens being strawberry-roan, others deep dark grey or brown, and others so light in colour as to appear almost white at a distance. The under parts are little lighter than the body, while the head and face have dark brown markings. The latter markings are characterised by the white streak in front of the eye being separated by a dark band from the white of the muzzle. The ears are very large, and the mane is small and erect.

The horns of bulls seldom exceed 30 inches in length, measured along the curve, but specimens measuring 33 and 35 inches have been recorded. This species has a large range, extending from Cape Colony to Abyssinia, and westwards to the Gambia. There are several local races, differing from one another in general colour, in the extent of the dark markings on the face and limbs, and in the length of the tufts of hair on the ears.

The species is nowhere numerous, and it is seldom that as many as twenty are seen together.

The blaauwbok (*H. leucophæus*) was a smaller but nearly allied species from the Cape, which has long been extinct. It derived its Dutch name from the bluish hue of the coat, and its head was uniformly coloured.

The handsomest member of the genus is the sable antelope (*Hippotragus niger*), which is rather smaller than the roan antelope, but has much longer horns, smaller ears and eye-tufts, and a longer and more abundant mane, partly pendent (page 727). With the exception of portions of the face, buttocks, and under parts, the coat is deep glossy black, the contrast formed by the white of the under parts being very striking; the markings on the face differ from those of the roan antelope in that the white streaks in front of the eyes are continued to join the white of the muzzle, and separated by a dark streak from that of the throat. The horns of the males not infrequently attain a length of 42 or 43 inches, but may reach as much as 46, or even 51 inches along the curve. In the females 36 inches seem to be the maximum.

The sable antelope is a southern species, ranging as far north as Uganda, and being most abundant in Mashonaland. This antelope, unlike the various species of oryx, frequents forest-clad highlands. In Mashonaland it is met with in herds of from ten to twenty individuals, although so many as fifty may be seen together. Mr. F. C. Selous observes that, "as a rule, the sable antelope runs very swiftly and has good bottom; but in this respect different individuals differ considerably, as is the case with all animals, and I have run down without much difficulty individual sable antelopes and roan antelopes, and one gemsbok, whilst others have gone clean away from me. The sable antelope is often very savage when wounded, and, like the roan antelope and gemsbok, will commit terrible havoc amongst a pack of dogs. Indeed, I have known one to kill three dogs with three consecutive sweeps of its long, scimitar-shaped horns." From having been discovered by Sir Cornwallis Harris, it is frequently termed the Harris buck by the inhabitants of the Cape. Those who have seen this antelope in its native wilds are impressed with its beauty and majestic appearance.

Extinct antelopes from the Pliocene deposits at the foot of the Himalaya indicate the former existence of the genus *Hippotragus* in India, and it was, perhaps, represented in Europe during the same epoch.

GAZELLES

The large group of antelopes known as gazelles is the first of an assemblage of several genera differing considerably from those yet noticed. Most are of small or moderate size, and the majority are inhabitants of the deserts of the Old World. All have narrow upper molar teeth like sheep, and their muzzles are similarly covered with hair. There is frequently a gland below the eye, and the tail is either short or of moderate length. As a rule, the horns are compressed, and lyrate or recurved, or cylindrical and

A GROUP OF BEISA

spiral, with distinct rings for a considerable portion of their length, and the skull has large pits in the forehead.

The name gazelle is derived from the Arabic *alghazal*, which is the native title of both the Arabian gazelle and the dorcas.

Gazelles are among the most elegant of all antelopes, and characterised by their sandy colour and the presence of a white streak on the side of the face from the base of the horn nearly to the nose, cutting off a dark triangular patch in the middle of the forehead, the streak itself being usually bordered externally by a diffused dark line. The horns, which are commonly present in both sexes, are lyrate or recurved, compressed oval in section, and completely ringed throughout the greater part of their length. The knees are generally furnished with tufts of hair. Glands are present on the feet, and the gland—when there is one—below the eye is small and covered with hair. Most of the gazelles do not exceed 30 inches in height, although the mohr reaches 36 inches. The species of the genus *Gazella* are mainly found in the deserts of Asia and North Africa, two of the Asiatic species living at great elevations. Several species of fossil gazelles occur in the Pleistocene and Pliocene deposits of Europe and India. The whole group forms the sub-family *Antilopinæ*.

Gazelles may be divided into groups according to the colour and the presence or absence of horns in the females, and, as the species are so numerous, one from each group will suffice for special notice.

THE SPRINGBUCK

The springbuck (*Antidorcas euchore*) is a South African species representing a genus by itself, distinguished by the presence of a stripe of long white erectile hairs running down the middle of the back, and by having only two premolar teeth in the lower jaw. Both sexes are horned. In height the springbuck stands about 30 inches, and the black horns are lyrate, with about twenty complete rings, and in the males attain a length of from 10 to 17 inches. The general colour is dark cinnamon yellow, but there is a dark brown stripe on the flanks dividing the cinnamon of the sides from the white of the under parts, and a dark streak running through the eye. There is more white on the face than in typical gazelles, the central dark area of the forehead being reduced to a small patch below the horns. The snow-white hairs on the back have a length of 3 or 4 inches (page 728).

In eastern South Africa the northern range of the spingbuck extends to about latitude 20°, its limits being marked by the forests south of the Mababi River; westwards of Lake Ngami, however, it extends farther north, reaching Benguela and Angola on the west coast. It is still found in the north-west of Cape Colony, and throughout the Transvaal and Griqualand West, while it is abundant on the borders of the Kalahari Desert.

The springbuck derives its name from its habit of suddenly leaping into the air, and is remarkable both for the large numbers in which it formerly occurred, and for its periodical migrations. Writing of one of these migrations, Gordon Cumming states that "for about two hours before dawn I had been lying awake in my waggon, listening to the grunting of the buck within 200 yards of me; imagining that some large herd of springbucks was feeding beside my camp, but, rising when it was light and looking about me, I beheld the ground to the north of my camp actually covered with a dense living mass of springbucks, marching slowly and steadily along. They extended from an

opening in a long range of hills on the west, through which they continued pouring like a flood of some great river, to a ridge about a mile to the north-east, over which they disappeared—the breadth they covered might have been somewhere about half a mile."

Vast, however, as must have been the numbers on this occasion, Boers informed the narrator that they were nothing to those that had been witnessed in some *trek-bokken*, when the animals extended over a succession of flats, instead of being confined to one alone, and were crowded together like sheep in a fold throughout a long

A ROAN ANTELOPE BULL

day's journey, as far as the eye could reach. So dense were the moving masses that if a flock of sheep became intermingled with the herd, it was swept along without hope of escape; and it is said that even a lion in those days might be thus entrapped. Livingstone suggested that these migrations were due to the grass in the Kalahari Desert becoming so tall as to impede the springbuck from obtaining a clear view of the surrounding country.

THE DORCAS GAZELLE

The Dorcas gazelle (*Gazella dorcas*), which is a well-known representative of a group of the gazelles in which the white of the rump does not encroach on the fawn colour of the haunches, and both sexes have lyrate or sublyrate horns, inhabits the deserts of Egypt, Algeria, Syria, Palestine, and parts of Asia Minor. It stands barely 24 inches at the shoulder; and the horns are relatively long and slender, with their tips incurved, their length being sometimes a little over 13 inches. This beautiful little antelope is of extremely delicate build, and is remarkable for its great speed. When running, it appears to skim the ground like a bird, and often takes leaps of a yard or more in height.

Closely allied to this species is the isabelline gazelle (*G. isabella*) of Kordofan and Sennar, distinguished by the tail being rufous, instead of black, above. Other species are the korin (*G. rufifrons*) of Senegal; Sundevall's gazelle (*G. lævipes*) of Sennar; and the black-tailed gazelle (*G. tilonura*) of Bogosland, the last-named being characterised by its superior size, reaching 29 inches at the shoulder, and the horns varying from 7 to 10¼ inches in length.

THE INDIAN GAZELLE

The Indian gazelle (*Gazella bennetti*) is a member of a subgroup distinguished by the horns not being distinctly lyrate, but having a slight S-shaped curvature when seen from the side. The general colour of this species—the ravine-deer of Indian sportsmen—is light chestnut above, while the tail is blackish. In height the buck stands 26 inches at the withers, and the horns, which usually have fifteen or sixteen rings, average 10 to 12 inches in length along the curve.

HEAD OF CHIRU

This species inhabits the plains of Central and North-Western India. It is commonly found in parties of from two to six, although occasionally from ten to twenty may be found together. Its swiftness is such that it can seldom be taken with dogs, but it does not leap in the air like the dorcas. Mr. Blanford writes that this gazelle "keeps much to waste ground, especially where that is broken up by ravines, but it is seldom seen on alluvial plains, and it haunts cultivation less than the [Indian] antelope. It is frequently found amongst scattered bushes or thin tree-jungle, and may be met with on undulating ground even on the top of hills ; it is commonly found amongst sand hills, and is nowhere so abundant as in parts of the Indian desert. It lives on grass and the leaves of bushes, and I believe never drinks, for it is common in tracts where there is no water except from deep wells."

Other members of this group are Kennion's gazelle (*G. fuscifrons*) of Seistan, the edmi gazelle (*G. cuvieri*) of Morocco and Algeria, which reaches the height of $27\frac{1}{2}$ inches, Loder's gazelle (*G. leptoceros*) of Algeria and Nubia, the Arabian gazelle (*G. arabica*), and Speke's gazelle (*G. spekei*) of the plateau of Somaliland. The last is of small size, and remarkable for the loose, flabby skin on the nose, and is further distinguished by the length of its hair and dull colour. The length of the horns ranges from $9\frac{1}{2}$ to $11\frac{1}{2}$ inches.

THE GOITRED GAZELLE

Another group is formed by certain Asiatic gazelles, which differ from all other members of the genus by the females being hornless. Of these, the goitred gazelle (*Gazella subgutturosa*) inhabits the highlands of Persia, but is represented in Seistan by *G. seistanica*. The former has lyrate horns, with incurved tips, which may have from sixteen to twenty-five rings ; and the tail is not surrounded by a white disc. In Mongolia it is replaced by the larger Mongolian gazelle (*G. gutturosa*), characterised by a shorter

HEAD OF GRANT'S GAZELLE

tail, and white rump and legs. In the three species the throats of the bucks have a goitre-like swelling in the breeding season.

Another member of the group is the goa, or Tibetan gazelle (*G. picticaudata*), which is distinguished by the white disc round the rump, the long winter coat, short ears and tail, the greatly-curved horns, and the uniform colour of the face. The height is 24 inches, and the large horns measure 15 inches in length, the number of rings varying from twenty to thirty. This gazelle inhabits the Tibetan plateau at elevations of from 13,000 to 18,000 feet, and goes in small parties of from two or three to a dozen. It is less shy than other species. Przewalski's gazelle (*G. przevalskii*) is an allied species from Mongolia, and the Saikik gazelle (*G. yarcandensis*) represents the group in Yarkand.

LARGER GAZELLES

The last group of the gazelles is characterised by the white of the rump extending forwards in an angle into the fawn colour of the haunches, both sexes having horns, which are frequently longer than in the other groups, and the animals themselves being also large. Perhaps the handsomest member of the whole genus is the East African Grant's gazelle (*G. granti*).

This gazelle has longer and finer horns than any other species, their length being frequently as much as 26 inches, while in one instance a length of 30 inches has been recorded. The general colour of the upper part of the body is fawn, and there is typically no dark band on the flanks dividing the fawn colour from the white of the under parts. On the neck and back the hair

HEAD OF DIBATAG

has a kind of wavy appearance, somewhat like the pattern on watered silk. This gazelle is common on the open plains of East Africa, where it is found in small parties comprising from ten to fifteen does and fawns, accompanied by a single adult buck.

In Masailand, on the east coast to the north of Zanzibar, Grant's gazelle is replaced by the smaller Thomson's gazelle (*G. thomsoni*), in which the horns are smaller and thinner, not exceeding $15\frac{3}{4}$ inches in length. This gazelle is also distinguished by the broad dark brown band on the flanks

HEAD AND NECK OF GERENUK

dividing the fawn of the body from the white of the belly. The largest of the group is the dama, or addra (*G. dama*), ranging from Senegal and Morocco to the Sudan, and standing 36 or 37 inches at the withers, and still higher at the rump. It has relatively short lyrate horns, and no dark band on the flanks, with an unusually large amount of white on the buttocks. The horns curve forwards at the tips. Another fine species is the aoul (*G. sœmmerringi*), inhabiting the lowlands of Somaliland, Abyssinia, and the Sudan. In the dama gazelle the length of the horns may be 12 inches; while in the aoul, or Sœmmerring's gazelle, this varies from about 12 to fully 20 inches.

The height of the latter species at the shoulder is about 35½ inches. It is characterised by its very massive lyrate horns, marked with about eighteen rings, and curving strongly inwards at the tips; while it may also be distinguished from the dama by its longer ears, bordered with black externally, and the more strongly-defined and nearly black markings on the face. This is the finest of the Somaliland gazelles, and was formerly found in small herds close to the shore.

FRENCH MUSCAT GAZELLE

THE DIBATAG

Nearly allied to the gazelles is the dibatag (*Ammodorcas clarkei*) of Somaliland, which has the face markings of the gazelles, but is distinguished by the regular upward and forward curvature of the rather short horns, which are ringed in front at the base. The females are hornless, and the skull is intermediate between that of the gazelles and the gerenuk. The neck is very long, the tail thin and long, and the rings on the horns from five to ten in number.

The general colour is deep cinnamon, darker than in any of the gazelles. These antelopes are local in Somaliland, but common in parts of the interior. When running, they throw the tail upwards and forwards, and incline the long neck backwards,

MALE KORIN GAZELLE

so that the two look as if they would touch each other.

THE GERENUK

A still more remarkable antelope is the gerenuk, or Waller's gazelle (*Lithocranius walleri*), an East African species, ranging from Somaliland to the Kilimanjaro district. The most peculiar feature about this species is the excessively long neck, which has led to its being likened to a miniature giraffe. The horns of the bucks curve forwards at the tips in a hook-like manner, and are usually about 13 inches in length, although they may reach 17 inches. The skin is distinguished by a broad dark brown band down the middle of the back, which in its widest part measures 7 or 8 inches across, and forms a contrast to the rufous fawn of the flanks and limbs. The skull differs from those of the gazelles in its dense and solid structure, as well as the relative shortness of its facial portion, its straightness, and the small size of the cheek teeth.

Colonel Swayne states that "the gerenuk is found all over the Somali country in small families, never in large herds, and generally in scattered bush, ravines, and rocky ground. I have never seen it in the cedar forests, nor in the treeless plains. Gerenuk are not necessarily found near water; in fact, generally in stony ground with a sprinkling of thorn-jungle. The gait of this antelope is peculiar. When first seen, a buck gerenuk will generally be standing motionless, head well up, looking at the intruder, and trusting to its invisibility. Then the head dives under the bushes, and the animal goes off at a long, crouching trot, stopping now and again behind some bush to gaze. The trot is awkward-looking, and very like that of a camel; the gerenuk seldom gallops, and its pace is never very fast. In the whole shape of the head and neck, and in the slender lower jaw, there is a marked resemblance between the gerenuk and the dibatag."

FEMALE CUVIER'S GAZELLE

This antelope subsists more by browsing than by grazing, and may be observed standing up on its hind legs, with outstretched neck, and its fore feet resting against the trunk of a tree in order to pluck the foliage.

BLACKBUCK

The handsomely-coloured blackbuck, or Indian antelope (*Antilope cervicapra*), is the sole representative of its genus, and at the same time the last member of the present group (page 729). The blackbuck stands about 32 inches at the shoulder, and has a short and compressed tail, large glands, with a linear aperture below the eyes, tufts of hair on the knees, and small but distinct lateral hoofs. The horns of the bucks rise close together, and

SABLE ANTELOPES

are cylindrical, divergent, and spiral, with complete blunt rings throughout their length. The number of turns in the spiral of the horns varies from less than three to as many as five, and there is great variation in regard to the degree of divergence of the horns. The usual length of horns varies from 16 to 20 inches in a straight line, and in peninsular India the length seldom exceeds 22 inches, but in Rajputana and Harriana the horns are longer, and sometimes attain 28¾ inches.

Does and young bucks are yellowish fawn above and on the outer sides of the limbs, and white on the under parts; the two colours are sharply defined, and just above the line of division there is a distinct pale streak. Save for a rufous patch on the nape of the neck, old bucks are blackish brown above, and on the sides of the neck and the whole of the face, with the exception of a white ring round each eye. In very old individuals the blackish brown becomes almost completely black. Occasionally does have small recurved horns.

The blackbuck is an inhabitant of open plains from the foot of the Himalaya nearly to Cape Comorin, and from the Punjab to Lower Assam; and is most abundant in the United Provinces, Rajputana, and portions of the Deccan. It frequents grassy districts or cultivated lands, and is found in herds, which

may comprise hundreds, or even thousands, but more usually number from ten to thirty, or even fifty does, accompanied by a single old buck. Blackbuck feed at all hours, although they generally rest during the middle of the day. Like springbuck, blackbuck frequently leap high into the air when running. The speed and endurance of these antelopes are well known; and they are seldom pulled down on good ground by greyhounds. In heavy sand, or on soft ground during the rains, they are, however, easily overtaken by good dogs, and wounded buck may be ridden down.

Young fawns are generally concealed by the does in long grass. The bucks utter a short grunt, and the does a kind of hissing sound, when alarmed. During the pairing season the bucks engage in frequent combats among themselves. When taken young, the black-buck can be easily tamed, but the males are apt to be dangerous at certain seasons.

R. LYDEKKER

SHOOTING THE BLACKBUCK

By MAJOR F. G. ALEXANDER

The blackbuck is generally regarded as the budding Indian sportsman's earliest prey. I remember well how my fingers quivered and my heart throbbed when I first pressed trigger on a buck. The size of the animal varies very much, and one can say that, unlike the sambar, the average length of horns of the blackbuck and the average weight of its body depend greatly upon the locality, whereas very large and very small sambar are found together in all the jungles I have visited. The shortest horned and smallest buck are to be found in the Deccan, and within that area if you kill a buck with horns 18 or 20 inches in length, they are regarded as above the average. I have shot over 200 buck in the following districts: the Deccan, Bundelkhand, Rajputana, North-Western Provinces, Bhopal, Hyderabad, Surat, and elsewhere. The largest horns are to be found about Bikanir. In the Deccan, the finest horns and beasts I have shot roamed in a small native state called Akulkote. Next to the Bikanir buck that found in Bhurtpore territory is the finest. In the Bikanir desert herds a hundred strong used to exist in 1883.

I have not read any discussion on the difference of size in buck living in different districts, but I think that salt has a great deal to do with the superiority of the Bikanir animal. Salt is as necessary to the well-being of an animal as it is to mankind. I once remained at Surat during the monsoon. My bungalow was beside the Nerbudda, rolling majestically with its volume of water to the sea. On each side of the river, close to the sea, I found antelope, and the animals were above the average. I watched them licking the frost-like surface of salt left here and there by evaporation. Sambar instinctively appreciate it. Saltpetre is found in large quantities about Bikanir, and I know that many sportsmen have endured the dreary pilgrimage to that inhospitable region to secure fine heads.

Albinos, I learn from a trustworthy source, are commoner in the North-Western Provinces than

anywhere else. The variety in the colours of buck skins is infinite. But I have only shot—at Patus, in the Deccan—one albino with pink eyes and white skin, excepting the saddle, where the colour was very faint ochre. I saw another albino at Malligaon, in the Deccan, but failed to kill it. I have also shot, at Salut, in Bundelkhand, a semi-albino with dirty-white skin and whitish horns. The colour of that animal's eyes was amber, and I regard it as a rarer beast than the pure albino. Fair antelope are to be found at Ahmedabad, though not of the Bikanir class. Ahmedabad horns are unusually thick, and the spirals are more gradual, and the horns straighter than most horns I have seen, but their length is not remarkable.

I have found blackbuck as a rule on the open plain, but in four separate places I discovered them in jungles frequented by the wild boar. The first place was a grass jungle interspersed with thick bushes near the Residency, Bhurtpore ; the second was a range of thorn, cactus, and grass jungle between Patus and Seroor (Deccan) ; the third possessed the same grass and thorns, and was near to Erinpura, Rajputana, where there were also wild pigs and a tiger ; the fourth was Sholapore. Near the old racquet court—which is closely connected with an historical event of the Indian Mutiny—is a thick grass and bush jungle by the road which leads to Bijapur. It was the home of the quail, the wild boar, the florikin, and the blackbuck.

Male antelope often separate from a herd and become for a time solitary beasts, and such animals were the ones I interviewed in the patches referred to. I never found a herd of antelope in such places. At Erinpura, whilst after quail, etc., a buck has often risen within a few feet of me. I think that when the antelope bounds in long grass, it does so for a look round, and not for exercise.

The natives, especially in the Bombay Presidency, have two ways by which they slaughter antelope. It is immaterial to a native whether the prey is male or female, so long as the victim reaches the cooking-pot. The first arrangement is to plant about twenty or more flags

THE BLACKBUCK   Photo C. V. Peel

in an area frequented by antelope. The flags are mounted on sticks about six feet in height, and placed about fifty yards apart in the shape of a V. Many men engage in the hunt, but at the apex of the V are one or two men concealed in pits or behind artificial screens. They are armed with muzzle-loading guns loaded with slugs. The object of the beaters is to drive the herd within the jaws of the V. When once they have succeeded in doing so, the herd finds itself with flags waving to the right and left of it.

The farther the herd moves the nearer are the flags, until at last it arrives at the head of the V in what natives call a " gŏbra " (disconcerted) condition, and the herd then stands still within a few yards of the masked

gunners, who drench it with slugs. The other plan is to lay out a continuous line of nooses, extending sometimes for five hundred yards. The nooses are composed of the sinews of antelope, and pegged at short intervals with pieces of antelope horn or wood. I once collected a bullock-cart load of such nooses and, in the interest of sport and fair play, burned the lot.

Sometimes natives, when following a blackbuck through a jowaree field, will hood themselves with the skin and horns of a buck, and so arrange things that the horns only are visible to the beast they are pursuing. This device is dangerous to the natives, as a sporting subaltern may be about, and be unaware of the black man's disguise.

Once in the Akulkote State a curious incident happened to me. I had a long shot at a blackbuck, and the bullet superficially struck the base of one of its horns. The horn became unscrewed and flew into the air, and the poor beast had to endure the misery of a bleeding core. I picked up the horn, but did not secure the buck. Those who know the formation of buck horns will understand how such an incident could occur. I dare say other sportsmen have done what I did. I have often knocked off a horn, including the core, with a bullet, but only once unscrewed a horn from the core. The longest horns I ever saw were 31 inches in length. The beast was killed near Bikanir by Major Percy Smith. The same officer killed many others with horns over 28 inches in length near the same place. Doe antelope rarely possess horns, but I saw one specimen killed by Colonel Yule of the Devonshire Regiment near Nowgong, Bundelkhand. I have shot buck with extraordinary horns both in Bhurtpore territory and near Delhi. Once I killed a buck with one horn 26 inches in length, the other horn being curled like that of a ram, but if you kill a buck with six spirals, you may be satisfied that it is a specimen out of the common.

F. G. ALEXANDER

THE CHIRU

In addition to possessing a peculiar gazelle, the barren plateau of Tibet is the home of an antelope remarkable for the swollen nose and long horns of the bucks. This is the chiru (*Pantholops hodgsoni*), the sole representative of the genus to which it belongs (page 692). In many respects the chiru is allied to the saiga, but the nose is less convex, and the nostrils open anteriorly instead of downwards. The horns, which—as in all the following members of this group—are present only in the bucks, are black, long, erect, laterally compressed, and sublyrate, with rings in front for the lower two-thirds of their length. There is no gland below the eye, and the skull lacks the pits between the eyes. In height the male chiru stands 32 inches at the shoulder, and is covered with very thick, close fur, which becomes woolly near the skin. The colour is pale fawn above and white below ; the whole face and a stripe down the front of each leg being black or dark brown in the bucks. The horns frequently reach 24 and 26 inches in length, and one pair has been recorded of 27½ inches. There are only two pairs of premolar teeth. The chiru probably inhabits the whole of the Tibetan plateau, at the same elevations as the Tibetan gazelle.

In summer the sexes live apart; and these antelopes are often found in parties of from three to four individuals, but sometimes in large herds. They frequent the open rolling plains or broad river valleys, and generally feed at morning and evening. Chiru are in the habit of excavating hollows in the sand, in which they lie concealed during the day. The young are born in summer, one being produced at a birth. This and the next two species are only distantly related to the gazelles.

THE SAIGA

From the peculiarly bloated appearance of the nose of the male, the saiga (*Saiga tatarica*) of the steppes of Eastern Europe and Western Asia is one of the most ungainly of antelopes. In size it may be compared to a sheep, and its whole build is clumsy. The nose is very large, convex, and inflated, with the nostrils opening downwards; and the face has a small gland below the eye. The ears are small and rounded; and the tail is of moderate length. The lyrate horns are rather short, completely ringed, and of an amber yellow colour. In summer the general colour of the upper parts is tawny yellow; but in winter, when the hair increases in length, the tint is greyish, and, in fact, externally nearly white; the face, under parts, and the lower surface of the tail being always white. The horns usually attain a length of from 10 to 12 inches along the curve, but may be over 14 inches.

SAIGAS

Saigas are found in large herds, sometimes comprising several hundred individuals during summer, but these split up into small parties in winter; the old males always remaining with the herds. Some members of the herd keep watch while the others sleep. Although saigas when first started can run swiftly for a short distance, they soon become blown. When caught young, they can be easily tamed, and will follow their owners like dogs.

The range of the saiga embraces Southern Russia and South-Western Siberia; its headquarters being the Kirghiz Steppes. A century ago it extended as far as the confines of Poland, and it is gradually retreating towards the east of the Volga. In summer the saiga wanders as far north as the districts inhabited by the reindeer; while in winter it migrates south, and thus comes into contact with the goitred gazelle.

In the Pleistocene period, the saiga had a much more extensive range westwards, its fossil remains having been obtained from the caverns and superficial deposits of Hungary, Belgium, the South of France, and England. In Moravia, remains of a saiga differing from the living species by having

six, in place of five, lower cheek teeth, have been found. From the occurrence of saiga remains in Western Europe, together with those of other mammals now characteristic of the Steppes, it has been inferred that steppe-like conditions and climate formerly prevailed over portions of that area.

PALA

The South African antelope known by the name of pala or impala (*Æpyceros melampus*) is a rather large species, standing a little over 3 feet in height, and of a dark red colour above, gradually shading into white below. There is no gland on the face below the eye, and the feet are distinguished by the absence of the lateral hoofs, and the presence of a pair of black, glandular tufts of hair at the back of the hind pair. The horns of the males are lyrate, widely divergent, and somewhat spiral, with about a dozen complete and widely separated rings. The ordinary length of pala horns does not exceed 16 inches; but there are specimens of 23 and 24 inches, measured in a straight line. The pala is found throughout Southern and South-Eastern Africa. These antelopes are nowhere more plentiful than along the Chobi, and may often be seen in herds of from twenty to one hundred together. "There are very few males in comparison with the number of females," writes Mr. F. C. Selous, "though I have sometimes seen a herd composed entirely of rams, ten or fifteen in number. They are like thick corn along the river's bank, and are seldom seen at a distance of more than a mile from water; and there is no more certain sign of the proximity of water than the presence of impala antelopes."

In Nyasaland, Mr. Crawshay states that they frequent sandy plains covered with mimosas and low scrub near the rivers. He observes that "no antelope I have seen can compare with the impala in fleetness of foot, and certainly no other can display such wonderful leaping power; they go off like the proverbial arrow from the bow, and, with most beautiful gliding bounds, cover the ground without apparently the least effort. When alarmed they often give utterance to a sharp bark." From its red colour, the pala is known to the Boers as the rooibok.

Years ago pala were to be met in large droves over a great part of Africa, and are still found in numbers in some districts of British Central and East Africa, as well as on the Upper Zambezi.

On the west coast, in Angola and Hasholand, the genus is represented by the Angola pala (*Æ. petersi*), distinguished by the presence of a purplish streak down the middle of the face, from the eyes to the upper part of the nose, and also by a similar streak through the line of the eyes.

REEDBUCK

The reedbuck (*Cervicapra arundinum*) is the typical representative of a sub-family group of African antelopes—the *Cervicaprinæ*—with horns only in the males, narrow, goat-like, upper molar teeth, and either hairy or naked muzzles. There is generally a gland below the eye, which may be very small; and the skull usually has large, unossified spaces below the eyes and distinct pits in the forehead. The horns may be either large, lyrate, widely spreading, and thickly ringed, or small and upright; and the tail is either of medium length or short.

The reedbuck is characterised by comparatively small horns, which bend forwards somewhat after the manner of those of the dibatag, the presence of a bare gland-patch below each ear, the bushy and comparatively short tail, which does not reach to within some distance of the hocks, and the very small lateral hoofs. In height this antelope stands nearly 3 feet. The short, smooth, and almost woolly fur is pale brownish fawn on the upper parts, with a tinge of orange on the head; the under parts and inner sides of the limbs being dirty white. Very old does become much paler, in fact almost white. The

THE BOHOR REEDBUCK

ordinary length of the horns is from 12 to 13 inches along the curves, although they occasionally reach 15 and 16 inches.

Formerly reedbuck were met with throughout Central South Africa, where there are open grassy or reedy valleys traversed by streams, but they are now practically exterminated in Bechuanaland, and rare in the Transvaal, although still common in many districts, such as the Chobi valley. They generally associate in pairs, and it is seldom that more than three or four (of which one or two will be young) are seen together, although sometimes as many as eight may feed within a short distance of one another.

Mr. F. C. Selous mentions that "although the reedbuck is never found far from water, it always keeps on dry ground, and when chased I have never seen one take to boggy ground, but have noticed that rather than cross a narrow stream of water they will make a long detour." Indeed, when hunted, these antelope invariably seek refuge in bush, or by flight into the open dry country. The males, if suddenly frightened, sometimes utter a whistling sound. In pace this species is slow, and it is one of the easiest of African antelopes to stalk.

The South African mountain reedbuck (*C. fulvo-rufula*) is a smaller species, standing only about 28 inches at the shoulder. It has long and coarse reddish brown hair on the upper parts, while beneath it is white. The horns are seldom more than 8 or 9 inches in length, and bend forwards in a sharp sweep, without any outward inclination. The West African bohor (*C. redunca*) is closely allied to the last, being nearly similar in size and colour, but the small horns, seldom exceeding 9 inches in length, form distinct hooks. In Abyssinia the species is represented by another race (*C. redunca bohor*), with widely expanding incurving horns. A third race (*C. redunca wardi*), distinguished by its larger size and rougher coat, inhabits East Africa.

WATERBUCK AND KOBS

The antelopes included in the genus *Cobus* are water-loving animals, typically of larger size than the reedbuck, and associating in herds. Their horns are long, sublyrate, and ringed nearly throughout; the tail is longer than in the reedbuck, and tufted at the end. As in the latter, the gland below the eye is rudimentary. Most of the species are greyish brown or reddish in colour, but in a few the old bucks are black. The muzzle is naked; and the skull may be distinguished from that of the reedbuck by the premaxillary bones reaching upwards to join the nasals.

The waterbuck (*Cobus ellipsiprymnus*), which stands 4 feet or more at the withers, is characterised by its long and coarse greyish roan coat marked by an oval white ring on the buttocks, extending above the tail, by a white gorget on the throat, a streak of the same on part of each eye, and some white near the muzzle (page 730). Good horns average about 28 inches along the curve, but they may measure 30, 31, or even 36½ inches; their colour is grey. Waterbuck inhabit Southern and Eastern Africa, extending as far north as the river Shebeyle, in Somaliland, and are never found in herds of more than twenty.

They are partial to steep stony hills, and are often found at a distance of more than a mile from the nearest river, for which, however, they always make when pursued. Though heavy-looking antelopes, they can clamber with wonderful speed and sureness of foot up and down the steepest hillsides. In Nyasaland waterbuck are found in greatest numbers on large swampy plains overgrown with coarse grass, tall reeds, and papyrus, where in the wet season it is almost impossible to get at them; unlike other antelopes, except the reedbuck, they do not appear to leave the lowlands in the rains, but keep to the plains all the year round. Waterbuck are less difficult to stalk than reedbuck, but their flesh is so coarse and stringy as to be almost uneatable.

The defassa waterbuck (*C. defassa*) is a widely-spread species, with several local races, differing from the typical waterbuck by having a large white patch on the rump, as well as by the absence of a gorget on the throat. The typical race, which is rufous, with a large amount of white round the eyes, is a native of Abyssinia and Kordofan.

Two very handsome, but smaller, species from the White Nile, namely Mrs. Grey's kob (*C. maria*) and the white-eared kob (*C. leucotis*), are characterised by the black upper parts of the old bucks ; the young bucks and the does at all ages being rufous. In the former species, which stands about 38 inches at the shoulder, the horns are long and doubly curved, and the backs of the ears white ; while in the second the white extends forwards to the eyes, and there is also a white gorget, while the horns are shorter and less curved.

Among the smaller members of the group, a well-known species is Buffon's kob (*C. coba*), which stands about 35 inches at the shoulder, with white on the inner sides of the ears, the under parts, the inner surfaces of the limbs, the tip of the tail, and a ring round each fetlock, the front of the fore legs being black. Good horns vary in length from 17 to 20 inches. Typically from West Africa, it ranges across to East Africa, where it is represented by a distinct race.

The lechwe (*C. leche*) and the puku (*C. vardoni*) are two allied species from South Central Africa, both of which were discovered by Livingstone. The puku is about the size of the pala, standing some 3 feet 3 inches at the shoulder ; the coarse and shaggy hair is of a uniform foxy red colour, with no black markings down the front of the forelegs. The horns are rather small, without much forward curvature, and with the rings not extending so high up as in the lechwe ; their length varying from 13 to 16 inches, and in one instance reaching 20 inches.

The puku is plumply built, with a very erect carriage. The lechwe is distinguished by its superior size and the black fronts of the fore legs ; the general colour being pale rufous, with the under parts and rings round the eyes whitish. The horns seldom exceed 30 inches in length, although they have been recorded of 34 inches. The lechwe is strictly a swamp-dwelling antelope, and, when undisturbed, can be approached very easily. Generally these animals are to be seen standing knee-deep or belly-deep in the water, lazily cropping the aquatic plants, or reposing close to the water's edge. Puku are usually met with in herds of from three to twelve, although occasionally so many as fifty may be seen. They are found on dry ground close to the edges of the rivers, but when pursued will take readily to the water. Puku and lechwe are never found together, although the latter may associate with pala. A lechwe (*C. smithemani*) in which the upper parts

of adult bucks are blackish inhabits the Lake Mweru district and North-Eastern Rhodesia.

THE RHEBOK

The rhebok, or vaal rhebok (*Pelea capreolus*), is the first representative of the second division of the cervicaprine group, in which the species are mostly of small size, and characterised by short and nearly upright horns. Of this sub-group the rhebok, which stands about 30 inches at the withers, is the largest species. The horns are placed wide apart over the eyes, and are sharp, slender, and well ringed, rising nearly vertically with a slight forward bend, but with little divergence. Their cross-section is elliptical, and their length from 7 to 11 inches. The gland below the eye and the corresponding depression in the skull are wanting. The muzzle is naked, the tail short, broad, fan-like, and bushy, and the hair thick and rather woolly. The colour is light greyish fawn, passing into white beneath.

KLIPSPRINGERS

This antelope is an inhabitant of hilly and mountainous districts in Southern and Eastern Africa, and its habits much resemble those of the chamois. Mr. Drummond states that it is "extraordinary how their delicate limbs escape injury when they take bound after bound, like an india-rubber ball, in places that a cat would shudder at." Rhebok only descend at night from the mountain tops and ridges for the purpose of drinking. They are usually found in parties of from six to seven to as many as a dozen.

THE KLIPSPRINGER

Even more active than the rhebok is the diminutive klipspringer (*Oreotragus saltator*), which derives its name—meaning "rock-jumper"—from its unrivalled power of leaping from crag to crag. This little antelope stands about 22 inches in height, and is characterised by its peculiarly thick and brittle coat, of which the hairs are hollow internally. The colour of the upper parts is speckled yellow and olive. The small, straight horns of the male rise vertically from the head and incline slightly forwards at their tips ; their length averaging only about 4 inches, so that they are overtopped by the large ears. The hoofs, although somewhat clumsily shaped, are so small that all the four feet could easily stand upon a penny-piece.

The range of the klipspringer extends from the Cape throughout Eastern Africa so far north as Somaliland and Abyssinia, where these pretty little antelopes are found so high up as eight or nine thousand feet above the sea. The rounded form of their hoofs enables klipspringers to obtain foothold on the smallest projections, and they are consequently able to bound up the sides of the steepest cliffs ; these antelopes are exclusively confined to hilly districts. They were formerly abundant at the Cape, but have now become comparatively scarce, and it is seldom that more than a pair are seen together, though, in places where they are numerous, as many as three or four may be in company. The flesh is tender and well-flavoured.

ORIBI

The easiest way of distinguishing the pretty little fox-coloured African antelope known as the oribi (*Oribia scoparia*) from the duikerboks is the presence in the former of a small patch of bare glandular skin below each ear ; a feature it possesses in common with the reedbuck. Why these two groups of antelopes, which are by no means nearly related, should alone possess these bare gland-patches is unexplained. Oribis have also a large gland below each eye ; but no tuft of long hair between the short, spike-like horns of the buck. The true oribi is a southern species, ranging as far north as the Zambezi, of a tawny yellow colour above and white below, with a black patch on the forehead between the horns in the bucks, and the moderately bushy and tufted tail, which is black for its terminal two-thirds. The horns of the bucks, which do not usually exceed 5 or 6 inches in length, although they are known to reach 7 inches, are ringed for about a couple of inches at the base. Oribis stand from about 24 to 26 inches at the shoulder, and have conspicuous tufts of hair at the knees, as well as small lateral hoofs.

In addition to the typical oribi, there are several other species, one of which is found on the western side of the continent in Gambia, while others extend the range of the group along the eastern side as far north as Abyssinia. Oribi are found in parties of two or three on open ground, but are very local. Their colour harmonises closely with the ground, and their speed is very great. The flesh forms excellent venison.

GRYSBOK AND STEINBOK

These two well-known little South African antelopes are distinguishable from the oribi by the absence of the bare glandular ear-patch and of tufts of long hair at the knees, as well as by the horns of the bucks being smooth and rising nearly vertically from the skull, and by the smaller size of the pits for the eye-glands in the steinbok. The grysbok (*Rhaphiceros melanotis*)—pronounced rysbok—which ranges as far north as the Zambezi, and stands about 22 inches at the shoulder, may be recognised by the mingled chocolate-red and white hairs, very large ears, and the presence of small lateral hoofs. In the steinbok (*R. campestris*), which is a paler antelope with a uniformly tawny coat, the lateral hoofs are lacking.

A connecting link between the two is formed by the Uganda steinbok (*R. sharpei*), the most northern member of the group, which combines the white-

BUFFON'S KOB

stippled coat of the grysbok with the absence of lateral hoofs. In male steinboks the horns usually attain a length of about 4 inches, but rarely may be 6 ; and the tail is of moderate length, and of the same colour as the back. This little antelope frequents either open country or thin forest, but avoids mountainous districts, and is common throughout South and East Africa as far north as the Zambezi. Although abundant, these animals are difficult to find, owing to the careful manner in which they conceal themselves.

PIGMY ANTELOPES

Typical mouse-deer, as well as small true deer, being absent from Africa, their place in that continent is taken by numerous fairy-like species of tiny antelopes, among which the so-called royal antelope (*Neotragus pygmæus*) of Guinea is one of the smallest, standing about only 12 inches at the shoulder, and with the simple spike-like horns of the buck scarcely projecting above the hair, which is rufous fawn in colour.

Together with its immediate relatives, this antelope may be distinguished from the grysbok and steinbok by the horns sloping backwards nearly in the plane of the face ; lateral hoofs are wanting. In the great Semliki forest the group is represented by Harrison's antelope (*N. harrisoni*), and on the Zanzibar coast and certain neighbouring islands, as well as in Mozambique and Zululand, by the so-called suni antelopes (*N. moschatus* and *N. livingstonianus*), which are of somewhat larger size, ranging from 13 to 15 inches in shoulder-height.

DIK-DIKS

Certain curious little antelopes from North-Eastern and Eastern Africa are characterised by their almost trunk-like muzzles, which suggest a resemblance to the tapir. The longest-known of these so-called dik-diks is the species, termed by the Arabs Beni-Israel, but by naturalists Salt's dik-dik (*Madoqua saltiana*), so named on account of having been discovered by the early Abyssinian traveller, Sir Henry Salt (1780–1827). From all the preceding groups of pigmy antelopes these are distinguished by the presence of a tuft of hair on the crown of the head and by the hairy, elongated, and puffy muzzle, as well as by the horns of the males sloping backwards in the plane of the face. The skull is characterised by the great size of the aperture for the nose and the shortness of the nasal bones, while the last molar tooth in the lower jaw, instead of being composed, as in other ruminants, of three distinct lobes, has either only two such lobes, or two with a mere rudiment of the third. The female of the Beni-Israel is only 16 inches in height.

In Central Somaliland, Kilimanjaro, and Damaraland this species is replaced by Kirk's dik-dik (*M. kirki*), differing from the first in having a rudiment of the third lobe in the last lower molar, in its more puffy nose, and in the horns being cylindrical instead of being flattened on the inner side. There are several other East African dik-diks. These tiny antelopes jump up from the tufts of grass like hares, and are so common in parts of Somaliland that two or three may be killed at a shot. When disturbed, they start up with great bounds, uttering a shrill cry; the flesh has an unpleasant musky flavour.

DUIKERBOKS

Impressed with the speed and agility with which it disappears into covert, the old Dutch settlers at the Cape christened one of the commonest of the smaller antelopes of the country the duikerbok, or "diving-buck" (*Cephalophus grimmi*). The name belongs, of course, only to this typical species, but it may be conveniently extended to include the whole group, which is a very large one. These antelopes, which are exclusively African, are mainly inhabitants of thick forests, although the typical species frequents brush-covered or open country. They are characterised by the small, straight horns, which are generally present in both sexes, being placed far back on the skull and separated by a long tuft of hair. The gland below the eye is small, and is peculiar in opening either in the form of a slit or as a row of small pores. The muzzle has a large naked portion, and the tail is very short. The upper molar teeth have broad and square crowns, and thereby differ markedly from those of the pigmy antelopes, grysbok, oribi, and dik-dik, which collectively constitute the sub-family *Neotraginæ*.

The majority of the duikers are light and elegantly-built antelopes of comparatively small size, and of a more or less uniform colour, and are all very similar in structure. From their inhabiting jungle-like or forest country, they are frequently spoken of as bushbucks, but since that name is also employed for another group, its use is best avoided. A few species are larger, one attaining the size of an average donkey. According to modern views, duikerbok alone constitute the sub-family *Cephalophinæ*.

The true duiker is found in bush-covered districts from the Cape to the Zambezi and Nyasaland, and on the west coast ranges as far north as Angola. It stands about 26 inches in height, and is characterised by the absence of horns in the female, and by those of the male rising upwards at a sharp angle to the plane of the nose. The ears are very long and narrow, and the colour typically yellowish brown, with a more or less marked grey tinge; but there is great variation in this respect, some skins tending to reddish and others to greyish, while the amount of white on the under parts is also variable. The length of the horns is usually from 3 to 4 inches, although they may reach 5 inches. In Abyssinia it is

THE CROWNED DUIKER

represented by a smaller race (*C. grimmi abyssinicus*), standing 16 or 17 inches in height, and of a yellowish fawn colour; and there are other races in Eastern Africa. In West Africa occurs a species known as the crowned duiker (*C. coronatus*), with a bright yellow coat.

Among the numerous other species the red buck, or Natal duiker (*C. natalensis*), which stands about 24 inches at the shoulder, differs in its horns, present in both sexes, inclining backwards in the plane of the nose. It is also distinguished by its bright reddish bay colour, shorter and broader ears, smaller horns, and larger head tuft. Owing to the sudden rushes they make when disturbed, these antelopes are difficult to shoot; and their flesh is unpalatable. There are many other more or less nearly-allied species, such as the philantomba (*C. maxwelli*) of Sierra Leone.

The little South African blue buck (*C. monticola*) claims attention as the smallest member of the genus. These antelopes, which swarm in the Natal jungles, stand only 13 inches at the shoulder, and are smaller and lighter than a hare, and of a bluish mouse colour, with the tiny straight horns scarcely showing above the tuft of hair.

Another member of the group is the much larger banded duiker (*C. doriæ*) of West Africa, which takes its name from the eight or nine black transverse bands crossing the back and loins, and gradually narrowing to a point on the flanks; the ground colour being a golden brown. The coloration is unique among ruminants, and recalls that of the Tasmanian wolf among the marsupials.

Two species of the genus call for mention on account of their great superiority in size over most of its other representatives. One of these is the yellow-backed duiker (*C. sylvicultor*) of West Africa, represented by closely allied races or species in North-East Rhodesia and the Ituri Forest; and the other Jentink's duiker (*C. jentinki*) from Liberia. The former stands about 2 feet 10½ inches in height, and is of a blackish colour, with the hind part of the middle of the back marked by a yellowish white line of long hair. The second is rather smaller, and greyish on the body, with the head and neck black, and the legs, lips, and inner sides of the ears whitish. The tuft of hair on the head is small and inconspicuous.

GNUS

The last group of the antelopes, forming the sub-family *Bubalinæ*, is represented by the gnus, or wildebeests, and their allies the hartebeests and blesbok, and is confined to Africa. All are of large size, and characterised by the presence of horns in both sexes, as well as by the withers being more or less elevated above the level of the haunches. The muzzle is naked, and there is a small gland below the eye, marked by a tuft of dark hairs. The tail is long, and the colour mostly uniform. The horns may be either somewhat lyrate or recurved, and at their origin are placed more or less closely together. The bony cores of the horns are honeycombed with cavities, as in cattle, but the upper molar teeth differ from those of the latter in their narrow crowns, without an additional column on the inner side. Nevertheless, it has been suggested, from the study of their internal anatomy, that gnus are really related to cattle, and more especially to the African buffalo.

Gnus are ungainly-looking antelopes, distinguished by their broad and short heads, in which the muzzle is of great width, and fringed with long bristles, so that the nostrils are separated from one another by a considerable interval. The neck is furnished with an erect mane of stiff hairs, and the long tail is thickly haired throughout. The nearly smooth, cylindrical horns are situated on the highest point of the skull, and curve outwards and downwards, and then bend upwards near the tips. In the young, however, the horns are straight and diverging, placed at some distance below the highest point of the skull, and separated from one another by a wide space at the base covered with hair. These straight horns persist as the tips of those of the adult, the curved basal portion of the latter being a later development. In aged bulls the horns approximate at their bases, so as to form a helmet-shaped mass completely covering the part of the skull, as in the Cape buffalo.

The true, or white-tailed gnu (*Connochætes gnu*), also known as the black wildebeest, is a southern species whose northward range was originally marked approximately by the Vaal River. It is all but, if not completely, extinct as a wild animal, although some are preserved on a few estates in South Africa.

Standing about 4½ feet at the shoulder, it is characterised by the downward and finally upward curvature of the horns, the upright mane, the long hair fringing the chest, the long white tail, and the uniform brown colour of the coat.

In South Africa gnus favoured the open country, and never wandered far from water. When quaggas were abundant, both animals were found together, often in company with ostriches, and at a later date a solitary gnu might often be observed feeding among a herd of sassabi or bonte-quagga.

In describing the habits and appearance of the white-tailed species, Gordon Cumming wrote as follows : " Wheeling about in endless circles, and performing the most extraordinary varieties of intricate evolutions, the shaggy herds of these eccentric and fierce-looking

THE ORIBI

animals caper and gambol round the hunter on every side. While he is riding hard to obtain a shot at a herd in front of him, other herds are charging down wind on his right and left, and, having described a number of circular movements, they take up positions upon the very ground across which he rode only a few minutes before.

" Singly, and in small troops of four or five individuals, the old bull wildebeests may be seen stationed at intervals throughout the plains, standing motionless during a whole forenoon, coolly watching with a philosophic eye the movements of the other game, uttering a loud snorting noise, and also a short sharp cry which is peculiar to them. When the hunter approaches these old bulls, they begin whisking their long white tails in a most eccentric manner ; then, springing into the air, start prancing and capering, and pursue each other in circles at their utmost speed. Suddenly they all pull up together to overhaul the intruder, when the bulls will often begin fighting in the most violent manner, dropping on their knees at every shock ; then, quickly wheeling about, they kick up their heels, whirl their tails with a fantastic flourish, and scour across the plain enveloped in a cloud of dust."

In addition to their speed, wildebeest are remarkable for their extreme tenacity of life ; and, owing to the vigorous use they make of their horns, are awkward creatures to hunt with dogs. Occasionally they can be approached within easy range by fair stalking, although they may be killed by watching at their drinking-holes at night. Both kinds of gnu are characterised by their great speed and endurance.

If possible, the brindled gnu (*Connochætes taurinus*), or blue wildebeest, as it is called by the Boers, is an even stranger-looking animal than its white-tailed cousin, its very long, straight face giving it a somewhat melancholy and dejected look, which becomes nothing less than comic when it indulges in the caperings characteristic of both kinds of gnu. From the white-tailed species the brindled gnu is distinguishable at a glance by its superior size, horizontally directed horns —which, although thinner, recall those of the African buffalo—longer face, thin, pendent mane, the presence of a fringe of long hair on the throat, and the absence of long tufts on the muzzle and lower part of the chest, and the dark and less elongated hair of the tail. The colour of the coat ranges from a grizzled roan to slaty or blackish brown, with more or less well-marked darker vertical stripes on the neck and fore quarters, these being most conspicuous in light-coloured specimens. In stature the bull stands about 4 feet 3 inches at the withers.

The horns have a span of from 2 feet to 2 feet 2 inches ; and in a specimen in which the span was 2 feet 1¾ inches, the greatest length of each horn along the hinder curve was 19½ inches, and the basal girth

13½ inches. This gnu replaces the white-tailed species north of the Orange River. It is still met with on the western borders of Griqualand West and the eastern edge of the Kalahari desert, and from Mashonaland to Lake Ngami in suitable districts. Near Kilimanjaro it is found in large herds, as is likewise the case in some other districts. In the typical southern race the whole of the face, mane, and throat fringe are dark ; but in Nyasaland occurs a race (*C. t. johnstoni*) with a white

higher than the haunches, and this feature, together with the great length of the face, communicates an ugly and ungainly appearance to the whole animal. These characters, however, are less strongly marked in the blesbok and bontebok and some of the intermediate species. The cows differ from those of wildebeests in the presence of only two in place of four teats.

The cama originally ranged from the plains of Cape Colony as far north as Matabililand and Mashonaland, but it has been exterminated from most of its southern haunts. It stands about 4 feet at the withers, its general colour is reddish brown, with a pale yellowish patch on each side of the haunches, and black markings on the forehead and nose. The hair of the face is reversed as high up as the eyes, or even to the horns, whereas in the bubal this reversal extends only for a distance of one or two inches above the muzzle. The horns are long, and boldly ringed, diverging from one another in the form of a V, with their tips directed suddenly backwards at a right angle, and the bases curved away behind the plane of the forehead. Their length varies in good specimens from 20 to 26 inches.

A PARTY OF GNUS

chevron on the face, while in the Kilimanjaro race (*C. t. albojubatus*) the throat fringe and a few hairs in the mane are yellowish white.

HARTEBEESTS

The air of melancholy dejection characteristic of the brindled gnu is likewise observable in the hartebeest (*Bubalis*, or *Alcelaphus*, *cama*) of South Africa ; this being due to the great length of the face, which is, however, much narrower than in the gnu. In the early days of Cape Colony the Dutch gave the name of hartebeest to this species from its fancied resemblance —perhaps in colour—to a hart or stag ; and it was known to naturalists by the excellent name of *Alcelaphus*, or elk-stag, till some wiseacre thought of resuscitating the name *Bubalis*, which ought to be restricted to the buffaloes. The hartebeest, or cama hartebeest, as it may be called to distinguish it from its relatives, is the typical representative of a large assemblage of antelopes, all exclusively African.

All of them differ from wildebeests in their long and pointed heads, terminating in a narrow muzzle, the ringed and often lyrate horns, the absence of a mane on the neck or throat, and the short and less thickly-haired tail. In consequence of the narrowness of the muzzle, the nostrils are closely approximated. The horns are compressed, and ringed for a considerable portion of their length, and in form are more or less lyrate, with their tips frequently bent suddenly backwards.

In the more typical species the withers are much

The cama is one of the fleetest of South African antelopes, and possesses such strength as to render it almost impossible for anything under a whole pack of strong and swift hounds to bring it to bay.

In the neighbourhood of Victoria Nyanza the cama is replaced by a local race, *B. lelwel jacksoni*, of the lelwel hartebeest, distinguished by the uniform pale colour of the face ; the hair being reversed for a distance of only about 4 inches above the muzzle. The horns are of about the same dimensions as those of the cama, ranging in length from about 20 to 24 inches along the front curve, with a basal girth of 12 inches. The typical *B. lelwel* is a native of the Sudan.

THE BUBAL HARTEBEEST

In North Africa these antelopes are represented by the bubal hartebeest (*Bubalis boselaphus*), the smallest member of the group, standing only 3 feet 7 inches at the shoulder, and of a uniform bright bay colour throughout. The face is extremely elongated, and the horns, which, like those of the cama, are perched on a crest situated on the very summit of the skull, are comparatively short and thick, of a deep black colour, with the rings extending nearly to their tips. They diverge from one another in a U-shaped form, and have their tips bent suddenly backwards, nearly, but not quite, at a right angle. Their length varies from 13 to 14½ inches. The western hartebeest (*B. major*), of the Gambia and Cameruns, is a much larger but closely allied species, with enormously massive horns, which may be just over 26 inches in length, with a girth of 13½ inches.

THE KONGONI

The kongoni, or Coke's hartebeest (*Bubalis cokei*), of British and German East Africa, typifies a group of three species distinguished from all the preceding forms by the wide expansion of the horns. The other two members of this group are the tora (*B. tora*) of Nubia and Abyssinia and the sig, or Swayne's hartebeest (*B. swaynei*) of Somaliland.

In all these species the hair of the face is reversed only for a distance of 2 inches or less above the muzzle. In the sig the colour is reddish chestnut, the face being marked by a broad purplish streak extending from a little distance below the eyes. The horns expand very widely, rising at first nearly in the plane of the face, and then forming a right angle with the middle line of the forehead; their smooth tips being bent at right angles to the base, and directed immediately backwards. Their length varies from 15 to 18¼ inches.

Coke's hartebeest is reddish brown on the upper parts and greyish brown beneath, the head being dark rufous in front and fulvous on the sides, and thus

THE KONZI

The konzi (*Bubalis lichtensteini*) is a very distinct species, inhabiting the Zambezi region and Nyasaland, and characterised by its small horns, much expanded and flattened at their bases. They incline at first upwards and outwards, and then inwards, with the tips directed backwards and upwards, so as to enclose a kind of vase-shaped space, their length ranging from 14 to 22 inches. The skull is also shorter than in any of the foregoing species. The colour is lighter than in the Cape hartebeest, the tail, knees, and the front of the legs being black, while the face is without any dark markings, but the buttocks usually have a pale yellow patch, and the under parts are also yellowish.

In Nyasaland this species is very generally met with in the hills, if not too steep and rocky, and in the plains, but prefers a flat or undulating country, well-wooded and with intervening open glades. It is frequently found feeding with waterbuck or zebras, and goes in small herds of from five or six to fifteen or twenty. Its vitality appears to be nearly equal to that of the waterbuck.

THE HIROLA

One of the least ugly—it is impossible to use the word beautiful in this association—members of the group is the hirola, or Hunter's hartebeest (*Damaliscus hunteri*), from the southern borders of Somaliland, on the river Tana, distinguishable by the white chevron on the forehead, and the peculiar form of the long horns, and, with the following species, representing a second genus. This antelope stands about 4 feet at the withers, and is uniform chestnut brown in colour, with a rather long tail, and white under parts. The chevron on the forehead has its angle directed upwards, and terminates in rings surrounding the eyes. The horns, after inclining upwards and outwards for a short distance, run vertically upwards for a much greater length, with long smooth tips, their length being about 22 inches in males. The face is of considerable length, but the hind quarters do not slope away in the same manner as in the cama.

This antelope frequents the grassy plains principally, but is also found in thick bush. It is generally met with in herds of from fifteen to twenty-five individuals. It runs with rather a heavy gallop, like a typical hartebeest. Mr. Hunter, its discoverer, states that the hirola

THE KILIMANJARO BRINDLED GNU

very different from that of the sig. The horns are also shorter and less widely expanded than in the latter. On the other hand, the tora has the whole face of a uniform pale isabelline tint, like that of the body; the horns being fully as long as in the sig, but rising more rapidly from the base, then coming farther forwards, and projecting much more in the backward direction. Good tora horns vary from 15 to 21 inches in length.

seemed to have more vitality than any other antelope he ever killed. This species, he remarks, " does not extend down to the coast, but we saw them as far as the farthest point we reached—about two hundred and fifty miles—up the river Tana, at a place called Mussa."

THE KORRIGUM, OR TIANG

Ranging across Africa, from Senegal on the west to the Bahr-el-Ghazal and Somaliland on the east, is the korigum, or tiang (*Damaliscus corrigum*), characterised by the comparatively short horns being regularly lyrate, ringed nearly to their tips, and curving backwards without any distinct angulation. In this species the face is only of moderate length, and the withers, as in the sassaby, are not greatly higher than the rump; the face having a broad black band from the roots of the horns to the nose. Most races of the tiang inherit marshy districts, but one from the Sudan is found in the desert.

THE SASSABY

Much longer known than the last is the nearly-allied sassaby, or bastard hartebeest (*Damaliscus lunatus*), widely distributed in South Africa as far north as the Zambezi. The horns, which seldom exceed 12 inches in length, diverge widely from their bases, and are then inclined inwards and upwards, without any angulation. The

KONZI HARTEBEESTS

On the Mababi flat at the end of the dry season large herds congregate, and in former years several hundreds might be seen at one time. They are the fleetest and most enduring antelopes in South Africa. In regard to hunting, the Hon. W. H. Drummond observes that he does not consider sassaby difficult for a good shot, as standing chances of from one hundred and fifty to two hundred yards are easy to obtain, and they will often allow the sportsman to walk up to within that distance before attempting to take to flight; while, when wounded, they are unable to go far, and easy to finish; and their flesh may be classed with that of the choicer antelopes.

BLESBOK AND BONTEBOK

The blesbok (*Damaliscus albifrons*) and its cousin the bontebok (*D. pygargus*) are smaller South African antelopes and the last representatives of the group. In both the horns are compressed and regularly lyrate, with the rings strongly marked, and extending nearly to the tips; for a short distance they run almost parallel, and then curve backwards, their usual length being about 15 inches, although a pair of $13\frac{1}{4}$ inches is on record. Both species are characterised by their brilliant purple red colour, and the broad white " blaze " down the face, from which the blesbok takes its name.

The bontebok is distinguished by the white blaze on the face generally continuing without interruption right up to the root of the horns, and by the white patch on the buttocks surrounding the tail, of which the upper portion is also white. On the other hand, in the blesbok the blaze on the face is divided by a transverse dark line just above the eyes, and there is no white on the rump above the tail, and the latter is wholly brown. In height the blesbok stands about 3 feet 2 inches or rather more at the withers, but the bontebok may reach from 3 feet 2 inches to 3 feet 11 inches.

Bontebok were confined to the plains south of the Orange River, beyond which they were replaced by the blesbok. Both species formerly existed in thousands, but are now practically exterminated

colour of the coarse hair is dark purplish red, becoming almost black along the back, and with a broad blackish mark down the face. In height this antelope stands about 3 feet 10 inches, and the horns usually range from 13 to $15\frac{1}{2}$ inches in length. Sassaby are never found in hilly country or thick jungle, but frequent downs free from bush, or else open forest country with treeless glades.

as wild animals, although preserved on a few farms in South Africa.

Remains of an extinct hartebeest occur in the Pliocene strata at the foot of the Himalaya, and it may be inferred from this and the facts mentioned above that the essentially African groups of sable antelope, waterbuck, and hartebeests, and probably also kudus, were formerly represented on the plains of India.

PRONGBUCK

THE North American prongbuck, or prong-horned antelope (*Antilocapra americana*), commonly known in its own country as the antelope, much resembles an antelope in appearance, but differs from all members of the family *Bovidæ* in the sheaths of the horns giving off a short branch about the middle of their length from their front edge, while the sheaths themselves are periodically shed, and afterwards replaced by a new growth. In consequence of this difference, it is generally referred to a family by itself, the *Antilocapridæ*; but Mr. M. W. Lyon has expressed the opinion that it might preferably be regarded as representing a subfamily of the *Bovidæ*.

As additional characteristics may be mentioned the large number of external glands, namely, a pair behind the lower jaw, another pair on the hips, two pairs between the hoofs, a pair on the hocks, and a single one on the hind part of the back in advance of the rump-patch.

The prongbuck stands about 3 feet in height at the shoulder, and some 3 inches more at the rump, and is of a light and graceful build, with the head carried very high. The head is of moderate length, with the muzzle hairy except for a narrow line in the middle of the upper lip, and large and pointed ears.

The horns, which are usually present only in the males, although sometimes well developed in females, rise vertically above the eyes, and are much compressed from side to side, and curved slightly backwards at the tips, while the anterior process is inclined upwards and forwards at an angle of about 45 degrees to the main axis. The bony cores are dagger-shaped, without any branching.

The tail is extremely short, not exceeding 3 inches in length, and the feet have small hoofs and no traces of lateral hoofs. There is no gland on the face below the eye, neither are there any tufts of hair on the knees.

The colouring of the prongbuck is decidedly handsome and striking, the hair of the upper parts and outer surfaces of the limbs being chestnut. The hair on the back of the neck, which is of chestnut tint, is lengthened into a kind of mane. The face is brownish black, but the summit of the head above the eyes, and also the ears, cheeks, and chin, are white. White also prevails on the lower portion of the throat, the under parts, and the inferior half of the flanks, and extends upwards to form a large patch on the rump, which includes the tail. Usually the throat is crossed by three russet yellow transverse bars, of which the uppermost is continuous with the dark area of the lower jaw.

The lower portion of the limbs is white. The horns are black, save at the tips, where they become yellowish, and their usual length is about 12 inches, although they may grow to 17 inches, with a span of 20 inches.

At birth, which takes place in the spring, the fawns are hornless, but by the middle of summer the first horns have made their appearance in the shape of small cones buried in the hair of the forehead, and by the autumn these attain a length of about an inch. Early in winter these horny cones, or caps, are shed, leaving a pair of hair-covered knobs about half an inch in length in their places. Within a week these knobs are covered with a small cap of horn, which

THE PRONGBUCK

continues to increase in size by growth at the base for a period of a year, when it will be about 6 inches long, forming a straight unforked spike. Early in the following winter these horns are dropped, leaving horn-cores about $1\frac{1}{2}$ inches long, covered as before with hairy skin.

New horns begin to form immediately on their tips, while at the base of the front of the core appears a second point of horn, destined to become the prong by a conversion of the epidermis of the skin covering the core into horn, the horny cap at the tip of the core and the horny summit of the prong eventually becoming welded into one continuous horn. This process is repeated annually, with a gradual increase in the size of the successive horns until the maximum development is attained; this usually occurring at the end of the fifth year.

That the horns of the prongbuck are shed annually was long and persistently urged by the hunters of Fort Union; but these statements were received with incredulity by naturalists, who scouted the idea, and it was eventually proved that the hunters were right, and the naturalists in error. The colouring of the prongbuck is essentially protective, the white under parts and throat-bands counteracting the dark shade thrown by the body when the animal is standing in full sunlight.

The habitat of the prongbuck is restricted to the temperate regions of the western portion of North America, and there is no evidence that it ever occurred to the east of the Mississippi, while it only impinges on that river in its upper reaches. These ruminants originally inhabited all the regions, except wooded districts and high mountain ranges, lying to the west of the Mississippi within the limits of the United States, and up to 1855 they were abundant in California, and not uncommon in the open parts of Oregon, but they have now almost, if not completely, disappeared from both these states. In latitude their range extended from the tropics to the 54th parallel, and within these limits they frequented by choice the open prairie country, avoiding thickly timbered districts or high, naked mountains.

As regards habits, prongbuck are shy and timid creatures, avoiding their enemies with great intelligence, but sometimes betrayed into danger by extreme curiosity. Although swifter than any other native North American ungulate, they are somewhat short-winded, and cannot maintain their speed for any length of time. Prongbuck are essentially gregarious, individuals of both sexes and of all ages congregating in herds from the beginning of September to the end of February. By the beginning of March, according to Dr. Canfield, the does separate from the band one by one to drop their kids, of which they produce two at a birth.

HEAD OF PRONGBUCK
Showing newly growing horns

After a little time the does collect with their young, probably for mutual protection against coyotes ; the old bucks in the meanwhile go off alone, each by himself, or at most two together, leaving the young bucks and young does in small bands. The old bucks for a month or two then wander a great deal, and are seen in the timber lands and other places where they never go at any other season of the year. After two or three months, the young bucks and does join the old does and kids, and finally, by the first of September, all are together once more. Any particular band of antelopes does not leave the locality where it grows up, and never ranges more than a few miles in different directions.

During the pairing season the bucks are combative, and frequently engage in contests among themselves. When about to give birth to offspring, the female proceeds to the middle of one of the numerous patches of cactus in the haunts of these animals, and there by means of a series of bounds, in the descent from which the cactuses are cut to pieces by her sharp hoofs, clears a space in the centre. Here the young are born, and remain for some time, secure from wolves, which are unable to penetrate the cactus fence. Danger, however, is experienced from eagles, and in protecting their young from these birds the antelopes display great courage.

In spite of their extreme speed, prongbuck are poor jumpers, and appear unable to leap over any large object that may be in their path ; this incapacity being attributed to the open nature of the country which these animals frequent. Mr. Caton states that if a prongbuck on the plains desires to cross the railway lines, when alarmed by the cars, as is sometimes the case, it will strain every muscle to outrun the train and cross ahead of it, as if it suspected a purpose to cut him off from crossing, and thus many an exciting race has been witnessed between muscle and steam.

When excited during its gambols with its fellows, or by the emotions of rage or fear, the hair of the white patch on the rump rises up, and assumes a more or less curved radial position from a central point on each side of the vertebræ. From these points the hairs radiate in every direction, only they are as nearly erect as their curved radial position will permit. The patches when in this condition have been aptly compared to large white chrysanthemums. They are, of course, guiding signals to the members of the flock.

Prongbuck are readily tamed when in captivity, and all who have eaten it bear testimony to the excellence of the flesh. The brittle nature of the hairs renders the coat of little value, and the skins are not much used for leather. As might be inferred from the nature of their habitat, prongbuck are exclusively grazing animals, and in captivity avoid browsing on leaves, except when no other food is available.

In localities where they have not been much disturbed prongbuck are not very difficult to approach within range. The case is, however, very different in districts where they are frequently hunted.

According to Mr. D. Bray, the ostrich, with its vaunted power of vision, is near-sighted when compared with the antelope. The giraffe may surpass the latter, not from having superior eyes, but from their greater elevation, and therefore greater scope. The deer cannot be named in this respect. Even when roaming on the prairie, it has not the knack of detecting an intruder that an antelope possesses. Mr. D. Bray never had any trouble in getting within 200 yards of an ostrich, in any fairly suitable place ; yet, with years of experience in this and other kinds of prairie-shooting, he at first found it difficult to get within 600 yards of an antelope, and then it was invariably wide awake, fully able to take care of itself.

Fossilised remains of prongbuck occur in some of the superficial Pleistocene deposits of North America. Mr. W. D. Matthew has described, under the name of *Capromeryx*, a ruminant from the Tertiary formations of North America regarded as the direct ancestor of the prongbuck. He considers that both animals are descended from a group of ruminants termed " antilopine deer," characterised by the possession of antlers approximating to those of deer, with teeth more like those of antelopes. The antlers, which are forked or several times branched, are provided usually, or invariably, with a " burr," whence it would appear that they were annually shed. On the other hand, they are smooth, which suggests that they were permanently invested with " velvet."

Another rather deer-like extinct American ruminant, *Cosoryx*, also has been regarded as near akin to the prongbuck. This had short antlers, which by simplification and the development of a horny sheath, coupled with permanent retention, may have given rise to the horns of the prongbuck. If these extinct species be ancestral to the prongbuck, there can be little doubt as to the right of the latter to represent a family.

THE GIRAFFE

TILL the beginning of the twentieth century giraffes were the only known existing representatives of the family to which they belong (*Giraffidæ*); but the discovery of the okapi in the great equatorial forest of East Central Africa brought to light an entirely distinct type clearly referable to the same family, although very different in form and appearance from its typical members. Extinct ruminants closely allied to the okapi, however, had been previously known from the Tertiary deposits of Southern Europe, while others less nearly related occur in the corresponding formations of India.

The inclusion of the okapi and its extinct relatives in the same family as the giraffe has rendered it necessary to modify to a considerable extent the old definition of the group; and it has been found that the most easily recognised distinctive character is afforded by the lower front teeth. In all ruminants—that is, the hollow-horned group, on the one hand, and the antlered group, or deer, on the other—the outermost of these four pairs of teeth, corresponding to the canines of other mammals, have simple, chisel-like crowns. In the giraffe and okapi, on the contrary, the crowns of these teeth are very much expanded and divided by a cleft down the middle into two semi-distinct lobes; so that this tooth is described as bi-lobed. As giraffes, and probably okapis, feed by stripping off the leaves of branches with their long extensile tongues and flexible upper lips, it is probable that the bi-lobed crowns of the outer pair of lower front teeth are designed to aid in this combing action.

All the teeth of the giraffe tribe have the outer surface of enamel very coarsely wrinkled, somewhat like the skin of the large black slug; and the upper cheek teeth have broad, low crowns, more like those of many deer than those of the majority of the ox tribe.

Another distinctive feature of the existing members of the family is to be found in the character of the main, or only, pair of horns, which consist of sharp, simple, conical, or compressed cores of bone at first completely separate from the underlying bones of the skull, and covered with hairy skin continuous with that of the head. In the giraffe these horns are surmounted with tufts of bristly hair, but in the okapi are crowned with small caps of bare bone. Structurally these horns, which make their appearance before birth, are nearer to the antlers of deer than to the horns of the hollow-horned ruminants. The length, slenderness, and extensibility of the tongue is another characteristic feature of the family.

The only other generic character to which it is necessary to allude now is the absence of lateral hoofs in both giraffes and okapis—a feature which separates them from the members of the deer tribe, although shared by a few of the hollow-horned ruminants.

The family is confined at the present

NORTH AFRICAN GIRAFFES

day to Africa south of the Sahara, and appears to have never reached America.

Owing to the remarkable length of its neck and limbs, coupled with its large bodily size, the giraffe (*Giraffa camelopardalis*) is by far the tallest of all mammals. In addition to its elongated neck and limbs, it is characterised by the depth and shortness of the body, the great elevation of the withers, as compared with the hind quarters, and the long and delicately formed head, with large eyes, and the pair of horn-like appendages covered with skin which surmount the skull and slope backwards nearly in the plane of the face. In addition to these paired horns, there is typically a dome-like bony protuberance occupying the middle line of the skull between the eyes, which may be conveniently termed the third horn. The ears, although large, are narrow and pointed, the eyes are full and prominent, the big, slit-like nostrils can be closed at the will of their owner, and the hairy upper lip is broad and prehensile, while the tongue is remarkable for its length and the distance it can be protruded beyond the lips, so as to act as a grasping organ of appreciable power. From the nape of the neck to the withers runs a relatively short and erect mane; the tail is of considerable length and terminates in a large tuft of long hair, and there are tufts of black hair on the summits of the horns. The feet are large and heavy.

The skull is characterised by the great elevation of the forehead and face above the level of the eyes, this being due to the development of a number of air-cells in the bones. There is also a large unossified space immediately below the eye.

HEAD OF BARINGO GIRAFFE

Showing the five horns

The general type of colouring consists either of a network of light lines on a tawny ground, or of dark blotches on a buff ground. The typical giraffe of Nubia is characterised by the presence in the male of a distinct third horn, the white, unspotted legs, and by the markings taking the form of a network of white lines on a fawn ground. Races approximating more or less closely to this type extend at least so far south as the neighbourhood of Lake Baringo and Mount Elgon—that is to say, considerably south of the equator; one of these, *G. c. rothschildi*, having the markings in the bull nearly black, and an additional pair of rudimentary horns on the back of the skull.

On the other hand, when the southern districts of the continent are reached, the frontal horn of the adult bull giraffes is reduced to a more or less inconspicuous irregular boss, while the legs have become spotted right down to the hoofs. Giraffes displaying these two characteristics occur as far north as the northern Transvaal. The nearest approach to a transition between these two extreme types is displayed by the giraffes of the Kilimanjaro district, which have the lower portion of the legs partially spotted, and tend to show less development of the third horn. In these Kilimanjaro giraffes (*G. c. tippelskirchi*) the markings take the form of irregular star-like dark blotches on a fawn ground; but in the southern *G. c. capensis* the dark blotches are of less irregular shape.

In addition to all these, there is the very strikingly coloured Somali giraffe, which, while agreeing with the northern type in cranial characters, strikes out a line altogether its own in the matter of marking and colour, although in these respects it merely displays an ultra-development of the northern type. Nevertheless, it has been regarded as indicating a species apart from the one including all the other races, and known as *G. reticulata*. It is marked by a very large-meshed network of narrow white lines on a liver-coloured ground, thus presenting a pronounced contrast to the blotched type of body-colouring and spotted legs characteristic of the southern races.

Apart from the Somali giraffe, which certainly differs in colour and marking more from all the others than do the latter among themselves, the tendency to a gradation from the northern three-horned and white-stockinged to the southern two-horned and spot-legged type points to the advisability of regarding the local colour-forms as races rather than species.

Although giraffes still hold their own in Nubia and Kordofan and are abundant in Eastern Africa, in the south their numbers and range have been greatly reduced. They have practically disappeared from large areas to the south of the Zambezi, and their headquarters are now the parched desert country forming the north Kalahari. Probably they are most abundant in the districts lying immediately south of the Botletli River, on the northern border of the Kalahari Desert. Most of this district is waterless for a great portion of the year, and cannot be hunted unless the sportsmen are accompanied by water-carts. Here giraffes may be seen in parties of fifteen or twenty, while as many as seventy or eighty have been observed together. To the east of the Kalahari giraffes are not uncommon, as is also the case in parts of the Chobi Valley; while in Matabililand and Mashonaland they are scarce. Southwards of the Limpopo they have been exterminated.

The giraffes inhabiting the northern Kalahari Desert cannot touch water for some seven or eight months of the year; and the same is true with regard to those found in other waterless districts. Hence the Bushmen state that these animals never drink at all. This, however, is disproved by the following quotation from Mr. Selous, who writes that on a certain occasion he reached camp " a little before sundown, just in time to see three tall, graceful giraffes issue from the forest a little distance beyond, and stalk across the intervening flat, swishing their long tails to and fro, on their way down to the water. It is a curious sight to watch these long-legged animals drinking, and one that I have had several opportunities of enjoying. Though their necks are long, they are unable to reach the water without straddling their legs wide apart. In doing this, they sometimes place one foot in front, and the other as far back as possible, and then by a series of little jerks widen the distance between the two, until they succeed in getting their mouths down to the water; sometimes they sprawl their legs out sideways in a similar manner." This posture has to be assumed not only when drinking, but when the animal desires to pick up a leaf from the ground, or on the rare occasions when it grazes.

The food of giraffes consists almost exclusively of leaves, plucked by the long, flexible tongue, aided by the lips and lower front teeth. The senses of sight and hearing are highly developed, and the lofty position of the head gives to the soft and liquid eyes a wide field of view. The giraffe's chief means of defence is by kicking out with its legs; the blows

ELAND

"Eland are the largest of all antelopes, and differ from most other members of their group in having horns in both sexes, spirally twisted on their own axis and directed upwards and outwards."

KUDU

"Kudu are fond of browsing on the tender shoots of trees and shrubs, especially in the dry season, when the grass has been burnt off.   When alarmed, they sometimes give vent to a low bark audible only at close quarters."

thus delivered being of terrific force and power. This mode of attack is employed by the cow in defending her young against Carnivora, and likewise in the contests which take place among the males during the pairing season.

From observations made on captive specimens of the northern race, pairing time is either in March or the early part of April, the young being born in May or June of the following year. A single fawn is produced at a birth, and the little creature in three days after its appearance in the world is able to trot by the side of its dam.

The speed and endurance of giraffes are alike considerable. When running, the tail is carried twisted in a cork-screw-like manner over the back, and the neck inclined somewhat forward. Their gait is peculiar, and takes the form of a kind of awkward gallop, " their hind legs," writes Mr. F. C. Selous, " being straddled out at each step and coming—one on each side—in front of the fore legs. If you only look at their bodies and necks from behind, they appear to be sailing or gliding along without making any movement at all. They get over the ground, however, at a great rate, and it requires a good horse to run one down. The great thing is to press them to their utmost speed at first, when, if fat, they soon get blown and can be ridden into, and, if the wind right up to one's waggons, just like an ox or an eland. At a hard gallop they can, however, spin along for miles."

The flesh of the giraffe is stated to be excellent.

Fossil giraffes are found in the Pliocene rocks of Greece, Persia, the Siwalik Hills at the foot of the Himalaya, and China. All these extinct forms appear to have been closely allied to the living African species, although in some instances the length of the limbs seems to have been proportionately somewhat less.

R. LYDEKKER

OKAPI

BY SIR H. H. JOHNSTON

The giraffe group has a comparatively long history as a family, as old as the deer, it may be, and older than the development of the Bovidæ. There are indications that the Giraffids may have originated in North America, but the earliest remains of giraffe-like forms as yet discovered in India and China date back to the end of the Miocene period. A less-specialised type of giraffe existed in China in the Pliocene, in India in the same period, in Persia, Greece, and Russia. From these regions it must have migrated southwards into Africa, becoming extinct to the north of the tropic and in India; partly through changes in the land surface, the advance of the glacial cold, and the attacks of man. In India the giraffid family had attained strange developments in size and antlers, such as the *Sivatherium*, the *Brahmatherium*,

GIRAFFE WALKING

and the *Vishnutherium*. In Persia, Asia Minor, and Greece there were smaller forms less specialised, such as the hornless *Helladotherium* and the much smaller *Samotherium*.

The Samotherium, like its gigantic but near relation, the giraffe, seems to have fled southwards to Africa before the Pleistocene cold, and, like the giraffe, no doubt plunged into the wilder parts of tropical Africa to escape the fierce attacks of carnivorous man, and there was transformed into the creature which we now know by the name of " okapi."

The okapi (*Ocapia johnstoni*) is a small giraffid compared to its relations, living and extinct. It is about the size of a large mule, but stands higher at the shoulders, though not so disproportionately high as is the case with the giraffe. The neck is long in proportion to the body, but in the living animal is not necessarily held upright, as it is in the giraffe, but is extended m o r e horizontally, especially when feeding ; still, the general direction of neck and quarters is that of the giraffe in an incipient form.

The ears are very large, the " horns " exist only in the adult male, and are short pedicels of bone about three inches in length, rising from the frontal bones above the eyes, and directed backwards. At the extremity there is a small pointed piece of naked bone which seems like the vestige or the first fore-shadowing of a separable bony antler. The eye is large, the nostrils are hairy, and the tail is fairly long, with a small black tuft of hair at the extremity. The coloration and markings are peculiar, the cheeks and much of the face at the side being greyish white like the interior of the ears, while the rest of the head and the backs of the ears are dark sepia brown. The coloration of the neck and body ranges from bluish black to deep vinous brown, but the legs are mostly cream-coloured, tinted with orange, and striped longitudinally with black stripes, or patches. The hind quarters are marked with white stripes edged with orange, and the tail is blackish chestnut (page 779).

It has been one of the surprises of the twentieth century that a mammal so large and so eccentrically coloured could have remained unknown to science down to 1901. The history of the discovery, in which the present writer was much concerned, is as follows :

There were early stories brought back from West Central Africa by Dutch travellers and traders in the eighteenth century which, joined to some other wandering legends of French or British origin, caused Philip Henry Gosse, famous for his classic work on the birds of Jamaica, to write and publish a book about 1861 on possible discoveries of strange beasts in Central Africa. In this book he revived these Dutch descriptions of a strange animal, about the size of the okapi, which dwelt in the innermost recesses of the great Central African forest, and which was quite possibly the unicorn of tradition.

When the present writer was a boy this book was a source of great interest to him, and he rose up from reading it determined some day to explore Africa for himself, and to see if he could find any particles of fact to support this story of the unicorn still lingering in the heart of Africa.

Consequently, when in 1899 he visited Sir Henry Stanley to say good-bye to that prince of African explorers before starting on a special mission to Uganda, Stanley said to him, " If you get a chance, mind you take a dip into that wonderful Ituri forest, which, I am sure, contains some strange beasts not yet made known to science. You may find there the donkey that the pygmies told me they caught in pitfalls, or you may succeed in getting the huge black pig which I know lives in that forest, for I have seen it on more than one occasion rush past when we were fighting our way through the tangle of undergrowth."

In the early spring of 1900 I was obliged to intervene in the affairs of some Congo pygmies who had been carried off by force from Belgian territory by an enterprising showman who wished to exhibit them at the Paris Exhibition of that year. The Belgian authorities requested me, after releasing the pygmies, not to send them back unaccompanied, or they would certainly be recaptured and enslaved by bigger negro tribes. I therefore kept them with me for several months, until I was able myself to make a journey to the Congo frontier. While they were my guests we conversed on many subjects with the aid of an interpreter who had mastered something of their Bambute language.

I remembered Stanley's story of the wild donkey that was caught in pits. Dense as the pygmies were on many matters on which they were questioned, they hastened to answer this particular query. They *did* catch such an animal as I had described in pits, and they called it o'api—one or two said o'ati, which brought the name very near to Stanley's term for it, atti. On asking them what it was like they at first pointed to a tame zebra, and subsequently to a mule, and said that it was like a cross between the two, being partly striped, but having big ears like the mule. As to horns, they were very uncertain.

When I reached the frontiers of the Congo State, and was being hospitably entertained at the Belgian station of Mbeni, I repeated these stories of the pygmies, and both the Belgian officer, Lieutenant Meura, and his Swedish colleague, Lieutenant Eriksson, at once replied that they knew of the animal and had indeed eaten its flesh, though they had never seen it alive. As to its affinities, it seemed to them less like a horse than an antelope, and they were sure that it had more than one toe on each hoof, though whether it had three or two they could not remember. They also thought it had no horns.

I was now eager to start in search of this strange animal, and was duly furnished with guides for the purpose. Seeing how shy the okapi has proved to be, it is possible that in the short space of time at my disposal I might have been no more fortunate in my attempt to shoot one than had been all the Europeans who have followed me in this quest. Still, I spoilt what chances I might have had of seeing, if not shooting,

this rare creature, by the prepossession which had now got hold of me that I was in search of a new type of horse, possibly a surviving three-toed horse which had taken to the densest forest in Africa as its last refuge.

Consequently, when on the second day of our journey we crossed a little stream-valley in the dark forest, and saw imprinted in the sand cloven-hoof marks rather like those of an eland, and about the same size, and my native guide excitedly declared I was now on the track of the okapi, as these people called it, I repudiated the idea, saying that these wonderful footprints were either those of a forest eland or a bongo, and that such animals being known I could look for them another day. What I wanted was the imprint of a single hoof.

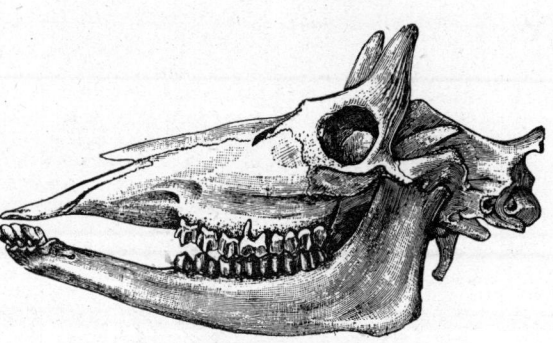

SKULL OF THE SAMOTHERIUM

They were much mystified, but continued to assert that the okapi had two hoofs like an ox. After three days' journey I came to a halt, because my followers were ill with the forest fever. In the village where we rested, the natives used as bandoliers for their guns, or additions to their scanty clothing, handsomely marked pieces of hide—brownish black, orange, and creamy white. They at once attracted my attention and seemed to me to be the pieces of the skin of an entirely new type of zebra. These, however, I was told were taken from the okapi whenever it was caught in pitfalls. Everyone being positive as to this, I now believed I held—as I did—portions of the skin of this unknown beast. On returning to the Belgian headquarters at Mbeni my belief was confirmed. The Congo officials told me that I had pieces of okapi skin. They were good enough to promise, as various causes had prevented me from staying any longer, that when the next okapi was caught by their soldiers or native neighbours in a pitfall, they would endeavour to secure the entire skin, and also the skull.

Some months afterwards this promise was redeemed by Mr. Eriksson, who forwarded to me in Uganda the skin and skull of the large female okapi, which is now in the British Museum of Natural History. He also sent a second and smaller skull. Directly these specimens came under my notice I recognised their giraffine characters—the complete absence of any " false hoofs," the bifoliate lower canines, the hairy muzzle, and slit-like nostrils, and the indications that if " horns " were developed they would be three in number, as in all the types but one of existing giraffes—namely, a single bony prominence above the nasal bones, and two prominences on the forehead above the eyes. The possible existence of these bony projections was slightly indicated in the larger of the two skulls, and this was intensified by the twirls of hair in the skin of the head. These prominences, or nascent " horns," were indicated in my original sketch, although I failed to find anything to indicate that the development of " horns " passed beyond these slight swellings in the bone or suggestive wisps of hair.

At the time I examined the skin and the two skulls, there were with me, as porters, natives of the Congo forest, who at once recognised the animal, though they did not know its name as okapi, but apparently called it something like " ndumba." They were questioned as to its carriage in life, its habits, and so forth, and from their information, together with a close and careful study and measurement of the skin and outline of the skull, I made a water-colour drawing which should as nearly as possible represent this mysterious animal in the living form. Then the skin and the two skulls were most carefully packed and labelled, half in fun, *Helladotherium*, and sent to Professor (afterwards Sir) E. Ray Lankester at the British Museum, accompanied by an explanatory letter. By the same post I sent a description of the beast to the "Times," under the title of "A New Mammal."

Having guessed this new beast of the Congo forest to be a giraffid, I named it provisionally as a species of *Helladotherium*. I was without any books of reference, but had some recollection that the large, hornless giraffids of Asia Minor and Greece were included under that generic name. As a matter of fact, that okapi is much more nearly related to the extinct *Samotherium* than to the *Helladotherium*.

After long delays in transport, this valuable package reached the hands of Sir E. Ray Lankester, who, having seen the water-colour drawing about a month before at the soirée of the Royal Society, had been inclined to put down the whole discovery to a piece of misplaced humour on my part. But the specimens soon convinced him of the reality of the discovery and the correctness of the guess as to the okapi's affinities. Curiously enough, after the despatch of drawing and specimens, the late Mr. W. G. Doggett and myself had, in the course of our journeys in the north-eastern part of the Uganda Protectorate, shot specimens of a giraffe which had five bony prominences on the head instead of the normal three, and I had ventured to telegraph this fact to Dr. P. L. Sclater.

The telegram appeared in the "Times" concurrently with the announcement of the genuineness of the okapi, and Sir E. Ray Lankester, confused—one might almost say—by my good luck, attempted to explain away the "five-horned giraffe" by arguing that the telegram must have been transmitted in French, and that I had telegraphed "sans cornes," or hornless, which by the telegraph operator had been changed into "cinq cornes." The five-horned giraffe was subsequently named after Mr. Walter Rothschild. My original specimens, with the five bony prominences, are to be seen in the British Museum. One of these was shot by Mr. Doggett, who was in my service as a taxidermist and collector, and the other by myself, together with two females without the extra two horns, also in the collection of the British Museum.

The question of naming the okapi led to a certain degree of confusion. Dr. P. L. Sclater, then Secretary of the Zoological Society, having received from me in 1900 strips of okapi skin which I had myself obtained in the forest, had decided that they must belong to a new type of zebra, and consequently named the animal *Equus johnstoni*. When Sir E. Ray Lankester created a new genus for the reception of the okapi, he latinised the name into *Ocapia*, and, in view of Dr. Sclater's action, continued my name as a specific classification. Thus in 1901 this beast appeared as the *Ocapia johnstoni*. The sex of my adult specimen was indeterminate. If it was a male, then it was clearly hornless.

In 1902, the attention of the Congo State authorities having been aroused as to the interest of this new

animal, Commandant Liebrechts sent to Brussels several other specimens of the okapi, and further examples were obtained by other officials and explorers. From these it was evident that the male of the okapi, or of one species of okapi, possessed "horns," or ossicusps far exceeding in length and size the faint indications I had already signalised. Yet the female forms sent home in these subsequent years were distinctly smaller than my specimen in the British Museum, which, if a male, was hornless. Also, on comparing my original pieces of okapi skin with the perfect skin due to the joint activities of Captain Eriksson and myself, there were found to be slight differences as to the placing or the length of the white stripes. Therefore certain British zoologists discriminated between the okapi of 1900 (that of the skin stripes) and the okapi of 1901. The hypothetically perfect form of the 1900 specimens was still called *Ocapia johnstoni*; but the well-established type of 1901 was styled *O. erikssoni*, or, by the Belgian naturalists, *O. liebrechtsi*. Finally, it was decided by the Belgian biologist, M. Jules Fraipont that there was but one valid species, *Ocapia johnstoni*. If this be the case, then the female okapi (which is hornless) is larger than the horned male.

Meanwhile, the Belgian authorities of the Congo Museum at Tervueren were steadily accumulating material for the adequate description of *Ocapia*. Mons. Jules Fraipont—already well known for his anthropological researches and his description of

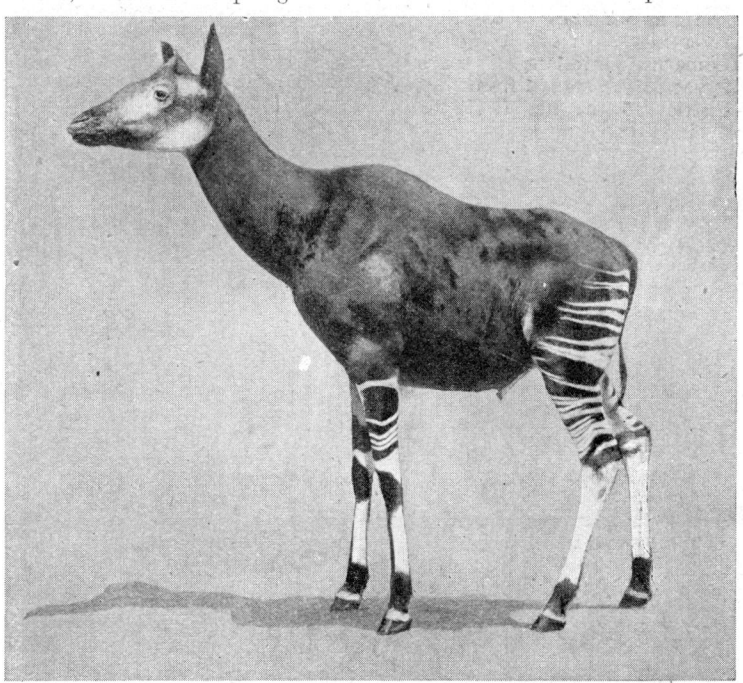

A MALE OKAPI
From the stuffed specimen in the Natural History Museum, Paris

extinct reptiles found fossil in Belgium—was entrusted with the task of producing a monograph on the okapi. This magnificent work, published by the Congo State in September, 1907, restored the Sclater-Lankester name of *Ocapia johnstoni*, and decided, apparently, that there was but one species extant of this beast, so far as could be decided from existing specimens and local research.

To a slightly different local variation or subspecies was applied tentatively the designation of *O. liebrechtsi*.

But, with the information at our disposal, it is still uncertain whether the okapi may be divided into distinct local forms. We know at present only its skin and bones, and no examination has been made of the "soft parts"—musculature and intestines.

In 1902, the okapi, under the name of *Ndumba*, was rediscovered on the Aruwimi river by the missionary explorer, George Grenfell, who, long cut off from European news, knew nothing of its revelation in 1900–1. The okapi, so far as is yet known, inhabits the densest portions of the forest of the northern and eastern part of the Belgian Congo, its range north-eastwards being limited by the abrupt edge of the forest on the lofty plateaus which overlook the Rift valley of Lake Albert, the Semliki, and Lake Edward.

From this great angle of the Congo forest it extends westwards through the forested regions between the Wele, or Upper Mubangi, and the northern course of the Congo river to the Mongala river, and even the vicinity of the Lower Mubangi, but does not, so far as we know, cross that river in the direction of the Cameruns hinterland. Nor has it yet been recorded from any district to the north of the Wele-Mubangi river, nor to the south or west of the main Congo. Its southern limit is the vicinity of Nyangwe, and its eastern, the western edge of the great Tanganyika-Kivu-Edward Rift valley. It has not been recorded from anywhere far east of Nyangwe because of the disappearance of forest in that direction. Captain Eriksson has stated

HEAD OF
MALE OKAPI

HEAD OF FEMALE
OKAPI

that the okapi is found in the Balolo country to the south of the Northern Congo between the rivers Lopori and Chuapa, but this assertion has not as yet been proved by the obtaining of any specimen. Nor has any specimen, so far, been obtained from the western side of the Congo-Lualaba opposite Nyangwe.

About 1906 a medical officer attached to the Northern Nigeria Government penetrated into the southern part of the Upper Benue basin, where there are great forests connected more or less with those of Southern Nigeria. He reported that in this region of forests an animal was found which, from the native description, must be identical with the okapi. But the region where one would next expect to hear of it as still living would certainly be the hinterland of the Cameruns, which in many respects approximates so closely in fauna to the equatorial belt of the Congo.

The writer of this article has made close inquiries on recent visits to West Africa as to the existence of the okapi in the dense forests of Sierra Leone, Liberia, the Gold Coast, and Southern Nigeria, but has never been able to get any hint of its existence there from natives who, on the other hand, readily identified pictures of other beasts of their forest, and gave interesting information as to their habitat. There is a remarkable correspondence in fauna between the true West African forests of the Gulf of Guinea and the great Cameruns-Congo forest that stretches between the Bight of Biafra and the frontiers of Uganda.

Yet in several genera of mammals this coincidence breaks down. For instance, the gorilla in various species is present in the forests between the northern Cameruns and the frontier of Uganda. So, also, is the great black forest pig (*Hylochœrus*), whose discovery was predicted by Stanley, Grenfell, and the present writer from independent sources of inquiry, and followed that of the okapi within two years. There are peculiar rodents of the familyt *Anomaluridæ*. There is the large otter-like insectivore, Potamogale, there is the primitive guinea-fowl of Luango (*Phasidus*), and there are a number of other beasts, birds, and reptiles of the great forest whose range extends over the same course between the Cameruns and the Uganda Protectorate, but which are not represented in the great forest belt of true West Africa.

The okapi, so far as present researches go, belongs exclusively to the Cameruns-Congo fauna, but has not so far been obtained actually from the Cameruns. There is no trace of it at all in West Africa. Probably its line of migration towards the Central African forest lay through the Bahr-al-Ghazal region and the valley of the Nile. In Syria or in the vanished extensions of Continental Greece and Asia Minor it differentiated, no doubt, from the common parent of the *Samotherium*. It lingered possibly till quite late in human history in the more forested regions of the Egyptian Sudan, and may even have been the animal type which in sculpture and design suggested to the Ethiopian Egyptians the representation of the god Seti.

Okapis are timid, inoffensive animals, living ordinarily in couples, male and female, with the addition of a calf or half-grown young. Occasionally okapis have been seen in small herds of ten to twenty individuals. The creature is said to have a voice like a cow; in which case it differs totally from its near ally, the big giraffe, which is absolutely voiceless. Its favourite food is stated to be the leaves of zingiberaceous or amarantaceous plants akin to the banana order; or the leaves of tall aroids. The natives, at any rate, assert that it lives on nothing but leaves, and does not browse. It affects the very densest and darkest parts of the forest, and easily conceals itself from the sight of all but the Congo pygmy by remaining perfectly immobile amidst the tall vegetation. The colour surface of its body would be broken up to the inexperienced eye by the sharp black and white of the striped portions, while the blackish chestnut of the upper parts of the body would assimilate with the rotting leaves of these foliage plants or the dark, sodden tree trunks.

H. H. JOHNSTON

THE RED DEER

THE last representatives of the true ruminants, or Pecora, are the deer tribe (family, *Cervidæ*), the distinctive feature of which is the almost universal presence in the males of the branched appendages to the skull known as antlers. These antlers are not present in all the members of the family, and the naturalist has, therefore, to rely partly on other characters in defining the group. Still, as antlers are the most characteristic feature of the deer tribe as a whole, their importance cannot be overrated, and they accordingly demand first consideration.

With regard to the meaning of the term "antler," the word is derived from the old French *antoiller*—a corruption of late Latin *antoculorum* ("before the eyes")—which was originally applied to the branch of the antler descending over the forehead, and now designated the brow tine. At a subsequent period the word "antler" seems to have been employed indifferently for all the branches of these appendages, while still later it was used to designate the entire appendages themselves. It is in the latter sense that it is now employed, the various branches of the antlers being termed "tines."

In addition to being generally more or less branched, the most characteristic feature of an antler when fully developed is that its outer surface is rugged and devoid of any covering of skin or horn. In fact, for all practical purposes, an antler may be regarded as a mass of dead bone borne for a certain period by a living animal. Save occasionally, as a specific peculiarity, antlers are shed once every year, and, except in the reindeer, are present only in the male sex. They arise from a pair of longer or shorter bony pedicles situated on the skull above and behind the eyes, and forming part of the skull itself.

When the antlers of a stag have been recently shed, these bony pedicles are completely covered with skin, and merely form small prominences on the upper part of the forehead. In a short time, however, there appear on the summits of these pedicles small velvety knobs, which are highly sensitive and tender, and supplied by an unusual number of blood-vessels.

These knobs are formed by a deposition of bony matter, and increase rapidly in size. In young deer and a few of the smaller species their growth is limited to the formation of a simple spike without a fork, but in the adults of the more typical kinds of deer they branch into a smaller or larger number of tines, until they finally assume the form of the complete antler. The whole antler is then completely invested with a soft and sensitive skin, clothed with exceedingly fine hair, termed the "velvet."

When, however, the growth of the antler is completed in its upper part, a deposition of bony matter takes place at its base, above the point of union with the pedicle of the skull, in the form of a prominent ring. This ring constricts the blood-vessels supplying the velvet, and ultimately causes them to dry up. In consequence of this cutting-off of the supply of blood by the ring or "burr," the velvet itself likewise dries up, and is eventually removed by the animal rubbing its newly-formed antlers against the stems of trees or other convenient objects. The antlers are then complete. They attain their full development shortly before the pairing season, and during that period they are employed as weapons in the contests which take place between the males of all species of deer. Subsequently the living bone beneath the skin below the burr of the antlers is absorbed, when the antler itself is shed, to be renewed in the following season in the same manner as before.

Although before shedding the antler is in most cases practically dead bone, in some species of deer, at any rate, it may be traversed internally by a few blood-vessels.

In the first year the antler forms merely a simple conical spike, and this type is retained in certain South American species throughout life. In the following year it gives off a branch near the base, and this form constitutes the highest development attained by some of the smaller species. In the more typical deer, however, the antlers become more and more branched with each succeeding year, till in the red deer they may occasionally have as many as forty points. The amount of bony matter annually secreted to form the antlers of the larger deer is enormous, antlers of the red deer having been obtained which weighed upwards of 74 pounds, while those of the extinct Irish deer would probably have scaled 100 pounds during life.

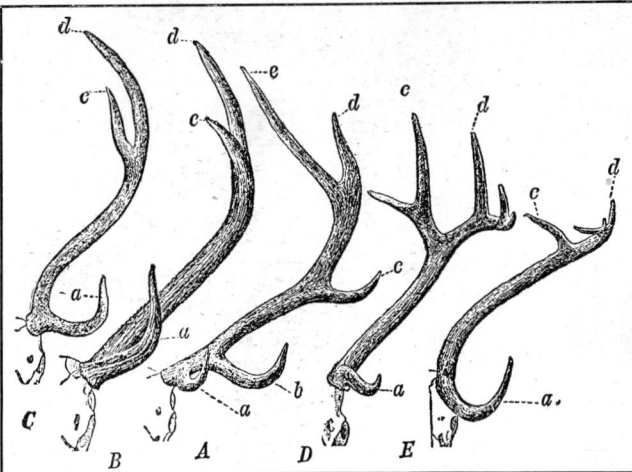

LEFT ANTLERS OF ASIATIC DEER

A, hangul, or Kashmir deer ; *B*, sambar ; *C*, spotted deer ; *D*, swamp deer ; *E*. thamin ; *a*, brow tine ; *b*, bez tine ; *c*, trez tine ; *d*, *e*, anterior and posterior surroyals.

The different tines borne by the antlers of the red deer and other species have received distinct names, and, as it is important that these should be understood, they may be referred to at once. In the red deer group (*A* of the accompanying figure) the shaft or beam of each antler carries three tines on its lower front edge, of which the lowest (*a*) is termed the brow tine, the second (*b*) the bez tine, and the third (*c*) the trez tine, or sometimes the royal tine. The summit of the beam may either be divided merely into two or three tines, or it may be split up into an almost indefinite number of snags, radiating outwards from a kind of cup ; but, in any case, these terminal snags, irrespective of their number, are collectively termed surroyals, or the crown of the antler. In many species of deer the bez tine of the antler is wanting, as is often the case in Scottish red deer.

It remains to mention certain characters which will aid in distinguishing from other ruminants those members of the deer family in which the antlers are wanting. In the first place, all deer have a large vacant, or unossified, space in the skull in advance of the socket of the eye, which is so extensive as to prevent the lachrymal bone from coming in contact with the nasal bone, as it does in the hollow-horned group. Of

RED DEER HIND AND FAWN

Deer are for the most part inhabitants of forests or grass jungles, and are never found in desert districts. They are an older group than any of the other typical ruminants, making their appearance in the lower portion of the Miocene period, where the species were of small size, and for the most part unprovided with antlers, while, when these were present, they were of a simple type, comparable to those of the modern muntjacs. That the group originated in the northern part of the Old World may be regarded as certain; and it made its way into North America—where the place of the deer tribe was taken during the Tertiary period by hoofed mammals more or less nearly related to the camels—at a comparatively late epoch by way of what is now Bering Strait. Having effected an entry into the New World from the north, the group afterwards made its way into South America when that continent became connected with North America; its south and tropical American representatives becoming markedly different from those inhabiting other parts of the world.

All deer possess a pair of large glands on the face, situated just below the eyes, and known as larmiers. In addition to these, many of them have a gland, marked by a tuft of long hair differing in colour from that of the rest of the leg, on the outer side of the lower portion of the leg overlying the cannon bone. In other cases there is a gland on the inner side of the hind leg, just below the hock. These hock and foot glands sometimes occur in the same species. While the face glands are probably connected with the sexual function, the glands on the legs and feet are most likely for the purpose of aiding these ruminants to ascertain the whereabouts of their fellows.

Deer present some interesting features in connection with colouring. From the fact that, with the exception of elk, reindeer, and a few of the other species, the young have fawn-coloured coats spotted with white, it may be considered certain that this was the original type of colouring. The adults of many species, however, have acquired a more or less uniformly coloured coat, sometimes with a light-coloured rump patch, probably for the purpose of better resemblance to their surroundings. Others, however, retain the spotted coat in the adult condition, either at all seasons, as in the chital or Indian spotted deer, or only in the summer, as in the fallow deer and the Japanese sika deer and its relatives. And it is noteworthy that, while those species which retain the spotted livery throughout the year are denizens of the tropics, those in which this dress is worn only during summer are

less importance is the circumstance that the first molar tooth in each jaw has a short crown. As a rule, tusks, or canine teeth, are present in the upper jaw; and since these are always developed in those species unprovided with antlers, they afford a ready means of distinction from the *Bovidæ*, in which upper tusks are never developed. Moreover, with the single exception of the musk-deer, no member of the family has a gall-bladder, which is so constantly present in the *Bovidæ*.

From prongbuck and giraffe deer are distinguished by the well-developed lateral hoofs in both feet. Moreover, while in the *Bovidæ* these lateral toes are represented merely by the bones of the toes themselves and the terminal hoofs, a large number of deer have remnants of the lower extremities of their supporting metacarpal and metatarsal bones on each side of the cannon bone in the form of splints. In all deer the end of the muzzle is naked, and there is a gland in front of the eye.

Although numerically far inferior to the *Bovidæ*, the deer family includes a large assemblage of species, which may be grouped under several generic headings, and have a wide geographical distribution. In the Old World, deer are found over the greater part of Europe and Asia, but are entirely unknown in Africa south of the Sahara—the Ethiopian region of naturalists. Three Old World species, representing as many genera, namely, the wapiti, the elk, and the reindeer, extend into North America, but the other New World deer, which range as far south as Chile, belong to quite a different type from any of those inhabiting the Eastern Hemisphere.

inhabitants of temperate climates. Obviously, this is connected with the persistence or fall of the leaves, and it is probable that all the species which have this spotted dress are in the habit of lying, like fallow deer, in the shade of trees, where their colouring harmonises with the chequered shade thrown by the sun's rays.

Another noticeable feature in many species with uniform coats is the great difference between the colour in summer and winter, shades of chestnut and warm brown prevailing at the former season, and grey in winter.

Although at other times fairly amenable, stags, especially those of the larger species, become exceedingly vicious and spiteful in the pairing season, ploughing up the ground and displaying paroxysms of rage and passion. At this season a wapiti stag is one of the most dangerous animals in existence, and, in fact, nothing less than an incarnate fiend.

The red deer (*Cervus elaphus*) of Europe, the typical representative of the genus *Cervus*, belongs to a group containing several species distributed over Europe, Asia north of the Himalaya, Northern Africa, and North America, and well characterised by the form of the antlers. These, when fully developed—as shown in *A* of the figure on page 715—have both a brow and a bez tine, and a nearly cylindrical beam, splitting up into two or more points at the summit. The tail is short, and the buttocks are very generally marked by a light disc-like patch, which includes the tail; while the rest of the coat of the upper parts is more or less uniformly coloured, although it may be darker on the neck than elsewhere. All the members of the group are of large size, and their young are spotted.

The red deer itself is characterised by the crown of the antlers in the adult having at least three points, and thus forming a cup, the total number of points being not less than twelve in cases where the bez tine is developed. Such a stag is called a royal hart. The number of points in the crown may, however, be greatly increased, as is shown in many antlers from the Irish bogs. In one such Irish bog antler the total number of points, if the two antlers were symmetrical, would have been thirty; but instances are recorded where there are as many as forty-five and even sixty-six points. The latter number, however, must be regarded as abnormal. Such antlers, and even larger ones, were not uncommon on the Continent a few centuries ago, many magnificent examples being preserved in old German castles, the collection at Moritzburg being especially rich.

An adult red deer stands fully 4 feet at the shoulder. The hair on the throat forms a long fringe, most developed in the pairing season. During summer the colour of the coat is bright reddish brown, with the head and legs somewhat greyer, the throat pale grey, and the patch on the buttocks yellowish white. In winter, when the fur becomes longer and softer, the colour tends to brownish grey. Wild stags are occasionally found white, the tendency to albinism increasing in the domesticated state. Good wild Scottish stags weigh about 280 pounds (20 stone), but may range up to 420 pounds (30 stone); and a park stag killed at Woburn in 1836 weighed 476 pounds (34 stone) as it stood. These weights are exceeded by the stags of Eastern Europe and Asia Minor, where antlers varying from 46 to 48½ inches in length have been obtained. Those of Scottish and Irish stags, however, rarely exceed 33 inches, although some of the latter may reach 35 inches.

The red deer has a wide distribution in the temperate regions of Europe and Western Asia, ranging through Asia Minor into Northern Persia. Formerly, indeed, it was probably found throughout the forest regions of Central Europe, but has been exterminated in many districts. In Scandinavia it is found only in a few forests in Sweden and in some of the Norwegian islands, and remains in the larger forests of France and Germany; while it is more abundant in Austria, Hungary, Servia, Transylvania, Poland, and the Danubian States. In parts of Greece, Italy, and Spain, as well as the islands of Corsica and Sardinia, it is less plentifully represented. In the British Isles it is only in the Scottish Highlands that wild red deer are met with abundantly, and then only through being preserved on an extensive scale. They are, however, also found on the moors of Devon and Somerset, in certain districts of Ireland, such as Killarney and Connemara, as well as in the Hebrides. So late as the reign of Queen Anne wild deer were common in Wolmer Forest, Hampshire, while a few lingered in Epping Forest till the early part of the nineteenth century.

Red deer abound in the Caucasus, and apparently also occur in the Crimea, although absent from Russia generally. The typical representative of the species is the red deer of Sweden, from which the deer of several countries differ to an extent sufficient to have led to their being distinguished as local races. Whatever may be the case with these, it is certain that the red deer from the Caspian provinces of Persia, commonly known as maral, constitute a distinct local race of the species

RED DEER STAG REPOSING

C. elaphus maral, characterised by its large size, the dark under parts, and the frequent retention of spots on the back of the hinds, is distinct. Closely allied, if not identical, red deer occur in Asia Minor and the Caucasus; but the Hungarian race may be distinct. The red deer of North-Western Africa, commonly known as the Barbary deer, constitute a small-sized race, *C. e. barbarus,* while another and still smaller race, *C. e. corsicanus,* inhabits Corsica; both being characterised by the absence of the bez tine of the antlers.

Fossil remains of red deer are found in the caves and superficial deposits of Europe, these fossil antlers being larger than most modern specimens, measuring in some cases 40 inches in length.

Like most of their tribe, red deer are gregarious; but, except during the pairing season, full-grown stags remain apart from the other members of the herd, and generally frequent higher ground. On the Continent this species is almost exclusively a forest-dweller, remaining concealed during the day in thick covert, and only venturing out to feed in the open glades or adjacent cultivated lands with the falling shades of evening. On the other hand, Scottish red deer inhabit open hills, and have for concealment only the glens.

The pairing season commences in the latter part of September or beginning of October, and lasts for about three weeks, when the venison is rank and unfit for table. At this season, writes Mr. W. Scrope, "the harts swell in their necks, have a ruff of long wiry hair about them, and are drawn up in their bodies like greyhounds. They now roll restlessly in the peat pools till they become almost black with mire, and feed chiefly on a light-coloured moss that grows on the round tops of the hills, so that they do not differ so entirely from the reindeer in their food as some naturalists have imagined. This is a very wild and picturesque season. The harts are heard roaring all over the forest, and are engaged in savage conflicts with each other, which sometimes terminate fatally.

"When a master hart has collected a number of hinds, another will endeavour to take them from him. They will fight till one of them, feeling himself worsted, will run in circles round the hinds, being unwilling to leave them; the other pursues, and when he touches the fugitive with the points of his horns, the animal thus gored either bounds suddenly on one side, and then turns and faces him, or will dash off to the right or the left, and at once give up the contest. The conflict, however, generally continues for a considerable time, and nothing can be more entertaining than to witness, as I have often done, the varied success and address of the combatants. It is a sort of wild joust, in the presence of the dames, who, as of old, bestow their favours on the most valiant.

"In solitary encounters, there being no hinds to take the alarm, the harts are so occupied, and possessed with such fury, that they may be occasionally approached in a manner that it would be vain to attempt at any other time." An instance has been recorded where the antlers of two stags fighting in this manner became so firmly interlocked that the victor, unable to disengage himself from his dead antagonist, was held captive till killed by a forester. After an interval of eight months and a few days from the pairing season—that is, generally in the early part of June—the fawns are produced, there being rarely more than one at a birth. The fawn is dropped in high heather, and left concealed there during the day by the hind, who returns to visit it in the evening.

Mr. Scrope states that the dam makes her offspring "lie down by a pressure of her nose, and it will never stir or lift up its head the whole of the day, unless you come right upon it, as I have often done. It lies like a dog, with its nose to its tail. The hind, however, although she separates herself from the young fawn, does not lose sight of its welfare, but remains at a distance to windward, and goes to its succour in case of an attack of the wild cat or fox, or any other powerful vermin."

The old stags shed their antlers about February or March, according to the nature of the season, but those of the young bucks are retained for some time longer. In spite of traditions as to the great age attained by stags, the ordinary limit of life is about twelve years, although a few individuals may survive to twenty years.

Red deer are essentially shy and wary animals, and, in the open districts which they frequent in Scotland, can detect an enemy at an immense distance. When all the members of a herd are together, the chief duty of watching appears to fall on the hinds, but at other times the stags have to depend on their own alertness. When their foes are in sight, deer will watch them with the greatest coolness and circumspection, but they become anxious and restless when they have reason to suspect the presence of a concealed enemy.

A WAPITI STAG IN WINTER

In Scotland, deer are killed only by driving or stalking, but wild red deer are hunted with hounds in Devon and Somerset. Formerly it was the custom in Scotland to surround a large tract of country with a circle of beaters; and deer-driving on a large scale is still practised in Austria and some other parts of the Continent. When hunted, as, indeed, at other times, red deer take freely to water; and when a wounded stag is hotly pursued by hounds, he generally seeks refuge in the mountain streams, where his length of leg gives him a great advantage over his pursuers. When disturbed, deer invariably run up wind.

THE HANGUL OR KASHMIR STAG

The Himalaya and the countries immediately north and east are the home of several species allied to the red deer, but with antlers of somewhat different type. The best known is the hangul (*Cervus cashmirianus*), which stands about 4 feet 4 inches at the shoulder, and differs from the red deer in that each antler usually has only five tines, so that no cup is formed at the crown, which is simply forked. Moreover, the whole beam of the antler is more curved, with the main tine of the surroyals inclined inwards ; while the bez tine is generally longer than the brow tine, or the reverse of the usual condition in the red deer. Occasionally six or seven points may be developed in the antlers.

In colour this deer is brownish ashy when in the winter coat, with the hairs speckled, and the rump patch, which is white bordered with black, intruding only to a small extent on to the upper surface, and not including the tail, but prolonged down the hind portion of the hams. This deer, commonly known to sportsmen as the barasingha, although that name properly belongs to a very different species, inhabits the mountains around the valley of Kashmir, extending eastwards to Kishtwar, but reappears in the Sze-chuen province of North-Western China in the shape of a much paler and greyer race, *C. c. macneilli*.

In Kashmir the hangul, which is essentially a forest deer, is found in summer at elevations of from 9,000 to 12,000 feet. In winter, however, it descends to the valleys during heavy falls of snow, and at such times is ruthlessly attacked by the villagers, as many as five hundred head having been slaughtered on a single occasion. These indiscriminate slaughters, together with the more orthodox pursuit by English sportsmen, have so thinned the ranks of this deer, that it is now comparatively rare. In summer hangul are found singly or in small parties, the old stags being usually solitary ; but in winter they collect in herds.

The antlers of the stags are shed about March, and the new ones do not attain their full development till October. In that month, and through November, the stags are continually calling ; this being the proper shooting season. The fawns are born in April, so that the period of gestation appears to be only about six months, or considerably less than in the red deer. Hangul are seldom confined to one region, but roam from forest to forest, preferring grassy glades alternating with dense

YELLOW-RUMPED WAPITI

forest, where there is a copious supply of water. I once saw a small party of these deer on the Ladak side of the mountains bounding Kashmir, where there is no forest.

In the pairing season the stags utter a somewhat wapiti-like squeal, quite unlike the roar of a red deer.

In the Tarim valley and neighbouring districts of Eastern Turkestan the place of the hangul is taken by the Yarkand stag (*C. yarcandensis*), distinguished by the large light rump patch, which includes the tail, the light rufous fawn colour of the coat, and the fact that when the antlers are five tined, as is usually the case, the terminal fork is almost at right angles to the middle line of the head—just the reverse of the condition in the wapiti.

Another member of this group is the large but imperfectly known shou, or Sikhim, stag (*C. affinis*), inhabiting the upper part of the Chumbi valley and some of the valleys of Bhutan, but also represented in the San-po valley near Lhasa. The characteristic feature of the five tined antlers, which may measure as much as 54 or 55 inches in length, is the sharp bend at the third tine, and the forward inclination of the portion immediately above, coupled with the inward bend of the tips. The general appearance of this deer seems to be distinctly wapiti-like.

In the neighbourhood of Lhasa this group is represented by Thorold's deer (*C. albirostris*), easily recognised by its white muzzle and the somewhat flattened and smooth four or five tined antlers, in which the bez tine is absent.

THE WAPITI

Till well into the second half of the nineteenth century wapiti (*Cervus canadensis*), persistently miscalled " elk " in their native country, were regarded as an exclusively American type, but are now known to be strongly represented in Central and North-Eastern Asia by deer closely related to the American species, of which they may be classed as local races. Wapiti are distinguished from the hangul and the shou—to which they are more nearly related than to the red deer—by the form and proportions of the antlers, which are characterised by their general smoothness, and the tendency to a flattening and expansion of the upper tines, and more especially by the great length and stoutness of the fourth tine, which is situated nearly in the same plane as those above, this lying nearly parallel to the long axis of the body. The antlers have a marked backward curvature and want of convergence in the upper part of the beam.

Wapiti are dark brown on the head and neck, creamy grey on the flanks and thighs, and blackish on the under parts of the body, with the legs brown, and the rump patch, which includes the very short tail, straw-coloured, bordered below with black. The height of a full-grown stag is rather more than 5 feet 4 inches (16 hands) ; the usual weight is about 700 pounds, but it is reported that large stags may exceed 1,000 pounds, although some full-grown females do not scale more than 400 pounds.

In the fifth year the antlers develop five points, but after that period the number increases irregularly, and there are frequently more snags on the one antler than on the other. Very rarely is there any approach to the cup in the crown of the antler distinctive of the red deer. Antlers of wapiti attain very large dimensions. Of two fine pairs in the collection of Mr. Otho Shaw, the respective dimensions are, in inches, length $49\frac{1}{2}$, span 54, basal girth 8, and length $55\frac{1}{2}$, span $48\frac{3}{4}$, basal girth $7\frac{1}{2}$; while in two examples belonging to Mr. E. S. Cameron the lengths are respecively $53\frac{1}{2}$ and $55\frac{1}{4}$ inches, the spans $47\frac{1}{4}$ and $44\frac{1}{2}$ inches, and the basal girths just above the burr $9\frac{1}{2}$ and 10 inches. Lengths of 70, 66, and 65 inches are on record.

The range of the wapiti has been greatly restricted by the advance of civilisation, while incessant pursuit on the part of sportsmen has reduced its numbers in a corresponding degree. These fine deer were formerly found in nearly all parts of the United States, in Mexico, and in British America as far north as the 60th parallel of north latitude, but are now met with only in the remotest mountain fastnesses of the Missouri River, or in the forests of British America. The largest herds remaining outside of the National Yellowstone Park occur in the Olympic Mountains of Washington and among the mountains of Vancouver Island. Many remain in the Cascade and Rocky Ranges, but do not congregate there in large herds as in the Coast Ranges. Up to about 1880 there were many secluded districts in Colorado, Wyoming, and Montana, where, during the late autumn and winter, wapiti might be seen in herds of many thousands, whereas it is seldom that a hundred can now be found together.

The habits of wapiti are very similar to those of red deer, the old stags living apart from the main herd during the greater part of the year, and in the pairing season taking exclusive possession of a party of hinds, after having vanquished their rivals in fight. The shedding of the antlers is late, generally taking place in full-grown stags during the latter part of December or the first half of January. The new antlers begin to sprout in March or April, and are fully complete by the middle of August. At this time the old stags begin to call, the note being a prolonged squeal very like that of the hangul, and has been compared to the bray of a donkey; and it is suggested that the wapiti has on this account received the nickname of "jackass deer," bestowed on it by the traders in the Rocky Mountains.

During May wapiti desert the lower hills to take refuge in the higher ranges, getting as near as possible to the snow line without leaving the upper belt of forest. The hinds then leave the herds to give birth to their fawns in the most secluded thickets. Usually a single fawn is produced at a birth, although twins are not very infrequent. The hind will fight to the death in the defence of her helpless offspring against the onslaught of puma, bear, or coyote; and at such times gives utterance to a loud cry, which at once brings to her aid any members of the herd that may be in the vicinity, all of which unite in driving off the foe.

Wapiti are promiscuous, not to say coarse, feeders. All the grasses and most of the weeds within reach are taken freely, the leaves and twigs of deciduous trees being alike enjoyed. A considerable proportion of their daily food should be leaves and twigs, but, if deprived of these, they will keep in good condition on herbaceous food alone. In winter they will take the coarsest food, even that which cattle and horses would reject being eaten freely. The venison, although unlike that of other deer, is of fine flavour, and said to be more nutritious than any other meat.

A combat between two male wapiti during the pairing season is described by Mr. Perry as follows: "The challenger, when approaching a band, or harem, blows a loud whistle of defiance. (Take a half-pint bottle and blow strongly into it, and the sound so produced will be similar to the call of the male wapiti during the

A WAPITI STAG IN SUMMER

rutting season.) This whistle is at once answered by the ruler of the herd, who steps boldly forth to do battle with the intruder. With heads lowered between their fore feet, the two adversaries walk around waiting for an opening, and when one is thrown off his guard the other makes a savage rush; but his opponent instantly recovers, counters the charge, and as they rush together the antlers strike each other with such terrific force that the report can be heard for a long distance. Slowly retreating, bellowing, grumbling, and grinding their teeth in a paroxysm of rage, they again circle around, and when an opportunity is afforded, make another charge, which is countered as before.

"The challenging wapiti usually does most of the offensive fighting until he finds, if such be the

FORMOSAN DEER IN SUMMER DRESS

case, that he is the weaker; then he sullenly retires, bellowing as he goes. These battles are seldom fatal, and during the rutting season are an everyday occurrence. Ugly wounds often result from them, and sometimes a prong of an antler is broken in the affray."

Wapiti differ from the majority of the deer tribe in that they do not feed during the night, although they are on the move with the first streak of dawn. From that time till about eight in the morning they continue feeding almost without interruption, after which they indulge in a midday siesta. During this rest they can be easily approached. About four o'clock in the evening they once more feed, in which occupation they continue till dusk. In winter they are often pressed for food; and when the snow lies deep on the ground each party occupies a small area, over which the snow is trampled down as hard as ice, while all the trees are gnawed bare both of bark and leaves as high as the animals can reach.

When wapiti were found on the prairies, the Indians were accustomed to hunt them on horseback by forming a wide circle of mounted men, from whom a certain number were detached to harass the unfortunate animals until they were brought to a standstill. Another favourite method was by forming a cordon of horsemen and driving a whole herd over a precipice; but at the present day the more sportsman-like method of hunting is almost exclusively employed. The wapiti is an animal far less difficult to approach than the red deer, while a comparatively slight wound will kill it.

There are several races of Asiatic wapiti, such as the Manchurian *C. xanthopygus*, some of which are

kept by the farmers in the Altai in a half-tamed condition, for the sake of their antlers, which are sawn off while in the velvet and exported to China, where they realise a high price, and are used, when ground to powder, for certain medical purposes.

SIKA DEER

The well-known and graceful sika deer (*Cervus sica*) of Japan is the typical representative of a group distinguished by the constant absence of the bez tine, and the consequent reduction of the normal number of tines in the antlers to four, as well as by the coat being profusely spotted with white in summer, although generally uniform brown during winter. The length of the tail is also much greater than in the red deer group, while the large white patch on the buttocks is completely bordered with black, and consists of much longer hairs, which can be erected and expanded into large white bunches, as in the prongbuck. All the deer of this group are inhabitants of Eastern Asia.

The typical sika of Japan and North China stands somewhat lower at the shoulder than a fallow deer, and has the ground colour of the fur dark or yellowish brown, with the greater part of the tail white. These deer are very abundant in northern Japan and parts of China, where they frequent dense forest, generally in hilly regions. The only way of shooting them is by beating the country with a large number of men. The Japanese deer has been introduced into several parks in Ireland and England. In Manchuria it is replaced by a larger race, *C. sica manchuricus*.

The finest member of the group is, however, the Pekin deer (*C. hortulorum*), from Manchuria, in which the stags are nearly as large as red deer, although the hinds are much smaller. In the summer dress the stags are reddish brown with large white spots, while the hinds are bright rufous. In winter both sexes become dull brown, the coat being very long and shaggy in the hinds. These deer are met with in large herds in the Manchurian forests, and are represented by another race, *C. s. kopschi*, in the Yangtse valley. The Formosan sika (*C. taëvanus*) is of the approximate size of the Japanese species, from which it differs by the spots persisting during winter; the tail being white, with a black streak down the middle of the upper surface. These deer are caught in traps by the inhabitants of Formosa, by whom, as well as by the dwellers on the island of Samasana, they are kept as pets.

In the stag shown in the annexed figure the antlers are only partially developed, and still in the velvet.

FALLOW DEER

The fallow deer (*Cervus dama*) is one of two representatives of a group of the genus *Cervus* characterised by the antlers being rounded at the base, but widening in the upper part into a flattened palmate expansion. In front there is a large brow antler, forming rather more than a right angle with the beam, above which is a trez tine given off at some distance below the beginning of the palmation; while the hind edge of the latter carries three or four small sharp snags, of which the lowest is longer and placed considerably below the others, so that it may rank as a distinct back tine.

In height fallow deer stand nearly 3 feet at the withers, and have small heads, large ears, and relatively long tails, which are dark above and white beneath, and when running are turned up to show the white, which, with that of the buttocks, forms a " recognition mark." The general colour is some shade of fawn or yellowish brown, darker on the head and neck, and marked on the body in summer with a number of large white spots. The under parts, inner sides of the limbs, and the under surface of the tail are white ; and there is a dark line running down the back from the nape of the neck to the end of the tail. There is, however, a tame blackish brown variety in which spots are wanting at all seasons, and specimens may be seen exhibiting every gradation from white to nearly black. The hair is comparatively short and fine, and there is no mane on the neck and throat. The upper jaw has no tusks. Good antlers vary in length from 19 to 27 or even 31 inches in length.

The fallow deer is a native of North-Western Africa and the countries bordering the Mediterranean, and in a wild state still exists, at any rate, in Asia Minor as far along the south coast as Adana. From these countries it is generally believed to have been introduced into Central Europe, where it flourishes well, although needing protection during winter in the more northerly regions. From the occurrence of antlers of the type of those of fallow deer in some of the superficial deposits, it has been supposed that this species is really an indigenous British animal, but these fossil antlers belong to an allied extinct species known as *C. browni*.

Other remains from a cave in Derbyshire referred to the existing species are stated to have been found with those of undoubted Pleistocene mammals at all horizons in the undisturbed strata. But as fallow deer remains are unknown from any other Pleistocene British cave, and since fallow deer are just the kind of animals whose carcases would be carried into caves by hyænas, the association of the Derbyshire bones with extinct mammals has been doubted. The argument is no doubt a strong one, but if the bones are rightly identified, it seems difficult to account for their occurrence among the Pleistocene remains otherwise than as being contemporary. It may be added that numerous fallow deer remains have been described from the peat of Denmark.

Fallow deer associate in large herds, the bucks apart from the does, except in the pairing season and early winter, when both sexes consort. Most persons are familiar with the bold and confident manner in which they approach man, when well accustomed to his presence. Like other species, fallow deer feed on herbage, but are specially fond of horse-chestnuts, which the bucks knock down from the branches with their antlers. The pairing season begins in September, and the doe goes eight months with young. As a rule, a single fawn is produced at a birth, although there may occasionally be two ; the alleged instances of triplets being apparently incorrect. The young male exhibits the first signs of his antlers in his second year, when they make their appearance as simple snags ; the deer being then called a " pricket." In the fifth year the antlers attain their full development, although some additional small points may be added in the following season.

It has been stated that the dark variety was introduced into England from Norway by James I., on account of its hardy constitution, but this is incorrect, since this breed existed in Windsor Park so far back as 1465. The fallow deer of Windsor Park include both the spotted and the brown breeds, but in Epping Forest only the latter occur.

Writing of the fallow deer of Epping Forest, Mr. J. E. Harting states that they " have held their own, in spite of all difficulties, until the present time, and have strangely preserved their ancient character in regard to size and colour. Locally they are referred to as ' the old forest breed,' and are comparatively small in size, of a uniformly dark brown colour, with very attenuated antlers—peculiarities which have no doubt been brought about by continued isolation, without the admixture of any fresh stock for many generations.

FALLOW DEER

" It is remarkable that no individuals of the true fallow colour—*i.e.*, yellow dun—or spotted with white, are ever seen in this forest. This in some measure proves the antiquity of the stock, which would otherwise show in their progeny a reversion to one or other of these varieties, which elsewhere are so common. The keepers assert that not only are there no spotted or fallow varieties here, but that they have never observed any spotted fawns, the latter being dark like their parents. If this observation be correct, it is very remarkable ; for it is generally supposed that the fawns of all fallow deer are spotted at birth, and that, except in the permanently spotted variety, the spots disappear with age. The attenuation of the antlers is also very noticeable, the palmation being reduced from a hand's-breadth to about the width of two fingers. There can be no doubt that, from long isolation and continued breeding in and in, the herd has considerably degenerated. They do not associate in one herd, but roam about in small parties, keeping to the thickest underwood and most unfrequented parts of the forest." The venison of the fallow deer is superior to that of red deer.

The Persian fallow deer (*C. mesopotamicus*), from the mountains of Luristan, in Mesopotamian Persia, differs from the ordinary kind in that the trez tine of the antlers is placed nearer to the small brow tine, and that the main palmation of the beam takes place below instead of above the middle, as well as by the fact that the tail is white on all sides for the greater part of its length. The two species are closely allied, and will breed freely together.

In this place may be noticed an extinct deer from the superficial deposits of Europe, which appears to be related to fallow deer, although it is impossible to tell whether it had a spotted or a uniformly-coloured coat. The typical and largest representative of this species is the gigantic Irish deer (*C. giganteus*), often incorrectly spoken of as the "Irish elk," in which the widely-palmated antlers were larger and more massive than in any other species. In this magnificent deer the antlers have a short and nearly cylindrical basal portion of the beam, given off almost at right angles to the axis of the skull.

Above the burr is a descending brow tine which is flattened and generally forked. As soon as the

HEAD OF PERSIAN FALLOW DEER

beam expands it gives off from the front edge a trez tine, and nearly opposite to it, on the hind edge, a back tine corresponding to the one similarly situated in the fallow deer. Above these tines the antlers expand to their fullest width, and terminate in five or six snags, of which the topmost have a nearly upright direction. In unusually fine examples, the antlers of the Irish deer may have a span of over 11 feet from tip to tip, and the height of the animal was fully 6 feet at the shoulder.

Although the Irish deer takes its name from the common occurrence of its remains in the bogs of Ireland, it is by no means confined to that country, but is also found in the caverns and superficial deposits of England and parts of Scotland, as well as on the Continent, where its range extended from Italy in the south to Russia in the north. That the Irish deer lived within the human period is proved by the occurrence of its remains in association with stone implements ; and it has been considered that the *Schelk* of the Nibelungenlied of the twelfth century refers to this deer, although it may mean a wild stallion.

The typical Irish deer differs from the fallow deer in

the form and direction of its antlers, but a connecting link is formed by the race known as *C. giganteus ruffi*, from the superficial deposits of Germany, which was of somewhat inferior dimensions to the former. In Ruff's deer the antlers are directed upwards and outwards nearly after the fashion obtaining in the fallow deer, while the plane of the palmated portion is placed in the same longitudinal direction as in the latter. The terminal snags are also shorter and inclined more inwardly than in the Irish deer, but the flattened and expanded form of the brow tine indicates a closer connection with the latter.

THE CHITAL AND SAMBAR GROUP

The chital, or spotted deer, of India and Ceylon, also known as the axis (*Cervus axis*), is the first representative of a group of deer from South-Eastern Asia, in which the cylindrical antlers have three tines on each side ; the bez and trez tines being absent, and the beam terminating in a simple fork. In the spotted deer the brow tine of the antlers is given off nearly at a right angle with the beam ; and the whole length of the antlers is about three times that of the skull in average specimens ; the hind tine of the terminal fork being considerably longer than the one in front.

Chital vary considerably in height in different localities, bucks from Northern and Central India standing from 3 feet to 3 feet 2 inches at the withers, whereas in Southern India the height seldom exceeds from 2 feet 6 inches to 2 feet 8 inches. In Ceylon the species is represented by a distinct small race. The neck and throat of this deer are devoid of mane, the tail is relatively long, pointed, and thin, and the cheek teeth are characterised by the height of their crowns.

The ground colour of the coat is rufous fawn, with the whole body marked by large white spots, which are present at all ages throughout the year, and tend to arrange themselves in longitudinal lines. The head and neck are uniform brownish, and there is a black line running from the nape of the neck to the end of the tail. White prevails on the inside of the ears, the chin, the upper part of the throat, the under parts of the body, and the insides of the limbs, as well as on the under surface of the tail. As in the case of the fallow deer, a blackish variety is occasionally met with, in which the spots are only faintly indicated. A buck standing close upon 3 feet in height weighed 145 pounds.

Although the antlers of the spotted deer are typically three-tined, there is not infrequently a number of small points or "sports" at the junction of the brow tine with the beam, but such sports are rare higher up. The average length of the antlers of the larger race of the species is about 30 inches ; but examples reaching 38 and 38¾ inches in length, with a girth of 5¾ inches above the burr, have been recorded. Great difference exists in regard to the degree of divergence or span of the antlers ; in two examples, of which the respective lengths were 34 and 34½ inches, the span in the former case was only 24 inches, against 30½ inches in the other. This deer is found nearly throughout India and Ceylon, but in the Himalaya occurs only on the outermost spurs, and is unknown on the plains of the Punjab, Sind, a large part of Rajputana, Assam, and all the countries to the east of the Bay of Bengal. On the hills of Southern India it is found at elevations of from three to four thousand feet above the sea.

The name chital refers to the dappled hide of this deer, which is, perhaps, the most handsome member of its tribe as regards colour and form, and is certainly one of the most characteristic of the mammals of India. It is generally found among bushes or trees in the neighbourhood of water, and in bamboo jungles, while it frequents both hilly tracts and plains, and never wanders far from its drinking places. "So long," writes Dr. W. T. Blanford, "as it has a wild tract of bush or ravines for shelter, it appears to care little for the neighbourhood of man. Many of its favourite haunts are in some of the most beautiful wild scenery of the Indian plains, and lower hills on the margins of rippling streams with their banks overgrown by lofty trees, or in the grassy glades that open out amidst the exquisite foliage of bamboo clumps.

"Spotted deer are thoroughly gregarious, and associate at all times of the year in herds, sometimes of several hundreds. They are less nocturnal than sambar, and may be found feeding for three or four hours after sunrise, and again in the afternoon for an hour or two before sunset. They generally drink between eight and ten o'clock in the morning, the time varying with the season of year, and repose during the day in deep shade. They swim well, and take readily to water. They both graze and browse."

There is great range of variation as regards the date of the pairing season and the shedding of the antlers; bucks with fully-developed antlers being met with at all times of the year. In Northern India the pairing season, however, seems to be generally during the winter, although young fawns may apparently be met with at any season.

Remains of deer apparently allied to the chital are found in the Pliocene formations of the south of France, thus indicating that the axis type of antler is an old one.

Nearly allied to the chital are several deer from South-Eastern Asia distinguished by the brow tine of the three-pronged antlers forming an acute, instead of nearly a right, angle with the beam.

Of these deer the well-known Indian sambar (*Cervus unicolor*) is the largest, and is distinguished by the fact that the typical Indian race is whole-coloured at all ages. Externally the sambar is characterised by its coarse wiry hair, which on the neck and throat of the adult stag is elongated to form an erectile mane. The ears are large and broad, and the tail thick and of moderate length. In colour the coat is nearly uniform dark brown throughout, tending, however, in some specimens to a more or less well-marked yellowish, and in others to a greyish tinge. The chin, under

ANTLERS

1. CHITAL
2. SWAMP-DEER
3. SAMBAR

parts, and inner surfaces of the limbs are always yellower, and may be yellowish white. The height of the buck varies from 4 to 5 feet, and possibly rather more at the withers; and large specimens have been killed weighing 560 and 700 pounds.

The antlers are generally characterised by their rough external surface and freedom from sports; and in Indian examples the two tines of the terminal fork are nearly equal in length, although in other districts there is great variability in this respect. In India fine horns attain a length of about 36 inches, but such dimensions are seldom reached in the countries to the east of the Bay of Bengal. As regards shape and girth, there is a great amount of variation in sambar antlers. In a fine pair, of which the extreme length was 38½ inches, the span was 37¾ inches, and the basal girth 8⅝ inches; whereas in another pair, while the length was only 32½ inches, the span was 38 inches and the girth 9 inches. The longest recorded pair measured 48 inches in length, but their girth at the middle of the beam was only 6 inches, against 8½ inches in a pair measuring 38 inches in length. Perhaps, however, the finest-known pair is one in which the length is 44 inches, the span being 45¾ inches, and the girth just above the brow tine 7¾ inches. There is also an equally-marked difference in regard to the degree of development of the ridges and furrows on the antlers.

The sambar occurs typically in the wooded undulating or hilly districts of India and Ceylon, but in Cachar and the countries east of the Bay of Bengal it is represented by a race, *C. unicolor equinus*, in which the fawns are spotted, and the front tine of the terminal fork of the antlers is shorter than the back one, instead of the two being subequal. In the Philippine and Ladrone Islands the species is represented by the small Luzon sambar (*C. u. philippinus*), which is not much larger than a hog deer, with light rings round the eyes; while in Formosa its place is taken by the somewhat larger, white-legged *C. u. swinhoei*.

Another race, which exists in the Sze-chuen province of North-Western China, is known as *C. u. dejeani*, and attains a very large size. In the Himalaya sambar range to elevations of nine thousand or ten thousand feet, and they are commonly found on the highest mountains of Southern India and Ceylon. They are seldom seen on the alluvial plains frequented by the chital, and are absent from the sandy desert tracts of Sind, the Punjab, and Rajputana.

Dr. W. T. Blanford observes that the sambar "is the woodland deer of South-Eastern Asia generally, and is more widely and generally distributed than any other species. Although it does not shun the neighbourhood of man to the same degree as *Bos gaurus* does, it is only common in wild tracts of country. It comes out on the grass slopes, where such exist, as in the Nilgiris and other hill ranges, to graze, but always takes refuge in the woods. It is but rarely found associating in any numbers; both stags and hinds are often found singly, but small herds from four or five to a dozen in number are commonly met with.

"Its habits are nocturnal; it may be seen feeding in the morning and evening, but it grazes chiefly at night, and at that time often visits small patches of cultivation in the half-cleared tracts, returning for the day to wilder parts, and often ascending hills to make a lair in grass amongst trees, where it generally selects a spot well shaded from the sun's rays. It feeds on grass, especially the green grass near water, and various wild fruits of which it is very fond, but it also browses greatly on shoots and leaves of trees. It drinks, I believe, daily, though this has been doubted, and certainly travels long distances to its drinking-places at times."

As regards the date of the pairing season and the time of shedding the antlers, there appears to be a still greater amount of variation than is the case in the chital, and it is stated that stags have been known to retain their antlers for two or more years. It appears, however, that in peninsular India the pairing season is usually in October and November, but in the Himalaya in the spring. Similarly, while in the former area the antlers are most frequently shed in March, in the latter the shedding-time is deferred for a month later. Usually there is one fawn at a birth.

During the pairing season sambar assemble in large numbers, and the old stags utter at morning and evening, and sometimes in the night, loud roarings, which have been described as a "metallic-sounding bellow.'

In the islands of the Malay region occur several small sambar-like deer, among which the rusa of Java (*C. hippelaphus*) is readily distinguished by the hairs

INDIAN SPOTTED DEER

being marked by dark and light rings, and thus communicating a speckled appearance to the coat, as well as by the smaller ears, and longer and slenderer antlers, in which the hind tine of the terminal fork is much the longer. Local forms of this species are the Timor deer (*C. hippelaphus timorensis*), a small, thick-set animal, scarcely half the size of the smaller race of the true sambar, and also the Moluccan *C. h. moluccensis*, in which the general build is more slight and graceful.

Another allied, but smaller, species is Kuhl's deer (*C. kuhli*), from the Bavian Islands between Borneo and Java, which resembles a sambar in its uniform colour, but differs in having a skull resembling that of the hog deer, and displaying the same absence of tusks in the upper jaw. The colour of the coat is pale brown, but the individual hairs are ringed with alternate tints, instead of having the uniform hue of those of the hog deer.

Very different from all other members of this group is the Philippine spotted deer (*C. alfredi*), which resembles the chital in having at all ages and all seasons a spotted coat. This deer, which stands about $2\frac{1}{2}$ feet at the withers, is dark chocolate brown in colour, with about six longitudinal rows of somewhat indistinctly-marked yellowish spots. The antlers are comparatively short, and have the front tine of the terminal fork directed inwardly, while the outer surfaces of the ears are nearly devoid of hairs.

R. LYDEKKER

IN THE JUNGLE WITH SAMBAR
BY MAJOR F. G. ALEXANDER

I have come across the sambar in many jungles, and for a long time thought that there were two distinct varieties, namely, the greater and the lesser sambar. Not being a systematist, I offer no opinion on the matter, beyond remarking that the Bheels of Central India call the larger the tailia, and the lesser the peelia, sambar. In colour the tailia is very dark brown. The term "tailia" signifies "dark oil," whilst "peelia" suggests that the animal is of a yellowish colour. Though the blackbuck is, on the average, large or small according to the locality in which it roams, very large and very small sambar are

GROUP OF INDIAN SPOTTED DEER

found in the same jungles. I have, as a sportsman, devoted my attention to the larger specimens, and I have observed that the tailias are not only bigger, but that their horns are more massive.

I have rarely shot what might be termed an "intermediate," but I generally allowed the peelias to go unmolested unless my followers were in want of food. I have compared the skulls of old tailias and old peelias, and found a vast difference in their formation. I could tell by footprints, after some years of practice, whether I was following the larger or lesser beast. Eccentricities in horns—I mean in regard to extra points—are more common in the smaller specimens.

I am fairly certain that the sambar sometimes passes a year without shedding its horns, and my reasons for supposing so are as follows. I have often shot beasts whose horns were abnormally smooth and nearly white, the crusty surface of the horn having disappeared. I have also picked up horns and examined them, and the surfaces of the very smooth horns suggested that they had been for over a year on their owner's heads. I once shot at Mount Abu, in September, a sambar one of whose horns was very long and perfectly smooth, and I was surprised to find that the other horn was shorter and in velvet. I therefore came to the conclusion that the deer had in the previous year got rid of one horn only.

Many people have advanced theories in regard to the shedding of horns. At one time I supposed that weevils found a home in the dried up blood channels connecting the once living upper bones, namely, the antlers and their ever-living pedestals. After consideration and consultation with scientific naturalists, I think there are two reasons why stag deer endeavour to shed their antlers.

Firstly, because the upper bones, namely the antlers, contract at the base, and as they die a rasping sensation is created between the base of the antlers and their pedestals.

Secondly, that, whilst foraging at night, the antlers collide with the trunks of trees and thereby jar the base of the antlers and their pedestals, causing the beasts continual annoyance.

Stags are mostly in velvet until November, and the rutting season is virtually over in March, when they begin to shed their horns; but my biggest stag was killed on June 1, 1892, a very late period for a stag to possess horns.

There are two ways by which sportsmen pursue the sambar. One is by beating, the other by stalking; I have always preferred the latter.

I think that the finest sambar occur in the Asseerghur jungles, and the method I adopted to kill them was to send men before break of day in pairs to the top of the passes to mark the deer down as they returned from their nocturnal feed in the valleys. At daybreak the sambar climbs the hill or roams and selects a spot

A SAMBAR STAG

for his daily siesta. When once recumbent he remains there, unless disturbed, for the day. As soon as my shikarees marked down a beast, one of the men came to my camp and the other men remained on guard, to be sure that the animal was still on its form and undisturbed. I have often sent pairs of men overnight to distant hills with food and water for the same purpose. At about 11 a.m. I have proceeded to the spot, and invariably found the sambar still quiescent.

In the course of the beating the sambar exhibits a sagacity wanting in the gaur. If surrounded, it will often double on its tracks and lie low under a bush. When wounded it will hide itself as the ibex does, and I have known a sambar, which was severely wounded, plunge into a pool and sink therein, leaving only its antlers and a portion of the head exposed to view. This effort of concealment was twice attempted on a certain occasion.

When stags are fighting, a sportsman has his great opportunity. They are so engrossed in the conflict that they can be approached, even though the wind is unfavourable. Once I shot two fighting stags with a right and left from my rifle, and on another occasion shot the victor of a battle. The beaten animal had retired just before I arrived on the scene. I saw both engagements with my glasses from the valley below, and the three belligerents shot by me bore severe scars of combat. The finest stag I am cognisant of was shot in the Asseerghur jungles by the late Colonel Cole of the 9th Bombay Infantry. Its horns in length were 48 and 47 inches respectively. I have killed forty-two stags in various jungles, and the finest beast I ever shot also met its death in the Asseerghur jungles. One horn measured $44\frac{1}{2}$ inches in length, and the other was a shade shorter; the circumference round the burr was 9 inches, the beam at its thickest was $7\frac{3}{4}$ inches, and the span was 39 inches.

The Bundelkhand animals, especially at Salut, are very fine, but the beams of the horns are not on a par with the average tailias of Asseerghur.

I have found the sambar in small and in large herds, but I think the most beautiful sight I ever gazed upon when hunting them was a herd at daybreak (twelve in number) passing me on a tree-clad hillside at Salut, Bundelkhand. I was sitting alone on the off-chance of finding game as the sun rose. Suddenly across my front a lovely herd of sambar passed at a trot; there were three stags but only one of them worthy of a bullet. I killed it. The scenery of that slope was worthy of an artist's brush—sunshine and shadow, peace, and silence, save for the tramping herd, the sunshine shifting from the tree-tops to the hillside. The distant view of wild country below intersected by ravines is still in my mind's eye. It reminded me of walks I had often taken to watch the rising sun from an exalted point amongst the deodars on Jacko, Simla.　　F. G. ALEXANDER.

SPRINGBUCK

"The springbuck derives its name from its habit of suddenly leaping into the air; and is remarkable both for the vast numbers in which it formerly occurred, and for its periodical migrations."

E

G. Bx & Co.

M. Kuhnert

SABLE ANTELOPES

"The sable antelope is a southern species ranging as far north as Uganda, and being most abundant in Mashonaland. This antelope generally frequents forest-clad highlands."

BLACKBUCK

"Blackbuck feed at all hours, although they generally rest during the middle of the day. Like springbuck, blackbuck frequently leap high into the air when running."

WATERBUCK

"Waterbuck are partial to steep, stony hills, and are often found at a distance of more than a mile from the nearest river, for which, however, they always make when pursued. Though heavy-looking antelopes, they can clamber with wonderful speed and sureness of foot up and down the steepest hillsides."

THE HOG DEER

The small hog deer, or para (*Cervus porcinus*), of India and Burma, stands only some 24 inches in height at the withers. In build this small species is characterised by the relative shortness of its legs, while the tail is rather long, and there is no mane on the neck and throat. The comparatively short antlers are mounted on very long bony pedicles, and after giving off the brow tine have a nearly straight beam up to the small terminal fork, the front branch of which is longer than the hind one. There are no tusks in the upper jaw.

In colour the coat of the para is brownish, with a more or less decided yellowish or reddish tinge, each hair being tipped with white, so as to produce a speckly appearance. The under parts are much darker than the back, and the under surface of the tail and the inside of the ears are white. The coat becomes paler in summer, and is then generally marked with light brown or white spots, which may be limited to one or two rows on each side of a dark streak down the back. The young have the whole body spotted till they attain the age of six months, or thereabouts. The antlers seldom exceed 10 or 12 inches in length.

In India the hog deer is confined to the Indo-Gangetic plain, where it ranges from Assam to the Punjab and Sind, and is unknown in the peninsula, though it has been introduced into Ceylon. It occurs along the Terai at the foot of the Himalaya, and from Assam its range extends into Burma and Tenasserim, and thence into Siam, where it is represented by an unspotted race (*C. p. hecki*).

THE HOG DEER

Para swarm on many of the low alluvial plains, to which situations they are mainly, if not exclusively, restricted. Here they frequent the grass jungles of moderate height, avoiding the taller ones which give shelter to the buffalo and rhinoceros, although sometimes they may be met with among trees. As a rule, hog deer are solitary creatures, and it is seldom that more than two or three are found together, although several may inhabit one patch of jungle. The pairing season is September and October, and the antlers are generally shed in April.

The hog deer is an ungainly animal when moving, and both its English and Latin names have been derived from the hog-like manner in which it rushes through the long grass when disturbed, keeping its head low, and galloping without the bounding action of most deer. Hog deer are generally shot from elephants, and afford good sport, although difficult to hit, since, as a rule, the only indication of their presence is a sudden rush in the long grass. Hog deer may be speared on favourable ground, and give splendid runs, being very fast, and usually affording a much longer chase than a boar; but there are instances of their deliberately charging horses, and with their sharp antlers they can inflict severe wounds.

THE SWAMP DEER

The swamp deer (*Cervus duvauceli*) differs from the Indian deer hitherto noticed in that the antlers carry more than three tines. This distinctive character has not escaped the notice of the natives of India, by whom the species is designated barasingha—that is, "twelve-tined." This deer is a rather large species, the bucks standing from 3 feet 8 inches to 3 feet 10 inches at the withers. The neck is maned, the tail of moderate length, the muzzle long, and the hair rather fine and rather woolly.

The antlers are smooth and somewhat flattened, and give off the brow tine nearly at right angles to the beam; after which the beam continues without branching for a considerable distance, finally dividing into a fork, of which the two prongs again branch. In the great majority of antlers the inner branch of the main fork has two, and the outer three, tines, but the number of points is often much greater, reaching from sixteen to twenty, or in some examples even more.

In its winter dress the colour of the swamp deer is bright yellowish brown above and paler underneath; but in summer the upper parts are reddish brown, generally more or less spotted with white, while the under parts and the lower surface of the tail are pure white. The young are spotted.

Average-sized antlers of the barasingha measure about 30 inches along the curve; but a length of 38 inches has been recorded. Large stags weigh from 460 to 570 pounds.

The swamp deer is confined to India, where it has a local distribution, being found along the foot of the Himalaya, from Assam to some distance west of the Jumna, and in some districts in the Indo-Gangetic plain, such as the Bengal Sandarbans and Rohri in Sind. It is also common in certain portions of Central India, especially in the valley of the Narbada, where its habitat is limited to the area clothed with forests of the sal tree.

Swamp deer, although sometimes found in open forest, generally keep to the outskirts of the woods, and frequent flat or undulating grass lands, more or less interspersed with trees. In winter they are gregarious, herds of from thirty to fifty head being often seen, while, in some districts, herds of several hundreds have been observed during September and October. In Assam the bucks are met with singly, with the antlers for the most part still in the velvet, so that the shedding time is probably, as a rule, not later than February. These deer are mainly grazers, and are said to be much less nocturnal in habits than sambar, being not infrequently seen grazing in the forenoon, and again early in the afternoon.

SCHOMBURGK'S DEER

Schomburgk's deer (*C. schomburgki*), of Siam, is an allied species, of which the antlers are distinguished by the extreme shortness of the beam below the bifurcation, and the great length of the brow tine. Each antler usually carries five points, and specimens vary in length from 27 to 30 inches in good examples. This deer is very rare in collections, and nothing seems to be known with regard to its habits.

THE THAMIN

An altogether unique form of antler is carried by the stags of the thamin, or Eld's deer (*Cervus eldi*), in which the brow tine curves down over the forehead, so as to form an almost continuous sweep with the beam, the latter being curved at first backwards and outwards, and then slightly forwards, after which it divides into a short fork, of which the two prongs may split up into as many as eight or ten points. The upper surface of the brow tine often carries a number of short points, and there is very generally a distinct snag at the point where that tine joins the beam. In some cases the upper part of the beam is much flattened. In height, this species stands nearly the same as the swamp deer.

In winter the colour of the coat of the bucks is dark brown, but in summer yellowish fawn, nearly like that of the does at all seasons ; the under parts being pale brown in winter and white in summer. The fawns lose their spots at an early age. In winter the hair is coarse and shaggy. Average-sized antlers measure about 40 inches from the tip of the brow tine along the curve to the extremity ; but one specimen of 54 and another of 59 inches have been recorded.

Thamin frequent low, swampy grounds in Manipur, Burma, the Malay Peninsula, Cambodia, Siam, and the island of Hainan ; the Siamese form representing a distinct race, known as *C. eldi platyceros*. Thamin associate usually in herds of from ten to fifty or more, but occasionally much larger numbers are found together. Sometimes they may enter the fringe of the forest in places for shade during the day, but generally keep to the open plains. In some places in the Irawadi delta and Martaban they are found in plains where, during the dry season, no fresh water is procurable. They are frequently seen in swamps, and feed on wild rice and other plants growing in such situations. The period of shedding the antlers varies from June in Manipur to September in Lower Burma. The hinds utter a short, barking grunt, while the call of the stags is a more prolonged sound of the same nature

MUNTJACS

The group of small Asiatic deer typified by the Indian muntjac (*Cervulus muntjac*) differs so decidedly from all those hitherto noticed that they are referred to a separate genus, distinguished from *Cervus* by the short, simple, two-tined antlers being mounted on pedicles of the skull as long as or longer than the antlers themselves, and diverging upwards from the middle line of the lower part of the forehead, where they begin as rib-like bars. From this feature, muntjacs have been termed rib-faced deer.

The brow tine of the antlers is short, and directed upwards, while the tip of the undivided beam is more or less inclined inwards. The skull has a very large depression for the reception of the gland below the eye, and the bucks are furnished with long projecting tusks in the upper jaw. The lateral toes are peculiar, in that they consist of the hoofs only, without any trace of the bones of the digits themselves.

Muntjacs are confined to India, Burma, Siam, China, and the Malay region, and evidently indicate an ancient and generalised type of the deer family. They appear to be represented in the Pliocene formations of Europe, and are probably nearly related to a still earlier group of extinct European deer, known as *Palæomeryx*, in which the antlers were either totally wanting or of very small dimensions.

The Indian muntjac, also known as the barking deer, and in Hindustani as the kakar, stands from 20 to 22 inches in height at the shoulder, and has a coat of deep red chestnut, becoming darker on the back, and paler and less brilliant below ; the chin and upper part of the throat, as well as the hind portion of the under surface of the body, and the inner sides of the thighs and lower surface of the tail being white. The face and limbs are brown, and there is a black line on the inner surface of the pedicles of the antlers, extending some distance down the ribs on the face. The antlers are generally only some 3 or 4 inches in length, on pedicles of some 4 or 5 inches, but sometimes reach the length of 5, and occasionally even 10½ inches.

The kakar is essentially a forest-dwelling deer, restricted to hilly regions, its range including suitable districts throughout India, Ceylon, Burma, and Siam, whence it extends through the Malay Peninsula to the islands of Sumatra, Java, Borneo, and Hainan. With such a wide range, there is, of course, a number of local variations, which may best be regarded merely as races, although classed by some naturalists as distinct species.

BARASINGHA HIND AND FAWN

These deer are solitary creatures, usually found singly or in pairs ; the name of barking deer being derived from their peculiar cry ; and many visitors to hill stations in the Himalaya, who may never have seen a kakar, must probably be well acquainted with its voice, which is wonderfully powerful for such a small animal. The cry, of which it is rather difficult to convey a correct idea by words, although it may perhaps be best described as a hoarse, resonant bark, may frequently be heard in the mornings and evenings, and it is also often uttered when the deer is alarmed, when it hears any loud or unusual sound, or suspects the existence of any danger. Occasionally a kakar will continue to bark, at short intervals, for an hour at a time, when advantage may be taken of this betrayal of its whereabouts to stalk the animal.

Kakar are adepts at making their way at speed through the most dense jungle, and run with the head low and the hindquarters elevated. When running, a peculiar rattling sound is produced, which has been supposed to originate in the mouth, although in what manner is unknown. The bucks, when attacked by dogs, use their tusks, which curve outwards in a peculiar manner, as weapons of defence, and are able with these to inflict gashes of considerable depth.

Although young kakar are apparently to be met with at all seasons of the year, the chief pairing time in Northern India is during January and February ; the fawns, which may be one or two in number, being born in the following June or July. The bucks shed their antlers in May, and their renewal is completed by August. Kakar venison is considered superior to that of most Indian deer.

There are several other kinds of muntjac in addition to the Indian species, among which Fea's muntjac (*C. feæ*), from Tenasserim, is rather smaller and darker than the Indian species, with a tuft of hair between the antlers, and a much shorter tail, the latter appendage being altogether white, except for a narrow black streak down the middle of its upper surface.

The mountains near Hankow, in Central China, are the home of Sclater's muntjac (*C. sclateri*), characterised by the bright yellow hair of the head and neck, while that clothing the body and limbs is of a more sombre hue, the front of the fore legs being black. Nearly allied is the Sze-chuen muntjac (*C. lachrymans*), in which the face seems to be browner. The smallest member of the group is Reeves's muntjac (*C. reevesi*), from Southern China and Formosa, in which the colour of the whole fur is brighter than in any other species, while the pedicles of the antlers diverge less from one another, and the hollow in the skull for the gland below the eye is of unusually large size.

Finally, the hairy-fronted muntjac (*C. crinifrons*), the handsomest of all, from the neighbourhood of Ningpo, is distinguished by the long tuft of hair on the forehead and top of the head, in which the minute antlers are almost entirely hidden. This species stands about 24 inches in height at the shoulder ; and the general colour is brown, with the upper part of the head bright chestnut, which, with the white of the under parts and lower surface of the tail, forms a striking contrast to the sombre colouring of the body.

A THAMIN STAG

TUFTED DEER

Nearly allied to the muntjacs are the three small species of Chinese tufted deer, of which Michie's deer (*Elaphodus michianus*) inhabits the neighbourhood of Ningpo, in the province of Chekiang, on the east coast, while *E. ichangensis* comes from the mountains of Ichang, in the Hupei province of Central China, and the typical *E. cephalophus* inhabits Sze-chuen ; the three kinds being easily distinguished by the characters of the skull. In all of them the antlers are extremely minute and unbranched, while their supports take the form of long pedicles, which, instead of diverging, as in the muntjacs, are convergent. Then, again, the rib-like ridges occurring on the face of the muntjacs are absent, as are also certain small glands found on the forehead of the latter.

As in the muntjacs, the bucks of these deer are furnished with long tusks in the upper jaw, although their extremities are not turned outwards. Their hair is so coarse as to have been compared to small quills, and on the forehead is lengthened so as to form a kind of horseshoe-like crest on the tuft.

In Michie's deer the colour of the coat is greyish black, each hair being white for a considerable distance above its base, and the face and neck uniformly dark grey, while the crest on the forehead and portions of the ears are dark brown.

In the Sze-chuen tufted deer the coat of the head, neck, and fore quarters is dark brown, each hair being brown above and whitish beneath, while a pure white ring divides the two colours ; consequently there is a speckled appearance in the coat of the anterior part of the animal. In the hind part of the body the white rings on the hairs are absent, and the colour of the coat is consequently uniform dark brown, becoming a still deeper shade on the feet and the crest on the forehead. The ears have a transverse black bar, with white tips and edges, the under parts of the body and the lower surface of the tail being also white.

Michie's deer is abundant in the reeds bordering the rivers in the neighbourhood of Ningpo and other parts of Eastern China, but the Ichang species is found high up in the mountains, this being probably the case with the Sze-chuen tufted deer.

REINDEER OR CARIBOU

The reindeer (*Rangifer tarandus*) is distinguished from other members of the deer tribe by the occurrence of antlers in both sexes, although those of the female are of smaller dimensions ; while, like most of the deer

A PAIR OF INDIAN MUNTJACS

remaining for notice, it also differs from those already described in the structure of the fore feet. In all the deer hitherto considered, which, with the exception of the wapiti, are exclusively Old World types, the lateral metacarpal bones of the fore feet, which originally supported the lateral toes, are represented only by two small splints lying on each side of the upper end of the cannon bone.

On the other hand, in the reindeer and most of the following species these lateral metacarpal bones are represented only by their lower extremities, and thus still support the toe bones of the lateral hoofs. This difference may not, perhaps, appear of much significance, but as there are other indications of affinity between the members of the two groups into which the deer family is thereby divided, it is probably of considerable importance in classification. The majority of the deer with this type of foot structure are either common to the northern regions of both

hemispheres, or are restricted to the New World, the roebucks and the Chinese water deer being the only exclusively Old World forms.

Reverting to the reindeer, in addition to the presence of antlers in both sexes, the genus is distinguished from all other deer by the form and position of these appendages, for, instead of being placed low down on the forehead, they take their origin on the upper part of the skull, immediately over the occipital ridge, and are accordingly far behind the eyes ; while as regards shape they are distinguished by the great development of the brow tines in the stags, which are more or less laterally compressed, branched, and palmated, and descend to a greater or less degree over the face, so that their lower edge sometimes almost touches the nose. Then, again, there is such an amount of variation that scarcely any two reindeer can be found in which the antlers are precisely similar ; while frequently those of opposite sides differ in the same individual.

The antlers are very long in proportion to the length of the skull, and above the brow tine, which is also branched and often palmated, the narrow beam, after giving off the bez tine, is continued backwards for some distance, till it bends forward at an angle, usually having a small back tine at the bend. The beam is then continued upwards and forwards till it becomes palmated near the extremity, with a variable number of points on its hind border. In the reindeer of the New World and Northern Asia the antlers exhibit the greatest complexity, the brow tine of one side being frequently enormously developed and greatly palmated, while on the other it is aborted.

In build reindeer are somewhat heavy animals (p. 780), with short and rather stout limbs, terminating in large hoofs. The main pair of hoofs are rounded, broad, and short, with the intervening cleft very deep and wide ; and the lateral hoofs are unusually large and flattened from front to back. In traversing snow fields the two main hoofs spread out sideways, while the lateral pair come in contact with the snow, by which means a large extent of surface is afforded to support the weight. The muzzle of the reindeer differs from that of all the deer hitherto mentioned in being clothed with soft hairs of moderate length.

The neck has no distinct mane, but the throat is fringed with long and rather stiff hair. The ears are relatively smaller than in any other deer, and thickly covered on both sides with hair. The hair clothing the body is from an inch to an inch and a half in length, and somewhat crimped, or waved, while beneath this is a coat of woolly under fur. The general colour of the European reindeer is dark cinnamon brown above, with the face, neck, and throat whitish, and the nose, ears, limbs, and a band on the flank dark brown. There is more or less white in the region of the tail, which usually has a tinge of brown at the root and on the upper surface ; and there is often a distinct white ring round each fetlock. The hoofs are black, and the antlers yellowish, wearing white in places. Reindeer fawns are uniformly coloured like the adults.

The various races of reindeer differ considerably from one another in respect of height, but the stags of the larger American kinds stand about 4½ feet at the withers, and may weigh 350 pounds, although unusually fine specimens reach nearly 400 pounds. In regard to the length of the antlers, fine examples vary from 48 to about 59 inches, although one pair from Canada is known in which the length reaches 62 inches. There is great variation in regard to the span of the antlers, and the number of points they carry, the longest specimens having in many instances by no means the greatest girth.

Reindeer inhabit the northern regions of both the Eastern and Western Hemispheres, and are divisible into a large number of more or less well-defined local races, regarded by some naturalists as distinct species.

The typical *Cervus tarandus* of Linnæus is the wild reindeer of the highlands of Swedish Lapland which is now extinct in Sweden, where it extended southwards to Dalecarlia; but it appears to have been identical with the wild Norwegian reindeer, and the tame mountain reindeer of Swedish Lapland and the adjacent districts of Norway, and probably also with those of Northern Finland. To the east of the Scandinavian Peninsula wild reindeer are, or were recently, found in Northern Finland, whence their range extends northwards into the peninsula of Kola, and southwards along the Russo-Finnish frontier through Carelia, while, in winter, at any rate, their wanderings sometimes carried them south of Lake Ladoga. These Finnish reindeer (*R. t. fennicus*) are noted for their large size and heavy antlers, the height at the shoulder reaching to 47½ or 48 inches, and at the loins to 50½ or 51½ inches.

The typical Swedish reindeer, on the other hand, stands only 44½ inches at the shoulder, and 45¾ inches at the loins. The two races are also distinguished by difference in the form of the skull and its constituent bones. Other Old World races are the Spitzbergen reindeer (*R. t. spetsbergensis*), the Novaya Zemlya reindeer (*R. t. pearsoni*), and the Siberian *R. t. sibiricus*; the two latter approximating to American reindeer which are noticed later in the large size and expansion of the brow line.

In the Old World reindeer are found nearly as far north as the extreme limits of land, while they extend from Scandinavia and Lapland in the west to Eastern Siberia. In the Ural region their southern limit reaches in the Kirghiz steppes to about 52° N., and they are still met with in the wild state in the neighbourhood of Orenburg. In European Russia they are found in the forests of the Government of Kazan as far south as latitude 54°; and it is stated that in this district they attain very large dimensions, while the females are reported to be without antlers. In Scandinavia wild reindeer are, however, now becoming rare.

Domesticated reindeer are kept in Siberia, Lapland, and part of Norway, as well as in the northern districts of the Government of Perm, but appear to be unknown in the Orenburg region. They were introduced into Iceland in 1870, where they flourish, and in 1892 sixteen head were landed in Alaska. This introduction of domesticated reindeer from Siberia into Alaska has turned out a thorough success. The Eskimo proved themselves well fitted to keep and train the animals, and it is hoped that in the future the country will have large herds of these valuable animals, which will prevent the Eskimo from becoming a burden to the revenues of the United States, as would otherwise have been the case owing to the diminution in the numbers of the whales, seals, walruses, bears, and so forth, which formerly constituted their means of subsistence.

The Scandinavian domesticated breed, which is chiefly used by the Lapps for purposes of draught, is considerably smaller than the wild race; but in Siberia the tame breed is of larger size, mainly used for riding. The reindeer is, almost literally, necessary to the existence of the Laplander.

In regard to the northern limits of reindeer in the Old World, it appears that, although they have not been found in Francis Joseph Land, they occur at Cape Chelyuskin, as well as in Novaya Zemlya and Spitzbergen, and in the still more northerly Phipps and Parry Islands, which lie between 80° and 81° N. In some of these desolate regions reindeer are still very numerous, even where, as in Spitzbergen, they are incessantly hunted. Regarding their abundance in the islands last named, it has been suggested that they immigrate from Novaya Zemlya, although it is more probable that, if such immigration does take place, it must be from some Arctic land to the north-north-east.

Baron Nordenskiöld observes that "the life of the wild reindeer is best known in Spitzbergen. During the summer it betakes itself to the grassy plains in the ice-free valleys of the island; in late autumn it withdraws—according to the walrus-hunters' statements—to the sea coast, in order to eat the seaweed thrown up on the beach. In winter it goes back to the lichen-clad mountain heights in the interior of the country, where it appears to thrive exceedingly well, though the cold during winter must be excessively severe; for when the reindeer in spring return to the coast they are still very fat, but some weeks afterwards, when the snow has frozen on the surface, and a crust of ice makes it difficult for them to get at the mountain sides, they

MICHIE'S TUFTED DEER

become so poor as to be scarcely eatable. In summer, however, they speedily eat themselves back into condition, and in autumn are so fat that they take prizes at an exhibition of fat cattle."

Admiral von Wrangel, who had an opportunity of seeing the periodical migrations of reindeer in Siberia, relates that the moving masses might be reckoned to include thousands, split up into herds of two or three hundred head. On one of these occasions "two large migrating bodies of reindeer passed at no great distance. They were descending the hills from the north-west, and crossing the plain on their way to the forests, where they spend the winter. Both bodies of deer extended farther than the eye could reach, and formed a compact mass narrowing to the front. They moved slowly and majestically along, their broad antlers resembling a moving wood of leafless trees. Each body was led by a deer of unusual size, which my guides assured me was always a female."

These southerly winter migrations are of considerable importance in regard to the former occurrence of reindeer in Central and Southern Europe, for, since their remains are not infrequently found in association with those of the hippopotamus, in such localities the climate could hardly have been otherwise than comparatively mild. Accordingly, the most probable hypothesis seems to be that in the Pleistocene period the reindeer, driven by the intense cold of the more northern portions of its habitat, travelled southwards during the winter till it reached regions where the rivers were suitable for the hippopotamus.

At the present day reindeer are unknown in the Old World to the south of a parallel running a little below the southern shore of the Baltic, but it appears probable that in the time of Julius Cæsar they were met with in the Black Forest of Northern Germany, although whether as permanent residents or as winter immigrants cannot now be ascertained. In the British Isles remains of reindeer are commonly met with in England, Scotland, and Ireland, and it was long considered that in Caithness the species survived till the middle of the twelfth century, although later researches discountenance this idea. Reindeer remains are also found over the Continent, occurring so far south as the valleys of the Dordogne and Garonne in France.

In America, where they are invariably known as caribou—a name said to be derived from *carrebœuf*, or "square ox" —the various local races which have been named may be arranged round two central types, namely, the woodland caribou (*R. t. caribu*), in which the antlers are short, much bent, and carry much branched lower tines, and the Barren Ground caribou (*R. t. arcticus*), in which the beam is of great length and slight curvature, with a long interval between the bez and the upper tines, and less expansion of the brow and bez tines.

In both races the brow, or lower, tines are much more expanded than in Scandinavian reindeer, and generally unsymmetrical, one being much larger than the other.

Numerous races of caribou have received distinct names, but it will suffice to mention that there is great variation among them in the matter of colour, the lightest being the Newfoundland *R. t. novæ-terræ* and the Ellesmere Land *R. t. pearyi*, which are nearly white, while the darkest is *R. t. osborni*, of the Cascade Mountains, in which the greater part of the body is chocolate, or even blackish, brown.

A correspondent in Newfoundland has informed me that caribou possess a gland between the front hoofs similar to that of sheep, which secretes a strong-smelling yellow fluid. It is further stated that caribou, when they cross the trail of a human being, first of all put their noses to their feet, and then rush off at full speed. What can be the meaning of this action is not easy to conjecture, as it would naturally be imagined

UNDER SURFACE OF FOOT OF REINDEER

that the scent of the foot-glands would overpower and obscure that left by the human footprints. It is commonly said that American caribou have never been domesticated, but the same correspondent informed me that he had tamed several, and had a pair which might have been put in a sleigh if they had been old enough. These two animals on one occasion escaped to the woods for a period of five days, but, on being followed, returned to their owner as soon as he came in sight.

The Barren Ground caribou, which is found only in the barren Arctic districts lying to the north of the forest region of North America, is abundant in the desolate country northwards of Fort Churchill, whence it extends to the confines of the Arctic Ocean. Despite its larger antlers, it is much inferior in point of size to the woodland caribou. Although confined in summer to the Barren Grounds, this reindeer makes extensive southerly migrations in autumn, in order to spend the winter in the forest regions tenanted by the woodland caribou. It appears, however, that even when inhabiting the same districts, the two races invariably remain completely apart, and show no tendency to intermingle.

The woodland caribou, on the other hand, is an inhabitant of the forest districts lying to the south of the barren northern lands. It inhabits Labrador and Northern Canada, thence ranges south to Nova Scotia, New Brunswick, the northern part of Maine, and Lower Canada on both sides of the St. Lawrence, and so in a westerly direction to the country north of Quebec and the vicinity of Lake Superior. It never migrates towards the north in summer, as is the habit of the Barren Ground caribou, but makes its migration in a southerly direction; this difference in the direction of the migration of the two races being very remarkable. The antlers are short and stout, with no long unbranched portion of the beam; one of the brow tines being enormously expanded, and the bez tines also broad.

Woodland caribou feed on leaves, grasses, and aquatic plants, but their great resource is lichens. They frequent marshy and swampy grounds more than any other deer except elk, for which they are admirably adapted, and where they are well protected from pursuit. In winter they resort to the dense forests on higher ground. Like European reindeer, caribou are animals of great endurance and speed, and can trot faster than most horses. In disposition they are shy and wary, and a successful stalk requires all the powers of the sportsman. To hunt these animals in deep snow on foot, or on the open ground with dogs, is said to be mere waste of time, as in the one case, by the aid of their broad hoofs, they make their way over the snow without difficulty, while in the other they easily distance and tire out their pursuers. Woodland caribou migrate in herds of from one hundred to two hundred, or even as many as five hundred head.

The season when caribou are most easily killed is during March and April, the snow having then a thin cake of ice on the surface, through which the animals are constantly breaking, and are thus run down without much difficulty by hunters on snow-shoes.

There appears to be a lack of information as to the breeding habits both of the caribou and the wild reindeer of the Old World. The pairing season of the Barren Ground caribou is said to be in the winter, while that of the woodland race is in September. In

A HERD OF REINDEER IN ALASKA

the case of the latter, the antlers of the stags are shed in December, but those of the hinds do not fall until the spring. The fawns are produced in May, and are either one or two in number.

ELK OR MOOSE

The largest living representative of the deer family is the ungainly, long-legged animal known in Europe as the elk, and in North America as the moose (*Alces machlis*), which differs from all other deer in the form and setting-on of the antlers of the male; these displaying considerable local and individual variation in form.

In build the elk is characterised by the length of its limbs, its short neck, very long and flapping ears, and the great length and narrowness of the head, which terminates in a broad, overhanging muzzle, covered with short fine hair, except for a small triangular spot just below the nostrils. The extremity of the muzzle is flexible, and the eyes are small and sunken. The antlers, instead of emerging from the forehead at an acute angle with its middle line and inclining forwards, as is the case in all living representatives of the genus *Cervus*, project at right angles to the middle line of the forehead, and in the same plane as its surface. Their basal portion consists of a short, cylindrical beam, without any tine, and beyond this beam they expand into an enormous basin-like palmation.

In the young, on the other hand, the antlers consist of three or four simple tines; and this condition may persist throughout life. Usually, however, in older animals, the palmated portion is divided into a small anterior and a larger posterior moiety; but in the adult, especially of the American race, these two coalesce into a single palmation, elongated from back to front, and containing a number of short and irregular snags on its outer edge. The antlers of fine specimens may weigh as much as 60 pounds; the antlers in one notable head having a span of 65 inches, a length along the palmation of 41 inches, and a width across the same of 24 inches, but a span of 66 inches is on record. The

antlers do not reach their full dimensions till the animal has attained its ninth year.

The skull of the elk differs from that of other deer in the extreme shortness of the nasal bones, and the consequently very large cavity of the nose. The upper molar teeth have very low and broad crowns. The tail is so short that it is scarcely more than a rudiment.

The elk carries its short neck nearly horizontally, and therefore somewhat lower than the elevated withers; and it is this feature which so largely contributes to the awkward and uncouth look of the animal. The feet have long, sharply pointed hoofs, very different in appearance from those of reindeer; and the lateral hoofs are very large and loosely attached.

In the male the hair is long, coarse, and somewhat brittle, and elongated into a slight mane on the neck, shoulders, and throat; while in colour it varies from very dark brown to yellowish grey, the lower portion of the legs being often dirty white. The female is lighter coloured than the male during the winter season. In both sexes the hair is softer and finer in summer than in winter, and during the latter season an abundant supply of woolly under fur is developed. Young elk have also brighter-coloured and sleeker coats than aged individuals, and in the latter the fading of the winter coat with the advance of spring is more noticeable than in the former. The fawns are uniformly coloured like the adults.

The height of the elk varies from 5 feet 9 inches to 6 feet 9 inches, or, in Alaska, perhaps rather more. The weight of an average adult male elk is about 700 pounds, but large specimens will reach 900 or 1,000, and, it is said, even as much as 1,200 pounds.

Adult male elk, and occasionally females, have a curious pendulous appendage on the throat formed by a dilatation of the skin, and covered with long and coarse blackish hairs. This appendage may vary in length from 4 to 10 inches, and is known to the American hunters as the bell; its use is unknown.

With the exception that it occurs in Alaska, the elk has a distribution very nearly the same as that of the reindeer, although it does not extend so far north, and is limited by the northern extension of trees, elk being essentially forest animals. In Europe, although now greatly diminished in numbers, elk are found locally in Scandinavia, Eastern Prussia, Lithuania, and parts of Russia, such as the neighbourhood of Orenburg, the government forest near Moscow, and the districts bordering the River Samaria in Astrakhan. Thence they extend eastwards into the sub-Arctic portions of Siberia, although their extreme limits in this direction are not fully ascertained.

Some years ago an elk was shot in Galicia, which had probably wandered from a more northerly latitude. In the time of Pallas elk were also found on the northern slopes of the Caucasus; while the Nibelungenlied mentions them as inhabiting the Black Forest. During the prehistoric period their distribution was still more extensive in Europe, and their remains have been found in many parts of England, the most southerly point being Walthamstow, in Essex. In the still earlier deposits of the Norfolk Forest Bed the species was preceded by the broad-fronted elk (*A. latifrons*).

A COW MOOSE IN ITS NATIVE HAUNTS

In North America the range of the elk appears to have extended originally from about 43° to 68° N., its northern limit being generally marked by the southern border of the Barren Grounds. Elk have been seen so far south as the Ohio and as far north as the Mackenzie River. Although specially protected, elk, however, are rapidly disappearing from the forests of North America. Formerly, indeed, the slaughter was terrible, there being a statement to the effect that on one occasion several hundreds were shot in New Brunswick merely for the sake of their hides; their carcases being left to rot on the ground. They are still comparatively common in Alaska, but have more or less completely disappeared from certain districts where they were formerly abundant.

Elk feed more upon the leaves and twigs of trees than upon grass, and their length of limb enables them to pluck such nutriment with facility, while the shortness of their necks renders them unfitted for grazing, unless in places where the grass is unusually tall, when they merely pluck the tops. In Northern Europe and Asia birch, willows, aspens, and poplars afford a large proportion of the leafy food of the elk, but in North America both evergreen and deciduous trees contribute their quota. Various lichens and mosses are also eaten, but in winter, when the whole country is deeply buried in snow, elk have to depend solely on twigs and buds of trees. In order to obtain the foliage of saplings which are above their reach, elk—in America, at least—have a habit of straddling on either side of the stem with their fore legs, and then gradually pressing down the tree with the weight of their body.

In America elk begin feeding with the first signs of dawn and continue till sunrise, after which they repose or ruminate till ten or eleven o'clock. From that time they feed again till about two, when they take another period of repose till four or five, and then feed till dusk, when they lie down for the night.

Mr. Lockhart states that elk "generally lie down with their tails to windward, trusting to their senses of hearing and smelling, which are remarkably acute, to warn them of approaching danger from that quarter. They can use their eyes to warn them from danger to leeward, where hearing, and especially smelling, would be of little use. While sleeping or chewing the cud, their ears are in perpetual motion, one backward, the other forward, alternately. They also have the remarkable instinct to make a short turn and sleep below the wind of their fresh track, so that any one falling thereon and following it up is sure to be heard or smelt before he can get within shooting distance."

In summer the favourite resorts of the American elk are in the neighbourhood of swamps, rivers, or lakes where long grasses which can be easily reached grow in rank abundance. In winter, however, elk generally betake themselves to higher grounds, although always those clothed with dense and almost impenetrable forest. When disturbed, elk, in spite of their great bulk, make off with extreme rapidity and almost perfect silence, even in the thickest covert, always when possible selecting moss-clad and yielding ground over which to make their way. During summer these long-legged deer wade belly-deep in the lakes and swamps to feed on water lilies and other aquatic vegetation.

In winter elk in America are in the habit of consorting in small parties, often comprising a male, female, and the young of two seasons, and taking up their quarters in what is termed a moose-yard. "The yard," writes Mr. C. C. Ward, "is situated in some part of the country where there is an abundant growth of young deciduous trees, such as the white birch, poplars, maple, and mountain ash; these, together with a few of the coniferous trees, the balsam fir and juniper, form the staple diet of the moose. Some writers maintain that the bull moose never yards with the female and young, but this is disproved by my own experience as a moose-hunter. I have on many occasions found and killed males occupying the same yard with the old and young females." It appears, however, that very old males generally make a yard for themselves, and remain alone throughout the winter.

The antlers of the adult elk are shed in America during January, and the new pair attain their full development in August. During the time that the antlers have been in the velvet the male elk has spent most of his time in the marshes and swamps, feeding on the leaves of the yellow water lily, and frequently protecting himself from the attacks of mosquitoes and other insect torments by standing neck-deep in the water. With the complete development of his antlers, he sallies forth from these retreats to begin calling, and to enter upon a series of combats with his rivals for the possession of the females. These contests appear to be fully as fierce and determined as those of red deer ; and Mr. Ward records finding in a lake the skulls of two elk, with their antlers inextricably inter-locked, which had evidently perished after one of these encounters.

The fawns are born in the following May, and are either one or two, or, very exceptionally, three in number. They are of a dark fawn colour, but often with a slight dappling. The females, before the birth of the fawns, seek out the most sequestered spots, such as islands in lakes and rivers, and swamps and prairies, which are liable to be overflowed at certain seasons of the year, where they will most likely be free from the attacks of wolves and bears. Some writers assert that at such seasons they also endeavour to avoid the males, but this is denied by Mr. Ward, who believes that the male is never very far away from his consort. Mr. Lockhart states that when the fawns are very young and helpless, " the mother in their defence will even attack men. At such times her appearance reminds

by any ordinary horse. If, however, they can be forced into a gallop, elk soon become blown, and can then be readily ridden down.

Although the appearance of elk when exhibited in menageries is ungainly and awkward, in their native forests no one can fail to be impressed with the majesty and grandeur of the male elk in the glory of his spreading antlers.

It appears to be only in the north-eastern districts that the practice of calling with a birch-bark pipe is followed, as the custom is stated to be unknown in the Rocky Mountains. In regard to this mode of proce-dure, Mr. Ward states that " the Indian, having selected a favourable position for his purpose, generally on the margin of a lake, heath, or bog, where he can readily conceal himself, puts his birchen trumpet to his mouth and gives the call of the cow moose in a manner so startling and truthful that only the educated ear of an Indian could detect the counterfeit. If the call is successful, presently the responsive bull moose is heard crashing through the forest, uttering his blood-curdling bellow or roar, and rattling his antlers against the trees in challenge to all rivals." In other districts

A COMBAT BETWEEN RIVAL MALE ELK
From a photograph supplied by the Natural History Museum, New York

one forcibly of a vicious horse. She raises her head, throws back her ears upon her neck, and sniffs or blows like a horse ; then she bounds towards her enemy, striking the ground with her fore feet, and her eyes glittering with rage."

The favourite pace of the elk when in rapid motion is a long swinging trot ; and it is said that so long as the animal keeps to this pace it cannot be overtaken

the call of the male is imitated by drawing the shoulder bone of a moose against the dry bark of a young tree, and any male that may be in the neighbourhood advances to answer the challenge of the supposed rival. In the Rocky Mountains the male moose, instead of uttering the bellowing call, gives vent to a loud and prolonged kind of whistle, while the female is stated to be completely silent.

A favourite mode of hunting, when the snow lay deep on the ground, was by running moose down in snow-shoes ; but accidents were frequent, more especially during spring, when the snow was covered with a thin crust. At such times, if the hunter happened incautiously to run too near, the moose would turn suddenly, and, leaping on his pursuer, trample him under foot.

In British America the Indians in winter were accustomed in deep snow to make a kind of fence of three poles, tied equidistant from each other, a little taller than a man, stretching for two days' march between lakes, or a lake and a river, or between two mountains, or in any place where the moose were wont to pass. Spaces were left vacant in this fence, where snares were set, in which the animals became entangled as they passed through.

The flesh of elk, in spite of some coarseness of grain, is regarded as excellent venison, although with a slight musky taste. The large and fleshy nose is esteemed the greatest delicacy, and reported to be absolutely unrivalled. Elk manage to maintain themselves in fair condition throughout the winter, so that their flesh is eatable when that of ordinary American deer is poor, dry, and unpalatable.

Owing to slight differences in colour and the form of the antlers, the American elk (*A. machlis americanus*) is regarded as a distinct race ; the Alaskan race (*A. m. gigas*) being also distinguished on account of its great size.

The East Siberian elk (*A. m. bedfordiæ*) is characterised in many instances by the slight palmation of the antlers, but antlers of the same general type are also met with in Scandinavian elk. A coloured representation of an elk will be found on page 831.

ROEBUCK

The roebuck (*Capreolus caprea*), while agreeing with reindeer and elk in the conformation of the bones of the lower part of the fore legs, differs from both in the form of its antlers. In common with all the antlered species described in the sequel, it differs from more typical deer in the absence of a brow tine to the antlers, which are forked at some distance above their base. All the species of roedeer are confined to the Old World (page 832).

The roebuck, when fully adult, stands about 26 inches in height, and has antlers somewhat less than twice the length of the head. These antlers are rough, and have a straight and nearly cylindrical beam, rising for some distance nearly vertically from the skull, and then giving off one forwardly directed tine from its front edge, after which the beam curves backwards and terminates in a simple fork. The roe's antler is therefore three-tined, like that of the Indian spotted deer, but differs in that, instead of having a true brow tine, the first tine is not given off till about the middle of the length. The average length of the antlers is from 8 to 9 inches, but a few reach 13 inches. They are more subject to malformations than those of any other species, and sometimes show a mass of ill-formed tines.

Roebuck have relatively short heads, with moderate ears, small glands below the eyes, and the naked portion of the sharp muzzle small and not extending beyond the nostrils. Normally there are no tusks in the upper jaw, and the tail is rudimentary. The neck is rather long and slender, and carried high above the level of the back ; and the limbs are slight and delicately formed. In summer the colour of the coat is foxy red, with little or no rump patch ; but in winter, when it becomes thicker and finer, the colour changes to speckly brown or olive, with a large white rump patch. There are some black and white markings on the lips, and the under parts and the insides of the limbs are pale yellowish fawn. The coat of the fawns is spotted with white. The weight of a full-grown buck may reach 60 pounds.

The roebuck is indigenous to the British Isles and the greater part of Europe, extending northwards to the south of Sweden, and southwards to Italy and Spain, while eastwards it ranges into the Southern Caucasus, Palestine, and perhaps Persia.

Their fossil remains occur in the superficial deposits of England and the Continent ; but at the present day roebuck are found wild within the limits of the British Isles only in Scotland and the neighbourhood of the Blackmoor Vale, in Dorsetshire, where they were reintroduced in the early part of the nineteenth century.

In Scotland roedeer are found chiefly in the woods, or on the immediately adjacent moors, but never wander far out in the open hills, although they venture on to the cultivated lands in search of food. They feed

ROEBUCK AND DOE

ROE DOE AND FAWN

European species, to which it is closely allied, the difference between the summer and winter coats being nearly as well marked.

WATER DEER

Among the tall reed beds fringing the banks of the Yang-tse-Kiang occur numbers of a small deer differing from any of the species hitherto noticed in that while both sexes are totally devoid of antlers, the males are provided with long scimitar-like tusks in the upper jaw. This deer is the Chinese water deer (*Hydropotes*, or *Hydrelaphus*, *inermis*), which in both these features resembles the musk deer (p. 746), although in other respects it is allied to the more typical representatives of the present section of the family.

The water deer, which is of the approximate dimensions of the Indian muntjac, is a long-bodied and short-limbed species, with light reddish brown fur. One of the most remarkable peculiarities about this small deer is that the does produce from three to six fawns at a birth. The coat of the young is faintly marked with white spots, arranged in ill-defined rows. The number of young produced, coupled with the absence of antlers in the bucks, indicates that the Chinese water deer is in all probability the survivor of a very ancient type of deer. These deer are commonly found in parties of two or three, and, when disturbed, arch their backs and scud away at a great pace in a series of quick leaps. They are usually killed with buckshot.

The resemblance of the skull of the male to that of the musk deer is merely due to both animals being apparently direct descendants of the common ancestral type, from which the more specialised members of the family have been evolved; it being well ascertained that in most or all of the early Tertiary deer the males were devoid of antlers and furnished with long upper tusks. When antlers were developed to their full extent, so as to become efficient weapons of defence, the need for tusks disappeared, and the tusks consequently dwindled or were lost. The muntjacs, in which the antlers are short, present a kind of middle stage of evolution, the tusks having become much smaller than in the water deer, though larger than in many species of superior size.

PÈRE DAVID'S DEER

A very remarkable deer—the milu, or Père David's deer (*Elaphurus davidianus*)—of which large herds were formerly kept in the Imperial Hunting Park near Pekin, differs from all the other members of the fork-antlered group in having the same type of foot structure as the red deer group. The large and branching antlers of the stags have the beam forking at a comparatively short distance above the burr, and the front prong of this fork again dividing, while the hind prong is very long, straight, and undivided (page 129).

The tail is long and bushy—longer, in fact, than in any other deer—and the neck in the stags is maned. A tuft of long hair on the outer side of the upper half of the hind cannon bone marks the position of a gland; but the gland so commonly present on the inner side of

in the early morning and towards evening, and associate in small family parties, while they make regular tracks through the woods to their feeding grounds. Their usual food is grass and other herbage, as well as the young shoots of such trees and bushes as they are able to reach. The speed of the roe is not great, but the animal is a good leaper, and, when running, its pace is a bounding gallop.

The antlers of the adult bucks are shed about the end of the year, and the new ones are generally fully developed by the latter part of February. The pairing season takes place during July and August, at which time the bucks are exceedingly pugnacious.

The fawns are born in the spring, usually early in May, and in Scotland about one doe out of five or six will produce two fawns at a birth in favourable seasons. No account of the roe would be complete without some reference to the extraordinary fact that, although the pairing season takes place in July or August, and the young are not produced till the following May, yet the period of gestation is only five months. The explanation of this appears to be that the ovum lies dormant for some four and a half months, that is, until December, after which it develops in the ordinary manner.

Certain extinct deer found in the Pliocene deposits of the Continent have been considered to belong to the same genus as the roe.

In the northern portion of the Caucasus the place of the European species is taken by the much larger Asiatic, or Siberian, roebuck (*C. pygargus*), which ranges eastwards through the Altai and Tian Shan to Eastern Siberia; the Tian Shan form being regarded as a distinct race. This species stands from 30 to 34 inches at the shoulder, and frequently has antlers of from 13 to 15 inches in length. It is a paler-coloured animal than the European roebuck, with shorter and more hairy ears, long and dense winter coat, and a very large white rump patch. The antlers are very rough and heavily knotted, or "pearled."

In Manchuria the group is represented by *C. manchuricus*, or *bedfordi*, which is only slightly larger than the

the hock in the American deer is absent. The adults of this species are uniformly tawny, but the young are spotted. The gait of this deer is remarkably donkey-like. In height the stags stand about 3 feet 9 inches at the shoulder.

The original home of this very curious deer is unknown, although there is some reason to believe it may have been Turkestan. During the Boxer

THE PUDU

rebellion in 1900 the walls of the Imperial Hunting Park were breached by a flood, when all the deer escaped, and were killed and eaten by the peasantry. It is believed that the only survivors of the species are those kept in the Duke of Bedford's park at Woburn.

The young stags at Woburn present the remarkable peculiarity of growing two pairs of antlers in the same year, of which the first is much smaller than the second; but later only a single pair is produced. The colour of the coat, which is long and shaggy in winter, is rufous fawn; the hair on the shoulder radiates from a large whorl, and there is another whorl farther back.

AMERICAN DEER

With the exception of the wapiti, the reindeer, and the elk, which are Old World types, the deer of America differ essentially from those of Asia and Europe in the structure of the bones of the lower part of the fore limb; while they also differ from all, except the reindeer, in the nasal passage of the skull being completely divided by a longitudinal vertical partition of bone. The latter feature serves at once to distinguish the skulls of reindeer and American deer from those of any other species of *Cervus*.

The antlers of American deer, in their fully developed type, are also essentially different from those of the majority of Old World deer, although in their forked structure and absence of brow tine they approximate to those of roebuck and the milu deer. The structure of these antlers is explained later, but it may be mentioned here that, starting from the simple spike-like antlers of the brockets of South and Central

America, there is a transition through a simply forked antler to the complex type exhibited by the mule deer, and it will accordingly be convenient to begin the account of these deer with those in which the antlers are simple.

All the American deer are uniformly coloured above in the adults, and all have narrow and naked muzzles. The length of the tail is subject to a great amount of specific variation; and, in addition to the peculiar feature already noticed as distinguishing the hind aperture of the nasal passage, the skulls of these deer are characterised by the large dimensions of the unossified space in front of the eye, and the small size of the pit for the reception of the gland.

THE PUDU

The tiny little deer from the Chilian Andes known as the pudu (*Pudua pudu*), although allied to the brockets, is so distinct as to necessitate its reference to a separate genus. Scarcely larger than a hare, this pigmy has a rounded head, with rather large ears, between which in the males is a pair of minute spike-like antlers, placed comparatively near together. The tail is very short, and the hair reversed on the crown of the head above the antlers, The colour is greyish fawn, passing into bright chestnut on the lips, forehead, ears, back, and lower portion of the legs; the under surface being lighter. There are no tusks in the upper jaw, and the skull differs from those of all the other American deer except the guemals in the premaxillary bones, which form the extremity of the muzzle, extending upwards to join the nasal bones covering the cavity of the nose. The ankle joint exhibits certain peculiarities of structure unknown in any other species.

MAZAMA

The second group of American deer is represented by several small species, commonly known as brockets, which are confined to the central and southern half of the continent, and are distinguished by their unbranched spike-like antlers, and by the hair on the middle line of the face radiating in all directions from two points, one situated on the crown of the head, and the other just below the eyes. They are further characterised by the large extent of the naked portion of the muzzle, which completely surrounds the nostrils, and also by the spotted coat of the fawns. The tail is of medium length, and the upper jaw may or may not have tusks.

The name "brocket," it may be mentioned, properly belongs to young red deer stags with their first spike-like antlers, and has been applied to the small South American deer on account of the somewhat similar character of their cranial appendages. One of the best-known species, the red brocket (*Mazama rufa*), which ranges from Guiana and North-Eastern Brazil through Peru to Paraguay and Northern Argentina, is a rather clumsily built deer, standing 27 inches in height at the withers, and of a uniform reddish brown colour.

In Southern Brazil it is represented by a smaller race (*M. r. simplicicornis*), standing only 21 inches in height, and distinguished by its lighter and more elegant shape, as well as by the more decided brown colour of the coat, especially in the young. Other species are the Ecuador brocket (*M. tema*), inhabiting Southern Mexico, Ecuador, Colombia, Venezuela, and Guatemala, and the wood brocket (*M. nemorivaga*), from Trinidad, Guiana, Colombia, Brazil, and Argentina, both of which are only 19 inches in height. The former has a coat of a full glossy red colour, with the face and legs shaded bluish brown ; while the latter differs from all the rest by the pepper-and-salt colour of its hair. Several other species have been named, of which the smallest is the Brazilian *M. nana*. In the caverns of Lagoa Santa, in Brazil, fossil remains of brockets occur which probably belong to species still inhabiting the same districts.

Brockets are found either alone or in pairs, and never collect in herds ; a male and female apparently associating for life. The does usually produce a single fawn at a birth, in December or January, and the young are able to follow their mother in from three to five days. The speed of brockets is considerable, but not enduring, and they can easily be ridden down by a good horse, while, when the covert is not too thick, hounds will generally capture them within half an hour.

GUEMALS

Another group is represented by two South American species of medium size, confined to the Andes and Patagonia, where they are known as guemals. They are distinguished by the antlers forming a single fork, of which the front prong is the longer, and is projected forwards in the manner characteristic of all the American deer, by the presence of tusks in the upper jaws of both sexes, and also by the uniform colour of the fawns.

Of the two species, the Chilian guemal (*Mazama*, or *Xenelaphus*, *bisulca*) ranges from Santiago to the Strait of Magellan, but is far more scarce in the northern than in the southern portion of this tract, while the Peruvian guemal (*M. antisiensis*) is from the highlands of Peru. In the Andes the Chilian species lives at high elevations, but in Patagonia inhabits the plains.

PAMPAS AND MARSH DEER

The pampas deer (*Mazama*, or *Blastoceros*, *bezoartica*), locally known as the guazuti, like its larger relative the marsh deer (*M. dichotoma*), has a more complex type of antler than the guemals. While in the pampas and marsh deer the two prongs of the antlers are nearly equal in size, in the white-tailed deer the anterior prong is greatly developed at the expense of the posterior. Further, while the white-tailed species has a large sub-basal tine rising from the inner side of the front of the antler some distance above the burr and directed upwards, in the marsh deer this snag is reduced to a mere rudiment.

The pampas deer and its larger relative are characterised by the antlers being regularly forked, with the hind prong—and sometimes also the front one—again forking, and having no sub-basal snag above the burr. The two species are further characterised by the absence of tusks in the upper jaw, the shortness of

the tail, and the uniform colour of the fawns, while they are likewise distinguished by the direction of the hair on the withers being reversed, so as to incline forwards. Both species are confined to the eastern side of South America.

The pampas deer, which stands about 2½ feet at the shoulder, ranges from Paraguay and Uruguay through Argentina to Northern Patagonia. The antlers are characterised by the great development of the forked posterior tine at the expense of the unbranched front tine, the number of points thus being three. The hair is thick, coarse, and glossy, and on the upper parts light reddish brown in colour. The lower parts of the flanks, as well as the chin, throat, chest, and a strip of the limbs, are dusky, while the under parts, inner sides of the limbs, the under side and tip of the tail, and the inside of the ears are white.

The pampas deer, very generally known as *Cariacus campestris*, is the largest and most common ruminant in the districts from which it takes its name. It frequents dry and open parts of the country, and is generally found in pairs or small parties, the old bucks being, however, solitary.

The male of the pampas deer possesses an unpleasant and penetrating effluvium, which can be detected at a distance of several miles. During the day these deer generally lie concealed among the tall pampas grass, coming out to feed at sunset, and continuing throughout the night. Their speed is very great, and it is only by

MALE AND FEMALE VENEZUELAN BROCKETS

the best horses they can be ridden down, while even then, if they have a considerable start, they are pretty sure to escape. The fawns are born in winter and spring, and it does not appear that there is ever more than one at a birth. Both parents assist in protecting their young, and the doe is especially clever in aiding the escape of her fawn. The alarm cry of the pampas deer is a low, whistling bark, but this is never uttered when the doe has a fawn by her side.

The marsh, or guazu, deer (*Mazama dichotoma* or *Cariacus palustris*) is found in South Brazil, Paraguay, Rio Grande do Sul, and Uruguay ; its westerly range being limited by the Parana River. The antlers of this deer are larger and more complex than those of the pampas deer, both prongs of the main fork being strongly developed, and each again subdividing ; the hind prong being also generally rather the heavier of the two. In contrast to the pampas deer, the marsh deer seeks out swamps and lakes, where it delights to enter the water or wallow in the mud. The general colour of the marsh deer is bright foxy red in summer and browner in winter, with the front of the legs, from the knees and hocks downwards, black. The coat is somewhat coarse and shaggy.

THE WHITE-TAILED DEER

The last main group of the American deer is typically represented by the well known white-tailed, or Virginian, deer (*Mazama*, or *Dorcelaphus*, *americana*), referred to in older works as *Cariacus virginianus*. The group includes the largest species, and nearly the whole of those found in the northern half of the continent. These deer are collectively distinguished by the large size and complexity of the

PAMPAS DEER

antlers, which differ from those of the other groups by the presence of a larger or smaller sub-basal snag, and also by the absence of tusks in the upper jaw, and the spotted coat of the fawns.

The white-tailed deer occurs typically in eastern North America, and stands about 3 feet 1 inch at the shoulder, but it is represented by a great number of local races, which gradually diminish in size from north to south, and also exhibit a decreasing complexity of antler and a greyer tone of colour. To mention them in detail is unnecessary, but it may be stated that while in the New England States and Canada the white-tail (*M. a. borealis*) is rather larger and greyer than the typical race, in Texas the species is represented by the so-called fan-tailed deer (*M. a. texensis*), which is small and grey, with poor antlers ; and in Arizona by *M. a. couesi*, which is also small in size and pale in colour, and lacks the black margins to the ears found in other races.

Considering these and many other local forms as referable to a single species, the white-tail will have a range extending right across the American continent from east to west, and from south to north from Canada to Mexico. The main distinctive characteristic of this species is to be found in the antlers, in which the anterior prong of the main fork shows a great development at the expense of the hind one. This abortion of the hind prong, however, is compensated by a corresponding growth of the sub-basal snag. These snags, like the main prongs of the antler, are subject to extraordinary abnormal developments, so that the variations which occur in the antlers of the white-tail are only paralleled by those found in the reindeer. The tail is long.

The summer coat of the white-tail is bright rufous chestnut, or bay, from which it derives its common local title of red deer, although in winter the coat becomes of a greyer tinge ; but at all seasons the throat, a ring above the muzzle, a spot above and below the eye, portions of the inside of the ear, the inner surfaces of the limbs, and the under parts are white. There is also a black band on the chin. The long and bushy tail is brown above and white below, and as this appendage is raised when the animal is running, the name of white-tail is appropriate. In build this deer is the most elegant and most graceful of all its compatriots. Unusually fine bucks are stated to weigh as much as 200 pounds, and occasionally more.

With regard to the local variation in size and colour in this species, although in a given neighbourhood there is no great difference in the size of the individuals, in widely different localities there is a permanent and constant difference of size. Thus, though in the north all the deer are large, as we proceed south there is a progressive decrease, till in Northern Mexico and the neighbourhood of the Gulf of Mexico the deer have so diminished in size that it is difficult to believe that they are specifically identical with their northern representatives. Similarly, we find in the mountainous regions of the west an increase in the amount of white on the tail and body, which has given rise to the notion that the western white-tailed deer is a distinct species, this difference not being constant, according to Mr. Caton, even among the deer of the west, where many specimens cannot be distinguished from those found in Illinois or Wisconsin.

Although shy and timid in the extreme, and at first retreating rapidly before the advance of civilisation, these deer soon regain confidence, and come back to their ancient haunts. Their speed is great, and they are excellent and rapid swimmers, even young fawns while still in the spotted coat taking readily to the water. During long-continued deep snow these deer frequently collect in parties, sometimes of considerable size, and form " yards," like elk.

There is considerable variation in the time of changing the grey dress of winter for the red coat of summer, as there is in the date when the antlers of the bucks are shed, these differences being apparently mainly due to the severity or mildness of the winters. The pairing season, during which the bucks, like those of other deer, are exceedingly pugnacious, lasts from the latter part of October till the beginning of December.

The fawns, which are nearly always two in number, are mostly born in May. They retain their white spots till September, when both young and old assume their winter dress. The fawns are easily tamed, if captured sufficiently young. In bucks of the first year the antlers form unbranched spikes, while in the second year they are simply forked, without any branching of the two prongs, although the sub-basal snag makes its appearance at the same time.

White-tailed deer also extend into South America, where they are represented in Ecuador and Colombia by the small so-called bare-eared deer (*M. a. gymnotis*), distinguished by the large flapping ears, of which the outer surface is naked, by the extreme narrowness of the head, and the more slender form ; and in Peru and Bolivia by *M. peruviana*.

THE MULE DEER

The most specialised of all the American deer as regards size and complexity of antlers is the mule deer (*Mazama*, or *Dorcelaphus*, *hemionus*), so called on account of the enormous size of its ears. In this deer, often known as *Cariacus macrotis*, the antlers, when compared with those of the white-tail, have recovered the relative importance of the posterior prong, and also show a proportionate reduction of the sub-basal snag, so that they are much more regularly forked. At the same time the main strength of the beam is drawn into the hind prong, and intermediate forms occur both in this and the white-tail which bridge the gap between the extremes, and leave no doubt as to their intimate relationship. In general the front prong is simply forked, while the second divides into three or more snags in adult bucks; but instances occur where the hind prong is unbranched, while in some individuals of the white-tailed deer the same prong is divided.

The antlers of the second year are simply forked, in the third year the hinder prong is also forked; but the forking of the front prong and the development of the sub-basal snag does not take place till the assumption of the fourth set of antlers. A head is recorded in which the length of the antlers was 32 inches, with an extreme span of 37 inches.

In height the mule deer is fully equal to the white-tail, but is more stoutly built and much less graceful, with proportionally shorter limbs, while the ears are nearly double the dimensions of those of the latter. The tail is short, and quite unlike that of any other deer, being cylindrical, naked below, and covered above with short white hairs, terminating in a long brush of black ones.

In summer the coat of the mule deer is very thin and sparse, and generally of a reddish colour, with a large white patch on the buttocks; but in winter the colour is steel grey, the individual hairs being tipped with black. There is much more white on the face than in the white-tailed deer. In the Californian race (*M. h. californica*) the colour is more decidedly red, and there is a black line running along the middle of the upper surface of the tail, and the ears are smaller. Other races, ranging south to New Mexico, have been named.

The mule deer is found throughout the greater part of the Missouri River district, thence westwards on the plains, in the Rocky Mountains, and in the Sierra Nevada. Its habitat has not been very much restricted by advancing civilisation, as this deer is much less alarmed by the invasion of its haunts than is the wapiti. Instead of running in the even manner of the white-tail, mule deer progress by a series of bounds, all their feet leaving the ground simultaneously; and for a short distance the pace is rapid, although it soon slackens. As in the case of the white-tailed deer, the number of fawns produced at a birth is nearly always two, which are born at the end of May or beginning of June, and retain their spots till September. The pairing season is in September and October.

By the hunters in Colorado this deer is commonly spoken of as the black-tail, although that name properly belongs to the next species.

BLACK-TAILED DEER

The Columbian black-tailed deer (*Mazama*, or *Dorcelaphus, columbiana*) has a very restricted distribution, being confined in its typical form to the mountain ranges bordering the Pacific in the neighbourhood of the Columbia River, and unknown to the east of the Sierra Nevada, but represented by local races in Alaska and California. This deer is rather smaller than the mule deer, with relatively smaller ears, but nearly similar antlers. The comparatively short cylindrical tail is black throughout, except for the basal third of the under surface.

THE WHITE-TAILED DEER

The general colour of the coat in winter is grey, darker on the back, and tending to reddish brown on the head, with white on the under parts and throat, the face brownish grey, darker on the forehead, and the legs dark cinnamon. The most distinctive feature of the species, however, is the gland on the outer side of the hind cannon bone, which is circular and surrounded by a ring of white hairs. In the mule deer the same gland is covered by an elongated patch of brown hair running up the greater part of this portion of the limb; and in the black-tail there is a similar but much less elongated tuft. In summer the colour changes to bay.

MUSK DEER

The musk deer (*Moschus moschiferus*) differs so remarkably from all other deer that it forms a sub-family by itself, and some naturalists consider it as the representative of a distinct family. These peculiarities are chiefly internal; among the most important being the presence of a gall-bladder to the liver, as in hollow-horned ruminants, while the brain is much less convoluted than in other deer. The absence of antlers in both sexes cannot be taken as a character of more than generic importance, since this feature occurs in the Chinese water deer.

The musk deer is somewhat clumsily built, and stands about 20 inches in height at the shoulder, and is clothed with peculiarly coarse, brittle, and rather long hair, somewhat resembling pith in structure.

The skull is characterised by the presence of upper tusks, which in the males may be 3 inches in length, and project considerably below the jaw. All the limbs are of considerable length, and the hind pair are longer than the front ones; the hoofs are narrow and pointed, and the lateral pair unusually large. The ears are very large and the tail is short, terminating in the male in a tuft, but hairy throughout in the female. The male has a peculiar sac-like gland in the skin of the abdomen, which yields the musk of commerce.

The general colour of the coat is rich dark brown, more or less speckled and mottled with grey and tawny; the individual hairs having black tips, beneath which is a ring of white, while for three-quarters of their length they are white at the base. The chin, the inner borders of the ears, and the inside of the thighs, and not infrequently a spot on each side of the throat, are whitish, while the under parts and the inner surfaces of the limbs are paler than the body. Some musk deer are considerably paler than ordinary, while in others there is a more or less marked yellowish tint, and others, again, are blacker. The young are spotted.

The musk deer is found throughout the Himalaya as far west as Gilgit, and thence extends through Central Asia into Siberia. In Kansu, in the north-west of China, it is replaced by a nearly allied species (*M. sifanicus*). In the Himalaya it is seldom found below elevations of eight thousand feet in summer, and in Sikhim it occurs above twelve thousand feet.

Musk deer are found either in pairs or alone, and in the Kashmir Himalaya are generally met with in the birch forests above the zone of pines. Sometimes, however, they may be seen at lower levels among thick covert. In habits they have been compared to hares, and, like these animals, they make a " form," in which they lie concealed during the day, their feeding time being in the morning and evening. They seem capable of enduring almost any degree of cold, against which the peculiar nature of their thick coat is sufficient protection.

Musk deer are stated to utter a kind of hiss when alarmed, and when captured give vent to a series of screams; with these exceptions they appear to be silent, even in the pairing season. From observations on some captive musk deer in Nepal, it appears that the sexes come together in January, and that the fawns are born in June. Usually there is a single one at birth, but occasionally two are produced.

The musk, when fresh, is soft and moist, of a brownish colour, with a rather unpleasant smell. It soon hardens and dries, and acquires the all-powerful scent of musk. When removed from the dead animal, the secretion is tied up in a portion of the hairy skin covering the gland, and is then known as a " musk-pod." Each pod contains on an average about an ounce of musk, and in India sells for about sixteen rupees.

English sportsmen hunt musk deer either by walking through the forests they frequent, and examining every ravine and hollow, or by having the jungles driven by natives. On the other hand, the natives themselves capture these little deer in a wholesale manner, which is described as follows by General Macintyre: " A low fence is made of boughs, etc., along the ridge of a hill, sometimes a mile or more in length. At intervals of 100 or 150 yards are gaps. The musk deer, crossing the ridge from one valley to another, come across this fence, and, to save themselves the trouble of jumping

MUSK DEER

over it, walk alongside until, seeing a little gap, they try to go through it. But in each gap a noose of strong string is placed on the ground and tied to a stout sapling bent downwards. The noose is so arranged that, when the deer tread inside it, the sapling is loosed and flies back, leaving the noose tied tightly round the animal's leg. The people visit these fences every two or three days, and secure the deer thus caught, and repair the fences and nooses, which are often carried away or destroyed by larger game."

CHEVROTAINS

THE deer family are the last of the true ruminants, or Pecora, and these are followed by smaller groups of ungulates, which, although ruminants in the general sense of the term, yet differ so widely from the Pecora, and also from one another, that each is regarded as constituting a section of equal value with the latter. These two groups are—firstly, the small deer-like animals known as chevrotains, or mouse deer ; and secondly, the camels ; the latter term including not only the true camels of the Old World, but the South American llamas.

Both agree with the true ruminants in having crescent-like (selenodont) molar teeth, but while chevrotains are probably descended from the ancestral stock which give rise to the deer, camels have originated from a totally different stock, and have acquired their crescent-like teeth independently of the true ruminants. In addition to forming two distinct families, these two groups have also received names of a superior grade, thus bringing them on to a platform equivalent to that occupied by the Pecora. For the chevrotains the term Tragulina is adopted, while that of Tylopoda is employed for the camels.

The elegant little creatures known as chevrotains, or mouse deer, forming the family *Tragulidæ*, are so like small antlerless deer in appearance, that they are commonly regarded as nearly allied to the musk deer, near which they were once placed by naturalists ; but when examined anatomically they are found to depart widely from the deer family.

Chevrotains agree with the true ruminants in the absence of incisor teeth in the upper jaw, and resemble the musk deer in the presence of upper tusks, or canine teeth, which in the males attain a considerable length, and project below the upper lip. They also agree with true ruminants in that the canine teeth of the lower jaw resemble the incisors, to the outermost pair of which they are approximated so as to form a continuous series. The three molar teeth and the last premolar tooth in the upper jaw, together with the lower molars are also of a crescent-like type ; but with this, the resemblance to the true ruminants ceases.

In the first place, the three premolar teeth, with the exception of the last in the upper jaw, instead of being crescent-like, have their crowns elongated and narrow, with sharp cutting edges. Then the second, or axis, vertebra of the neck has a simple conical peg (odontoid process) projecting in front, by which it articulates with the first, or atlas, vertebra, whereas in the true ruminants this process is spout-like.

The limbs in chevrotains have the fibula, or smaller bone of the lower leg, complete, instead of represented only by its lower end. Moreover, each foot has four complete toes—that is to say, the metacarpal and metatarsal bones, respectively supporting the toes of the fore and hind feet, are complete, and extend alongside of the cannon bone from the basal joints of the toes to the wrist and ankle joints, instead of either being represented by their upper or lower extremities alone, or wanting. In one of the chevrotains the cannon bone of the fore limb is divided into its two component metacarpal elements ; while in the other it is wider and less completely soldered than in the ruminants. Finally, instead of the four distinct compartments characteristic of that of the true ruminants, the stomach of the chevrotains has only three such chambers.

The chevrotains are divided into two genera, the first of which, *Tragulus*, is Asiatic and the second, *Dorcatherium*, African. The true, or Asiatic, chevrotains are represented by several species, of which the range extends from India and Ceylon through the Malay Archipelago to the Philippines. They are characterised by the two middle metacarpal bones of the fore limb being fused into a cannon bone, and the small size of the lateral toes. With the exception of the pigmy antelopes of Africa, they are the smallest of the living representatives of the ruminating ungulates, and much resemble agutis in appearance and habits.

THE NAPU OR MALAY CHEVROTAIN

Of living species of the genus, one is confined to India and Ceylon, while the others are found in the regions east of the Bay of Bengal. The Javan chevrotain (*Tragulus javanicus*), or napu, the smallest of the group, is greyish above, with the sides brightening to rufous, and a dark line, which may be nearly black, running along the nape of the neck. The under parts are whitish, more or less mixed with rufous, but there is generally a broad reddish or brown stripe running up the front of the chest. This chevrotain has a wide geographical distribution, extending from Java to Cambodia, Cochin China, Tenasserim, the Malay Peninsula, Sumatra, Borneo, the Philippines, and a number of the smaller Malay islands. All these island races have received distinct specific names, among which the Sumatran *T. j. napu* is larger than the Javan race, standing 13 inches at the shoulder, and characterised by its dark, smoky grey colour, with the under parts greyish white, and devoid of rufous or tawny edgings. The Philippine race (*T. j. nigricans*) is also dark coloured.

A second species is the kanchil (*T. kanchil*), typically from Sumatra, but with a number of local races in the Malay Peninsula and islands. It is chiefly distinguished from the napu by its superior size. In common with the former and the next species, it has a bare tract on the throat and the hind side of the hocks, which are wanting in the Indian chevrotain.

Another Malay species is Stanley's chevrotain (*T. stanleyanus*), probably from the Malay Peninsula, and intermediate in size between the Javan and Sumatran races of the napu ; in colour, all the upper parts are bright rufous.

The Indian chevrotain (*Tragulus meminna*) differs from all the other species in having white spots on the body, the tail shorter, and the whole of the chin and throat, as well as the hind surface of the hock, uniformly covered with hair. It is of medium height, standing from 10 to 12 inches at the withers, and weighing from 5 to 6 pounds. In colour, the upper parts are brown of variable shade, minutely speckled with yellow, while the flanks are spotted with white or buff on a brown ground ; the spots being more or less elongated, and often passing into short longitudinal stripes. This chevrotain is found in Southern India and Ceylon at elevations below two thousand feet, extending northwards as far as Orissa on the east coast, and to the Western Ghats near Bombay on the west. Remains of a fossil chevrotain have been discovered in the Pliocene rocks of the Siwalik Hills.

All chevrotains appear to be very similar in habits, and have a way of walking in a mincing manner on the extreme tips of their hoofs, which communicates a stiff and rigid appearance to the legs, and has given rise to the popular notion that these animals have no joints. They lie concealed in grass or jungle, and only venture out to feed in the evenings and mornings. They are timid and shy, but in confinement soon become tame and gentle, and have been known to breed. Writing of the Indian species, Colonel Tickell observes that it " is found throughout the jungly districts of Central India—Chutia Nagpur—but from its retired habits is not often seen. It never ventures into open country, but keeps among rocks, in the crevices of which it passes the heat of the day, and into which it retires on the approach of an enemy. In these the female brings forth her young, two in number, generally at the close of the rains or the commencement of the cold season. The male keeps with the female during the rutting season, about June or July, but at other times they live solitary." The napu chevrotain, which is very common in the Malay Peninsula, inhabits dense thickets, and produces either one or two fawns at a birth.

WATER CHEVROTAIN

The water chevrotain (*Dorcatherium aquaticum*), which ranges from the West Coast of Africa through the forest region to the Ituri Forest in East Equatoria, is the surviving representative of a genus, *Dorcatherium*, widely spread in the Old World during the Pliocene and Miocene epochs of the Tertiary period. Indeed, the genus was originally founded upon the evidence of one of these extinct species, the living form having been afterwards described under the name of *Hyomoschus*.

The water chevrotain (p. 83) is mainly distinguished from the true chevrotains of Asia by the feet being shorter and stouter, with relatively larger lateral toes, and, above all, by the fact that the two middle metacarpal bones remain completely separate. The living species is slightly superior in size to the largest of the Asiatic chevrotains, and resembles the Indian in having the body spotted and striped with white. The general colour of the coat is olive, with a large amount of white on the throat, chest, and under surface of the tail ; the upper part of the body is spotted, while the flanks are marked with longitudinal white stripes, larger and more continuous than those of the Indian chevrotain.

These chevrotains frequent the borders of the equatorial region, where their habits are more like those of pigs than deer. They take readily to the water, in which they both swim and dive.

The water chevrotain has three premolar teeth in the lower jaw, but in the somewhat larger extinct species found in the Pliocene and Miocene strata of Europe there were four pairs of these teeth. The species occurring in the Pliocene of the Punjab was of still larger dimensions, and affords an instance of the intimate connection existing between the Tertiary mammalian fauna of India and that of Africa at the present day.

In its separate metacarpal bones

THE WATER CHEVROTAIN

the water chevrotain makes a decided approach towards the pigs ; and in the Tertiary deposits of Europe and North America there occur numerous small ungulates, which appear to have connected the chevrotains with deer. Such is *Gelocus*, from the lower Miocene of France, in which the middle metacarpal bones were separate, while the metatarsals were fused into a cannon bone ; the genus has been regarded as the common ancestor of the two families. *Prodremotherium* of the upper Eocene of France, has cannon bones in both limbs, while in the American *Hypertragulus* both the metacarpals and metatarsals were separate.

CAMELS AND LLAMAS

THE camels of the Old, and the llamas of the New World form a group of ruminating ungulates (family *Camelidæ*), distinguished widely both from the true ruminants and the chevrotains, which probably had a distinct origin from more primitive even-toed ungulates.

An important point of distinction is that the front of the upper jaw is furnished with incisor teeth; it is true, indeed, that in the adult state there is only a single pair of these teeth remaining, but in young animals there are, as in pigs, three pairs. Then, again, both jaws are furnished with tusks, or canine teeth; those of the lower jaw being sharply pointed, and separated by an interval from the incisors, instead of resembling the latter and forming with them a continuous series, as in the chevrotains and true ruminants.

The molar teeth have tall and crescent-shaped crowns, which, however, are not precisely similar to those of the chevrotains; and one or sometimes more, of the premolar teeth generally has a simple pointed crown, like that of a canine, and is not in contact with the other teeth of the cheek series.

The limbs are long, and the thigh is placed nearly vertically, so that the true knee is more detached from the small hind quarters of the body than is usually the case in ungulates. The lower portion of the legs is composed of a cannon bone followed by two toes, without any trace of the lateral toes or their supporting bones. The cannon bone differs, however, from that of true ruminants in that the two pulley-like surfaces at the lower end, instead of being placed side by side and furnished with a distinct ridge in the middle of each, are divergent and perfectly smooth.

The bones of the first joint of the toes are also longer and more expanded at their lower ends than in true ruminants; the second pair being broad and flattened, while the third forms mere nodules, unlike the symmetrical ones of the true ruminants. The feet form broad, expanded cushion-like pads—from which the group derives its title of Tylopoda—of which the under surface is undivided, while the front shows a division into two toes, each of which bears a broad nail on the upper surface. The ankle joint differs from that of true ruminants in that the two bones lying immediately below the astragalus remain distinct, whereas in the former they unite into a compound bone termed the naviculo-cuboid.

A further distinction is to be found in the divided upper lip, like that of a hare; while the elongated neck is characterised by the great length of its vertebræ. These vertebræ exhibit certain peculiarities of structure the consideration of which need not be discussed here; but it must be observed that they resemble those of true ruminants in that the process in front of the second vertebra, by which it articulates with the first, is spout-shaped, this being an instance of a similar structure acquired independently in two distinct groups. The head is carried high in the air, with the upper part of the neck nearly vertical, and is unprovided with either horns or antlers. The stomach has three compartments, of which the first two are provided with a number of cells or pouches capable of being closed by the action of muscles, and containing only fluid. The bones of all the members of the family are remarkable for their extremely solid and ivory-like structure.

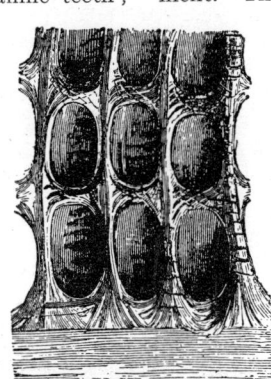

WATER-CELLS IN STOMACH OF CAMEL

Camels and llamas differ from other mammals in possessing oval in place of circular red blood corpuscles; and in this respect they resemble reptiles and birds, although the blood corpuscles preserve the mammalian feature of the absence of a nucleus. In 1909 it was pointed out by Dr. J. B. Cleland that camels present another resemblance to reptiles in the fact that their temperature exhibits considerable diurnal fluctuations dependent upon the temperature of the external air, instead of being unaffected by changes in the environment. The experiments were made in 1907 on camels imported into Australia from India. At the time when the experiments were conducted the days were usually very hot, the temperature rising on some occasions to 100° Fahr. in the shade, while the nights were comparatively cool. The diurnal oscillation in the body temperature of the camels reached in some cases 8° Fahr., the low temperatures occurring in the early morning, after which there was a gradual rise in the temperature of the blood as the warmth of the air increased. The animals were restless and impatient to be off in search of food at the time of lowest temperature. The low blood temperature may be attributed to the coolness of the mornings, the abstention from active exercise during the night, and perhaps to the completion of the ruminating process some hours previously. On the other hand, the high evening temperatures may be attributable to the fact that camels sweat visibly only over a small area on the back of the neck, this area being much too small, considering the bulk of the animal, to assist materially in maintaining the bodily temperature at an invariable mean under the influence of great solar heat and active exertion. Hence, the keeping down of the temperature under such conditions must be brought about chiefly by invisible perspiration and vasomotor processes. The small amount of visible perspiration given off must be of considerable advantage to an animal inhabiting tropical deserts.

Dr. Cleland asks whether there is any connection between the two reptilian features, namely, the oval blood corpuscles and the oscillating temperature found in camels, as it is frequently the case that an animal exhibiting one low feature often displays a second. The oval blood corpuscles are, however, apparently due to reversion or new development, as it is impossible to regard them as directly inherited from reptilian ancestors; and if this be so, a somewhat similar view must be taken of the other phenomenon.

The camel family, in proportion to its extent, is more valuable to mankind than any other group of even-toed ungulates, only one species being unknown in the domesticated condition, while one is found exclusively in that state. The Old and New World representatives constitute distinct genera.

The camels of the Old World, of which there are two species, are characterised by their great bodily size and bulk, and the presence of one or two large fatty humps on the back, as well as by having six upper and five lower cheek teeth on each side of the jaws, the total number of teeth being thirty-four. Their ears are comparatively short and rounded; and the hair is very irregularly disposed, being in some places very long and shaggy, and in others short and close, although never partaking of the nature of wool. The feet are broad, with the toes imperfectly separated; and the tail is comparatively long, reaching nearly to the hocks, and furnished near the end wi h long hair forming a terminal tuft.

Callous pads, on which the animal rests when lying down, and which are present at birth, are found on the chest, elbows, wrists—commonly called knees—and the true knees. The whole form of these animals is far from beautiful, while the head is positively ugly, this want of bodily beauty being accompanied by a viciousness of temper and general stupidity of disposition which can scarcely be paralleled among domesticated animals.

THE ARABIAN CAMEL

The Arabian camel (*Camelus dromedarius*), found both in Africa and Asia, and characterised by its single hump, is a long-limbed animal, with a comparatively short coat of hair, and soft feet adapted for walking on yielding sandy soil, and standing from about 6 feet 8 inches to 7 feet in height. The head is comparatively short, with a long and sloping muzzle, and convex forehead. The eyes are large, with a soft expression, and the small rounded ears are placed far back on the sides of the head. The upper lip overhangs the lower, and the large slit-like nostrils can be closed at will. The long neck is laterally compressed, and thickest in the middle, and the body is massive and rounded. The contour of the back rises from the setting on of the neck to the loins, and then falls rapidly away to the tail.

The hump, when the animal is in good condition, stands upright, but it alters considerably in shape according to age. The richer the food of the camel, the larger is its hump ; while, when the food is poor and dry, the hump decreases in size, and accordingly in the rainy season this appendage attains its maximum development, while in the dry months it proportionately shrinks. In high-conditioned camels, the hump should form a regular pyramid, and occupy at least a quarter of the whole length, but when the animals are half-starved it almost disappears.

The hair is soft, and on the hind part of the head, the neck and throat, the shoulders, the hump, and the upper part of the fore legs longer than elsewhere. The colour of the hair is very variable, although a light sandy is the most common hue ; there are, however, white, grey, brown, and even totally black camels, but those of the last-named colour are held by the Arabs to be worthless.

There are numerous breeds differing more or less from another, and the Arabs recognise no fewer than twenty distinct strains. Roughly speaking, they may be divided into two classes—namely, baggage camels and riding camels, or dromedaries. The peculiarly unpleasant motion of even the best camels is due to the circumstance that the two legs of one side move simultaneously. The ordinary pace of a baggage camel is from two and a half to three miles an hour when fully loaded, but a good dromedary will keep up a pace of from eight to ten miles an hour for a long period.

Arabian camels are found in the domesticated condition in all parts of Africa lying between the Mediterranean and 12° N., while in Somaliland they extend as far south as 5° N. They are also widely distributed in South-Eastern Asia, ranging from the lowlands of Afghanistan and Bokhara, where they impinge on the habitat of the two-humped Bactrian camel, through North-Western India, Persia, Asia Minor, Syria, and Arabia. In Asia Minor and Khorasan, there is a race of half-breeds between the Arabian and the Bactrian camel, known in the last-named country as the Bóghdi camel. It has the two humps of the Bactrian species, but the long limbs of the Arabian, and appears to be a product of crossing a male of the former with a female of the latter. Arabian camels have been introduced into the Canaries, Australia, North America, Italy, the South of Spain, and Zanzibar.

There has been much discussion as to what country was the original home of the Arabian camel ; but it has been considered that Arabia has the best claim. Some light is thrown on the question by the occurrence of fossilised remains of extinct camels in the Pliocene rocks of the Siwalik Hills, and also in beds belonging to the succeeding Pleistocene period in Algeria ; and as so many African genera of mammals which occur fossil in India apparently migrated thence to their present home, it seems likely that the same may have been the case with the camels. The Arabian camel, or its immediate parent, may, therefore, have sprung from an Indian ancestor, and thence made its way through Arabia and Syria into Northern Africa.

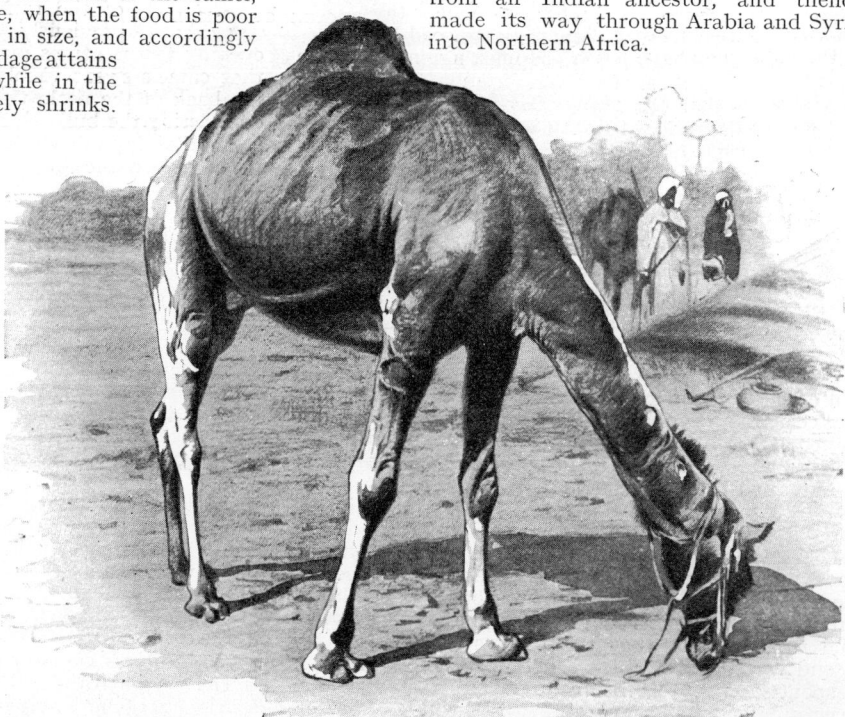

THE ARABIAN CAMEL

The Arabian camel is essentially an animal fitted to exist only in dry or desert districts, and consequently attempts to introduce it into the moist and wooded regions of Southern India and Equatorial Africa have failed. Where the climate is at all favourable, its introduction into new regions has generally been attended with success. In Australia, for example, the introduction of camels has been a success, and they have proved invaluable in the expeditions undertaken to explore the deserts of the interior.

The food of the camel in its natural state probably consisted entirely of branches and leaves of trees, and although grain is now largely given, a certain amount of green food is essential to the animals' health. No matter how thorny the boughs may be, they are acceptable to the camel, and it is marvellous how the animals manage to eat such food without injury to their mouths. On such a diet, or even on dates, camels will do well; but when compelled to work for days with little or no food, they soon break down, as was disastrously shown in the first expedition to Khartum. For a few days, owing to the peculiar conformation of their stomachs, camels can exist comfortably without water, but their endurance in this respect is often taxed sadly beyond its capability.

Although the camel is undoubtedly the most valuable and most useful of all animals in dry and desert countries, its disposition and temper are of the very worst description. In addition to its ordinary surliness and want of attachment to its master, the male camel during the pairing season is subject to almost uncontrollable outbreaks of rage; and, at the same time, owing to a swelling of the uvula, makes a loud bubbling noise, most unpleasant to the human occupants of the camp. An instance of the savage disposition of camels is afforded by the habit they have, when passing a mounted man on a narrow path, of turning their heads suddenly round and endeavouring to inflict a bite on the rider's arm or shoulder; and a camel's bite is exceptionally severe.

In addition to its value as a beast of burden, the camel is also esteemed by the natives of many countries on account of its milk and flesh, while its hair is woven into ropes and cloth, and in some parts of India its bones are used in lieu of ivory for inlaying and turning. The milk is extremely thick and rich, although unsuitable for use with tea or coffee, as it immediately curdles.

From remote antiquity camels have been kept in enormous herds by Eastern nations. In modern times the Arabs of the Sudan possess immense herds, which in the rainy season are driven northwards in thousands; and in some parts of North-Western India very large numbers of camels are kept by the natives (p 43). When the young camels are too feeble to undergo the fatigues of a day's march, they are slung in nets on the backs or by the sides of some adult members of the drove. A single calf is produced at a birth, after a gestation of rather more than eleven months, and is suckled by the dam for at least a twelvemonth.

Camels have a great aversion from crossing even the smallest stream, and swim either imperfectly, or not at all, without assistance; this aversion doubtless indicating that their original home was in desert lands.

THE BACTRIAN CAMEL

The Bactrian camel (*C. bactrianus*) of Central Asia is distinguished from the Arabian species not only by its double hump, but also by its inferior height, stouter and more clumsy build, shorter legs, and harder and shorter feet, as well as by the greater length and abundance of the hair. This animal is, indeed, in all respects better adapted for a rocky and hilly country than its southern congener, its shorter and stouter limbs rendering it far less liable to accidents in traversing precipitous ascents. The largest development of hair occurs upon the top of the head, the neck and shoulders, the upper part of the fore limbs, and the humps.

The Bactrian camel is found in nearly all the desert regions of Central Asia lying between Afghanistan and

AN ARABIAN CAMEL WALKING

Turkestan, and China and Southern Siberia. In the regions lying to the east of Yarkand occur droves of these animals living in a wild condition, which are probably descended from domesticated individuals escaped from captivity. These wild camels differ from the ordinary domesticated breed by the smaller size of the humps, the more distinct pads on their so-called front knees, and certain peculiarities in the conformation of the skull.

Major C. S. Cumberland states that this " camel is very shy in its habits, and, so far as I could ascertain, has never been caught and domesticated. The natives told me that no horse in the country could catch the camels in the deep sand of the region they frequent. They vary in colour, like the domesticated species, from dark brown to lightish dun. Their origin has yet to be traced. I take it that they have sprung from camels which escaped when the district known as Takla Makan was buried in a great sand-storm some two centuries ago. Tradition relates that no human beings survived, but it is likely enough that some of the camels and horses did so, and this was the origin of the wild camels and ponies which are found in the district."

In the deserts of Tibet some, at least, of the camels are in all probability really wild. Fossil camels found in Rumania and Russia are probably the ancestors of the living two-humped species.

Bactrian camels feed chiefly on the saline and bitter plants of the steppes, which are rejected by almost all other animals. They display a partiality for salt, drinking freely at the brackish water and salt lakes so common throughout their habitat. Instead of confining themselves to a strictly vegetable diet, these camels will, when pressed by hunger, readily devour almost anything they may come across, including felt blankets, bones and skins of animals, flesh, and fish.

BACTRIAN CAMEL IN THE ZOOLOGICAL GARDENS, LONDON

The pairing season occurs during February, March, and April; and the young, of which one is produced at birth, are not born till thirteen months later, so that the period of gestation is considerably longer than in the Arabian camel. At birth the young are so helpless in the domesticated state that they have to be attended with the greatest care, but they soon gain strength, and in about a week are able to eat. They are weaned at an early period for the sake of the milk of the parents, which is largely used by their owners. In their third year they are ridden on short journeys, while in their fifth they attain their full stature and vigour, and with good management are said to be serviceable until they attain the age of some five-and-twenty years. In Mongolia and the Kirghiz steppes the Bactrian camel is fully as important to the nomad inhabitants as is its southern cousin.

R. LYDEKKER

STORIES OF THE CAMEL

It would have caused surprise, no doubt, had the suggestion been made to Captain Scott that he should take camels with him for his Antarctic trip, begun in the summer of 1910. For, as Sir Ernest Shackleton's hardy little ponies killed themselves by a misguided passion for sand, possibly the result of a camel cavalcade for Captain Scott might not have been more auspicious. Still, when the Klondike was being opened up at the close of the nineteenth century, the suggestion to commandeer the powerful Siberian camel was under consideration in certain quarters. Men had been sent from Canada and the United States to fetch reindeer and their Lapp drivers from the far north-eastern corner of Arctic Europe, to the intent that the animals might act as beasts of burthen where no other animals might so fitly go.

The suggestion as to the employment of the Siberian camel emanated from that astute authority, Herr Carl Hagenbeck. "The best animal for the Klondike," he wrote to the late Mr. C. J. Cornish, "is the big Siberian camel. These animals transport all merchandise from China to Russia, and can stand Siberian cold as well as the greatest heat. They never need shelter, and sleep out in the deep snow. . . They can carry from five hundredweight to six hundredweight, and also go in harness and pull as much as a big horse. They can cross mountains as well as level country."

Seeing that the Arabian camel has been introduced to help in colonising Australia, it would have been a little romantic to have had its hardier cousin opening the way to the golden, frozen North.

Europeans know very little of this camel, for in Europe it is rarely seen. Travellers who have visited the great Russian fairs, where end the trade routes to and from the East, are familiar with tales of its powers and endurance. De Quincey knew something of the attributes of the beast when he described that terrible retreat of the Tatar host from the Volga to the Great Wall of China, when, saved alone by their strong long-suffering camels, the flying horde, reduced from six hundred thousand to three hundred and fifty thousand, after a five months' retreat, plunged, together with their pursuers, into the waters of the Lake of Tengs, "like a host of lunatics pursued by a host of fiends."

Of oxen, cows, mules, asses, sheep, and goats none remained—only the camels. These animals, on which they had started in the snows of winter, and crossed the ice of the Russian rivers, these, says our author, "looking like the mummies of some antediluvian animals, without the affections or sensibilities of flesh and blood—these only lifted up their speaking eyes to the eastern heavens, and had to all appearances come out of this long tempest of trial unscathed and hardly diminished." They had borne the rigours of winter which left men, women, and children lying frozen stiff and dead in circles around the camp fires.

The camel did not find its way to the Klondike goldfields, so happily there arose no labour complications to vex the soul of a government. It was different in Australia. Queensland squatters had some few years ago to lament a serious lack of transport facilities. They were being eaten off their farms by rabbits, because they could not get wire netting carried out to them; and when their wool was ready for market, they could not get it carried. Hence camels were introduced. Up rose gentlemen with what they were pleased to consider vested interests in the carrying trade. The camels would kill the calling of the carrying trade, they said, hence the camels must pad the hoof elsewhere. But the Premier would not ban these new friends of the farmer. The agitation was hasty and ill-considered, he said, the camels' presence was due only to drought, which made it impossible for the usual carrying teams to travel. Wire netting must go up country to the rabbit boards, and wool must come down from the colonists. So the camel remained, and will remain.

It is not in Australia, however, that the full utility of the camel is appreciated. The Laplander alone knows the full value of the reindeer, and it is eastward far that the camel's full worth is realised. The hair and milk of the camel are indispensable to the Arab, and the sole source of fuel supply is the dung of the camel.

One of the unexplained antipathies of animals is that of horses for camels. To train a horse to endure the presence of a camel is as difficult for the owner of a circus or menagerie as to make it learn some elaborate trick. Success is attained, of course, where horses have to accustom themselves to the proximity day and night of beasts of prey of which ordinarily they go in terror. But an untrained horse has an instinctive aversion to the camel, and it has been noticed that where these animals have been tethered at any particular spot, horses will shy and refuse to go near the place, even after the camels have gone their way, with the rest of the show, to another town. E. A. B.

LLAMAS

Under the title of llamas may be included all the existing South American representatives of the camel family, although that name properly belongs only to a domesticated breed of the larger of the two wild species. All existing llamas are smaller in size and lighter in build than the camels, and owing to the absence of any hump on the back depart less widely from the ordinary type of ungulates. Their pointed ears are relatively much longer than in camels, while their thickly-haired tails are reduced to little more than stumps. The feet are narrower and more pointed than in their Old World relatives, and have the toes more completely separate, each being furnished with a distinct pad on the sole. The body is covered with a thick coat of long hair of a woolly nature, and there are fewer callosities on the limbs than in camels. The head is proportionately longer than in the latter, and has a tapering and sharply-pointed muzzle, the neck being relatively thinner.

The skull has one tooth on each side of the upper jaw less than in camels, the missing tooth being the isolated sharp-pointed premolar situated in the latter in the middle of the gap between the tusk and the main series of cheek teeth. There are only thirty-two, instead of thirty-four, teeth; but the premolar tooth in the lower jaw, which is of very small size, not infrequently falls out in the adult, and reduces the number to thirty.

Llamas are confined to the western and southern regions of South America, and can live only where the climate is temperate or cold. On the western side of the continent they are restricted to the higher ranges of the Andes and Cordilleras, but in many parts of Patagonia and in Tierra del Fuego they flourish on the plains at the

sea-level. In the neighbourhood of the Equator they are found at elevations of between 12,000 and 16,000 feet above the sea, and never descend lower than between 6,000 and 7,000 feet. During the rainy season the wild species inhabiting the mountains ascend to the limits of vegetation, but in the hot season descend to the valleys, where sustenance is alone to be found. They live in larger or smaller parties, and sometimes congregate in herds comprising many hundreds. All are characterised by the singular habit of spitting at intruders.

THE VICUGNA

The vicugna (*Lama vicugna*), which is the smaller of the wild species, is of a uniform light-brown colour, becoming paler on the under parts and limbs, and with light markings on the face and jaws. The build is light and graceful, the head is relatively short, and there are no naked callosities on the hind legs. This species is confined to the mountains in the district between Southern Ecuador and Central Bolivia, which includes the whole of Peru.

During the wet season of the year vicugnas seek the highest ridges of the Cordilleras, where plant life is sparse. On account of the softness of their feet, they prefer upland meadows, and avoid stony, naked peaks, while they still more carefully shun glaciers and snow-fields. In the hot season, on the other hand, they descend into the higher valleys; the reason of this

BACTRIAN CAMEL (MALE)

reversal of the usual plan of migration apparently being that in the Cordilleras the vegetation on the higher ridges is withered up by the heat of the dry summer season, and that such herbage that remains is only to be found in the valleys, where it is nourished by springs or swamps. Vicugnas feed all day, and a flock is seldom seen lying down.

During the pairing season the males fight fiercely for the supremacy of the flocks, each of which comprises one male accompanied by from six to fifteen females. The male always remains a few paces behind the flock, and gives notice of approaching danger by a shrill whistle, at the same time rapidly advancing ; the flock

VICUGNAS

then collects, and swiftly gallops off, the male bringing up the rear, and often stopping to observe the foe.

In February the female gives birth to a single fawn, which as soon as it comes into the world is endowed with remarkable speed and endurance. The young males remain with their dams until full grown, when they are expelled from the flock by the united force of females. These young males unite in separate bands of from twenty to thirty head, and as such flocks have no special guardian, but all the members are constantly on the alert, they are exceedingly difficult to approach. During the pairing season incessant fights take place among these male flocks, and the animals then utter a peculiar neighing sort of cry audible at a great distance.

THE GUANACO

The guanaco (*Lama huanacos*) is a rather larger and heavier-built animal than the vicugna, with a longer head, larger skull, and distinct naked patches on the knees of the hind legs. A full-grown male measures 4 feet in height at the shoulder, and from 7 to 8 feet in length. The thick and woolly hair is of a pale reddish colour, longest and palest on the under parts. The species extends from the mountains of Ecuador and Peru, where it occurs with the vicugna, to Patagonia and Tierra del Fuego.

In the mountains guanacos appear very similar in their habits to vicugnas, but they are often seen in

larger flocks, which may include as many as one hundred or even five hundred head. The pairing season is in August and September, and the young are born ten or eleven months afterwards. These animals are very wild and wary, and frequently the first evidence of their presence near the hunter is their loud neighing alarm cry, which makes itself heard from afar. They display extreme curiosity, are easily domesticated, and in the wild state have no notion of defending themselves

A singular circumstance connected with the guanacos is their alleged habit of resorting to certain particular spots when they feel their end approaching. On this point Darwin observes that " on the banks of the Santa Cruz, in certain circumscribed spaces, which were generally bushy and always near the river, the ground was actually white with bones. On one such spot I counted between ten and twenty heads. I particularly examined the bones ; they did not appear, like some scattered ones which I have seen, gnawed or broken, as if dragged together by beasts of prey. The animals in most cases must have crawled before dying beneath and amongst the bushes." Although mentioning that wounded guanacos invariably make their way towards the river, Darwin did not attempt any explanation of this strange habit ; but Mr. W. H. Hudson, after stating that this habit is only developed among the guanacos of Southern Patagonia, suggests that it is due to an inherited instinct, derived from a time when the animals were accustomed during a period of exceptional cold to seek refuge beneath the cover of the bushes growing in the sheltered river valleys.

The true llama (pages 52, 61) is a domesticated breed of the guanaco, fully as large as its wild prototype, and very variable in colour, although generally white, or white spotted with brown or black, and more rarely completely brown or black. The skull is very similar to that of the guanaco, and the knees have the same naked patches. In appearance the llama is a long-necked and long-limbed animal, with comparatively short hair falling little below the lower line of the body.

Bred by the ancient Peruvians as a beast of burden, or for riding, it was chiefly characteristic of the southern portion of Peru, where, before the Spanish conquest, enormous numbers were kept. Only male llamas were used as beasts of burden, the smaller females being kept for their milk and flesh. When not in active use, the herds were kept on the higher mountain pastures, where they temporarily associated with wild guanacos. The distinction between llamas and alpacas from as far back as tradition extends, coupled with the antiquity of the Peruvian civilisation, indicates that the domestication of the wild guanacos took place at a very early period.

Llamas produce only one offspring at a time, so that their rate of increase is not rapid. Usually the calves are suckled for about four months, but in one breed the period is longer ; and it is stated that the young of two successive seasons may not infrequently be seen suckling at the same time.

The alpaca is a smaller animal than the llama, and is bred for the sake of its wool, which is of great fineness and length, reaching in some specimens almost to the ground ; the usual colour being very dark brown or black. As to the origin of the alpaca, the old view of the vicugna being the parent stock is untenable, and the guanaco is the true ancestor. Mr. Oldfield Thomas observes that the size of the alpaca, " although less than that of the llama, is far greater than that of the vicugna ; its skull and teeth agree with those of the former, and the naked patches on the legs, so distinctive of the guanaco as compared with the vicugna, are very often, although not always, present, the exceptions being easily explainable in the case of an animal bred and selected for generations solely with an eye to the thickness and extent of its furry covering. The occasional growth of the fur over the naked patches is not therefore to be wondered at. The probabilities also are much in favour of the Peruvians having domesticated one wild species rather than two, and of their having gradually developed two races out of it—the one large, strong, and suitable for the carriage of burdens, and the other smaller in size, but exceptional in its capacity for producing a quantity of wool."

Alpacas are kept throughout the year in large herds on the high plateaus of Bolivia and Southern Peru, and only driven down to the villages at the shearing season. The wool is of two kinds—a longer and coarser, and a finer and shorter ; the former being termed by the Peruvians *hanaska*, and the latter *kumbi*.

The Incas dyed both kinds with bright and lasting colours, and wove them into cloth and blankets. Alpaca wool was introduced into England, but it was not till 1836 that, owing to the enterprise of Sir Titus Salt, it became commercially available. It was first manufactured into cloth in his factory at Bradford, and afterwards in the great mills which he built at Saltaire.

Attempts have been made to acclimatise the alpaca in Europe and Australia. A large herd was imported by the thirteenth Earl of Derby, and established at Knowsley, and it was thought that these animals might be successfully introduced into the highlands of Scotland, but if the attempt was ever made, it had no permanent results. In Australia three hundred head were introduced, but

ALPACAS

in five years they had dwindled to a dozen, and the experiment does not appear to have been repeated. Probably one of the great difficulties in successfully introducing llamas into other countries is to find a locality where they can be left almost to themselves, and yet where they will be safe. The climate of Britain is too damp, and in this respect parts of Australia would be much more suitable.

The alpaca goes with young eleven months, and produces but one at a birth. Its flesh is as excellent as that of the llama.

EXTINCT CAMEL-LIKE UNGULATES

As already mentioned, extinct camels occur in Europe, India, and Northern Africa, while fossil species of llamas—some as large as camels—are found in Eastern South America. In addition to these, the Pliocene and Miocene formations of the United States have yielded remains of a number of species of extinct genera of camel-like ungulates, from which both camels and llamas have probably been derived ; and as no such forms have hitherto been discovered in Europe, North America may be regarded as the original home of the family, from which the ancestor of the modern representatives of the group migrated southwards across the Isthmus of Darien, and westwards by way of what is now Bering Strait into Asia. In the older Tertiary formations of Patagonia the group is unknown.

Some of these North American extinct camels, such as *Procamelus*, were not unlike existing members of the family, but had four premolar teeth in each jaw. In the Miocene are found still more generalised forms, having the typical number of forty-four teeth—that is, with three pairs of incisors in each jaw—while one kind (*Poëbrotherium*), no larger than a fox, had the main metacarpal and metatarsal bones of the feet separate, and showed traces of the bones of the lateral toes. From this form a transition can be traced to others with four complete toes, and molar teeth surmounted with simple cones instead of crescents.

Camels and llamas were, therefore, derived from primitive ungulates quite independently of the true ruminants. Not improbably a number of extinct Tertiary North American ungulates, such as the so-called oreodonts (*Merycoidodon*) belonged to the camel stock, which was then the dominant artiodactyle type in the Western Hemisphere, as were hollow-horned ruminants, deer, and chevrotains in the Eastern. One of the American Tertiary camels (*Alticamelus*) rivalled the giraffe in proportions and stature.

THE PIG TRIBE

ALL the ungulates hitherto described are characterised by their power of ruminating, with which are associated crescent-like, or selenodont, molar teeth, and, with one exception, the presence of a cannon bone in the limbs. There are, however, generalised representatives of the even-toed group of ungulates, such as pigs and hippopotamuses, which lack the power of rumination, and have molar teeth and limbs of a different structure.

At the present day there is a great gap between the types with crescent-like molars and the pig-like ungulates ; a gap so wide that earlier naturalists failed to recognise the relation that really exists between the two. This gap is, however, bridged over by a number of extinct ungulates.

In the upper molar of a modern ruminant the crown is surmounted by four crescentic columns of considerable height, and separated by deep pocket-like pits, while in the corresponding tooth of many extinct ungulates the same columns, although still crescent-like, are much lower, and separated by quite shallow valleys, of which the base is visible from the surface.

From such a tooth there is but a step to the tooth of *Anoplotherium*, in which, however, the front inner column of the ruminant molar is divided into two moieties, so that the tooth becomes five-columned. The *Anoplotherium* was a two or three toed ungulate from the Oligocene rocks of Europe, furnished with the full number of forty-four teeth. The columns of the tooth in *Ancodus*, although low, have an imperfect crescentic shape, but in the more pig-like genus known as *Anthracotherium* of the same horizon this structure is far less apparent, and the columns assume the form of flattened cones. From such a tooth the transition is easy to the type of tooth in the extinct pig known as *Hyotherium*, in which each tooth carried four low, conical, hillock-like columns, or tubercles.

From the hillock-like form of the columns the type of tooth found in the pigs is known as the bunodont (from Gr. *bounos*, a hillock), in contradistinction to the selenodont (Gr. *selene*, the crescent moon) form distinctive of all ruminating ungulates. This essential difference in the structure of their molar teeth is the most readily recognised characteristic by which pig-like ungulates are distinguished from all those already treated ; but from the transition between one type and the other indicated by extinct forms, it is clear that true ruminants, chevrotains, and camels are severally descended from bunodont ancestors.

Pigs and their allies are further distinguished from true ruminants and camels by the metacarpal and metatarsal bones of the two main toes of the feet remaining distinct instead of being fused into a cannon bone, while in the fore limb at least the lateral toes are likewise furnished with complete supporting bones. In these respects the pigs

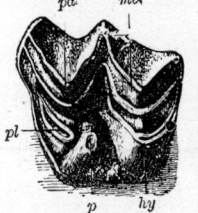
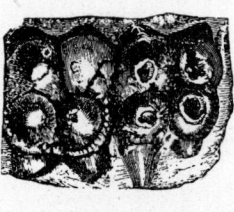

Anoplotherium   Hyotherium
LEFT UPPER MOLAR TEETH

are, however, approached by the water chevrotain ; and they also resemble all chevrotains in having a conical process on the front of the second vertebra of the neck for articulation with the first of that series.

All members of the pig-like group—technically known as Suina—have front or incisor teeth in their upper jaws, and their lower tusks are quite unlike, and distinct from, the incisors. Further, in correlation with the absence of the power of rumination, the stomach is less complex than that of ruminants, and may be perfectly simple and comprise only a single chamber. Pig-like animals existed at a date when ruminants were unknown.

Existing pig-like ungulates are generally divided into the three families of pigs, peccaries, and hippopotamuses.

Pigs, or swine (family *Suidæ*), are distinguished from other members of the group to which they belong by the following characters. The head and skull are greatly elongated, and the muzzle terminates in an abruptly truncated mobile snout, with a disc-like naked surface at the extremity, in which are situated the nostrils ; the disc being supported by an additional separate bone at the extremity of the skull. The feet are narrow, and carry four completely-developed toes, of which the hindmost do not touch the ground in walking, while the adjacent surfaces of the main pair are flattened.

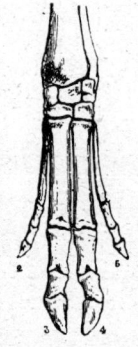

BONES OF LEFT FORE FOOT OF PIG

The molar teeth are narrow, the last one in both upper and lower jaws being more or less elongated ; and the large tusks grow continuously throughout life, those of the upper jaw curving upwards, instead of pointing downwards after the usual fashion. Swine have large flapping ears, and rather long cylindrical tails, with a tuft at the end. Their bodies are more or less sparsely clothed with bristly hairs, and their stomachs are quite simple. Like all unspecialised ungulates, they have the neck short, thick, and imperfectly differentiated from the body and the head, the latter being consequently carried low. The whole of the existing members of the family are restricted to the Old World, and chiefly frequent damp or swampy districts where they are fond of wallowing in wet mud.

EUROPEAN WILD BOAR

The typical representatives of the pig family, such as the European wild boar, are characterised by having forty-four teeth, among which the last molar in each jaw is greatly elongated, while the thick and short upper tusk is turned sharply upwards, and has a large smooth facet worn on the

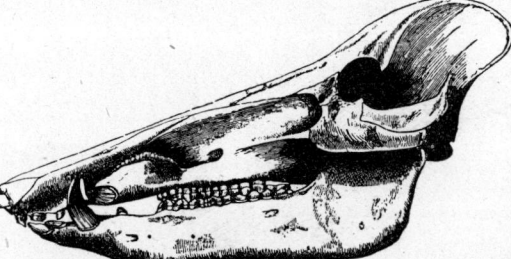

SKULL OF THE BEARDED PIG

outer side of its upturned extremity by the abrasion of the inner surface of the extremity of the lower tusk. Consequently, if either tusk happens to be broken, the opposing one continues to grow indefinitely, and, from its curved form, generally pierces some portion of the skull with its tip, thus ultimately leading to the death of the animal which has met with an accident of this nature.

In addition to the bristly hairs, there is generally a more or less developed woolly under fur. The skull of pigs, besides the presence of the additional bone in the snout already mentioned, is remarkable for the great length of the nasal bones, and the high elevation of the crest of the occiput. In wild pigs the profile of the face is straight, although in most domesticated breeds more or less concave. Pigs are exceedingly prolific, and the young of all the wild species of the typical genus are marked with light longitudinal stripes, although these markings are very rarely developed in domesticated breeds.

The distributional area of the genus, before it was curtailed by human agency, was extensive, comprising the greater part of Europe, Southern and a portion of Central Asia, Japan, the islands of the Malay region, and Northern Africa. Domesticated pigs have been turned loose in many parts of the world, such as America, the West Indies, and New Zealand, where they have given rise to descendants tending to revert more or less completely to the wild type, some even producing striped young.

Although some species are markedly distinct, pigs are a puzzling group, scarcely any two naturalists being in accord as to the number of existing species.

The type of the genus is the European wild boar (*Sus scrofa*), ranging over Europe, Northern Africa, and part of Western and Central Asia. In Asia it extends into Mesopotamia, Persia, Baluchistan, probably Afghanistan, Yarkand, and North-Western China. It was formerly abundant throughout the British Isles, as is attested not only by historical evidence, but by its remains in the peat mosses and fens; and boar hunting was a favourite pursuit of our ancestors. Although the exact date of the extermination of the species in the British Isles is unknown, wild boars existed in Oxfordshire in 1339, in Suffolk in 1572, and in Chartley Forest, Staffordshire, so late as 1593; and it is probable that in Scotland, and perhaps in Ireland also, they may have lingered still later. In many parts of the Continent, and especially in the Black Forest, they are still abundant (page 833).

EUROPEAN WILD SWINE

mane, of long black bristles running from the nape of the neck along the back, and by the rather more complex structure and larger size of the last molar tooth in each jaw. The usual height of the Indian wild boar varies from 30 to 40 inches at the shoulder, but it is stated that a specimen has been killed standing upwards of 43½ inches; while the weight ranges from 200 to considerably over 300 pounds. When extracted from the jaw, the lower tusk of a fine boar usually measures about 8 or 9 inches in length, but specimens of 9¼ and 10 inches have been recorded. The Indian wild boar is found in suitable spots throughout India, Ceylon, and Burma, and also in the wooded districts of the outer Himalaya, extending into the interior as far as Kashmir.

Wild pigs frequent moist or marshy situations, where there is plenty of covert, their great characteristic being the habit of turning up the ground with their snouts in search of food, leaving marks by which their presence in a district can be instantly recognised. It is this habit which renders them so specially obnoxious to the cultivator. During the day the Indian wild boar makes its lair in any convenient covert, in tall grass, in reeds, or sugar-cane or in bushes or forest, while not infrequently standing crops other than sugar-cane afford the necessary shelter. In the mornings and evenings these swine wander forth in search of food, in cultivated districts devastating the crops, but away from human haunts depending chiefly upon roots, those of a kind of sedge being particular favourites.

Wild pigs will readily feed on the carcases of animals and other carrion, and in Assam they are stated to be in the habit of digging out fish which bury themselves in the mud during the dry season. They are less nocturnal in their habits in remote districts than in those where they are much disturbed. While the females and young associate in droves or "sounders," usually comprising from ten to a dozen head, and rarely exceeding twenty, old boars are solitary. The number of young produced at a birth by the European species varies from six to ten, after a gestation of four months; and frequently two litters are produced in a year.

The lower tusks of the wild boar, which project about three inches from the jaw, and are kept with edges as sharp as razors by wear against those of the upper jaw, are most formidable weapons, capable of ripping open a horse at a single stroke. Like the European, the Indian species is among the boldest and fiercest of all animals, charging men, horses, or elephants time after

INDIAN WILD BOAR

The Indian wild boar (*S. cristatus*) is closely allied to its European cousin, but somewhat taller, with a thinner coat of hair and no under fur; and it is more especially distinguished by the presence of a crest, or

time without a moment's hesitation, and in spite of the most desperate wounds. Indeed, the injuries that a wild boar will sustain without loss of life are perfectly marvellous. A correspondent of the "Asian" newspaper related that he once killed an old boar, in the skull of which the broken extremity of the tusk of another boar was firmly embedded, with its point penetrating into the brain cavity a short distance behind the left eye.

Although the speed of a wild pig is considerable, yet it cannot be maintained for a long distance, and accordingly either a boar or a sow may be easily overtaken by a well-mounted horseman after a comparatively short run. Both as regards speed and inclination to fight, however, there is considerable local variation among the wild pigs of India; the large, heavily-built animal found in Bengal being much more disposed to show fight than the lighter pig of the Punjab, which has a greater turn of speed.

In spite of its boldness, the Indian wild boar seldom makes unprovoked attacks; but when once roused nothing will stop it. An instance is on record of a boar charging, overthrowing, and ripping open a camel; and there are several well-authenticated cases of boars having attacked and killed, or beaten off, tigers.

DOMESTICATED SWINE

Much discussion has taken place as to the origin of the numerous domesticated breeds of swine, and very diverse views have been expressed by different writers; some urging that certain of the earlier races found in Europe had an Eastern origin, while others regard the whole of them as descended directly from the European wild boar. The earliest evidence of the existence of domesticated swine in Europe is afforded by remains found on the sites of the prehistoric lake-dwellings of Switzerland. These were regarded by Professor Rütimeyer as indicating two quite distinct breeds—one nearly allied to the European wild boar, and the other more resembling some of the Asiatic kinds.

Professor George Rolleston failed, however, to detect evidence of Asiatic affinity in any of the prehistoric swine of Europe, and accordingly came to the conclusion that they were all probably derived from the European wild species, although there might have been some crossing with an Asiatic stock. It must be confessed that this view is, at first sight, the more probable; and that the original domesticated races of different parts of the world have been derived from the wild species inhabiting the same districts. This is the opinion of Dr. W. T. Blanford, who states that the tame pig of India is derived from the wild boar of the country, with which it probably interbreeds. In modern times, however, there has certainly been a great amount of intercrossing between the various breeds of domesticated swine; and many of the races now most esteemed in Europe have a large proportion of Asiatic blood in their veins.

The effects of domestication have been very marked in the swine, although the degree of variation from the wild type depends largely upon the amount of care that has been bestowed upon the breed. The European domesticated breeds differ from all wild species by the concave profile of the face; while as a rule domesticated races have uniformly-coloured young. Indeed, whenever the young of domesticated swine are striped, a recent crossing with a wild race may reasonably be suspected. When domesticated pigs revert to a wild condition, this striping is, however, frequently resumed.

Domestication invariably greatly reduces the size of the tusks of the boars, which in some breeds are very small indeed; and in this respect we have a reversion to extinct species of swine, in the earlier forms of which the tusks were only slightly developed. There are also modifications in the form of the hinder part of the skull, in the number of joints in the backbone, and in the length of the intestines. Equally marked differences obtain in the shape of the ears, which in some of the inferior breeds are large, flapping, and pendent, while in the superior breeds they are small and erect.

As regards bodily form, we have but to contrast the long-legged, large-headed, and thin-bodied "grey-hound pig" of Ireland with some of the best modern breeds to see how enormous is the difference in this respect.

INDIAN WILD SWINE ON THE HILLS OF JAIPUR
Photo, H. C. White Co.

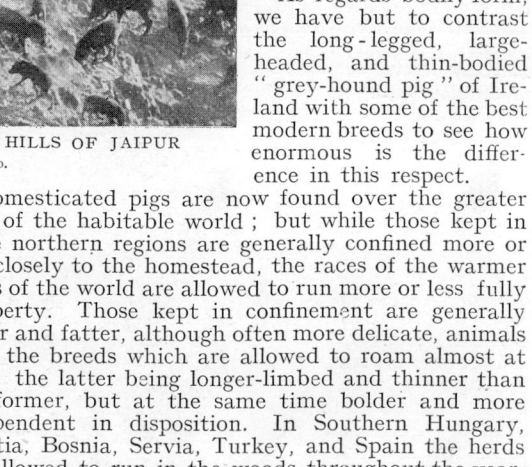

Domesticated pigs are now found over the greater part of the habitable world; but while those kept in more northern regions are generally confined more or less closely to the homestead, the races of the warmer parts of the world are allowed to run more or less fully at liberty. Those kept in confinement are generally larger and fatter, although often more delicate, animals than the breeds which are allowed to roam almost at will; the latter being longer-limbed and thinner than the former, but at the same time bolder and more independent in disposition. In Southern Hungary, Croatia, Bosnia, Servia, Turkey, and Spain the herds are allowed to run in the woods throughout the year, but in less warm districts they have to be taken in and fed during the winter. In the Sierra Nevada of Spain these herds ascend to an elevation of some nine thousand feet above the sea, and thus become expert climbers.

Of the curious Japanese masked pig, Darwin writes that it "has an extraordinary appearance, from its short head, broad forehead and nose, great fleshy ears, and deeply-furrowed skin. Not only is the face furrowed, but thick folds of skin, which are harder than the other parts, almost like the plates on the Indian rhinoceros, hang about the shoulders and rump. It is coloured black, with white feet, and breeds true. That it has long been domesticated there can be little doubt; and this might have been inferred even from the circumstance that its young are not longitudinally striped." From a study of its skull, Professor Nathusius regarded the masked pig as nearly allied to the Chinese breed ; but, as Darwin remarks, " if this be really the case, it is a wonderful instance of the amount of modification which can be effected under domestication."

R. LYDEKKER

BRITISH DOMESTICATED PIGS

At the present time pigs are found in greater or smaller numbers on most farms in the United Kingdom, and they further act in the useful capacity of tenants to the sty attached to the majority of cottages. In such positions they are particularly valuable for utilising with profit the waste products of the dairy, field and garden. When refuse of this sort is available, or scraps from the house and kitchen are forthcoming, a pig can be economically fattened, either for market or home consumption, with a very small addition of purchased food in the form of meal. Again, as a meat producer, in proportion to the amount of food consumed, the hog—with the exception of the milk-fed calf—far surpasses all other domesticated animals.

In fact, the pig has been called " the most economical meat-making machine in the hands of the British farmer." And this is all the more evident when it is remembered that one hundredweight of digestible food will produce at least twice as much pork as it will beef or mutton.

The original type of pig found in Great Britain was a huge, gaunt, roach-backed, long-legged, slow-growing brute much resembling its ancestor the wild boar, and the gradual development to the neat, compact, flesh-producing animal of to-day has necessarily been slow. The present breeds of swine of the United Kingdom have been improved chiefly by crosses made with foreign and native breeds, and by greater care being exercised in the methods of management and feeding. This crossing with foreign breeds, especially the Chinese pig (*Sus indicus*), was principally carried out during the first half of the nineteenth century.

As is well known, certain parts of the carcase of a pig are more valuable for purposes of sale than others. It should, therefore, be the breeder's object to raise an animal that has these parts best developed.

The type of pig now required for purposes of feeding for bacon and in demand by the bacon curer may be described as follows : The head and neck should be light and the shoulder free from coarseness, as these parts do not command so high a price. The body should be long and deep with well-sprung ribs, giving a wide back and loin capable of being well packed with flesh, as here the valuable cuts are situated, and a good side of bacon is a primary object. The thighs should be thick, the legs short, and the hair long and silky.

Sufficient depth in the region of the heart is also desirable, as it shows a good constitution, Further, the bone below the knee and hock (cannon)

should be fine, as this indicates lightness of offal and a tendency to the development of lean meat.

PRINCIPAL BREEDS OF PIGS

In selecting a breed of pigs for any particular district the question of colour must be taken into consideration, as, owing to local prejudice, white pigs are favoured in some markets and black in others. If a farmer, therefore, breeds pigs of a colour not in fashion in his neighbourhood he may suffer considerably as regards the price obtained should he wish to sell in the local market. The colour, however, has nothing whatever to do with the thriving properties of the animal.

WHITE BREEDS

LARGE WHITE YORKSHIRE. The large white Yorkshire is one of the best breeds of pigs, and is particularly well suited to the requirements of the farmer, and highly prized by bacon curers. It is large in size without being coarse, the proportion of offal produced is small, and the meat is sufficiently lean for modern requirements. It is handsome and symmetrical in appearance, comes early to maturity, is very prolific, and may be used for purposes of either pork or bacon. It is hardy in constitution, of a good disposition, and the sow is an excellent mother.

The colour should be white and free from black hairs ; the head moderately long and wide between the ears ; and the body should be long, level, wide and deep, with broad loin and well-developed hams.

MIDDLE WHITE YORKSHIRE. This breed, which originated by a cross between the small and large white, takes after the latter in appearance, but is not so long and the body rather more compact. The head also is shorter, the face more dished, and the snout somewhat turned up ; the ears are more upright, the legs shorter, and there is a greater abundance of fine, soft hair. Further, these pigs do not produce such a good proportion of lean meat as the large white, and are, therefore, not so profitable to the farmer as bacon producers. In these circumstances they are rather better suited for the production of pork than bacon, and consequently there is a demand for middle white boars for crossing purposes by breeders who aim at producing pork for the market.

A MIDDLE WHITE SOW   Photo, Vinton.

SMALL WHITE YORKSHIRE. These pigs are now very little bred in the United Kingdom, except in a few special cases where a market exists for small pork. For their symmetry of form, quick-feeding properties, and smallness of offal they may be taken as an excellent example of the skill of the breeder. They are somewhat delicate in constitution, and care has to be exercised in feeding, as they tend to lay on excessive quantities of fat in proportion to lean meat, appearing at some of the fat-stock shows as mere balls of lard. They cannot, therefore, be looked on as a farmers' pig for general utility purposes. The special characters are a pure white colour, head very short and dished, with broad and turned up snout and heavy jowl ; ears pricked, and body broad, deep and compact.

LINCOLNSHIRE CURLY-COATED. This is a large-sized, white-coloured local breed from the east coast of Lincolnshire. The face is shorter than that of the large Yorkshire, and there is an abundance of long curly hair when the coat is fully grown. The ears are pendent and not pricked like those of the Yorkshire. It is claimed for the breed that it is hardy, prolific, of good disposition, and feeds quickly, producing equally good pork and bacon.

COLOURED BREEDS

BERKSHIRE. The Berkshire is one of the best-known breeds, and very popular in England and abroad.

A SMALL WHITE BOAR   Photo, Vinton

Owing to the care bestowed upon it by the early breeders and its many excellent qualities, it was at one time considered the most important of the pure breeds, and was much used for crossing purposes. During recent years, however, the tendency has been to breed more on fashionable than utility lines. The colour is black with a white blaze on the face, white feet, and white tip to the tail. The head is neat with erect ears, and the object now is to get the face as short and well-dished as possible. The body should be broad and straight, with a wide, level back.

LARGE BLACKS. These pigs have been bred for a good many years in different parts of England. The outcome of the formation of the Large Black Pig Society at the end of the nineteenth century has resulted in the development of a bacon pig on similar lines to the large white, and killing to about eight scores dead weight when about seven to eight months old. It also has a quiet disposition, good constitution, feeds quickly, and is very prolific. It is black in colour, with a head of medium length and long, thin ears hanging well over the face. The body is long and level, well sprung in the rib, and capable of producing a good side of bacon.

TAMWORTH. This is of a reddish, or rusty, colour, and probably the oldest breed of pigs in England. It is hardy and prolific, and much in favour for purposes of home curing, as it yields a large side of lean bacon of excellent quality and flavour. The head is of a fair length, and the snout is long and straight, being quite in contrast to that of the small white or the modern type of Berkshire. The ears are rather large and erect, and carried slightly forward. The body is long and straight, the girth deep, and the loin wide. The skin is of a flesh colour, and covered with an abundance of long, straight, fine hair of a golden red, which gives the characteristic colour to the pig.

The principal objection to the Tamworth in the past has been its slowness in coming to maturity, but this fault is being remedied by care and selection.

CROSS-BRED PIGS

For ordinary feeding purposes a first cross between two pure breeds often produces a pig better adapted to provide a good carcase of bacon than the pure breeds themselves. When crossing, consideration must be taken as to the points of the respective breeds, and it is not wise as a rule to go beyond a first cross. The following crosses may be recommended as yielding first-rate types of bacon pigs: (a) Large Yorkshire boar and Berkshire sows; (b) Large Black boar and Berkshire sows. The first of these crosses is particularly favoured by bacon curers.

GENERAL MANAGEMENT

In starting to breed pigs great care must be taken in the selection of the breeding stock. A number of points should also be considered before determining upon the choice of variety. Thus, the kind of pigs generally kept in the district should be noted, and a study made of the requirements of the local market before a decision is finally come to. It is further necessary to have some ideal as to the type of pigs one wishes to breed, and to select the boar and sows accordingly.

It is best to choose a boar, if possible, from a good mother of prolific strain, and he should have an even temper and quiet disposition. Well-developed teats in the male are a good sign.

The young boar may be used when six to eight months old, and it is wise to mate him at first with fully-grown sows. He should be kept in ordinary store condition, and not be pampered. He must have plenty of exercise, and, treated with care, he ought to prove useful and last for a number of years.

His food should consist principally of sharps, or coarse bran mixed with barley meal, fed to him in two meals daily. A little corn in the shape of old peas, beans, or oats is useful, and may be given as a midday feed.

Young sows should be chosen with good points according to the variety, a quiet disposition, and not

A TAMWORTH BOAR   Photo, Vinton

less than twelve evenly-placed teats. Gilts may be put to the boar at from six to eight months old or upwards.

The period of gestation is 113 days, or sixteen weeks. Sows, therefore, if mated in October or April will farrow in February or August, which latter are generally considered good months for producing spring and autumn litters respectively.

Seven or eight pigs may be looked on as a sufficient number for a gilt to rear in her first litter, but the more pigs brought up under favourable conditions the better, as in the second litter those pigs which suck teats that have been sucked by the first litter obtain more milk and thrive better than others.

A gilt's capabilities may be judged by the way she rears and suckles her first litter, and the opinion thus formed will determine whether she should be bred from again or sent to the fattening pen.

A good disposition is a matter of great importance in a sow, as occasionally well-bred gilts of handsome appearance may be purchased which develop savage instincts when they come to farrow—not only objecting to the attendant who is watching their interests, but sometimes going so far as to destroy their own offspring. Some knowledge, therefore, of the mother and other ancestors of any young sow—especially as regards temper—will be a great advantage before effecting the purchase.

Some care is necessary in feeding the sow for the first few weeks after farrowing, and nothing is better for this purpose, if available, than well-soaked bran or sharps mixed with a little skim milk or buttermilk. If everything goes on satisfactorily, a small quantity of meal may be gradually added to the ration so as to assist the sow in producing an abundant flow of milk. The young pigs should be weaned at eight weeks old, the process being gradually performed between the seventh and eighth week.

FEEDING

A very common and erroneous idea often prevalent in the rural mind is that a pig can be kept and expected to thrive under the most unwholesome and insanitary conditions. They are, therefore, allowed to wallow in a filthy sty on a rotten accumulation of litter, which is seldom removed until the unfortunate pig has found its way to the butcher. The feeding is also performed in a haphazard and slovenly manner, accumulations of garbage being allowed to remain in the trough from one feeding-time to another. There can be no greater fallacy, and no wonder, under such conditions, pigs are often considered not only as unprofitable, but as an intolerable and unsavoury nuisance.

A LARGE BLACK SOW   Photo, Vinton.

Pigs, if given the opportunity, however, will be found most respectable animals, showing great intelligence in keeping themselves clean and attending to their personal comfort. Thus, if housed in a sty with an inner and outer court, they will be found to keep their bed in the inner-covered part clean, dry, and comfortable, and will deposit their excrement in a corner of the open yard. Sties should, therefore, be provided with hard floors, such as cement concrete set with a proper slope so as to allow for surface drainage, as sties of this description can be kept clean by brushing. A sufficient supply of clean, sweet straw

should also be available for the pig's bed in the inner court, and this should be changed periodically as soon as it shows signs of becoming soiled.

The feeding of these animals must be carried out in a cleanly and methodical manner, no more food being put into the trough at one time than the occupants of the sty will clear up before the next meal. Under these conditions, which necessitate little extra labour when systematically carried out, pigs will be found to be healthier, to thrive and grow better, and make a much larger return for the quantity of food given than when kept in a filthy and insanitary state.

As in the case of beef and mutton, the public taste

A BERKSHIRE BOAR   Photo, Vinton.

for pork has considerably altered. What is now required is a young carcase of sweet flesh suitable for consumption as fresh pork, or capable of being turned into sides of lean, mild-cured bacon. In these circumstances the old custom of feeding pigs up to two years old or more, and killing so as to produce huge carcases, largely composed of fat, has almost entirely died out.

The type of pig at present in most demand is one which will fatten quickly and be ready for the butcher at some seven or eight months old, when it should yield a carcase of from 160 to 170 pounds in weight. This is the kind of animal now sought after by the bacon curer, and to produce pigs of this stamp it is necessary to keep the animals going steadily on without a check from the time of weaning till they are fit to go out. The ancient custom of keeping a number of hungry stores hanging about the premises for many months on end, with the object of picking up a promiscuous living, has thus entirely gone out of date. The young pigs should, therefore, be run as rapidly growing stores till they are about five months old, and then be quickly finished off on a more concentrated ration, consisting largely of barley meal, in from eight to twelve weeks.

Two great points to pay attention to in the successful feeding of young pigs are cleanliness and warmth, and these factors are quite as important as the question of food. As the little pigs' stomachs are small, they should be fed four times a day immediately after weaning, and as they get stronger this may be reduced to three times daily. On no account must they be overfed at first, and a mixture of bran and sharps, with a little skim milk or wash, will be found a suitable diet. Care must be taken to avoid giving foods which have decidedly heating properties, such as wheat-meal and pea-meal, in any quantities to young pigs during the early stages of their existence; but meal may be gradually introduced, and increased by degrees as the fattening period advances. Experiment has clearly shown that as the weight of a pig advances, so does the amount of food required to produce a given increase; so the sooner a pig is fattened off the better prospect there is of leaving a margin of profit for the feeder.

It is necessary to say only a few words with regard to the cottager's pig. Here the object is not only to produce a wholesome carcase of meat for home consumption or sale, but also to turn to profitable account a lot of waste material from the garden and allotment, together with wash or scraps from the kitchen, and at the same time to produce a quantity of valuable manure for subsequent use.

In these circumstances the rapid fattening of the pig at the earliest possible moment is not the prime object

THE RED RIVER-HOG

of the labourer and small-holder, and feeding to somewhat heavier weights till from twelve to fourteen months old often suits his purpose better.

As to statistics, the pig trade is a fluctuating one, the total number of animals in the United Kingdom rising and falling every few years, and never exceeding some 4,500,000. The reason of this seems to be due to the fact that when good prices are obtainable in the home markets everyone starts breeding, and the price goes down, with a consequence that many of the breeding sows are then disposed of.

On the other hand, we find that pig products to the value of some £20,000,000 sterling are imported annually into the United Kingdom, which roughly represents 5,000,000 pigs per annum. These figures point to the fact that the home production is inadequate to the demand.

The question of whether a part of this great quantity of bacon could not be grown profitably at home turns on the possibility of running factories on sound business principles in various parts of the country. Private bacon factories yield large profits, and there seems no reason why these should not be established by farmers themselves, and conducted on co-operative lines with every prospect of success.

DRYSDALE TURNER

THE MALAY PIG

In both the European and Indian wild boar the upper or hind surface of the lower tusk, which has no enamel, inclines obliquely outwards, and is broader than the outer surface ; and the same feature occurs in the banded pig (*Sus vittatus*) of Sumatra, which takes its name from the presence of a broad reddish or whitish band running from the middle of the snout along the upper lips to disappear on the sides of the neck.

Varieties of this type are also met with in Java, Cochin China, and Formosa, the pig from the latter island having been named *S. taëvanus*. Near akin is the Japanese pig (*S. leucomystax*), and the small Andamanese *S. andamanensis*. Whether the New Guinea pigs (*S. papuensis* and *S. niger*) are really wild members of this group or modified descendants of European tame pigs is still doubtful, although the general character of the fauna of New Guinea supports the view that they were introduced.

A second group is typified by the warty pig (*S. verrucosus*) of Java, in which the hind or upper unenamelled surface of the lower tusk is narrower than the outer one, concave, and set nearly in the long axis of the skull. Unlike that of the banded pig, which is short, the skull is elongated, with comparatively simple and primitive cheek teeth, which are relatively short. There are also three small warts on each side of the face, the largest situated just below the eyes and carrying long bristles. The small *C. celebensis* of Celebes, and the Philippine *S. philippinensis*, are probably only varieties of this species. Very distinct, however, is the bearded pig (*S. barbatus*), of Borneo, distinguished by the great elongation of the head and skull, and the presence of a tuft of long hair near the muzzle.

In the island of Pulo Bultam, adjacent to the Malay Peninsula, occurs a closely allied pig which has been described as *S. oi*, and another member of the same group apparently is met with in the peninsula itself. From the inordinate length of the face, these remarkable pigs have a distinctly comical appearance.

THE PIGMY HOG

On account of its diminutive size a separate heading may be accorded to the pigmy hog (*Sus salvanius*) of the forests at the foot of the Himalaya in Bhutan, Sikkim, and Nepal. These tiny pigs are scarcely larger than hares, standing only about 11 inches at the shoulder. They are brown or blackish brown in colour, with small, naked ears, very short tails, and only three pairs of teats in the female instead of the usual six. From the little that is known of the habits of these pigs in the wild state, it appears that they live in herds of from five to twenty head in grass jungle, and that the old boars remain with the sows. Probably the number of young produced at a birth is less than in other pigs.

BUSH-PIGS

In Africa south of the Sahara the place of the European and Asiatic wild swine is taken by the bush-pig (*Potamochœrus chœropotamus*)—the boschyark of the Boers—which differs in having one pair fewer of cheek teeth, owing to the absence of the first premolar on each side of the lower jaw, while frequently the corresponding upper tooth is also wanting in the adult. The molar teeth are also distinguished by their simpler structure, the last in the lower jaw having the third lobe much reduced in size. The ears have tufts of long hair, the tusks are scarcely larger than those of domesticated pigs, and the snout is unusually elongated.

On each side of the face are two pairs of large swellings, due to the development of ridges of bone, the lower pair being placed on the sheaths of the upper tusks. The typical bush-pig, ranging from South to Central Africa, usually has the hair greyish brown, but in Nyasaland it is represented by a distinct race. It is specially characterised by the form of the swellings on the face. These pigs frequent thick forest, although occasionally found in thorny bush and among reeds in the river valleys.

These ingulabi, as they are called by the natives, do an immense amount of damage to the sweet potatoes and fields, and have in consequence been exterminated in many districts. Their habits appear to be very similar to those of ordinary swine.

The red bush-pig or red river-hog (*P. porcus*) is a West African species distinguished by the form of the skull ridges and by the brilliant reddish colour of the hair (page 834). As in the first species, the bristles of the neck, back, chin, and throat are elongated into a distinct mane, and the tail terminates in a small tuft. The prevailing colour is either shining brownish red with a tinge of yellow, or dark reddish yellow, but the forehead, ears, and limbs are blackish, while the mane on the back, part of the margins of the ears and the tips of their pencils of hair, the eyebrows, and a streak under the eyes and the margins of the cheeks are white or whitish ; the under parts being whitish grey, and the snout grey. These brilliant contrasts of colour make the red bush pig decidedly the handsomest member of the swine family.

These pigs are found in large herds, and frequent moist forests and the banks of rivers, while they are occasionally seen on the mountains. The first living example of this species brought to Europe was exhibited in the London Zoological Gardens in 1852, since which date many specimens have been imported into Europe. A third species, *P. hassama*, inhabits Abyssinia, and a fourth, *P. larvatus*, Madagascar.

Numerous fossil pigs are found in the Pliocene and Pleistocene Tertiary deposits of the Old World, several of which may be referred to the genus *Potamochœrus* ; these fossil pigs occurring in Europe, North Africa, India, and China. One of the most remarkable is the titan pig (*P. titan*) from the Siwalik Hills, at the foot of the Himalaya, in which the length of the skull is 23 inches, against 16 in an average-sized Indian wild pig, so that the height of the animal could not have been much less than that of a fair-sized mule. The same deposits have also yielded remains of an extinct species which did not exceed the living pigmy hog in point of size.

Still more noteworthy are Falconer's pig (*P. falconeri*) from the Siwalik Hills, and some allied species from the Pleistocene deposits of Southern India and Algeria, which in the extreme complexity of the lower teeth approximated to the wart hogs. The Auvergne pig (*Sus arvernensis*), from the Pliocene of France, is believed, on the other hand, to be related to the typical pigs. In most of these extinct species the tusks of the boars, as already mentioned, were relatively small. The fossil bush-pigs afford another instance of the occurrence of modern African types in India during the Tertiary period.

BABIRUSAS

The extraordinary development of the tusks in the males of the animals to which the Malays have given the name of babirusa (meaning " pig deer ") is so

THE CELEBES BABIRUSAS

remarkable as to suggest at first sight the idea of a malformation. Babirusas, of which there are two species, are inhabitants of Celebes and the neighbouring island of Boru, and take their name from these abnormally developed tusks, which have led the Malays to liken them to the antlers of the deer. In the boars the long and slender upper tusks, although curving upwards like those of an ordinary wild pig, instead of

H

protruding from the margins of the jaws, arise close together near the middle line of the face, and thence, after being directed upwards for a short distance, sweep backwards, frequently coming into contact with the surface of the forehead, and are then finally directed forwards at the tips. The lower tusks have the same upwards and backwards direction as those of the upper jaw, but are frequently less strongly curved, although in other cases the direction of their sweep is not very different from that of the latter. Both pairs of tusks are devoid of enamel, and, as there is no abrasion of the one pair against the other, both grow uninterruptedly; the upper tusks occasionally attaining a length of 14½ inches, exclusive of the portion buried in the socket.

In addition to the peculiar conformation of its tusks, babirusas differ from ordinary pigs in the diminished number of teeth, of which the total is only thirty-four; the missing teeth comprising the outermost incisors and the first two premolars on each side of both the upper and lower jaws. The molar teeth are characterised by their simple structure and the small development of the third lobe of the last one in each jaw.

The Celebes *Babirusa celebensis* has a nearly naked skin of dark ashy grey colour, sparsely covered with hair along the line of the back, and thrown into numerous wrinkles. The ears are small, the tail is short and devoid of a terminal tuft, and the back is much arched. The female has small tusks, and only a single pair of teats. The height at the middle of the back is about 42 inches. The young, of which there are either one or two at a birth, are devoid of stripes. The Boru species, *Babirusa alfurus*, is a much more hairy and greyer animal.

The peculiar character of the tusks, the reduction in the number of the teeth, and the uniform colour of the young, indicate that babirusas are more specialised than ordinary pigs. At the same time, the simple structure of the molar teeth suggests that they are directly descended from one of the extinct genera of pigs in which a similar type of dentition obtains.

In habits babirusas seem to be very similar to other wild swine; moist forests, cane-brakes, and the banks of rivers and lakes where abundance of water plants are to be found, being their favourite resorts. Here these swine collect in larger or smaller herds, sleeping by day and going forth to feed at night. Babirusas are excellent swimmers, not only entering lakes to feed on water plants, but also traversing small channels of the sea separating one island from another. Their gallop is lighter than that of the wild boar, the senses of smell and hearing are very acute, and the grunt is very similar to that of other swine. The young, which are born in February, are of very small size, and require great attention on the part of the sow. Much discussion has arisen as to the use of the

THE FOREST HOG

tusks of the male babirusa. It has been suggested that they may be for the purpose of protecting the eyes when the animal is rushing through dense forest; but if this were so, how are we to account for the slight development of these organs in the sows? On the whole, Dr. A. R. Wallace considers it probable that the tusks were at one period useful to their owner, and were then kept of moderate size by wearing against one another, but that, for some reason, they have become of no benefit to the animal, and have assumed a monstrous growth like that occurring in the lower tusk of a wild boar when the corresponding upper one has been accidentally broken off.

FOREST HOG

Not long after the discovery of the okapi, evidence was obtained of the existence of another previously unknown large mammal in the great African equatorial forest, and the genus *Hylochœrus* was established in 1904, on the evidence of specimens brought home from the East African Nandi Forest by Mr. R. Meinertzhagen, after whom the species was named *H. meinertzhageni*. These huge hairy black swine are related to the wart-hogs, but have a less specialised type of skull and teeth, and thus serve in some degree to connect the latter with the bush-pigs, with which they agree in their abundant coat of hair.

Although much smaller, the tusks have the curvature of those of the wart-hogs, and there is a similar reduction of the upper incisor teeth to a single pair. The face carries a pair of great warty growths, not unlike funguses. The Nandi Forest and the Kenia district are the home of the typical race of these enormous swine; but a second race occurs in the Ituri Forest of East Central Africa, and a third in the Cameruns.

WART-HOG

As Africa possesses in the red river-hog the handsomest representative of the swine family, so in the wart-hog (*Phacochœrus œthiopicus*) it is also the home of the most hideous member, not only of that group, but of the whole ungulate order.

The wart-hog is characterised by the enormous size of the head, in which the lower part of the face is extremely flat and broad, with a huge warty protuberance below each eye, between this and the tusk being two other warts of smaller size. The head is also distinguished by the great length of the muzzle, and the consequent backward position of the eyes; while the hideous physiognomy is completed by the huge tusks with which the jaws of both sexes are armed, those of the upper jaw being considerably longer than those of the lower, or just the reverse of what occurs in the true pigs.

This difference in the proportionate length of the upper and lower tusks in the two groups is due to the fact that in the wart-hogs the lower pair only bite against the inferior surface of the upper ones, instead of wearing away their whole summits. The upper tusks are devoid of enamel except at their tips, and these small caps are worn away at an early period. They curve in an upward and inward direction, and sometimes project as much as $8\frac{3}{4}$ inches from the jaw, having a basal girth of 5 inches. The shorter and more slender lower tusks have a nearly similar curvature, and are coated throughout with enamel.

The tusks are not the only peculiarity in the dentition of the wart-hogs. In young animals there are thirty-four teeth—namely one pair of upper and three pairs of lower incisors, a pair of tusks in each jaw, and six cheek teeth on each side of the upper, and five in the lower jaw. In the adult, however, the incisors and anterior cheek teeth tend to disappear, till in some instances the tusks and the last molars alone remain, thus leaving a total of eight teeth; this paucity in the number of cheek teeth being compensated by the enormous size and complex structure of the single molar remaining in each jaw. This tooth is composed of a number of small elongated cylindrical denticules, closely packed together; its total length from back to front being something over 2 inches, and its height proportionately great, although its width is small. This is, however, only an extreme development of the structure already referred to as occurring in certain extinct species of bush-pigs; and, in possessing such a single tooth on each side of the jaws in the adult condition, the wart-hog may be compared to the elephant.

The body is massive and nearly cylindrical, the ears are small and sharply-pointed, the tail is long and tufted at the tip, and the neck and back are furnished with a

MALE WART-HOG

mane of long bristly hair, the rest of the body being nearly naked. The young are uniformly coloured.

The wart-hog is typically an inhabitant of South-Eastern Africa, but is represented in Abyssinia by a local race, *P. a. africanus*. The normal height is about $27\frac{1}{2}$ inches at the shoulder.

Accounts of the habits of the wart-hogs are not so full as might be desired, and there is some discrepancy between those given by different observers; the statement made by the Austrian naturalist Von Heuglin that these animals habitually repose on swampy ground, or even in water, not being borne out by later writers. The northern race is found everywhere in Abyssinia, from the level of the sea at Annesley Bay to heights of 9,000 or 10,000 feet in the highlands of the interior.

In South-Eastern Africa — where they are known to the natives by the name of indhlovudawani— wart-hogs are found on the plains in light thorn jungles; and they are abundant in the districts around Mount Kilimanjaro. In these regions they generally occupy the deserted burrow of an aard-vark, or other animal. The Hon. W. H. Drummond states that wart-hogs occupying such burrows "have a most curious mode of exit when they bolt—a dangerous one if you are not up to it. As they emerge from a hole, they turn a somersault on to the back of it, instead of coming straight out like an ordinary animal, and as that is just the spot where one would naturally stand, more than one man has had his legs ripped open before he learnt the wisdom of experience."

As the number of teats in the female is only four, it may be inferred that few young are produced at a birth.

PECCARIES

THE peccaries of America differ so markedly from Old World swine that they are regarded by many naturalists as representing a separate family, *Dicotylidæ*, although by others they are classed as a sub-family of the *Suidæ*. The most important differences between the two groups are that the upper tusks of the peccaries have their points directed downwards instead of upwards, that their hind limbs have three instead of four toes, while instead of the simple stomach of the Old World swine, the peccaries have a complex one approaching that of the ruminants.

Peccaries have a total of thirty-eight teeth, that is to say, a pair of incisors in the upper jaw, and a premolar on each side of both jaws less than the wild boar. The downwardly directed upper tusks, which are at first completely covered with enamel, are of small size, with sharp cutting edges behind; while those of the lower jaw are directed upwards, outwards, and slightly backwards, and are received in notches in the sides of the opposite jaw just in front of the upper tusks. The last molar tooth in each jaw lacks the hind lobe characteristic of the Old World swine, and the fourth

premolar tooth in the upper jaw resembles the first molar in having four tubercles on its crown, instead of only three.

In addition to the difference in the number of toes in the hind feet, peccaries are further distinguished by the upper ends of the two larger metacarpal and metatarsal bones being united, so as to make an approach to the formation of cannon bones. In this respect, as well as in the complex structure of the stomachs, and the presence of four tubercles on the last upper premolar teeth, peccaries are one step in advance of their allies of the Old World.

A unique feature in these animals is the presence of a large gland in the middle of the back, from which is secreted in abundance an evil-smelling oily substance. In appearance, peccaries are not unlike small hogs, but with very slender limbs; they are devoid of externally visible tails, and their snouts are much elongated and extremely mobile. The ears are small and pointed; and the body is covered with thick bristle-like hairs, elongated into a mane on the neck, and forming a fringe on the throat and hind quarters. The young are uniformly-coloured, like their parents, and never exceed two in number at a birth.

Of the two best-known species, the collared peccary (*Dicotyles tajacu*) is the smaller, and ranges from Arkansas and Mexico to the Rio Negro in Patagonia. This species stands from about 13½ to 15½ inches in height at the shoulder. The bristly hairs are parti-coloured, and the hue of the coat is blackish brown, becoming yellowish brown mingled with white on the flanks. The under parts are brown, and the upper portion of the chest is white, while a broad yellowish white stripe runs from the hind part of the shoulders obliquely downwards to the chest.

In Texas it is represented by an allied species, *D. angulatus*, extending into Arizona, North-Eastern Mexico, Sonora, and Yucatan, of which several local races have been named; and other species, or races, have been described from Central America and Colombia.

The white-lipped peccary (*D. albirostris*) is a very distinct species, rather larger than the collared peccary, its height at the shoulder varying from 15½ to nearly 18 inches. It is distinguished by the presence of a large white spot on the lower jaw, and the white lips, the colour of the hair being greyish black. There is also a difference in the mane and fringes on the neck of the two species. The range of the white-lipped peccary includes the region lying between British Honduras, Paraguay, and Argentina.

Peccaries are forest-dwelling animals, but while the collared species are found only singly or in pairs, or in small parties of from eight to ten, the white-lipped peccary associates in large herds.

Both species frequent the densest and most extensive forests, dwelling in the hollows of trees, or in burrows excavated by other animals, or among bushes and grass.

Peccaries wander about both by day and night, and when it is scarce make long migrations in search of food. Their chief food consists of fruits and roots; and their teeth and jaws are of such strength as to enable them to crack with ease the hard seeds of palms. In inhabited districts peccaries inflict much damage on growing crops, and vary their diet with carrion, worms, or insects.

Fossil remains of peccaries occur in the Upper Tertiary deposits of

COLLARED PECCARIES

both North and South America, many of the northern ones being referred to the extinct genus *Platygonus*.

Certain extinct Pliocene and Miocene hog-like animals seem to indicate the parent stock from which both peccaries and true pigs have been derived. Of these *Chærohyus*, from North America, comes closest to the peccaries, while the Old World *Hyotherium* is more like the pigs. *Listriodon* is another European type, in which the molars have a pair of transverse ridges instead of four tubercles. None of these was unusually large, but the genus *Entelodon*, which is common to the Miocene and Oligocene strata of Europe and North America, includes pig-like animals nearly as large as a hippopotamus. For another huge pig-like animal allied to Entelodon from the Loup Fork beds of Nebraska the name *Dinochærus hollandi* has been suggested. The chief grounds for the generic separation of this species appear to be the geological horizon and the immense proportions of the animal, of which the skull measures no fewer than 35 inches in length. It is perhaps allied to the imperfectly known *Tetraconodon* of the Indian Siwaliks.

Finally, *Chæropotamus*, from the upper Eocene of Europe, connects the type of molar tooth characteristic of the pigs with that of the *Anthracothere*.

HIPPOPOTAMUSES

ALTHOUGH the Greek term "hippopotamus" and its English equivalent "river-horse" are etymologically objectionable ones to denote the animals now claiming consideration, yet the former is so firmly established in European languages that it would be impossible to change it. The Dutch term "see-kuh," commonly translated "sea-cow," but which might equally bear the interpretation "lake-cow," and a name used by the Arabs which means "water-buffalo," are far less objectionable; but a title equivalent to "river-swine," which is said to have been conferred on these animals by the ancient Egyptians, is, from a zoological standpoint, the best.

The common hippopotamus (pages 86, 883) and a much smaller species from West Africa typify by themselves a family (*Hippopotamidæ*), which is also the last group of the even-toed ungulates. Hippopotamuses are bulky animals, with round, barrel-like bodies of great length, short and thick legs, and enormous heads, in which the muzzle is angular and greatly expanded transversely, and has no trace of the terminal disc characteristic of swine and peccaries. Indeed, the ugly head appears as if it were too large and heavy for its owner, since the animal may frequently be seen resting its muzzle on the ground, as though to relieve the neck from the strain of its weight. The portion of the skull in front of the eyes is much longer than that behind them; and the sockets of the eyes are completely surrounded by a very prominent bony ring, which has an almost tubular form. In the pigs, on the other hand, the sockets of the eye is open behind. The prominence of these sockets causes the relatively small eyes of the hippopotamus to project far above the level of the forehead.

The ears are small and rounded, and the slit-like nostrils placed rather close together on the highest point of the broad, bristly muzzle; while both ears and nostrils can be completely closed at the will of the animal. The neck is short and powerful, and the body so deep that when the animal is walking on soft mud the under surface comes in contact with the ground. Disproportionately short for the size of the animal, the tail is laterally compressed from side to side.

The short and broad feet are furnished with four well-developed toes, all of which touch the ground when walking, and are encased in rounded black hoofs, of which the middle pair has not the inner surfaces flattened; so that the hippopotamus lacks the cloven hoof of the pigs and ruminants. The toes are partially connected by webs. Although there are a number of bristles on the muzzle, and also a few on the sides of the head and neck, as well as at the extremity of the tail, the skin of the hippopotamus is naked; it is also rather rough and warty, and of enormous thickness.

The gigantic mouth, when opened to the widest, is one of the ugliest sights in nature, looking like a huge red cavern, from the edges of which project the enormous tusks and incisors. The tusks, or canines, are the largest of the teeth in the jaws, and are curved backwards in a bold sweep, with their extremities obliquely bevelled off by mutual attrition; they grow throughout life, and the points of the upper pair are directed downwards. The incisor teeth also grow during the whole period of existence, and thereby differ from those of pigs, which form roots.

In the existing species there are not more than two pairs of these teeth, and while those of the upper jaw

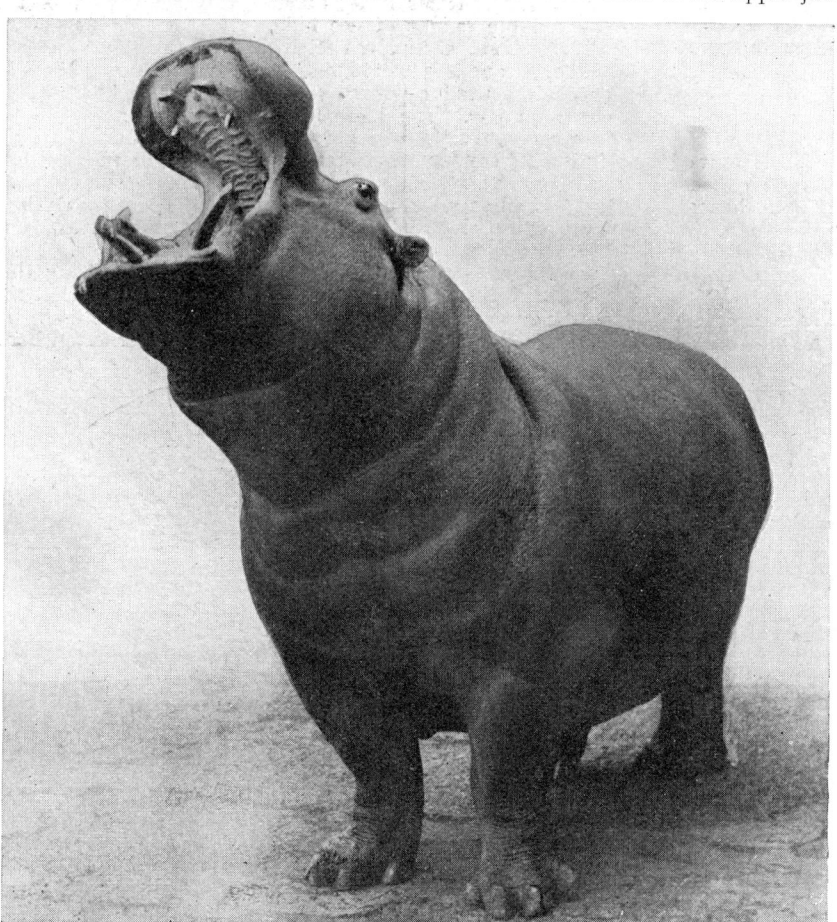

THE HIPPOPOTAMUS

are directed downwards, the lower ones project forwards in advance of the jaw. The sides of the jaws are provided with seven pairs of cheek teeth, of which the four premolars have sub-conical pointed crowns, while the broad molars carry four distinct columns, which, when worn by use, show on their summits well-defined trefoil-shaped surfaces of ivory surrounded by a rim of enamel. A peculiarity in the lower jaw is the presence of a hook-like flange at its hind extremity.

Summarising the result of the foregoing description, it may be observed that hippopotamuses are entitled to rank as a distinct family on account of the following differences from pigs and peccaries, namely, the broad and expanded muzzle, not terminating in a disc ; the sub-equal size of the hoofs, all of which touch the ground, and the absence of the flattening in the opposing surfaces of the middle pair ; the continually-growing incisor teeth ; the complete ring of bone round the socket of the eye ; and the hook-like flange at the hind extremity of the lower jaw.

The typical, or common, hippopotamus (*Hippopotamus amphibius*) is far the larger of the two living species, and, next to the elephant, the bulkiest of existing land mammals. A male which lived for many years in the London Zoological Society's Gardens measured 12 feet from the tip of the snout to the root of the tail, the length of the latter appendage being 22 inches, and its total weight was about 4 tons. Sir Samuel Baker states that in an old male measured by himself the length was 14 feet 3 inches from the snout to the end of the tail, the latter being about 9 inches ; and he estimated the weight of the hide, when freshly removed, at about 5 hundredweight. The height at the shoulder is about 3 feet 8 inches. This species is further characterised by having two pairs of incisor teeth in each jaw, the middle lower pair being of larger dimensions than the others.

The colour of the skin is slaty copper-brown, tending more to blackish brown on the back and purplish brown beneath. There is, however, considerable sexual and individual variation in this respect, and the hue of the skin also varies according as the animal has recently emerged from the water, or is thoroughly dry. Dr. Livingstone stated that while the males are of a dark colour, the females are yellowish brown ; and when these animals first leave the water the upper parts appear brownish blue and the under parts almost flesh-coloured, but when thoroughly dry the colour of the back is blackish brown or slaty. Sir John Kirk observed in East Africa nearly pure white and also spotted individuals, while in others only the feet were white. In certain cases a more or less distinct reddish, purple, or yellow tinge has been noticed. One of the largest recorded pairs of lower tusks has a total length of 31½ inches along the curve, and a basal circumference of just over 9 inches.

That the hippopotamus formerly inhabited Lower Egypt is indicated by the occurrence of its remains in the mud of the Delta, while this is also confirmed by the frequency with which it is depicted in the ancient frescoes of that country. Teeth have been dug up at Kalabshi, a short distance above the first cataract, but at the present day the animal is not met with north of the neighbourhood of Dongola, in the Sudan, between the second and third cataracts ; and even there it is comparatively rare, although a certain number take refuge in the wooded islands between Abu Hamed and Berber. Above Khartum hippo-

potamuses are found in large numbers. Generally, the hippopotamus inhabits most of the African rivers and lakes lying between 17° N. and 27° S. ; that is to say, in the south it is found in the upper course of the Limpopo. Formerly its distribution embraced the greater part of Cape Colony. In East, South, and West Africa the hippopotamus comes much nearer to the coast than in the north, and in many districts it is to be found quite close to, or even in, the sea itself.

On the other hand, in Abyssinia these animals are found dwelling in Lake Tzana-Dembea, at an elevation of six thousand feet above sea-level. The existing species is unknown in Madagascar ; but from the reference to it in the Bible, under the name of behemoth, it is possible that it may have inhabited Palestine within the historic period.

In the Pleistocene and upper portion of the Pliocene epoch a large hippopotamus, which appears specifically indistinguishable from the living kind, was widely spread over Europe, extending from Italy in the south to England in the north. These fossil hippopotamuses were, however, of much larger dimensions than at least the average of the existing race.

In England the range of the animal extended so far north as Yorkshire, and it is remarkable that in several English localities remains are found lying side by side with those of the reindeer. It has been attempted to explain this association of such southern and northern types by assuming that in the Pleistocene period the summers were very hot and the winters very cold, and that during the summer the hippopotamus wandered northwards into regions tenanted in winter by the reindeer. There are, however, difficulties in the way of accepting this explanation, not the smallest being the fact that the African hippopotamus is not a migratory animal. It may, however, be confidently assumed that, wherever remains of hippopotamus are found, the rivers must have been free from ice throughout at least the greater part of the year.

The hippopotamus is more essentially an aquatic animal than any other ungulate, the greater portion of its time being spent in the water, where its movements are far more rapid and natural than on land. As the carcase of a hippopotamus when freshly killed sinks rapidly to the bottom, its specific gravity when the lungs are inflated with air cannot be far, if at all, below that of water, and the animal is consequently enabled to stay without difficulty at the bottom of a river or lake, where it can run with ease and speed. When undisturbed, the average duration of time during which a hippopotamus remains under water

HIPPOPOTAMUS SWIMMING

does not exceed five minutes ; but in regions where these animals are much hunted the length of the immersion is often much greater, sometimes extending to as much as ten minutes.

Sir Samuel Baker mentions that when on the Upper Nile in a steamer travelling about ten knots an hour, it was not till the engineer increased the pace by putting on full steam, that they were able to overtake

A GROUP OF HIPPOPOTAMUSES IN THEIR NATIVE HAUNTS ON THE TANA RIVER, BRITISH EAST AFRICA

a hippopotamus swimming about a hundred yards in advance of the vessel. When a hippopotamus comes to the surface, it generally spouts up a column of water by the violent blowing-out of air through the nostrils, accompanied by a loud, snorting noise; but these animals are wont to learn caution when much persecuted.

A peculiarity of the hippopotamus is that when swimming in the water and about to dive, it gradually subsides by slowly sinking the hind quarters and afterwards the rest of the body, instead of sinking down head foremost. When on a high bank and suddenly frightened, however, it will not hesitate to precipitate itself headlong into the water.

Regarding the general habits and haunts of the hippopotamus, Dr. Livingstone states that on the Chobi and other large rivers the banks are marked by numerous furrows made by these animals in ascending during the night to graze on the herbage of the adjacent lands, and adds that, as they are guided back to these paths solely by scent, if a heavy rain comes on during their nocturnal excursions they are unable to find their way back to the river, and stand helpless on the land. The males remain in company with the females, although a few very aged individuals of the former sex may lead more or less solitary lives.

"The still reaches," continues the same observer, "are their favourite haunts, as elsewhere the constant exertion necessary to keep themselves from being carried down the stream disturbs their nap. They remain by day in a drowsy, yawning state, taking little notice of things at a distance. The males utter loud, snorting grunts, which may be heard a mile off. The young ones stand on the necks of their dams, and their small heads appear first above the surface as they rise to breathe. The dam, knowing the more urgent need of her calf, rises more frequently when it is in her care. In the rivers of Loanda, where they are in danger of being shot, the hippopotamuses gain wit by experience; for while those in the Zambezi expose their heads, the others keep their noses among the water plants, and breathe so quietly as to elude all observation."

On the banks of the White Nile, the favourite haunts of hippopotamuses are the dense masses of tall reeds fringing the river, where they pass a considerable portion of their time in marshy retreats among the canes; such dens would be impervious to human beings, and would not be observed unless from a vessel on the river. The tangled mass of vegetation is pierced in numerous places by dark tunnels, bored out by the bulky forms of the animals, and these gloomy routes form the channels of retreat, where they retire to sleep. Females, with their calves, are especially fond of these impervious bowers, where they are secure from molestation by man or beast.

The hippopotamus is a purely herbivorous animal, and from its gigantic bulk consumes an enormous amount of food. The capacious stomach, which when extended, measures about 11 feet in length, is capable of containing between five and six bushels; this giving some idea of the vast quantity of nutriment the creature requires. In uncultivated districts grass and various water plants—more especially lotus and papyrus—afford the chief supply; but where the land adjoining the rivers is under cultivation, the damage done to crops of rice, millet, maize, and sugar is incalculable.

It is not only the amount they actually eat, although this is large enough, but the quantity damaged in their passage to and fro. Water plants are dragged up by the roots from the beds of rivers and lakes when not too deep, and, after being brought to the surface, are devoured at leisure. When starting for their nocturnal excursions in the fields, these animals seldom leave the river till about an hour after sunset and do not return till dawn. On such expeditions they make a prodigious snorting and grunting, which may be heard for long distances.

Usually a single offspring is produced at a birth, and no one appears to have seen a female hippopotamus accompanied by more than two calves. The period of gestation is a little short of eight months, and the young may be brought forth at any season of the year. The mother is sedulous in her attention to her offspring, but the male is apt to be evilly disposed. Males are constantly fighting among themselves at night, apparently irrespective of any pairing season, and a wounded animal may be furiously attacked by a comrade.

The full age attained by the hippopotamus in its wild state has not been ascertained, but, since a calf brought to the London Zoological Society's Gardens in 1850 survived till 1878, the duration of life must be considerable.

In disposition the hippopotamus is described as comparatively timid, but when a boat passes unexpectedly into the middle of a sleeping herd, or comes close to a solitary individual at night, the results are apt to be serious. Sir Samuel Baker states that, when travelling by night in an ordinary boat on the Nile, " there is no possibility of escape should a hippopotamus take it into his head that your vessel is an enemy. The creature's snort may be heard at a few yards' distance in the darkness, and the next moment you may be overturned by an attack from beneath, where the enemy was unseen."

Formerly hippopotamus ivory was valued for the manufacture of artificial teeth, and in the early part of the nineteenth century fetched as much as twenty shillings per pound. Now, however, the animal is hunted solely for its hide and fat, or for the sake of its flesh as food. The hide is used for whips, and for facing revolving wheels employed in polishing steel. A good hippopotamus will yield about 200 pounds of pure fat, and the flesh is always palatable, that of the young calf being delicious. The feet of the latter make an excellent stew, and its skin a soup which has been compared to turtle.

Hippopotamuses thrive in captivity, and breed not infrequently. The first specimen exhibited in the London Zoological Society's Gardens was captured on the Upper Nile in 1849, and brought to England the next year.

THE PIGMY HIPPO-POTAMUS

The Liberian or pigmy hippopotamus (*Hippopotamus liberiensis*) of Western Africa is a much smaller animal, not exceeding a pig in dimensions, and weighing only about 400 pounds. It also differs structurally from the common species in having only a single pair of incisor teeth in the lower jaw, although a small tooth of the second pair may sometimes occur on one side.

The colour of the back is slaty black, while that of the under parts is dirty greyish-white, and of the sides greenish slaty grey. The height at the shoulder is about 2 feet 6 inches, and the total length 6 feet, of which 7 inches are occupied by the tail.

This diminutive species inhabits Guinea, Liberia, and Sierra Leone, and its habits are said to be more like those of wild swine than those of its gigantic cousin, as, instead of traversing well-beaten paths, it wanders great distances in the woods. Dr. Büttikofer was uncertain whether the Liberian hippopotamus is nocturnal or diurnal in its habits, although he was inclined to believe it is diurnal. It lives either solitary or in pairs, and never associates in troops like the larger species.

A later observer, Captain Murray, states that usually these hippopotamuses seem to begin their wanderings about dusk, although a large specimen was seen at Daru in broad daylight. This, however, appears to have been very exceptional behaviour, since not one of the numerous natives hunters questioned on this subject by Captain Murray could recall a similar instance.

Whenever it is possible, these animals greatly relish a mud bath, and if there be a suitable spot in the neighbourhood, it will almost certainly have nightly visitants. Taking into consideration its bulky shape, and the very dense bush through which it has to pass, the pigmy hippopotamus is wonderfully ghost-like and quiet in its movements, unless disturbed, its presence being only detected by the faintest rustle. Consequently, it is an extremely difficult animal not only to approach, but also to trap, as it scents the taint of man with extraordinary acuteness.

EXTINCT HIPPOPOTAMUSES

Among extinct species of the genus, the Cyprian hippopotamus (*H. minutus*) appears to have been no larger than the Liberian species, though it resembled the ordinary living African one in the number of its lower incisor teeth. The form of the canines and incisors, however, is the same as in the pigmy species, while the pattern of the molars is even simpler than in the latter, and therefore much more so than in *H. amphibius*.

On the other hand, the small Maltese hippopotamus (*H. melitensis*) is more nearly allied to the Liberian species. Intermediate in size between the Maltese and the common hippopotamus was Pentland's hippopotamus (*H. pentlandi*), found in the rock fissures and caves of Malta and Sicily. The vast quantities in which the remains of the last extinct species are found in the Sicilian caves presents a puzzle, since hippopotamuses are not the sort of

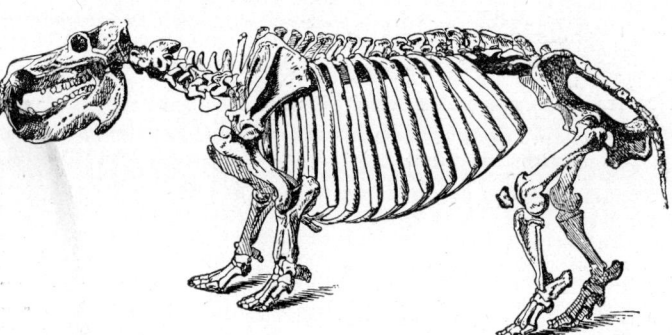

SKELETON OF HIPPOPOTAMUS

animals which one would expect to frequent such habitations. Some years ago many shiploads of teeth and bones of this species were imported into England from Palermo for the manufacture of charcoal.

Although hippopotamuses are now unknown in India, during the Pleistocene and Pliocene epochs they were abundant in that country. In the Pleistocene of the Narbada valley in Central India remains of two species of the genus are met with ; one of these (*H. palæindicus*) being characterised by the presence on each side of the lower jaw of a small incisor tooth between the two larger ones, corresponding to those of the common African hippopotamus ; while in the second Narbada species (*H. namadicus*) both upper and lower jaws were provided with three nearly equal-sized pairs of incisor teeth.

The same condition in respect of the incisor teeth also obtains in the Siwalik hippopotamus (*H. sivalensis*) from the Pliocene rocks at the foot of the Himalaya, and likewise in the Pliocene Burmese hippopotamus (*H. iravadicus*) and the Algerian hippopotamus (*H. bonariensis*), which was also of Pliocene age. Two extinct species of hippopotamus (*Hippopotamus lemerlei* and *Hippopotamus madagascariensis*) have been discovered in the superficial deposits of Madagascar ; both being allied to the larger African species.

ODD-TOED UNGULATES

THE three groups of hoofed mammals known as tapirs, rhinoceroses, and horses are the sole living representatives of an assemblage of Ungulata differing in many important respects from all those already described, and collectively constituting a distinct primary division of the order. The most obvious external characteristics of these animals are displayed by their feet, in which the toe corresponding to the third or middle finger of the human hand, or the middle toe of the human foot, is always larger than any of the others, and symmetrical in itself. In all the even-toed ungulates, instead of the third toe being symmetrical in itself and larger than any of the others, it is symmetrical to a line drawn between itself and the fourth toe, and equal in size to the latter, with which it forms a pair.

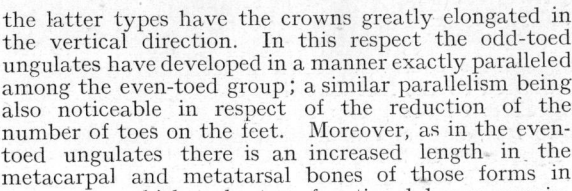

Although in the members of the present group the number of toes in the foot is frequently three, it may be increased to four or diminished to one ; yet in all these variations the symmetry of the third digit is preserved. And it is on account of the prominence of this digit that the group has received the designation of the odd-toed, or perissodactyle, ungulates.

Another distinctive feature of this group is to be found in the conformation of the astragalus of the ankle-joint of the hind foot. This bone is characterised by its deeply-grooved, pulley-like superior surface, while inferiorly it is abruptly truncated ; and, unlike that of the even-toed group, it has not a special surface for articulation with the fibula, or smaller bone of the leg.

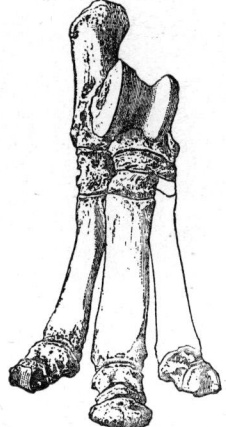

BONES OF RIGHT HIND FOOT OF EXTINCT RHINOCEROS

The astragalus of the even-toed ungulates is, on the other hand, a more elongated bone, with its lower surface highly convex, and divided into two distinct moïeties. A third very important characteristic of the limbs of the odd-toed ungulates is that the femur, or bone of the upper segment of the hind leg, is furnished with a projecting crest on the upper part of its hind surface known as the third trochanter ; this trochanter being quite unknown among artiodactyle, or even-toed, ungulates.

The foregoing characteristics of the feet are alone sufficient to distinguish the odd-toed ungulates from the even-toed group, but there are also certain other features—especially connected with the teeth—which it is advisable to notice. As regards the cheek teeth, the premolars in the upper jaw are generally as complex as the molars, whereas in most members of the even-toed group they are simpler. Then, again, all the upper cheek teeth, with the exception of the first, in most of the earlier and more primitive representatives of the group are characterised by carrying six cusps on their crowns, of which the middle and inner one on each side

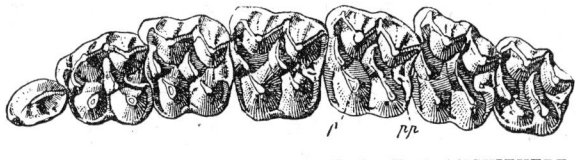

THE LEFT UPPER CHEEK TEETH OF THE ANCHITHERE

tend to unite more or less completely, and thus form a pair of oblique transverse ridges, extending across the crown to the two outer columns ; the two latter also uniting to form a longitudinal outer wall to the tooth.

From this primitive type of tooth all the more specialised developments may be derived ; and while the earlier forms have low-crowned molar teeth, some of the latter types have the crowns greatly elongated in the vertical direction. In this respect the odd-toed ungulates have developed in a manner exactly paralleled among the even-toed group ; a similar parallelism being also noticeable in respect of the reduction of the number of toes on the feet. Moreover, as in the even-toed ungulates there is an increased length in the metacarpal and metatarsal bones of those forms in which only two functional bones remain, so in the present group there is a similar elongation of the single metacarpal and metatarsal (cannon) bones in its one-toed representatives, namely, the members of the horse family. It is only of late years that the importance of parallelism in the development of allied groups of animals has been fully recognised, and in no group are there better examples of this feature than in the ungulates, where it is displayed in several groups, and affects totally different parts of the skeleton.

The lower cheek teeth of the odd-toed ungulates very generally differ from those of the other main group in that the last of the series resembles those in advance of it in having two lobes, this feature being distinctive of the whole of the existing members of the group. On the other hand, in all the living representatives of the even-toed group, with the exception of some of the dik-dik antelopes, the corresponding tooth has three distinct lobes. Generally the lower cheek teeth of the present group carry two transverse ridges or a pair of crescents, one in front of the other, on their crowns. It may be added that all odd-toed ungulates have simple stomachs, and that in no case is the liver provided with a gall-bladder.

With the exception of the tapirs, which are common to the Malay region and Central and South America, all existing odd-toed ungulates are Old World animals ; while all the three family groups are represented by a comparatively small number of species, which, with the exception of the horses, are much inferior in number of individuals to the majority of even-toed ungulates.

These circumstances point to the conclusion that, as a whole, the odd-toed ungulates are a waning group— a conclusion fully supported by its past history. Rhinoceroses and horses, for instance, were abundantly represented during former epochs in the New World ; while the rocks of both hemispheres have yielded fossil remains of an enormous number of extinct generic, and even family, types of odd-toed ungulates, several of which serve to connect the three living groups.

What may have been the reason of this gradual waning of the odd-toed ungulates, and the great development of the even-toed group during geological epochs, is not easy to divine. Perhaps the former group is one of a lower and less adaptive nature than the latter.

The horse tribe forms an exception to the other members of the group, as regards number of species and individuals, and belongs to a branch raised to a platform as high as that occupied by the hollow-horned family in the other group. It is difficult to understand why horses became extinct in the New World, unless they were exterminated by pumas or bacteria.

TAPIRS

The tapirs (family *Tapiridæ*) are the least specialised of all the existing odd-toed ungulates, their peculiarly antediluvian appearance suggesting this even to the unscientific observer. Their generalised character is indicated by the fact that they differ from other living members of the group in having four toes to their fore feet, although their hind feet resemble those of rhinoceroses in being tridactyle. In the fore feet the three main toes correspond to the three middle fingers of the human hand, while the small external one represents the fifth or little finger.

The tapirs are further characterised by the production of the extremity of the muzzle into a short cylindrical proboscis, at the extremity of which are situated the nostrils. The form of the body is heavy and ungainly, the limbs being relatively short and stout, and the tail scarcely more than a rudiment. The eyes are small in proportion to the size of the head, and the erect and oval ears are of moderate size. The thick skin is smooth, and covered with a scanty coat of short hair, usually of uniform colour in the adult, although in the young striped and spotted with white.

The skull is rather short, narrow, and high, its most distinctive features being the enormous size of the aperture of the nose, and the absence of any bony bar dividing the socket of the eye from the channel on the side of the brain case. The teeth are forty-two in number, or two less than the full typical mammalian number, the missing ones being the first premolar on each side of the lower jaw. The short-crowned cheek teeth are separated from those in the front of the jaws by a long gap, and the tusks, or canines, are small, those of the upper jaw being inferior in dimensions to the outermost pair of incisors. The upper cheek teeth have two transverse ridges and an outer longitudinal wall, while those of the lower jaw carry a pair of transverse ridges alone.

In the limbs all the bones are fully developed and distinct from one another, and the toes are encased in long and rather oval hoofs, while inferiorly the foot is furnished with a large callous pad, which takes a share in supporting the weight of the body. Except when the soil is soft and yielding, the small outermost toe of the fore foot scarcely touches the ground.

Existing tapirs have a remarkable geographical distribution, a solitary species being found in the Malay region, while all the others are restricted to Central and South America. Still more remarkable is the fact that, instead of all the American species being closely allied, two are nearly related to the Malay tapir; while the other two form a distinct group. A flood of light on this remarkable instance of what is known as discontinuous distribution is thrown by the discovery of remains of extinct tapirs in the middle and upper Tertiary rocks of Europe—including those of England—and China, while nearly allied or identical forms occur in those of the United States. Such remains are also found in the cavern deposits of Brazil, which belong to the later Pleistocene epoch. Since these extinct forms belong to the existing genus, tapirs may be regarded as amongst the oldest of living mammals.

Whether the group originated in the Old or the New World, it is certainly a northern one, and only obtained entrance into South America at a comparatively recent date while it never penetrated into Africa. In the Old World, where they were once so abundant, they have dwindled to a single species, existing in small numbers in the Malay Peninsula, Sumatra, and Borneo, while in the Western Hemisphere they occupy a much larger area, and are represented by several species. With regard to the probable ancestors of the tapirs, some remarks are made on a later page.

Except for the fact that the Malay species differs from the rest in colour, the various kinds of tapirs are remarkably alike, both in respect of bodily form and habits. But while four of the species are found at or near the sea level, the fifth inhabits comparatively high elevations in the Cordilleras.

Tapirs are solitary, nocturnal, shy, and inoffensive animals,

SKELETON OF MALAY TAPIR

chiefly frequenting the depths of shady tropical forests and the neighbourhood of water, to which they resort for the purpose of bathing, and in which they often take refuge when pursued. They feed exclusively on vegetable substances, such as young shoots of trees and bushes.

Tapirs are peculiar in that the whole of the four premolar teeth on each side of the upper jaw are preceded by milk teeth, while in the pig and other even-toed ungulates the first of these teeth never has a deciduous predecessor, as, indeed, is the case in other groups of mammals. Some rhinoceroses, however, resemble tapirs in having the first premolar preceded by a milk tooth, although this seems to be merely an individual, and not a specific peculiarity. A second peculiarity—at all events, in the Indian species—is that the lungs, instead of having a separate membranous bag, are in contact with the walls of the chest; the same feature occurring in elephants.

THE MALAY TAPIR

The Malay tapir (*Tapirus indicus*), which is the largest of the whole group (page 60), and differs from all the others in its parti-coloured skin, stands from 3 to 3½ feet at the withers, and about 4 inches more at the rump, its length along the curve from the tip of the snout to the root of the tail being about 8 feet. In the adult the colour of the head and front of the body, as well as the limbs, is dark brown or black; while the body from behind the shoulders to the rump and the upper part of the thighs is greyish white, as are also the ears (page 884). On the other hand, the newly-born young are brownish or velvety black, marked with spots and longitudinal streaks of brownish yellow on the sides, and of white beneath; the change from the young to the adult coloration taking place between four and six months after birth.

The Malay tapir is found in the peninsula from which it takes its name, whence it extends northwards to Tenasserim, and also occurs in Sumatra, and perhaps Borneo.

Owing to its retiring nature, the Malay tapir is seldom seen in its native haunts, and information as to its habits is consequently meagre. Indeed, nothing is known as to its breeding habits, although it seems to be ascertained that only one young is produced at a birth. Although seen so rarely, the tapir is by no means uncommon in the interior of the Tavoy and Mergui provinces, but it avoids the inhabited parts of the country. When taking to the water, it is said to plunge in and walk along the bottom, instead of swimming.

In spite of its shy and retiring habits, this tapir, if captured at a sufficiently early period, can be readily tamed, and exhibits considerable attachment to its master. It has been stated that when lying down in a district studded with large grey boulders a Malay tapir is almost invisible ; but, in spite of this, it is probable that the division of the body into a dark and a light area is for the purpose of breaking up the outline of the entire animal, and thus rendering it inconspicuous at a moderate distance.

AMERICAN TAPIRS

Of the New World tapirs the longest known is the Brazilian species (*T. americanus*, or *terrestris*), originally described by Linnæus as a terrestrial species of hippopotamus. In common with the other American kinds, the adult is of uniform dark brown or blackish colour (page 60), although the young are striped and spotted after the manner of the Asiatic species. The snout is shorter than in the latter, the hind part of the head more elevated, and the crown of the head and the neck are furnished with a short, stiff, upright mane. The margins of the ears are white. This species inhabits the forest districts of Brazil, Paraguay, and the northern part of Argentina.

The second member of this group is Roulin's tapir (*T. roulini*), which is a mountain species inhabiting the Cordilleras of Ecuador and Colombia at an elevation of from seven thousand to eight thousand feet above the sea, and locally known as the pinchaque. It has a less vaulted skull and a rounder neck, without distinct crest, than the lowland species, from which it is further distinguished by the presence of a long white spot on the chin.

The two remaining species are Baird's tapir (*T. bairdi*), ranging from Mexico to Panama, and Dow's tapir (*T. dowi*), restricted to Guatemala, Nicaragua, and Costa Rica, which constitute a second group of the genus distinguished by the characters of the skull. In the three species of the first group the nasal cavity is perfectly open in advance of the roofing bones of the skull ; but in the members of the second group this cavity is divided by a vertical partition in the middle line, similar to that one in the skull of the extinct woolly rhinoceros.

Brazilian tapirs confine themselves exclusively to the thickest parts of the forests, carefully avoiding all open spaces, and forming regular pathways along which they travel in search of food and water. In the forest itself it is generally difficult to come across them, but when travelling on the rivers by boat tapirs may be often seen in the early morning, when they come to the bank to drink. Although mainly nocturnal, in the densest and darkest portions of the forest tapirs may be encountered abroad during the daytime. They are fond of gambolling in the water and rolling in soft mud, so that their hides often become thickly plastered, probably as a protection against the bites of insects.

The males, except during the pairing season, are said to be completely solitary, and even family parties are rarely met with ; and, except when several have been temporarily collected by the attraction of unusually good pasture, it is very seldom that more than three are seen in company. Tapirs begin to feed in the evening, and probably continue throughout the greater part of the night.

These animals are slow and deliberate in their movements, usually walking with their snouts close to the ground, and by the aid of scent or sound detecting the presence of foes with extreme acuteness. When frightened, they rush blindly forwards, crashing through bushes or splashing through water in precipitate flight. The Brazilian tapir is an excellent swimmer, crossing the largest rivers with facility, and even diving, although with what object is not ascertained. Not improbably it may also walk along the beds of shallow rivers and lakes, as was observed to be the habit of a specimen of the Malay species kept in captivity at Barrakpur.

The chief sound made by the Brazilian tapir is a peculiar shrill whistle, which has little volume in comparison with the size of the animal. This whistle is uttered at all seasons, and is not, as has been supposed, restricted to the pairing season ; the Malay species is reported to give vent to a very similar sound. When suddenly disturbed, the Brazilian tapir utters a loud snort. Although in general perfectly harmless animals, fleeing hurriedly before the smallest dog, tapirs will sometimes attack their enemies fiercely, this being more especially the case with females that have been deprived of their young. In such instances they rush violently at their foes—human or otherwise—and after knocking them down, trample upon and bite them after the manner of wild swine.

In Brazil the food of the tapir is largely composed of palm leaves in districts remote from cultivation, but at certain seasons these animals subsist almost exclusively on fallen fruits, while in other districts swamp grasses and water plants form

BRAZILIAN TAPIR AND YOUNG

their chief nutriment. In the neighbourhood of plantations they frequently do much harm to the crops of sugar-cane, melons, and the like, and are especially dreaded by the proprietors of cacao plantations for the amount of damage they inflict on the young plants. Salt seems particularly grateful to their palate, and in order to obtain it they will eat the saline earth found in many parts of South America.

In captivity they are fond of sweet substances, and become almost as omnivorous as swine.

RHINOCEROSES

ALTHOUGH inferior in length of body, and probably also in weight, to the hippopotamus, the larger species of rhinoceros exceed that animal in height, and, therefore, claim the position of being the mammals next in point of size to elephants. Unlike tapirs, the various species of rhinoceros, all of which are now confined to the Old World, differ very markedly from one another in structure—so much so, indeed, that by many naturalists they are divided into several genera —and there is also considerable disparity in point of size. All existing rhinoceroses (family *Rhinocerotidæ*) differ from tapirs in having only three toes on both fore and hind feet, but since there are some extinct species with four toes to the front limbs, this point of distinction cannot be regarded as very important.

The presence of one or two horns in the middle line of the front of the head might at first sight be regarded as a more valuable distinctive character, but since these appendages are always or, at least, frequently absent in the female of one of the living Indian rhinoceroses, and are invariably wanting in certain extinct kinds, other features must be sought in order to distinguish these animals from tapirs.

Such characteristics are found in the cheek teeth. In the molar teeth of the upper jaw the two outer columns of the primitive tooth have completely coalesced so as to form a continuous external wall to the crown, this wall being sinuous, and in some cases forming a prominent buttress at the front outer edge of the crown. From this outer wall proceed two continuous oblique transverse ridges, or crests, separated from one another by a deep valley, which is interrupted by projecting processes from one or both ridges, and sometimes also from the outer wall. This middle valley is usually free from cement, and its form, as also the relative height of the whole crown, varies considerably in the different species.

Instead of having the simple transverse ridges found in those of tapirs, the lower cheek teeth of the rhinoceroses have a pair of crescents, placed one in front of the other. On each side of both jaws are seven cheek teeth ; but the last molar in the upper jaw differs from the rest in having its hind ridge more or less aborted, so that the form of the crown is generally triangular.

As regards their front teeth, the different species of rhinoceros present a considerable amount of variation, some having such teeth in both jaws, while in others they are totally absent ; but there are never any canine teeth or tusks in the upper jaw, and the number of upper incisor teeth does not exceed two pairs. In the lower jaw there may be a pair of large pointed and nearly horizontal tusks, and between them a small pair of incisor teeth.

All living rhinoceroses are animals of large size and heavy build, with the legs comparatively short and stout, although less so than in the hippopotamus. Each of the toes is furnished with a relatively small, but broad and well-defined hoof-like nail. The head is large and elongated, with a concave profile, and the erect oval ears are placed very far back. The eyes are very small in proportion to the size of the head ; and the upper lip is generally, although not invariably, prehensile, and prolonged beyond the extremity of the lower one. The thick skin is either naked, or sparsely clad with hair, and may be thrown in certain parts of the body into a series of deep folds. The tail is thin and of moderate length.

The horns, which form the characteristic feature of the physiognomy of the living species, are composed of a closely-packed mass of horny fibres, growing from the skin, and having no connection with the bones of the skull, although there are prominences on the latter beneath each horn. The skull is characterised by its elevated occipital region, long curved profile, the absence of any bony bar at the hind part of the socket of the eye, and the large size of the nasal bones, which are completely fused together. In those species with one horn, this is carried upon the nasal bones, and the front horn of those with two of these appendages has a similar situation ; but the second horn, when present is placed on the frontal bones.

Rhinoceroses are stupid and somewhat timorous beasts, generally striving to escape from man, although when brought to bay exceedingly fierce, and consequently, from their great size, very dangerous. Although the African species are entirely dependent on their enormous horns as weapons of offence and defence, the Asiatic kinds, in which the horns are smaller, rely chiefly upon their sharply-pointed lower tusks, which are capable of inflicting terrific gashes. All are mainly nocturnal ; and while some resemble tapirs in frequenting tall grass jungles and swampy districts, others prefer more or less open plains.

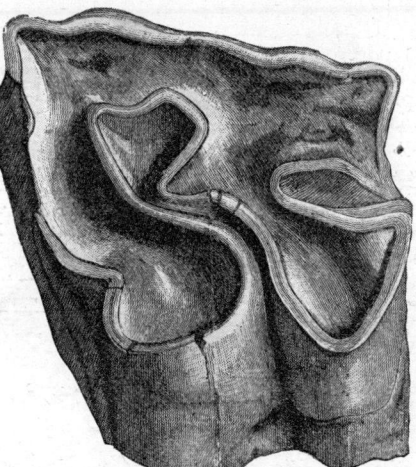

LEFT UPPER MOLAR OF A SIWALIK RHINOCEROS

Their food is entirely vegetable, but while some species subsist almost exclusively on grass, the food of others consists mainly of twigs and small boughs of trees, this difference in diet being correlated with a difference in the structure of the molar teeth. At the present day these animals are restricted to South-Eastern Asia and Africa, and they may be divided into two main groups according to their geographical distribution, the Asiatic group being again subdivided into two minor groups.

THE INDIAN RHINOCEROS

The great one-horned Indian rhinoceros (*Rhinoceros unicornis*) is the one which has been longest known in Europe from living examples, a specimen having been sent to Portugal so long ago as 1513 ; it is the largest of the Asiatic species, and carries a single nasal horn. In common with the other two species inhabiting Asia, this rhinoceros (p. 885) is characterised by the skin being thrown in places into thick folds, and by the presence of teeth in the front of the jaws.

With the exception of that of the tail and ears, the skin is naked, and on the sides of the body is studded with a number of large convex tubercles, recalling the heads of the rivets in an iron boiler, these being largest on the fore and hind quarters, where they may be as much as an inch in diameter. The skin of the body is divided into a number of shield-like pieces by the aforesaid folds. There is one fold before and behind each shoulder, marking off a large triangular shield covering the shoulder, and a second in front of each thigh dividing the large saddle-shaped body-shield from one on the the hind quarters. The folds behind the shoulder and in front of the hind quarters continue completely across the back, but the one in front of the shoulder inclines backwards and dies close out to the second great fold. Other folds form great rolls of skin on the neck, while there are others below the shields on the fore and hind quarters, and one situated behind the buttocks which forms a groove for the reception of the tail.

The head of the Indian rhinoceros is very large in proportion to the body, with the occipital region of the skull much elevated ; and the ears are large, with their tips fringed with hairs. The horn is large in both sexes, and the colour of the skin a uniform blackish grey. In height the Indian rhinoceros stands 5 feet to $5\frac{3}{4}$ feet at the shoulder. In a male standing 5 feet 9 inches at the shoulder measured by General A. A.

and forwards grinding motion, and not a champing action, such a mode of mastication being similar to that existing in horses and cattle.

So far as is known, this rhinoceros is confined to the country from which it takes its name, although it appears to be represented in the hill country north of Burma by an allied species. Nowadays it is still abundant in the Assam plain, and, although long supposed to be almost unknown in the countries west of the Tista valley, likewise in the Terai lands of Nepal, where a large number were killed or captured in 1908. Formerly its range extended so far west as Rohilcund, while not improbably about 1850 it may have occurred in the grass jungles of the Ganges valley at the north end of the Rahmahal hills in Bengal. In the early part of the sixteenth century it ranged over the Punjab as far westwards as Peshawur ; and since its fossilised remains are found in the United Provinces, the Narbada valley, and Madras, it may be inferred that it formerly

THE INDIAN RHINOCEROS

Kinloch, the length from the tip of the snout to the root of the tail was 10 feet 6 inches, the length of the tail 2 feet 5 inches, and the girth of the body 9 feet 8 inches. The length of the horn is seldom more than a foot, although there are stated to be instances of horns 2 feet in length, and one formerly in the British Museum measured 19 inches.

The Indian rhinoceros is further characterised by its teeth. As a rule, there is but a single pair of broad incisors in the upper jaw, although in some cases there may be a smaller pair behind them. In the lower jaw there is one pair of long, triangular, pointed tusks, and between them a pair of small cylindrical incisors which can be of no functional importance. The upper molar teeth have tall crowns, and are distinguished by the presence of a small vertical plate projecting from the outer wall into the extremity of the middle valley. It will be obvious that this flat plane of wear of the cheek teeth implies that the jaws have a backwards

ranged over the greater part of peninsular India in localities suited to its habits.

The Indian rhinoceros is a denizen of the great grass jungles that cover such a large portion of the plains, and from this fact, coupled with the general resemblance of its molar teeth to those of the African white rhinoceros, which is known to be a grass-eater, it may be assumed that its food is chiefly grass. It chiefly frequents such spots as are on swampy ground ; and although it is a solitary animal, General A. A. Kinloch states that he has known half a dozen roused from a belt of not more than half a mile in length by three hundred or four hundred yards in width. The Indian rhinoceros is fond of a mud bath.

Although there are many stories extant as to its ferocity, and more especially its enmity to the elephant, it is generally quiet and harmless. Even when wounded, it seldom charges home ; but when it does attack, the sharp lower tusks are used much after the same manner as are those of a wild boar. The only sound that this rhinoceros utters is a peculiar grunt, repeated at frequent intervals during excitement. Its usual gait is a long swinging trot, although when disturbed it can break into an awkward, but very rapid gallop. Only a single calf is produced at birth, but there is some uncertainty as to the length of the period of gestation, an old writer stating that it is nine months, while a more recent authority affirms that it is nearly or quite double as long.

The Indian rhinoceros thrives well in confinement, and frequently lives in that state for a long period. One specimen acquired by the London Zoological Gardens in 1834 lived till 1849, while a second, purchased in 1850, died in 1874, and a third, presented in 1864, survived till 1906. Dr. W. T. Blanford states that he has heard of captive specimens living fifty or sixty years, and Mr. Brian Hodgson was of opinion that the natural term of the animal's life is upwards of a century.

THE JAVAN RHINOCEROS

The Javan, or lesser one-horned, rhinoceros (*Rhinoceros sondaicus*) is a smaller animal than the last, with the head relatively less large in proportion to the body, although its height at the shoulder is scarcely, if at all, inferior. The skin, which is nearly or quite naked, lacks the large tubercles of the Indian rhinoceros ; while the fold in front of the shoulder, instead of inclining backwards, is continued right across the body like the other two main folds. Superficially, the skin is divided by a network of cracks into a number of small mosaic-like discs. The great folds of skin which are so conspicuous in the neck of the Indian rhinoceros are much less strongly developed ; and the colour is a uniform dusky grey. The skull is less elevated than in the larger species in the occipital region, but there is the same number of front teeth.

In structure, however, the upper molar teeth are simpler, and their crowns are not so tall. Measurements of wild individuals appear to be very few, but

Burma and the Malay Peninsula to Sumatra, Java, and Borneo ; its partially fossilised remains occurring in the latter island.

Dr. W. T. Blanford observes that this species " is more an inhabitant of the forest than of grass, and although it is found in the alluvial swamps of the Sandarbans, its usual habitat appears to be in hilly countries. It has been observed at considerable elevations both in Burma and Java." Indeed, there is evidence that it probably ascends occasionally to as much as seven thousand feet above the sea-level.

This species being a forest-dwelling one, while its molar teeth are of the same pattern as those of the leaf and branch eating black African rhinoceros, it is pretty certain that its food must be of similar nature to that of the latter. In disposition the Javan rhinoceros is said to be more gentle than the large Indian species, and it is not infrequently tamed by the Malays. The horns are never large, and afford poor trophies to the sportsman.

In the Pliocene rocks of the Siwalik Hills at the foot of the Himalaya occur remains of a single-horned rhinoceros (*R. sivalensis*), which appears to have been closely allied to the Javan species, of which the original home may accordingly have been India. More remarkable is the occurrence of remains of a fossil rhinoceros in the interior of the Himalaya, at an elevation of about sixteen thousand feet above the sea-level, which also seems to have been related to the same species. It may be added that another fossil Indian rhinoceros (*R. palæindicus*) appears to have been the forerunner of the great Indian rhinoceros ; its molar teeth (page 774) approximating to those of the latter, although of a rather less complex structure.

THE SUMATRAN RHINOCEROS

The last of the living Asiatic species is the Sumatran rhinoceros (*Rhinoceros sumatrensis*), mainly characteristic of the countries to the east of the Bay of Bengal, and occurring rarely in Assam, although a specimen has been obtained from Bhutan. From Assam it ranges through Burma and the Malay Peninsula to Siam, Sumatra, and Borneo ; but it is unknown in Java.

This is the smallest of all the living rhinoceroses, and differs from the two preceding species in carrying two horns, while it is further distinguished by its hairiness, although there is a certain amount of variation in this respect. As a rule, the greater part of the body is thinly covered with brown or black hair of considerable length, while there are larger or smaller fringes on the ears and tail. The rough and granular skin varies in colour from earthy brown almost to black, and has the folds much less developed than in the single-horned species, only the one behind the shoulders continuing right across the back.

The two horns are placed some distance apart, and when fully developed are thick and massive at the base, but very slender above, the front and longer one sweeping backwards in a graceful curve. In many specimens, however, the horns are very short, and in examples kept in confinement they may be worn down to mere stumps. The Sumatran rhinoceros differs from its two Asiatic cousins in having lost the pair of small incisor teeth in the lower jaw, in the front of which only the tusks remain.

CHITTAGONG RACE OF THE SUMATRAN RHINOCEROS

in a large female the height at the shoulder was $5\frac{1}{2}$ feet. The female is generally or invariably hornless.

This species has a more extensive distribution than its larger cousin. There is no evidence that it ever occurred in peninsular India, but it is found in the Bengal Sandarbans and portions of Eastern Bengal, while it has been met with in the Sikkim " terai." From the valley of Assam it ranges eastwards through

In addition to the variation in the degrees of development of the hair, this species shows considerable differences in colour, and also in the relative breadth of the skull. A specimen from Chittagong exhibited in 1872 in the London Zoological Gardens was characterised by its large size, pale brown colour, smooth skin, short and rather thickly-tufted tail, and long, fine, reddish-coloured hair; the latter forming a long fringe on the ears, of which the insides were naked. It had also a wider head than ordinary. It was regarded as a distinct species, but really indicates only a local race (*R. sumatrensis lasiotis*) of the present species. Another race (*R. s. niger*), characterised by its small size and blackish skin, inhabits the Malay Peninsula.

There is considerable local variation in regard to the dimensions of this species, but from 4 feet to 4½ feet represents about the average height at the shoulder. In the above-mentioned Chittagong specimen the height at the shoulder was 4 feet 4 inches, and the length from the tip of the snout to the root of the tail 8 feet; the weight of the animal being about 2,000 pounds. On the other hand, in an adult female from the Malay Peninsula, the shoulder height was only 3 feet 8 inches.

There is also great variation in regard to the length of the horns, the hind one being in some cases reduced to an almost invisible knob. In one Bornean example the front horn was 4½ and the hind one 2 inches in length; in a second, while the front horn measured 5 inches, the hind one was a mere knob; and in a third, the front horn had a length of 19 inches with a girth of 16 inches, the second horn being fairly developed, although not more than about 3 inches in height. A single specimen of a front horn had a length of 11 inches, with a basal girth of 11½ inches; but a length of 32 inches along the curve has been recorded.

The molar teeth of this species are almost indistinguishable from those of the Javan rhinoceros, and as its habits appear to be very similar to those of the latter, the diet of the two is probably also alike. The Sumatran rhinoceros inhabits hilly forest districts, and has been observed in Tenasserim at an elevation of four thousand feet above the sea. It is a good swimmer, and is reported to have been seen swimming in the sea in the Mergui Archipelago. Although shy and timid in the wild state, in captivity it soon becomes tame.

In Borneo the Dyaks are very partial to the flesh of this species as an article of diet, and the Kyens—a race very distinct from the Dyaks—sell the horns for barter for a high price to the Chinese, who import them to China for medicinal purposes. The horns are ground into powder for some diseases, while others are cut into minute fragments to carry about the person. This rhinoceros has become extremely rare in Sarawak, on account of the value set upon its horns, but in Central and North Borneo in old jungle it is more plentiful.

A huge two-horned extinct rhinoceros (*R. platyrhinus*) from the Pliocene of the Siwalik Hills appears to be allied to the Sumatran species, although it has teeth of the type of those of the living Indian species. More nearly allied to the Sumatran animal is *R.*

THE BLACK RHINOCEROS

hundsheimensis of the Tertiary of Austria. Schleiermacher's rhinoceros (*R. schleiermacheri*) of the Miocene and lower Pliocene deposits of France and Germany also appears to have been closely allied to the Sumatran species.

THE BLACK RHINOCEROS

Africa is the home of two very distinct species of the group, commonly known as the black and the white rhinoceros; and although there does not appear to be any very marked difference in the colour of their hides, these names are so well-known that they are preferable to any that have been proposed as substitutes.

Both these species are furnished with two horns, which attain a greater development than in any of their Asiatic relatives, from all of which the African rhinoceroses are distinguished by the absence of permanent folds in the skin, and the want of both incisor teeth and tusks in the adult state; such teeth if they occur in the young being rudimentary and functionless. In consequence of this want of front teeth, the extremities of both the upper and lower jaws are much shorter than in the Asiatic species; and while in the latter the nasal bones are narrow and terminate in a point, in the African rhinoceroses they are rounded and truncated in front. In both kinds the skin of the body is almost entirely naked and comparatively smooth, but there is generally a little fringe or tuft of hairs on the ears and tail.

The black rhinoceros (*R. bicornis*), which is the smaller of the two species, has the wider distribution, extending, in suitable districts, through Eastern and Central Africa, from Abyssinia and Somaliland in the north to Cape Colony in the south. From the character of the upper lip this species is sometimes spoken of as the prehensile-lipped rhinoceros, while in Southern and Eastern Africa it is variously termed the boreli or upetyani, the keitloa, and the kulumani ; these different native names referring to differences in the relative proportions of the two horns.

The species is best characterised by the pointed and slightly prehensile upper lip, the small and rounded nostrils, and the position of the eyes a little behind the continuation of the axis of the second horn. The ears are of moderate length, and furnished with a fringe of hair along the upper edge, while in some cases they are rounded above, although in others more pointed. There is a considerable amount of variation in respect of the length and amount of the fringe of hairs on the margins of the ears.

In the molar teeth the crowns are low, with a well-marked buttress at the front outer angle, the middle valley not divided into two by a cross-partition, and the surface of the crown when worn raised into two distinct ridges. The latter feature shows that the jaws have a somewhat champing, instead of a completely grinding action ; and since this species feeds almost exclusively on twigs and leaves, it may be assumed that molar teeth of this pattern always indicate a similar diet for their owners. The horns are well developed in both sexes, the front one generally curving backwards and having a moderately expanded and rounded base, above which the front surface is also rounded, or even reduced to a sharp edge. The second horn, when well developed, is usually straight, and almost dagger-shaped, with fore and aft cutting edges.

HEAD OF THE BLACK RHINOCEROS

As regards dimensions, in an adult female from Abyssinia described by Dr. W. T. Blanford the length from the tip of the snout to the end of the tail measured along the curves was 6 feet 9 inches, of which 1 foot 9½ inches was occupied by the tail, and the height at the shoulder was 4 feet 8½ inches. These dimensions are, however, exceeded by males, which may stand from 5 feet 6 inches to 5 feet 8 inches at the shoulder.

The proportions of the two horns to one another vary greatly, the front one being in some cases much longer than the hind, while in others the two are nearly or quite equal, and, more rarely, the second horn may be the longer. There is, however, in South Africa a complete transition from the one to the other type, so that not even local races can be established in that part of the continent on such differences.

In regard to the length attained by the horns of this species in Abyssinia and other parts of North-East Africa, the front horn rarely exceeds 23 or 24 inches, but much larger dimensions are recorded in South and East African specimens. Examples of the front horn, for instance, are recorded as measuring 44, 43, 41, 40, and 38½ inches in length ; but with the exception of the last, in which its length is 21 inches, in none of these examples are the dimensions of the second horn recorded. Front horns of a long, slender, and much compressed type from East Africa have been made the type of a distinct species, under the name of *R. holmwoodi*, but indicate, at most, nothing more than a local race of the black species.

In Abyssinia this rhinoceros is confined to the lower elevations, not ascending above some five thousand feet. In the valley of the Anseba, Dr. W. T. Blanford writes, it inhabits the dense thickets on the bank of the stream, which are intersected in all directions by the paths made by these animals, which enter the thick jungle early in the morning and " rest until one or two o'clock in the day, then they leave the thickets and go out to feed, usually remaining, however, amongst high bushes. At the time of year in which we visited the country, rain generally set in in the afternoon, and, even if it did not rain, the sky was overcast. In the clear weather the rhinoceroses are said never to appear before evening. They are great browsers, feeding chiefly on the young shoots and branches of acacia and other trees, or on fruits ; so far as I could see, they do not generally eat grass. Their movements are very quick, their usual pace being a smart trot, and the numerous tracks show that they move about a good deal." The snort of alarm or rage uttered by the creature when disturbed has been compared to the noise of a locomotive rather than to the sound of any other animal.

Mr. F. C. Selous states that this rhinoceros, like the white African species, exhibits extraordinary activity in getting over hilly and rocky ground, and that it can traverse places which at first sight appear utterly impracticable for an animal of its bulky and apparent clumsy build. The present species always walks with its nose carried high in the air, whereas the white rhinoceros walks with its muzzle close to the ground ; and while in the case of the former the calf invariably follows its mother, in the latter case the calf as constantly precedes its parent.

Mr. Selous says that he was only once charged by a black rhinoceros, and this after strong provocation, and even then the animal did not charge home ; and he considers that vicious individuals are comparatively few and far between. " These animals," he writes, " are very quick and restless in their movements, and either very inquisitive or mistrustful of their eyesight, for usually, when disturbed by anyone approaching from below the wind, they will jump up with a snort, gaze fixedly at the intruder, then, with another snort, trot quickly a few steps nearer, stand again, move their heads with a quick motion, first to one side then to the other, advance again, perhaps, and finally, when shouted at, whisk quickly round and trot away in grand style, with tail screwed up over their backs."

In South-Eastern Africa both species of rhinoceros leave their lairs about four o'clock in the afternoon. The lair is in an extremely sheltered and deeply-shaded spot. In the Kilimanjaro district, however, rhinoceroses are stated to lie out in the open plain during the day.

THE RED DEER

"Red deer are essentially shy and wary animals, and in the open districts which they frequent in Scotland can detect an enemy at an immense distance. When all the members of a herd are together the chief duty of watching appears to fall on the hinds, but at other times the stags have to depend on their own alertness."

OKAPIS, FROM A PAINTING BY SIR H. H. JOHNSTON

"Okapis are timid, inoffensive animals, living ordinarily in couples, male and female, with the addition of a calf or half-grown young. The creature is said to have a voice like a cow."

THE SAMBAR

"Its habits are nocturnal; it may be seen feeding in the morning and evening, but it grazes chiefly at night, and at that time often visits small patches of cultivation in the half-cleared tracts, returning for the day to wilder parts."

OKAPIS, FROM A PAINTING BY SIR H. H. JOHNSTON

"Okapis are timid, inoffensive animals, living ordinarily in couples, male and female, with the addition of a calf or half-grown young. The creature is said to have a voice like a cow."

The black rhinoceros is met with in Southern Africa either solitary or in family parties of two or three. In the latter case it is usually a female accompanied by her calf; but Sir John Willoughby met a male, female, and half-grown calf together. Occasionally several full-grown individuals are seen together, Mr. Drummond stating that on one occasion he met with a party of six or seven. Sir John Willoughby relates that once he shot one of a pair of these rhinoceroses, which was immediately fiercely attacked and rolled over by its companion. When a cow rhinoceros is killed, the calf generally remains by the dead body of its parent, from which it can with difficulty be dragged away.

Like most other large African animals, the black rhinoceros is rapidly decreasing, from the incessant pursuit to which it is subjected in the southern and eastern portion of the continent. In 1881 it was still fairly common in South-Eastern Africa, although it had been nearly exterminated in the regions of the west; but only a few then remained on the Chobi, while between that river and the Zambezi there was none, and the natives said that there never had been any in that district. Northwards of the Zambezi they were at that time again to be met with, and thence they extend through the whole of Central Africa to Abyssinia and the Sudan. In the Kilimanjaro district Sir John Willoughby's party found them very plentiful in 1886, having on one occasion seen as many as sixteen head during a single day's march.

The immediate ancestor of this species appears to have been the extinct thick-jawed rhinoceros (*R. pachygnathus*), of which a series of finely-preserved remains have been obtained from the well-known fresh-water deposits of Pikermi, in Attica, belonging to the Pliocene period.

WHITE RHINOCEROS

The largest member of the group is the white rhinoceros (*R. simus*), also known as the square-mouthed, or Burchell's, rhinoceros, which, in addition to its great size, is characterised by its ugly, broad, and bluntly-truncated muzzle and the absence of a prehensile extremity to the upper lip, as well as by the great proportionate length of the head; this, in large specimens, being more than a foot longer than in the black species. The nostrils form long, narrow slits; the eye is placed entirely behind the line of the second horn; and the ear is very long, sharply pointed at the extremity, with only a very small tuft of hairs, and its lower portion completely closed for some distance, so as to form a tube. The front horn attains a greater length than in the black species.

In the skull the extremity of the lower jaw forms a much, wider and shallower channel than in the black rhinoceros, and the structure of the upper cheek teeth is different. These teeth resemble in general structure those of the great Indian rhinoceros, having very tall crowns, with flat, grinding surfaces, no distinct buttress at the front outer angle, and the outer portion of the middle valley cut off by a partition. They are, how-

ever, quite peculiar among existing species, in having a large amount of cement investing the interior and filling up the valleys of the crown. Moreover, the third molar in the upper jaw, instead of being triangular in shape, closely resembles the tooth in front of it; a peculiarity found elsewhere only among certain extinct hornless species. Despite its name, the white rhinoceros differs but little in colour from the black species, the general hue of both being a slaty grey.

In height this rhinoceros is known to reach $6\frac{1}{2}$ feet at the shoulder, and it is said that specimens were formerly obtained which slightly exceeded these dimensions. As regards length, it is probable that this never exceeded about 14 feet; one of the specimens referred to below has a length of 12 feet 1 inch, and a height at the shoulder of 6 feet 2 inches.

There is even more variation in the relative length of the horns than in the black species, the second horn being sometimes a mere stump, and occasionally almost wanting. In other specimens, however, it may attain a length of 2 feet, while in some instances both horns are comparatively short. The front horn is characterised by the great size and squared form of the base, and the flattened front surface; it is longer and generally more slender in cows than in bulls. It displays considerable variation in shape. In adult bulls it curves, as a rule, backwards in a more or less bold sweep, the individuals exhibiting this form being known to the Bechuanas by the name of mohohu.

In other examples, mostly, if not invariably, cows, the front horn is slender and nearly straight, with a forward inclination in its upper half; specimens with this type of horn being designated by the natives kabaoba. When the front horn has a forward inclination near the tip, and attains the length of about a yard, the point touches the ground as the animal walks along when feeding, and such horns consequently always show a flat surface on the front of the tip, produced by friction.

HEAD OF WHITE RHINOCEROS

In the northern race of the species, whose horns formed an important article of commerce in the Sudan during the Middle Ages, and may have given rise to the legend of the unicorn, the front horn of the cow appears to be shorter. The longest-known horn of the white rhinoceros is one of a cow—the so-called kabaoba type—which was formerly in the possession of Roualeyn Gordon Cumming, and measures $62\frac{1}{2}$ inches in length; and there is also a fine specimen, of the same type, in the British Museum, of which the length is $56\frac{1}{2}$ inches. In a horn of the mohohu type a length of 54 inches is recorded. In examples where both horns have been preserved, the length of the front one in one case is $37\frac{3}{8}$ inches, and that of the hind one, $17\frac{7}{8}$ inches, while in another these dimensions are 33 inches and 13 inches. At the time when these rhinoceroses were abundant it was the ambition of every South African chief to possess a long staff, or *kerrie*, made from a front horn, and it is, therefore, probable that the largest dimensions recorded above may have been exceeded.

D 31
K

For years the white rhinoceros was believed to be confined to South Africa, although its characteristic front horns had for centuries been exported from the Sudan; but the species is now known to inhabit the southernmost portion of the Bahr-el-Ghazal province of the Egyptian Sudan and the district of Lado, in the Congo State, situated in the heart of Africa, five degrees north of the Equator. This northern white rhinoceros (*R. simus cottoni*) differs from the southern animal in certain features in the skull, and in the skin having a somewhat tuberculated character.

In South Africa the range of the white rhinoceros was always limited, and apparently never extended north of the Zambezi. For the last century or so the species has been unknown to the south of the Orange River, but there is a tradition that it formerly roamed over the greater part of Cape Colony. About the middle of the nineteenth century, when Gordon Cumming and, later, C. J. Andersson made their hunting tours, the white rhinoceros was comparatively common in parts of the Kalahari Desert, Ngamiland, and various districts between the Orange and Zambezi rivers. Indeed, Gordon Cumming states that on one occasion he saw upwards of twelve of these magnificent animals together in long grass, and Andersson and Chapman speak of having shot so many as eight in a single night while the victims were drinking at a water-hole during the dry season. The numbers thus met with, however, were probably drawn together from over a large tract of country, as drinking-places were few and far between.

In 1874 Mr. F. C. Selous met with a considerable number of these rhinoceroses on the Chobi, but on again visiting the same district in 1877 came across traces of only two, while in 1879 they had completely disappeared. In North Mashonaland there was still a considerable number between 1878 and 1880, while others were to be met with in a small tract on the Sabi River in South-East Africa. About 1882, however, Mr. Selous was only able to find a single specimen in Mashonaland, and it was then thought that this animal, which fell to his rifle, was actually the last of its race. In a remote corner of Mashonaland, however, some half-dozen were found living in 1892, two of which were afterwards shot and brought to England. In the north of the Kalahari Desert the species had been completely exterminated some years before 1890.

In treating of the black African rhinoceros, reference was made to the exclusively grass-eating habits of the white species, and the consequent restriction of its habitat to open grassy plains; and allusion was also made to its habit of walking with its head carried close to the ground; and likewise to the fact that the calf always precedes its mother when walking. It may be added that the mother appears to direct the course of her offspring with her long front horn.

As regards the time of feeding and taking repose, the habits of this species closely resemble those of the black kind. Mr. Selous states that "their sight is very bad, but they are quick of hearing and their scent is very keen; they are, too, often accompanied by rhinoceros-birds, which, by running about their heads, flapping their wings, and screeching at the same time, frequently give them notice of the approach of danger.

"When disturbed, they go off at a swift trot, which soon leaves all pursuit from a man on foot far behind; but if chased by a horseman they break into a gallop, which they can keep up for some distance. However, although they run very swiftly, when their size and heavy build are considered, they are no match for an average good horse.'

These animals were found in pairs or in parties of three, although sometimes considerably more might be seen together. Although there is some difference of opinion as to the temper and disposition of the black species, all sportsmen agree that the white rhinoceros was generally a harmless and inoffensive creature. Still, when wounded it would occasionally charge; and from the enormous size of the animal such a charge was a serious matter for those against whom it was directed.

EXTINCT RHINOCEROSES

Reference has been made to certain extinct species of rhinoceroses which approximate closely to some of the existing members of the group. Besides these, there is a multitude of extinct species, which ranged not only over Europe and Asia, but also North America. It has been suggested that America was the original home of these animals, whence they migrated to Asia and Europe; but the evidence seems equally in favour of the migration having been in the opposite direction.

These extinct rhinoceroses occur throughout the Tertiary period as far down as the Oligocene division; and even at that low horizon many of the species may be referred to the living genus, although in most cases they were unprovided with horns, while some of them had four toes to each fore foot. Rhinoceroses are, therefore, even more ancient animals than tapirs.

Mention has been made of a rhinoceros from Greece

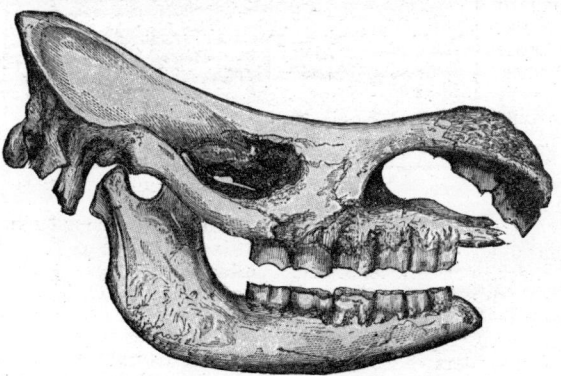

SKULL OF AN EXTINCT RHINOCEROS FROM THE BRICK-EARTH OF ESSEX

which was closely allied to the black African species, but there were also several other extinct Old World kinds resembling the existing African rhinoceroses in the presence of two horns and the absence of front teeth, while in some cases there is evidence that their skins were of the smooth type. One of the most remarkable of these species is the woolly rhinoceros (*R. antiquitatis*), so called from the thick coat of woolly hair with which its body was covered. Skeletons, bones, and teeth of this species have been found in the cavern and other superficial deposits of the greater part of Europe, including England, while entire carcases occur frozen in the ice of the Siberian "tundra." From these frozen specimens it has been ascertained not only that the skin was covered with woolly hair, but that it was devoid of the permanent folds characterising the Asiatic species.

The horns of the woolly rhinoceros appear to have rivalled in size those of the living African white rhinoceros. From the structure of the upper molar teeth it would seem probable that the woolly rhinoceros was a grass-eater; but in Siberia portions of needles of conifers and of twigs of other trees have been found in the interstices of the molar teeth, from which it has been assumed that the animal was a branch-eater. Possibly in Siberia it may have been compelled from lack of other food to feed upon leaves and twigs, while in the more southern portion of its range it resembled its allies in being a grass-eater. In the form of the skull, which is of great length, and in the structure of the molar teeth, the woolly rhinoceros comes very close to the white rhinoceros, of which, indeed, it may be regarded as the northern representative. About 1907 a mummified rhinoceros—presumably the woolly species—was discovered in the oil strata of Russian Poland. The skin of the head, of one forelimb, and of a considerable portion of the body is preserved, and appears to be in wonderfully good condition. The preservation of the soft parts is due, of course, to the oil in the stratum, which has probably converted much of the tissues into a kind of adipocere. Although horns of the aurochs have been discovered in peat, this is the first instance of the preservation of the skin of an extinct animal in oil.

During the Pleistocene period there were other species of rhinoceroses without front teeth inhabiting England and other parts of Europe, which had upper molar teeth of the general type of those of the black African species, although their skulls were very different. Of these, the leptorhine rhinoceros (*R. leptorhinus*) and the megarhine rhinoceros (*R. megarhinus*) are found in the brick earths of the Thames valley and other superficial deposits; while the Etruscan rhinoceros (*R. etruscus*) occurs in the somewhat older Forest-Bed of the Norfolk coast, and also in the upper Pliocene beds of Italy and France. The leptorhine and megarhine species have tall-crowned cheek teeth, and are characterised by the presence of a vertical bony partition in the skull dividing the two chambers of the cavity of the nose. In this respect they resemble the woolly rhinoceros; a rudiment of the same feature also occurring in the living Javan rhinoceros.

The Etruscan rhinoceros, on the other hand, has shorter-crowned cheek teeth, and no such bony partition in the nasal cavity. That these three species browsed on leaves and twigs may be pretty confidently inferred from the structure of their upper molar teeth; while a carcase found embedded in the ice of Siberia, belonging to either the leptorhine or the megarhine species shows that these had smooth skins like the living rhinoceroses of Africa.

Throughout the middle Tertiary rocks of Europe, as well as in the Pliocene and Miocene of India, there is found a number of rhinoceroses differing from any living species in the total absence of horns, while in those cases where their limbs are known the fore feet were provided with four toes. Some of these animals were of very large size, and their jaws were furnished with large front teeth. Moreover, in one of the Indian representatives of this hornless group, the last molar tooth was of nearly the same form as that in front of it, instead of being triangular. That all these species subsisted on leaves and boughs may be inferred from the structure of their short-crowned molar teeth; and here it may be observed that all the older ungulates had short-crowned cheek teeth, adapted for champing twigs and leaves rather than for masticating grass; whence it may be concluded that grassy plains are a recent feature in the history of the globe.

Hornless rhinoceroses also occur in the Tertiary deposits of North America, but at least the majority of these resembled existing types in having three toes on each fore foot; while their limbs were relatively shorter than in their Old World allies, and their bodies more elongated. Finally, there were certain other small rhinoceroses from the lower Miocene of both Europe and the United States in which the skull

THE WHITE RHINOCEROS

carried a very small pair of horns transversely placed.

In addition to the above, there are a number of allied extinct species which connect the true rhinoceroses with more generalised extinct types of odd-toed ungulates. Such, for instance, is the *Amynodon*, from the Miocene Tertiary of North America, which was a rhinoceros-like animal with no horn, and the full typical number of forty-four teeth; all three upper molars were alike, and none of them had the processes projecting into the middle valley which are found in those of all true rhinoceroses. Probably *Amynodon* also occurred in the lower Miocene and upper Eocene rocks of France. There were other allied types, but the above example is sufficient to show that the earlier rhinoceroses were far less different from tapirs and some extinct generalised forms, noticed later, than their modern representatives.

The rhinoceros family also includes a remarkable animal known as the *Elasmotherium*, which flourished during the Pleistocene period in Siberia. This creature was probably as large as the white rhinoceros, and, like that species, has no teeth in the front of the jaws. The skull had a bony partition in the cavity of the nose, and carried on the forehead an enormous protuberance which, during life, doubtless supported a horn of very large size. The most remarkable feature about the elasmothere is, however, to be found in the structure of its cheek teeth, which, while formed on the type of those of the rhinoceroses, are greatly elongated, and have their enamel so much folded as to present some resemblance to those of the horse. Indeed, the elasmothere presents a relationship to a rhinoceros somewhat similar to that which the horse exhibits to certain extinct ungulates noticed in the sequel. The elasmothere is considered to trace its descent directly to the large hornless rhinoceroses, or aceratheres, of the Miocene period.

R. LYDEKKER

THE HORSE TRIBE

By R. I. POCOCK, F.L.S., F.Z.S.

THE existing species of *Equidæ*, commonly called horses, asses, and zebras, and referred to the genus *Equus*, differ so entirely in appearance from tapirs and rhinoceroses, that it is difficult to persuade the uninitiated that close relationship exists between them. That such nevertheless is the case is proved by their anatomical and osteological characters, and by the past existence of a host of now extinct species representing a practically complete series of types intermediate in character between tapir-like animals and modern *Equidæ*. These extinct forms, moreover, fully confirm the conclusion established by the study of the *Equidæ* themselves, that the latter are highly specialised organisms which in the course of ages have been evolved slowly, and probably gradually, from a much simpler and more generalised type of mammal. Tapirs, however, form a collateral branch off the main line of equine descent, and will only be briefly referred to later in connection with the origin of the pattern and colour of the *Equidæ*.

From the ancestral stock to which they can be traced horses have deviated mainly in three particulars, namely, increase in size and stature, reduction in the number of the toes, and modification of the structure and mode of growth of the grinding teeth.

In a horse's leg the part below the knees and hocks, which correspond respectively to the wrist (carpus) and ankle (tarsus) of other mammals, there is a single, long, strong, and complete bone, the cannon bone, representing the middle metacarpal or metatarsal of the normal hand or foot. This bone is jointed at its lower end to a series of three short bones or phalanges, corresponding to the three bones of a finger or toe, the third bone of the series, which is alone in contact with the ground, being expanded and, in the living animal, encased in horn to constitute the hoof. The two phalanges between the hoof and the cannon bone are the "pastern," and the joint between the pastern and the cannon bone is called the "fetlock."

Thus the horse stands upon a single digit of each foot, which corresponds to the third finger or toe of the human hand or foot. The evidence for this is as follows. In existing members of the *Equidæ* there are attached to the back and sides of each cannon bone two much smaller bones, the "splint bones," which, although complete at their upper ends where they abut against the bones of the knee and hock joints, taper away inferiorly, and cease some little distance above the fetlock. These "splint bones" are the reduced second and fourth metacarpals or metatarsals of the normal mammalian foot. In some extinct species which preceded horses in geological time, they were terminated by three phalanges which projected as low as the middle of the pastern, and, no doubt, carried hoofs comparable to the so-called false hoofs of ruminant ungulates.

These extinct forms, therefore, were three-toed horses. The best known of them are *Merychippus*, also called *Protohippus*, from the Miocene of North America; and *Hipparion* of the European and Indian Pliocene. The lateral toes of these horses did not, however, reach the ground, and were probably functionless.

In certain still earlier forms, however, like *Mesohippus* and *Anchitherium* from the Oligocene, the splint bones and their terminal phalanges were relatively much larger and longer, suggesting that these animals walked on three toes like a rhinoceros. It may be added that *Mesohippus* and *Anchitherium* are usually referred to the family *Palæotheriidæ*, which is in many respects intermediate between tapirs and horses.

Finally, in earlier deposits of Eocene age occur perissodactyle fossils (*Hyracotherium*, *Pachynolophus*), with four complete toes, like those that may be seen on the fore legs of tapirs, the additional digit being the fifth. Nevertheless, in these animals the whole region below the carpus and tarsus already showed the beginning of the thinning and lengthening of the component bones, which are carried to a much greater extreme in the genus *Equus*.

It is highly probable that the many-toed shorter-legged forerunners of horses were to a varying extent plantigrade and adapted to locomotion on soft soil, and walked on a large pad behind the middle toe of the feet, just as tapirs and rhinoceroses do. A useless vestige of this pad still persists in most existing species of the horse tribe as the "ergot," a small area of thick horny naked skin on the back of the fetlock. Somewhat similar patches of naked, horny skin are also found in all existing species above the knee on the foreleg, and in most true horses, in the restricted sense of the word, below the hock on the hind leg.

The function and significance of these so-called "chestnuts" or "warts" is unknown. It has been suggested that, like the "ergot," they are vestiges of pads; and those on the hind legs, judging from their position, may conceivably be so. But those on the front legs occupy too high a position to fall in with this theory, and it is not improbable that they represent a tactile sensory organ found in exactly the same position in many species of mammals, often unrelated to one another, like cats and lemurs; or they may be

STAGES IN THE DEVELOPMENT OF THE HORSE
A. Hyracotherium; *B.* Orohippus; *C.* Mesohippus; *D.* Merychippus; *E.* Pliohippus; *F.* Modern domesticated horse (with special points named)

glandular patches secreting an odorous substance, which by adhering to vegetation enables a strayed member of a herd to rejoin his companions when out of sight.

The evolution of horses in size and stature may be briefly mentioned. *Hipparion* and *Protohippus* were about the size of ordinary donkeys; still smaller was *Pliohippus*; *Anchitherium* and *Mesohippus* have been compared to sheep; while *Hyracotherium* was no larger than a hare.

The teeth of horses supply evidence of progressive evolution not less important than that supplied by the legs. They also furnish valuable characters for distinguishing the species, and are useful from an economic standpoint as approximately accurate indices of age. The permanent dentition normally consists of six incisors above and below, separated from the six grinders on each side by a long space, which contains the canines or tusks in stallions, but is practically toothless in mares, the canines being absent or vestigial in that sex. The grinding surface of the crown of each incisor is impressed with an enamel-lined pit, which forms an elliptical "mark" on the surface. As the tooth wears away with use, the shape of this mark gradually alters year by year, and ultimately disappears altogether, vanishing earlier from the central than from the lateral incisors, and from the lower jaw a few years before it goes from the upper. At twelve years no trace of it is left in the upper jaw.

After twelve years a horse's age can be roughly guessed by the position of a groove on the outer upper incisors. This groove appears at the root of the tooth at about ten years, reaches half-way down at fifteen, extends the entire length of the tooth at about twenty, occupies the lower half of the tooth at twenty-six, and gradually becomes reduced in length after that time. Up to the age of five years, when the permanent incisors are in use, the age can be estimated from year to year by the number of teeth in the jaws as the milk teeth are gradually replaced by the permanent set.

But the chief interest in the dentition of the *Equidæ* lies in the structure of the grinding teeth. These are normally six in number on each side above and below, the last three being molars which have no milk predecessors, and the first three premolars, or grinding teeth, which have milk predecessors. Occasionally, however, there is in recent horses an additional small premolar, the "wolf tooth," at the beginning of the series. This tooth may be present on one side only of either upper or lower jaw, and it has been observed in zebras and donkeys, as well as in true horses, both living and extinct. Its presence, however, is due to the common and accidental inheritance of a character possessed by the ancestors of all horses; and since its presence is not a sign of affinity between existing species, it cannot in itself be regarded as such between existing and extinct species.

Setting aside this archaic premolar, the six remaining grinding teeth are approximately alike in structure and shape, the premolars of the upper jaw being somewhat larger than the molars. They are long, prismatic, and deeply embedded in the jaw, and since they continue to grow until the animal is advanced in years, the effects of wearing away are counteracted. A tooth of this

kind is called "hypsodont" both in horses and other mammals. Each molar consists of a number of vertical dentine columns, individually highly irregular in shape, in accordance with which the coating of enamel forms an intricate pattern of complicated folds.

The spaces or "valleys" between the columns are filled with a substance called cement, so that when the summits of the columns are evenly worn down by use, the grinding face of the tooth forms a flat, irregularly quadrate area, the ivory, or dentine, of which is bordered externally by a complexly folded ridge of very hard enamel, while its surface is marked with two equally irregular patches of cement, also narrowly bordered by enamel. On the inner face of the tooth a deep infolding of enamel partially separates a small column from the rest of the tooth. This is called the antero-internal or simply the inner pillar, because it is situated in the anterior part of the inner surface of the tooth. It is of some importance in classification on account of the variation in development it presents in different horses. It is much shorter, for example, in horses like Arabs than it is in cart-horses; while in the extinct three-toed horse (*Hipparion*) it was completely separated from the adjacent column instead of being joined thereto by a narrow neck, as in all existing members of the family. According to the length of the grinding surface of this column, as measured by the investing enamel, horses' teeth may be briefly described as "long pillared" or "short pillared."

When the molar teeth cease to grow, they develop roots like those that were present in the short teeth with low crowns, called brachydont teeth, characteristic of tapirs and early ancestors of the horse family.

That horses are descended from species with forty-four instead of forty teeth is suggested by the occasional presence of the "wolf

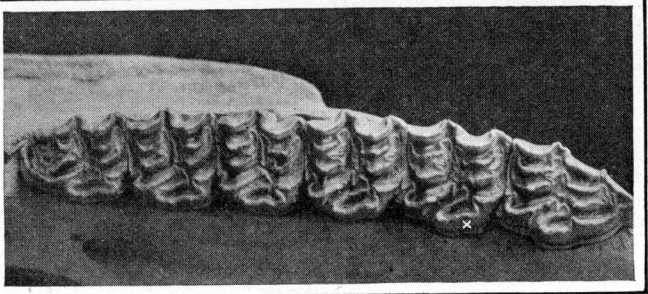

GRINDING TEETH OF UPPER JAW OF FULL-GROWN HORSE
x Inner pillar

tooth" or small first premolar. Confirming this, we find that even in such comparatively late forms as the three-toed *Merychippus* (*Protohippus*) this tooth was comparatively large and prominent. In this genus also the crowns of the molars were shorter than in modern species. In still earlier forms like *Anchitherium* and *Hyracotherium* the dentition was much more like that which is characteristic of mammals in general, that is to say, only the roots were embedded in the jaw, and the crowns, which were low, were furnished with ridges or cusps, the spaces between which were not filled in with cement, and there was no counteraction of the effects of wear by long continued growth.

As has been already stated, it is highly probable that, like tapirs, these early ancestors of the horse lived in moist, soft-soiled localities, as the structure of their feet suggests. No less forcibly does the structure of their teeth suggest that they fed upon vegetation of a succulent kind, and easily masticated by small, ungrowing teeth. On the other hand, their descendants, the horses, are eminently adapted for swift progression over hard, unyielding ground, and for feeding upon coarse herbage and other hard-fibred plants that flourish on mountain, desert, steppe, or open plain; and the structural changes that have accompanied the evolution of horses have been in adaptation to these conditions of life.

The true horses, then, constituting the family

Equidæ, may be defined as perissodactyle ungulates with pitted incisors separated by a long space from the grinding teeth, which, with the exception of the first premolars, when present, are markedly hypsodont, continue growing to an advanced age, and have a grinding surface exhibiting a complicated pattern of enamel,

GREY'S QUAGGA (EXTINCT)   *Photo, York & Sons*

dentine, and cement, those of the upper jaw being furnished with an inner pillar; with the orbit encircled behind by bone; and with the legs terminated by a single functional digit, the third of the typical mammalian foot, although the second and fourth digits were often present in a reduced form in some extinct genera.

This definition includes not only *Equus* itself, but such extinct forms as *Hipparion* and *Pliohippus* and *Merychippus*, mentioned above, as well as certain South American genera like *Onohippidium* and *Hippidium*; but it excludes the less specialised genera, *Anchitherium*, *Pachynolophus* and *Hyracotherium*.

In the genus *Equus* the inner pillar of the upper molars is united to the adjacent column by a narrow bridge, the lateral digits are only represented by the splint bones concealed beneath the skin, and in the skull the apex of the angle formed by the junction of the nasals with the maxillæ extends at most as far back as a vertical line passing behind the first permanent premolar tooth.

This last character, apart from others, serves at once to separate *Equus* from *Hippidium*, *Onohippidium*, and *Pliohippus*, in which the angle in question is continued nearly as far back as the orbit. A special interest attaches to *Onohippidium*, from Pliocene, and *Hippidium*, from Pliocene and Pleistocene deposits of South America, from the suggestion, made by Mr. Lydekker, that representatives of these genera may have been the horses alleged to have been discovered in South America by the first Europeans who landed there. Although this fact has been disputed, there is no doubt that these genera became extinct in comparatively recent times. As will be hereafter explained, the horses now existing in South America are descended from animals introduced by the Spaniards.

In popular language the living species and varieties of the horse family, whether domestic or wild, are known as horses, asses, and zebras; and this classification was formerly expressed in scientific language by calling true horses *Equus*, asses *Asinus*, and zebras *Hippotigris*; *Equus* comprising the species without hock callosities, with a flowing mane and forelock and a tail covered with long hair up to the root; and *Hippotigris*, the species differing from *Asinus*, at least in having the head, mane, neck, and shoulders striped. This classification, however, is not in accordance with modern knowledge, for it is now known that absence of hock callosities is by no means an uncommon feature in some breeds of horses; also that in the wild horse the mane is short, erect, and without forelock, at all events in the summer, and that the hair on the basal part of the tail is short as compared with the long terminal tuft. The characters, therefore, regarded as distinguishing true horses from asses, which justified the name *Asinus*, no longer hold good.

Moreover, the asses themselves comprise species belonging to two very distinct groups, one inhabiting Asia, the other Africa, and it is by no means certain that the Asiatic asses are not almost as closely related to true horses as they are to the African asses. The zebras, including quaggas, are still more heterogeneous, it being by no means established that the species formerly included under *Hippotigris* are sufficiently closely related to each other and sufficiently distinct from horses and asses to justify their union under one name. Too much importance must not be attached to the existence of stripes, because, in the first place, as will be hereafter explained, there are very strong reasons for thinking that all members of the horse family are descended from ancestors striped after the manner of zebras in general, and because, in the second place, some of the quaggas were comparatively so little striped that in general appearance they were at

BURCHELL'S QUAGGA

least as much like true horses as fully striped zebras.

In the following pages, therefore, the existing species of the horse family are referred to the single genus *Equus*, and described in the order named, under the following headings—quaggas, mountain zebras, Foa's zebra, Grévy's zebra, African asses and their domestic descendants, Asiatic asses, horses wild and domestic.

QUAGGAS

The trivial and scientific designations of the quagga (*Equus quagga*) are derived from the name " quaha " or " quacha," given to South African representatives of the species in imitation of their cry. It so happens that the first example to be made known to naturalists came from the Cape flats and is now extinct ; but striped equine animals with the same cry and the same structural characters are now known to range through the whole of East Africa from Abyssinia to Zululand, and thence westwards to Southern Angola.

Distributed over an area so vast and so varied in its physical features and exposed to widely different conditions of climate and temperature, the species exhibits marked local variations in colour and pattern, forming distinguishable geographical races or subspecies. The northern and eastern races so far south as Mashonaland are fully striped with black and white or pale fawn to the hoofs ; but southwards from Mashonaland occur races in which the stripes exhibit more and more marked signs of disappearance from the legs, belly, and hind quarters ; those that formerly inhabited Cape Colony, to which the name quagga was first applied, showing in some cases hardly a trace of striping even on the posterior part of the body.

These, as well as some of the decidedly striped more northern races, were known to the Dutch colonists, who, by way of emphasising the difference, spoke of the latter as bontequaggas ; but when the relatively less striped races became extinct, the term bontequagga dropped out of use amongst the Dutch, who to this day comprehensively speak of all the South African races as quaggas ; and since no competent authorities now doubt that these animals belong to the same species as the existing North African and the extinct South African races, the scientific and vernacular term

last characteristic being the distinguishing feature of the pattern of the species ; the stripes on the thighs are broad and on the legs numerous and close set ; the spinal stripe is distinct and widens behind over the saddle and croup, where it is usually separated from the adjoining stripes of the body and quarters.

THE MOUNTAIN ZEBRA

Of these northern forms the best known is Böhm's quagga (*E. quagga boehmi*) from British and German East Africa. Nearly allied to it are Jalla's quagga (*E. quagga jallæ*) from Southern Abyssinia ; and Crawshay's quagga (*E. quagga crawshayi*) from Southern Nyasaland. Related to the last is a quagga from North Eastern Rhodesia to which the name *annectans* has been given, a race characterised by the great breadth of the dark as compared with the light stripes.

South of the Zambezi in Mashonaland occurs Selous's quagga (*E. quagga selousi*), of the same general stamp as Böhm's quagga. In the latter faint stripes called " shadow stripes " are sometimes observable between the principal stripes on the quarters. These are also present in Selous's quagga ; but in more southern forms they increase in distinctness and extent concomitantly with the disappearance of the stripes from the legs. Chapman's quagga (*E. quagga chapmanni*), which ranges from Damaraland to the Transvaal, differs from Selous's quagga in having the legs, below the knees and hocks, sparsely striped. The reduction of the leg stripes is carried still further in Wahlberg's quagga (*E. quagga wahlbergi*), from Zululand, a race which is also distinguished by the great reduction in width of the principal stripes upon the hind quarters ; by the distinctness of the shadow stripes on this region, and by their forward extension to the withers.

Still more different from the northern races is Burchell's quagga (*E. quagga burchelli*), from Bechuanaland, in which the stripes have almost vanished over the hind quarters up to the root of the tail, and on the fore legs up to the shoulder, leaving the legs whitish and almost unstriped ; the body stripes no longer reach the middle line of the belly, and the shadow stripes sometimes extend as far as the head. In some of these quaggas, too, the lighter areas are ochre brown,

CHAPMAN'S QUAGGA

" quagga " may be extended to the whole series.

In the fully striped races of this species the stripes on the body extend to the median ventral line, those on its anterior half behind the shoulder-stripe, four or five in number, being vertical, while the remainder turn sharply backwards dorsally, no fewer than four forming a bold sweep back on to the hind quarters, this

so that there is no longer the sharp contrast between the dark and light stripes seen in the northern types.

The next stage in variation is reached by various races, all now extinct, which formerly ranged southwards from the Orange River Colony over Cape Colony to the flats round Cape Town. The typical quagga, of which only a coloured illustration is extant, was very like a dark-tinted Burchell's quagga, except that the stripes over the croup were broken up into spots. In other races, as shown by mounted specimens, the obliteration of the pattern was carried still further, so that only the head, neck, and shoulders were distinctly marked; the tendency of the obliteration being to produce a nearly uniformly brownish, or in some cases chestnut, animal with pale legs. But even the few specimens of Cape Colony quaggas that have been preserved show practically a complete gradation from Burchell's quagga to chestnut-tinted individuals with narrow dark stripes only on the head, neck, and shoulders.

Between eleven and twelve hands at the withers is the average height of quaggas. Adapted essentially for living in the plains, quaggas have broader hoofs than the mountain zebra and African asses ; the ears are markedly smaller than in other African species of *Equidæ*, and the callosities are intermediate in size between those of the mountain and Grévy's zebras. The voice may be described as a ringing bark, comparable in shrillness to that of a small dog, and representable by the syllables " quă hă hă," " quă hă hă," rapidly repeated and sharply uttered, a cry quite unlike the neigh of a horse or the bray of an ass or of Grévy's zebra.

When South Africa was first colonised by Europeans, quaggas were exceedingly common on the flats and plateaus of Cape Colony, where they associated in troops, quite commonly mixed with ostriches, white-tailed gnus, and other antelopes. They were finally exterminated by the Boers in the Cape and Orange River Colonies ; and the same fate is rapidly overtaking Burchell's quagga of Bechuanaland, of which, as in the case of the Cape Colony races, only a few mounted specimens have been preserved, although a few may still be seen in various menageries of Europe and America.

The habit of herding together practised by ostriches, gnus, springbok, and quaggas is probably for the mutual benefit of the species concerned. It seems likely that the senses of sight, scent, and hearing are developed in a varying degree in the different species, and that through one of these channels the proximity of a dangerous enemy would be detected by the members of one of the associated species before it became apparent to the others. Ostriches, for instance, by reason of their stature and keen vision would discover the presence of man or lions by sight long before they would be visible to quaggas or gnus. The quaggas, on the other hand, would become aware of their approach by scent before the ostriches, which are defective in this sense, took the alarm. And it is well

GRÉVY'S ZEBRA

known that with animals of this kind fear is extremely infectious, for when one member of a troop, however heterogeneous, begins to run, the rest are on the *qui vive* in a moment, ready to follow suit.

MOUNTAIN ZEBRA

The mountain zebra (*E. zebra*), which takes its vernacular name from its occurrence in the mountains of Cape Colony, as opposed to the plains where the quagga was found, was the first species of zebra to be scientifically described and named by Linnæus, who regarded the specimen he saw depicted as the male of the typical quagga. With the exception of the belly, on which the stripes are absent or evanescent, this species is covered with numerous stripes over the head, neck, body, and legs down to the hoofs. The stripes are for the most part narrow and close-set, except on the quarters, where they are very broad and widely spaced. The spinal stripe is exceedingly narrow and linear, and is joined throughout its length to the transverse stripes of the body, the great majority of which run vertically up to it, only the two uppermost of the stripes on the quarters passing obliquely downwards and forwards on to the body in front of the " stifle-joint," as the true knee of the hind leg is called.

The uppermost of these, called the croup-stripe, passes on each side to the root of the tail, forming a triangular space, which is crossed transversely by stripes running from the median spinal stripe and becoming progressively shorter towards the tail. This pattern, formerly supposed to be distinctive of the mountain zebra, is called the " gridiron." On the muzzle there is a considerable amount of tan.

The mountain zebra is a small, sturdily-built animal, standing about eleven and a half hands at the withers. The ears are long and asinine and the hoofs very narrow, with a remarkably broad, uncompressed " frog," as the hinder part of the sole is termed. The chestnuts are exceptionally large ; much larger, in fact, than in any other species of *Equus*. The hair along the spine grows forwards from the withers, and there is always a pendent lappet of skin or small dewlap on the throat, two features in which this species differs from all other members of the genus *Equus*.

In the typical Cape Colony race of this zebra the dark stripes are wider than the light stripes, and the latter are whitish or pale ochre ; but in Southern Angola another race has been recently discovered, in which the pale bands are relatively much wider and darker ochre in tint. This was named *Equus zebra penricei*, and probably hardly differs from another imperfectly known race from German South-West Africa named *E. zebra hartmannæ*.

Although formerly abundant in all the hill regions of the extreme south of Africa, as far east as the Drakensberg Mountains, this species, owing to reckless slaughter by the Boers, was rapidly verging on extinction in Cape Colony, until protective means were taken to preserve the few herds that remained in inaccessible parts of the country. These herds number up to a dozen individuals, one of which is set apart as a sentinel who warns the rest by a shrill cry of the approach of danger, when the whole herd gallops away, covering the precipitous ground with speed and precision.

To exaggerated reports of the difficulty experienced in breaking adult specimens of this species to harness must be attributed the popular but erroneous belief that all zebras are untameable, a belief the falseness of which has been demonstrated again and again in other species of zebras and quaggas, and more than once in connection with the one now under discussion. In captivity this species is remarkably silent, seldom uttering more than an angry squeal, an attribute in which it differs markedly from quaggas and Grévy's zebras. Although its voice has been described as a neigh, it is highly improbable that it resembles in reality the neigh of a horse.

FOA'S ZEBRA

Foa's zebra (*E. foai*) is a very rare species, confined, so far as is known, to the mountains opposite Tete, on the north bank of the Zambezi, where a few specimens were obtained by the traveller after whom the animal was named. The stripes are very narrow and numerous, the legs being fully banded both outside and inside to the fetlocks, which are black, and the stripes on the body extending to the ventral middle line. The hind quarters are marked up to the summit of the croup with many narrow, obliquely longitudinal stripes, of which the uppermost three are confluent with the last of the body stripes, which descends almost vertically just in front of the stifle joint of the hind leg.

Between the shoulder stripes and the hind quarters the body is marked with about ten vertical stripes, of which only the last stripe close to the hind quarters turns backwards over the croup; the spinal stripe is distinct and rather broad, and is separated from the body stripes almost throughout its extent; but on the summit of the croup short transverse stripes pass laterally from its vicinity to the adjacent stripes of the quarters, forming a narrow gridiron such as is seen in some races of quaggas.

There are thirteen narrow stripes on the neck from behind the ears to the shoulder stripes. The ears are moderately long and the chestnuts on the fore legs small. Although probably most nearly related to Crawshay's quagga, Foa's zebra differs from all the subspecies of *E. quagga* in that the dorsal ends of the stripes on the posterior half of the body, with the exception of the last, do not turn obliquely backwards towards or over the croup.

GRÉVY'S ZEBRA

Grévy's zebra (*E. grévyi*) was named after the President of the French Republic, in whose time the first specimens to be made known to science were sent to France from Shoa by King Menelik of Abyssinia. There is abundant evidence, however, that this handsome species was not only known to Europeans in the Middle Ages, but was the real Hippotigris of the Roman circus.

This zebra, the largest and, in some respects, the handsomest of all the striped *Equidæ*—large specimens standing up to about thirteen hands at the withers —differs both in pattern and structural characters from all other species. The stripes on the head, body and legs, which are fully marked to the hoofs, are narrow, numerous, and close-set. On the middle of the neck they are commonly broader. On the body they run vertically from the spinal area as far back as the quarters, but do not pass on to the belly.

The spinal stripe is broad and separated from the upper ends of the body stripes from the beginning of the lumbar region by a pale area which widens considerably on the croup, the croup itself being marked with very narrow stripes inclining obliquely downwards and backwards, and passing into the narrow longitudinal stripes on the thighs. The muzzle is mostly ashy grey. The neck is deep and short, and the head correspondingly long and heavy, so that the mouth may reach the ground for grazing.

The ears are long and flexible, but their most remarkable characteristic is their great width, a feature in which they are quite unlike the ears of all known members of the horse tribe. The callosities are exceedingly small, and the hoofs, though small, are oval, with the " frog " broad behind. In the typical race from the highlands of Shoa, the coloration is markedly black and white ; but in Somaliland there occurs a different race, known as *E. grévyi berberensis*, in which the dark stripes are chocolate-brown, and the intervening light stripes ochre, the entire tint of the animal being much more uniform.

The voice of Grévy's zebra is an unmistakable bray, closely resembling that of the African wild ass, and probably betraying closer relationship between these two species than between Grévy's zebra and any other existing species of *Equus*. It consists of a shrill squealing inspiration followed by a loud roaring expiration, the latter only differing from the corresponding effort of the donkey in being louder, more guttural, and deeper in tone.

These zebras are gregarious, associating in droves of less than a dozen to over twenty individuals. They frequent open country more or less overgrown with scrub, but are never found in thick bush. As is the case with asses and quaggas, the mare, which is fully equal to the stallion in size, carries her young about twelve months, and the foal, which is born any time from May to August, is remarkable for the extension of the mane from the shoulder to the tuft of the tail. The stripes on the posterior half of the body also are brown, while those of the head, neck, and fore parts are quite black.

NUBIAN WILD ASSES

AFRICAN WILD ASS & DOMESTICATED ASSES

Although the name *Equus asinus* was given by Linnæus to the domestic asses of Europe, the title has been extended to the wild African form, in accordance with the belief that at least one of the subspecies of the latter was the parent stock of the former. The prevailing colour is a pale slate-grey turning to sandy grey in the winter—at least, in some cases. The muzzle is white with ashy lips ; there is a white ring round the eye, and white on the belly and frequently on the legs. The mane and tail-tuft are mostly black and there are usually a dark spinal stripe, a cross stripe on the shoulder, and frequently indistinct or very distinctly defined stripes on the legs, these stripes being subject both to individual and local variation, and forming the basis for named varieties and geographical races.

The variety or race whence domestic asses are mainly, perhaps wholly, derived has a large dark patch upon the base of the ear as well as one at the tip, and the legs are grey, usually with indistinct markings, the spinal and shoulder stripes persisting. This form is said to occur in Nubia at the present time, but its exact locality is unknown, and in all probability it formerly extended much farther north.

South of Nubia proper, in the Eastern Sudan, on both sides of the Atbara river, occurs another race, known as *Equus asinus africanus*, with the ears black only at the tip, and the legs white and unstriped, save for a patch on the fetlocks. This is replaced in Somaliland by a third race, resembling the last in the colour of the ears, but with the legs very decidedly striped, and the spinal and shoulder stripes absent or nearly so. This is named *E. asinus somaliensis*. A form resembling the latter in the striping of its legs, but with the spinal and shoulder stripes well developed, as is usually the case in *E. a. africanus*, and in those intermediate between the two, has been named *E. africanus tæniopus ;* but its exact geographical area is uncertain.

In general characters, then, wild asses resemble domesticated breeds. They have short, deep necks and long heads, long, moderately broad and pointed ears, strong but slender limbs, and narrow hoofs, with the frog wide behind. Large specimens stand about 12 hands at the withers, and somewhat higher at the croup. They are swift of foot and graceful in their movements, their action when trotting with a long, striding step, the neck carried erect and the head at right angles to it, being peculiarly fine. The voice is the well-known bray, resembling in all essential respects that of Grévy's zebra.

As the wild prototype of domestic asses, the species just described has proved of great service to man, both as a beast of burden and for producing, when crossed with horses, the still more useful mule. Descended from a species adapted to an arid semi-desert environment where the mean annual temperature is about 80° F., domesticated asses do not thrive in northern latitudes, and are unable to withstand exposure to cold to the same extent as horses. This fact, coupled with in-

sufficient feeding and general neglect on the part of their owners, who belong mostly to a class unable to afford to keep the superior but more expensive horse, has led to deterioration, both in size and strength, of the asses of North and North-Western Europe, as compared with the wild animal. But in some of the countries of South Europe, in Egypt, Syria, and Persia, where conditions are more favourable, and where special attention has been paid to their breeding and welfare, the wild stock has been improved in the matter of size, and breeds suitable for different purposes have been developed.

The breed which presents the greatest departure from the ancestral stock is the Poitou ass, which ranges in height from about 13½ to 16 hands, and is characterised by a very large head, enormous ears, usually a long and shaggy coat, and hanging mane, comparatively thick legs and broad hoofs. Somewhat resembling a cart-horse in build, this ass is used in Poitou almost exclusively for the lucrative industry of breeding heavy-weight mules. For producing mules of lighter weight, the less clumsily-built Andalusian and Catalonian asses are reared in Spain. Except in colour and size, these animals, from which the Poitou breed is believed to be descended, differ but little in general features from wild asses. Like the Poitous, they are pale grey or nearly black in colour, the black being the most favoured of the two varieties. In Egypt, Persia, and Syria dirty white is a very common colour, and in these countries asses are much more used for riding, driving, and agricultural pursuits than in Spain and France.

Since they are not employed on any extensive scale for mule-breeding, no great attention has been paid to the question of size, and they do not reach the stature seen in more western breeds. Some of them, nevertheless, are very fine animals, being elegant in shape and docile in temper. They are principally used for riding.

Another breed of heavier build is used for ploughing and farm labour, and a third, characterised by a long body, is commonly employed in Damascus for draught purposes. Many of the eastern donkeys, however, are degraded animals, no larger than those of English towns. Still smaller are the dwarfed donkey of India, belonging to the Mahratta or Gudha breed. Although standing no more than 7½ or 8 hands at the withers, these little asses are remarkably vigorous and hardy.

When these small and active Gudha asses are compared with the huge, unwieldy, heavily-built Poitou breed, it will be seen that, although descended from a single species, domesticated asses differ extraordinarily from each other, not only in stature and bulk, but also in thickness of limb, breadth of hoof, and the nature of the mane. Allowing for the small amount of attention that has been given to the production of artificial breeds, the difference may be compared with those that exist between various breeds of horses. In one point in particular, however, the variation between asses is not nearly so marked as in horses—namely, in colour. Asses are not nearly so much

THE KIANG

addicted to partial albinism, and the normal grey colour of the wild species varies mainly in two directions, becoming intensified to produce black, and lightened to produce white; chestnut or bay asses being unknown.

ASIATIC WILD ASSES

The wild asses of Asia constitute a perfectly natural group, chiefly distinguished from those of Africa by having shorter and narrower ears, and by being sandy or rufous fawn instead of grey in colour (page 886). Several geographical types are distinguishable, but there is at present no agreement as to whether these should be regarded as true species, or merely as subspecies of one widely varying form. Nevertheless, it is quite certain that the differences between them are far less important and deep-seated than those which separate the zebras from each other. The muzzle, belly, legs, and the backs of the thighs are always lighter than the sandy or rufous fawn body; usually, indeed, they are whitish. The mane and tail-tuft are mostly black; there is always a distinct and broad spinal stripe, and occasionally faint stripes on the shoulders and on the knees and hocks.

BOKHARA ONAGER IN WINTER COAT

The voice must be described as a bray, since it consists of a squealing inhalation, followed by a more guttural exhalation; but, like the mountain zebra, these animals are remarkably silent, at all events in captivity, and never noisy, as are the African asses, Grévy's zebra, and quaggas. The stifled and suppressed bray that they utter has no resemblance to the neigh of a horse.

Like African asses, Grévy's zebras, and quaggas, the mares carry their young about a year, whereas in horses the period of gestation is a month less. Of these asses, the largest and handsomest is the kiang (*E. kiang*) of Tibet. Standing about 13 hands at the withers, and rather higher at the croup, the kiang is a powerfully-built animal, with strong legs and moderately broad hoofs. The general colour of the short summer coat is pale chestnut, which becomes darker and browner in the longish, shaggy, winter coat. With this is sharply contrasted the creamy white tint of the muzzle, of all the lower part of the neck, and of the belly and legs; the white of the thighs scarcely extends above the root of the tail. The ears are shorter and more equine than in the rest of the Asiatic forms, and have a dark patch at their base as well as at their tip.

North of the Himalaya the kiang ranges at least from Lhasa to Ladak, at elevations up to about 16,000 feet above sea-level. They live in the plains in small troops. The feeding herd is guarded by a sentinel, which watches the surrounding country at a distance of 100 or 200 yards from the rest, and when danger threatens gives a signal of alarm, whereupon the whole herd makes off at a brisk trot or canter, stopping now and again and wheeling round, as if in curiosity, to inspect the pursuer. They are never found far from water and are strong and fearless swimmers, boldly crossing broad and swift-flowing rivers. In this respect they are unlike African asses, which are notorious for their dislike of fording streams.

Although the exact northern range of the kiang is unknown, it is probable that the species does not extend north of the Kuen Lun Mountains. At all events the wild ass of Mongolia, the chigetai, or dziggetai (*E. hemionus*), is a very different animal. He is smaller and more lightly built than the kiang, but the hoofs are broader and rounder. Moreover, he quite lacks the parti-coloured appearance of the kiang, the whole of the upper side being, according to the season, paler or darker fawn, which gradually fades into dirty white on the belly, and into a paler shade of fawn on the lower portion of the neck and on the legs. The ears, too, have no dark patch at the base, and the middle of their hinder portion is largely white. Wild asses of this type have been observed at Kobdo, in North-Western Mongolia. They are said also to occur in Turkestan, and to be identical with the "koolan" of the Tatars.

In the deserts of South-Western Asia the dziggetai is replaced by a closely allied ass, the onager of classical writers, which occurs in Persia, Syria, Baluchistan, and Western India as far south as the Ran of Cutch. The onager (*E. onager*) is represented by several local races, which differ principally from each other in colour. The white of the lower surface and of the legs is more sharply marked off from the fawn of the upper parts than in the dziggetai, but less so than in the kiang, and the light tint of the back of the thighs extends above the root of the tail, and is continued as a pale line along the broader spinal stripe. The black tip to the ears is smaller than in the other two, and, as in the dziggetai, there is no dark patch at their base. Onagers stand about 11 hands at the withers; the legs are fine and slender, and the hoofs narrow.

The race which comes nearest to the dziggetai is the so-called Indian onager, or ghorkhar (*E. onager indicus*), which ranges from the plains of Western India into Persia, and at least so far north as Bokhara. Persian examples are intermediate in tint between the kiang and the dziggetai, and the black and broader spinal stripe extends to the tail-tuft. Distinguishable from the ghorkhar by its slightly higher stature, and by the presence of a larger and more conspicuous white patch on the croup, is a second subspecies known as *E. onager casteneus*, of which the locality is doubtful, although the only known specimen is alleged to have come from Kobdo, in Mongolia.

In the typical form of this species described from Western Persia, south of the Caspian Sea, the white areas observable in the ghorkhar are greatly increased in extent, so that the animal may be described as whitish, with three large pale fawn blotches, one involving the upper part of the head and of the neck, the other the middle of the body, and the third the outside of the thigh. The spinal stripe extends on to the tail, but does not reach the tuft, and is considerably broader over the saddle and croup than in the ghorkhar or dziggetai. A fourth race found in Syria and Mesopotamia, and known as *E. onager hemippus*, appears to be closely allied to the last, but its characters are not sufficiently well known for description.

MONGOLIAN WILD HORSE AND DOMESTICATED HORSES

Although a horse of any kind can be distinguished at a glance from all other kinds of *Equidæ*, it is not easy to frame a definition of the species, because the differences are largely differences of degree, and because domesticated horses seem to be descended from several distinct species, an origin which has resulted in a confused mixture of structural character.

There are reasons, however, for thinking that the horses concerned in the ancestry of modern breeds were, with one possible exception, much darker below the knees and hocks than above them, a character not found in any of the asses, zebras, or quaggas, and that, whatever may have been the case with regard to the head and body, the mane was not striped, as it is in all quaggas, however nearly uniformly coloured they may have been. For the rest, there is always more hair upon the basal half of the tail than is seen in the other species; the ears, however large, are always relatively smaller than in the smallest-eared Asiatic asses and quaggas; the hoofs, however narrow, are generally relatively broader than in the broadest-hoofed members of these species, and, when hock callosities are absent, the mane is full and hangs over the neck and forehead, and the tail is furnished with long hair up, or nearly up, to the root. Finally, the voice is a neigh, and quite unlike that of the other species where it is known.

Until recently it was commonly held that the supposed ancestor or prototype of domesticated horses had long ceased to exist as a genuine wild species, and, in spite of rumour to the contrary, derived from Kirghiz and Cossack sources, it was never seriously doubted that the so-called wild horses of the steppes of Asiatic Russia were the descendants of strayed or abandoned animals, like the mustangs of the prairies of North America and the droves of feral horses of the South American pampas.

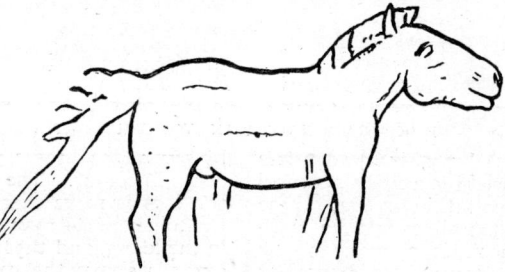

PREHISTORIC DRAWING OF A HORSE RELATED TO PRZEVALSKY'S HORSE

Interest in the question, and in the question of the ancestry of domesticated breeds, was reawakened in 1881 by the discovery of an apparently true wild horse in Mongolia; but it was not until twenty years later that a drove of the foals of these animals was imported to Europe from the neighbourhood of Kobdo, east of the Altai Mountains in Central Asia. But these foals were not sufficiently alike to inspire confidence in the purity of the breed of all of them; and although they have been reared and bred from in various menageries and parks, we do not as yet know for certain the true characters of the wild species, which was named Przevalsky's horse (*Equus przevalskii*) after its discoverer, for it appears that more than one type is at the present time passing under that name in Europe.

One kind, however, seems to be marked off from all domesticated breeds. This, which may be regarded as a genuine wild animal, is a pony with a large head, a rounded forehead, an erect or hog-mane, and a tail furnished in its basal part with hairs short as compared with those forming the long terminal tuft; with ergots on all four fetlocks, and callosities on the hind as well as on the fore legs, and with the legs moderately slender and the hoofs not broad. The general colour is dun, becoming paler on the nose and belly, while the mane, tail-tuft, ear-tips, and lower halves of the legs are black; there is also a narrow black spinal stripe, traces of a stripe or stripes on the shoulders, and indistinct stripes above the knees and hocks. In the winter the coat is long, the mane falls a little to one side, and the beard on the lower jaw and the fetlock tufts are longer than in the summer; but even in the winter the pale-coloured hair on the base of the tail only measures from two to four inches in length.

In the skull the molar or cheek teeth are unusually large, with long inner pillars; correlated with the size of the teeth are jaws of great massiveness, and other characters not seen in the skulls of domesticated horses, not even in those belonging to the Kalmucks or Cossacks, as would certainly be the case if Przevalsky's horses, of the type above described, were the descendants of escaped or abandoned ponies belonging to those tribes. Nevertheless, it is probable that this horse is one of the species concerned in the ancestry of domesticated breeds. For the rest, we must turn to other sources of information.

There are good grounds for the belief that the *Equidæ* were evolved in North America, and that in pre-glacial Tertiary times they migrated into the Old World by a continuous land connection between Siberia and Alaska, when the mean temperature of those latitudes was much higher than at present. Fossil remains from deposits of Pliocene and Pleistocene age prove that several distinct species of horses existed in those early days in Europe, North Africa, and North India.

These species are referable to two groups, one group, mostly of Pliocene age, containing animals characterised by slender limbs and a short inner pillar to the anterior grinding teeth of the upper jaw, and the other of Pleistocene age, containing species with thicker limbs and a long inner pillar to the teeth in question.

Of the slender-limbed, short-pillared species, one of the most important is the Siwalik horse (*Equus sivalensis*), so called from the Siwalik Hills of North India, where its remains were first discovered. This horse was about 15 hands high, and had a broad forehead, a convex profile, and a long, tapering face bent downwards on the cranial portion of the skull. Of Steno's horse *E. stenonis*), which also belongs to this section, and has left its remains in Britain, France, and other European countries, less is known with certainty beyond the fact that the pillars of the molars were even shorter than in *E. sivalensis*, and that individuals of the species sometimes reached a height of about 15 hands.

A third species was smaller than the two just mentioned, and had still thinner legs; the face was fine and narrow, but only slightly bent upon the cranium. Fossil remains of this type have been found in Pliocene deposits of France and Italy, and that the species lived in Pleistocene times is suggested by bones that have been discovered in South Devonshire, France, and Algeria.

Belonging to the second group of horses—namely, those with stout limbs and long-pillared molars—those best known had a broad-browed skull with the face almost in a line with the cranium. The slender-limbed short-pillared, and stout-limbed long-pillared horses, are believed by Professor Ewart to have been the species mostly concerned, in conjunction with Przevalsky's horse, in the formation of modern breeds.

That horses inhabited Western Europe in great numbers in post-glacial times, and were hunted and eaten by Palæolithic man, is shown by the accumulation of bony remains in human encampments of that period, of which the most famous is at Solutré, in France. This heap of bones seems to contain fragments of skeletons referable to two well-marked species, one of which was slender-limbed and lightly built, while the other was of a sturdy form with a large head and thick legs. Confirmation of the belief that several distinct species were known to Palæolithic man is supplied by certain rude engravings executed by him on pieces of horn and the walls of caves, and representing various types of horses, differing from each other in the size and shape of the head, the structure of the mane and tail, and in thickness and length of limb. These engravings also suggest that horses of more than one species were tamed and used for transport at an early date.

However that may be, it is practically certain that the horses in question had been evolved by natural causes, and owed nothing of their structural characters to man's intervention. Since, therefore, there were several species available for domestication, it is in the highest degree improbable that only one species was selected for the purpose.

All these facts and inferences point to the conclusion that domesticated breeds are descended from more than one originally wild species ; and this is borne out by the structure of the skull, teeth, and other parts of the skeleton, as well as by the external features of horses themselves. But owing to long - continued crossing and recrossing, the original differences between them have largely broken down, so that the unravelling of the ancestry of domesticated breeds is a task of extraordinary difficulty, to which naturalists have only recently begun seriously to address themselves.

Linnæus applied the name *Equus caballus* to domesticated horses in general ; and there does not appear to be any horse of unmixed breed in Sweden or elsewhere to which the name can be restricted. The duncoloured Norse horse to which it has been applied has been shown by Professor Ewart to be producible by crossing two distinct Scottish breeds. One of these is a strongly-built, thick-legged Highland pony, held to be probably the least modified representative in existence of the robust horse of Solutré.

A typical horse of this breed is low in stature, but strongly built, with short, stout legs and broad hoofs.

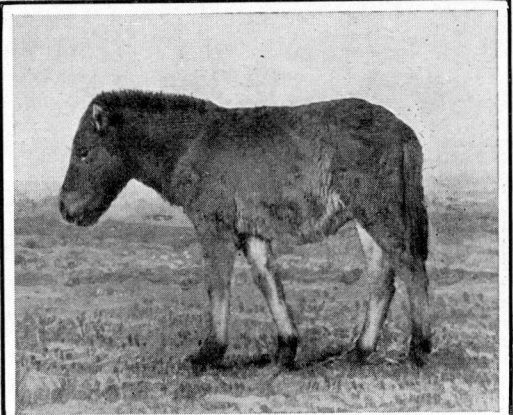
FOAL OF MONGOLIAN WILD HORSE

The mane is profuse, and the tail, which is thickly haired to the root, is set on low, the croup being distinctly sloped. The colour is dun, with black points, and the mane and tail are mostly black ; there is also a black spinal stripe, stripes over the knees and hocks, and frequently also on the head. Although very like Prževalsky's horse in colour, as well as in having hock callosities, this horse differs from the Mongolian animal in the structure of the mane, tail, limbs, skull, and teeth. It is believed to be the main stock whence the so-called garrons of the Highlands of Scotland and the active Clydesdales of former generations are mainly descended. The latter, crossed with larger Flemish cart-horses, seem to have resulted in the magnificent Clydesdales of to-day (page 799).

These are closely allied to the so-called shire horses of England, now employed for pulling drays and heavy carts ; and the shire horse itself seems to have been produced by crossing heavily-built horses imported from Flanders and Belgium with the old English war-horse, which was especially serviceable for carrying armour and armour-clad warriors. It was for these purposes that the large and thickly-set so-called great horses were fostered and developed as armour was gradually increased in amount and weight. With the introduction and perfection of firearms, rendering armour useless, these chargers ceased to be useful for the object for which they were bred, so that when the concomitant improvements of roads opened up possibilities of heavy vehicular transport, they were made use of for the purpose already mentioned.

Another breed belonging no doubt to this stock is the sturdy Suffolk Punch, long famous for strength and weight - pulling capacity. Thus it appears that the heavily-built horses already discussed trace their descent, in part at all events, from horses closely akin to *Equus robustus* of the Pleistocene. This broad-hoofed horse, which existed in Britain in the Bronze Age, is believed by Professor Ewart to have been adapted to a life in forests and wooded upland valleys. Other species, however, have probably contributed characters to the above-mentioned strains. For horses allied to *E. przevalskii*, *E. sivalensis*, and *E. stenonis* existed in Great Britain in the first century; and it has been suggested that the last-named, which was stouter-limbed than *E. sivalensis*, may have played

TARPANS

an important part in the formation of shires and other heavy breeds, just as *E. sivalensis* seems to have been largely concerned in the formation of English " thoroughbreds," as well as of some Irish horses.

Skeletal remains of a small-toothed, slender-limbed horse resembling the modern Celtic pony in all essential respects attest the introduction of this pony into Ireland in the pre-Christian era, and its existence in

DARTMOOR BREED OF CELTIC PONY

Britain in the Bronze Age. Evidence of the same kind shows that this horse flourished in England in Pleistocene times, and that it is identical with the third species of short-pillared, slender-limbed horse mentioned above as one of the forms from which modern breeds have been derived. This horse is believed by Professor Ewart to have become differentiated at an early date into a northern race, the Celtic pony, and a southern race, which spread into North Africa, and gave rise to the Barb and Arab of historic times.

The other pony above referred to, which, by being crossed with the stout, broad-hoofed Highland specimen, yielded a Norwegian dun horse, came from the Hebrides, and was of a very different type from its mate. It belonged to the breed just mentioned called the Celtic pony (*Equus celticus*), which occurs in Iceland—where alone the pure type is said to exist—in Finland, the Faröe and Shetland Islands, the Hebrides, Connemara, Wales, and parts of England. A pure-bred specimen stands about 12 hands, and is very like Przevalsky's horse in colour. The head, however, is small and well formed ; the legs and hoofs are fine, and there are no callosities on the hind legs, and the fetlocks lack the ergots, features in which it shows decided affinity to Arabs.

The mane and forelock are luxuriant ; the coat is heavy in the winter, and the tail is furnished throughout the greater part of its length with long, persistent hairs ; but quite at the base the hairs are short, annually shed, and stiff, and arranged so as to form a pad on each side. During a driving winter storm these ponies turn their backs to the wind, so that the snow accumulates on this tuft of hair and prevents the thinly-clad skin on the inner side of the thighs from being chilled.

Some Shetland ponies closely resemble the Iceland specimens above described ; others are more sturdily built, like miniature cart-horses, and have hock callosities, ergots, and the tail-pad poorly, if at all, developed. Like Faröe and Hebridean ponies, these appear to have a larger or smaller admixture of " forest " pony blood in their veins.

It is highly probable, as Professor Ridgeway has shown, that the forerunners of these ponies were taken to Iceland, the Hebrides and Faröe Islands by settlers from Ireland ; and it is in the west of Ireland that remnants of the same stock still linger among modern Connemara ponies. These at the present time are, however, a mixed breed, the characters of which are gradually swamping those of the Celtic pony, just as the characters of the latter have been to an even greater extent already obliterated in the moorland ponies of Wales, Devonshire, and the New Forest.

The close resemblance between " Arabs " and Celtic ponies has already been alluded to. In a pure-bred Arab the head is small, with a sinuous profile, the face being convex between the eyes and depressed in front of them, with a delicate, tapering muzzle ; the tail, which is long-haired to the root, is set on high, the croup being flat instead of sloped ; the legs are slender, and not expanded towards the fetlocks and hoofs, the latter being small and well rounded ; the mane is long, but not so thick or luxuriant as in the Celtic pony ; finally, the chestnuts on the hind legs and the ergots on all four fetlocks are not infrequently absent. The colour is variable, but bay, with black points, mane, and tail, is usually regarded as that of the primitive stock. The height is generally between 14 and 15 hands. The skeleton naturally conforms to the shape of the body, the pelvis, for example, being set on more horizontally than in the breeds with a sloping croup.

Several different breeds of Arabs are distinguished, but they merely differ from each other in points of minor importance. A better-marked local variety from Morocco, commonly called the Barb, is perhaps as famous in history as the Arab itself. Agreeing closely with the Arab in most features, the Barb is chiefly distinguished by having the quarters less flat, and the tail inserted at a lower level, as in the Celtic pony.

Until recently it was commonly held that the home

SHETLAND PONY

of the Arab horse, which has been variously named *arabicus*, *asiaticus*, *africanus*, and *libycus*, was the country from which the breed takes its name. Professor Ridgeway, however, has shown from historical data that this belief is erroneous, for the horses that made their appearance in Babylon, Palestine, and Greece not long before 1500 B.C. were coarse, thick-set animals. Moreover, the nomad Arabs of Arabia had no horses until after the Christian era—whereas the Egyptians are known to have possessed horses at least as early as 1500 B.C.—and these horses appear to have resembled modern Arabian or Barb horses in all essential respects, differing totally from the horses of which the Greeks and Babylonians became possessed at about that date. And classical literature proves that as early as 1000 B.C. North African horses were highly esteemed and eagerly sought for by the nations of the Mediterranean area, among whom they were famed for swiftness of foot. Nevertheless, it is practically beyond doubt that the ancestor, or ancestors, of this horse entered Africa from Europe or Asia, or from both sources, at a time when the union between these three continents was much more intimate than it is at the present time.

As has already been said, Professor Ewart believes the Libyan horse to have been a southern offshoot of the slender-limbed, short-pillared species, which also gave rise to the Celtic pony in the north ; and fossil remains closely akin to this type have been discovered in Pleistocene deposits in the south of France and North Africa. On the other hand, Mr. Lydekker considers the Libyan horse to be lineally descended from *E. sivalensis*, the essential characters of which have been described, this opinion being founded upon the structure of the skull of modern Arab horses. There seems, however, to be no certainty that Arabs are of unmixed descent, and it is possible that both the above named species may be involved in their ancestry.

The high appreciation of the qualities of North African horses in ancient times lasted without diminution down to the time of the development of the English thoroughbred, which, on account of its superior speed and strength, has to all intents and purposes supplanted the Barb and Arab in modern times. Thus from early historical periods there are records of the introduction of horses of North African descent into the countries of Europe and Asia bordering the Mediterranean, whence in course of time they made their way northwards and were crossed with horses already in use, like the shorter, more clumsily-built animals of central Europe, which were used for the chase and warfare by the Germans, Sigynnæ, Scythians, and other barbarian tribes. This, and much more concerning North African and other horses, has been fully discussed by Professor Ridgeway ; but the exact extent to which North African blood has affected modern breeds is uncertain.

The most famous breed of modern times whose essential qualities are largely, at all events, traceable to North African blood is the English thoroughbred, a horse which, although the finest in the world for the particular purpose—that is to say, racing—for which it has been bred, cannot claim unmixed purity of descent. English racehorses of the present day are the descendants, perfected by generations of selective breeding, of horses of North African origin, imported from the time of James I. downwards, and crossed with English breeds of mixed descent. The most famous of these imported horses were three stallions brought to England in the latter part of the seventeenth and the early part of the eighteenth centuries, namely the Byerly Turk, the Darley Arab, and the Godolphin Barb,

which have given rise to the best strains of racers of the present time. Long prior to this, however, both Turkish and Barb horses had been introduced into England for hunting and racing. It was with mares bred mainly from these that the three stallions above mentioned were crossed, thus laying the foundation of the modern type of racehorse. It may be added that the historically famous Irish hunters were derived from

DARLEY ARABIAN
From a contemporary painting

Spanish horses of Barb descent imported into Ireland several hundred years ago.

To an infusion of thoroughbred blood, greater or less according to requirements, with the blood of old English horses may be traced the main characteristics of many domesticated breeds. Cavalry horses are probably the descendants of the heavy armour-carrying chargers of the Middle Ages, modified by a thoroughbred cross, which has eliminated a good deal of the robustness, and substituted pace and a lighter build. Heavy-weight hunters may be obtained by crossing thoroughbreds with Cleveland Bays or with Suffolk Punches if exceptional strength is required ; and Cleveland Bays were bred in Yorkshire from a Barb stallion and cart-mares, when a powerful yet fairly light and swift horse was wanted for coach driving. Good sturdy carriage horses and strong hacks are made by blending thoroughbreds with Suffolk Punches ; the offspring of Clydesdales or Shires and thoroughbreds are first-rate van horses, and lightly-built ladies' hacks are obtained by crossing small thoroughbreds with Welsh, Exmoor, or Connemara ponies.

English thoroughbreds were exported to North America towards the end of the eighteenth century. From these and from subsequently added blood have sprung the best American lightly-built horses, of which the trotter is perhaps the most famous. But long before that date the States possessed horses descended from feral animals which had escaped from the early Spanish settlers or been abandoned by them. These horses, or "mustangs," were at all events mainly of Barb descent, like the feral horses of the Argentine pampas, which had also been taken there by colonists from Spain.

In the East, North African blood, it has been claimed, has left its stamp upon the Kathiawar ponies of India, and also apparently more or less upon the ponies of Burma, Sumatra, Java, and other islands of the Malay Archipelago, which were, perhaps, brought southwards into these countries from Mongolia, and may be, in part, at all events, modified descendants of Przevalsky's horse; but certain peculiarities in the skull of some of these ponies seem to suggest a different, but at present unknown, origin.

However that may be, indications of their descent from Przevalsky's horse are to be seen in domesticated Mongolian and Korean ponies, and also in the Tarpan or feral horses of the Russian Steppes. Some of the latter, indeed, seem to be a nearly pure cross between Przevalsky's horse and the Celtic pony. That Przevalsky's horse, or a form closely akin to it, was an inhabitant of Western Europe in prehistoric times there is a good deal of evidence to prove, and it has been

ENGLISH THOROUGHBRED RACEHORSE

said that some of the existing Connemara ponies bear strongly upon them the impress of descent from that wild species.

EVOLUTION & SIGNIFICANCE OF COLOUR & PATTERN

From the foregoing account of Przevalsky's horse and of the Celtic, forest, and Arab horses, which are believed to be existing representative types of distinct species or races from which modern breeds are to a great extent descended, it may be inferred that the general colour of ancestral horses was brown or dun, with black mane and tail-tuft and black "points," that is to say, black below the knees and hocks. But domesticated horses are exceedingly variable in colour, presenting every gradation from black to white, through various shades of brown, chestnut, dun, and grey. They are also greatly addicted to partial albinism, which in blacks, chestnuts, and bays shows itself sometimes as a white "star" on the forehead, a "blaze" down the face, or white "bracelets" or "stockings" on the legs or as larger or smaller patches on the body; at other times as white hairs intermixed with black or brown hairs on the body and neck, giving rise to roan of various shades. Partially white horses may be "thoroughbred" according

to the stud-book, but they are "sports" from the zoological standpoint. So, too, must blacks, chestnuts, and whites be dismissed respectively as melanistic, erythristic, and albinistic sports. That chestnuts do not adhere to a primitive type of colour may be inferred from the redness of the mane and tail, the hairs of which in all wild *Equidæ* are mostly black; and it is highly improbable that any of the ancestors concerned in the origin of domesticated breeds were black or white, because these colours, except in rare cases and under certain conditions are eliminated by natural processes on account of their conspicuousness.

Apart from actual colour, horses of almost all breeds quite commonly show the pattern which is called "dappled" or "pummelled." This consists of a dark network surrounding pale spots or blotches. Less commonly, but by no means infrequently, they show dark stripes on various parts of the body, head, and limbs. Indeed, from the frequency with which stripes appear, especially in foals of domesticated horses, Darwin was led to suppose that horses, as well as self-coloured asses, are descended from species marked like zebras in a general way. He also thought that the dappled pattern was derived from stripes. The true significance of "dappling" is not clearly understood, but it is generally admitted that Darwin's explanation of the presence of vestigial stripes on otherwise nearly self-coloured species is correct.

The further question now arises : Is it possible to refer the pattern of zebras and quaggas to an earlier stage ? That there was an earlier stage is suggested by the fact that vertical stripes are a very unusual style of pattern in mammals as a whole; and that where it occurs, as in the cat family, for instance, it is traceable to the fusion of spots which have arisen from the breaking up of longitudinal stripes. Now, it was shown (page 786) that the *Equidæ* are descended from somewhat tapir-like ancestors.

It is, moreover, known that the young of all existing species of tapirs are dark brown or blackish animals marked with a profusion of longitudinal white stripes, or of white spots showing a definite longitudinal arrangement, a pattern no doubt characteristic of the ancestors of tapirs which were closely related to the ancestors of horses. When we find, moreover, that the pattern of young tapirs coincides in some important details with that of zebras and quaggas, in the longitudinal arrangement, for instance, of the white stripes upon the legs and hind quarters, in the presence of a dark spinal area set off on each side by a white stripe, and of white tips to the ears, and in other particulars that could be mentioned, it is difficult to avoid the conclusion that the pattern of zebras has been derived from such a pattern as is seen in young tapirs.

Hence, contrary to the usually accepted view, the white or ochre marks in zebras are in reality the stripes, and the dark marks the ground colour ; and when, as in the case of grey African asses, sandy or reddish fawn Asiatic asses, and dun or bay horses, the dark marks are reduced to mere vestiges, these are the remnants not of the stripes, but of the original ground colour, the greater part of which has been obliterated either by the development and extension of the stripes, that have become intensified in tone, or by the fading away of the ground colour to the same tint as the stripes. The fact that both these processes have combined to produce some of the nearly self-coloured, now extinct, races of Cape Colony quaggas from a fully striped quagga of the Mashonaland type, removes any difficulty that might be felt in applying the above-given explanation to the coloration of African and Asiatic asses and dun or bay horses.

Again, the analogy of other mammals suggests that the intermediate stage between the longitudinal white stripes of tapirs and the vertical white stripes of zebras was the disintegration of the white stripes of the former into white spots, which were at first irregularly arranged and subsequently fused into vertical bands. Hence it is possible that the dappled pattern of domesticated horses, which consists of pale spots upon a darker ground, may represent this early stage in coloration to which the horses possessing it have reverted. Reversion to a primitive pattern not uncommonly occurs when individuals of different varieties are crossed; and, as we have seen, domesticated horses seem to be descended from several different stocks. Of all dappled horses those that show this pattern in its most emphasised form are dapple-greys. Some of these may be described as blackish horses covered with white spots, and it is possible that their coloration represents more nearly than that of any other the stage in the evolution of equine coloration which preceded the striped pattern of zebras.

To those who have only seen zebras in museums and menageries it may seem incredible that their coloration, conspicuous though it be under artificial conditions, in reality makes for concealment in the natural haunts of the species. Yet the testimony of observers in the field is unanimous that at close quarters in the dusk

CLYDESDALE HORSE   Photo, Vinton

of twilight and at a distance in the open in broad daylight zebras are difficult to see on account of the blending of their black and white stripes to a uniform grey. It is also the case that when they take cover their pattern harmonises with the shadows cast by the foliage and with the rays of sunlight that are sifted through it.

Critical examination of the nature and arrangement of the stripes shows that their design helps to destroy the unity of bodily shape which more self-coloured species exhibit. In the first place, the ends of the stripes, except on the belly in some cases, everywhere cut the periphery at right angles, thus repeatedly breaking up the continuity of the outline. In the second place, the stripes differ in direction in certain parts of the body, those, for instance, of the hind quarters and limbs, and even of the posterior part of the body in fully striped quaggas, lying obliquely or at right angles to those of the whole or the fore part of the body, so that the appearance of two distinct objects is presented to the eye as it travels from one region to the other; and this effect is often still further increased by regional differences in the thickness of the stripes, for the thickly striped areas appear to be parts of an object which are nearer the observer than are those that are narrowly striped. It is to this combination of factors that the procryptic effect of the coloration of zebras and fully striped quaggas is due.

Some of the southern and extinct races of quaggas, however, had almost attained perfection in a different style of obliterative coloration

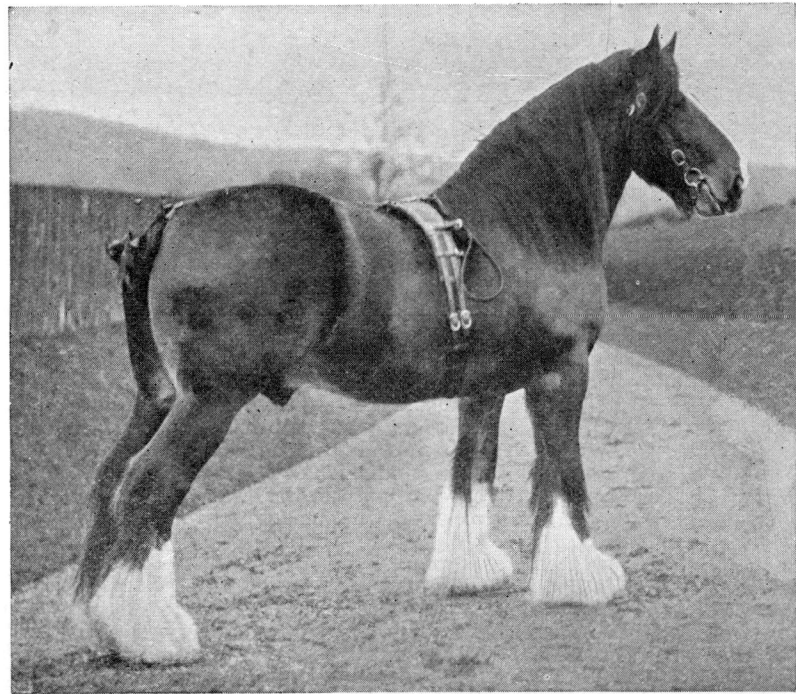

SHIRE HORSE   Photo, Vinton

L

in conformity, apparently, with life in a less diversified environment. That is to say, the lower parts of the body and limbs were white, whereas the upper parts approached a uniform brown hue, the comparatively slight distinction between the darker and lighter marks having been, it may be supposed, practically invisible at a distance. The meaning of this style of coloration, so well exemplified by Asiatic and African asses, is clearly understood. The darker upper side tones down reflected top lights, and the pale underside counteracts shadow, so that the visible shape of the convex and solid body is obliterated, and the asses in question, which are tinted above so as nearly to match their desert surroundings, melt into the landscape when looked at from afar.

Then, again, the significance of the whiteness at the back of the thigh in Burchell's quagga, in the extinct races akin to this animal and in Asiatic asses is probably two-fold. When these animals lie on the ground in their habitual attitude of rest, this white area is brought into line with the white of the belly and counteracts the shadow thrown by the hind quarters; but when they are up and on the move it makes them conspicuous from behind to others near at hand, and acts as a guide-mark, enabling the members of a troop to follow the flying leaders in the event of a panic at night. This probably is also the meaning of the conspicuous white area on each side of the spinal stripe on the croup of Grévy's zebras.

The difference in coloration between Asiatic asses and Przevalsky's horse indicates a difference of environment. Although this horse now inhabits the steppe country of Central Asia, there are some reasons for thinking that at one time not so very long ago it was more addicted to a forest life, like the broad-hoofed so-called "forest-horse" of Europe. This was probably at the time when its dun-coloured coat was much more distinctly striped than it is in the foals of the species at the present day. A horse so coloured would not differ greatly in pattern from a tiger, essentially an inhabitant of forest or jungle, with the tints of which its colour is in very close harmony. And if dapple-grey was ever the colour of an ancestral horse, it is easy to believe that this pattern, compounded of white spots and a black network, was as serviceable in the way of concealment as the black and white stripes of zebras are known to be. Especially would it lend itself to this end if the horses habitually took cover in woods, through the foliage of which the sunrays filtered, dappling the leaves and tree-trunks with spots of light.

MULES

In all cases where experimental breeding has been tried, it has been found possible to produce hybrids between different species of *Equidæ*. Sometimes these hybrids are completely sterile both *inter se* and with their parent forms, like mules and hinnies, which are produced by crossing *Equus caballus* with *Equus asinus*. At other times, however, the progeny appears to be partially fertile. A male hybrid, for example, bred at Knowsley between an African wild ass (*E. asinus*) and a mountain zebra (*E. zebra*)

formed a fertile union when paired with a bay pony mare. This fact, coupled with the sterility of mules, suggests that sterility depends, as would be expected, upon the degree of relationship between the species concerned; for there are reasons to believe that the mountain zebra and African ass are comparatively nearly allied forms, whereas it would be perhaps impossible to choose two species of *Equus* with less in common than the horse and the African ass.

But up to the present time experimental breeding has not been conducted on a sufficiently extensive scale to permit of any accurate conclusions being formed on this point. There is no complete and up-to-date record of all the hybrids that have been bred; but horses, Asiatic asses, African asses, mountain zebras and quaggas have all been crossed with each other. And it may be added that a hybrid between Chapman's quagga and a mountain zebra was regarded, until its history was known, as a distinct species which passed under the name of Ward's zebra. It is an interesting fact that, when quaggas of Chapman's race are crossed with bay ponies, the progeny, termed zebrules and zebrinnies, takes after the horse in colour, but is marked with narrow, close-set, dark stripes, quite unlike those of the quagga parent in width, number, and largely also in direction. Though like mules in the matter of sterility, these hybrids have shown themselves to be extremely useful animals for draught and carriage in tropical countries where horses do not thrive; but, since it can hardly be claimed that they are superior to the long-established mule, bred from species that have been domesticated from time immemorial, it is not likely that any great attention will ever be paid to rearing them.

A MULE
Photo, W. S. Berridge
Bred from a Spanish jack and an English thoroughbred mare

Mules, as commonly understood, are the progeny of horses and asses; but technically the term is restricted to the hybrid of the male ass, or "jack," and the female horse, or mare, the converse cross of the male horse, or stallion, and the female ass, or "jenny," being called a "hinny" or "jennet." Whichever way the cross be made the hybrid takes after the sire in appearance and the dam in size. Hinnies, therefore, in spite of showing greater superficial resemblance to horses than mules do, have never been much in request, on account of the lack of size and strength inherited from their asinine dams. Nevertheless, they are used to a certain extent in Ireland, and have proved most serviceable beasts of burden. Large Spanish and French asses, however, are used almost entirely for breeding their own kind, the production of "jacks" for mule-getting being the main purpose for which they are kept. Mules, in many respects, and for particular kinds of work, are greatly superior to horses. Relatively to their size they are more powerful, more enduring, less particular in the matter of food, less liable to disease, and longer-lived, a combination of qualities which makes them much cheaper to keep. Besides, when properly treated, they show none of the vice and obstinacy connoted by the epithet "mulish."

R. I. POCOCK

EXTINCT ODD-TOED UNGULATES

We have already (page 786) traced the modern single-toed horse as far back as the *Hyracotherium* of the lower Eocene London clay. A step back brings us to the still earlier *Phenacodus*, in which each foot had five complete toes, while the molar teeth had their crowns with small isolated tubercles instead of ridges. This small primitive animal, with a most generalised type of structure, appears then to be the undoubted ancestral stock from which the modern horse has been slowly produced by a process of evolution, which was going on throughout the long ages of the whole Tertiary period ; and it is at least noteworthy that the true horse only made its appearance on the globe at or about the same time as his master, man.

In addition to the animals referred to above, as forming the direct ancestral line of the modern horse, there were a number of other more or less closely-allied types belonging to the odd-toed group. Among these some of the best and longest known are the palæotheres (*Palæotherium*) from the upper Eocene strata of Europe, of which, so far back as the early portion of the nineteenth century, nearly complete skeletons, discovered in the gypsum quarries near Paris, were described by Cuvier. These palæotheres were tapir-like animals, with three toes to each foot, and molar teeth approximating to those of the anchithere in structure, but with a more elongated neck. While some of the species were not taller than a sheep, others must have fully equalled the largest tapirs in size. They probably resembled tapirs in having a short trunk to the snout, and likewise in the general mode of life.

The lophiodons (*Lophiodon*) are somewhat older animals, mainly characteristic of the Middle Eocene strata of Europe. Some were as large as a rhinoceros ; and their upper molar teeth approximate to those of tapirs in having the outer columns conical, instead of assuming the flattened form characteristic of the palæotheres. The lower molars, moreover, differ from those of the palæotheres in having their transverse ridges nearly straight instead of crescent-like ; and the total number of teeth is only forty, owing to the loss of the first premolar in each jaw. So far as is known, the number of toes to the feet was the same as in tapirs ; and while the true lophiodons apparently indicate a group which died out without leaving any descendants, certain allied forms probably indicate the ancestral stocks of both tapirs and rhinoceroses.

In the Miocene period there existed in North America certain gigantic rhinoceros-like ungulates which, while belonging to the odd-toed group, were quite unlike any other forms, and approximated in bulk to elephants. These titanotheres (*Titanotherium*), as they are called, had skulls somewhat like those of rhinoceroses, but furnished with a pair of bony processes placed transversely in the region of the nose, which were sometimes forked at the tips. The limbs were massive, and furnished with four toes in front and three behind. Some of the species had the full number or forty-four teeth, placed in close apposition to one another ; but in others the whole of the lower and one pair of the upper incisors were wanting. The upper molars differ markedly from those of other odd-toed ungulates, consisting of four columns, of which the outer ones are flattened, and those on the inner side more or less conical. The teeth are further remarkable for the extreme lowness of their crowns.

It was long supposed that those bony horn cores were sheathed with horn after the bovine fashion, but they exhibit a total absence of impressions of blood vessels such as are seen on those of cattle and antelopes, and also on those of the extinct group of giant horned reptiles, and they also display on the summit of each main prominence, as well as on those of the secondary ones, a distinctly rugose structure, comparable to, although coarser than, the rugosity on a rhinoceros skull which causes the horn. This has led Professor R. S. Lull to doubt the probability of the titanothere's bony horn cores being invested with hollow sheaths, and he thinks it likely that while the greater portion of these prominences was clothed with skin, the rugosities at the summits were surmounted by horns like those of a rhinoceros. This conception may perhaps render the creature somewhat more grotesque, but it would surely provide it with offensive and defensive weapons, which, with its evident prowess, would make the titanothere peerless among its contemporary mammals.

A titanothere referred to the genus or group *Megacerops* stands about 7 feet 4 inches at the withers, and measures rather more than 12 feet in length. The proportions are those of a rhinoceros, although the limbs, in order to support the enormous weight of the body, are less angulated, and primitive features are displayed by the shortness of the back and in the structure of the fore foot. Indeed, if the description of the latter is correct, the definition of the suborder Perissodactyla requires modification, for the fore foot of this titanothere is stated to be four-toed and

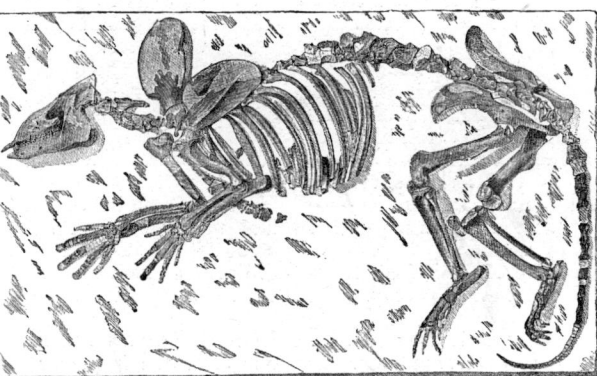

SKELETON OF THE PHENACODUS
Discovered in the lower Eocene of Wyoming, U.S.A.

symmetrical, with the main axis lying between the third and fourth digits after the artiodactyle fashion.

The Tertiary strata of North America have also yielded remains of smaller but allied ungulates, such as *Palæosyops*, which extend downwards to the highest beds of the Eocene, and have no bony processes on the skull.

The most extraordinary modification of the odd-toed ungulate type is, however, presented by the chalicotheres (*Chalicotherium*), which are common to the Pliocene and Miocene deposits of Southern Asia, Europe, and the United States. In these animals the molar teeth were of the type of those of titanotheres, but the limbs terminated in long curved claws, very similar to those of the pangolins or scaly ant-eaters, described later. Indeed, so like are the limbs of the chalicothere to those of the last-named animals that they were originally regarded as indicating members of the same group.

Mr. O. A. Peterson, from the evidence of specimens referable to the genus *Moropus*, has come to the conclusion " that *Moropus* is, excepting its unguiculate feet, essentially a perissodactyle in structure ; that the laterally compressed and cleft condition of the terminal phalanges is quite distinct in some of the early perissodactyla, and that by adaptation the unguals of *Moropus* were specially modified, and their differences from the ordinary type should not be regarded as of ordinal importance."

HYRAXES

WITH the exception of the extinct phenacodus, the whole of the ungulates already described are characterised by certain peculiarities in the structure of that part of the fore foot corresponding to the wrist joint of human anatomy. In the two horizontal rows of bones forming the wrist the constituent elements are arranged alternately to one another, and none of these animals has more than four toes to any one foot ; while in no case do they walk on the whole sole of the foot in plantigrade fashion. Then, again, the huckle bone, or astragalus, in the ankle joint, is always deeply grooved.

On the other hand, in most of the ungulates remaining for consideration the component bones of the two rows of the wrist joint are placed directly one over the other. This type of structure, it will be obvious, is inferior from a mechanical point of view to that distinguishing the wrist joint of the typical ungulates. The existing, and many of the extinct, ungulates we are about to describe frequently have five toes on each foot, and not less than four functional ones, with a rudiment of a fifth, on the fore foot. They may also walk partly or entirely in the plantigrade manner ; while in the ankle joint the upper surface of the huckle bone is generally flat. In all respects, therefore, so far as foot structure is concerned, these animals are less highly organised than the ungulates already described. The sole living representatives of ungulates with this generalised type of foot structure are the small hyraxes, of which there are numerous kinds, and the two species of elephants. The latter are, however, the last survivors from a number of kindred animals ; and there once existed several other groups of more or less nearly-allied ungulates which are now totally extinct.

Beyond the generalised structure of their feet, there is little in common between hyraxes and the elephants, which respectively form the representatives of two groups as distinct from one another as is the odd-toed from the even-toed group of the typical ungulates. It is, however, important to mention that both groups originated in Africa—a fact which may indicate near affinity between their earliest ancestors. Elephants have been enabled to survive to the present day by the development of a highly specialised dentition, and, perhaps, also owing to their huge bodily size, while the small hyraxes are sufficiently protected by their habits.

The small animals generally known as hyraxes, from one of their scientific names, constitute the suborder Hyracoidea and the family *Procaviidæ*, or *Hyracidæ*. They are so like rodents in external appearance and habits that in the English version of the Bible they are designated by the term "coney," which is the old name of the rabbit.

This rodent-like appearance is largely due to the fact that the jaws are armed in front with long, curved teeth, adapted for gnawing, and separated by a long gap from the teeth of the cheek series, although these front teeth are in reality very different, both in form and number, from those of rodents. In the upper jaw there is a pair of incisor teeth of semicircular form and growing throughout life in the rodent manner. Instead, however, of being chisel-like, they are triangular in section, and terminate in sharp points, their outer and inner front surfaces being covered with enamel,

BONES OF UPPER PART OF THE LEFT FORE FOOT OF A TREE HYRAX

which is wanting on the hind surface. In the lower jaw are two pairs of front teeth, of which the outermost are nearly straight, with long, conical crowns divided into three lobes ; both pairs of these teeth are, however, rooted, and, therefore, quite unlike the continually-growing single pair in the rodents. The cheek teeth, which are seven in number on each side of both the upper and lower jaw, approximate in structure to those of either the rhinoceros or the palæothere, there being some amount of variation in the form and height of the crowns of these teeth in the different species.

Like other ungulates, hyraxes have no collar bones (clavicles), and the tail is reduced to a mere stump. In the fore foot there are four functional toes, of which the outermost is smaller than the others ; the first digit being represented by a mere rudiment. The hind foot has only three toes, of which the innermost is furnished with a long curved claw, while the other two, like all those in the fore foot, carry broad and short nails, somewhat like those of a rhinoceros. All the bones of the limbs are fully developed and separate from one another ; and the thigh bone, or femur, lacks the distinct third trochanter characterising the odd-toed ungulates. In many species the socket of the eye is completely surrounded by bone, but in others it is partially open behind.

Hyraxes are alert little animals, with sharply-pointed muzzles and small rounded ears ; their bodies being covered with a thick coat of nearly uniformly-coloured hair, which varies in length in the different species. Near the middle of the back is a gland, surrounded and partly covered by a patch of hairs differing in colour from those on the rest of the body. Frequently the central part of this gland is naked—in one species for a length of fully two inches—but it is generally concealed by the convergence of the surrounding hairs. In most species the female has three pairs of teats, one of which is placed near the fore limbs, while the other two are situated posteriorly ; but in three species of tree hyrax there is but a single pair.

The various species of hyrax, about a score in number, are confined to Africa, Arabia, and Syria. In Africa they are found in the extreme south at the Cape, and thence range along the eastern and western coasts about as far north as 20° N., while they also occur in the central equatorial region. They are usually found in rocky districts, at elevations varying from near the sea-level to upwards of eleven thousand feet. All the species are now included in the single genus *Procavia*, or *Hyrax*, and as it will be unnecessary to notice all, attention will be directed only to some of

TREE HYRAX

the better known. Of these the Abyssinian hyrax (*P. abyssinica*), which agrees with the majority in the light colour of the patch of hairs surrounding the gland on the back, is of medium size ; the total length of a female specimen being 20 inches, and the height at the shoulder 8 inches. The fur is coarse and harsh, and in specimens from high elevations somewhat elongated, but short in those from the lowlands. The light spot round the gland is very small and inconspicuous.

According to Dr. W. T. Blanford, these hyraxes "live in rocky or stony places. A large pile of loose blocks, especially if there are precipices around, is sure to be inhabited by them. They are frequently found, too, in rocky watercourses. They appear to feed at night and very early in the morning, their principal food being the leaves and young shoots of trees and bushes. During the day they lie out upon the rocks in the shade, or retire, especially towards midday, beneath the rocks. They are timid and wary, rushing into their holes at the smallest intimation of danger. The only sound I heard made by them was a shrill squeak when suddenly a-larmed. They can climb over smooth surfaces of rock in a wonderful manner, their large feet aiding them in obtaining a hold." The typical race of this species occurs in the highlands of Abyssinia, the lowland form being of considerably smaller size. Its habits may be taken as characteristic of all the species, with the exception of those frequenting trees.

A GROUP OF BURTON'S HYRAXES

Two other species inhabit Southern Abyssinia, namely, the Shoan hyrax (*P. shoana*), and Bruce's hyrax (*P. brucei*). The former, which inhabits Southern Abyssinia and Shoa, and is nearly or quite the largest of the group, differs from all others except the Cape hyrax in having the spot on the back entirely black, and is distinguished from the latter by the great length of its soft and silky hair. Bruce's hyrax, which ranges from Southern Abyssinia to Somaliland and Mozambique, is a small species, with the spot on the back long and narrow, and yellowish or whitish in colour. It has been found at elevations of from seven thousand to eight thousand feet. Burton's hyrax (*P. burtoni*), of North-Eastern Africa, is an allied species.

The Cape hyrax (*P. capensis*), confined to Cape Colony and Natal, where it is known to the Dutch colonists as the klip-das, or rock-badger, is characterised by the hair being soft and fine, and of medium length, with the spot on the back of an irregular oval form, and black in colour ; the general hue of the fur being dark sepia brown, speckled with pale yellow or white.

Professor H. N. Moseley writes that these animals " come out to feed in the mornings and evenings, but also bask sometimes in the hot sun at midday. They are very inquisitive, and sit up on a rock, and look at one, and then suddenly dash into their hiding-place. After a time, if one remains quiet, they come out for another look, and afford a good chance for a shot. Their cry of alarm is a short, hissing noise. They had young at the time of our visit [November], and I met with two litters, each of three young, which were about the size of very large rats, with soft chocolate-brown downy hair. The young play about on the rocks together like kittens, chasing one another, and darting in and out among the clefts "

The Syrian hyrax (*P. syriaca*), the only species found out of Africa, inhabits Syria, Palestine, the Sinaitic Peninsula, and Arabia. It is a small or medium-sized and rather variable species, with somewhat soft and shaggy hair of a dull orange yellow or fawn colour, and the spot on the back rather small, oval, and its component hairs yellow throughout their length. Canon Tristram states that these hyraxes produce from three to six young at a birth, but that four appears to be the ordinary number. He observes that " they are far too wary to be taken in traps, and the only chance of securing one is patiently to lie concealed, about sunset or before sunrise, on some overhanging cliff, taking care not to let the shadow be cast below, and thus to wait till the little creatures cautiously peep forth from their holes. They make a nest of dried grass and fur, in which the young are buried like those of a mouse. The flesh is much prized by the Arabs. We found it good, but rather dry and insipid, as dark in colour as that of the hare."

The equatorial forest belt is the chief home of a certain section of hyraxes which are unique among living ungulates on account of their arboreal habits, while some differ from their relatives in the females having only a single pair of teats. As well-known representatives of this group, mention may be made of the Kilimanjaro *Procavia valida*, distinguished from all the others by the bright fulvous hue of the under parts, *P. arborea* from Eastern and South-Eastern Africa, and *P. dorsalis* ranging on the west coast from Liberia to the Cameruns and Fernando Po. The last-named species is of large size, and characterised by its long shaggy fur, black at the base and white at the tips of the hairs, and the relatively large size of the head compared to the body.

The Kilimanjaro species is found at elevations of from seven thousand to eleven thousand feet in the dense forests clothing the mountain. They live entirely in the trees, making their lairs and breeding places in holes in the boughs and trunks, and are stated to make a great noise at night. A female captured by Sir H. H. Johnston gave birth to three young. Many are captured alive by the natives for the sake of their skins, of which several are sewn together to make cloaks.

In addition to a few species from the lower Pliocene strata of Greece, forming the genus *Pliohyrax*, hyraxes are represented in the Eocene of the Fayum district of Egypt by species as large as tapirs, described under the name of *Megalohyrax* and *Sagatherium*. From the absence of similar remains in the lower Tertiary formations of Europe, there is little doubt that hyraxes are originally an African group.

ELEPHANTS

From their peculiar bodily conformation, huge size, which exceeds that of all other terrestrial mammals, and the high degree of intelligence which they display, elephants (suborder Proboscidea, family *Elephantidæ*) have excited an amount of interest surpassing that accorded to most other animals. And in truth this interest is not misplaced, since elephants really are among the most extraordinary and most remarkable animals known to the naturalist. In the structure of their feet elephants are some of the most generalised of living mammals; and this is true also of the structure of the rest of their limbs. When, however, we consider the nature of their dentition, and their marvellously-constructed proboscis, we find them possessing characters of the highest specialisation; and it is this combination of generalised and specialised features which renders elephants so peculiarly interesting to the naturalist.

At the present day elephants are represented only by the Indian and African species, but in past epochs there was a number of extinct members of the group which serve to connect the living genus with ungulates of a more ordinary type; and since it is only by a thorough comprehension of the characters presented by the dentition of these extinct elephants that the structure of the teeth of their living representatives can be properly understood, it will be necessary to devote some attention to the fossil species.

The most striking external peculiarity of modern elephants and their immediate extinct relatives, and the one from which their title of proboscidians is derived, is the long, flexible trunk, or proboscis, into which the nose is produced; this having the nostrils at its extremity, and being used as an organ of prehension, and for conveying water to the mouth. The build of elephants is extremely massive and bulky, the head being of great proportionate size, the ears large and flapping, the neck very short and thick, and the limbs long and stout.

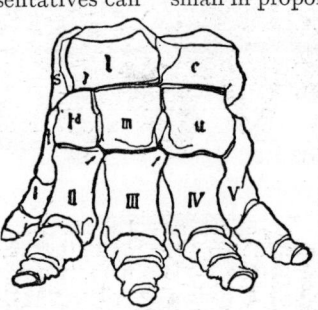

BONES OF LEFT FORE FOOT OF AN ELEPHANT

A peculiarity of the limbs is that the humerus in the fore and the femur in the hind leg are very long in proportion to the lower segments; the feet themselves being very short. The bones of the limbs are set nearly vertically one above another; and from this cause, together with the great relative length of the upper segments, the knee and elbow joints are not partially enclosed within the skin covering the body, as is the case in most ungulates. Consequently the knee of the elephant is more readily identified with that of man than is the case in that of the horse. It is owing to this peculiarity in the structure of its limbs than an elephant kneels down with its fore feet stretched out in front and the hind ones behind (page 815). The short feet are extremely broad, and have five toes each, of which the middle one is the largest; and from the extreme shortness of the feet the ankle bone is placed close to the ground, instead of being raised half-way up the leg, as in the horse. The whole of the toes are enclosed in a common skin, with a flat cushion-like sole; the positions of the toes being indicated by the broad, flat nails, of which there may be either three or four in the hind foot. The fore foot is broader than the hind one, and generally has five nails.

In most cases the males, and frequently the females also, have a pair of tusks in the upper jaw; these tusks corresponding to one of the pair of incisors of other mammals, and not to the tusks of the wild boar and hippopotamus, which are canines. There are no other front teeth in the upper and none at all in the lower jaw of the living species. The eyes are small in proportion to the size of the head; the tail is nearly cylindrical, and of considerable length, with a tuft of bristly hairs at the end; but the skin is nearly naked in the existing species. The female has a single pair of teats placed between the fore legs.

In addition to the proportions and position of the bones of the limbs, the two bones of the lower segment of each leg are distinct from one another, and in the ankle the huckle bone, or astragalus, is nearly flat both above and below, and of slight vertical thickness, but of great horizontal extent. The vertebræ of the back have very tall spines for the attachment of the powerful ligaments necessary to support the enormous weight of the head; and the ribs are of great length, and thus afford ample space for the viscera. The blade bone, or scapula, has a backwardly recurved process projecting from its spine; a nearly similar condition of this acromial process occurring in rodents.

From the enormous size of the skull it might be inferred that elephants have very large brains. This, however, is far from the case, the brain not only being small in proportion to the size of the animal, but also of a low degree of organisation. The brain occupies, indeed, only a comparatively small portion of the space lying between the socket of the eye and the region where the vertebræ of the neck articulate with the skull. The whole of the elevated upper portion of the skull is occupied by a mass of bone honeycombed into cells, and thus affords space for the attachment of the huge muscles of the jaws, and forms an adequate support for the trunk without unduly adding to the weight; the great size of this region being also essential in order to harmonise with the immense development of the lower part of the skull, which has to accommodate the enormous tusks and molar teeth. Similar cells also enter into the structure of the hind and basal region of the skull. Of other peculiarities in the conformation of the elephant's skull, it will suffice to mention that the nasal aperture is situated high up in the front of the face, and that the nasal bones are reduced to mere triangular nodules, instead of having the elongated form characteristic of most mammals.

The teeth afford some of the most essential characteristics of the group. Elephants have no canine teeth in either jaw, while in the living species tusks are developed only in the upper jaw. In the young elephant there is a minute pair of milk tusks, which are shed at a very early age. The permanent tusks, which are nearly cylindrical in section and taper to their extremities, continue to grow throughout the life of their owners, and thus remain permanently open at their bases, which are enclosed in sheaths of the premaxillary bones extending as high up in the skull as the aperture of the nasal cavity. In the young state the tusks of the living species of elephants are tipped with enamel, but this is soon rubbed off by use, when they consist of ivory alone. This ivory differs from that of other mammals in its structure, which renders it easy to distinguish elephant ivory from all other; and if a transverse section of a tusk be examined, it will be found to present a pattern like the engine-turning on the back of a watch-case, this pattern being absolutely distinctive of true ivory.

In their structure and mode of succession the molar or cheek teeth of elephants are unlike those of all other mammals. An elephant has a total of six cheek teeth on each side of both the upper and lower jaws; but instead of all being in use at once, in the existing species only two are ever above the gums at any one time, and one of these is only partly protruded; while in old animals only a single tooth remains on each side of both jaws. The molar teeth are elongated from front to back, and composed of a number of transverse ridges closely packed together. The anterior teeth are small, and include few ridges; but each succeeding tooth is larger, and comprises a greater number of ridges, reaching in the last molar of the Indian species to as many as twenty-four. The individual teeth succeed one another from the front backwards in an arc of a circle; and as the tooth in front is worn away, its place is gradually taken by the one rising from behind, till at length the sixth and last tooth alone remains. Although this mode of succession appears strange and peculiar, it is in reality only an ultra-development of what takes place among the pigs, and more especially in the African wart-hogs. In all pigs the last molar does not come into use till the teeth in front are considerably worn; and in the wart-hog the last molar is of unusually large size, and may be the only cheek tooth remaining in the adult condition, owing to those in front being shed. It should be added that while the last three cheek teeth of the elephants correspond to the true molars of an ordinary mammal, the three anterior ones represent the last three milk molars of such an animal as the pig, and not, as would at first sight appear to be the case, the premolars. That the three teeth in question are really milk molars is proved by the fact that in some extinct species they were vertically succeeded by teeth of simpler structure corresponding to the premolars of the pig.

In order to understand the structure of the molar teeth of the elephants, it will be advisable to take those of one of certain extinct species which, like Clift's elephant (*Elephas clifti*), from the Pliocene Siwalik formations of India and Burma, exhibit a simpler conformation than those of the existing species. Such teeth are composed of a number of low roof-like transverse ridges separated by open valleys. When unworn, these ridges are crowned by a number of small tubercles; but the effect of wear is to perforate the enamel of which the ridges are externally composed, and thus to reveal an elliptical surface of ivory surrounded by a narrow border of enamel. In the molars of *E. clifti* the valleys between the ridges are completely open and devoid of cement, but in the teeth of other species of nearly similar type they contain a certain amount of this constituent. Now it only requires that the ridges in a tooth like that of Clift's elephant should be greatly increased in height, with an equal diminution of their basal width, which would admit of a greater number being borne in the same length of space, and by the intervening valleys being completely filled with cement, to produce a tooth like that of the Narbada elephant.

In such a tooth the ridges become so tall as to assume the appearance of thin and nearly parallel plates, with their investing enamel thrown into a series of fine plications, or puckers; and the intervening valleys are so deepened and narrowed, that their contained cement is also in the form of exceedingly thin plates. When worn, such a tooth presents on its surface a series of narrow ellipses of yellow ivory, surrounded by elevated rims of the harder white enamel, marked by its characteristic puckers; while between the ellipses of enamel-bordered ivory come the layers of cement. The succession of layers in such a tooth is therefore arranged in the following order—cement, enamel, ivory, and so on. The worn crown forms a slightly convex or concave surface according as to whether it belongs to the upper or the lower jaw, marked by transverse ridges of different degrees of hardness and height, and thus yields a masticating instrument of great power and efficiency.

Elephants differ from all other mammals except tapirs in the fact that their lungs, instead of being enclosed in a membranous bag known as the pleuron, are in contact with the inner surface of the walls of the chest.

In their food elephants are strictly herbivorous, subsisting chiefly upon roots, twigs, leaves, and young shoots of trees, or grass and other herbage; such food being conveyed to the mouth by the aid of the flexible trunk, which is admirably adapted for such a purpose, as it is for drawing up water. There is, however, much popular misapprehension as to the other uses of the elephant's trunk. In addition to its use as a conveyer of food and water to the mouth, the trunk is the organ of touch and smell, and is altogether extremely delicate and sensitive. When any danger is impending, elephants, except in some cases when charging an enemy, invariably curl up the trunk out of harm's way. In regard to the alleged employment of the trunk of the Indian elephant for all manner of purposes, Mr. G. P. Sanderson observes that " the idea that he can use it for any purpose, from picking up a needle to dragging a piece of ordnance from a bog, is, like many others, founded entirely on imagination. An elephant might manage the former feat, though I doubt it; the latter he would not attempt. Elephants engaged in such work as dragging timber, invariably take the rope between their teeth; they never attempt to pull a heavy weight with the trunk. In carrying a light log, they hold it in the mouth as a dog does a stick, receiving some little assistance in balancing it from the trunk. Tuskers generally use their tusks for this and similar purposes, and are more valuable than females for work. An elephant is powerful enough to extricate a cannon from a difficult situation, but he does it by pushing with his head or feet, or in harness—never by lifting or drawing with his trunk."

An equal degree of misapprehension is prevalent as to the intelligence of elephants, at least so far as the Indian species is concerned; and all observers who have had practical experience of these animals are of

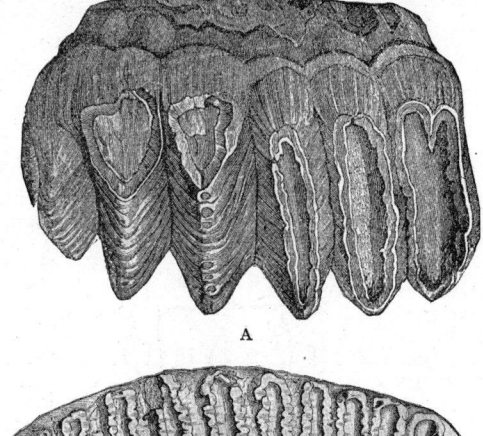

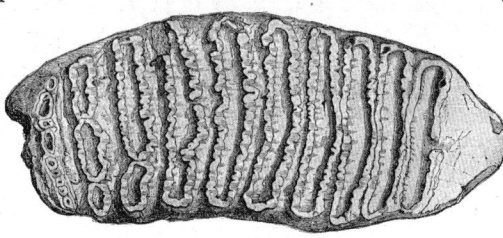

UPPER MOLAR TEETH OF (A) CLIFT'S ELEPHANT; (B) NARBADA ELEPHANT

opinion that their intellectual faculties have been greatly overrated. It is true that in captivity the Indian elephant exhibits marvellous docility and obedience, and is capable of learning to perform certain kinds of labour, such as stacking logs of timber, a task which at first sight appears to demand a considerable amount of intelligence. There is here, however, a great deal of confusion between intelligence and mere docility and capacity for receiving instruction; and there can be little doubt that the usefulness of the elephant is due to the latter rather than to the former trait. Indeed, the size and structure of the brain are sufficient to prove that the intellectual capacity of elephants is far inferior to that of dogs, and probably below that of most ungulates.

This view of their intelligence is confirmed by the fact that elephants, in spite of many statements to the contrary, are wanting in originality, and do not rise to the occasion when confronted by a sudden emergency or event beyond the range of their daily experience. As Sir Samuel Baker observes, an elephant " can be educated to perform certain acts, but would never volunteer its services. There is no elephant that I ever saw that would spontaneously interfere to save its master from drowning or from attack. An enemy might assassinate you at the feet of your favourite elephant, but it would never attempt to interfere in your defence; it would probably run away, or remain impassive, unless guided and instructed by the mahout. This is incontestable; the elephant will do nothing useful unless it is specially ordered to perform a certain work or movement." At the same time, in addition to its capacity for receiving instruction, an elephant has a very retentive memory, both for acts of kindness and of cruelty; and this has doubtless partly contributed to its character for general intelligence.

In this connection it may be observed that the Indian species, at any rate, differs from all other mammals in the readiness with which it may be tamed and domesticated when fully adult, nearly all those captured in India being quite mature before they undergo their training.

A curious circumstance in connection with elephants is that the bones of those which have died a natural death are scarcely ever found in the forests of India, and the same appears to be true with regard to Africa. It has been suggested that elephants resort to particular spots when about to die, as is known to be the case with the guanaco in South America (page 754), but as no such mortuaries have been discovered in India, this seems scarcely tenable.

INDIAN ELEPHANT

The Indian or, as it might be better termed, Asiatic elephant (*Elephas maximus*, or *E. indicus*), which is the more specialised of the two living species, and at the same time the one most familiarly known, is charac-

terised by its comparatively flat forehead, relatively small ears, regularly tapering and smooth trunk, and also by the nearly naked skin being smooth, and the tail having a row of long bristly hairs at the tip, and a few inches upwards, before and behind only. The fore feet have each, as a rule, five nails, and the hind ones four. Generally males alone have large tusks, those of the females being small and scarcely protruding beyond the jaws. In some males, known in India as machnas, the tusks, however, are not longer than those of females. The back of the Indian elephant is regularly convex, its middle point being higher than the withers.

The most important characteristic of this species is to be found in the structure of the molar teeth. In these teeth the plates of enamel-bordered ivory are very thin and closely approximated. The enamel is thrown into a number of fine puckerings, and each enamel-bordered area forms a greatly elongated and irregular ellipse. In the first tooth the number of ridges is usually four, in the second eight, in the third and fourth about twelve, in the fifth sixteen, while in the last it may be as many as twenty-four.

The colour of the skin is blackish grey, but there are frequently flesh-coloured mottlings on the forehead, the root of the trunk, and the ears. Occasionally so-called white elephants are met with, which are really albinos, the dark pigment being absent from a larger or smaller area of the skin; in Burma and Siam such albinos are highly valued, and considered as sacred or royal animals. Although the skin is nearly naked, it has a few sparsely-scattered hairs; there are also faint remnants of a woolly fur, similar to that fully developed in the extinct mammoth. This fact is important, since, taken in connection with its well-known intolerance of heat, it indicates that the Indian elephant is descended from a species inhabiting temperate or cold climates.

The height of the Indian elephant has been greatly exaggerated, although the tendency of recent observers has been rather to depreciate the maximum size which it may occasionally attain. On the average, the height of the adult male does not exceed 9 feet, and that of the female 8 feet, but these dimensions are sometimes considerably exceeded. Mr. Sanderson measured a male standing 9 feet 7 inches at the shoulder, and measuring 26 feet 2½ inches from the tip of the trunk to the extremity of the tail; and he records others reaching 9 feet 10 inches, and 10 feet 7½ inches at the shoulder. An elephant shot by General A. A. Kinloch stood 10 feet 1 inch. These dimensions, however, are exceeded by a specimen killed by Sir Victor Brooke, which is reported to have reached a height of 11 feet, and there is a rumour of a Ceylon elephant of 12 feet. That such giants may exist is indicated by a skeleton in the Museum at Calcutta, which is believed to have belonged to an individual living between 1856 and 1860 in the neighbourhood of the Rajmahal Hills, in Bengal. As now mounted, this enormous skeleton stands

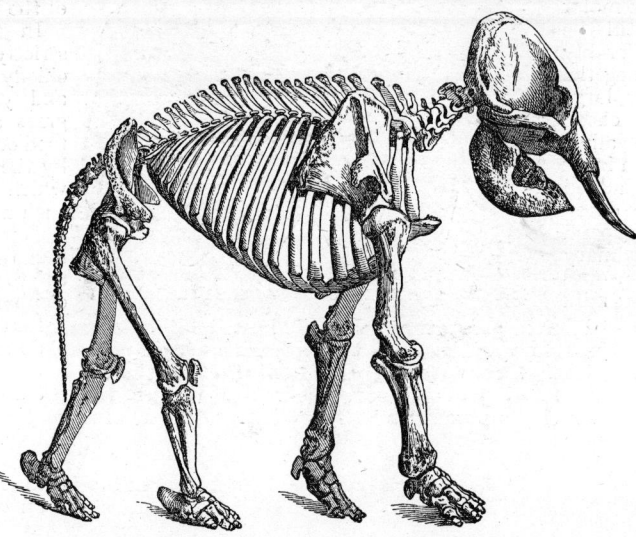

SKELETON OF THE INDIAN ELEPHANT

11 feet 3 inches at the shoulders, but it has been asserted that it is made to stand too low, and that its true height was several inches more. If this be so, there can be no doubt that when alive this elephant stood 12 feet. The height of an Indian elephant is almost precisely twice the circumference of its fore foot.

With regard to the maximum weight of this species, there is no information; but an immature male of 8 feet in height weighed 2 tons 17 cwt. 1 qr. and 25 lb., while a second, of 7½ feet in height, turned the scale at 2 tons 11 cwt. and 23 lb.

The tusks of the male vary greatly in length and weight. A pair obtained by Mr. Sanderson measured 5 feet along the curve, with a girth of 16 inches at the point of emergence from the jaw, their weight being 74½ pounds. The single perfect tusk of the elephant that was killed by Sir V. Brooke measured 8 feet in length, and nearly 17 inches in circumference, and weighed 90 pounds. This weight is, however, exceeded by a shorter tusk of about 6 feet in length, which reached 100 pounds; and two specimens obtained from the Garo Hills are reported to have weighed 155 and 157 pounds.

Since it is impossible to obtain accurate data as to the age which the Indian elephant may attain in its wild state, it is only possible to suggest an approximation to what this may be from captive specimens. Although full grown at the age of twenty-five, an elephant, as determined by the state of its teeth, is not then mature. A female captured in Coorg in 1805, when about three years of age, did not appear to be particularly old-looking in 1878, although she had then passed her prime. Other specimens have been known to live in captivity for over a century; and since the artificial mode of life in this condition cannot tend to promote longevity, it is probable that the estimate of a century and a half as the duration of life in the wild state is not excessive.

At the present day the Indian elephant inhabits the forest regions of India, Ceylon, Assam, Burma, Siam, Cochin-China, Sumatra, and Borneo, although there is an idea that its occurrence in the island last named may be due to human agency. In India elephants are still found wild along the base of the Himalaya as far west as Dera Dun, in places in the forest country between the Ganges and the Kistna as far west as Bilaspur and Mandla, in the Western Ghats as far north as 17° or 18°, and in some of the forest-clad ranges of Nagpur and farther south. They occasionally ascend the Himalaya to a great height, and are sometimes found at considerable elevations above the sea in Southern India, and in

Ceylon range near Newera Ellia to a height of over seven thousand feet. In former times their distribution in India was much more extensive.

Indian elephants chiefly frequent districts covered with tall forest, where the ground is undulating or hilly, and bamboos grow in profusion. During the hot months, in the early part of the year, they keep mainly to the densest portions of the forest, in the neighbourhood of water; but with the beginning of the rains, they venture into the open glades to feed upon the young succulent grass, and in the late summer in Madras descend at times to the lower jungles.

INDIAN ELEPHANTS

Contrary to opinion, the Indian elephant is exceedingly intolerant of the burning rays of the sun, to which it never voluntarily exposes itself. The dark colour of its skin and the immense surface attract an amount of heat which becomes almost intolerable when the animal is forced to carry a heavy load in the hot season; and even without a greater weight than the rider, elephants exhibit signs of distress when marching after nine o'clock in the morning. In cloudy and showery weather they move about a good deal during the time they are in the open country, and when travelling from one forest to another almost invariably march in single file.

Herds of elephants usually consist of from thirty to fifty individuals, all of which belong, as a rule, to a single family; although females and young males are said occasionally to migrate from their own proper herd to another. In some cases a herd may include as many as a hundred head; but when fodder is scarce, all the larger herds break up into smaller parties of from ten to twenty, these smaller parties keeping within a distance of two or three miles of one another, and re-uniting when conditions are more favourable. A female seems to be invariably the leader of the herd, although it may include males of all ages, and on the march the females, with their calves, occupy the van, while the tusked males bring up the rear. The old bulls are frequently solitary for a time, but generally each belongs to a particular herd, which it visits occasionally.

Solitary male elephants are known as "rogues," and are characterised by their fierce and quarrelsome disposition; but elephants that are permanently solitary are comparatively rare, the majority of so-called rogues really belonging to herds. These leave their companions, as a rule, merely for a time, in order to visit the cultivated lands, where the less venturesome females hesitate to follow, and where they do enormous damage to the crops.

The food of the Indian elephant is mainly composed of grass, leaves, and young shoots of the bamboo, stems, leaves, and fruits of the wild plantain, and the leaves, twigs, and bark of certain trees, more especially figs. The succulent nature of its food is in harmony with the structure of the molar teeth, which present a relation to those of the African species almost exactly analogous to that which exists between the molars of the white and those of the black African rhinoceros. In plucking tussocks of grass or branches of trees, the elephant coils the end of its trunk around them and tears them off ; the same method being employed in stripping leaves from a bough, or bark from a stem. Small objects, such as fruit, however, are picked up by the small finger-like process forming the termination of the trunk above the aperture of the nostrils. When drinking, elephants immerse the end of the trunk in water, which is sucked up to a distance estimated at from 15 to 18 inches in its tubes, and then emptied into the mouth. As a rule, the times of drinking are soon after sunset and shortly before sunrise. Grain is drawn up into the trunk, and then blown into the mouth.

Wild elephants roam about and feed during both the day and night, although they rest

INDIAN ELEPHANT CARRYING A HOWDAH

from nine or ten o'clock in the morning till three in the afternoon, and again from eleven at night till three in the morning. When sleeping, they lie down in the usual manner, and although the members of a herd scatter in all direction on any sudden alarm while feeding, they quickly reassemble.

When the season is not too cold, elephants are fond of bathing, or rolling themselves in wet mud, but unless the weather be exceptionally warm, they seldom indulge in such pastimes after sundown. When heated, they squirt water over their backs from their trunks, and when unable to obtain water externally, have the power of drawing fluid from their mouths or throats by the aid of the trunk. At times, when exposed to a scorching sun, they protect themselves by throwing dust, leaves, or straw on their backs.

The Indian elephant is an excellent swimmer, and is perhaps more thoroughly at home in the water than any mammal whose habits are not essentially amphibious or aquatic. Mr. Sanderson states that a herd of seventy-nine elephants under his charge once had a swim of six hours' duration, and, after a short rest on a sandbank, accomplished their journey by water in three hours more. An elephant swims very deep in the water, sometimes only showing the end of its trunk, but at others allowing the greater part of its head to appear above the surface. In the case of tame animals, the mahout, or driver, generally stands on the neck. The pace at which an elephant swims is estimated at about a mile an hour, but this depends on whether the animal is swimming with or against the stream. Unlike that of a hippopotamus, the body of a freshly-killed elephant floats.

In regard to movement on land, Mr. Sanderson observes that " the only pace of the elephant is the

walk, capable of being increased to a fast shuffle of about fifteen miles an hour for very short distances. It can neither trot, canter, nor gallop. It does not move with the legs on the same side together, but nearly so. A very good runner might keep out of an elephant's way on a smooth piece of turf, but on the ground in which they are generally met with any attempt to escape by flight, unless supplemented by concealment, would be unavailing." Elephants are totally unable to leap in either the horizontal or the vertical direction, and since their maximum length of stride is about 6½ feet, a 7-feet ditch forms an effectual barrier to progress. They are, however, capable of ascending or descending steep and difficult places with great facility, sometimes sliding down on their bent hind limbs. When a herd descends one of the steep alluvial banks bordering most Indian rivers, it is surprising how rapidly the soil becomes broken down under their weight so as to form a regular sloping road.

The Indian elephant, in different circumstances, gives vent to a variety of sounds, some produced in the trunk, while others originate in the throat. Of these utterances, the first, writes Dr. W. T. Blanford, is " the shrill trumpet, varying in tone, and expressive, sometimes of fear, sometimes of anger. Secondly, a roar from the throat caused by fear or pain. A peculiar hoarse rumbling in the throat may express anger or want, as when a calf is calling for its mother. Pleasure is indicated by a continued low squeaking through the trunk. Lastly, there is a peculiar metallic sound made by rapping the end of the trunk on the ground and blowing through it at the same time. This indicates alarm or dislike, and is the well-known indication of a tiger's presence." Though the sense of smell is strongly developed, both sight and hearing do not appear to be acute.

At most seasons the Indian elephant is a timid animal, much more ready to flee from a foe than to attack. Solitary " rogues " however are frequently an exception to this rule, and sometimes assault passers-by. Indeed, there are instances of a " rogue " taking up a position near a road, and rendering it impassable to travellers. Females with calves are at all times dangerous to approach. When an Indian elephant charges, it does so with its trunk tightly curled up, and it attacks by trampling its victim with its feet or knees, or, if a male, by pinning it to the ground with its tusks. At certain periods the male elephant is subject to paroxysms of excitement, supposed to be due to sexual causes, and is highly dangerous, not only to human beings, but to its fellows. The creature is then said to be *mast*, or " mad," and the onset of such attacks is indicated by the copious flow of a dark tar-like liquid from two small orifices in the forehead. At the first indications of a seizure, domesticated elephants should be promptly secured.

Not the least remarkable fact connected with elephants is the circumstance that, in India at least, they very rarely breed in captivity, thus showing the profound effect which the change from a wild to a domesticated mode of life has on the animal's entire organisation. In some parts of Burma and Siam calves are, however, produced much more freely from captive females. A young elephant was born in London in 1902, and one in Copenhagen in 1907

The ordinary period of gestation is about nineteen months, but in some cases it may be a month less, while in others its duration may be as much as twenty-two months. As a rule, the young are born in autumn, from September to November; and there is generally one produced at a birth, although in rare instances twins occur. The new-born calf, which stands about a yard in height, and weighs about 200 pounds, is coated with a comparatively thick coat of somewhat woolly hair; it suckles its parent with its mouth, and not, as has sometimes been supposed, with its trunk.

An immature female elephant is worth about £150, while good working females will realise from £200 to £300. Tuskers, however, are far more valuable, ranging from £800 to £1,500 or £1,600, or even more if all their " points " be perfect.

Domesticated elephants (p. 47) are largely employed in India for the transport of heavy camp baggage, for dragging timber to the rivers, and in lieu of horses for artillery, and are of special value in traversing districts where roads are either wanting, or are so bad as to be impassable for other animals when laden. Elephants may be employed either as beasts of burden or of draught, and in the former case their loads should not exceed half a ton for continuous marching, while in hilly districts they should be reduced to about seven hundredweight. In dragging timber of moderate dimensions, a short rope is attached to one end of each log, which the elephant seizes between his teeth, and thus raising his burden from the ground, half carries and half drags it away. Tuskers are both stronger and more useful than females,

HERD OF INDIAN ELEPHANTS IN A STOCKADE IN CEYLON
Photograph, Underwood & Underwood, London

since their tusks often aid them in the performance of their duties.

The majority of elephants employed in such tasks belong to what the native term the inferior castes, tuskers of the finest and most approved form being far too expensive to be put to such uses. The majority of such elephants are purchased by the native princes, by whom they are used in state pageants; the taller the animal, the greater its value.

Elephants are extensively employed in tiger-shooting, and in many districts this sport can only be enjoyed by the aid of these animals. For sporting purposes the elephant carries a howdah, which should be so constructed as to combine lightness with strength, and allow of the occupant firing from it with equal ease in any direction. One of the most remarkable features connected with the taming of the Indian elephant is

the extent to which its natural timidity in the presence of its dreaded enemy the tiger may be overcome by means of careful training.

Evidence of the former existence of the Indian elephant in Mesopotamia is afforded by the Assyrian " Black Obelisk," dating from 840 B.C., on which is sculptured an elephant, supposed to be of the Indian species. Taken by itself the evidence of this obelisk does not appear convincing, as the elephant depicted might have been imported into Assyria from Egypt; but much greater weight attaches to a famous text of Amenemhib, in the reign of Thothmes III., which runs as follows : " He [the king] hunted 120 elephants for the sake of their tusks. I engaged the greatest among those which attacked his highness. I cut his trunk through while yet alive; he pursued me, when I went into the water between two rocks. Then my royal lord rewarded me with golden gifts." The events of this narrative occurred in the land of Ni during an expedition to Syria. Ni being a town in Naharain— now Mesopotamia — close to the boundary stone erected by Thothmes III. immediately east of the Euphrates. This record seems to be pretty conclusive, and is supported by the fact that the name of the elephant is the same in Egyptian and Assyrian (*eb* and *habba*) as in Tamil (*hab*).

Further evidence is afforded by the fact that during the Crimean war Colonel J. M. Giels discovered near Khanus, in the Erzerum district of Armenia the remains of a fossil elephant, of which three teeth were brought home and presented to the British Museum. Subsequent investigation showed that these came from a skeleton embedded in a river deposit containing recent shells, of which the bones and tusks were in a friable condition. The molar teeth were declared by Dr. Hugh Falconer to be intermediate in character between those of the mammoth and those of the Indian elephant, the resemblance to the living being greater than to the extinct species; and for this Armenian elephant the name of *Elephas armeniacus* was proposed. There can, however, be little doubt that it is nothing more than a local race of the Indian elephant, and should accordingly be known as *E. maximus armeniacus*.   R. LYDEKKER

THE INDIAN ELEPHANT, WILD AND TAME
By MAJOR F. G. ALEXANDER

I concur in the opinion that the elephant in its wild state is far from intelligent. The brain is small and of a very low order, and the easy capture of the creature in keddas is sufficient to prove that it is deficient in sagacity. But when educated, it becomes a totally different being. Its bump of obedience is largely developed. It understands Hindustanee in a way which is incomprehensible to the ordinary mortal. If it is told to stop—" Dutt, dutt " are the words used—it stops; other expressions are employed to make it attack, lower itself on its haunches, retreat, and so on ; different languages being, of course, used in different districts.

Once on the banks of the Nerbudda I was watching a mahout scrubbing an elephant ; having scrubbed one side of its body the mahout, in Hindustanee, bade the beast turn over. The elephant did so at once. When its toilette was completed the mahout was hungry.

In a Bundelkhand beat I have had as many as five elephants at one time over ground full of snakes. In answer to numerous inquiries, mahouts assured me that the animal is impervious to snake poison.

The sporting elephant which will face a tiger's charge is worth a good deal of money. I engaged one from the commissariat at two rupees a day, which I had to pay for its food. I was told it was staunch, but at the sight of a tiger it bolted, and nearly caused two men who were riding on its back on a pad to be killed by overhanging branches.

Forest officers are not allowed to shoot wild elephants unless the animals attack them, or have been gazetted to be slaughtered. As much as a thousand rupees and the tusks has been earned by an officer who shot a dangerous rogue in the Doon forests. A friend shot a rogue in *mast* which had actually stopped the traffic on the Bombay and Baroda railway.

It is not generally known that not so very long ago commissariat elephants, like the British soldier, possessed defaulter sheets. An elephant

TAME INDIAN ELEPHANTS AIDING IN THE CAPTURE OF A WILD ELEPHANT

With him was his little black child, and again he spoke to the elephant in Hindustanee : "Brother, I am going to cook my dinner, look after the baba, and see that he does not get near the river." With that he placed the child between the elephant's trunk and fore feet, and went off to the river bed to cook his food. Several times the child tried to escape, but the recumbent elephant, with a tenderness almost human, gently curled its trunk round the child and drew him back to where his father had deposited him. I was very much impressed with the scene. The father continued his cooking, and appeared to have absolute confidence that the child was in safe custody.

It has been stated that elephants rarely breed in captivity. I am able to affirm that in the 'eighties they used to breed in Punna State, Bundelkhand, where I have seen a tiny baby elephant, which measured about 3 feet 6 inches at the shoulder. I believe the young rarely live to maturity, as they are so worried and pulled about by the natives, who all want to play with the baby.

I have been informed by an experienced forest officer that he once, and only once, found the skeleton of a dead elephant on an almost inaccessible mountain above the Doon. Elephants die, and if they perished on the plains, in populous districts their carcases would soon grow noisome. During the Afghan war an elephant was buried in the Bolan Pass. In the hurry of movements it was not interred deeply enough, and the carcase made travelling in the pass more unpleasant than usual. The officer who found the skeleton was not inclined to romance, so I think it is highly probable that elephants, on the point of death, repair to an elevated and almost inaccessible spot to die.

having misbehaved himself was sentenced usually to a thrashing with iron chains by two brother elephants, and sometimes one or other of the castigators afterwards found himself a defaulter, and his quandom victim helped to put *him* through the mill.

There is one fact about the elephant which is extraordinary. It knows to an ounce what it is entitled to receive in the matter of food, such as chupatties, goor, sugar-cane, and the like, and if its keeper ventures to make money out of the provender he stands in danger of his life. I know many cases in which mahouts have been killed by domesticated elephants simply because the beasts had been deprived of their proper food. This, clearly, was the result of education. In the cases of commissariat elephants sentenced to be punished for various misdeeds, deprivation of food was never allowed to be one of the sentences.

When I first went out shooting on an elephant the mahout ordered it to lift me on to its head. I put my foot on the elephant's trunk with some misgivings, but after a time I regarded the elephant as a gentle creature with kind and patient manners. One officer whom I knew fired at a charging tiger ; the sportsman was in a howdah, and the bullet from the right barrel was erratic and entered the elephant's skull, fortunately wide of the brain. The elephant never exhibited any animosity towards the offender, and eventually the hole filled up.

There is no question but that the educated elephant very soon recognises a tyrannical mahout, or a kind keeper, and, small as its eye may be, it is quicker to detect the presence of a tiger than is the human eye.

F. G. ALEXANDER

THE MAMMOTH

As being closely allied to the living Indian species, the extinct elephant of the Pleistocene deposits of Europe and Northern Asia, known as the mammoth (*Elephas primigenius*), may be conveniently noticed in this place (see pp. 30, 31). So close is the relationship between it and the Indian elephant that it may be a question whether they are more than varieties of one species, specially modified for the climates of their respective habitats. It is true that the tusks of the mammoth are more curved upwards than those of the Indian elephant, and assume a spiral curvature, while the plates of the molar teeth are narrower and more numerous. These, however, are differences which scarcely constitute more than a well-marked variety; and it is noteworthy that in Asia Minor the place of the mammoth was taken by the Armenian elephant, which had molar teeth intermediate between those of the mammoth and those of the living Indian elephant.

In Siberia, where carcases have been found preserved in the frozen soil, the body of the mammoth was covered with a thick coat of brownish woolly fur, among which was a number of longer bristly black hairs, but it is not certain that the animal was thus protected in the more southern and warmer portions of its habitat. Apart from this, the fact that the Indian elephant retains traces of a woolly covering similar to that of the mammoth shows that in this respect there is no essential difference between the two, and indicates that the development or loss of the hairy coat was due to climatic conditions.

The mammoth is found in great abundance in Siberia, its remains becoming more numerous the farther north we proceed. In Northern Europe, with the exception of the district to the east of the White Sea, it is rare or unknown, none of its remains having been discovered in Norway, and few in Denmark and Sweden. Although rare in Scotland and Ireland, remains are extremely common over the greater part of England and a large area of Central Europe. They abound in France and Germany, and in Italy extend as far south as Rome, but are unknown south of the Pyrenees. Great numbers are dredged from the Dogger Bank in the North Sea. From Eastern Asia the mammoth travelled across what is now Bering Strait into Alaska, but in the United States, as far south as Texas and Mexico, its place was taken by the Columbian mammoth (*E. columbianus*).

That the mammoth lived in Siberia in the area where its frozen remains are found may be deemed certain, and there is evidence that the climate of these regions was less inclement than it is at present. This, however, only renders it the more difficult to account for the manner in which its remains were—as they must have been—frozen up in the soil immediately after death. Some have called in the aid of a sudden cataclysmic change from heat to extreme cold, but it is difficult to accept such a theory, although without some such explanation the mode of entombment remains a complete puzzle. In Europe the mammoth seems to have made its first appearance before the great cold of the Glacial period, thus tending to show that it never inhabited a country with a very cold climate.

Numerous finds of frozen carcases of mammoths in the soil of Siberia have been recorded, but it may be safely asserted that these form only a small proportion of the remains brought to light by the action of the weather during the historic period. Of the recorded examples, almost the earliest was one found on the River Alasega in 1787, and somewhere about the same time another appears to have been discovered at the mouth of the Lena, while a third occurred in 1805 on the shores of the Polar Sea.

The most celebrated of the earlier finds is the one recorded by Adams, in 1806, which was disclosed by the gradual melting of the ice on a peninsula at the mouth of the Lena. The first indication of this carcase was noticed by a native in 1799, who observed a hummocky mass in the ice, which melted in the summer of 1801 sufficiently to show one tusk and the side of the monster. The carcase was then entire, showing the eyes and trunk well preserved, and the thick coat of wool and hair clothing the skin. During the cold summer of 1802 the ice melted little, but in the following year the carcase slid down on to a sandbank, and in 1804

STUFFED CARCASE OF MAMMOTH FROM THE SANGAR-YURACH RIVER
Photographed from the original in St. Petersburg Academy

a native hacked out and carried off both tusks. It was not till two years later that Adams arrived on the scene, by which time the dogs of the natives had consumed nearly all the flesh, while one limb had been removed bodily. The rest of the skeleton and a large amount of hair were taken to St. Petersburg.

Another mammoth mummy was discovered in 1840 on a tributary of the Yenisei, and its skeleton taken to the museum at Moscow. Some long stiff hair, of a reddish colour, found with this specimen probably belonged to the mane, the existence of such a mane having been proved by the rough sketches of Adams's specimen made by the natives. A half-grown mammoth, with part of the skin remaining, was discovered in 1843 near the River Taimyr, only a comparatively short distance from the Polar Sea. Some time between 1840 and 1850 a well-preserved carcase was discovered in the circle of Yakutsk, on the banks of the Kolyma, which had a long mane extending from the head to the tail, and fragments of twigs, on which the animal had been browsing shortly before its death, were found between its teeth.

Between 1860 and 1862 the natives discovered another frozen carcase on a tributary of the Lena, and an expedition from St. Petersburg, which arrived too late, was despatched to secure the prize. The summer of 1867 revealed another of these frozen carcases, near the Polar Sea in the neighbourhood of the Alasega, and some distance beyond the northern limit of trees. About the same time news arrived of the discovery of a mammoth on the Kolyma; while a third was discovered in 1870 near the Alasega, and a fourth in 1900.

The last of these was discovered by Yakuts in the sandy bed of the Sangar-Yurach river. The discovery was communicated to the governor of Yakutsk, who telegraphed to the St. Petersburg Academy of Science, which despatched an expedition to secure as much as possible of the remains. These were prepared for transport in a tent, when the temperature was many degrees below freezing, at a point some 120 miles distant from the Arctic Ocean, whence they started on their journey to the Russian capital. The journey to Bulun, a distance of 1,200 miles, was accomplished in sledges drawn by reindeer in a fortnight; but it took six months for the freight to reach its destination, the cost of the expedition and transport amounting to £1,700. The carcase is that of a rather small mammoth, and although lacking tusks, is unique in retaining the trunk, as well as certain other portions of the body not preserved in other examples.

These isolated finds convey no idea of the number of mammoths that inhabited Siberia at a time when its climate must have been far less rigorous than at present, and in order to form some opinion on the subject attention must be given to the trade in mammoth ivory. It appears that in 1872 no fewer than 1,630 of these tusks, and in the following year 1,140, were imported into England, and it may be estimated that for a long time fully 120,000 pounds weight of fossil ivory found its way year by year into the market. This means that, within a period of twenty years, the remains, in various stages of completeness, of over 20,000 mammoths must have been discovered, which affords ample proof that

Siberia was as thickly inhabited by these animals as was Africa by the elephant of modern times. About 14 per cent. of the tusks imported afforded first-class ivory, in addition to which about 17 per cent. was capable of being used where ivory of the best quality was not required.

Despite a very general opinion to the contrary, the mammoth was a puny beast in comparison with the lordly African elephant, its height apparently not exceeding 9½ feet—a stature easily beaten by some Indian elephants, and altogether outclassed by the African, which not infrequently reaches 11 feet 4 inches, and may in some cases touch 12 feet. Despite the insignificant stature of the mammoth, there were, however, giants in the old days which altogether eclipsed the African species; for the American *E. imperator* and the European *E. meridionalis* and *E. antiquus* stood certainly 12½ feet high, and possibly reached the height of 13½ feet.

According to Mr. G. E. Pilgrim, these records are beaten by the Narbada elephant of India (*E. a. namadicus*), of which the height at the shoulder is estimated to have been at least 16 feet, the estimate being based apparently on an imperfect thigh bone, or femur, which, when complete, is considered to have measured no less than 69 inches in length. As the two ends of this bone are entire, the length could be calculated with a fair approximation to accuracy from the corresponding part of the skeleton of an existing elephant, and, from my recollection of other bones in the Calcutta Museum, I think Mr. Pilgrim's estimate of the height of the fossil species is not excessive.

THE AFRICAN ELEPHANT

The African elephant (*Elephas africanus*) differs widely from its Asiatic congener, not only in external form, but also in the structure of its molar teeth, the males also reaching larger dimensions than those ordinarily attained by the latter (page 67). The most striking external characteristic of the African species is the enormous size of the ears in some of the local races. In repose, they completely cover the shoulders, but during periods of excitement are elevated at right angles, and communicate a most extraordinary appearance to them.

The head is also much more convex in the region of the forehead, the eye is larger, and the extremity of the trunk, instead of having one long finger-like process on its front edge, has two nearly equal-sized processes, one in front and the other be-

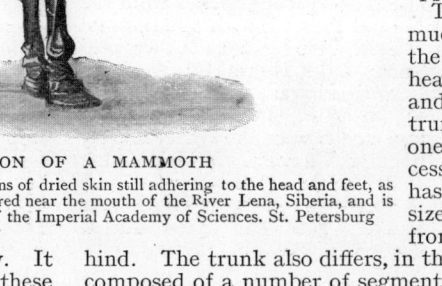

SKELETON OF A MAMMOTH

This complete skeleton, with remains of dried skin still adhering to the head and feet, as seen in the illustration, was discovered near the mouth of the River Lena, Siberia, and is now in the Zoological Museum of the Imperial Academy of Sciences. St. Petersburg

hind. The trunk also differs, in that it looks as though composed of a number of segments of different calibre, like the joints of a collapsible telescope. The colour of the skin is somewhat darker. In general form the African species is distinguished by the middle of the back being hollowed, and the shoulder the highest point; while the hind foot carries three, in place of four, nails. As a rule, both males and females are furnished with well-developed tusks. which attain

THE AFRICAN ELEPHANT

larger dimensions than those of the Indian elephant; but in Eastern and Northern Abyssinia all the elephants appear to be almost tuskless, or to have very small and short tusks ; and in certain localities the cows are generally tuskless. The molar teeth are distinguished by the smaller number and greater thickness of their plates, each of these plates expanding in the middle in an angulated form, so that when worn it presents a lozenge-shaped area of ivory bordered by enamel ; nor is the enamel puckered in the manner characterising the molars of the Indian species. The number of plates in the first molar is usually three ; in the second, six ; in the third and fourth, seven ; in the fifth, eight ; and in the last, ten.

In regard to the dimensions of the African elephant, it may be noticed that a male killed in South Africa by the late Duke of Coburg, which stood 10 feet at the withers, had a length of 23 feet 5 inches from the tip of the trunk to the end of the tail, with a maximum girth of 16½ feet, its weight being 4 tons 8 cwt. and 4 lbs. In one killed near Lake Nyasa by Sir John Kirk the height at the withers was 10 feet 3 inches, the total length 25 feet 2 inches, and the maximum girth 18 feet. These dimensions were, however, largely exceeded by those of " Jumbo," formerly in the London Zoological Gardens, whose height at the withers was 11 feet, and his weight 6½ tons. An Abyssinian elephant standing 11 feet 8½ inches has been killed, and it is probable that in some instances 12 feet may be reached.

In regard to the dimensions of the tusks, about 140 pounds may be given as the average weight of a pair in full-grown males from the Sudan ; but, owing to the exclusive use of one tusk for digging, the two would not be of equal weight. A single tusk sold in London in 1874 weighed 188 pounds ; one mentioned by Sir Samuel Baker weighed 172 pounds ; while another recorded by Sir John Kirk had a weight of 160 pounds, a length of 9 feet 4 inches, and a girth of 20½ inches. A fine specimen in the collection of the British Museum has a length of 10 feet 2 inches, and a weight of 228 pounds ; but the largest known tusk is one from East Africa in the possession of Sir E. G. Loder, which measures 10 feet 4 inches long, with a girth of 26 inches, and weighs 235 pounds. The longest tusks are a pair from East Africa, their respective lengths being 11 feet 5½ inches and 11 feet 11 inches, and their united weight 293 pounds.

Although its fossilised remains have been found in the superficial deposits of Spain, Sicily, and Algeria, the species is now confined to Africa south of the Sahara, where it was formerly spread over the whole of the wooded districts. Owing, however, to constant persecution for the sake of its tusks, the numbers of the African elephant have been greatly reduced, and these animals have now practically been exterminated from large areas in the southern portion of the continent.

In the districts lying to the south of the Zambezi, with the exception of a few scattered herds in the more unfrequented parts of Matabililand and the extremity of North-Eastern Mashonaland, elephants some years ago were only met with in anything like fair numbers in the impenetrable bush of the low-lying coast country in the region of Sofala Bay. A few herds might remain in the extreme north and north-east of Ovampoland, bordering on the Cuneni and Okavango Rivers ; but the last herd frequenting the Botletli and the neighbourhood of Lake Ngami was destroyed in 1889 by Bechuanas ; but a good many still survived in the country between the Chobi and Zambezi. Some herds are preserved in a protected state by the Government in the forests in the east of Cape Colony. In East

Africa elephants are still fairly plentiful in the Kilimanjaro district, where they ascend at certain seasons to an elevation of nine or ten thousand feet among the damp forests clothing the sides of the mountain. They are found at heights of from seven to eight thousand feet above the sea-level in the Abyssinian highlands.

Some idea of the appalling destruction of elephants which still goes on in the heart of the continent may be gleaned from a statement by Herr E. C. Schillings, to the effect that the number of tusks annually imported into Antwerp alone represents the slaughter of no fewer than 18,500 elephants.

Numerous local races of the African elephant, differing from one another in bodily size, the degree of development of the tusks, and the size and shape of the ears, have been described. The West African Camerun elephant (*E. a. cyclotis*), has, for instance, nearly circular ears, while those of the Sudani race (*E. a. oxyotis*) are very large and pointed, and those of the East African *E. a. knockenhaueri* small and triangular.

All observers seem agreed that the African elephant is a more powerful and more active animal than its Asiatic cousin, displaying marvellous capacities for getting over precipitous and rocky ground, and being altogether more rapid in its movements, while most writers consider its disposition decidedly fiercer than that of the other species. Although there is probably some local difference in this respect, it is far less intolerant of intense solar heat than the Indian species, and in the Sudan these animals may be observed enjoying themselves in the blazing sun in the hottest hours of the day among plains of withered grass, many miles from jungle.

The difference in the structure of their molar teeth would of itself be an indication of a marked distinction in the diet of the two species ; and from the analogous instance of the two African species of rhinoceros it would be inferred that the nutriment of the African elephant is composed of coarser and harder substances than those eaten by the Indian species. From his experience in the Sudan, Sir Samuel Baker observes that " the African elephant is a more decided tree-feeder than the Indian, and the destruction committed by a large herd of such animals when feeding in a mimosa forest is extraordinary ; they deliberately march forward, and uproot or break down every tree that excites their appetite. The mimosas are generally from 16 to 20 feet high, and, having no tap-root, they are easily overturned by the tusks of the elephants, which are driven like crowbars beneath the roots, and used as levers, in which rough labour they are frequently broken. Upon the overthrow of a tree, the elephants eat the roots and leaves, and strip the bark from the branches by grasping them with their rough trunks."

Mr. F. C. Selous bears testimony to the digging habits of the elephant in South-Eastern Africa, stating that he has seen large areas of sandy soil ploughed up by their tusks in the search for roots.

In digging, the elephant uses one particular tusk—nearly always the right—which, in consequence, is much more worn than the other, and which is termed by the Sudanis *hadam*, or "servant." A curious question arises whether this preferential use of the right tusk discloses any relation to right-handedness in man.

In Southern Africa, at least, elephants drink almost every night, but only rarely during the day. In that part of the continent they seek the deepest shades of the forest during the heat of the day, generally sleeping in a standing posture.

African elephants associate in herds of varying size,

SUDANI ELEPHANTS
Photographed by Captain S. S. Flower in the Zoological Gardens, Giza, Egypt

apparently family parties ; but the old bulls may be solitary, in pairs, or in small parties, and keep apart from the larger herds, which usually consist of young males, females, and calves. One of the largest herds seen by Mr. Selous was estimated to contain from one to two hundred head, but such assemblages are rare. In many parts of Africa, including Abyssinia, Kilimanjaro, and the Sudan, elephants undertake periodical migrations, probably necessitated by the supply of food, or the ripening of certain kinds of fruit in particular districts. At such times the old bulls rejoin the herds to which they belong.

Although the Indian elephant can keep up for 200 yards or so a pace at the rate of fifteen miles an hour, its speed really does not exceed six or eight miles an hour. The African elephant, on the other hand, while maintaining a maximum of fifteen miles an hour for perhaps 300 yards, settles down to a pace of ten miles an hour, which can be kept up for at least that period of time. The relatively longer limbs and stride of the African species bear out this view as to its speedier movements.

The sense of scent is very strongly developed in this species, inasmuch as it can discover the presence of a human being at an immense distance when the wind is favourable. As soon as an elephant scents a man, it starts off at once at a rapid pace, which will be maintained sometimes for hours ; and since in most parts of Africa the wind is constantly veering, this constitutes one of the great difficulties in elephant-stalking. On the other hand, the sight of these animals is most defective, nor is their hearing particularly good. On account of these deficiencies, it is possible to approach a wild African elephant from the leeward to within a very short distance ; and I have been informed, on good authority, that a hunter once wagered that he would write his initials on the hind quarters of one of these animals while alive, and actually succeeded in so doing.

Attempts have of late years been made to domesticate the African elephant in the Congo State, with a fair amount of success.

The testimony of those who have had experience of both the African and the Indian elephant points to the conclusion that the former is the more dangerous animal and the more ready to charge. The females, especially those that are barren and have small tusks, are said to be far more dangerous than males, frequently charging without the least provocation, even when unwounded ; and it is stated that hunters will sometimes take the trouble to kill one of these worthless females before attacking the tuskers. Indeed, the Hon. W. H. Drummond is of opinion that the greater number of accidents that have occurred in African elephant-shooting may be attributed to females. The African elephant, unlike its Indian cousin, charges with trunk uplifted and loudly trumpeting.

Although highly appreciated by the natives, the flesh of the African elephant is coarse and rank, but portions of the trunk, although tough, are said to be fairly good. Baked elephant's foot, cooked in the skin, and scooped out like a Stilton cheese, was formerly considered a dainty, but most of those who have tasted it express their dislike of the dish. R. LYDEKKER

STORIES OF AFRICAN ELEPHANTS

Thousands of people who visit the Zoological Gardens come away with the belief with which they went, that the African elephant cannot be tamed. Yet the only male elephant in the Zoo at the present time is a son of Africa, and the biggest elephant ever seen in

YOUNG AFRICAN ELEPHANTS LYING DOWN
Photograph supplied by Mr. Carl Hagenbeck

captivity in Europe—Jumbo—was a native of the Dark Continent, as was also his mate, Alice.

The man in the street may be forgiven his acceptance of a common tradition in this matter. Virchow, the great scientist, believed the story, and when Herr Hagenbeck imported five African elephants, suggested that he should attempt the impossible—that he

should train them. A challenge of this sort never found Herr Hagenbeck reluctant, and, to the professor's vast astonishment, he replied that if he (Virchow) cared to call on the following afternoon he should find the elephants broken in, notwithstanding the fact that no previous attempt had been made to train them. The appointment was duly made, and Hagenbeck set to work upon his task.

Several agile Nubians were offered rewards to seat themselves upon the animals, and retain their seats. The natives soon clambered into position, but the elephants were alarmed and disconcerted. Not viciousness, but fright, impelled them to rid themselves of their burden. They rushed about the arena, trumpeting loudly, and finally shook themselves with such vigour that three of them succeeded in unseating their riders. Food was now given to the elephants, which were thus persuaded to permit a renewal of operations. Three quickly yielded to the natives' blandishments, and were ridden until nightfall. Next morning the other two capitulated, and all five bore riders upon their backs as to the manner born.

The next difficulty was to get them to carry inanimate burdens. Sacks were filled and strapped in pairs over their backs. The pressure of the burdens against their flanks excited even more alarm in the brutes than had their riders. Caresses and exhortations, and the still more persuasive effects of generous gifts of food, however, soon overcame all objections, and by midday all bore their burdens, whether of men or merchandise, with complete equanimity. Virchow arrived with a party of friends later in the afternoon, and was surprised to see the wild animals of the previous day converted into docile beasts of burthen. The handsome sums which African elephants' earnings have contributed to the revenue of our own Zoological Gardens are further evidence of the fact that *Elephas africanus* can be as readily domesticated as his Asiatic cousin.

The fact that the African elephant, when charging, carries the trunk high, is proof that the animal has a dread of injury to that member. Experience would show, however, that in captivity this sense is apt to be dulled. Alice met with an extraordinary mishap through neglect of a precaution which, in a state of freedom, not the youngest elephant would forget. Her fidgetty nature had caused her to be roped while her stable was being cleared out. A cable, attached to an iron ring in the floor, secured one of her legs. Suddenly her scream of pain called the attention of her keeper, and it was found that she had torn off the end of her trunk. In trying to pull up the ring to which her rope was fastened, she had caught the end of her proboscis under the ring, and trodden upon the latter. While her foot was thus pressing down, she had endeavoured to pull her trunk away, with the result described. After suffering great pain and alarm, she recovered from her injury, and remained at the Zoo to mourn the departure of Jumbo.

It is conceivable that, happening at another time, the shock which this injury caused might have sufficed to kill her. There is no other large animal which so

M

soon succumbs to the unexpected. Mighty elephants have been known to lie down and die when a load has been more than they can manage, or to expire when mastered in an attempt to resist capture.

This curious "softness" must have been largely responsible for an extraordinary disaster which overtook three African elephants owned by Mr. Hagenbeck. They arrived tired from a long journey, ate well, and lay down to sleep. In the middle of the night their owner was called up, and found one elephant already dead and the others dying. A colony of fierce rats had made their homes beneath the flooring of the elephant houses, and, attacking the soles of the elephants' feet, had caused severe wounds. But the wounds in themselves were insufficient to account for the death of these three great animals ; fright must have been largely responsible. This is a fair deduction from the fact that an elephant owned by our own Zoological Gardens, known to be greatly frightened by thunder, actually expired from terror during a midsummer storm which broke over the gardens some years ago.

The removal of Jumbo, the great African elephant, gave the British public the biggest excuse for hysteria that it has had for many years. Jumbo had reached an age when it was no longer safe to keep him in the crowded Zoological Gardens. He might have caused a disaster at any moment. Only one man dared go near him ; the others were armed lest he should break out.

The council of the society, therefore, closed with an offer from Barnum of £2,000 for the fine but dangerous beast. There was a great outcry in the papers against the sale. The society were likened to slave-dealers, and the transaction to the sale of Uncle Tom. The society had no right, it was urged, to dispose of so rare and valuable a specimen ; their charter only gave them the right to acquire, not to sell. What greater right had they to sell this unique treasure than the National Gallery to sell a masterpiece ? An application to the High Court to restrain the society from completing the sale was made, and an interim injunction was granted pending investigations. Eventually the court decided unreservedly in favour of the society.

Then came the difficulty of getting the animal away. He refused to budge, and people wept, declaring that the poor beast could not bear the thought of leaving his home and family. He had no family, by the way. It was shrewdly suspected that the keeper who had charge of Jumbo did not want him to go, and privately gave him a sign which made him lie down when called upon to enter the truck prepared for him. At any rate, Barnum called this keeper to him and suggested that he should take a holiday and let another man superintend. Further, he offered the man generous terms to accompany the elephant to America. The keeper accepted the offer, but begged not to be given a

YOUNG AFRICAN ELEPHANT

holiday. Next day he resumed work, and without great difficulty got Jumbo safely boxed up and away.

E. A. B.

EXTINCT PROBOSCIDEANS

In addition to the mammoth, there are a number of other extinct elephants more or less closely allied to the living species, together with others of a totally different type. All are confined to Europe, Asia, and North Africa, the only American species being the Columbian elephant alluded to above.

The earliest species allied to the Indian elephant is the Sutlej elephant (*E. hysudricus*) from the Pliocene rocks of the Siwalik Hills, in which the plates of the molar teeth are very thin, but less tall and less numerous than in the living species. The skull resembles that of the latter, and it is possible that this species may have been the ancestor of both the Indian elephant and the mammoth.

The Pleistocene deposits of the Narbada Valley in Central India yield the remains of the Narbada elephant, alluded to above as being the largest of all elephants. Although formerly regarded as a distinct species, it is now considered to be a local race of the European straight-tusked elephant, under the name of *E. antiquus namadicus*. It is characterised by its very short skull, which has an enormous ridge running transversely across the forehead. This species ranged eastwards to Japan.

The straight-tusked elephant (*E. antiquus*), from the Pleistocene deposits of Europe, differs from the mammoth in its smaller and comparatively straight tusks, and the fewer and wider plates in the molar teeth, of which the crowns are generally narrow. Indeed, some of these teeth come so close to those of the African elephant as to indicate the near relationship between that species and the fossil one. The straight-tusked elephant ranged from Yorkshire to Algeria, and is represented in India and Japan by the above-mentioned Narbada race.

We are so accustomed to regard elephants as the giants of creation that it is at first difficult to believe in the existence of a species not exceeding 3 feet in height. Yet pigmy elephants (*E. mnaidriensis, E. cypriotes,* and *E. melitensis*), of which the smallest is considered to have reached only those diminutive proportions, were abundant in Malta, Cyprus, and some of the neighbouring islands during the Pleistocene period ; their remains occurring in caverns and rock fissures. These elephants, many of which are not larger than a donkey, appear to have been closely related to the living African species, and were probably dwarfed in size in accordance with the small area of the islands they inhabited.

The southern elephant (*E. meridionalis*), from the upper Pliocene rocks of Italy and France, and also found in the Forest Bed on the coast of Norfolk, and at

Dewlish, in Dorsetshire, was one of the largest of the European species, its height, as already mentioned, having been estimated at from 12½ to 13½ feet. The molar teeth of this giant have wide crowns, with the plates very broad and widely separated from one another, and somewhat less numerous than in the African species. The flat-headed elephant (*E. planifrons*), from the Pliocene rocks of the Siwalik Hills, was an allied Indian species, distinguished from all other true elephants by the fact that two of the milk molar teeth were vertically replaced by premolars; this elephant having eight more teeth than any other species, and thereby showing evident traces of closer kinship with the mastodons.

The so-called stegodont elephants — named thus from the roof-like form assumed by the ridges of their molar teeth—of India and other parts of South-Eastern Asia, form an interesting group, almost completely connecting the true elephants with the mastodons. The molar teeth of this group are characterised by the small number of the ridges—in this instance six—which are very low and wide, with the shallow intervening valleys devoid of cement. In other species of the group the ridges were somewhat more numerous and more elevated, while the valleys were partially filled with cement; and these serve to connect Clift's elephant with species like the southern elephant. The tooth of Clift's elephant (page 805) agrees with that of existing species in having the transverse ridges undivided by any distinct longitudinal cleft.

Another of the stegodont elephants (*E. ganesa*) is remarkable for the enormous size of its tusks, those in a skull preserved in the British Museum measuring 12 feet 9 inches in length, with a maximum girth of 26 inches. Representatives of this group also occur in China, Japan, and Java.

The stegodont elephants so closely connect the living species with the extinct mastodons that the division between the two groups is somewhat arbitrary; and as the species of mastodons most nearly related to the stegodont elephants are found in the same regions as the latter, it may be inferred that the evolution of elephants from mastodons took place in South-Eastern Asia.

Mastodons are distinguished by their molar teeth having comparatively few transverse ridges, which are low, and more or less completely divided by a longitudinal cleft into inner and outer columns. These ridges are separated by valleys in which there is little or no cement; and when worn down by use they exhibit more or less trefoil-shaped surfaces of ivory,

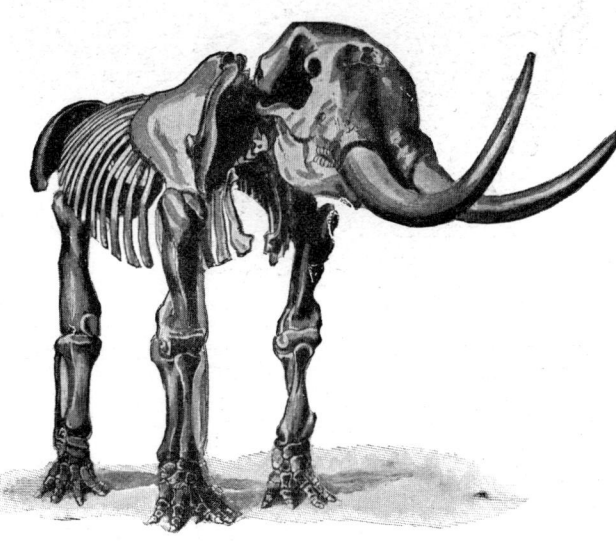

LAST UPPER LEFT MOLAR OF INDIAN MASTODON

quite different from the elongated ellipses formed in those of the true elephants. In the third, fourth, and fifth molar teeth of the stegodont elephants the number of transverse ridges is usually more than six, but in the mastodons is generally either four or three, although occasionally there may be as many as five, while the sixth or last molar generally has only four or five such ridges, in place of from nine to eleven found in the stegodont elephants. In all these respects mastodons exhibit a less specialised type of structure than that existing in the elephants, and thereby approximate to ordinary ungulates. The simpler dental structure is accompanied by the circumstance that portions of three molar teeth may be in use at the same time, whereas in elephants only two such teeth are present simultaneously on one side of the jaw. Nearly all mastodons had premolar teeth vertically replacing their milk molars, in the same manner as in other ungulates.

Early in the first half of the nineteenth century Dr. Hugh Falconer demonstrated that in respect of dental characters there is a practically complete gradation from the elephants of to-day to the ridge-toothed, or stegodont, elephants of the Tertiary formations of the Siwalik Hills, which, with the exception of the much simpler structure of their cheek teeth, are in all respects true elephants. And these ridge-toothed elephants are to be regarded as the immediate ancestors of the elephants of to-day. From these ridge-toothed elephants there is, in turn, an equally complete gradation into what may be called the short-chinned mastodons (*Mastodon*); that is to say, into elephants with cheek teeth of a still simpler type of structure, but in which the lower jaw is tuskless and terminates in front in the short spout characteristic of modern elephants.

There are, however, other mastodons (*Tetrabelodon*) in which the front of the lower jaw is produced into a long trough-like chin, considerably exceeding in length the rest of the skull, and terminating in a pair of small tusks which project upwards at an obtuse angle to the general line of the jaw. In the European species of long-chinned mastodons (*T. angustidens*, etc.) these tusks were present in both sexes, but in one Indian species, as shown by specimens of this portion of the jaw from the Punjab, they appear to have been restricted to the males. The upper tusks of these mastodons, instead of curving upwards like those of elephants, were somewhat bent down at the tips, so as to cross the extremities of the lower pair; and in this respect they are evidently one degree less far removed from the corresponding teeth

SKELETON OF AMERICAN MASTODON
From the Pleistocene of Benton County, Missouri, U.S.A.

of ordinary mammals. Now it is these long-chinned mastodons which have enabled naturalists to solve the problem of the origin and evolution of the elephant's trunk. Obviously, a creature with a lower jaw of this inordinate length must have had the upper half of the muzzle, or, in other words, the nose and upper lip, prolonged to an equal degree; and it is therefore quite clear that these long-chinned mastodons had an extremely exaggerated pig's muzzle. If we ask what was the reason for this extraordinary development, it may be replied that the long-chinned mastodons had evidently been developed from shorter-legged animals without any corresponding elongation of the neck to balance the lengthening of the limbs. Consequently, in order to enable them to reach the ground with their lips it was imperative

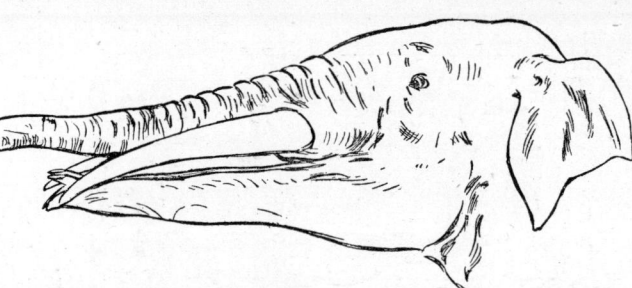

HEAD AND TUSKS OF LONG-CHINNED MASTODON

that the muzzle should be lengthened. And it is perfectly easy to understand how the muzzle lengthened *pari passu* with the increasing length of limb. Doubtless these long-chinned mastodons were able to graze; but their increase in bodily stature may have been for the purpose of enabling them also to browse after the manner of the Indian elephant.

No sooner had the long-chinned mastodons attained their full development of muzzle and tusks, than it would appear the whole arrangement was found unwieldy and inconvenient; the rigid lower jaw preventing the upper half of the muzzle from acting as a flexible proboscis. At all events, we may assume that this was the case from the rapidity with which the structure was modified and altered. Owing to the soft nature of most of the parts, the details of how this was accomplished are not quite clear.

Broadly speaking, it may be stated, however, that as the size of the animals of this group continued to increase—for, it should be mentioned, elephants are much larger animals than mastodons—the upper half of

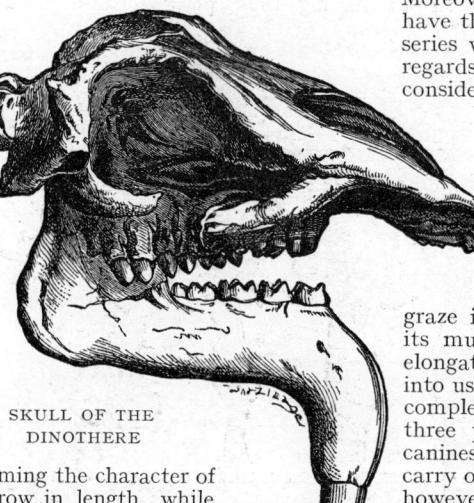

SKULL OF THE DINOTHERE

the muzzle, which was now assuming the character of a true proboscis, continued to grow in length, while the long trough-like chin of the lower jaw lost its tusks and began to contract in length, till it finally disappeared altogether, leaving only the short spout found in the front of the lower jaw of the elephant as a witness to its former existence. With this disappearance of the lower half of the long muzzle the upper half became converted into the trunk of the modern elephant, which serves to convey nutriment into a mouth now incapable of approaching within a long distance of the ground. The elephant's trunk is, therefore, nothing more than the greatly prolonged nose and upper lip; and the ridges to be seen on the two sides of its lower surface are, in fact, neither more nor less than remnants of the margins of the lip itself. Such, in brief, is the history of the evolution of this marvellous organ.

We have thus traced the Indian elephant into such a widely different animal as the long-chinned mastodon; and it must be added that, so far as available evidence goes, the transformation appears to have taken place in Asia. It remains to trace the long-chinned mastodons into connection with smaller animals of less abnormal structure, and for this we are indebted to Egypt, in the early Tertiary deposits of which country we meet with the earliest known ancestors of the elephants.

Here it is necessary to observe that even the long-chinned mastodons have a dentition of a highly-modified and specialised type. The front teeth, as already mentioned, are reduced to a single pair of tusks, or incisors, in each jaw; while of the cheek teeth there are, at most, but portions of three in use at any one time on the same side of each jaw, the hind teeth of this series coming into use as the front ones are worn away and shed. Moreover, with the exception of the first one or two, each tooth carries at least three transverse ridges.

From the aforesaid Egyptian deposits have been obtained remains of an animal—known as *Palæomastodon*—nearly allied to the long-chinned mastodons, but with a somewhat shorter chin to the lower jaw, and with both pairs of tusks relatively smaller and inclined somewhat more downwards or upwards, as the case may be. Moreover, although the cheek teeth still have three ridges each, nearly the whole series was in use at the same time. As regards size, the *Palæomastodon* was considerably smaller than the long-chinned mastodons—in some instances very markedly so.

A stage further in the line of evolution is presented by another Egyptian Eocene mammal, the *Mœritherium*, a creature but little larger than a tapir. From the length of its neck, it could evidently graze in the ordinary manner, although its muzzle may have been somewhat elongated. The teeth, which all came into use at the same time, form a fairly complete and regular series, these being three pairs of incisors, together with canines, while most of the cheek teeth carry only two ridges apiece. Already, however, we notice elephant-like characters in the superior size and abnormal direction of the second pair of incisors in each jaw; teeth destined to become the tusks of the long-chinned mastodon.

Somewhat off the line of the descent of the elephants, is the remarkable dinothere (*Dinotherium giganteum*), remains of which are found in the Miocene and Pliocene rocks of Europe and India, in which there appear to have been no upper tusks, but the extremity of the lower jaw was sharply bent down, and terminated in a pair of massive and somewhat curved tusks. There were no canine teeth, and the cheek teeth carried transverse ridges; but the whole of the permanent series of cheek teeth were in use at the same time, and their ridges were low and simple, and either two or three in number.

EXTINCT SHORT-FOOTED UNGULATES

There are several extinct groups of ungulates differing so markedly from all living forms that they cannot be included in any of the groups into which the latter are divided, and consequently have to be classed in groups by themselves.

The name of short-footed ungulates, Amblypoda, is applied to one of these groups which is confined to the Eocene division of the Tertiary period, and is more developed in the United States than in Europe. It is represented in both continents by the coryphodons (*Coryphodon*) of the lower and middle Eocene beds, and in America by the uintatheres (*Uintatherium*) of the upper Eocene. In these animals the feet are very short, and each provided with five toes, the mode of walking being partly plantigrade. The molar teeth have short crowns and the ridges arranged in a V-shape in those of the upper jaw, and it must also be noticed that the two bones in the forearm, as well as those in the lower leg, are quite distinct from one another.

The coryphodons were animals which may be compared to bears, and possessed the full typical number of forty-four teeth, with the tusks (canines) well developed. They had no horn-like processes to the skull. In the fore feet only the terminal bones of the toes touched the ground, but in the hind pair the whole sole was applied to the ground, in the same manner as in a bear, a skeleton of which is shown on page 481.

The American uintatheres, on the other hand, were much larger animals, rivalling the Indian rhinoceros in bulk. Their skulls are furnished with three pairs of bony processes, which during life were probably covered with horn ; and the upper tusks are developed into enormous sabre-like teeth, protected by a descending flange on each side of the front of the lower jaw. There are no incisor teeth in the upper jaw, and the first premolar tooth is wanting in both jaws, the total number of teeth being thirty-four. Both feet resembled the fore feet of the coryphodons in general structure, and the bones of the limbs approximate to those of elephants.

The brain is marvellously small in proportion to the size of the skull and body, indicating that these animals must have been of a stupid and sluggish nature. The uintatheres are evidently a specialised development of the coryphodon stock, which died out with the appearance of the former.

The movements of coryphodons were probably very similar to those of elephants, and these animals most likely walked with a shuffling and ambling gait, and may have been even more awkward from the inflexibility of the ankle. In compensation for the probable lack of speed, they were, however, most formidably armed with tusks ; these weapons, particularly in the upper jaw, being better developed and generally more robust than those of Carnivora. In length, one of the American species was probably about 6 feet.

Although the uintatheres were only made known to science in the second half of the nineteenth century, their skulls and bones long ago attracted the attention of wandering Indians, and squatters and trappers whose business led them into the district known as the Bad Lands. On returning to civilisation, these pioneers brought news of the skeletons of marvellous monsters staring at them from the rockbound cañons, and at length these won the notice of Professor Leidy, who made these strange creatures known to the world. The region where these remains occur consists of bare, treeless wastes of naked stone, rising here and there into terraced ledges and strange tower-like prominences, or sinking into hollows where the water gathers in salt or bitter pools. Under the cloudless sky, and in the clear, dry atmosphere, the extraordinary colouring of the rock forms the most striking feature of the weird landscape.

CONJECTURAL RESTORATION OF THE ARSINOITHERIUM

The coryphodons and the uintatheres severally represent a distinct family group—the *Coryphodontidæ* and the *Uintatheriidæ*. A third family, the *Arsinoïtheriidæ*, is typified by a most remarkable animal from the Eocene of Egypt known as *Arsinoïtherium*. Queen Arsinoë's animal, as the name means, was evidently more or less intimately related to the short-footed ungulates, although its exact systematic position is not yet finally settled by naturalists.

The skull of this extraordinary beast, of which an illustration is given on page 615, is very short and high, and furnished with a pair of small horns above the eyes and a second pair of immense horns in front, which appear to be merely enlarged nasal bones, and are supported by a bridge passing across the nose cavity to join the tip of the upper jaw. The brain is rather more developed than in the uintatheres, and the teeth, which form a regular and uninterrupted series, unbroken by large tusks or gaps, are taller, probably to suit a diet of dry vegetation requiring a large amount of grinding.

EXTINCT SOUTH AMERICAN UNGULATES

During early Tertiary times, when it formed an island continent, separated from the land to the north, South America was the home of numerous extinct ungulates quite unlike those found in any other part of the world, which, while resembling in some respects the odd-toed group, represent one or more perfectly distinct suborders. Among these, one of the most remarkable is *Macrauchenia*, the typical representative of the suborder Litopterna. The members of this group are characterised by having cheek teeth approximating in structure to those of the European palæotheres, the upper molars having their outer wall divided into two distinct lobes. Although the long toes are arranged in the same manner as in the odd-toed group of ungulates, and are never more than three in number, the structure of both the wrist and ankle joints is different. Thus, in place of the component bones of these joints alternating with one another, they are arranged directly one above another, after the linear type characterising modern elephants.

The huckle bone, or astragalus, of the ankle resembles that of the odd-toed group in being grooved superiorly, but the heel bone, or calcaneum, differs in having a small surface for the articulation of the fibula, or smaller bone of the leg, as in the even-toed group. The long vertebræ of the neck, although showing the same flat terminal ends characterising the allied extinct South American groups, are peculiar in regard to the position of the canal for the great artery of the neck, and in this respect agree with camels and llamas alone among living ungulates. The thigh bone, or femur, has a small third trochanter representing the larger one characteristic of the odd-toed group. In build, the members of the present group were tall, slender ungulates, with long legs, feet, and neck; and thus very different in appearance from the toxodonts, which were short-limbed, short-necked, and heavily-built animals.

The Litopterna are divisible into two families, of which the first (*Macraucheniidæ*) is represented by the macrauchenia and certain allied forms, and characterised by the presence of forty-four teeth, forming an uninterrupted series in the jaws. Macrauchenia itself, which was discovered by Darwin in the superficial deposits of Patagonia, was an animal somewhat larger than a horse, but resembling a llama in general appearance, and presenting the remarkable peculiarity of having the aperture of the nostrils in the skull situated in the middle of the forehead. During life it is probable that the muzzle terminated in a short trunk. In the lower, or Miocene, Tertiaries of Patagonia the family was represented by smaller and less specialised forms such as *Oxyodontotherium*, in which the nostrils are more normal in position, and the crowns of the molar teeth lower and simpler.

In the second family, or *Proterotheriidæ*, represented principally in the lower Patagonian Tertiary deposits, the teeth are reduced in number, and form an interrupted series, a pair in both the upper and lower jaw being much longer than the rest. In these proterotheres the molar teeth have a considerable resemblance to those of palæotheres; but the feet are of the general type of those of the three-toed horses, or hipparions, and in the genus *Thoatherium* only the middle toe was functionally developed, just as in the modern members of the horse family. In fact, these animals probably looked very like ponies; but in the skeleton the terminal bones of the toe were cleft, and the radius and ulna in the fore limb, and the fibula and tibia in the hind limb, were severally distinct.

In another group from the Miocene deposits of Patagonia the species are of large size, and possess rooted cheek teeth of a rhinoceros-like type, and lacking the marked curvature of the crown characterising those of the toxodonts. The vertebræ of the neck are comparatively short, with flattened articular surfaces, and the lateral canal piercing the transverse process in the ordinary manner. The wrist and ankle joints

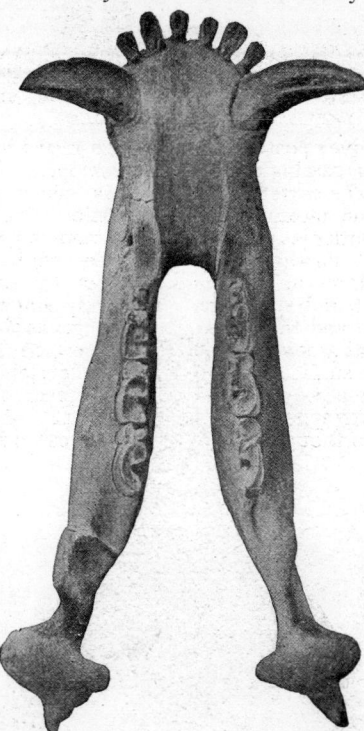

LOWER JAW OF THE ASTRAPOTHERE

were probably of the linear type; the calcaneum articulates largely with the fibula; and the astragalus is quite flat, and furnished with a large head for articulation with the navicular bone. The femur, when known, has a large third trochanter.

The group, which may or may not belong to the Litopterna, is distinguished from the Amblypoda by the structure of the cheek teeth, and not improbably by the number of digits having been three in place of five; and it is decidedly the most generalised of the South American extinct ungulates, as is especially shown by the flattened astragalus. The remarkable similarity of the molars of *Astrapotherium* to those of rhinoceroses must be considered as due to parallelism, since the structure of the ankle in the apparently allied *Homalodontotherium* indicates that the group diverged from the common ancestor before modern odd-toed ungulates had acquired their characteristic foot structure.

In *Homalodontotherium*, representing a family by itself, the teeth comprise the full number of $i. \frac{3}{3}, c. \frac{1}{1}, p.m. \frac{4}{4}, m. \frac{3}{3}$, and have no gap; the canines being rooted and of relatively small size, and the molars with comparatively short crowns. The upper premolars are nearly as complex as the molars, and the third upper molar is not markedly different from the two preceding teeth. The lower molars are in the form of double crescents, of which the front one develops a loop like that found in the corresponding teeth of horses. It is stated that the toes terminated in claws. The one known species was an animal of the approximate size of the Sumatran rhinoceros (page 776).

The gigantic astrapothere, which represents the family *Astrapotheriidæ*, differs from the last genus in the more specialised and reduced dentition, the enlarged teeth of each jaw taking the form of permanently growing tusks, which are worn in nearly the same manner as those of pigs. The molars are more distinctly rhinoceros-like in structure, those of the upper jaw having taller crowns than those of the homalodonto-there, with a large posterior valley, and a well-developed projection in the middle valley. The last of the series has the same triangular form as in the majority of species of rhinoceros, and the premolars are simpler than the molars. In the lower jaw the molars form nearly simple crescents, very similar to those of rhinoceroses, but the hind crescent of the third of the series is more elongated.

The dentition may apparently be represented by the formula, $i.\frac{1}{3}, c.\frac{0}{1}, p.m. \frac{2}{1}, m. \frac{3}{3}$; the premolars being separated from the incisors or canines by a long gap.

The front of the apex of the upper tusk is worn to an oblique facet by the friction of the lower canine. In the lower jaw the tusk is considerably smaller than in the upper jaw, but is still triangular in section, although with the sharp edge in front; the inner

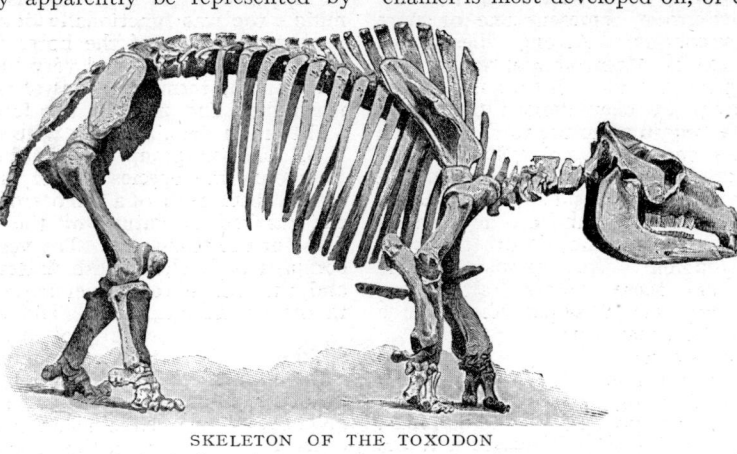

SKELETON OF THE TOXODON

surface being concave anteriorly and convex posteriorly, but the outer one wholly convex, and passing imperceptibly into the small hind surface. The extremity of the latter is worn into a long oblique facet, in the same manner as in the corresponding tooth of a peccary.

The six lower incisors are inclined forwards, and arranged in a circle so as to fill up the interval between the tusks; and their crowns are short and spatulate, with the upper surface slightly concave and the lower one convex; a deep longitudinal groove traversing the middle of each of these surfaces to unite in a notch in the middle of the unworn crown. In the lower jaw the tusks correspond to canines, and it looks at first sight as though the same would hold good with those of the upper jaw, but from the analogy of the proterothere it is more probable that they really belong to the incisor series.

Another group of these curious South American ungulates is formed by the toxodonts (suborder Toxodontia), which may be defined as ungulates with tall-crowned and curved cheek teeth, some or all of which grow from persistent pulps, either permanently or during a considerable portion of life; while at least one pair of incisors in each jaw is rootless, and the third upper incisor, when present, is placed in the line of the cheek teeth. The vertebræ of the neck are short, with flattened articular faces to the bodies, and the vertebral artery piercing the transverse process in the ordinary manner. The wrist is of the alternating type, but the ankle joint is formed on the linear plan. The astragalus is slightly grooved on its superior face, and inferiorly is like that of the odd-toed group, having no head for the navicular; but the calcaneum, which is truncated inferiorly, has a large articular surface for the fibula, as in the even-toed section. The number of toes varies from five to three, the middle one being larger

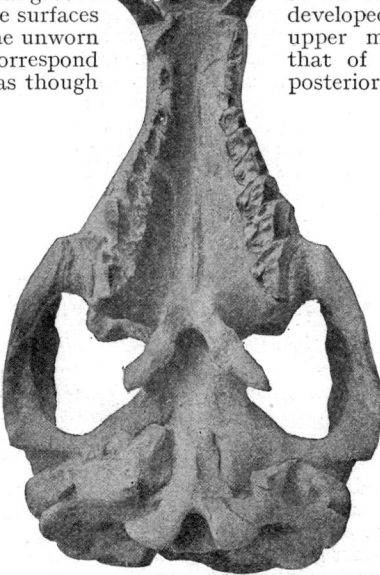

UNDER-SURFACE OF SKULL OF THE NESODON

than any of the others, and symmetrical in itself. The femur may or may not have a third trochanter. The number of trunk vertebræ in the typical genus *Toxodon* is twenty, or intermediate between that of the even and the odd-toed groups. In form the cheek teeth of the less specialised forms approximate to the odd-toed plan of structure; and in all the genera the enamel is most developed on, or even confined to, the outer sides of the cheek teeth, although there may be vertical bands on some of the other surfaces.

The toxodon was of the size of a large rhinoceros, and characterised by the long and curved crowns of its molar teeth, which continued to grow throughout life. There are only two pairs of incisor teeth and no tusks in the upper jaw, although in the lower jaw the full number of these teeth is developed. The feet are furnished with three toes.

This genus occurs in the superficial deposits of Argentina, but is replaced in the Miocene Tertiaries of Patagonia by the allied nesodons (*Nesodon*), which may be defined as toxodonts of medium or small size, in which the limbs, and probably also the neck, were relatively longer and more slender than in the typical genus; while all the teeth, with the exception of the second upper and third lower incisors, developed roots in the adult state, and the upper molars were of a type approaching that of the odd-toed group, with a distinct posterior valley, and the middle column forming a lobe projecting into the middle valley. The second upper and the third lower incisors formed a pair of permanently growing tusks, which were, however, not fully developed till late in life.

Even more strange than the toxodon was the smaller typothere (*Typotherium*), which represents a remarkable approximation in the characters of its skull and teeth to rodents. While the molars are not unlike those of the toxodon, the upper incisors are reduced to a single chisel-shaped pair, and there are no tusks in either jaw. The lower jaw carries one large pair of chisel-like incisor teeth, behind which is a much smaller second pair. The typothere differed from all living ungulates, and thereby again resembled rodents, in having collar bones (clavicles). The occurrence of all these remarkable ungulates, so utterly different from those of all other parts of the world, indicates that during the Miocene period South America, with its many peculiar types of edentates, was completely cut off from the northern half of the New World. Later the two areas became connected, and the incursion of northern types led to the extermination of all the original ungulates of South America.

ORDER VII. SIRENIA

THE CHARACTERISTICS OF THE SEA-COWS

By R. LYDEKKER

THE purely aquatic mammals known as manatis and dugongs, or sea-cows, together with the rhytina, or northern sea-cow, which became extinct within the last two centuries, constitute by themselves an order known as the Sirenia. Although as well fitted for an aquatic life as the cetaceans, these se-acows have no relationship with the whales, and were derived independently from terrestrial mammals ; such resemblances as exist between sirenians and cetaceans being entirely of an adaptive nature, and due solely to the fact that the two groups lead a somewhat similar mode of life. Researches show that sea-cows are closely related to elephants, so that the Sirenia are a specialised offshoot from the proboscidean stock.

Although existing sirenians resemble cetaceans in having their fore limbs converted into flippers, and in having lost all traces of the hind limbs, while the tail is converted into a horizontally expanded rudder-like organ, comparable to the flukes of whales and dolphins, their general conformation is very different. In the first place, although the body is somewhat cetacean-like, without any well-defined neck and with no distinction between trunk and tail, it is markedly depressed, instead of more or less compressed from side to side.

The head departs little from the ordinary mammalian type, being comparatively small in proportion to the body, with the summit rounded, and the nostrils, which are double and capable of being closed at will by valve-like flaps, placed above the extremity of the abruptly truncated muzzle. The back fin, commonly present in cetaceans, is totally wanting ; and in the flippers, although the whole of the toes are enclosed in a paddle-shaped mass of integument, traces of nails are in some cases retained.

The eyes of sirenians are small, with imperfectly developed lids, and the minute aperture of the ear is unprovided with any external conch. The small mouth has thick, fleshy lips, furnished with a number of bristly hairs, which persist throughout life. The skin is thick, and either finely wrinkled or rugged and bark-like, sometimes with thinly distributed fine hairs. The female has a single pair of teats placed on the breast.

The teeth are very variable, being totally wanting in the northern sea-cow, but well-developed in the two living genera, in which they consist of incisors and cheek teeth. In structure, however, the cheek teeth of the manati are different from those of the dugong ; while in the former group their number is much greater than among less aberrant mammals. The living forms possess rudimentary milk teeth, and in some extinct species such teeth were well developed. Certain extinct members of the order, moreover, were furnished with a complete set of teeth, comparable to those of ordinary mammals. All the recent species have horny plates on the palate and on the opposing surface of the lower jaw.

In the skeleton the bones are distinguished by their solid and dense structure ; this being especially noticeable in those of the skull and ribs. The skull is depressed, and has a more or less distinctly deflected beak-like snout, much flattened from side to side ; and is further characterised by the very large size of the aperture of the cavity of the nose, which is somewhat pear-shaped, and placed relatively farther back than usual. In the living forms the nasal bones are either rudimentary or absent, but in some fossil species are better developed, and partially roofed over the nasal cavity in the ordinary manner. This abortion of the nasal bones in both sirenians and cetaceans is doubtless due to the necessity for a large nasal aperture in the skull, owing to the peculiarities in the respiration of these animals.

The vertebræ are singular in that during the young state they do not show separate plate-like ossifications at each end of their bodies, like those developed in other mammals. Rudiments of these so-called epiphyses, however, have been shown to exist in the extremely young state, and were more fully developed in certain extinct forms. As in cetaceans, none of the vertebræ in the hind region of the trunk unites to form a sacrum ; and it is evident that a solid immovable structure in this part of the backbone would be not only a serious disadvantage to a swimming animal, but also of no use to one which has no hind limbs to support.

Sirenians resemble ungulates in having no collar bones. In the fore limb the upper bone, or humerus, is of considerable length, and differs from that of cetaceans in having distinct pulley-like surfaces at its lower end for the articulation of the bones of the fore arm (radius and ulna), thus permitting of a certain amount of free motion at the elbow joint. The two bones of the fore arm, however, are generally united at the lower end. The number of digits is five, and none of these contains more than the ordinary number of three joints, in addition to the metacarpus. None of the recent sirenians shows any trace of the hind limb, although the pelvis is represented by a pair of splint-like bones ; but in some fossil forms there was a rudimentary thigh bone, or femur.

There are several peculiarities connected with the soft internal parts, but it will suffice to mention that the lungs are extremely long and narrow, extending beneath the back bone nearly as far back as the last rib ; to permit of this backward extension, the midriff, or diaphragm, is placed very obliquely. The larger arteries of the body form peculiar net-like expansions in certain regions, which render sea-cows able to remain beneath the surface for a longer period than would otherwise be possible, as partly oxygenated blood can be retained for some time in these structures before it is passed through the heart.

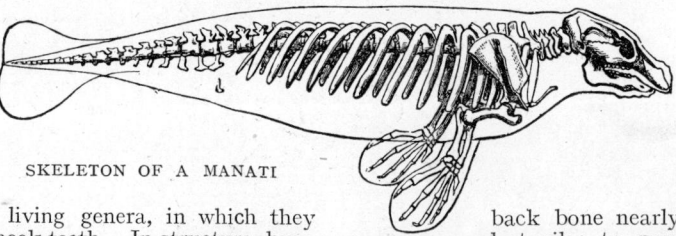

SKELETON OF A MANATI

Some curious resemblances exist between the sirenian and the cetacean tongue. In that organ in the dolphin, for instance, there have been found certain peculiar pits occupying the position of the circumvallate

A YOUNG MANATI CAPTURED OFF THE COAST OF SOUTH FLORIDA

papillæ in other mammals, and very similar pits in the dugong occupy the position of the foliate papillæ. Whether these pits are connected with the sense of taste is uncertain, although the occurrence in both cases of ganglionic cells in the pits is in favour of such a function. An important difference between the sirenian and cetacean mouth is the presence in the former of large salivary glands, which are wanting in the latter.

Although manatis and dugongs never leave the water, and are as well adapted for an aquatic life as whales are, yet they cannot swim in the rapid manner characteristic of many of the latter, and are never found inhabiting the open sea. They frequent shallow seas and bays, lagoons, estuaries, and large rivers. As regards their food, sea-cows are entirely herbivorous, browsing upon seaweed or other aquatic plants. They are slow and sluggish in their movements, harmless and inoffensive in disposition, and endowed with a comparatively small amount of intelligence.

Sea-cows produce a single offspring, which is attended with assiduous care by its parent. When suckling, the females raise their heads and breasts above the water, and exhibit the young clinging to them, and partially supported by their flippers; and there can be little doubt that this habit has given origin to the legendary mermaid.

The living members of the order, which generally associate in small herds, frequent the coasts and larger rivers on both sides of the Atlantic, and also those of the Red Sea, the Indian Ocean, parts of the Bay of Bengal, and Australia. The northern sea-cow, however, was an inhabitant of the cold regions of Bering Sea, and during the Tertiary period sirenians were distributed over the greater part of the globe, so that the group is on the wane.

Each of the three genera of sirenians that have existed during the historic period is frequently regarded as entitled to constitute a family by itself, but they are all so nearly allied, and so closely connected by fossil forms, that it seems preferable to regard them as members of a single family—the *Halicoridæ*.

The following table sets forth the classification of the Sirenia.

ORDER VII.
Sea-Cows, or Manatis and Dugongs—Sirenia

FAMILY
Sea-Cows—Halicoridæ

GENUS 1
Manatis—Manatus
SPECIES

American manati	Manatus americanus
Senegal manati	M. senegalensis
Amazonian manati	M. inunguis

GENUS 2
Dugongs—Halicore
SPECIES

Dugong	Halicore dugong

GENUS 3
Northern Sea-Cow—Rhytina
SPECIES

Northern sea-cow (extinct)	Rhytina gigas

EXTINCT SEA-COWS

Felsinotherium	Prorastomus	Eosiren
Metaxytherium	Eotherium	Protosiren
Halitherium		

MANATIS

The manatis—so named from the hand-like use of the flippers when nursing the young—are characterised by the nostrils being situated at the apex of the muzzle, by the rounded margin of the expanded tail, and by the presence of three minute rudimentary nails on each of the flippers. In the skull, the beak and extremity of the lower jaw are comparatively small, and slightly bent downwards. The incisor teeth are rudimentary, being concealed beneath the horny plates of the mouth, and disappearing before the animal becomes adult. On the other hand, the cheek teeth, of which a great number are developed in each jaw, have squared crowns, with transverse ridges, and present some resemblance to the lower teeth of the tapir and the early forerunners (*Moeritherium*) of the elephants. Generally there are seldom more than six pairs of these teeth in use at the same time on one side of each jaw, the front ones falling out before those farther back have come into use. In the skeleton manatis present the remarkable peculiarity of having only six vertebræ in the neck, and are therein almost unique among mammals.

Manatis attain a length of about 8 feet. Their dark, greyish skin is marked by a number of fine wrinkles, and, at least in the young condition, is covered with very fine, sparsely distributed hairs.

One of the most peculiar features connected with the manatis is to be found in the conformation of the mouth; the upper lip being prehensile, so that the animal is able to introduce food into the mouth without the assistance of the comparatively insignificant lower lip. The front of the muzzle is of triangular form, with the apex, in which are situated the nostrils, upwards; the lower border of this triangle being bounded by two rounded fleshy pads, forming the angles of the upper lip. "When the animal," writes Professor A. H. Garrod, "is on the point of seizing, say, a leaf of lettuce, the pads are diverged transversely in such a way as to make the median gap of considerable breadth. Directly the leaf is within grasp, the lip-pads are approximated, the leaf is firmly seized between their contiguous bristly surfaces, and then drawn inwards by a backward movement of the lower margin of the lip as a whole.

The appearance produced by the movements of this peculiar organ is very much the same as that of the mouth in the silkworm and other caterpillars whilst devouring a leaf, the jaws in these insects diverging and converging laterally, in a very similar manner during mastication." In regard to the mechanism for closing the nostrils during submersion, Garrod adds that "these circular orifices have each a flap-valve, which forms the floor or inferior wall of the nasal tubes when the animal is breathing, but which rises and completely occludes it when closed."

Manatis are found in the rivers and on the coasts of the two sides of the tropical portions of the Atlantic, but are mainly fluviatile, ascending the larger rivers, such as the Amazon, almost to their sources. There are three well-defined species, namely, the American *Manatus americanus*, the closely allied African *M. senegalensis*, distinguished from the former by the characters of the skull, and the small and nailless manati (*M. inunguis*) from the Amazon and Orinoco.

In young manatis the brain chamber and the enclosing portion of the skull are short, and it is not until mature life that they attain the characteristic elongation. The tympanic and petrosal bones of the ear do not fuse to form a petro-tympanic bone.

The dentition of the manatis is of a secondary type, so far as the exceptional number of the cheek teeth is concerned, while the extension of the skull in the line of the body axis, the markedly forward inclination of the orbital region, and the small eye-sockets, or orbits, are all features indicative of adaptation to an aquatic life, while the comparative lateness of this adaptation is indicated by the preservation of the original condition in the structure of the internal ear.

As regards distribution, the nailless species is now mainly confined to the Amazon basin, although it still survives in the Rio San Francisco, while formerly it was met with for a considerable distance along the Brazilian coast. The American manati, on the other hand, is chiefly a Central American species ranging little south of the main stream of the Orinoco.

Owing to the constant persecution for the sake of their oil and hides, manatis have much diminished in numbers, and in most accessible districts are now comparatively scarce. The first living manati brought to England was received in the Zoological Gardens in London early in August 1875, but did not long survive, and a second specimen was obtained in March 1889. A third lived in the Brighton Aquarium for

A MANATI

sixteen months. All were fed chiefly upon lettuce, although they would eat other vegetables.

The following remarks were made by Professor Garrod on the one first acquired by the Zoological Society : " Looking at the living animal generally, the most striking peculiarity was the sluggishness of its movements ; when crossing its pond there was none of the lateral movement of the body so characteristic of the seals. All flexions were up and down, the whole trunk bending a little in that direction, the base of the tail doing so freely at a clearly marked transverse fold-line in that region. An opportunity occurred for seeing it out of the water, when its pond was drained dry for a short time. From my observations on this occasion it

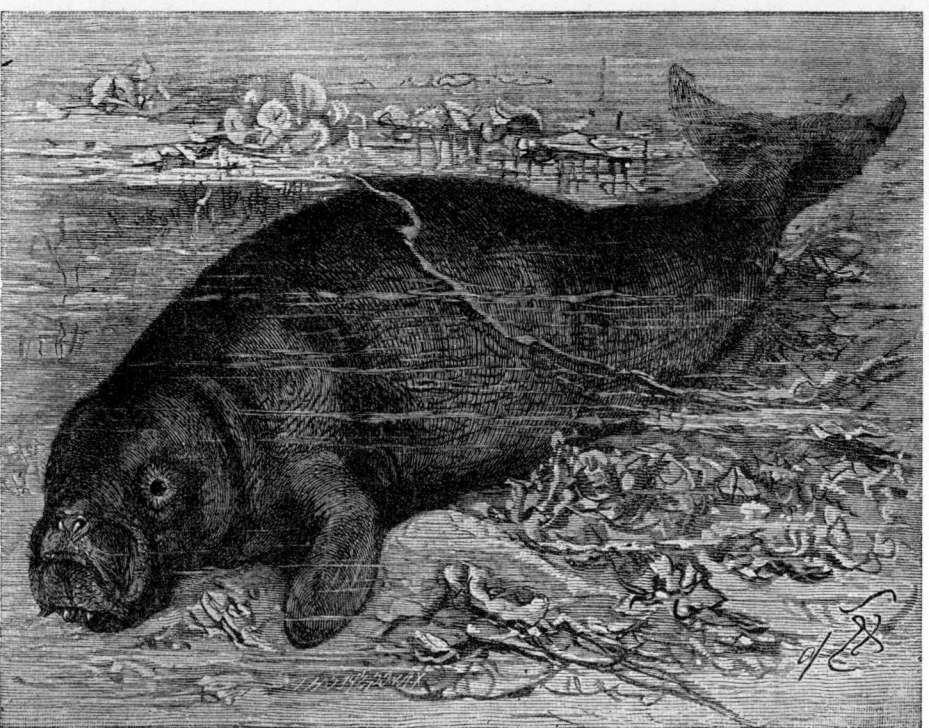

THE DUGONG

was perfectly evident that the manati is purely aquatic in habits, and that it never willingly quits the water. When on land, it seemed perfectly unable to advance or recede, the only movements it performed being that from its belly to its back, and vice versâ.

" The power of moving the slightly exserted elbow was considerable, whilst that of the wrist was small but apparent. It used its limbs much more freely than do the seals, sometimes employing the extreme margins of the paddles to assist in introducing food into its mouth, at others employing them in progression along the bottom of the pond, during which time the swimming tail could not be brought into play to any extent."

The flesh of the manati, which is very light in colour, is eaten by the natives of the Amazon region, and has been compared to pork, but the fat is reported to have a disagreeable flavour.

THE DUGONG

The dugong (*Halicore dugong*), or, as it should be termed from its Malay name, duyong, is a very different animal (page 130), both externally and as regards the structure of its skull and teeth, from the manati. Externally it is characterised by the nostrils being situated on the upper part of the muzzle, by the tail being crescent-shaped and concave posteriorly, and by the absence of any trace of nails on the flippers. The skull is characterised by the great thickness and massiveness of the beak and the extremity of the lower jaw, both of which are sharply bent down, so as to form almost a right angle with the long axis.

The teeth, which grow throughout life, in the adult state comprise a pair of incisors in the upper jaw, and five molars on each side of both jaws. In the females the incisors are small and do not pierce the gum, but in the males they assume the form of rather large

and nearly straight tusks, partially coated with enamel, and directed downwards. The molars are cylindrical, the last in each jaw being more complex than the others, and looking as if composed of two cylinders joined together. These teeth have no enamel ; and some of the front ones are shed before those behind come into use. There can be little doubt that the molars of the dugong present one step in the process of degeneration which resulted in their complete disappearance in the northern sea-cow.

In colour the dugong is either uniformly bluish grey, or the under parts may have a more or less distinct whitish tinge. The normal length varies from 5 to 7 feet, but they occasionally measure from 8 to 9 feet. In a specimen of 8½ feet in length, the maximum girth was 6 feet.

Dugongs are found on the shores of the Indian Ocean, for about fifteen degrees on each side of the equator, from Eastern Africa to Australia, and likewise around the Red Sea. They are not uncommon on parts of the coasts of Ceylon and the Andaman and Nicobar Islands. Although it has been considered that the dugong of the Red Sea, together with the one found on the Australian coasts, is specifically distinct from the typical dugong, this is extremely doubtful.

Except that it is a marine animal, never ascending rivers, and feeding chiefly on seaweed and marine grasses, the dugong is very similar in its mode of life to the manati. Formerly, these animals occurred in large herds comprising several hundreds, so fearless of man that they would allow themselves to be touched with the hand. Now, however, they are only to be met with in twos or threes, or small parties, and have become very shy and wary.

Dugongs, like manatis, do not voluntarily leave the water, and, further, it is suggested that they seldom enter brakish, and are incapable of living in fresh water. Much interest attaches to the existence of a slimy coating for the protection of the eye, a similar coating also occurring in whales, although in the latter it is of an oily nature, in order to prevent it from being too easily washed away by the sea water. Dugong fishing is practised as a regular industry on the Australian coast, the clear, limpid oil bearing a high value. The flesh is described as of excellent quality and flavour. The natives of Torres Strait are in the habit of using dugong skulls and ribs for the decoration of their huts.

NORTHERN SEA-COW

On his return in 1741 from a voyage of discovery to Alaska, the navigator Vitus Bering had the misfortune to be shipwrecked on the island which now bears his name ; this island, and the adjacent Copper Island, together with some islets, constituting the Commander group, which lies in Bering Sea, at a distance of about one hundred miles from the coast of Kamchatka. At the time of their sojourn, Bering and his companions found the shores of these islands inhabited by a pre-viously unknown animal, evidently allied to the manati, but of much greater dimensions. This was the northern sea-cow (*Rhytina gigas*) then found in vast numbers on the islands, but which within a period of thirty years from that date appears to have been exterminated. Indeed, had Bering not been accom-panied by the naturalist, Georg Wilhelm Steller, we should probably never even have heard of the existence of this animal, except for some slight mention in the accounts of certain contemporary voyagers. No skins and only some imperfect skeletons of the animal were preserved by the survivors of Bering's party ; but of late years a considerable number of more or less imperfect skeletons have been reclaimed from the frozen soil of the Commander Islands.

This gigantic sea-cow differed from its allies in having no teeth, the functions of which were performed by horny plates covering the palate and opposing surface of the lower jaw. The head was very small in proportion to the body, and the extremities of the jaws were bent somewhat downwards. The tail was forked, after the manner of that of the dugong; while the flippers were very small and truncated, and covered with bristly hairs. Steller states that there were no bones in the hand, and none has hitherto been found.

The skin was naked, and covered with a thick, rugged epidermis, compared to the bark of a tree ; in places this epidermis was an inch in thickness, and so tough that it required the use of an axe to cut it. The skin, according to

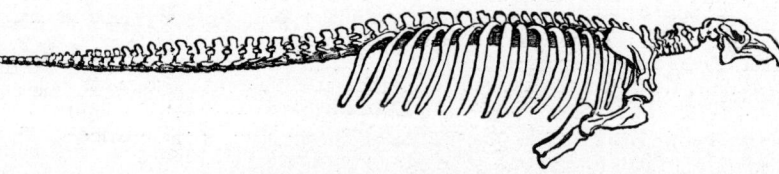

SKELETON OF NORTHERN SEA-COW

Steller's description, was dark brown in colour, some-times marked with streaks or spots of white ; but a drawing of the animal left by Waxell, the navigator of Bering's party, represents it as marked with alternate dark and light transverse stripes. The skeleton measures 19½ feet in length, which would indicate a length of about 20 feet in the living state, but Steller states that the animal sometimes attained a length of from 25 to 30 feet. The girth of the body was 19 or 20 feet, and the estimated weight 8,000 pounds.

With the exception of a single rib from Altu, no remains of the northern sea-cow have been obtained elsewhere than on Bering and Copper Islands. It is, however, almost impossible to believe that such a large animal could always have had such a restricted distri-bution, and it is probable that, when discovered, this sea-cow was already on the wane, and that the Com-mander Islands were its last resorts from a more extended distribution. Not the least remarkable circumstance is that, although closely allied to the typical dugong, it should have inhabited such a cold and northerly region.

At the time of its discovery, the northern sea-cow was abundant in the bays and river mouths of the Commander Islands, where it lived in herds of con-siderable size. It fed chiefly on seaweeds, and more especially the tangle which grows so abundantly in the northern seas. It was described as stupid, sluggish, and comparatively helpless, unable to dive, and not infrequently washed ashore by the waves. From inability to dive, these sea-cows were compelled to obtain their food in shallow water, and from being often unable to approach the shore during the storms of winter they were generally in poor condition by the spring.

EXTINCT SEA-COWS

Throughout a large portion of the Tertiary period various species of extinct sea-cows were common in Europe, the best known of these being the halithere (*Halitherium*), which forms in some respects a kind of connecting link between the manati and the dugong. It resembled the latter in having the extremities of the jaws deflected, and in the presence of a pair of tusks in the upper jaw, but its molar teeth were more like those of the manati, although with a pattern recalling that obtaining on the crowns of those of the hippopotamus. There are several features which indicate that this animal was a more generalised type than either of its existing allies, the premolar teeth having milk predecessors, while the skull was furnished with distinct nasal bones, and there were rudimentary hind limbs. Several allied genera have been described.

There is another extinct member of the order, which presents indications of a still closer affinity with ordinary mammals. This is *Prorastomus*, of which remains have been found in strata probably belonging to the upper portion of the Eocene period in Jamaica and Italy. This creature has three pairs of incisors, and a pair of canines, as well as seven or eight pairs of cheek teeth in each jaw, and thus approximates very closely to the ordinary mam-malian type, the front and premo-lar teeth havng milk predeces-sors. *Prorasto-mus* was probably the ancestor of the manati ; and it is interesting to note that the milk molars of the Italian Oligocene *P. veronense* resemble the permanent molars of the manati.

The most primitive member of the group is *Eotherium*, from the Eocene of the Mokattam Range, near Cairo, which possessed a complete pelvis, showing a well-marked obturator foramen. In this respect the genus differs from all other known members of the order, which are thus brought into connection with less specialised mammals.

The three Egyptian Eocene genera *Eotherium*, *Eosiren*, and *Protosiren* are regarded as the earliest known ancestors of the dugong group, and to these succeed *Halitherium* in the Oligocene, *Metaxytherium* in the Miocene, and *Felsinotherium* in the Pliocene.

ORDER VIII. CETACEA
GENERAL SKETCH OF WHALES AND DOLPHINS
By R. LYDEKKER

UNDER the title of cetaceans (order Cetacea) may be included those mammals known as whales, porpoises, and dolphins, which exceed even sea-cows in their assumption of a fish-like form and complete adaptation to a purely aquatic mode of life. Indeed, so like are cetaceans in outward appearance to fishes, that they are popularly regarded as belonging to that class, although in all essential features of their organisation they are true mammals, breathing atmospheric air by means of lungs, having warm blood, a four-chambered heart, the skull articulating with the first joint of the backbone by means of two condyles, and the cavity of the body divided into two chambers by a midriff, while they produce living young, which are nourished by milk drawn from the bodies of their mothers.

The assumption of a fish-like form by cetaceans is one of the best-marked examples of adaptive characters produced in order to fit the animals in which they exist for their external surroundings, and without

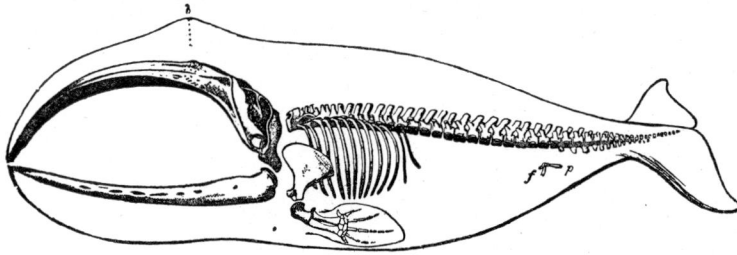

SKELETON OF THE GREENLAND WHALE

any sort of connection with their affinities. The fish-like resemblances of cetaceans are, moreover, not so close as might at first sight appear, since the tail fin, instead of being vertical, is horizontal, while the structure of the skeleton of the fore limb is different from that of any fish. As a general fish-like form of body is the best adapted for progression through water, this affords sufficient reason for its having been acquired in the present group; and it may also be mentioned that cetaceans resemble fishes in having the upper part of the body coloured dark, while the under parts are light, such a type of colouring rendering the animals in which it occurs not easily seen, either from above or below, when in their native element.

That whales are not even directly descended from fishes is evident from the fact of their breathing atmospheric air, by means of lungs, for if they had so originated they would certainly have retained fish-like gills, and thus have avoided the necessity of coming periodically to the surface for the purpose of breathing. It is probably for this reason that cetaceans have their tails with the expansion placed in a horizontal instead of a vertical plane, since the strokes of such a horizontally expanded organ are the best calculated to bring an animal rapidly to the surface.

The additional fact that cetaceans retain traces of the hairy covering so characteristic of mammals in general, affords evidence that they derive their origin from terrestrial mammals; and, coupled with the absence of hind limbs, is sufficient to disprove any notion that they themselves are in any way connected with the ancestral stock from which the other members of the class have originated. Cetaceans may, therefore, be regarded as some of the most specialised of all mammals.

For some years the idea was prevalent that the ancestral forms were to be sought among the primitive

extinct representatives of the hoofed, or ungulate, group. There existed, however, during the Eocene division of the Tertiary period certain whale-like creatures known as zeuglodonts, and, since their teeth are of a carnivorous type, it ought long ago to have been evident that if a kinship exists between these zeuglodonts and whales, the latter must have had carnivorous rather than herbivorous ancestors. As regards the zeuglodonts, discoveries made in the lower Tertiary deposits of Egypt have almost conclusively proved that they trace their origin to that primitive extinct group of Carnivora known as creodonts; and the question accordingly narrows itself down as to the nature of the relationship (if any) existing between zeuglodonts and modern whales and dolphins.

In the opinion of Dr. Stromer zeuglodonts are to be regarded as primitive cetaceans, with a nearer relationship to the toothed than to the whalebone whales; such resemblance as they present to seals being due to adaptation to a similar mode of life. The larger species, which attained a length of some 30 or 40 feet, became extinct without leaving successors, as is commonly the case among animals; and although the smaller typical kinds present more approximation to the toothed whales, it seems probable that the two groups underwent a parallel development, rather than that the one was ancestral to the other. The distinction between the two is specially manifested by the hind brain, or cerebellum, as well as by the form of the pterygoid fossa. On the other hand, the small zeuglodont known as *Protocetus* presents in its shorter snout and certain other features a more decided approximation to the toothed whales, especially some of their middle Tertiary representatives, and this suggests that modern whales are the direct descendants of some small, primitive, and at present unknown zeuglodont.

The leading characteristics of these zeuglodonts are described later (p. 857).

With regard to the terrestrial mammals to which cetaceans are most closely related, some uncertainty and difference of opinion still prevail among naturalists. The late Sir William H. Flower was inclined to consider that they show more resemblances to ungulates, especially the even-toed group; but the teeth of the earliest forms are unlike those of any ungulates and approximate much more nearly to those of carnivores; and, as stated above, a carnivorous ancestry is therefore probable. The few cetaceans inhabiting fresh water are somewhat less markedly different in structure from ordinary mammals than are the marine representatives of the order, which has suggested the idea that cetaceans were first modified for the assumption of an aquatic life from land mammals frequenting the banks of rivers, and that after having acquired natatorial powers in fresh water, they migrated to the sea, where they attained their present remarkable development. Against this may be urged the fact that zeuglodonts were marine.

Cetaceans are characterised by their fish-like form, the head passing imperceptibly into the body without any distinct neck, and the trunk gradually tapering to the tail, which terminates in a forked, horizontal fin-like expansion known as the "flukes." The head is large in proportion to the body, with a wide mouth, often furnished with a few bristles, at least in the young state. The fore limbs are represented by flippers, encased in continuous skin, showing no outward indications of digits, and without the slightest trace of nails or claws, while of the hind limbs there is not the least external sign.

With the exception of the sparse bristles in the neighbourhood of the mouth, the smooth and shining skin is devoid of all traces of hair; neither has it any structure corresponding to the scales of fishes. Beneath, it is underlain by the thick layer of oily fat termed "blubber," the function of which is to prevent the absorption of the heat of the body by the water. The majority of the species have a fin on the back, entirely composed of integument, and having no internal skeleton corresponding to the similarly situated fins of fishes. The eye is extremely small; and, as in fishes, the ear has no external conch, and opens by an exceedingly small aperture behind the eye. The nostrils, which may have either a single or double opening, are situated on the very summit of the head, and thus reach the surface before any other part when the animals rise horizontally.

In the skeleton the bones are remarkable for their loose and spongy structure, and in the living state are saturated with oil. The majority of the species have teeth, which may be confined to the lower jaw, and there represented only by a single pair. In all cases these teeth are of a simply conical or compressed form; and in many dolphins are much more numerous than in any other mammals. In no instance is there any replacement of the teeth, although in some species there are rudimentary successional teeth which never come to maturity; and from this it is considered that the functional teeth correspond to the milk series of those mammals in which there is a replacement. With regard to the great number of teeth present in some cetaceans, it has been suggested that this is due to the division of a number of trilobed teeth, like those of certain seals, into three parts, whereby three distinct teeth have been produced out of what was originally a single tooth.

In the baleen, or whalebone, whales the place of teeth is taken by the horny structure technically termed "baleen," but commonly known as "whalebone," the nature of which will be explained later. Even in this group, however, there are rudiments of teeth deeply buried in the gums of the young, and the structure of these rudiments is such as to indicate the origin of at least that group of cetaceans from mammals furnished with teeth of a complex type; and it is also inferred that these rudimentary teeth correspond with those of the permanent set in other mammals.

In conformity with the absence of any external indications of a neck, the vertebræ in that region of the backbone of cetaceans are abnormally shortened, so that even in the largest species this part of the column may not exceed a foot in length. This shortening of the neck, however, is not accomplished by any reduction in the number of the vertebræ from the normal seven, but by the shortening of the body of each vertebra until it assumes the form of a broad, thin plate (page 138). The necks of a giraffe and a whale present, therefore, the extremes in the modifications assumed by their constituent vertebræ, these joints undergoing the maximum degree of elongation in the one, and of abbreviation in the other. In many cetaceans the whole or a certain number of the vertebræ of the neck are welded into one solid mass. In the hind portion of the backbone the region of the tail is only distinguished from that of the trunk by the vertebræ, carrying chevron bones affixed to their undersurfaces, there being no mass of united vertebræ corresponding to the sacrum of land mammals.

The skeleton of the fore limbs exhibits all the segments characterising those of terrestrial mammals, although some of these are much modified. There are no collar bones (clavicles), but the shoulder blades, or scapulæ, are very large, and much elongated in the antero-posterior direction. The humerus, or bone of the upper arm, although much shorter than usual, has a free movement at its articulation with the shoulder blade; but its junction with the two bones of the forearm, like all the joints lower down in the limb, admits of scarcely any motion. Indeed, in all these joints the bones articulate by flattened surfaces closely applied to one another, and are bound together by fibrous tissue.

The bones of the forearm (radius and ulna) are elongated and flattened, and lie nearly parallel, one in front of the other. The number of digits in the flippers is usually five, although occasionally reduced to four; and in the second and third of these there are always more than the ordinary three joints below the metacarpus. The only rudiments of the hind limbs are a few small bones beneath the sacral region of the backbone representing part of the pelvis, and occasionally part of the limb itself.

In accordance with the position of the nostrils at its summit, the skull departs considerably from the ordinary type; but it will suffice to state that the supraoccipital bone extends forward to join the frontals, and thus excludes the parietal bones from taking any share in the formation of the roof of the middle line of the

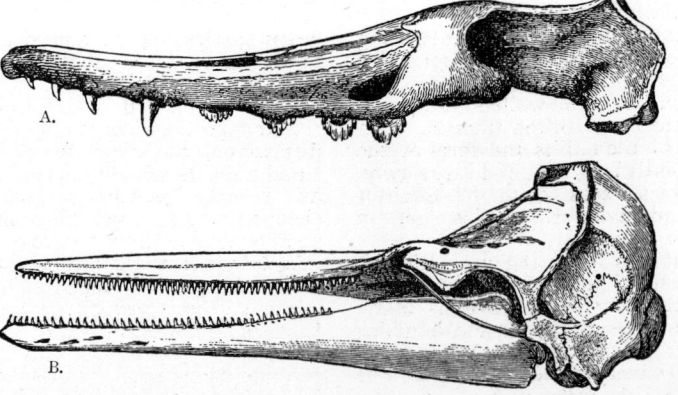

SKULLS OF (A.) ZEUGLODONT AND (B.) DOLPHIN

skull, while in front of the opening for the nostrils there is a more or less prolonged beak.

In regard to the soft parts, the stomach is always complex, and the female has two teats, placed far back on the abdomen. In order to enable these animals to swim with their mouths wide open, the upper part of the windpipe (larynx) is prolonged so as to reach the opening of the nostrils in the hind portion of the mouth, and thus form a closed tube leading directly from the external nostrils to the lungs.

There is frequently some misconception as to the so-called "spouting" or "blowing" of cetaceans. When a whale comes to the surface, after a longer or shorter period of submergence, its first act is to discharge the air from the lungs before taking a fresh inspiration, the air being expelled from the lungs with great force, and thus rising a considerable height above the surface. As it is saturated with water vapour at a high temperature the contact with the cold external air at once condenses this vapour, which forms a column of steam or spray. Frequently, however, a whale begins to "blow" before its nostrils are actually above the surface, and then a certain amount of water is forced up with the column of air.

Cetaceans include the largest animals now existing, and are only approached in size by some of the gigantic land reptiles which flourished during the Secondary period. As a group, they are comparatively modern, being unknown before the upper portion of the Eocene division of the Tertiary period. In the preceding Secondary period their place in the ocean was taken by huge marine reptiles, such as the ichthyosaurs and plesiosaurs, but as these seem to have died out at the close of that period, while whales are unknown in the early part of the Eocene, it would seem that there was an interregnum, during which the seas were not tenanted by any large animals except fishes.

From their oceanic habits and huge size, the study of the larger cetaceans is a matter of extreme difficulty, the majority of the specimens that are cast ashore not being seen by naturalists, while even in cases where opportunity is afforded for inspection, the bodies are usually more or less distorted from their proper form, while nothing can, of course, be learnt as to the habits of the animals. Such knowledge as we possess of the habits and form of the larger whales has consequently been acquired very slowly.

Cetaceans are found in all seas, from the Equator to within the Arctic and Antarctic circles, and in former years many of the larger species were extraordinarily abundant in certain regions, although they have been greatly reduced in numbers, and in some instances almost or completely exterminated. Many of the smaller forms known as porpoises and dolphins ascend rivers for longer or shorter distances, while some of these are exclusively fluviatile. With the exception of a dolphin from the rivers of the Cameruns, on the West Coast of Africa, which is reported to be herbivorous, cetaceans are carnivorous. Their food, however, is very varied, and the size of the animals devoured for food bears no sort of relation to the dimensions of their devourers.

The killer, or grampus, for instance, feeds on seals and some of the smaller cetaceans, and is, indeed, the only member of the order which subsists on warm-blooded animals, while, on the other hand, several of the toothed cetaceans prey on fishes of various kinds and others devour small crustaceans, jelly-fish, and the molluscs known as pteropods. The food of many of the

A GREENLAND WHALE ATTACKED BY KILLERS

larger species consists almost exclusively of squids and cuttles, and so small are the animals on which the Greenland whale feeds, that it is said that this species would be choked if it attempted to swallow a herring.

Although the killer is renowned for the ferocity of its disposition, the majority of cetaceans are harmless, timid animals, usually associating in companies known as "schools," which may sometimes comprise several thousands. As a rule, the members of a school display an affectionate disposition to one another, and numerous anecdotes attest the strong attachment and solicitude displayed by the females towards their offspring. Although some rorquals produce two young at a birth, the usual number is one.

Existing cetaceans are divided into two suborders, the one comprising the true, or whalebone, whales, in which the place of teeth is taken by baleen or "whalebone," and the toothed whales, characterised by the presence of functional teeth, at least in the lower jaw. These two suborders differ from one another in many important respects, and if both are derived from a single stock, their common ancestor must have existed at a comparatively remote epoch. It has, however, been suggested that whalebone and toothed whales originated independently of one another from distinct groups of terrestrial mammals; and if this view be correct, it will be evident that the cetacean order, as at present constituted, is a heterogeneous group.

R. LYDEKKER

CLASSIFICATION OF CETACEA MENTIONED IN THIS WORK

ORDER VIII
Whales and Dolphins—Cetacea
SUBORDER 1
Whalebone Whales—Mystacoceti
FAMILY
Whalebone Whales—Balænidæ
GENUS 1
Right Whales—Balæna
SPECIES
Greenland whale ....Balæna mysticetus
Black whale ....B. biscayensis
GENUS 2
Pigmy Whale—Neobalæna
SPECIES
Pigmy whale ....Neobalæna marginata
GENUS 3
Grey Whale—Rhachianectes
SPECIES
Grey whale ....Rhachianectes glaucus
GENUS 4
Humpback Whale—Megaptera
SPECIES
Humpback whale ....Megaptera boöps
GENUS 5
Rorquals—Balænoptera
SPECIES
Lesser rorqual..........Balænoptera rostrata
Indian rorqual ....B. edeni
Rudolphi's rorqual ....B. borealis
Common rorqual ....B. musculus
Sibbald's rorqual ....B. sibbaldi
Cetotherium (extinct)
SUBORDER 2
Toothed Whales—Odontoceti
FAMILY 1
Sperm-whale Tribe—Physeteridæ
GENUS 1
Sperm-whale—Physeter
SPECIES
Sperm-whale, or cachalot ....Physeter
macrocephalus
GENUS 2
Lesser Sperm-whale—Cogia
SPECIES
Lesser sperm-whale ....Cogia breviceps
EXTINCT SPERM-WHALES
Balænodon   **Prophyseter**
Thalassocetus   **Placoziphius**
Physeterula   **Hypocetus**
FAMILY 2
Bottle-nosed and Beaked Whales—Ziphiidæ
GENUS 1
Bottle-nosed Whales—Hyperoodon
SPECIES
Bottle-nosed whale ....Hyperoödon rostratus
H. planifrons
GENUS 2
Ziphius
SPECIES
Cuvier's whale ....Ziphius cavirostris
GENUS 3
Typical Beaked Whales—Mesoplodon
SPECIES
Sowerby's beaked whale....Mesoplodon bidens
Layard's beaked whale ....M. layardi

GENUS 4
Berardius
SPECIES
Arnoux's whale ....Berardius arnouxi
EXTINCT BEAKED WHALE
Eurhinodelphis

FAMILY 3
River Dolphins—Platanistidæ
GENUS
Susu—Platanista
SPECIES
Susu, or Gangetic dolphin ....Platanista
gangetica
FAMILY 4
Estuarine Dolphins—Iniidæ
GENUS 1
Inia—Inia
SPECIES
Dolphin of the Amazons ....Inia geoffroyensis
GENUS 2
Pontoporia—Pontoporia
SPECIES
La Plata dolphin........Pontoporia blainvillei
EXTINCT RIVERINE DOLPHINS
Pontistes   **Ischyrorhynchus**
Argyrocetus   **Champsodelphis**
Cyrtodelphis   **Acrodelphis**
Pontivaga   **Heterodelphis**
Argyrodelphis
FAMILY 5
Porpoises and Dolphins—Delphinidæ
GENUS 1
Narwhal—Monodon
SPECIES
Narwhal................Monodon monoceros
GENUS 2
Beluga—Delphinapterus
SPECIES
White whale ....Delphinapterus leucas
GENUS 3
Porpoises—Phocæna
SPECIES
Porpoise.............Phocæna communis
Black Sea porpoise ....P. relicta
GENUS 4
Indian Porpoise—Neomeris
SPECIES
Indian porpoise........Neomeris phocænoides
GENUS 5
Cephalorhynchus
SPECIES
Heaviside's dolphin ....Cephalorhynchus
heavisidei
White-fronted dolphin............C. albifrons
GENUS 6
Orcella
SPECIES
Irawadi dolphin............Orcella fluminalis
Bay of Bengal dolphin..........O. brevirostris
GENUS 7
Killer Whale—Orca
SPECIES
Killer, or grampus.............Orca gladiator

GENUS 8
Lesser Killer—Pseudorca
SPECIES
Lesser killer ....Pseudorca crassidens
GENUS 9
Blackfish—Globiocephalus
SPECIES
Blackfish, or ca'ing whale ....Globiocephalus
melas
North Pacific blackfish.........G. scammoni
GENUS 10
Risso's Dolphin—Grampus
SPECIES
Risso's dolphin..............Grampus griseus
GENUS 11
Lagenorhynchus
SPECIES
White-sided dolphin..Lagenorhynchus acutus
Pacific short-beaked dolphin.....L. crucigera
White-beaked dolphin..........L. albirostris
GENUS 12
Dolphins—Delphinus
SPECIES
True, or common, dolphin ..Delphinus delphis
Dussumier's dolphin...........D. dussumieri
Cape dolphin..................D. capensis
Red-bellied dolphin...........D. roseiventris
Slender dolphin...............D. attenuatus
Malay dolphin................D. malayanus
GENUS 13
Bottle-nosed Dolphins—Tursiops
SPECIES
Bottle-nosed dolphin.......Tursiops tursio
Indian bottle-nosed dolphin......T. catalania
Red Sea dolphin ....T. abusalam
GENUS 14
Steno
SPECIES
Rough-toothed dolphin.......Steno frontatus
Grey rough-toothed dolphin.....S. plumbeus
Speckled dolphin.............S. lentiginosus
GENUS 15
Long-beaked River Dolphin—Sotalia
SPECIES
Brazilian dolphin..........Sotalia brasiliensis
Cayenne dolphin..............S. guianensis
Tucuxi......................S. tucuxi
Pale river dolphin..............S. pallida
Fluviatile dolphin ....S. fluviatilis
Chinese white dolphin...........S. sinensis
Bornean dolphin..............S. borneënsis
Camerun dolphin ....S. teuxi
FAMILY 6
Shark-toothed Dolphins—Squalodontidæ
GENUS
Squalodon (extinct)
FAMILY 7
Primitive Whales—Zeuglodontidæ
GENUS
Zeuglodon (extinct)
Protocetus (extinct)
Prozeuglodon (extinct)
Eocetus (extinct)

WHALEBONE WHALES

THE whalebone, or true, whales constitute a single family (*Balænidæ*), with the following characteristics: They have no teeth after birth, but the palate is furnished with numerous horny plates of baleen or whalebone, which serve to strain from the water the small animals on which some feed. The skull is symmetrical, and the two branches of the lower jaw are outwardly curved, and joined at the chin by fibrous tissue only. The nostrils open externally by two distinct longitudinal apertures. In the skeleton the ribs are very loosely united with the backbone, articulating only with the horizontal transverse processes of the vertebræ, and having no connection with the bodies of the same; while the breast bone is composed of a single piece, to which only one pair of ribs articulates.

By the substitution of whalebone for teeth, as well as in the loose connection of the ribs with the backbone and the breast bone, and in the reduction in the size of the latter, whalebone whales are more specialised than the other group of cetaceans; this laxity of connection between the ribs and the other parts of the skeleton allowing of a greater degree of expansion of the cavity of the chest, and thus permitting a longer submergence. On the other hand, in the retention of the double apertures to the nostrils, and in the symmetrically formed skull, as well as in the position of a distinct olfactory organ, and certain other features of their organisation, the members of the present group depart less widely from the ordinary type of mammalian structure than do the existing toothed cetaceans.

Whalebone, which does not appear until after birth, is composed of two long series of flattened horny plates, placed transversely on each side of the palate, and separated from one another by an open space in the middle line. The plates vary greatly in length in the different species, and are triangular in form, with their broad bases attached to the palate, and their points hanging downwards.

THE ELK, OR MOOSE

"Elk generally lie down with their tails to windward, trusting to their senses of smelling and hearing, which are remarkably acute, to warn them
of approaching danger from that quarter.

THE ROEBUCK

" The roebuck is indigenous to the British Isles and the greater part of Europe, extending northwards to the south of Sweden, and southwards to Italy and Spain, while eastwards it ranges into the southern Caucasus, Palestine, and perhaps Persia.''

WILD SWINE

"Wild swine were formerly abundant throughout the British Isles, and boar-hunting was a favourite pursuit of our ancestors. In many parts of the Continent, and especially in the Black Forest, they are still abundant."

RIVER-HOGS

' These pigs are found in large herds, and frequent moist forests and the banks of rivers, while they are occasionally seen on the mountains.'

Although smooth externally, the inner edge of each plate is frayed out into a kind of fringe, thus giving a hairy appearance to the whole of the inside of the mouth when viewed from below. The plates attain the greatest length in the middle portion of the jaw, whence they gradually diminish in size towards the two extremities. Whalebone differs greatly not only in length, but likewise in its relative thickness and degree of elasticity in the different species. In colour it may vary from black to creamy white; while in some cases it is ornamented with stripes of dark and light. When feeding, the immense mouth is filled with water containing shoals of small creatures, and then, on the whale closing the jaws and raising the tongue, so as to diminish the cavity of the mouth, the water streams out through the narrow intervals between the hairy fringe of the whalebone blades, and escapes through the lips, leaving the prey to be swallowed.

Whalebone whales are divided into right whales, humpbacks, and rorquals or finners, severally representing as many genera, in addition to which there are certain others entitled to generic distinction. In whalebone whales the females are generally larger than the males.

GREENLAND WHALE

The Right whales, of which the Greenland whale is the best known representative (page 26), are characterised by the absence of a fin on the back, and of furrows in the skin of the throat, and also by the proportionately large size of the head, and the arched form of the sides of the mouth, which ascends in the middle far above the level of the eye. The flippers are relatively short, and contain five distinct digits; and the whole of the seven vertebræ of the neck are welded into a solid mass. The whalebone is long, narrow, very elastic, and black.

The Greenland whale (*Balæna mysticetus*) is a northern species, characterised by the enormous size of the head, which often exceeds one-third of the entire length of the animal, by the high arching of the mouth margins, and the great number and length of the whalebone plates. The latter in the middle region attain a length of 10 or even 12 feet, and their total number may exceed 380 on each side of the jaw. In order to afford room for such enormous structures, the narrow upper jaw is greatly arched from before backwards, while the two branches of the lower jaw are widely separated behind, and curve much outwards in the middle of their course (page 827).

When the mouth of the whale is closed, the slender extremities of the whalebone curve backwards in the direction of the throat, the longer ones in the middle of the jaw occupying the hollow formed by the shorter ones behind. When the jaws are opened for feeding, the plates spring downwards and forwards by their own weight, and thus fill up the whole space between the two jaws, irrespective of their degree of separation

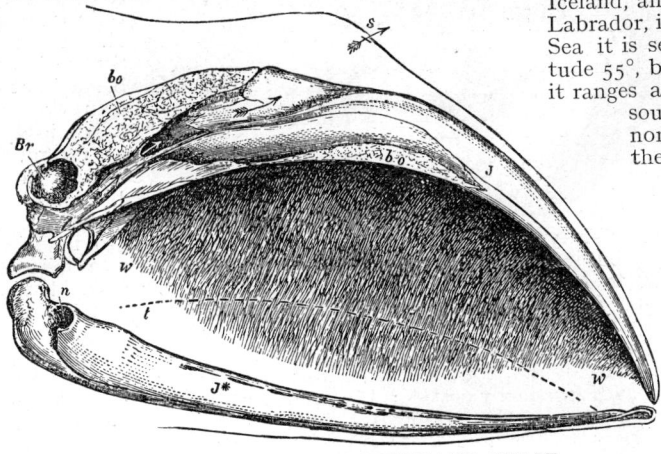

SECTION OF SKULL OF GREENLAND WHALE

Br, brain-cavity; J, J*, upper and lower jaws; *bo*, bones of roof of skull; *s*, blow-hole, with arrows leading from the cavity of the nostrils; *w*, whalebone; *t*, contour of tongue; *n*, aperture of nerve canal in lower jaw.

An effectual strainer is thus interposed between the sides of the cavity of the mouth and the external water, which prevents the food swallowed from escaping, while the water taken in at the same time has full means of escape upon the closure of the mouth.

The tongue is of very large size, and fills up the cavity between the two series of whalebone plates when the mouth is shut; and the stranded prey left upon its surface after the completion of the straining process is swallowed at leisure. The large lower lip, rising up at the sides above the extremities of the plates of whalebone, prevents them from being borne outwards by the rush of water as the mouth is closing.

The colour of the Greenland whale is black, but there is frequently more or less white about the throat, flippers, and in front of the flukes, while some specimens are pied all over.

The Greenland whale attains usually a length of about 50 feet, but examples have been recorded exceeding 60 feet, and it is probable that when the species was more numerous its size was greater. These whales yield about 130 barrels of oil, but specimens were formerly killed from which as much as from 200 to 280 barrels were obtained. The product of baleen may vary from 1,000 to over 3,000 pounds.

Inclusive of the so-called bow-head whale of Bering Strait and the Sea of Okhotsk, the Greenland whale has an approximately circumpolar distribution. In the North Atlantic the southern limits of this species may be approximately indicated by a line drawn from the coast of Lapland, in latitude 70°, to the southern point of Iceland, and thence to the coast of Labrador, in latitude 55°. In Bering Sea it is seldom seen south of latitude 55°, but in the Sea of Okhotsk it ranges about one degree farther south. With regard to the northern limits of this whale there is some diversity of opinion. Admiral Feilden, however, is of opinion that no whale could inhabit the frozen sea lying to the north of Robeson Channel, above Baffin Bay, in 82° N., and that none would be found in the neighbourhood of the Pole.

This species undertakes annual migrations of considerable extent, always travelling northwards in summer as the ice breaks up. Everything tends to prove that it is truly an ice-whale, for its home is among the scattered floes, or about the borders of the ice-fields or barriers. It is true that these whales are pursued in open water during the summer, but there are no instances of their capture south of where winter ice-fields occasionally occur.

The huge size of the mouth and the enormous development of the whalebone in this species are in correlation with the nature of the food, which is composed mainly of small shrimp-like crustaceans and swimming molluscs belonging to the group known as pteropods; a vast number of such minute creatures being necessary to afford sustenance to an animal of the dimensions of the Greenland whale. When feeding, these whales swim near the surface of the water with the nostrils and a portion of the middle of the back showing above.

D 72

O

Captain Scammon states that "they are often met with singly in their wanderings ; at other times in pairs or triplets, and scattered over the surface of the water as far as the eye can discern from the masthead. Towards the end of the season they are seen in large numbers, crowded together. These herds are called 'gams,' and they are regarded by experienced whalemen as an indication that the whales will soon leave the ground. Their manner of respiration is to blow seven to nine times at a 'rising,' then, 'turning flukes' —elevating them six to eight feet out of the water— they go down and remain twelve or fifteen minutes."

GREENLAND WHALE

Captain D. Gray, however, states that he has known a whale, when harpooned, stay under water for fifty minutes.

There is some degree of uncertainty as to the breeding habits of the Greenland whale, but it is probable that the pairing season is from June to August, and that the young are born in the following March, April, and May, although it has been suggested that the period of gestation is thirteen or fourteen months. The single offspring is believed to be suckled for about a year, during which time the whalebone is gradually developed. The affection of the female parent for her young is most intense, and if the former be captured there is little difficulty in securing her offspring.

The Greenland whale is a peaceful and timid animal, and seldom attacks the boats of its pursuers. The accidents which occur in hunting are mainly due either to its descending suddenly when first wounded, whereby the boat may be swamped or dragged under water, or to a too close approach to the animal when in its last terrible death-struggle, or "flurry," as it is called by the whalers. The ordinary speed of a Greenland whale, whether swimming at or below the surface, is estimated at about four miles an hour, but when the animal is frightened or wounded, its rate of progress is accelerated to about eight miles.

BLACK WHALE OR NORDCAPER

For many years, the Right whale inhabiting the North Atlantic, to which the Norwegians gave the name "Nordcaper," was known to naturalists as *Balæna biscayensis*, but it has been proposed to change this name to *Eubalæna glacialis*, on the ground that it is generically distinct from the Greenland whale,

while the term *glacialis* is earlier than *biscayensis*. Older naturalists regarded the "nordcaper" as, in all probability, a local form of the southern black Right whale (*B. australis*), but such a view does not appeal to modern American naturalists, who consider that, since the southern and northern black Right whales are separated by a zone of several thousand miles of warm equatorial water, which they do not cross, they must be specifically distinct. How closely related they are is not exactly known, but it is clear that their common ancestor crossed the equatorial zone when already a black Right whale, and the mere fact of isolation does not necessarily imply specific distinction.

Structurally, this species differs from the Greenland whale in its relatively smaller head, in which the contour of the lower lip is much more highly arched, and the whalebone considerably shorter, and in the number of ribs being fifteen, in place of twelve. It is also of smaller size, and yields less blubber, while its colour is wholly black. In its movements, this whale is said to be quicker, more active, and more violent than the other, and thus more difficult and more dangerous to kill.

In the North Atlantic, it was still not unfrequent in the latter part of the eighteenth century, and ranged so far north as Iceland and Norway, but for many years appeared to be all but exterminated in those seas. Several instances of whales probably belonging to this species having been seen or captured off the British coasts in the eighteenth century are on record, and it is probable that whales seen off Peterhead in 1806 and 1872 were of the same kind. An example was captured in the harbour of San Sebastian in 1854, a second in the Gulf of Taranto in 1877, and a third on the Spanish coast in the following year, and in the twentieth century a considerable number of individuals have been taken on both sides of the Atlantic. The former great scarcity was due to the Basque fishermen of the Biscayan ports, by whom the species was persistently hunted from the tenth to the sixteenth century. It was known to them as the "sletbag," and had become exceedingly scarce on the discovery of Spitzbergen in 1596, when the Basque whalers turned their attention to the more valuable Greenland species.

In the North Pacific black whales occur in Japanese waters, and also frequent the Australian and New Zealand seas, as well as those around the Cape of Good Hope. The southern limits of the black whale are not definitely known, but the species certainly does not penetrate the icebound Antarctic Ocean.

The southern black whale differs from the northern form by its longer whalebone, so that it is at any rate entitled to rank as a separate race, if not as a distinct species.

The nose of the black whale is furnished with certain honeycombed horny excrescences known as the "bonnet." For many years this "bonnet" was supposed to be a single structure, and has been regarded as a kind of corn, perhaps produced by the animal rubbing its nose against rocks, as this species has been observed to do, to get rid of the barnacles which are apt to infest it. This is not a very probable explanation of the origin of the "bonnet," and it has been disproved by South Georgian specimens of this whale, which show that the "bonnet," in place of being a single structure, is one of several horny bosses on the head of the southern black whale, and that these structures are developed in the fœtus. The bonnet itself is situated on the extremity of the muzzle, while behind it are two longitudinal rows of smaller excrescences, and there is a large boss above each eye ; the chin carries one large boss corresponding to the bonnet, and two longitudinal rows of smaller bosses, the uppermost of which is on the free margin.

These horny excrescences are completely honeycombed, and the chambers filled with so-called "whalelice," the whole bonnet being covered by an immense crawling mass of these lice, which are really crustaceans of the genus *Cyamus*. It seems highly probable that there is some definite correlation between the bonnet, inclusive of all the callosities, and the lice, and as the latter may be useful to the whale in keeping its skin clear of larval barnacles, the callosities may have been developed for their special protection. Whether the callosities have the same arrangement in the northern black whale remains to be proved.

During the Discovery expedition a previously unknown cetacean was found in the South Polar ocean. This was a blackish whale, some 25 feet long, having a tall, upright black fin, like that of a killer. Whether it was a whalebone whale, the future must decide.

Several species of Right whales have left their remains in the Pliocene deposits of Belgium and the east coast of England. One of these extinct forms appears to have been allied to the Greenland, and a second to the black whale, while the other two are smaller species unlike any now living.

PIGMY WHALE

A whale from the New Zealand, Australian, and South American seas is one of the smallest representatives of the group, and, while nearly allied to the Right whales, presents certain peculiarities in structure which entitle it to rank as the representative of a distinct genus. It derives its common name of pigmy whale (*Neobalæna marginata*) from its comparatively small size, the length never exceeding 20 feet, and being sometimes only 15 or 16 feet. Although agreeing with Right whales in having the skin of the throat smooth and all the vertebræ of the neck united into a solid mass, the pigmy whale differs in having a small fin on the back, in the whalebone, which is of great length and slenderness, being white, and also in the small and narrow flippers containing only three digits in their skeleton. The ribs, which are very broad and flattened, are seventeen in number. The whalebone of this species is more flexible, more elastic, and tougher than that of any other whale, and, if it could be obtained in any quantity, would fetch a higher price in the market than that of the Greenland whale.

GREY WHALE

The grey whale of the North Pacific (*Rhachianectes glaucus*), which takes its name from the bluish grey colour of its skin, is also the single representative of its genus, and serves as a kind of connecting link between the Right whales on the one hand and the humpback and rorquals on the other, and is probably

an ancient and generalised type. It agrees with the humpback in the absence of a fin on the back and the narrowness of the flippers, but resembles the rorquals in the relatively small size of the head, the elongated form of the body, the shortness and brittle nature of the whalebone, and the almost complete separation of all the vertebræ of the neck. A further approximation to the humpback and rorquals is made by the presence of a single pair of flutings in the skin of the throat. The male attains a length of from 35 to 42 feet, and the female from 40 to 44 feet, the length of the flippers being about 6½ feet. The colour is mottled bluish grey, becoming very light in some, while in others it is nearly black. The whalebone is relatively shorter than in any other species, scarcely exceeding 18 inches in length, and yellow in colour.

In the skeleton the ribs are remarkable for their shortness and great width, and the consequent narrowness of the spaces between them ; while the first two are more or less completely united to form a solid shield of bone. In the flippers the joints of the digits are very short and thick, and appear to be less numerous than in the rorquals. The blubber is solid and tough. with a reddish colour, and yields little oil.

At the present day the grey whale is confined to the North Pacific, and does not range farther south than 20° N. ; but from the evidence of certain bones found in the superficial deposits of the British Isles, and described under the name of *Eschrichtius*, it is not improbable that it formerly frequented the Atlantic.

This big whale is a migratory species, appearing on the coasts of California and Oregon for the purpose of breeding from November to May, and going northwards for the rest of the year. The females of this whale manifest the greatest affection for their young, and seek sheltered estuaries lying under a tropical sun, as if to warm their offspring into activity and promote their comfort, until grown to the size Nature demands for their first northern visit. When the

HUMPBACK WHALE SUCKLING ITS YOUNG

parent whales are attacked, they show a power of resistance and tenacity of life that distinguish them from all other cetaceans. This species has become very rare. and is in considerable danger of extermination.

HUMPBACK WHALE

The humpback whale (*Megaptera boöps*) belongs to the group of whalebone whales characterised by the presence of a number of longitudinal flutings in the skin of the throat, and of a fin on the back. It is distinguished from the rorquals by the comparatively large size of the head, the short and deep body, the small size of the fin on the back, and the enormous length of the flippers. The flukes are relatively large, and the flippers characterised by their scalloped margins. As in the grey whale and rorquals, the vertebræ of the neck are relatively longer than in the Right whales, and remain separate throughout life.

The whalebone, which is deep black, is short and broad, and of a coarse and only slightly elastic structure. In length the humpback varies from 45 to 50 feet, the flippers measuring from 10 to 14 feet in length. The colour of the body is black above, but often more or less marbled with white below, while the flippers may be either entirely white, or black above and speckled with white below. The skeleton of the flippers has four digits, with a great number of joints. Two young are frequently produced at a birth. The name humpback is derived from the prominence on

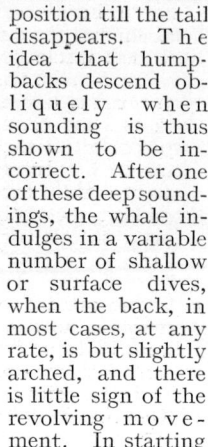

LESSER RORQUAL

the back, which carries the fin, but there is considerable variation in regard to the degree of its development.

When a whale leaps out of the water it is said to "breach"; when a fin is shown out of the water the action is termed "finning"; while, when the flukes alone are exposed, it is called "lob-tailing."

Humpbacks are found in nearly all seas, and it appears impossible to distinguish more than a single species, although some naturalists maintain that the one inhabiting the Persian Gulf is distinct from the common form. These whales are not uncommon off the eastern coast of Scotland during summer, and of late years a considerable number has been taken at the whaling stations established on the Irish coast, in the Shetlands, and in Norway. In South African waters they abound.

As regards the habits of humpbacks, Mr. R. C. Andrews states that when coming up to the surface these whales ascend obliquely, so that only the top of the head, as far back as the blow-holes, is visible, and as soon as this takes place the spout is delivered. The cloud of vapour, which rises vertically, is narrow at the base, but at once spreads out into a low, bushy column. The height to which the spout ascends is about 15 feet, but, as in other whales, the height and density of the column depend upon the length of time the animal has been below and the force of the expiration. A loud, harsh, whistling sound, audible for a considerable distance, and due to the rush of air through the blow-holes, accompanies the spout.

Inspiration, which lasts from two to four seconds, immediately follows the spout, and during this action the blow-holes are greatly distended so as to form a wide ellipse, and are at the same time protruded in a remarkable manner, so as to occupy a different position from that which they hold during expiration. The number of spouts delivered during each appearance at the surface depends upon the depth at which the whale happens to have been feeding—the greater the depth the greater the number of spouts, the maximum being usually six or seven.

In the case of both humpbacks and rorquals, big dives or soundings, when the whales descend to considerable depths, alternate with shallow intermediate dives, the positions assumed during these two actions being distinct and characteristic. In beginning a sound, after the completion of the spout, the humpback depresses its head and begins to revolve, after which the body is much arched and the back fin shown, when much of the body is above the surface; as the revolution continues the tail is drawn smoothly out of the water, and the whale assumes a vertical position till the tail disappears. The idea that humpbacks descend obliquely when sounding is thus shown to be incorrect. After one of these deep soundings, the whale indulges in a variable number of shallow or surface dives, when the back, in most cases, at any rate, is but slightly arched, and there is little sign of the revolving movement. In starting on one of these dives the flukes are not shown.

When sounding, humpbacks may remain below the surface from five to twenty minutes, the distance travelled depending apparently to a great extent on the amount of food to be obtained. When food is abundant the whale will frequently rise close to where it disappeared, but when nutriment is scarce it will often swim at a great pace and reappear a mile or more away from the spot where it sounded.

The amount of oil yielded by a humpback is very variable, a female with a large young one having scarcely any blubber; and while the amount of oil taken from some individuals does not exceed eight to ten barrels, in others the yield has been so much as seventy-five. Since the introduction of expanding harpoons humpbacks have been regularly hunted. When one of these whales is lying on its side with the body just submerged, the flipper of the upper side may stand out of the water like a gigantic white sword.

RORQUALS OR FIN-WHALES

The remaining living representatives of the whalebone whales are known as rorquals, or fin-whales, or sometimes fin-backs or razor-backs, and include four well-defined species. These whales are distinguished from the humpback by their more elongated and slender form and proportionately smaller head, which measures from one-fifth to one-fourth the total length, and also by the comparative shortness of their flippers, the latter being narrow and pointed, and varying from one-seventh to one-eleventh of the total length. The small and recurved back fin is placed about two-thirds of the distance from the head to the flukes, and the latter are smaller than in the humpback. The whalebone is short and coarse, and the lateral line of the mouth is consequently nearly straight, and does not rise above the level of the eye.

Rorquals are the commonest and most widely distributed of all the larger cetaceans, and far more active and speedy in their movements than Right whales; and since their yield of blubber is relatively small, while the shortness and inferior quality of their whalebone render it of much less value than that of the Right whales, they were formerly little molested by whalers. The increasing scarcity of the Greenland whale, however, and the enormous advance in the price of whalebone, coupled with the invention of harpoon-guns and expanding explosives, which render the capture of these animals far less difficult than in the old days, have led to both humpbacks and finners being regularly hunted; and numerous whaling stations have been established, where large numbers are taken. Rorquals are found in nearly all seas except those of the Antarctic regions, and the four well-defined species have an almost cosmopolitan distribution.

Some rorquals feed mainly on fishes, especially herrings and pilchards. When fishes are first captured, they are received into the large collapsible pouch in the throat till such time as they are swallowed. This pouch is formed of skin strengthened by bands of tendon, like the ribs of an umbrella, and when the pouch is collapsed the folds of skin between these ribs make the characteristic flutings on the throat.

LESSER RORQUAL

The smallest representative of the group is the lesser fin-whale, or rorqual (*Balænoptera rostrata*), frequently known, from its pointed muzzle, as the pike whale. The average length of this species varies from 25 to 30 feet, a length of 33 feet being very seldom exceeded. The colour of the upper parts is greyish black, and the whole of the under surface, inclusive of the flukes, is white; but the most distinctive characteristic is the broad band of white running across the upper part of the outer surface of the flippers, which forms a striking contrast to the black of the remainder. The flippers measure about one-eighth the entire length of the animal, and the number of pairs of ribs is eleven. The whalebone is nearly white.

This whale is by no means rare on the British coasts; but it is more common on the shores of Norway, where it is frequently captured in the bays and fjords. Known in North American waters as the sharp-nosed finner, this whal`, according to Captain Scammon, "frequently gambols about vessels when under way, darting from one side to another beneath their bottoms. When coming to the surface, it makes a quick, faint spout, such as would be made by a suckling of one of the larger cetaceans, which plainly accounts for whalemen taking it to be the young of more bulky species. At sea the sharp-headed finners are seldom seen in pairs, but wander solitary along, frequently changing their course in the depths below, and meandering along the whole continental coast of the North Pacific, occasionally visiting the large estuaries about the shore. They pass through Bering Sea and Strait into the Arctic Ocean, where they appear to be as much at home as their superiors in size."

The Indian rorqual (*B. edeni*), described on the evidence of the skeleton, appears to be closely allied to the lesser fin-whale, but attains somewhat larger dimensions than European examples, and is believed to have a few more vertebræ in the backbone. Probably, however, it is nothing more than a local race.

RUDOLPHI'S RORQUAL

The next species in point of size is Rudolphi's rorqual (*B. borealis*), which attains a length of from 40 to 45, or occasionally as much as 52 feet. In colour it is bluish black above, with oblong white spots, and more or less white on the lower side, although the under surface of the flukes, as well as both sides of the flippers, are coloured like the back. The back fin is smaller, and placed further back than in the lesser finner, while the flippers are very small, equalling only one-fourteenth of the total length. There are thirteen pairs of ribs, and the whalebone is black.

This species is rarer than other rorquals, and does not appear to have been recorded from the Pacific. It ranges as far south as Biarritz, and migrates northwards in summer as far as the North Cape, and either this or a closely allied species occurs in the seas around Java. Specimens have been recorded from the British Isles.

Rudolphi's whale differs from the other rorquals in feeding entirely on minute crustaceans, never touching fishes; and, in accordance with this difference in its diet, the edges of its whalebone are more frayed out and curling than in the other species. On the Finmark coast these whales appear sometimes singly, but more generally in schools of varying size, which may occasionally number about fifty. When migrating, or not engaged in feeding, they swim rapidly, and do not require to breathe so frequently as the other species. When they come up to blow, they make only one or two respirations, while the others take five or six.

While swimming under water, their course can be traced by the bubbles of air continually rising to the surface; and when gorging on the swarms of crustaceans found in the northern seas these whales swim slowly, with the muzzle and half the back above water. Rudolphi's whale appears never to utter a sound, and is timid and inoffensive in disposition. As a rule, a single young one is born at a time, but at least one instance of twins has been recorded. The yield of oil varies from fifteen to thirty barrels, and the value of one of these whales ranges from £27 to £33

COMMON RORQUAL

COMMON RORQUAL

The common rorqual, or fin-whale (*B. musculus*), averages from 60 to 65 feet in length, and rarely exceeds 70 feet. It is very elongated in form, with moderately large jaws, the flippers measuring one-ninth of the total length. The colour of the upper parts and the left side of the lower jaw is slaty grey, but the right side of the lower jaw and the under parts, including the inferior surface of the flukes and flippers, are usually white. The whalebone is slate-coloured at the ends, with the first two or three rows white.

The common rorqual is rarely found in the Mediterranean, but abundantly throughout the more northern seas of Europe, ranging as far as 70° or 75° N. It is likewise widely distributed in American waters, where it is commonly known as the fin-back; and it appears that the so-called southern fin-whale of New Zealand is not specifically separable. It is not uncommon off the British coasts, and has been taken in considerable numbers off Mayo.

These rorquals swim with great rapidity and strength, being second in this respect only to the next species, and are consequently taken with difficulty, except when explosive harpoons are used. Their habits appear to be very similar to those of the lesser fin-whale, and they are described as playing around vessels under way in similar fashion. They are frequently found alone, but occasionally assemble in schools of from ten to fifteen or twenty. When rising to breathe they inhale the air so rapidly as to produce a sharp

SIBBALD'S FIN-WHALE

sound which may be heard at a considerable distance, and is said to be perfectly distinguishable from that produced by any other species.

In 1909, an observer at the whaling station on the coast of Mayo took numbers of the small species of shrimp known as *Meganyctiphanes norvegica* in August of that year from the throats of a common rorqual and a Sibbald's rorqual; but off Norway, the former feeds chiefly on herrings. Rudolphi's rorqual, as already mentioned, feeds entirely on microscopic crustaceans, consuming not only the small crustaceans called *Euphausia*, but the more minute forms known as *Calanus finmarchicus* and *Temera longicornis*.

SIBBALD'S FIN-WHALE

The blue rorqual, or gigantic Sibbald's fin-whale (*B. sibbaldi*), has the distinction of being the largest of living animals. It is a somewhat stouter-built species than the last, and commonly attains a length of from 70 to 80 feet, and occasionally reaches 85 feet, or perhaps more. The colour is dark bluish grey, with some white spots on the chest, and the lower edges and under surface of the flippers white.

In American specimens, at least, there is a more or less marked yellowish tinge on the under surface of the body, which has given origin to the popular name, "sulphur bottom." The flippers are longer than in the other species,

measuring one-seventh of the entire length, and the jaws are also of more than usual proportionate size. The back fin is small, and situated comparatively near the tail. The whalebone is black, and there are usually sixteen pairs of ribs, compared with fifteen in the preceding species. This rorqual has a wide distribution, and in the Northern Hemisphere, after passing the winter in the open sea, migrates northwards in the spring towards the coasts for the purpose of breeding.

In the Bay of Bengal and the Arabian Sea, Sibbald's whale is represented by a local race (*B. s. indica*), which attains a length of 90 feet, and is said to have a somewhat more slender lower jaw than the European form. This whale differs somewhat in habits from the typical race, as it has been observed in the warm Indian seas during summer when the true Sibbald's whale is visiting the cool shores of Norway. In the Pacific this species is to be found at all seasons on the coast of California, thus confirming the view that the Indian rorqual is not specifically distinct. Sibbald's whale has been taken in the Firth of Forth, in the Shetlands, and off Mayo.

During their sojourn on the Norwegian coasts these whales subsist on crustaceans, and when in pursuit of these small creatures may be seen swimming on their sides. At other times they feed largely on sardines, sprats, and other fishes. Sibbald's whale is considered to be the fastest of all the larger cetaceans. It seldom "breaches," yet when it does so it exhibits its splendid proportions and its marvellous activity to the fullest degree. The invention of explosive harpoons has rendered the capture of Sibbald's whale comparatively easy, and it is hunted in the Shetlands, off Mayo, and at Hammerfest. One example measuring 85 feet in length yielded ninety barrels of oil.

STRANDED SPECIMEN OF SIBBALD'S FIN-WHALE

The Pliocene deposits of Belgium and the eastern coast of England yield remains of several kinds of rorquals, and likewise of a humpback,

Other whales from the Pliocene deposits of Europe constitute an extinct genus — *Cetotherium* — which, while nearly allied to the rorquals, exhibits certain features in the structure of the skull whereby it departs less widely from the ordinary mammalian type.

SPERM-WHALE GROUP

ALL the remaining cetaceans form a group distinguished from the whalebone whales by the absence of whalebone, and the presence of permanent teeth in at least the lower jaw. This group, comprising several existing families, is known as the Odontoceti, or Toothed Cetaceans, in contradistinction to the Mystacoceti, or Whalebone Whales.

In addition to the presence of teeth, the group is characterised by the following distinctive features : The two nostrils unite before they reach the surface, and thus open by a single aperture, which usually takes the form of a crescentic valvular slit placed transversely to the long axis of the head. In the skull the bones of the upper surface are formed unsymmetrically on the two sides, the nasal bones in existing forms being reduced to nodules, which have no share in roofing over the cavity of the nostrils. The two branches of the lower jaw are nearly straight, and of great vertical extent behind, while in front they come in contact with one another by flattened surfaces of larger or smaller extent, as is ordinarily the case among mammals.

The ribs are more firmly joined to the rest of the skeleton than is the case in whalebone whales, several of the anterior pairs articulating with the bodies as well as with the horizontal transverse processes of the vertebræ, while below they are joined to the breastbone by the intervention of so-called chest ribs, the breastbone itself usually consisting of several distinct portions, placed one behind the other. In all cases the flippers have five digits. Contrary to what obtains among the whalebone whales, the females of the larger species are smaller than the males.

SPERM-WHALE

The gigantic sperm-whale is the typical representative of a family which includes the lesser cachalot and a number of extinct cetaceans. In both living species functional teeth are restricted to the lower jaw, but there are numerous extinct *Physeteridæ* in which both jaws are furnished with a full series of teeth. In the existing species nearly all the ribs are two-headed ; the rib cartilages do not ossify ; the petroso-tympanic bones are firmly united to the skull, which has large crests behind the nostrils ; some of the cervical vertebræ are fused together ; the two halves of the lower jaw may have a long or a short union ; the blow-hole, which is situated on the left side, is longitudinal or oblique, with its concavity turned backwards ; the stomach is muscular, and the teeth in the lower jaw are numerous.

Although the teeth of the cachalot have no enamel, this is present in those of the extinct genera in which functional teeth are developed in the upper jaw, the number in the front upper jawbones, or premaxillæ, being limited to three pairs. In the existing sperm-whale teeth of an inch or so in length are embedded in the gums of the upper jaw, but never attain full development.

The sperm-whale (*Physeter macrocephalus*), or as it is frequently called from its French title, cachalot, is one of the largest of cetaceans, rivalling in size the Greenland whale, but, as with many other species, its dimensions have been considerably exaggerated, although it is possible that when the species was more abundant some individuals attained a size which is never reached at the present day. Be this as it may, the male sperm-whale attains a length of from 55 to 60 feet, but females are not much more than half these dimensions, while their form is proportionately more slender. The generic characteristics are to be found in the great proportionate size of the head, which equals about one-fourth of the total length of the animal, and in the number of the teeth being from twenty to twenty-five on each side of the lower jaw.

THE SPERM-WHALE

The ugly and ungainly appearance of the sperm-whale is chiefly due to the great height and abrupt truncation of the enormous muzzle, upon the summit of which is situated the S-shaped aperture of the nostrils, somewhat to the left of the middle line. The mouth, which is of great length and capacity, opens below, and at some distance behind the extremity of the muzzle. On the upper surface of the skull is a huge cavity, bounded behind by a tall vertical wall of bone, which is filled in the living animal with the substance known as spermaceti ; and in front of this hollow protrudes the long beak of the upper jaw, the gum of which contains the rudimentary teeth. The lower jaw is very long and slender, with its two branches united in the middle line for about half their total length.

The teeth, which are implanted in the lower jaw in a long groove, partially divided into sockets by incomplete bony partitions, are of large size, and, when unworn, pointed and recurved at their tips. They are composed solely of ivory, and the pulp cavity at their base remains open for a long period, although it generally becomes more or less completely closed in adult life, when the whole base of the tooth grows much flattened from side to side. The tongue and interior of the mouth are glistening white ; and the diameter of the throat is very large. The eyes, of which the left is smaller than the right, are placed somewhat above the angles of the mouth, and a short distance behind them are the minute apertures of the ear, which are said not to exceed a quarter of an inch in diameter.

At the junction of the head with the body is a distinct prominence in the middle line of the back, and half-way between this and the tail is a larger projection, followed by a number of smaller ones, and technically known as the " hump." There is no back fin. The flippers are placed a little behind and below the eyes, and seldom exceed 6 feet in length by 3 feet in width, and the maximum diameter of the flukes is about 15 feet. In colour the sperm-whale is either black or blackish brown on the upper parts, becoming rather lighter on the sides and under surface, and passing into silvery grey on the chest. Sometimes, however, piebald individuals are met with, and old males frequently become grey in the region of the muzzle and crown of the head.

The sperm-whale, which is essentially an inhabitant of the open seas, ranges over all the warmer oceans, and in summer wanders, at all events occasionally, far north. That the sperm-whale is in the habit of travelling immense distances is proved by the fact that specimens have been killed in the Atlantic bearing in their bodies spears that had penetrated them during a sojourn in the Pacific.

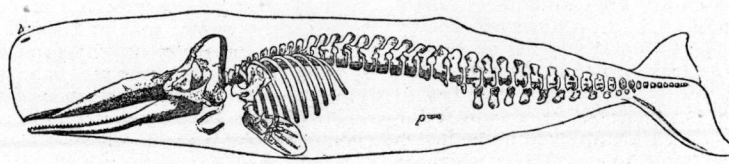

SKELETON OF A SPERM-WHALE

and likewise for that of their offspring ; and when one female out of a party is killed it is generally easy to capture several others. The young males, which are found in herds at certain times of the year, are, however, far less chivalrous in disposition, and leave a wounded companion to its fate.

The sperm-whale is distinguished from all other cetaceans by the regularity with which it comes to the surface to breathe, although there is some variation in this respect according to age. " When emerging to the surface," writes Captain Scammon, " the first portion of the animal seen is the region of the hump, then it raises its head and respires slowly for the space of about three seconds, sending forth diagonally a volume of whitish vapour, like an escape of steam ; this may be seen from the masthead at a distance of three to five miles. In respiring at its leisure, the animal sometimes makes no headway through the water ; at other times it moves quietly along at the rate of two or three miles an hour, or, ' if making a passage ' from one feeding ground to another, it may accelerate its velocity.

For many years it was believed that the sperm-whale was only an occasional straggler to British waters, but in the summer of 1903 no fewer than seven fully adult bull sperm-whales were killed in the northern seas by Norwegian, Icelandic, and Shetland whalers. These, however, formed only a small portion of the whole number that had wandered thus far north. The first record is on June 20, when two bulls out of an immense herd were killed in about 60° N.—that is, nearly the latitude of the Faroes. On the same day a third bull, 54 feet long, was taken about eighty-four miles east-south-east of Raidarfjord. No other whales were seen at this time.

On June 27 another bull—in company with which three or four other whales were seen—was killed sixty miles from the Shetlands. This bull is stated to have been 68 feet in length, with a girth of 40 feet. If this measurement be in a straight line, and not along the curve, it is a record, the skeleton of the old bull in the British Museum measuring just over 50 feet. The yield of oil by the Shetland bull was fifty-three barrels, or the same as in the 54-feet Raidarfjord specimen.

Sperm-whales are gregarious, and assemble in " schools," which in former days might comprise from fifteen to twenty to several hundred individuals, the females, or cows, with several old bulls, or "schoolmasters," accompanying them, forming one division, and the young bulls another. The old bulls are very jealous, and fights between the old and young for supremacy are usual. Formerly it was a common sight, when in the southern seas, to see these vast schools disporting themselves near the ship ; not so much or so frequently from the deck of a large liner as from a sailing ship, since the splash and noise of the former are apt to keep them at a distance.

It was a wonderful sight—the truncated head, the long shimmering greenish blue body, the vast jaws, the humped back and tapering tail, the immense size of the whales, and yet the easy motion, the graceful and noiseless movement, and the regular jet of water from the blow-holes. Sperm-whales, though frequently seen, are, as a rule, on passage at such times from one part of the ocean to another in search of molluscs, and they never play round the ship like porpoises. The females display much solicitude for the safety of one another,

" When in progressive motion, hardly an instant is required for inspiration ; the animal dips its head a little and momentarily disappears, then it rises again to blow as before, each respiration being made with great regularity. The number of its spoutings, when in a state of quietude, depends on the size of the whale. The same may be said as to the time it remains upon or beneath the surface of the ocean. With the largest bulls the time occupied in performing one expiration and one inspiration is from ten to twelve seconds, and a whale will generally blow from sixty to seventy-five times at a rising, remaining upon the surface of the sea about twelve minutes. As soon as ' his spoutings are out ' he pitches head-foremost downwards, then, ' rounding out,' turns his flukes high in the air, and, when gaining a nearly perpendicular altitude, descends to a great depth, and there remains from fifty minutes to an hour and a quarter."

During the spouting there is no sound heard. When swimming in the ordinary manner, with the hump just showing above the surface, it has been estimated that sperm-whales can attain a speed of about seven miles an hour, but when swimming with the head alternately in and out of the water the speed has been put at from ten to twelve miles an hour.

The female cachalot breeds at all seasons of the year, and generally a single young one is produced at birth, although twins are not unknown. At birth the length of the young sperm-whale is said to vary from 11 to 14 feet.

The chief food of the sperm-whale consists of squids and cuttles, but considerable quantities of fishes—comprising rock cod, albacore, and bonito—are likewise consumed. All these different kinds of food are procured at a considerable depth below the surface of the water, but the mode of capture is at present unknown. It is believed by some that when below the surface the whale remains stationary, and drops its lower jaw nearly perpendicularly, thus revealing the glistening white interior of the capacious mouth. This, it is alleged, serves to attract the animals upon which it feeds, and when a sufficient number have entered the trap the lower jaw is closed with a snap.

When a sperm-whale is vitally wounded it disgorges its last meal, and from the circumstance that some of the pieces of the arms of cuttle-fishes thus disgorged have measured 6 by 6 by 8 feet, an idea may be gained of the size of the cephalopods upon which these monsters feed.

The sperm oil yielded by the thick layer of blubber investing the body, and the spermaceti contained in the cavity of the head, are the two products for which the sperm-whale is hunted ; and since the former fetches a far higher price than ordinary whale oil, this animal is one of the most valuable of all the cetaceans. The spermaceti exists in the form of oil in the living animal, and is ladled out in buckets from the skull when the carcase is cut up. The spermaceti of commerce is produced by a process of refining. The use to the animal of this enormous mass of oil in the skull does not appear to be ascertained.

In addition to sperm oil and spermaceti, the substance known as ambergris—literally, grey amber—is also a product of the sperm-whale. It is not, however, usually taken from the animal, but is found floating in the sea, and has been ascertained to be formed in the intestines. This substance, which always contains a number of the beaks of the squids and cuttles upon which the whale has fed, although formerly employed in medicine, is now used exclusively in perfumery. It is worth as much as £4 10s. an ounce.

When harpooned or lanced, females and young males make the most frantic efforts to escape, and, being very active, give the most trouble to despatch. The larger whales, yielding eighty or more barrels of oil, being less active, are in most cases killed more easily. This is, however, by no means always so ; and there are many instances where large sperm-whales have turned with the utmost fury upon their pursuers and destroyed every object that came in their way, either by blows from the enormous flukes, or by attacking with the head and lower jaw. There are, moreover, well-authenticated instances, not only of sperm-whales demolishing the boats of a whaling-ship, but actually attacking and sinking the vessel itself ; and Captain Scammon considered it probable that many ships which have perished without leaving any clue as to their fate have been wrecked by these whales. As an instance of the ferocity of these whales, it may be mentioned that in 1851, when the ship Citizen was whaling in the Atlantic, a wounded cachalot, after attacking and demolishing one boat, made for a second, from which it was only diverted by its attention being transferred to a third. This third boat only escaped with difficulty, and the whale thereupon headed straight for the vessel itself, which was then approaching under full sail. By putting the head before the wind the rush of the whale was, however, avoided ; and before the animal could gather itself for a second charge it was seized with its death-throes and expired. In another case a sperm-whale, not content with having smashed a whale-boat, actually seized the timbers in its jaws and chewed them into matchwood.

Still more remarkable, because wholly unprovoked, was the attack on the brigantine Handa Isle, some 220 miles out from Sydney, made by a couple of cachalots on August 24, 1894. The vessel had left Mercury Bay, New Zealand, deeply laden with timber, and nothing was farther from her skipper's mind than to go whale-hunting, since he lacked the necessary appliances. One of the whales shirked the assault, and dived below the ship, but the other rammed the brigantine with its head, and caused her to reel from stem to stern, smashing in the side so effectually that the water poured in at the rate of one foot per hour.

LESSER SPERM-WHALE

The lesser sperm-whale (*Cogia breviceps*) is a rather rare species, differing widely both in size and form from the sperm-whale, and more resembling a porpoise. It agrees with the sperm-whale in having no functional teeth in the upper jaw, and a full series in the lower ; but the rudimentary upper teeth are reduced to a single pair, or may be wanting, and there are only from nine to twelve pairs of teeth in the lower jaw. These teeth, which are rather long and slender, with curved summits, differ from those of the sperm-whale in having a coating of enamel, and the two branches of the lower jaw are united for less than half their length.

The upper surface of the hind part of the skull is hollowed, with a thick elevated rim behind and at the base ; and the portion of the skull forming the beak is shorter and more rapidly tapering than in the larger species. This whale attains a length of about 10 feet. The head is about one-sixth the total length, and has a bluntly pointed muzzle, with the small mouth opening on the under surface, far behind the extremity. The back carries a large fin. The colour is glistening black above and paler beneath.

The lesser sperm-whale is known only from a comparatively small number of examples obtained from such widely separated areas as the Indian and Australian seas, the Cape of Good Hope, and the North Pacific, and it may accordingly be assumed that it has probably an almost cosmopolitan distribution, although it has not occurred in British waters. It yields spermaceti ; but nothing seems to have been ascertained in regard to its habits.

EXTINCT SPERM-WHALES

In the seas of the Pliocene portion of the Tertiary period, as well as in those of the somewhat older Miocene, sperm-whales of extinct species abounded, as is attested by the number of their fossil teeth found in the so-called Crags of East Anglia, and corresponding formations in other parts of the world. These extinct genera include *Balænodon*, *Thalassocetus*, *Physeterula*, *Prophyseter*, *Placoziphius*, and *Hypocetus*, all of which have teeth in both jaws. The last of these, which is common to the Miocene of North and South America, seems to be the ancestor of *Physeter* or *Cogia*, probably of the former.

The teeth differ from those of the sperm-whale in having a cap of enamel on the summit ; while some of them are characterised by their nearly circular cross-section, and by the swollen size of the aperture of the central pulp cavity.

SKULL OF AN EXTINCT SPERM-WHALE

BOTTLE-NOSED AND BEAKED WHALES

THE bottle-nosed whale and its near relatives the beaked whales represent by themselves a family (*Ziphiidæ*) nearly related to the *Physeteridæ*, but with certain distinctive features of its own. In many of the extinct genera both jaws carried teeth, but in the living species the functional dentition is reduced to one or two pairs of very large teeth in the lower jaw, which are larger in males than in females, and in the typical beaked whales have a thin layer of enamel. There are, however, minute teeth, to the number of 17 or 19 pairs, in both jaws of the latter which never cut the gum ; and in the extinct *Palæoziphius* there is little difference in the size of the individual teeth. The union between the two halves of the lower jaw is long in the more ancient, but short in the recent genus.

The skull is compressed into high crests, with thick and massive pterygoid bones, and the beak often formed by a massive rod of ivory-like bone. The first two cervical vertebræ are fused, but the condition of the others varies, all the latter being generally free in the typical beaked whales, while in the bottlenose all of them, as well as the first dorsal, are united. The flippers are situated higher up than in the sperm-whales.

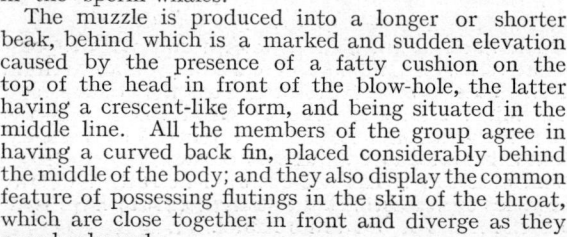

WATER-WORN SKULL, WITHOUT LOWER JAW, OF SOUTHERN BOTTLE-NOSED WHALE

The muzzle is produced into a longer or shorter beak, behind which is a marked and sudden elevation caused by the presence of a fatty cushion on the top of the head in front of the blow-hole, the latter having a crescent-like form, and being situated in the middle line. All the members of the group agree in having a curved back fin, placed considerably behind the middle of the body; and they also display the common feature of possessing flutings in the skin of the throat, which are close together in front and diverge as they pass backwards.

Like the sperm-whales, the members of this group are inhabitants of the open sea, and feed almost entirely upon squids and cuttles. Except the bottlenose, most of them are known mainly by stranded specimens ; and when any of these whales approach the shore they have no idea of saving themselves, but are almost invariably stranded. In this respect they resemble the sperm-whales ; and it would thus seem that whales accustomed to live in the open seas, and to seek their food at considerable depths, become confused and helpless when they reach shallow water. Most of them go about in pairs or alone ; but the bottlenose is in the habit of frequently associating in schools of considerable size.

BOTTLE-NOSED WHALE

The bottlenose (*Hyperoödon rostratus*) derives its name from the elevation of the upper surface of the head above the rather short beak and in front of the blow-hole into a rounded abrupt prominence. The lower jaw has merely a pair of small conical teeth at the extremity, which in the living state are concealed by the gum. In the skull the crests behind the aperture of the nostrils are greatly developed ; and in addition to these there is a pair of longitudinal bony crests lying on each side of the base of the beak, which in old males become of great size, with their front surfaces broad and flat.

This excessive development of the crests in the adult males produces a great difference in the appearance of the two sexes when adult, the females, like the young, having a beak distinctly projecting, whereas in the males it is almost buried beneath the elevated and flattened surface of the upper part of the head, which has a disc-like form when seen from the front. The flukes are not notched. In length the male bottlenose may reach as much as 30 feet, but the female does not exceed 24 feet. The young are black above, but with advancing age gradually pass to a light brown tint, the under parts being greyish white. Very old specimens turn almost yellow, with a white band round the neck, and the front of the head and beak also white.

The bottlenose is a migratory species confined to the North Atlantic. During the summer it ranges as far northwards as Spitzbergen, but how far southwards it travels in winter is not yet ascertained. In the early autumn some specimens are usually stranded on the coasts of Britain and the countries bordering the English Channel and North Sea ; but none is recorded from the shores of Spain, Western France, or the Mediterranean countries. The majority of such specimens are solitary and generally young, although sometimes an adult female with her offspring is taken.

In early spring these whales are to be met with occasionally after leaving the Shetland Islands, and thence northwards to the borders of the Polar ice, where they are more numerous. They also frequent the seas around Iceland, Greenland as far as latitude 77° N.; Western Spitzbergen, and Davis Strait, and it is highly probable that they may range as far as Novaya Zemlya. Although they do not venture in among the ice itself, they frequent the open bays along its margin for the shelter thus afforded from the open sea. They are generally to be found in herds comprising from four to ten, but many different herds may be in sight at the same time. The adult males are frequently solitary, but sometimes one may be seen leading a herd.

These whales exhibit little fear of ships, swimming around them and beneath the boats till their curiosity is satisfied. The herd remain around a wounded companion till its death, upon which they immediately desert. If, however, a second one be harpooned before the death of that first struck, and this process be continued, a whole herd may be killed at once. They exhibit great endurance of wounds and tenacity of life, old males taking out from three hundred to four hundred, and occasionally as much as seven hundred, fathoms of line. Their activity is stated to be very great, and at times they leap out of the water many feet into the air, and while so doing have time to turn their heads to look about them. When descending, they re-enter the water head-first, instead of falling helplessly on their sides as the larger whales have the habit of doing.

Their ordinary food consists of a bluish white cuttle-fish, 6 inches long and 3 inches in circumference and pointed towards the tail; the stomachs of several of these whales contained nothing but remains of these cuttles. In their search after food bottle-nosed whales descend to great depths, as they remain under water for a long period, and blow very heavily upon reaching the surface. When wounded, they will sometimes remain below for as much as two hours at a time, after which they will come up apparently untired. A second species (*H. planifrons*) inhabits the seas round South America.

The bottlenose yields spermaceti and an oil very similar to sperm oil, and capable of being used for the same purposes, an adult male producing about two hundredweight of spermaceti and two tons of oil. The protuberance on the front of the head of the female contains a small quantity of colourless oil twice the density of that obtained from the blubber; while in the male the same region is composed of solid fat.

A fossil bottle-nosed whale, apparently closely allied to the living species, has left its remains in the Pliocene Crag deposits of the eastern coast of England.

CUVIER'S WHALE

The rare cetacean known as Cuvier's whale (*Ziphius cavirostris*) differs from the bottlenose in having a pair of well-developed conical teeth at the extremity of the lower jaw, which are directed forwards and upwards. In the skull there are only slight indications of the longitudinal bony crests of the bottlenose, while the beak is longer and much more solid in structure, owing to the ossification of certain cartilages and their fusion with the adjacent bones. When viewed from above, the beak is triangular in form, gradually tapering from its broad base to its narrow extremity. A further point of difference from the bottlenose is to be found in the fact that only the first three, instead of the whole seven, of the vertebræ of the neck are united. The colour is believed to be black above and white below.

This whale, which forms in some degree a connecting link between the bottlenose and the typical beaked whales, appears to be known only from stranded specimens, which have been obtained from regions as remote from one another as the Shetland Islands, the Cape of Good Hope, Eastern South America, and New Zealand, so that its distribution appears to be as extensive as that of the sperm-whale.

BEAKED WHALES

The beaked whales derive their English name from the great development of the beak of the skull, which is long and narrow, and formed of extremely solid and ivory-like bone, while they take their scientific title (*Mesoplodon*) from the presence of a pair of teeth generally situated near the middle of each side of the lower jaw. Each of these teeth is pointed and much flattened, sometimes being elongated into a strap-like form, so as to overhang the beak of the skull; their position is variable in the different species, but generally some distance behind the extremity of the jaw. The skull has the same curving crests over the aperture of the nostrils as in the bottlenose, but no longitudinal crests. Usually only the first two or three of the neck vertebræ are united.

The massive beak of the skull is not infrequently picked up on the shores of regions where these whales are common, and similar beaks are among the commonest of cetacean remains found in the Pliocene Crag deposits of the Suffolk and Essex coasts, thus indicating that beaked whales formerly abounded in the English seas. These beaks are, perhaps, the most solid bones known, their material being as dense as ivory. In some cases a row of minute functionless teeth is present in the upper jaw, serving to show that the whales of this group are descended from ancestors possessing a full set of teeth in both the upper and lower jaws. Beaked whales are represented by several species, and range over most seas, although they appear more common in the Southern than in the Northern Hemisphere.

SOWERBY'S WHALE

The typical representative of the genus is Sowerby's whale (*Mesoplodon bidens*), of which eighteen specimens were taken between 1800 and 1889 in the North

BOTTLE-NOSED WHALES

Atlantic and its inlets, all but two occurring on the coasts of Europe. Seven of these were captured between 1800 and 1888, one taken in 1885 having been stranded at the mouth of the Humber, and at that time the only known English example. The first specimen known to science was captured off the coast of Elgin in 1800 ; and by its describer, after whom it is named, was called the two-toothed cachalot. Of late years several examples have been taken off Bergen by the Norwegians.

This whale usually attains a length of about 15 feet, and its teeth are of comparatively small size, and some-times only project slightly from the sides of the mouth when the jaws are closed. Above the nearly straight beak the head rises gently into a marked prominence in front of the blow-hole, behind which is another prominence, with the level of its summit continued backwards into the line of the back. The opening of the ear is so small as to admit only of the passage of a fine bristle. The usual colour of the upper parts is bluish slate, and that of the under parts whitish, but the latter may be nearly as dark as the back. The body is generally marked with a number of whitish streaks and spots, most numerous on the sides, and probably produced by the cuttle-fishes upon which these whales feed. A specimen captured at New Jersey in 1889 measured 12½ feet in length.

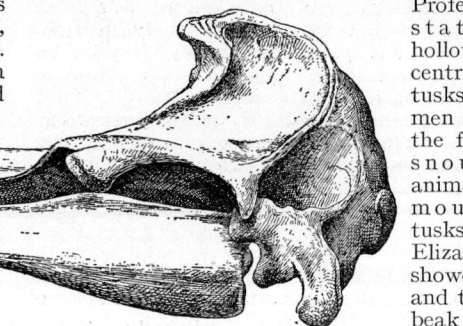

SKULL OF SOWERBY'S BEAKED WHALE

Whether Sower-by's whale ranges into the seas of the Southern Hemi-sphere is not definitely ascertained, although the genus is more abundantly represented there than to the north of the equator ; and it is still a question whether many of the southern forms, to which separate names have been given, are entitled to rank as distinct species, or should be regarded merely as races of the European one.

LAYARD'S WHALE

Layard's beaked whale (*M. layardi*), from the Cape of Good Hope and the seas of the other parts of the Southern Hemisphere, is a well-marked species, charac-terised by the enormous development of the strap-like teeth. Professor H. N. Moseley, in describing a skull of this species obtained at the Cape during the voyage of the Challenger, observes that " the two teeth in the adult animal become lengthened by continuous growth of the fangs into long curved tusks. These arch over the upper jaw or beak, and, crossing one another above it at their tips, form a ring round it, and lock the lower jaw, so that the animal can only open its mouth for a very short distance indeed. The tusks are seen always to be worn away in front by the grating of the confined upper jaw against them. How the animal manages to feed itself under these conditions is a mystery. It is remarkable that the main mass of each tusk is made up of what appears to be an abnormal growth of the fang.

" The actual conical tooth—that is, the original small cap of dentine [ivory] of the tooth of the young animal, which corresponds to the part of the teeth showing above the gum in other whales—does not increase at all in size, but is carried up by the growth of the fangs, and remains at the tips of the tusks as a sort of wart-like rudimentary excrescence." That these enormous teeth can be of no advantage to their owner appears perfectly clear ; and they must probably be regarded as an instance of semi-monstrous development analo-gous to the one displayed by the tusks of the babirusa. A specimen of Layard's beaked whale stranded at the Cape was said to be black above and white beneath, with the division between the two tints sharply defined. One measuring over 16 feet in length yielded eighty gallons of oil of a superior quality. A male stranded

near Port Elizabeth in 1907 measured 19 feet 2 inches in length. The colour of the back was dark brown, in-clining to black on the dorsal surface, gradually merging to brown on the sides and tail, and becoming whitey-brown or dirty white on the belly. Professor Moseley stated that there was a distinct line of demarcation between the black and the white, but in this specimen the blackish of the back gradually merged to brown on the sides and pure white on the belly.

Inspection of the muzzle proved that this whale was able to open its mouth from 4½ inches to 5 inches at the tip. The fleshy covering of the upper jaw beneath the teeth showed no mark or abrasion, indicating that the beak was opened only so far as the teeth allowed.

Professor Moseley stated that the hollowing-out of the central part of the tusks in his speci-men was caused by the friction of the snout when the animal opened its mouth; but the tusks of the Port Elizabeth specimen showed no such sign, and the skin of the beak displayed no indication of coming frequently into con-tact with a hard body. Judging from the width of the gullet, this whale does not require to open its mouth very wide ; and as the gullet is only from 1¾ inch to 2 inches in diameter, it indicates that the food consists of small morsels. The sharp enamelled tooth at the summit of the tusk is probably used for tearing and rending soft-bodied animals such as cuttle-fishes, and possibly for tearing aside seaweeds when in search of food.

ARNOUX'S WHALE

The last representative of this group is Arnoux's whale (*Berardius arnouxi*), from the southern seas, which attains a length of about 30 feet, and differs from all the other forms in having two pairs of teeth near the front of the jaw, the first pair being placed close to the tip of the jaw and larger than the second pair. They are of moderate size, flattened from side to side, pointed at the tips, and inclined directly forwards. The skull lacks the high crests above the opening of the nostrils characteristic of the three preceding genera, and the long and narrow beak is less solidly ossified than in the beaked whales. These whales are stated to have the power of raising and depressing their teeth.

EXTINCT BEAKED WHALES

Here it may conveniently be mentioned that certain fossil cetaceans from the Miocene Tertiary deposits of Europe and North America, described under the name of *Eurhinodelphis*, represent an extinct family—the *Eurhinodelphidæ*—which is related to the *Ziphiidæ*, but possesses distinctive peculiarities. Among these features are the small size of the pterygoid bones, the long, toothless premaxillæ, and the dolphin-like muzzle of the skull. The premaxillæ form the greater portion of the very long beak; the maxillæ carry from 37 to 60 conical teeth; and the skull is of the general type of that of the *Ziphiidæ*, in some cases slightly convex, in others with a bold transverse crest. The group is a primitive type related to the *Ziphiidæ*, although none of the species at present known can be regarded as ancestral to the latter.

RIVER AND ESTUARINE DOLPHINS

THE susu of the rivers of India and Burma, along with two South American species, respectively represent at the present day the families *Platanistidæ* and *Iniidæ*. They are characterised by having eight double-headed ribs and long beaks ; the costal cartilages ossify late in life ; the petrosal and tympanic bones are connected with the skull mainly by ligament ; the temporal fossa is large ; all the cervical vertebræ are free ; teeth are present in both jaws ; and the flippers are short and wide. They agree with true dolphins in having a numerous series of small teeth in both jaws, but differ in that the two branches of the lower jaw are united for more than half their length ; while the head is marked off from the body by a slightly constricted neck. They are also characterised by the ribs articulating with the vertebræ in a manner very similar to that which obtains in ordinary mammals.

In some respects these cetaceans are less specialised than the other living representatives of the order, and are, therefore, probably more nearly allied to the ancestral stock.

THE SUSU

Although commonly designated the Gangetic dolphin (*Platanista gangetica*), the single existing representative of the first family is better called by its name of susu, which refers to the rushing sound of the air exhaled by the animal when it comes to the surface to breathe. The susu differs from the two members of the other family (*Iniidæ*) in the slit-like form of the blow-hole, the presence of a cæcum, or blind appendage, to the intestine, the development of a high crest on each maxilla, and in the teeth undergoing remarkable changes with age. It inhabits the Indus, Ganges, and Bramaputra rivers, with their larger tributaries, from the regions where they leave the mountains to the sea ; and is characterised by its long, compressed beak, which is slightly enlarged at the extremity, by the back fin being rudimentary and replaced by a low ridge, by the triangular and fan-shaped flippers, by the very minute and rudimentary eye, and by the blow-hole forming a longitudinal slit. The conical and cylindrical teeth are rather large, and while sharply pointed in the young, in the adult they become much worn down by use. Towards the extremities of the jaws they are so closely placed as to be almost in contact with one another.

The skull is characterised by the development of enormous crests at the root of the beak, which almost meet in the middle line above the latter. In the males the beak is much shorter than in the females ; and there are generally about thirty teeth on each side of the jaws. The colour is blackish throughout. Females are larger than males ; the length of adults varies from 7 to 8 feet, but a specimen from the Jumna measured 12 feet. The susu is blind, and, indeed, sight would be useless to

SUSU, OR GANGETIC DOLPHIN

it in the turbid waters of the Indus at all seasons, and in the Ganges and Bramaputra at most periods of the year. It is never seen at sea, but to a certain extent is migratory in the rivers, since none is observed in the Hughli at Calcutta during the hot season from March to June, although they are commonly visible in the cold months from October to March. That they also remain in the tidal waters during the rainy season from June to October is proved by the fact that they are then frequently caught in fishing-nets, although they rarely show themselves above water. This dolphin has been obtained one thousand miles above Calcutta, and its upward range in the river is only checked by the presence of rocky barriers and the diminishing depth of the stream, aided perhaps by the increasing lowness of the temperature of the water.

Although these dolphins do not collect in herds, several may often be observed within a small area in the more placid reaches of the Indian rivers. Dr. J. Anderson writes that "it is difficult to say whether the Gangetic dolphin confines itself to limited areas when there is no disturbing cause at work, such as the rains, leading it to disperse itself over other channels and branches of the river which are not accessible to it in the dry weather. In rising to breathe, the platanista may either simply expose the upper surface of its head sufficiently to bring its blow-hole above water, or, what is more common, plunge out of the water upwards, forwards, and downwards, first exhibiting its long snout, followed by two-thirds of its back. At such times it emits a short, blowing sound, which doubtless has given rise to the term (susu), generally applied to it along the Ganges and Bramaputra. During the cold months, in the quiet reaches, it even becomes at times extravagant in its movements, and will leap altogether out of the water with the tail curved downwards. As a rule, however, its respiratory visits to the surface are leisurely executed.

"I have had the rare opportunity of narrowly observing the respiratory movements of this dolphin from having had one alive for ten days in captivity. In its place of confinement this individual rose slowly to the surface, exposing the blow-hole and a portion of its back. The blow-hole opened whenever it reached the surface of the water, the characteristic expiratory sound was produced, and so rapid was inspiration that the blow-hole seemed to close immediately after the expiratory act, and then the animal slowly subsided. The respirations were tolerably frequent, occurring at intervals of about one-half or three-quarters of a minute, and the whole act did not take more than a few seconds for its fulfilment."

The food of the susu consists principally of fishes and prawns, many of the fish consumed by it being mud-hunting species belonging to the catfish group (*Siluridæ*). These are doubtless captured by the dolphin probing for them in the mud with its long snout. The captive specimen above mentioned fed on the fishes with which it was supplied only during the night, but careful observations made on these dolphins in their native state prove that they feed by day as well. Sometimes they may be seen among the shipping in the Hughli at Calcutta, in search of their favourite prawns, during the daytime. The grain sometimes found in

INIA, OR AMAZONIAN DOLPHIN

their stomachs appears to be swallowed unintentionally.

The young are born from April to July, and it is very rarely that there is more than one at a birth. The period of gestation is believed to be from eight to nine months. It is said that the young will hold on by its mouth to the base of one of the flippers of its parent.

THE INIA

In the inia (*Inia geoffroyensis*), or freshwater dolphin of the Amazon, and the La Plata dolphin, which constitute the family *Iniidæ*, the opening of the blow-hole is crescentic, there is no cæcum to the intestine, the upper jaw does not carry crests, and the transverse processes of the lumbar vertebræ are very broad.

The inia more resembles a porpoise in appearance than does the susu. The long, cylindrical beak, which carries from twenty-six to thirty-three teeth on each side of the jaws, is peculiar in being furnished with a number of sparsely distributed bristle-like hairs. The teeth are characterised by having a distinct tubercle on the inner side of the base of their crowns, and the back fin is represented merely by a low ridge. The males attain a length of about 7 feet, but the females are little more than half the size. In general the upper parts are blackish and the under parts reddish, but some specimens are found which are either entirely blackish or wholly reddish. The eye is well developed, and the flippers have not the fan-like shape characterising those of the Gangetic dolphin. In the skeleton the breastbone is short and broad, and composed only of a single piece, and the horizontal transverse processes of the vertebræ of the hind portion of the trunk are remarkable for their great width.

The inia, or bouto, as the species is called in certain parts of South America, is entirely fluviatile, and inhabits the upper portions of the Amazon and its affluents, ranging over the area of country included between 10° and 17° S. lat. In addition to the inia,

there are certain species of dolphins belonging to the family *Delphinidæ* found in certain parts of the Amazon. One of these, called the tucuxi—a species of the genus *Sotalia*—when it comes to the surface to breathe rises horizontally, showing first its long, low back fin ; then draws an inspiration, and finally dives gently down, head-foremost. On the other hand, when the inia rises the top of the head is the part first seen ; it then blows, and immediately afterwards dips head-downwards, its back curving over, exposing successively the whole dorsal ridge. It thus seems to pitch heels-over-head, but does not show the tail fin. In addition to this peculiar motion, which seems to be very similar to that of the susu, it is distinguished from the tucuxi by its habit of generally going in pairs.

Both species are exceedingly numerous throughout the Amazon and its larger tributaries, but are nowhere more plentiful than in the shoal water at the mouth of the Tocantins, especially in the dry season. In the Upper Amazon a third pale flesh-coloured species is also abundant. In the broader parts of the Amazon, from its mouth to a distance of fifteen hundred miles in the interior, one or other of the three kinds mentioned is always heard rolling, blowing, and snorting, especially at night, and these sounds contribute much to the impression of sea-wide vastness and desolation which haunts the traveller.

LA PLATA DOLPHIN

The small La Plata dolphin (*Pontoporia*, or *Stenodelphis*, *blainvillei*), from the estuary of the Rio de la Plata, differs from the inia in the presence of a well-marked back fin and the extreme elongation of the jaws, which carry from fifty to sixty teeth on each side. In the skeleton the breastbone is long and composed of two distinct pieces ; and the transverse processes of the lumbar vertebræ are very broad, as in the inia, but the pterygoid bones of the skull are involuted, the sternal ribs (costal cartilages) are ossified, and the true ribs articulate with the vertebræ in the same manner as in the *Delphinidæ*. This species, which does not exceed five feet in length, is remarkable for its nearly uniform light brown colour, which harmonises exactly with the muddy water of the estuary of the La Plata.

EXTINCT RIVER DOLPHINS

The inia and the La Plata dolphin, together with the nearly allied extinct Argentine genus *Pontistes*, constitute the sub-family *Iniinæ ;* in addition there are two extinct sub-families, the *Argyrocetinæ* (with the genera *Argyrocetus*, *Cyrtodelphis*, *Pontivaga*, *Ischyorhynchus*, and *Champsodelphis*), and the *Acrodelphinæ* (with *Acrodelphis* and *Heterodelphis*). The *Argyrocetinæ*, of which the type genus is from the Miocene of South America, although several of the others are European, have flat skulls, very long beaks with a great number of teeth, and the frontal bones forming a broad zone on the forehead. In the *Acrodelphinæ* the frontal zone is narrower, and the teeth in the type genus have numerous accessory denticles, apparently representing the serrations on those of the extinct *Squalodon*. The Patagonian *Argyrodelphis* also belongs to this group.

PORPOISES AND DOLPHINS

THE whole of the remaining members of the existing Cetacea, including those commonly known as narwhals, porpoises, grampuses, and dolphins, are referred to a single family (*Delphinidæ*), which contains a far greater number of species than any of the others. All the members of this family are of small or medium size, and, with the exception of the narwhal and Risso's dolphin, are furnished with a numerous series of teeth in both the upper and lower jaws (page 828), the jaws themselves being either elongated or short. They are distinguished from the two preceding families by the union between the two branches of the lower jaw being always considerably less than half the entire length of the jaw itself, and likewise by the manner in which the ribs are articulated to the backbone, as well as by certain features in the base of the skull.

There are only four or five ribs with double heads ; the costal cartilages are fully ossified at an early age ; the petroso-tympanic bones of the ear, which differ in form from the corresponding bones of the *Physeteridæ* and *Ziphiidæ*, are united by ligament with the skull, and the blow-hole is situated on the right side and has the horns of the crescent pointing forwards. The nasal bones are short, the skull has no crests, and the teeth are smooth.

The family is divided into two sub-families, the *Delphinapterinæ* and *Delphininæ*, in the first of which all the cervical vertebræ are free, and in which are included only the narwhal and the beluga, or white whale. In the second sub-family at least the first two cervical vertebræ are united.

The majority of the dolphins—as it is convenient to term collectively the whole of the members of the family—are of marine habits, but many of them frequent estuaries and ascend tidal rivers, while a few are more or less exclusively freshwater in habitat. They have been divided into a considerable number of genera, but many of these are very closely allied, and mainly distinguished by differences in the skeleton.

NARWHAL

The strange-looking cetacean known as the narwhal (*Monodon monoceros*) differs from all other members of the family by the enormous spirally twisted tusk projecting from one side of the upper jaw of the male (page 92). This tusk is nearly always that of the left side, its fellow on the opposite side being only a few inches in length, and lying concealed within the bone of the jaw, while in the females both tusks remain in a similar rudimentary condition. The developed tusk of the male is composed solely of ivory, and its spiral twist always runs from left to right. In form it is cylindrical, and tapers more or less markedly from root to tip. Not infrequently the tusk attains a length of from 7 to 8 feet, or more than half that of the entire animal.

Very rarely narwhals are met with in which the right tusk is developed as well as the left, but there appears to be no known instance of the right tusk being developed while the left remains rudimentary ; and it is noteworthy that when the right tusk is developed it has the same left-to-right twist as its fellow. Apart from a few small rudimentary ones, which are irregular in their occurrence, the male narwhal has no teeth except the tusk, while the female—except for similar rudiments—is toothless.

The narwhal, as already mentioned, has all the vertebræ of the neck separate, but it agrees with several of the following genera in the blunt and rounded head, in which the muzzle shows no sign of being produced into a beak. A special character of the narwhal is the absence of a back fin, which is represented merely by a low and ill-defined ridge. The flippers are short, wide, and rounded ; and the colour of the skin is dark grey or dusky above and white beneath, the back and sides being irregularly mottled with various shades of grey. The entire length may vary from 12 to 16 feet. A tusk measuring 8 feet in length had a basal girth of $7\frac{1}{2}$ inches.

The narwhal is an inhabitant of the icy Polar seas and circumpolar in its distribution ; it is, however, apparently local in its range, being rarely found in the seas accessible to the whalers passing through Bering Strait. Although seldom occurring to the south of 65° N., there are three instances—one in 1648, a second in 1800, and a third eight years

A SCHOOL OF NARWHALS

later—of narwhals visiting the British coasts ; but from the extreme rarity of such occurrences these examples must have been carried by currents out of their proper habitat. From constant persecution, the numbers of the narwhal have been greatly reduced in the more accessible portions of its haunts, and it is now never seen on the coasts of Novaya Zemlya. It is however, more common at Hope Island, and large herds are reported from the seas between Spitzbergen and Novaya Zemlya.

On the north-west coast of Greenland narwhals are fairly common, although not numerous, but they are rarely seen to the south of Sukker-toppen (66° N.). Along the east coast they are more common than belugas, which they much resemble in habits. On the west coast they are only found in the northernmost part of Baffin Bay, but not until late in autumn. They migrate southwards later than the beluga, and their migration in that direction does not extend so far.

At Umanack they do not appear before November, and as early as March may be seen in Davis Strait moving northwards. Even on the north coast they are present in winter, and on the east coast proceed farther south than on the west coast. After the manner of belugas, they seek open holes when the sea suddenly freezes, and under ordinary conditions are found in open channels in the ice. Narwhals are gregarious, and when migrating often move in great herds.

It is noteworthy that fossil remains of the narwhal have been found in the so-called Forest-Bed of the Norfolk coast—a deposit laid down before the great cold of the Glacial Period, but when the temperature may have been steadily lowering, whereby Arctic animals were enabled to leave their more northerly haunts.

Of the habits of narwhals little is known. They are found in small schools, comprising from fifteen to twenty, and are extremely playful in their disposition. Much has been written as to the use of the tusk, although nothing very definite has been ascertained. That it is not employed for the purpose of procuring food is evident from the fact of its absence in the female. A more probable suggestion is that it is used by the males in combats among themselves for the possession of the females, in which case it should be regarded as a sexual appendage, analogous to the antlers of deer. The food of the narwhal is stated to be composed of cuttles and various crustaceans, together with small fishes. As a rule, only a single young is produced at birth, but an instance of twins is on record.

The narwhal is valued both for its ivory and its oil, the latter being superior in quality to ordinary whale oil. The ivory of the tusk is very dense in structure, and of a pure creamy white colour, but since the tusk is hollow throughout the greater part of its length, its value is much less than it would be otherwise. The price of narwhal tusks, although very variable, is considerable.

WHITE WHALE OR BELUGA

Nearly allied to the narwhal is the white whale, or beluga (*Delphinapterus leucas*), which is also an Arctic species. It resembles the narwhal in having the back fin represented merely by a low ridge, and it also agrees with that species, and differs from the other members of the family, in having all the vertebræ of the neck separate. The flippers are short, very broad across the middle, and bluntly pointed; and the short and rounded head is separated from the body by a slight constriction indicating the neck. The teeth, usually nine or ten in number on each side of the jaws, vary in size, and are often irregularly and obliquely implanted. The white whale attains a length of 16 or 16½ feet. In colour the young are light greyish brown, but the skin of the adult is pure glistening white.

WHITE WHALES, OR BELUGAS

When alive, the adult animal is singularly beautiful, the brilliant white hide scarcely even showing a spot, scratch, or wrinkle; but the young, when accompanying a school, look like shadowy ghosts.

The white whale ranges as far northwards as latitude 81° 35′, and it occasionally straggles as far southwards as Cape Cod, in Massachusetts, and the Scottish shores. It occurs in large herds on the coasts of Spitzbergen and Novaya Zemlya, and especially frequents the neighbourhood of the mouths of rivers, which it will ascend for considerable distances. Several instances of the occurrence of this species on the coasts of Scotland have been recorded; in the summer of 1879 a specimen was found near Dunrobin, Sutherlandshire, at ebb-tide, with its flukes caught between two short posts, to which a net was fastened. Near by lay a salmon, which the white whale was supposed to have been pursuing.

Except in the extreme south, the white whale is the commonest species on the west coast of Greenland, and on the western part of the north coast is numerous, as well as outside the east coast ice-belt, in the neighbourhood of Spitzbergen. It is migratory, in summer frequenting the waters as far to the north as the ice will permit, and in winter moving southwards. It is found in large numbers in Baffin Bay and at the entrance to Smith Sound in summer, but in autumn moves southwards along the west coast of Greenland, making its appearance off Disco in October and November, and at Godthaab (64° N.) in December. As a rule, the migration does not extend much farther south. Throughout the winter these whales frequent the whole of the central west coast, but about the end of April begin to return northwards, and in May and

June are again common in Disco Bay, from which in July they disappear completely. Should the sea not be frozen over, they are met with in winter off the north coast. On the east coast their migrations, so far as known, correspond nearly with those on the west.

White whales are sometimes caught by the ice forming suddenly over an extensive area of water, and in such case they repair in great numbers to a so-called "hole," which they keep open for breathing purposes. Generally, they exhibit a preference for the neighbourhood of land, and on migration along the west coast pass close along the shore, among the islands and up the fjords. When on these journeys, they move in herds, sometimes consisting of hundreds of both sexes.

Their food consists of fishes, such as cod, sea perch, and flounders, with shellfish and squids. In 1857 the number of these whales annually killed on the west coast of Greenland was estimated at between 400 and 500, and twenty years later at 600, while in 1894 more than double that number were killed.

This species is fairly rapid in its movements, more especially when in pursuit of fishes. When pursuing fishes like halibut and flounders, the beluga frequently enters shoal water, in which it can scarcely float, but in such situations is said to exhibit no alarm, and to make only slight efforts to reach deeper waters. In addition to fishes, white whales consume cuttles and various crustaceans.

In captivity the beluga is easily tamed, and exhibits considerable docility. A specimen was shown alive at the Westminster Aquarium in 1877, and another in 1878, but neither lived long.

The white whale is killed for its blubber, flesh and hide; a specimen measuring 16½ feet in length yielded one hundred gallons of oil. The Greenlanders dry the flesh for winter use, and in parts of Siberia sledge-dogs are mainly fed on it. The fat is considered a luxurious dish in winter. In Russia white whale skin is used for reins and traces, and imported in some quantities into England under the name of porpoise hide. In some of the Siberian rivers white whales are harpooned and lanced in the ordinary manner, but in other districts are taken in nets from June to September.

PORPOISES

The porpoise (*Phocæna communis*) of the European seas is the first representative of the second, or typical, sub-family of the *Delphinidæ*, in which at least the first two vertebræ of the neck are welded together. It is the best-known representative of a small genus distinguished from all others by the characters of the teeth. These are twenty-five or twenty-six in number on each side of the jaws, and are very small, with flattened spade-like crowns separated from the roots by a distinct neck; sometimes the upper border of the crown is entire, but in other cases it is divided into two

or three distinct lobes. In size porpoises are small; and the head has a rounded muzzle, without a beak, while there is a fin on the back. The skull has a broad palate, and the union between the two branches of the lower jaw is very short. There are frequently one or more rows of horny tubercles on the front edge of the back fin, or of the ridge which takes its place.

The porpoise is the best-known of all the cetaceans frequenting the British coasts, generally keeping near the shores, and often ascending the larger rivers to considerable distances. It is characterised by the sloping head, the equality in the length of the upper and lower jaws, and the length of the mouth exceeding half that of the flipper. The fin on the back is triangular in shape, and situated somewhat in advance of the middle of the total length. In length the porpoise measures about 5 feet, or rather more. The colour of the upper parts is dark slate, or blackish, but the sides become gradually lighter till the colour fades into the pure white of the under parts. In some cases there is a yellowish or pinkish tinge on the flukes.

The distribution of this species is extensive, comprising the North Atlantic and North Pacific Oceans, the North Sea, and the coasts of Europe. In Davis Strait it extends as far northwards as latitude 67° or 69°, and it also occurs on the Alaskan coasts, while southwards it extends in America to the shores of New Jersey and Mexico. In the Mediterranean it is rarely, if ever, seen.

Few sights are more interesting to watch than a shoal of these animals diving and sporting round a vessel, whether it be making rapid headway or lying at anchor. At one moment will be seen the roll of the arched back, surmounted by the fin, as the porpoise

PORPOISES BREACHING

swims along in a series of gentle curves; while at another the white belly will flash in the sunlight as the creature turns on its side or leaps out of the water. In the ordinary undulating mode of swimming, the porpoise just brings its blow-hole to the surface, breathes without checking its course, and then dips downwards, exposing the back fin, this elegant motion being continued without intermission. Throughout its course the flukes are the propelling instrument, the flippers being laid close against the sides during the onward movement, and only spread out to check its speed when the animal desires to stop.

The food of the porpoise apparently consists exclusively of fishes ; mackerel, pilchards, and herrings being especial favourites, although it also consumes salmon. The pairing season is said to be in the summer, and it is believed that the single offspring is produced after a period of six months' gestation. Three porpoises which were enclosed by a fence in the Wareham River in Dorsetshire many years ago are reported to have incessantly uttered distressing cries, continued by night as well as by day.

Formerly porpoises were esteemed in England for their flesh, but they are now taken mainly for oil, although the skin, despite its oily nature, is stated to be sometimes utilised. The leather commonly known as porpoise hide is generally made from the skin of the white whale. On parts of the coast of North America porpoise-shooting is practised by the Indians, the pursuit affording to the Passamaquody tribe their chief means of support. The average yield of oil is about three gallons per head, and in a good season an Indian may kill from one hundred to one hundred and fifty porpoises.

According to Dr. O. Abel, the porpoise of the Black Sea is distinct from the common species, the chief difference being apparently the form of the head. For this species the name *Phocæna relicta* has been proposed. Seeing that the common porpoise does not, as a rule, enter the Mediterranean, it is only natural to expect that its Euxine representative should be distinct. It is suggested that the reason why porpoises do not enter the Mediterranean is because the water is too salt for them. Dr. Abel has described a fossil porpoise skull from the Miocene strata of the Taman Peninsula as *Palæophocæna*, regarding it as representing an ancestral member of the group.

INDIAN PORPOISE

The Indian porpoise (*Neomeris*, or *Neophocæna*, *phocænoides*) is distinguished from the typical porpoises by the absence of the back fin and the reduced number of the teeth, of which there are about eighteen on each side of the jaws. Of small size—it is less than 4 feet in length—and generally of a more or less uniform black colour, with some whitish markings near and on the muzzle, it inhabits the shores of the Indian Ocean, from the Cape of Good Hope to Japan, and has been taken in many of the tidal rivers of India, and in the Yang-tse-Kiang, at a distance of nearly one thousand miles from its mouth.

This porpoise has a depressed area in the middle of the back, in which the skin carries a number of minute horny scales, supposed to be the remains of a bony and horny armour protecting the extinct zeuglodonts.

Mr. F. W. Sinclair states that it " frequents the tidal creeks, not ascending very far, and the sounds among the reefs and islands. It feeds chiefly on prawns, also

on small cephalopods and fish. It does not appear to herd in schools, more than four or five being rarely, if ever, seen together. Usually it is solitary ; the pairs seem to consist of female and calf more often than male and female. The young, one in number, are born, apparently, about October. The roll of this porpoise is like that of *Phocæna communis*. It does not jump or turn somersaults, and is, on the whole, a sluggish little porpoise." It appears to be found only in shallow water.

HEAVISIDE'S DOLPHIN

HEAVISIDE'S DOLPHIN

Heaviside's dolphin (*Cephalorhynchus heavisidei*), from the Cape of Good Hope, is the typical representative of a genus considered by some naturalists to include four species inhabiting the warmer seas of the Southern Hemisphere. These dolphins are of small size, and remarkable for their peculiar type of colouring which recalls that of the killer. The head is conical, without any distinct beak, and the teeth are small and sharp, varying in number from twenty-five to thirty-one on each side of the jaws. The back fin is triangular or ovate, and, except in one species, the flippers have a characteristic elliptical form.

The colour is black above and white below ; the white of the under parts terminating posteriorly in a trident-shaped form, with the lateral prongs of the trident extending obliquely upwards on the sides. The total length of Heaviside's dolphin is about 4 feet, and the number of teeth varies from twenty-five to thirty. The white-fronted dolphin (*C. albifrons*), from New Zealand, is a rather larger species, with thirty-one teeth on each side. Nothing seems to be recorded as to the habits of these species.

IRAWADI DOLPHINS

The upper waters of the Irawadi River are tenanted by a rather large dolphin or porpoise (*Orcella fluminalis*), which, together with a closely allied species or race (*O. brevirostris*) from the Bay of Bengal and its estuaries, as well as Singapore and Borneo, constitute a distinct genus. These dolphins are characterised by the globe-like head, without beak, and the comparatively few and small teeth, which occupy nearly the whole length of the jaws, and number from thirteen to seventeen in the upper, and from twelve to fifteen in the lower jaw. In form the teeth are conical and pointed, and they are set close together, those in the front of the jaws of old animals being directed outwards. The back fin is small and hook-like, and the flippers are of moderate size, broad at the base, and subovate in form.

These dolphins, which attain a length of from 7 to 7½ feet, are slaty or blackish in colour. In the Irawadi dolphin the colour is pale slaty above and whitish below, with numerous irregular streaks on the sides ; but in the one inhabiting the Bay of Bengal the skin is uniformly blackish without any streaks. The latter appears never to ascend the rivers beyond the distance influenced by the tides, while the Irawadi dolphin never descends to the estuaries.

The following account of the habits of the Irawadi dolphin is taken from Dr. John Anderson : " They never leave the deep water, and when they rise to breathe—which they do in periods varying from sixty to one hundred and seventy seconds, although occasionally exceeded—the blow-hole is first seen ; then, at the end of the inspiration, the head disappears and the back comes into view, and is gradually exposed as far as the dorsal fin, but the tail flippers are rarely visible. The act of breathing is rapid, so much so indeed that it requires a very expert marksman to take aim and fire before the animal disappears.

" I have observed some of them disporting themselves in a way that has never yet been recorded of Cetacea, as far as I am aware. They swam with a rolling motion near the surface, with their heads half out of the water, and every now and then fully exposed, when they ejected great volumes of water out of their mouths, generally straight before them, but sometimes nearly vertically. On one occasion I noticed an individual standing upright in the water, so much so that one half of its pectoral fins was exposed, producing the appearance against the background as if the animal was supported on its flippers. It suddenly disappeared, and again, a little in advance of its former position, it bobbed up in the same attitude, and this it frequently repeated. The Shan boatmen who were with me seemed to connect these curious movements with the season—spring—in which the dolphins breed."

The food of this dolphin apparently consists exclusively of fishes. Dr. Anderson adds that " the fishermen believe that the dolphin purposely draws fishes to their nets, and each fishing village has its particular guardian dolphin, which receives a name common to all fellows of his school ; and it is this superstition which makes it so difficult to obtain specimens of this cetacean."

KILLER OR GRAMPUS

One of the largest, and at the same time the most ferocious, of all the dolphin family is the killer, or killer whale, frequently also known as the grampus (*Orca gladiator*). It is characterised as a genus by its large size, and the conical and depressed head, devoid of a beak. The back fin is of great height, especially in the males ; and the flippers are large and broadly ovate. The teeth are comparatively few, varying from ten to thirteen on each side, and are much larger than in any dolphins yet noticed, being often an inch or more in diameter, and having an oval section.

The colour is striking, the upper parts and fins being black, while the lower jaw, chest, and under parts are whitish. The white area of the under parts, however, does not reach to the flukes, but extends posteriorly in a trident, of which the lateral and shorter prongs extend obliquely upwards on the flanks. There is a large white streak above and behind the eye, and frequently a purple crescentic area extends across the back behind the fin. The killer attains a length of at least 20 feet.

In spite of many nominal species having been recognised, there seems little doubt that the killer has a cosmopolitan distribution, ranging from Greenland to Australia. Although chiefly keeping to the open sea, killers occasionally ascend tidal rivers ; and three specimens were observed in the Thames in the spring of 1890, which entered the river during the night, and in the morning were seen swimming up and down the reach between Battersea and Chelsea bridges. After continuing there for several hours, they headed for the sea.

When at sea, killers may always be recognised by the tall and nearly vertical back fin. They associate in small parties, and subsist not only on fishes, but also on the flesh of other members of their own order, as well as on that of seals. At times both the long-finned males and the shorter-finned females may be found in the same school, while at other times the two sexes keep apart. The swiftness of the killer is such that it can overtake the smaller dolphins, which it swallows alive. Its voracity is insatiable, Eschricht stating that one of these animals was known to swallow four porpoises in succession, while from the stomach of another, whose length was 21 feet, were taken remains of thirteen porpoises and fourteen seals.

The Greenland whale is sometimes attacked by a party of killers (page 829). Writing on the subject of these attacks Captain Scammon says that " it is surprising to see those leviathans of the deep so completely paralysed by the presence of their natural although diminutive enemies. Frequently the terrified animal —comparatively of enormous size and superior strength— evinces no effort to escape, but lies in a helpless condition, or makes but little resistance to the assaults of its merciless destroyers. The attack of these wolves of the ocean upon their gigantic prey may be likened in some respects to a pack of hounds

KILLER OR GRAMPUS

holding a stricken deer at bay. They cluster about the animal's head, some of their number breaching over it, while others seize it by the lips and draw the bleeding monster under water ; and when captured, should the mouth be open, they eat out its tongue."

LESSER KILLER

A special interest attaches to the cetacean known as the lesser killer (*Pseudorca crassidens*) owing to its having been originally described on the evidence of a skull dug up in the Lincolnshire fens, which was long regarded as pertaining to an extinct species. This whale is distinguished from the killer by its smaller back fin, the pointed flippers, and the cylindrical roots of the teeth, as well as by certain features in the structure of the skull.

In colour the lesser killer is entirely black, and attains a length of about 14 feet. There are generally eight teeth in the upper jaw in each side, and ten in the lower jaw. This species appears to be cosmopolitan, having been met with in small herds on the coasts of Denmark, India and Tasmania.

BLACKFISH

The blackfish (*Globiocephalus melas*) derives its English name from its nearly uniform black colour, while its generic title refers to the characteristic globular form of the head. In size this species is one of the largest representatives of the family, attaining a length of about 20 feet.

In addition to its beakless, globular head, the blackfish is characterised by the long, low, and thick back fin, the long and narrow flippers, and the small size and number of the teeth, which are confined to the front of the jaws. The usual number of the teeth is from eight to twelve on each side of the jaws, but in a distinct variety, or species, from the Bay of Bengal they are rather fewer.

The skull is very broad and much depressed, and the union between the two branches of the lower jaw very short. In the typical form there is a large spear-shaped white area on the chest, extending from the corners of the mouth to the flippers. This white area is, however, absent in certain forms, which have been regarded as indicating distinct species.

The ordinary blackfish has a wide distribution, having been obtained from the coasts of Europe, the Atlantic coast of North America, the Cape of Good Hope and New Zealand. It has, however, been considered that the blackfish of the North Pacific (*G. scammoni*), and also the one found on the Atlantic coast to the south of New Jersey, are distinct species, and there is also the above-mentioned fourth species or race in the Bay of Bengal. In Europe the blackfish, or, as it is often called, the pilot whale, or ca'ing whale, is a frequent although irregular visitant to the British coasts, and occasionally extends its range so far north as Greenland. In the Mediterranean it appears to be rare.

The blackfish is the most gregarious of all cetaceans, assembling in herds which frequently comprise from two hundred to three hundred, and sometimes number as many as one thousand or even two thousand. The members of a herd blindly follow a leader, after the manner of a flock of sheep, and from this strange habit the species derives its names of pilot whale and ca'ing

BLACKFISH

(*i.e.*, driving) whale. Curiously enough, if the leader happen to run into shoal water and become stranded, the other members follow suit, and in this way large numbers are often captured by the inhabitants of Iceland and the Faroe, Orkney, and Shetland Islands. In disposition this species is mild and gentle. Its chief and favourite food is cuttle-fish, although it is also reported to eat fishes. The young, of which there is generally one at birth, are said to be born in late summer, and suckled through the winter.

RISSO'S DOLPHIN

Risso's dolphin (*Grampus griseus*) is a rare and rather large species, which appears to be the only representative of its genus, and is recognised by the peculiar streaked character of the skin, the stripes and colouring presenting much individual variation. It is distinguished from all other dolphins, except the female narwhal, by the absence of teeth in the upper jaw; while in the lower jaw there are only from three to seven small teeth on each side, and these confined to the anterior region of the jaw.

In external characteristics Risso's dolphin closely approaches the blackfish, but the front of the head is less completely globe-like, and the length of the flippers somewhat less. The mouth is obliquely placed, and the lower jaw shorter than the upper; while the back fin is high and pointed. The flukes are very narrow.

The colour is slaty grey, mottled, and very irregularly streaked. As a rule, the back, with its fin, and the flukes are dark grey or blackish, more or less tinged with purple, while the flippers are blackish, mottled with grey. The head and fore half of the body are light grey, of varying tint, and more or less tinged with yellow; the under parts are greyish white, and the whole body is marked with a number of irregular and unsymmetrically arranged light striæ.

In the young the colour is dark grey above and greyish white below, with the head yellowish white; the flukes being marked with five or more narrow and nearly vertical lines, placed at almost equal distances from one another. In length the animal measures about 13 feet when full grown.

Risso's dolphin appears to have an almost world-wide distribution, although not occurring in the Polar seas. It has been recorded from the North Atlantic and North Pacific, the North Sea, the Mediterranean, the Cape of Good Hope, and Japan, and several examples have been taken on the British coasts. Beyond the fact that its chief food consists of cuttle-fish, nothing definite appears to be known as to the habits of this species, but it is believed that the streaks on the body are caused by the hooks in the suckers of the cuttle-fishes which form its food; this explaining the irregular form and numerical variation of these markings.

SHORT-BEAKED DOLPHINS

Under the title of short-beaked dolphins may be included a group of several small species serving to connect the beakless forms with those possessing distinct beaks, and remarkable for their strongly contrasting colouring. They are generally characterised by the head having a short and not very well defined ploughshare - like beak, although in one species it is pointed and beakless. The fin and flippers are of moderate size; and the tail has very prominent ridges. The teeth are variable in size and number; the beak of the skull is flat, and not longer than the hinder part of the same, and the union between the two branches of the lower jaw is short. The colouring takes the form of two light-coloured areas of variable size on the sides, separated from one another by irregular, oblique dark bands. Representatives of this genus are found in most of the temperate and tropical seas, and two species have been taken off the British coasts.

DOLPHINS

THE WHITE-SIDED DOLPHIN

Of the two British species, the white-sided dolphin (*Lagenorhynchus acutus*) is blackish grey above and white beneath, with a broad band of yellowish brown between the two, in the middle of which is a large white patch; a narrow black band extends from the flukes nearly to the line of the back fin, and another runs from the base of the flipper to a point between the eye and the mouth, and the eye is surrounded by a black ring. The length varies from 6 to 8 feet. This species, which inhabits the North Atlantic and the North Sea, is not infrequently seen off the Orkneys, but is practically unknown farther south.

In the Pacific species (*L. crucigera*) of the short-beaked genus are presented marked contrasts of black and white. It has a short beak, only slightly marked off from the skull. In colour, the muzzle, the forehead, the back, and the fin, flippers, and flukes are black, while a broad black band runs from the eye and the base of the flipper along each side to the flukes; the other parts of the body being a more or less pure white.

THE WHITE-BEAKED DOLPHIN

Another species of this genus which has been met with on the British coasts is the white-beaked dolphin (*L. albirostris*), which resembles the white-sided dolphin in form, but has a more swollen head, a narrower and more sloping back fin, and longer flippers. It takes its distinctive name from the fact of the muzzle, including the extremities of both jaws, being white, more or less tinged with grey. The upper parts are black, the sides greyish, and the under parts white, frequently of a creamy hue, and there are three more or less distinctly defined whitish areas on the flanks, placed one behind the other, and more or less mottled with dark tints.

There is also a similar light area behind the blow-hole on the back, and another near the root of the flukes, but there seems to be considerable individual variation in regard to colouring. When freshly stranded specimens come under observation the black is often seen to be shot with a rich purplish tint, and the whole colour is then exceedingly beautiful. There are usually about twenty-six teeth on each side of the jaws, and the length attained by adults is from 8 to 9 feet. The white-beaked dolphin inhabits the North Atlantic, the North Sea, and the Baltic, ranging so far northwards as Greenland and Davis Strait. Several specimens have been captured in British waters.

DOLPHINS

The dolphin is the first representative of the second great group of the sub-family, which includes all the forms with distinct beaks, except the short - beaked dolphins just described. The beak is generally distinctly marked off from the forehead by a V-shaped groove, and, in the skull, considerably exceeds the brain cavity in length. In the skeleton the first two vertebræ of the neck are united, but the other five remain separate. All the members of the group are of comparatively small size, most of them not exceeding 10 feet in length. Dolphins associate in shoals, and feed mostly on fishes, although some also consume crustaceans and molluscs.

The true, or common, dolphin (*Delphinus delphis*), which apparently frequents all temperate and tropical seas, is the typical representative of its genus, which presents the following characteristics. The beak is long, and the back fin and flippers are elongated and falcate. In the skull the bony beak is long and narrow, and about twice the length of the region of the brain-case. The jaws are furnished with a numerous series of teeth, which vary from about forty to sixty-five on each side, and are sharply pointed, with their bases oval in section. The bony union between the two branches of the lower jaw is short.

The common dolphin has a slender body and small head, the beak being long and narrow, and the flippers about three times as long as broad, with their extremities pointed. There is considerable variation in colour, but usually the back is dark grey, the under parts are white or whitish, and the flanks marked by varying bands of grey or fulvous. The length is about $7\frac{1}{2}$ feet, and there are from forty-one to fifty teeth in the upper, and from forty-five to fifty-one in the lower jaw.

The species is occasionally met with around the coasts of Britain, but is much rarer off Scotland than in the south. The dolphin is said to utter a low murmuring sound. A single offspring is produced at birth, and is tended by the female with assiduous care. Formerly the flesh of the dolphin was eaten in England and other European countries.

There are several other species more or less allied to the common dolphin, although some of them are still imperfectly known. Such are Dussumier's dolphin (*D. dussumieri*), from the Malabar coast of India, and the Cape dolphin (*D. capensis*), from the Cape of Good Hope. The red-bellied dolphin (*D. roseiventris*), from the Moluccas and Torres Strait, is a small species not exceeding 4 feet in length, with forty-eight teeth on each side of the jaws, and a skull intermediate between that of the common dolphin and the next species.

The slender dolphin (*D. attenuatus*) may be taken as an example of a group of several species distinguished from the typical dolphin and its allies by the palate being nearly flat, instead of deeply hollowed on each side in its posterior portion, most of these being further distinguished by the skin being either spotted or marked with longitudinal bands. The slender dolphin is a spotted species from the Atlantic and the Cape of Good Hope, while the Malay dolphin (*D. malayanus*), from the Indian Ocean, which attains a length of 6¼ feet, is uniform ashy grey.

BOTTLE-NOSED DOLPHINS

The bottle-nosed dolphin, or, as it is often called, porpoise (*Tursiops tursio*), is the best known of several species constituting a genus distinct from *Delphinus*. The form of these dolphins is stout, with the beak shorter and more tapering than in the true dolphins, and the number of teeth considerably less—not exceeding from twenty-two to twenty-six on each side of the jaws.

The bottle-nosed dolphin, which attains a length of from 9½ feet to 12 feet, is usually purplish grey above, passing gradually into pure white on the under parts, but some specimens are black above and pale grey below, while others are grey all over.

This species appears to range over all temperate and tropical seas, and is occasionally met with on the British coasts.

As observed at Hatteras, in Carolina, these dolphins are abundant off the coast, and associate in schools of considerable size, fourteen having been secured at a single haul of the nets one morning, while in the afternoon of the same day no less than sixty-six were taken. In the spring the schools generally comprise a nearly equal number of each sex, and include animals of all ages ; but later in the season they are more uniform as regards sex and age, some herds consisting only of old males. It is believed that these dolphins migrate northwards in the spring, and southwards in the autumn, although a few remain at Hatteras throughout the year. The breeding season begins in the spring, but in the more northerly districts appears to be continued into the summer. The largest specimen caught at Hatteras measured 12 feet in length and yielded twenty-four gallons of oil, but the average product during the winter is only about eight gallons. Some idea of the number of these dolphins frequenting the Carolina seas may be gathered from the fact that between November 15, 1884, and the middle of the following May no fewer than 1,268 were caught at Hatteras.

Other species are *Trusiops catalania*, and *T. abusalam*, which have been taken in Indian waters and the Red Sea.

ROUGH-TOOTHED DOLPHIN

The rough-toothed dolphin (*Steno frontatus*), from the Indian and Atlantic oceans, is the typical representative of a genus comprising several more or less nearly allied species, mostly confined to the warmer seas. They are distinguished by the great length of the beak, which is distinctly marked off from the head and in the skull is narrow and compressed ; and also by the length of the bony union between the two branches of the lower jaw, which exceeds one-quarter the total length of the jaw. The teeth vary from twenty to twenty-five on each side of the jaws, and are of rather large size, with the crowns often marked by vertical groovings. The colour is variable in the different species.

The rough-toothed dolphin, which attains a length of 8½ feet, takes its name from its coarsely fluted teeth. The colour of the upper parts is purplish black, the sides being marked with rather large star-shaped spots, and of the snout and under parts white, tinged with purple and rose colour, and ornamented with purple spots. The grey dolphin (*S. plumbeus*) of the Indian Ocean has an extremely long beak, and is of a uniform leaden grey colour, with the exception of the extremity and under surface of the lower jaw, which are white. A third species from the Indian seas is the speckled dolphin (*S. lentiginosus*), which above is of a leaden grey colour, with numerous long, drop-shaped spots, most of which are pure white, but others slaty or black, while below it is white, more or less mottled with grey

THE ROUGH-TOOTHED DOLPHIN

LONG-BEAKED RIVER DOLPHINS

Under this title may be included several species closely allied to those of the preceding genus, but distinguished by their fluviatile or estuarine habits and the smaller number of joints in the backbone. Their teeth are always smooth, and the flippers very broad at the base.

Dolphins of this group are abundant in the upper portions of the Amazon, but there is considerable uncertainty whether these belong to one or to three species, or whether all or any of them are distinct from the Brazilian dolphin (*Sotalia brasiliensis*) of the Bay of Rio de Janeiro, nearly allied to which is the Cayenne dolphin (*S. guianensis*) of Guiana. In the Amazon there are several dolphins, one known as the tucuxi (*S. tucuxi*), a second as the pale river dolphin (*S. pallida*), and a third as *S. fluviatilis* ; these differing from one another chiefly in colour, the relative length of the fins, and the number of teeth. The pale dolphin has the upper parts and flukes yellowish white, and the under parts and flippers white.

Another representative of this group is the Chinese white dolphin (*S. sinensis*), from Quemoy Island, in the harbour of Amoy, and the Foochow and Canton rivers, characterised by its general milk-white colour, pinkish fins, and black eyes ; a second cream-coloured species being the Bornean dolphin (*S. borneënsis*). Perhaps the most interesting member of this group is the *Sotalia teuxi* from the estuaries and rivers of the Camerun district of Western Africa, which is reported to be of herbivorous habit. If this should be confirmed, this dolphin will differ not only from all the other members of the family to which it belongs, but from all other living cetaceans.

SQUALODONTS AND ZEUGLODONTS

IN addition to numerous extinct representatives of the existing cetacean families, to some of which reference has already been made, there are two extinct groups which cannot be included in either of the existing families, to the first of which the name of shark-toothed dolphins (*Squalodontidæ*) is applied, on account of the somewhat shark-like structure of their cheek teeth. In the characters of their skulls these cetaceans approximate to modern dolphins, from which they are distinguished by the teeth being of different characters in different parts of the jaws, as in ordinary mammals.

The squalodonts have a total of fifteen teeth on each side of both the upper and lower jaws; of which the first four are of simple structure, and correspond to the incisors and canines of other mammals; the next four, which are also comparatively simple, appear to represent the premolars; and the last seven have two roots, and laterally compressed triangular crowns, with sharp cutting edges, on which is a number of cusps arranged in a saw-like manner. The squalodonts, which are found in Miocene and Pliocene formations, both in the Old and New World, clearly form one step between modern cetaceans and ordinary mammals; and, so far as the structure of their teeth can be relied upon, appear to suggest a kinship between cetaceans and carnivores.

Very different from the above are the still earlier forms known as zeuglodonts (*Zeuglodontidæ*), which appear to be mainly or entirely confined to the Eocene Tertiary, and have been obtained from regions as far asunder as North America, Western Europe, the Caucasus, Egypt, Australia, and New Zealand. These primitive whales have long skulls, with an elongated muzzle, a broad forehead, the nasal opening placed about the middle of the length and roofed over by the nasal bones, and the brain case relatively small.

The bones of the internal ear and the position of the eye are essentially whale-like, as is also the lower jaw in the Upper Eocene species, which has a long alveolar canal, a long and loose union of its two halves in front, and a distinct coronoid process. The teeth, which are coated with enamel, are simply conical as far back as the canine or first premolar, and separated from one another by gaps up to the second premolar, but those farther back in the jaw are in contact, and have either two or three roots and compressed and strongly serrated triangular crowns. The normal dental formula is *i.* $\frac{3}{3}$, *c.* $\frac{1}{1}$, *p.m.* $\frac{4}{4}$, *m.* $\frac{3}{3}$, or the same as that of primitive carnivorous land mammals.

All seven vertebræ of the neck are free, and the first twelve rib-bearing vertebræ are very like those of land Carnivora, eleven of the fifteen ribs carrying two heads. The fore limb—especially the scapula, or shoulder blade—has a generally whale-like character, the bones of the upper arm and fore arm being distinctly flattened, and thus suggesting that the limb had the character of a flipper or paddle; but the articular surfaces of the limb bones are much better developed than in modern whales. No traces of hind limbs have hitherto been detected.

In association with the remains of these whale-like creatures have been discovered on more than one occasion solid bony plates, which appear to indicate that some zeuglodonts, at any rate, were furnished with a dermal armour on the back fin and some portions of the back somewhat resembled that of the South American glyptodont armadillos. Traces of a similar armour occur in an extinct Argentine dolphin, and tubercles found on the back fin of the common porpoise and on the back of the Indian porpoise may probably be regarded as the last remnants of this structure.

As a partial armour would be useless, it may be assumed that the ancestral cetaceans were fully protected by bony plates; but such a rigid panoply would be unsuitable to a pelagic type, such as *Zeuglodon* seems to have been, and it is accordingly presumed that the armour was restricted to part of the back. The presumption that the ancestral cetaceans were fully armoured must not, however, be taken to indicate that they were descended from mail-clad land animals. On the contrary, they themselves seem to have developed the armour, which may have been for the purpose of protecting them from the breakers and the attacks of sharks when they led an amphibious life on the coasts.

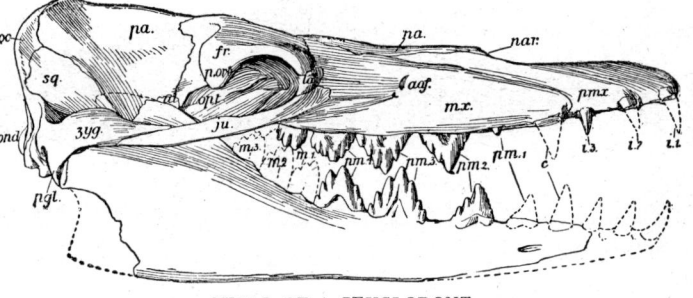

SKULL OF A ZEUGLODONT

The zeuglodonts of the Eocene of the Fayum district of Egypt, together with a species (*Protocetus atavus*) described by Professor E. Fraas from the limestones of the Mokattam Hills, near Cairo, form a series showing a complete transition, so far, at least, as the dentition is concerned, from the creodont Carnivora to the true zeuglodonts. In the earliest type, *Protocetus*, the skull is already practically that of a zeuglodont, the rostral portion, or beak, being, in fact, even more elongated than in some of the later forms, while the opening of the nostrils is situated nearer to the end of the snout. The teeth are most remarkable; the incisors are not known, but the rest of the dentition is practically that of a typical creodont, none of the teeth having assumed the peculiar serrated form characteristic of the later zeuglodonts. The canine is large, with a single though grooved root; the first premolar is much smaller, the second large and two-rooted, the third and fourth have posterior cusps and are supported by three roots, while the molars, which are small, are also three-rooted.

In *Prozeuglodon*, from the later Birket-el-Qurun series, the skull is likewise essentially of the zeuglodont type, although the external nostrils have shifted a little farther back. The canine is much larger than the teeth before and behind, and although the third and fourth premolars and the molars have serrated crowns, as in the later zeuglodonts, the premolars, at any rate, retain the inner buttress supported by a third root, so that in tooth structure this genus is intermediate between *Protocetus* and *Zeuglodon*.

Dr. Fraas has also described another annectant form, *Eocetus*, from about the same horizon, which attained a very large size; the skull approaching that of *Zeuglodon* in the position of the nostrils, and the teeth being of the creodont type and possessing inner, or third, roots.

CLASSIFICATION OF EDENTATA MENTIONED IN THIS WORK

ORDER IX. EDENTATA
GENERAL CHARACTERISTICS OF THE GROUP
By R. LYDEKKER

THE mammals which are now to be described include the sloths, ant-eaters, and armadillos of South America, together with two Old World families, and are collectively characterised by the total absence of front teeth, while in a few instances their jaws are entirely toothless. Strictly speaking, therefore, the title of the order, Edentata, applies only to such or its representatives as present the latter feature, but if the term be taken as indicating the absence of front teeth alone, it will be applicable to the whole assemblage, so far as existing forms are concerned.

In addition to this absence of front, or incisor, teeth, the edentates are characterised by the simple structure of their cheek teeth, which are composed solely of ivory and cement, without any trace of enamel ; and likewise by the fact that these teeth never form distinct roots, but grow continuously throughout life, and have their pulp cavities open inferiorly. Edentates usually also lack a functional series of milk teeth, although in certain cases these teeth are developed in a rudimentary condition, and in one instance actually cut the gums and come into use.

The foregoing are almost the only characters common to all edentates ; but these animals agree in being of a comparatively low degree of organisation, although many are specialised for particular modes of life. Their brains are relatively small, with the hemispheres, or anterior portion, frequently devoid of convolutions, and not extending backwards to overlap the hind portion, or cerebellum ; but in some cases the hemispheres are distinctly convoluted. Very frequently the shoulder blade, or scapula, is characterised by the great development of the anterior portion of its lower extremity ; this so-called coracoidal portion being sometimes marked off from the remainder of the bone by a perforation, and united with it by suture. Certain members of the order, such as armadillos and their extinct allies, are peculiar among mammals in possessing a bony cuirass in the skin, while the pangolins are equally remarkable for the coat of overlapping horny scales with which the entire body is invested.

From the absence of enamel on their teeth, and the presence of rudimentary milk teeth in some of their representatives, it is probable that edentates are somewhat degenerate types, descended from ancestors provided with a double set of enamel-coated teeth. It has, indeed, been suggested that the South American, or typical, edentates are descended from a group of curious lower Eocene North American mammals known as ganodonts (*Ganodontia*), which had a full series of enamel-coated teeth, and were probably not far removed from the ancestral stock of more ordinary mammals. *Psittacotherium*, *Calamodon*, and *Stylinodon* are the names of three well-known genera of this group.

The sloths, ant-eaters, and armadillos are entirely confined to the southern portion of the New World, and since it is these alone that form the typical edentates, the order is essentially American. Indeed, there is a considerable degree of doubt whether the Old World pangolins and ant-bears, which form its other representatives, are rightly included within the order ; their organisation being very different from that of the typical forms. They are placed in the order largely because they cannot satisfactorily be located elsewhere. The typical edentates have been always confined to the New World, in the southern half of which they attained their greatest development, the supposed fossil armadillos of France being probably based on the remains of reptiles. Some of the American extinct types are of the greatest importance to the naturalist, since they serve to connect most intimately such widely different forms as the sloths and the ant-eaters.

Although varying greatly in their mode of life, the whole of the edentates—both living and extinct—are either arboreal or terrestrial, none being modified either for flight in the air or for swimming in the water. While the purely arboreal sloths are entirely vegetable feeders, all the other members of the order, of which a few are also more or less arboreal in their habits, subsist on flesh or insects. Several of these carnivorous types are burrowers, and it is remarkable that the members of three distinct groups—namely, ant-eaters, pangolins, and ant-bears—subsist mainly, or exclusively, on white ants or termites ; the only other purely ant-eating mammals belonging respectively to the pouched and the egg-laying groups.

It is further noteworthy that while among the ant-eating edentates the true ant-eaters and the pangolins have entirely lost their teeth, those organs are retained in a comparatively high state of development in the ant-bear. At the present day the edentates are a waning group, the whole of the larger members of the order having died out, while those which remain have sought protection by the acquisition of either arboreal or burrowing habits, or by the development of a protective coat of mail to their bodies.

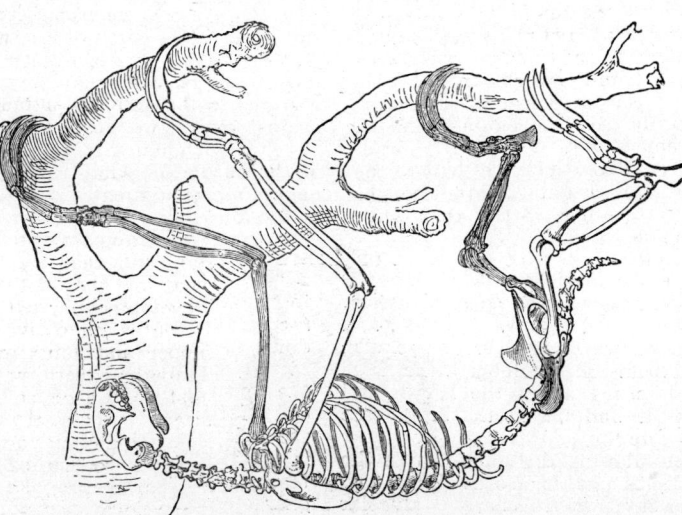

SKELETON OF THREE-TOED SLOTH

CLASSIFICATION OF EDENTATA MENTIONED IN THIS WORK

ORDER IX.
Edentates—Edentata

FAMILY 1
Sloths—Bradypodidæ
GENUS 1
Three-toed Sloths—Bradypus
SPECIES
Aï .... Bradypus tridactylus
.... B. infuscatus
GENUS 2
Two-toed Sloths—Cholœpus
SPECIES
Unau.................. Cholœpus didactylus
Hoffmann's sloth .... C. hoffmanni
EXTINCT GROUND SLOTHS
Megalotherium   Scelidotherium
Mylodon   Megalonyx
Glossotherium   Eucholœops

FAMILY 2
Ant-eaters—Myrmecophagidæ
GENUS 1
Great Ant-eaters—Myrmecophaga
SPECIES
Great ant-eater .... Myrmecophaga jubata
Central American ant-eater ...... M. centralis
GENUS 2
Lesser Ant-eater—Tamandua
SPECIES
Tamandua .... Tamandua tetradactyla

GENUS 3
Two-toed Ant-eater—Cycloturus [Cyclopes]
SPECIES
Pigmy ant-eater .... Cycloturus didactylus

FAMILY 3
Armadillos—Dasypodidæ
GENUS 1
Fairy Armadillos—Chlamydophorus
SPECIES
Pichiciago .... Chlamydophorus truncatus
Bolivian pichiciago .... C. retusus
GENUS 2
Six-banded Armadillos—Dasypus
SPECIES
Weasel-headed armadillo ..Dasypus sexcinctus
Hairy armadillo .... D. villosus
Fleecy armadillo .... D. vellerosus
Pigmy armadillo .... D. minutus
GENUS 3
Broad-banded Armadillos—Lysiurus
SPECIES
Tatouay .... Lysiurus unicinctus
GENUS 4
Great Armadillo—Priodon
SPECIES
Great armadillo .... Priodon gigas
GENUS 5
Three-banded Armadillos—Tolypeutes
SPECIES
Apar .... Tolypeutes tricinctus

GENUS 6
Peba Armadillos—Tatusia
SPECIES
Peba armadillo .... Tatusia novemcincta
Mulita .... T. hybrida
Shaggy armadillo .... T. pilosa
EXTINCT GIANT ARMADILLOS
Chlamydotherium   Hoplophorus [Lomaphorus]
Glyptodon   Dædicurus
Glyptotherium

FAMILY 4
Pangolins—Manidæ
GENUS
Pangolins—Manis
SPECIES
Indian pangolin .... Manis pentadactyla
Chinese pangolin .... M. aurita
Malay pangolin .... M. javanica
Long-tailed pangolin .... M. macrura
White-bellied pangolin .... M. tricuspis
Short-tailed pangolin .... M. temmincki
Giant pangolin .... M. gigantea

FAMILY 5
Ant-bears—Orycteropodidæ
GENUS
Ant-bears—Orycteropus
SPECIES
Ant-bear, or aard-vark ...... Orycteropus afer

SLOTHS

ALTHOUGH by older naturalists sloths (family *Brady-podidæ*) were regarded as ill-formed creatures destined to lead a miserable life on account of their misshapen limbs, no animals are in reality better adapted to their peculiar mode of existence; this being displayed not only in their elongated limbs, which are modified into hook-like organs of suspension, with the removal of all superfluous digits and the great development of the claws of those which remain, but also in the extraordinary resemblance of their coarse coat of hair to the shaggy lichens clothing the gnarled and knotted boughs of their native forests. It is noteworthy that while the monkeys of the same regions have mostly acquired a fifth limb by a development of the prehensile power in their tails, sloths have almost dispensed with tails altogether.

Sloths are characterised externally by their short and rounded heads, in which the ears are very small and buried among the fur, their rudimentary tails, and the excessive elongation of their fore limbs, of which the length far surpasses that of the hind pair. Both pairs of limbs are furnished with long and slender feet, in which there are never more than three toes, and the toes themselves are invested for nearly their whole length in a common skin, and terminate in long, curved claws of great strength.

The thick coat of long, coarse, and some-what brittle hair with which the whole of the body and limbs is invested is generally of a brownish or dull ashy grey colour, mingled with a greenish tint; each individual hair having a fluted or roughened external surface. The most remarkable feature connected with the coats, however, is the growth of a vegetable—a kind of alga—in the hairs themselves, the alga growing in the cracks or flutings of the coarse outer layer of the hair, and flourishing luxuriantly in the moist atmosphere of the South American forests, although quickly withering when the animals are brought to Europe. It is this extraneous vegetable growth which communicates the greenish tinge to the hair during life; and its object is doubtless to render the colouring of these creatures in still closer harmony

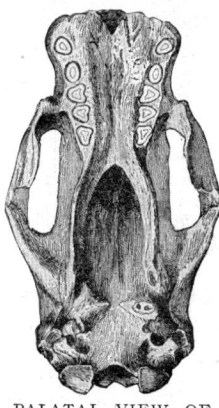

PALATAL VIEW OF
SKULL OF MYLODON

with their inanimate surroundings than would otherwise have been possible.

In the region of the back between the shoulders many sloths exhibit a patch of fine woolly under fur marked by longitudinal stripes of rich brown and orange, and it was long believed that the exposure of such patches was due to the animals rubbing or resting their backs against trees, and thus wearing away the outer coat; but it is much more probable that these patches partake of the nature of glands. The colour of this patch of under fur approximates to that obtaining in the coat of the ant-eaters, from which it may be inferred that both groups originally had bright-coloured fur, and that the long external dull-hued coat of the sloths has been a special development suited to their environment.

Sloths have five pairs of teeth in the upper and four in the lower jaw; the individual teeth, with the exception of the first pair in one of the two genera, being nearly cylindrical in form, and in all cases consisting of a core of ivory invested with a thick coating of cement. The skeleton is characterised by the presence of complete collar bones and the freedom of the two bones of the fore arm, which allows the hand to be supinated like that of man. The claws, however, are permanently fixed parallel to one another, so that the hand, like the foot, can be used merely as a claw. In the hind limb the foot is articulated obliquely to the bones of the leg, so that when on the ground the animal can walk only on the outer sides of its feet.

Of the soft parts, it will suffice to mention that the tongue is short and soft, while the large stomach, as in so many leaf-eaters and grass-feeders, is divided into several compartments. The windpipe is peculiar in being folded before reaching the lungs—a feature found elsewhere only in certain birds. The females have a single pair of teats on the breast.

AÏS OR THREE-TOED SLOTHS

The typical member of the family, commonly known as the three-toed sloth, or, from its native title, aï

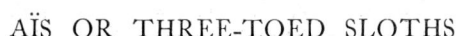

(*Bradypus tridactylus*), is characterised by the presence of three toes on both fore and hind feet. The teeth are all of nearly the same height, with their grinding surfaces deeply cupped ; the first tooth in the upper jaw being considerably smaller than any of the others, while the corresponding lower tooth is broad and compressed. The most remarkable peculiarity connected with the genus, however, is the presence of nine, instead of the usual seven, vertebræ in the neck—that is to say, it is the tenth vertebra from the head which first carries ribs articulating with the breastbone, although the ninth, and occasionally the eighth, vertebra is furnished with a pair of free floating ribs, which stop short of the breastbone.

There are several species of these sloths characterised by differences in colour, or the relative length of the hair on the face ; the colour being in some cases uniform, while in others there is a dark stripe across the shoulders. The aï inhabits the drier regions of the forests, while others frequent the permanently flooded districts.

Writing of the habits of the common three-toed sloth, Mr. H. W. Bates observes that the Indians call it aï ybyreté, or "sloth of the mainland," to distinguish it from *B. infuscatus*, which has a long black and tawny stripe between the shoulders, and is called aï ygapo, or "sloth of the flooded lands." Some travellers in South America have described the sloth as very nimble in its native woods, and have disputed the justness of the name which has been bestowed upon it. "The inhabitants of the Amazon regions, however, both Indians and descendants of the Portuguese, hold to the common opinion, and consider the sloth as the type of laziness. It is a strange sight to watch the uncouth creature, fit production of these silent shades, lazily moving from branch to branch. Every movement betrays, not indolence exactly, but extreme caution. He never loosens his hold from one branch without first securing himself to the next, and when he does not find a bough to grasp immediately with the rigid hooks into which his paws are so curiously transformed, he raises his body, supported on his hind legs, and claws around in search of a fresh foothold."

Sloths are mainly nocturnal, and, when moving or feeding, hang suspended back-downwards. When sleeping, they roll themselves into a ball, with the head tucked between the arms ; in this position they somewhat resemble the pottos among the lemurs (page 292), and it is then that they present the most striking resemblance to lichen-clad knots. They are found usually either in pairs or in small family parties, and are harmless and inoffensive in disposition. Their diet consists exclusively of leaves, young shoots, and fruits, the moisture contained in which renders

THREE-TOED SLOTHS

drinking unnecessary. Their favourite food is afforded by the large-leaved and milky cecropia trees.

In Darien and Venezuela, at any rate, sloths, according to Mr. Geay, confine themselves almost exclusively to the cecropia trees, and more especially to the species known to botanists as *Cecropia peltata*. These trees seldom exceed from about 16 feet to 22 feet in height, and their trunks are slender and carry only a few branches, of which the terminal twigs are sparsely clothed with leaves. They grow only in open valleys, where their tops stand clear of the low brushwood. In such trees are to be found the sloths, which generally take up their position in a fork, either for the purpose of basking in the sun or to enjoy their day's sleep.

They always sit with the head bent forwards on the breast, and the arms grasping the trunk of the tree so as to maintain the body in a nearly upright posture ; this statement being in accord with that of an early observer, Mr. Seitz ; and it is also maintained that sloths never hang back-downwards by their hook-like claws except when moving or feeding. If they ever sleep in this posture, it is only, as when in confinement, for lack of other accommodation, and the statement that they pass most of their time in the reversed hanging position is asserted to be an error.

Sloths ascend cecropia trunks with facility and comparative rapidity by clasping them with their arms. When they have stripped a tree of its foliage, they descend and make their way along the ground till they come to the foot of another. When travelling on the ground, they lean on one arm, and stretch the other forwards to its full extent until the claws get a grip of some hollow or object which will serve as a point of fixation, and then drag their bodies forwards. Confirmation of this is given by a French engineer, who has on several occasions come across sloths on the move. In a single night of seven or eight hours' duration a sloth was ascertained to have travelled over 500 yards in this manner.

The sense of hearing in these animals seems imperfectly developed ; and their small, dull, and reddish eyes do not appear capable of very acute vision. Indeed, on first observing a sloth its eyes look so devoid of brightness as to give the impression that it must be blind. A single young is produced at a birth, which, when it first comes into the world, is fully developed, having the body thickly clothed with hair, and the claws on the toes of the same proportionate length as in the adult. With these claws it clings fast to the long hair of its mother, clasping its arms round her neck.

Sloths are capable of enduring deprivation from food for protracted periods, and are also remarkable for the severe bodily injuries they are capable of sustaining, while they appear to be unaffected by doses of poison that would immediately prove fatal to other animals of larger size. On one occasion a three-toed sloth kept in captivity at Turin took no food for upwards of a month, and seemed none the worse at the end of its long fast. All these circumstances clearly point to the low organisation of these animals ; reptiles exhibiting a far greater tenacity of life than the higher mammals. Indeed, as a rule, the lower we descend in the animal kingdom, the greater becomes the power of sustaining injury.

UNAUS, OR TWO-TOED SLOTHS

The two-toed sloths, or unaus (genus, *Cholœpus*), of which there are at least two species, are characterised by having only two functional toes on the fore foot ; these two digits representing the index and middle finger of the human hand. The hind foot, however, has three toes, as in *Bradypus*. Unaus are further distinguished by their teeth, the first pair in each jaw being longer and stouter than the others, from which they are separated by a considerable interval. These anterior teeth assume, indeed, the characters of tusks, and have their summits obliquely worn away by mutual attrition. That they do not correspond to the true tusks, or canines, of other mammals, however, is shown by the fact that the lower ones bite behind, instead of in front of, those of the upper jaw (page 396).

In the common unau (*C. didactylus*) the number of vertebræ in the neck is the usual seven, but in Hoffmann's sloth (*C. hoffmanni*) it is reduced to six. Of these two species the former is restricted to Brazil, while the latter extends from Ecuador to Costa Rica. Hoffmann's sloth utters at rare intervals a cry like the bleating of a sheep, while when suddenly seized it gives vent to a loud snort. Generally speaking, the habits of unaus seem to be similar to those of aïs ; but it is remarkable that the alga growing in their hairs is quite distinct from the one found in the latter.

THE UNAU

EXTINCT GROUND SLOTHS

No account of the edentates would be complete without reference to the gigantic ground sloths (*Megalotheriidæ*), formerly so abundant in South America, as it is by their aid alone that we are able to comprehend the relationship of the true sloths to the ant-eaters (page 22). The largest of these creatures is the megalothere (*Megalotherium*), which rivalled the elephant in bulk ; while the mylodons (*Mylodon* and *Glossotherium*) and scelidotheres (*Scelidotherium*) are somewhat smaller forms. They may be described as possessing the skulls and teeth of sloths, and the backbones, limbs, and tails of ant-eaters.

The megalothere differs from most of the others in having the crowns of the teeth square and divided into wedge-shaped transverse ridges, owing to the variation in the hardness of their constituents, but in most cases the teeth are subcylindrical, with depressed centres. Ground sloths agree with sloths in having large and complete collar bones ; but, as may be inferred from the conformation of the lower jaw, approximate to ant-eaters in the elongation of their tongues. The majority of the ground sloths were South American ; but some species of mylodon ranged into North America, and the allied genus *Megalonyx* was exclusively North American.

Special interest attaches to one species of ground sloth (*Glossotherium darwini*) on account of the occurrence of portions of its skin in a cave at Ultima Esperanza, Southern Patagonia. Externally, the thick hide is covered with long, coarse, shaggy hair, of very similar character to that of modern sloths ; but its inner surface is studded with a number of small, smooth nodules of bone. Very similar nodules have been found in association with the bones of *Mylodon*, but as these are sculptured on one side, it has been suggested that they were external. The skin and bones of the Patagonian ground sloth were found buried in coarse chaff, the bones showing signs of having been cut by some sharp implement, while the chaff was evidently man's handiwork.

From these facts it has been inferred that this ground sloth inhabited the cave contemporaneously with aboriginal man, by whom it appears to have been kept in a semi-domesticated state. These aborigines seem to have been identical with the ancient Patagonians. *Glossotherium*, or *Grypotherium*, appears to have been a stouter-built animal than *Mylodon*, with the orbital region of the skull smaller ; while it was further distinguished by the presence of a bony bridge connecting the nasal bones with the tip of the upper jaw. *Scelidotherium* has a longer and more slender type of skull than that of either *Mylodon* or *Glossotherium*.

That the ground sloths were herbivorous is evident from the structure of their teeth ; while it is obvious that creatures which must have weighed several tons when in the flesh could not have been climbers. From the enormous width and massiveness of the pelvis of the ground sloths, coupled with the extraordinary size of the bones of the tail, it is probable that these animals were in the habit of procuring their food by supporting themselves on the tripod formed by the hind limbs and tail, and rearing their bodies against the trunks of trees, from which the boughs were then dragged down by the powerful arms. Possibly, however, the megalothere may in some cases have bodily uprooted trees, by first digging a hole at their roots with its powerful front claws, and then grasping the trunk with its arms and swaying it to and fro till it fell with a crash.

It may be added that ground sloths resembled ant-eaters and sloths in walking on the outer sides of their enormous fore feet, but differed from the latter in also applying only the outer side of the hind feet to the ground. All these gigantic forms lived during the Pleistocene and later epochs, but in the lower Tertiaries of Patagonia they are represented by the much smaller *Eucholœops*, in which the skull was only some 5 inches in length, and was furnished with teeth recalling those of the megalothere.

ANT-EATERS

Ant-eaters (family, *Myrmecophagidæ*) differ so widely in appearance and structure from sloths that it is difficult to believe at first sight in their close relationship; indeed, had it not been for the fortunate preservation of the remains of the ground sloths, it may be questioned whether naturalists would have fully understood the alliance of the two. As it is, we have an excellent example of the effects of adaptation to widely different modes of life in modifying the organisation of nearly allied animals. In the present instance the extinct ground sloths are probably the least removed from the original common type.

In the sloths the needs of a purely arboreal life have led to a great elongation of the fore limbs, coupled with the reduction of the digits to a few hook-like claws, and the functional loss of the tail. In the other group, the ant-eating habit has led to an extraordinary elongation of the skull, with the loss of all traces of teeth.

Ant-eaters are characterised by the body being clothed with hair, and the more or less marked elongation of the head, in which the mouth is tubular, and provided with a long worm-like tongue, while teeth are wanting. The mouth has only a small aperture at its extremity, through which, when feeding, the long extensile tongue, coated with viscid saliva, is rapidly protruded and as instantaneously withdrawn. The tail is always long, and in two species is prehensile. In the fore feet the middle toe is enlarged and furnished with an enormous curved claw, while the other digits are reduced in size, and some of them may be rudimentary. The hind limbs are as long as the front pair, and their feet terminate in four or five equal-sized, clawed toes.

In the skeleton the collar bones are generally rudimentary, although in one genus well-developed, and the ribs are remarkable for their breadth. In the soft parts the stomach is comparatively simple, and the brain more convoluted than in sloths. The heart is very small. As their name implies, ant-eaters are purely insectivorous.

GREAT ANT-EATERS

The great, or maned, ant-eater (*Myrmecophaga jubata*) is one of the two largest members of the family, and externally is characterised by the extreme elongation of its narrow head and the enormous mass of long hair clothing the tail (page 937). The anterior portion of the head forms a kind of cylindrical beak, which is of far greater length than the hind half, and carries the small nostrils at its tip. The eyes are minute, and the oval ears small and erect. The body is somewhat compressed laterally, and about equal in length to the tail, which is not prehensile. In the fore feet claws are present on all the toes except the fifth, that of the third being far larger than any of the others. When walking, the toes are bent back, and the weight of the body is supported on the upper surfaces of the third and fourth, aided by a hard pad at the extremity of the fifth. The hind feet, in which the toes are of nearly equal length, are comparatively short, and their soles are applied to the ground in walking.

The hair is stiff and bristly, although short on the head, and is of considerable though varying length on the body. On the neck and back it forms an upright mane, while on the fore limbs and flanks it becomes still more elongated and pendent. but attains its maximum development on the tail. where it may measure as much as 16 inches in length. The colour of the hair over a large part of the body is ashy grey mingled with black, this tint prevailing on the head, neck, back, flanks and hind quarters, fore legs, and tail. The throat, chest, under parts. hind feet, and under surface of the tail are blackish brown, and a broad black band, margined with white, extends obliquely upwards and backwards to terminate in a point on the loins. The length of the head and body is about 4 feet, the height at the shoulder being about 2 feet

In Central America the great ant-eater is represented by a second species (*M. centralis*), distinguished by skull characters from its southern representative. In the skull of the Brazilian ant-eater the frontal bones have a long point in the middle line projecting some distance between the two nasal bones, and thus being far in advance of the lateral portions of the former. In the Central American ant-eater, on the other hand, the frontals give off one median and two lateral processes of nearly equal length, the former of which only projects a short distance between the nasals.

The difference between the two skulls may be concisely defined by the statement that whereas in the Brazilian ant-eater the frontals penetrate the nasals by a long median process, in the Costa Rica species

GREAT ANT-EATER

the nasals send a couple of short processes into the frontals. Other differences of minor importance also occur between the skulls of the two forms. Whether any external differences distinguish the Central American from the Mexican ant-eater remains for future investigation.

In addition to the above-mentioned external features, there are certain points in the internal anatomy of these ant-eaters which demand attention. In the first place, the exceedingly elongated skull is characterised by the zygomatic, or cheek, arch being incomplete, and also by the fact that the passage above the bony palate, through which the animals breathe, instead of stopping short near the middle of the skull, is prolonged nearly to the hind extremity. This is brought about by the union in the middle line of descending plates from the bones known as pterygoids, this feature occurring elsewhere among mammals only in certain dolphins and one genus of armadillo. In consequence of this arrangement, the posterior, or inner, nostrils

GREAT ANT-EATER, WITH TAIL ELEVATED

of the great ant-eater open at the back of the skull instead of near its middle.

Another peculiarity of the skull is the absence of any postorbital process defining the hind border of the socket of the eye, which is consequently continuous with the temporal fossa, or large open space at the side of the hind portion of the skull. Then, again, the lower jaw is very long and slender, with an extremely short union in front between its two lateral branches, and without the process which usually ascends behind the socket of the eye for the attachment of the muscles of mastication. As in sloths, the females of the great ant-eater have only a single pair of teats on the breast.

Although distributed over the whole of the tropical portions of South and Central America, great ant-eaters are nowhere common, and from their nocturnal habits seldom seen. They frequent either the low, wet lands bordering the rivers, or swampy forests, and are strictly terrestrial in habits. The strong claws might lead to the supposition that these animals are burrowers, but this is not the case. They have, however, usually, regular lairs, or at least habitual places of resort, generally situated among tall grass, where they spend the day in slumber, lying on one side, with the head buried in the long fur of the chest, the legs folded together, and the huge tail curled round the exposed side of the body.

Except in the case of females with young, the ant-eater is, as a rule, a solitary creature. Its pace is a kind of trot, but when pursued it breaks into an awkward, shuffling, slow gallop. Its food consists exclusively of termites and ants, together with their larvæ; and in order to obtain these insects, ant-eaters tear open their nests or hillocks with the powerful claws of their fore feet. The ants or termites rush to the surface to investigate the cause of the disturbance, and are forthwith swept up in hundreds by the ant-eater's viscid tongue, which is protruded and withdrawn with lightning-like rapidity.

The breeding habits of ant-eaters are imperfectly known. A single young, however, produced by the female in spring, is carried about on the back of its parent for a considerable time. The period of suckling lasts for several months, and even when the young ant-eater has taken to feeding on insects, it does not leave its parent until she is again pregnant.

Usually the ant-eater is a harmless, inoffensive creature, which may be driven in almost any direction so long as it is not pressed too hard. If, however, driven to close quarters, it turns furiously on its assailant, which it attacks by hugging with its immensely muscular arms.

Natives assert that the ant-eater will face and attack the jaguar, and although the truth of this statement was denied by the traveller Azara, a later explorer believes it may be founded on fact. Like sloths, ant-eaters are exceedingly difficult to kill, their skin being so tough that an ordinary small hunting knife will make no impression, while their skulls may be battered with a heavy stone without producing any other effect than temporarily stunning the creatures.

These ant-eaters thrive fairly well in captivity in Europe, but spend most of their time in sleep, with the head, limbs, and tail folded up in the manner already mentioned. On awakening, they unfold themselves with considerable deliberation, sitting up at first on their hind quarters, with the legs stretched out rigidly in front, and the bird-like head swaying slowly from side to side. When walking in their usually slow and measured manner, the tail is stretched out in a straight line with the back, and the animal then presents a length of between 6 and 7 feet, of which the head occupies 1 foot, and the tail 3 feet. The small mouth and face are cleaned from any viscid saliva that may have adhered to them by being rubbed from time to time against the slightly bent knee. The flesh of the great ant-eater, although black in colour, and musky in odour, is eaten by the natives and negroes of South America.

TAMANDUA, OR LESSER ANT-EATER

The lesser ant-eater, or tamandua (*Tamandua tetradactyla*), is an animal of scarcely half the size of the great ant-eater, from which it is distinguished by its much shorter head, longer ears, uniformly short, bristly hair, and the prehensile tail, of which the extremity, together with the whole length of the inferior surface, is naked and scaly. The three middle toes of the fore foot have well-developed claws, of which the third is much larger than any of the others; while the first toe has only a minute claw, and the fifth is clawless, and concealed within the skin. The hind foot is very similar to that of the great ant-eater, and has five sub-equal clawed toes. The structure of the skull is essentially the same, and the collar bones are also rudimentary. The whole length of the head and body is about 2 feet, and that of the tail 6 inches less. As regards colour, there is a great amount of individual or racial variation. The hue of the fur, however, is yellowish white, with a more or less marked rusty tinge, but a broad black band extends from the sides of the neck, along the flanks, and becomes so deep on the hind quarters as to appear the predominating colour. The tip of the snout, together with the lips, eyelids, and the soles of the feet, are naked and black; and the ears are sparsely haired.

The tamandua—which is the Portuguese term for the animal, the native name being caguari—ranges through the tropical forests of South and Central America, and is mainly arboreal, its climbing powers being largely aided by the prehensile tail. Generally nocturnal, it may sometimes be seen abroad during the day. Its movements are more rapid than those of the great ant-eater; and when asleep it lies on its belly, with the head bent under the chest and covered with the fore feet, and the tail curled along the side.

The food of the tamandua apparently consists mainly of ants and termites, but it has been suggested that honey may also form a portion of its diet. It produces only a single young one. It is a commoner animal than the great ant-eater, and said to be generally found on the borders of the forests. Frequently it ascends to the top of the tallest trees. When pursued, it endeavours to escape by flight; but if hard pressed it turns on men or dogs in the same manner as its larger cousin, sitting up on its hind quarters, and trying to hug its foes in its arms.

PIGMY, OR TWO-TOED, ANT-EATER

The third generic representative of the family, the pigmy, or two-toed, ant-eater (*Cycloturus*, or *Cyclopes, didactylus*), is no larger than a rat. The skull is but slightly elongated; and the length of the head and body

somewhat after the fashion of the foot of a sloth. The fur is soft, thick, and silky, generally foxy red above and grey beneath, with the individual hairs greyish brown or black at the base, and yellowish brown at the tips.

The skull of this edentate differs from that of other ant-eaters in its shorter muzzle and the absence of the backward prolongation of the nasal passage on the palate. The lower jaw is less widely removed

TWO-TOED ANT-EATER

from the ordinary type. Another peculiarity in the skeleton is the presence of well-developed collar bones; and the ribs are so extraordinarily wide as to come nearly in contact with one another, and thus render the bony casing of the chest well-nigh continuous.

The two-toed ant-eater is exclusively arboreal, and has a somewhat restricted geographical range, inhabiting Northern Brazil, Guiana, and Peru, between 10° S. and 6° N., and also extending into Central America; its range thus includes the very hottest portions of the continent. In the mountains it ascends to an elevation of some two thousand feet above the sea. It is a rare creature, seldom seen even by the natives, and frequents the thickest portions of the forests, escaping observation through its arboreal habits and diminutive size. Like its larger relatives, it leads, except during the pairing season, a solitary existence, and is also nocturnal, sleeping during the day among the boughs. Its movements are slow and deliberate; but when so disposed it can climb quickly, always with the aid of the tail. Ants, termites, bees, wasps, and their larvæ are its food. When it has captured a large insect, it sits up on its haunches like a squirrel, and conveys the prey to its mouth with its paws.

Mr. Bates had one of these ant-eaters brought to him, which had been captured while slumbering in a hollow tree. He kept it for twenty-four hours in the house, where " it remained nearly all the time without motion, except when irritated, in which case it reared itself on its hind legs from the back of a chair to which it clung, and clawed out with its fore paws like a cat. Its manner of clinging with its claws, and the sluggishness of its motions, gave it a great resemblance to a sloth. It uttered no sound, and remained all night on the spot where I had placed it in the morning. The next day I put it on a tree in the open air, and at night it escaped."

THE TAMANDUA

is only 6 inches, and that of the highly prehensile tail a little over 7 inches. The fore feet have four toes, of which those corresponding to the index and third fingers of man alone have claws; the claw of the third toe being very much larger than that of the other. In the hind feet there are four nearly equal-sized toes, placed close together so as to form a hook-like organ

ARMADILLOS

THE armadillos, together with their near ally the pichiciago, constitute a well-defined South American family (*Dasypodidæ*), distinguished from other living mammals by the development of a number of bony plates in the skin, so as to form a more or less complete shield enveloping the body, from the presence of which armour the members of the family derive their Spanish title of armadillos. In general the bony shield of the back is formed by the union of quadrangular or many-sided plates, and is divided into an anterior and posterior solid portion, separated by a series of movable transverse bands, varying in number from three, or occasionally two, to thirteen. The anterior shield, into which the head and fore limbs may be more or less completely withdrawn, is termed the scapular shield; while the posterior portion, which is notched for the tail, is known as the lumbar, or pelvic, shield. The movable bands are composed of parallel rows of similar plates connected by flexible skin; and in some cases the degree of flexibility in this region is so great as to allow of the animal rolling itself into a complete ball.

One peculiar genus of extinct armadillo differs from all living forms in that the whole body-shield was composed of these movable plates. Usually a certain number of hairs protrudes between the bony plates of the armour, and in some cases these are so numerous as almost to conceal the armour, and give the appearance of a furry animal. Each bony plate is sculptured, varying in pattern in the different genera, and is overlain by a horny shield, developed in the cuticle, or epidermis, the bones themselves belonging to the true skin. The upper surface of the head is also protected by an armour of similar structure, and the tail is usually encircled by a series of bony rings. The limbs are likewise protected externally by a number of bony plates embedded in the skin, which do not, however, articulate together by their edges.

The fore feet are provided with very powerful curved claws adapted for digging, and varying in number from five to three; but in the hind feet the claws are of smaller size, and invariably five in number. The numerous teeth are small and simple, looking like small pegs fixed in the jaws, and in one genus the anterior teeth are preceded by a deciduous milk series. The tongue is considerably elongated, although to a less extent than in ant-eaters.

The elongated skull is characterised by the full development of the zygomatic, or cheek, arch, and the collar bones are complete. In the hind limbs, the bones of the second segment—tibia and fibula—differ from those of the other existing members of the order by being united at their lower extremities. Another peculiarity is that a variable number of the vertebræ in the middle of the neck are also immovably welded together. In the development of additional facets for mutual articulation, the vertebræ of the loins of armadillos resemble those of ant-eaters. The ribs are of considerable width, and the upper lateral processes of the back are specially developed for the support of the carapace.

Most of the species are of comparatively small size, the largest living one not exceeding three feet in length, exclusive of the tail; but in the Pleistocene of Argentina there occurs the gigantic *Dasypus retusus*, with a skull about a foot in length. In the Argentine

pampas the armadillos are as a rule diurnal, but in other districts many appear to be crepuscular or nocturnal. The majority are mainly or exclusively insectivorous, but one species consumes not only flesh, but vegetable substances.

In disposition armadillos are mostly harmless and inoffensive—a Gaucho, as he sharpened his knife on the back of one, remarking to Mr. Darwin, "They are so quiet (*Son tan mansos*)." All burrow in the ground, and so rapid is the act of burrowing that, as I have witnessed, if a horseman sees one of these animals, it is almost necessary for him to tumble off his horse in order to capture it before it disappears in the soft soil of the pampas. They run with considerable speed, some of the species merely touching the ground with the tips of their claws, and carrying the body elevated high on the limbs. They are found both on the open pampas and in the forests; and, with the exception of one or two species which range so far north as Texas, are restricted to the warmer parts of South and Central America. Their burrows are frequently found in the neighbourhood of the mounds erected by ants and termites; and although most of the species wander afield in search of food, a few lead an almost exclusively subterranean and mole-like life.

Except in the pairing season, armadillos are solitary creatures, and nearly always prefer flat, open country for their habitations. Although found in dry districts, they are said to be able to swim well and swiftly. In spite of the nature of their food, which, in addition to ants and other insects, includes snails and worms, the flesh of most armadillos is free from unpleasant flavour.

With the exception of the aforesaid species ranging into Texas and the adjacent States, armadillos, both recent and fossil, were long supposed to be confined to

PICHICIAGOS

South and Central America, inclusive of Mexico; but skeletons of extinct members of the group have been found in the lower Tertiary, or Eocene, formations of the United States. In place of the bony armour characteristic of the existing and later Tertiary members of the group, these primitive armadillos appear to have had their backs protected merely by a shield of hard, leathery skin. The discovery profoundly modifies current views as to the origin of the South American fauna, indicating that armadillos, at any rate, were immigrants into the southern half of the New World from the north; and this, again, seems to imply a temporary connection between North and South

America during the early part of the Tertiary period, during which the ancestors of the ungulates of South America also entered the country.

PICHICIAGO OR FAIRY ARMADILLO

One of the two smallest representatives of the whole group is the tiny creature known as the pichiciago, or pink fairy armadillo (*Chlamydophorus truncatus*), which differs so remarkably from the true armadillos as to constitute, with its ally, a sub-family. It was discovered by the American naturalist Harlan, at Mendoza in 1824, much to the astonishment of the

SIX-BANDED ARMADILLO

natives, who had no knowledge of its existence. For many years it was known only by two examples—one preserved in London and the other at Philadelphia—but of recent years a considerable number of specimens have been obtained, and it has been kept alive in the Zoological Gardens at Buenos Aires.

The pichiciago is only about 5 inches in length, with the shield, or mantle, covering the head and body pink, and the fur snowy white. The head is short, widest behind, and gradually tapering to the muzzle, where it terminates in a short and abruptly truncated snout, with small and rounded nostrils. The small and almost rudimentary eyes are nearly concealed among the long hair, and the ears are invisible, having scarcely any external conchs. The mouth is very small, with the lips hard and stiff, and the rather long and fleshy tongue conical, and covered above with warty protuberances. The teeth, of which there are eight in the upper and eight or nine in the lower jaw, are small and nearly cylindrical; those in the middle of the series being larger than those at the two extremities.

The neck is short and thick, and the body long and depressed, becoming gradually wider from the shoulders to the abruptly truncated hind extremity. The limbs are short, and the front pair is much more powerfully made than are the hind ones. Both are provided with five toes, but while in the fore limbs these are connected nearly to the bases of the claws, in the hind pair they are entirely free. The second claw in the fore foot is the largest, and the fifth the smallest, but the claws of all the hind toes are comparatively small. The tail, which protrudes through a notch in the lower border of the bony shield on the hind quarters, is short and inflexible, terminating in a flattened and pointed paddle-like expansion, and covered with a leathery skin, dotted over with small horny plates.

The whole of the upper surface of the body is covered with a continuous shield, or mantle, of quadrangular horny scales, underlain by very thin, bony plates; this mantle beginning in a point a short distance above the muzzle, and gradually increasing in width to the hind extremity of the body, where it is abruptly truncated. Instead of being firmly attached to the body throughout its extent, the mantle is only affixed along the line of the backbone, and consequently lies loosely on the hairy sides of the body, but on the head it is firmly joined to the bones. There are usually about twenty transverse rows of plates in the mantle; and, while the number of plates in each row at the hinder extremity of the head varies from seven to eight, on the loins there may be as many as twenty-four in a row.

The abruptly truncated hind extremity of the body is protected by a solid shield, composed of firmly welded plates of bone, overlain by thin scales of horn. This shield, which is slightly convex and forms a segment of a circle, the centre of which would be the notch in its inferior border through which protrudes the tail, is firmly welded to bony processes arising from the pelvis, and comprises five or six concentric rows of plates, the number in the uppermost row being about twenty, and that in the lowest only six. The entire shield is placed in a nearly vertical plane. Both externally and internally the mantle is smooth and devoid of hair. With the exception of the tail, the soles of the feet, the snout, and the chin, which are nearly naked, the whole of the skin is covered with a coat of long silky hair, forming a fringe along the edges of the mantle; this hair being longest on the flanks and limbs, and shortest on the upper surface of the feet, where it is intermingled with wart-like masses of horn. The female has a single pair of teats situated on the breast, as in armadillos.

The pichiciago is a rare animal, confined to the western part of Argentina, and least uncommon in the vicinity of Mendoza, where, as elsewhere, it frequents open, sandy dunes or their proximity, the vegetation in such spots consisting of thorny brushwood and cacti. Mr. E. W. White writes that, when walking, the pichiciago "plants both the fore and hind feet on the soles, and not on the contracted claws, carrying its inflexible tail, which it has no power to raise, trailing along the ground, and much inclined downwards from the body. As it begins to excavate, the fore feet are first employed; and immediately afterwards, supporting its body on the tripod formed of these and the extremity of the tail, both hind feet are set to work simultaneously, discharging the sand with incredible swiftness. The burrows, which are never left open, usually have but slight, if any, inclination to the horizon. Sluggish in all its movements, except as a fodient, in which capacity it perhaps excels all other burrowing animals, the *Chlamydophorus* performs the operation of excavation with such celerity that a man has scarcely time to dismount from his horse before the creature has buried itself to the depth of its own body."

Mr. White, who believes that the bony shield at the hind extremity of the body acts as a rammer in closing up the entrance to its burrow, is of opinion that when the creature desires to come above ground it emerges by digging a new exit. When in search of a spot in which to burrow, the pichiciago utters a sniffing sound, but is otherwise silent.

"So extremely sensitive is this delicate little burrower to cold," writes Mr. White, "that my living example, after passing a night in a box of earth covered with flannels, was found the following morning in a very exhausted condition. Wrapped in warm clothing and

parts of South A
differs from all th
by the elongated
their roots, by the
abdomen in additi
the fact that the
of the last pair in
milk teeth, each
permanent teeth,
number on each sid
of both the upp
and lower jaws, a
very small in pr
portion to the si
of the skull, and
not come into u
until the animal h
well nigh attain
its full dimensio
The head is narro
and produced in
a nearly cylindri
s n o u t, oblique
truncated at t
extremity, and t
bony palate of t
skull has a ba
ward prolongati
formed in the sa
manner as that

The body is l
nine movable ba
shields; the fo
the shoulders, a
Each bony plat
arranged in the
as long as the
part of its lengt
feet have four l
considerably la
carry five claw
and the fourth
the body of th
and that of the

In producing
the peba differ
It inhabits burr
on carrion, whi
for future con
diet, the peba
stated to be of

The mulita
shorter tail.
armadillo (T.
and the whole
as well as the
surface of the
light brown ha
So dense is th
completely co
for its mail-c
hairy mamma

EXTINC

Although th
does not rea
cene, or latest
America a nu
(family Glypt
attained a le
differed from
teeth—eight

placed near a fire, it soon revived. On taking it into my hand under a Mendozan midday sun it shivered violently, but whether through fear or chill it is impossible to say. Its normal paradise seems to be when the temperature of its residence is such as is produced by sand so hot as almost to scorch the hand; and yet, if cold be unfriendly, no less so is wet, for although its winter is spent beneath the earth, a fall of rain quickly drives it from its retreat. During summer it leaves its burrow at dusk to search for food; and, being truly nocturnal, moonlight nights are very favourable for discovering it."

A second and rather larger species of pichiciago (*C. retusus*) inhabits Bolivia, and is distinguished from the typical form by the mantle being attached to the skin of the back throughout its whole extent.

SIX-BANDED ARMADILLOS

With the exception of the peba armadillo and its allies, all other living armadillos are included in a single sub-family characterised by the division of the bony carapace on the back into scapular and lumbar shields, separated from one another by a variable number of movable bands. They all have moderate-sized ears, set at a considerable distance apart; the first and second claws of the fore feet are, when present, slender, and the females have a single pair of teats on the breast.

The weasel-headed, or six-banded, armadillo (*Dasypus sexcinctus*) is the type of a genus characterised by

GREAT ARMADILLO

having usually six or seven, but occasionally eight, movable bands in the carapace, each bony plate of which is marked by an elliptical row of punctures. The head is broad and flattened, with an obtusely pointed muzzle and rather small or moderate-sized ears, and the body is broad and much depressed. In length the tail is less than the head and body, and the plates on its basal portion form well-defined rings. Of the five toes in the fore feet, the first is the most slender, the second is the longest, while the three outer ones are the stoutest, and gradually diminish in size from the third to the fifth. They have a rounded inner border, and a sharp outer and lower edge.

The teeth, of which there may be either nine in the upper and ten in the lower jaw, or one less in each, are of large size, with the first upper pair generally implanted in the premaxillary bones. The common species, which attains a length of about 16 inches, exclusive of the tail, inhabits Brazil and Paraguay, but is replaced in Argentina by the closely allied peludo, or hairy armadillo (*D. villosus*).

The fleecy armadillo (*D. vellerosus*), from Argentina and the north of Patagonia, and the pichi, or pigmy armadillo (*D. minutus*), of Argentina, are much smaller species, the second distinguished by the absence of teeth in the premaxillary bones.

The different species vary somewhat in habits, the pichi being mainly diurnal, while in the cultivated districts of Argentina the peludo has become nocturnal. The pichi prefers a very dry soil, the sand dunes near the coast, where for many months it can never taste water, being its favourite resort; it often tries to escape notice by squatting close to the ground. All the species live in burrows, where in winter or spring the young are born; the number in a litter varying from two to four, although the female has only a single pair of teats. The young are born blind, but with their armour fully formed, although soft and flexible. They grow with great rapidity, and remain for several weeks in the burrows, but it is believed that they are not suckled for any very lengthened period, and soon learn to shift for themselves.

The armadillos of this genus are usually found alone, and most of them feed chiefly on ants and other insects, although they will also attack and devour small snakes, but the peludo is omnivorous. Mr. W. H. Hudson writes that the peludo " is an insect-eater still, but does not, like them, seek its food on the surface and on the ant-hills only; all kinds of insects are preyed on, and by means of its keen scent it discovers worms and larvae several inches below the surface. Its method of taking worms and larvae resembles that of probing birds, for it throws up no earth, but forces its sharp snout and wedge-shaped head down to the required depth; and probably while working it moves round in a circle, for the hole is conical, though the head of the animal is flat. Where it has found a rich hunting-ground, the earth is seen pitted with hundreds of these neat symmetrical bores.

" It is also an enemy to ground-nesting birds, being fond of eggs and fledgelings; and when unable to capture prey it will feed on carrion as readily as a wild dog or vulture, returning night after night to the carcase of a horse or cow as long as the flesh lasts."

Mr. Hudson adds that this armadillo resorts to a vegetable diet only when animal food fails; and states that on such occasions it will eat not only clover, but grains of maize, which are swallowed whole.

The peludo displays marked intelligence in capturing some of the animals on which it preys; a tame one being an adept at catching mice in a most ingenious manner. A peludo has been observed to kill a snake by rushing upon it and sawing the reptile in pieces by pressing upon it closely with the jagged edges of its armour, and at the same time moving its body backwards and forwards. The struggles of the snake were all in vain, as its fangs could make no impression upon the panoply of its assailant; and eventually the reptile

Q

slowly dropped
armadillo, whic
tail in its mout

The tatouay
unicinctus), of
best-known re
tinguished fron
or thirteen n
also by the t
in number or
lower jaws, ar
jaw the last c
advance of th
instead of clos
head has a si
banded armad
and rounded e
siderably shor
except for a fe
near the tip.
In the fore fe
much larger th
first and secon
short triangula
and the third
are ornamente
Next to the gr
largest of the
similar to tho
definite inforr

By far the
the great arr
of Surinam
nearly a yard
of the tail,
genus. While
dillo in the
bands in the c
the general st
feet, this spe
tinguished b
greater relati
ment of the 1
the small size
of the fifth, ar
larger numbe
which there
twenty to tw
each side of be
and the lowe
It is furth
ised by the s
elongated forr
the ears bei
rather small
tail, which is
in length te
being covere
in spiral row
There are
sixteen or s
exception of
which are v
The immens
dillo proclai
feed chiefly
averse from

STRANGER even than armadillos are the edentates commonly known as pangolins, or scaly ant-eaters, which may be compared in appearance to animated spruce-fir cones furnished with a head and legs. These animals constitute a family by themselves (*Manidæ*), in which there is but a single genus, *Manis*, and, like the remaining representatives of the order, are confined to the Old World. As already mentioned, the relationship of the pangolins to the New World edentates is more than doubtful, their internal anatomy being of a different type, and the joints of the backbone lacking the additional articular processes characterising most of the American edentates.

Pangolins are characterised as a family by the total want of teeth, and by the upper surface and sides of the body and the whole tail being covered with a series of large, overlapping horny scales. The limbs are short, with five toes on each foot ; and the long, worm-like tongue is capable of being protruded a great distance from the small mouth. The head is small, long, and pointed, with the eyes small, and the external conchs of the ears minute or rudimentary. The scales of the body extend on to the outer sides of the limbs, but are absent from the inner surfaces of the latter, as well as from the sides of the head and the inferior aspect of the body, all of which are sparsely covered with hair. There are often a few coarse, bristly hairs arising from between the scales.

All the toes have slightly curved claws, much longer in the front than in the hind feet, the third being larger than any of the others. In walking, the front toes are bent under the feet, and the weight of the body supported mainly on the upper and outer sides of the fourth and fifth toes. On the other hand, the hind feet are of the ordinary plantigrade type, and have the whole sole applied to the ground in walking. The female has one pair of teats, situated on the breast.

In the skeleton the skull is remarkable for its smooth and solid structure, and almost conical form. The zygomatic, or cheek, arch is incomplete, and there is no division between the sockets of the eyes and the pits at the hind extremity of the skull, while the palate is produced much backwards. The lower jaw is extremely slight and slender, without any ascending or descending processes. In many of these respects the skulls of the pangolins approach those of the true ant-eaters, but it must be remembered that such resemblances are purely adaptive, and brought about by the identical mode of life of the two groups. Two other points may be noticed in the skeleton—collar bones are wanting, and the terminal joints of the claws are deeply cleft.

According to Dr. H. W. Marett Tims, the jaws of a foetus of one of these animals were found to be provided with minute pointed outgrowths, which there is reason to regard as vestigial tooth germs rather than hair follicles. Some of these structures arise from the margin of the jaw, while others grow from the outer side, and if they were hair follicles some of the hairs would fringe the free margin, and others would grow outwards into the substance of the cheek. So far as can be determined, the histological structure of these growths suggests teeth rather than hairs. Assuming them to be the former, they indicate that the formula of the vestigial dentition is $\frac{3}{13}$ or $\frac{3}{14}$, that the teeth in the middle of the series were the largest, and that all were apparently of a simple peg-like type, recalling those of armadillos.

The pangolins, of which the largest species attains a length of about 6 feet, are confined to Africa south of the Sahara and South-Eastern Asia, Africa possessing the largest, and at the same time the greater number. Pangolins are essentially burrowing and nocturnal animals, feeding exclusively on ants and termites, which are captured on the long extensile tongue. They have the power of rolling themselves into a ball as a protection against foes, and when thus coiled up their muscular strength is such as to set at defiance any attempt to unroll them.

ASIATIC PANGOLINS

Asia is inhabited by three species of the family—namely, the Indian pangolin (*M. pentadactyla*), confined to India and Ceylon ; the Chinese pangolin (*M. aurita*), ranging from Nepal and Assam to China ; and the Malay pangolin (*M. javanica*), inhabiting the regions to the west of the Bay of Bengal as far as Celebes, and also occurring in North-Eastern India. All agree in having the whole of the outer surfaces of the limbs covered with scales, and in their tapering tails, on which the middle upper row of scales is continued uninterruptedly to the extremity.

In the first two species the front claws are about twice the length of the hind ones, the Indian pangolin having from eleven to thirteen rows of scales round the body, against from fifteen to eighteen in the Chinese species. On the other hand, the more slenderly built and longer tailed Malay pangolin differs from both the others in having the claws on the fore feet only slightly exceeding in length those of the hind limbs. In the Indian pangolin the length of the head and body is just over 2 feet, and that of the tail a foot and a half.

INDIAN PANGOLIN

The habits of all the three kinds are believed to be similar, although the Malay species is probably less of a burrower than the others. The Indian pangolin dwells either among the crevices and clefts of rocks, or in burrows of its own construction, such burrows extending to a depth of from 8 to 12 feet below the surface, and terminating

parts of South America, and certain allied species, differs from all the members of the family yet noticed by the elongated ears being closely approximated at their roots, by the female having a pair of teats on the abdomen in addition to the two on the breast, and by the fact that the permanent teeth, with the exception of the last pair in each jaw, are preceded by deciduous milk teeth, each furnished with two roots. The permanent teeth, which are either seven or eight in number on each side of both the upper and lower jaws, are very small in proportion to the size of the skull, and do not come into use until the animal has well nigh attained its full dimensions. The head is narrow, and produced into a nearly cylindrical s n o u t, obliquely truncated at the extremity, and the bony palate of the skull has a backward prolongation formed in the same manner as that of the great ant-eater (page 862).

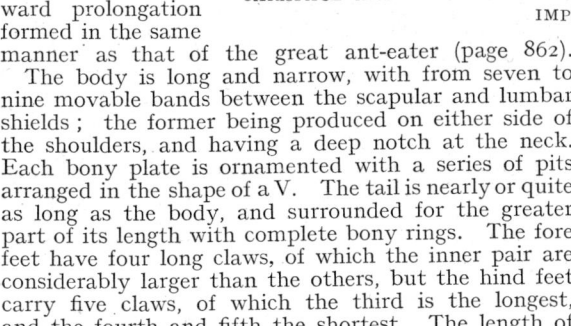

CARAPACE AND SKELETON OF GLYPTODON, WITH THE TAIL-SHEATH IMPERFECT

The body is long and narrow, with from seven to nine movable bands between the scapular and lumbar shields ; the former being produced on either side of the shoulders, and having a deep notch at the neck. Each bony plate is ornamented with a series of pits arranged in the shape of a V. The tail is nearly or quite as long as the body, and surrounded for the greater part of its length with complete bony rings. The fore feet have four long claws, of which the inner pair are considerably larger than the others, but the hind feet carry five claws, of which the third is the longest, and the fourth and fifth the shortest. The length of the body of the peba armadillo is about 16 inches, and that of the tail some 2 inches less.

In producing from six to twelve young at a birth the peba differs from all the species already noticed. It inhabits burrows in the open plains, and feeds largely on carrion, which is said to be stored up in the burrows for future consumption. In spite of this unsavoury diet, the peba is much hunted for its flesh, which is stated to be of delicate flavour.

The mulita is a smaller species, with a relatively shorter tail. A very remarkable form is the shaggy armadillo (T. pilosa), from Peru, in which the cheeks and the whole of the carapace, except the front margin, as well as the upper parts of the limbs and the under surface of the body, are covered with a thick coat of light brown hair of about an inch and a half in length. So dense is this hairy covering that the carapace is completely concealed, giving to the creature, except for its mail-clad head, the appearance of an ordinary hairy mammal.

EXTINCT GIANT ARMADILLOS

Although the carapace of the largest existing armadillo does not reach a yard in length, during the Pleistocene, or latest geological, period there existed in South America a number of gigantic armadillo-like edentates (family Glyptodontidæ), in some of which the carapace attained a length of between 6 and 7 feet. All these differed from living armadillos in having complex teeth—eight in number on each side of the jaws—

divided into three prisms by a pair of deep vertical grooves on each side ; and in all of them the carapace consists of a single solid shield, formed of a number of polygonal bony plates firmly united by suture. A peculiar species from Brazil known as the chlamydothere (Chlamydotherium) serves in some respects to connect the giant armadillos, or glyptodonts, with the true armadillos, having the carapace of the latter, but teeth approximating to those of the former. The typical species (Glyptodon clavipes) was about the size of a small r h i n o c e r o s, but others were smaller.

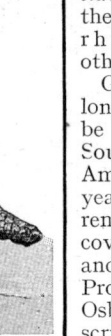

Glyptodonts were long supposed to be confined to South and Central America, but some years ago their remains were discovered in Texas, and more recently Professor H. F. Osborn has described and figured a fine carapace and tail-sheath of one of these strange monsters from the same state. It is regarded as representing a distinct generic type, under the name of Glyptotherium.

In all glyptodonts the skull was short, the feet were short and massive, generally with five toes in front and four behind, and the limbs were also short and massive. In the larger forms the bony plates of the carapace were fully an inch in thickness, and in all the species the head was protected by a bony shield, somewhat similar in structure to the carapace. In the typical genus Glyptodon the carapace was much vaulted, and its margins were ornamented with a number of large projecting tubercles ; while the tail was protected by a series of bony rings, also ornamented with bosses, gradually diminishing in size from root to tip (page 24). In one specimen the total length, along the curve of the back, from the nose to the end of the tail, is $11\frac{1}{2}$ feet, and the carapace measures 7 feet in length and 9 in width, inclusive of the curves.

On the other hand, in the mostly smaller forms known as Hoplophorus, or Lomaphorus, the carapace is less vaulted and devoid of bosses on the margin ; while the tail had several movable smooth rings at the root, and terminated in a long bony tube of more than a yard in length.

Another gigantic species from the pampas, distinguished by the tail terminating in a huge flattened club, armed during life with horns, is known as the club-tailed glyptodon (Dœdicurus). The surfaces for the attachment of the horn-like projections are situated near the extremity of the tail-sheath. In this species the plates are smooth and oblong, with two or three large perforations in each ; but in the Glyptodon they were ornamented, when young, with a kind of rosette-like pattern. In the Miocene strata of Patagonia the glyptodonts were represented by species of comparatively small size.

In common with sloths and ant-eaters, armadillos and glyptodonts, when they had effected an entrance into South America, were shut off from the rest of the world till that continent became united to North America, when a few members of nearly all the groups appeared north of the isthmus of Darien.

PANGOLINS

Stranger even than armadillos are the edentates commonly known as pangolins, or scaly ant-eaters, which may be compared in appearance to animated spruce-fir cones furnished with a head and legs. These animals constitute a family by themselves (*Manidæ*), in which there is but a single genus, *Manis*, and, like the remaining representatives of the order, are confined to the Old World. As already mentioned, the relationship of the pangolins to the New World edentates is more than doubtful, their internal anatomy being of a different type, and the joints of the backbone lacking the additional articular processes characterising most of the American edentates.

Pangolins are characterised as a family by the total want of teeth, and by the upper surface and sides of the body and the whole tail being covered with a series of large, overlapping horny scales. The limbs are short, with five toes on each foot ; and the long, worm-like tongue is capable of being protruded a great distance from the small mouth. The head is small, long, and pointed, with the eyes small, and the external conchs of the ears minute or rudimentary. The scales of the body extend on to the outer sides of the limbs, but are absent from the inner surfaces of the latter, as well as from the sides of the head and the inferior aspect of the body, all of which are sparsely covered with hair. There are often a few coarse, bristly hairs arising from between the scales.

All the toes have slightly curved claws, much longer in the front than in the hind feet, the third being larger than any of the others. In walking, the front toes are bent under the feet, and the weight of the body supported mainly on the upper and outer sides of the fourth and fifth toes. On the other hand, the hind feet are of the ordinary plantigrade type, and have the whole sole applied to the ground in walking. The female has one pair of teats, situated on the breast.

In the skeleton the skull is remarkable for its smooth and solid structure, and almost conical form. The zygomatic, or cheek, arch is incomplete, and there is no division between the sockets of the eyes and the pits at the hind extremity of the skull, while the palate is produced much backwards. The lower jaw is extremely slight and slender, without any ascending or descending processes. In many of these respects the skulls of the pangolins approach those of the true ant-eaters, but it must be remembered that such resemblances are purely adaptive, and brought about by the identical mode of life of the two groups. Two other points may be noticed in the skeleton—collar bones are wanting, and the terminal joints of the claws are deeply cleft.

According to Dr. H. W. Marett Tims, the jaws of a foetus of one of these animals were found to be provided with minute pointed outgrowths, which there is reason to regard as vestigial tooth germs rather than hair follicles. Some of these structures arise from the margin of the jaw, while others grow from the outer side, and if they were hair follicles some of the hairs would fringe the free margin, and others would grow outwards into the substance of the cheek. So far as can be determined, the histological structure of these growths suggests teeth rather than hairs. Assuming them to be the former, they indicate that the formula of the vestigial dentition is $\frac{3}{13}$ or $\frac{3}{14}$, that the teeth in the middle of the series were the largest, and that all were apparently of a simple peg-like type, recalling those of armadillos.

The pangolins, of which the largest species attains a length of about 6 feet, are confined to Africa south of the Sahara and South-Eastern Asia, Africa possessing the largest, and at the same time the greater number. Pangolins are essentially burrowing and nocturnal animals, feeding exclusively on ants and termites, which are captured on the long extensile tongue. They have the power of rolling themselves into a ball as a protection against foes, and when thus coiled up their muscular strength is such as to set at defiance any attempt to unroll them.

ASIATIC PANGOLINS

Asia is inhabited by three species of the family—namely, the Indian pangolin (*M. pentadactyla*), confined to India and Ceylon ; the Chinese pangolin (*M. aurita*), ranging from Nepal and Assam from China ; and the Malay pangolin (*M. javanica*), inhabiting the regions to the west of the Bay of Bengal as far as Celebes, and also occurring in North-Eastern India. All agree in having the whole of the outer surfaces of the limbs covered with scales, and in their tapering tails, on which the middle upper row of scales is continued uninterruptedly to the extremity.

In the first two species the front claws are about twice the length of the hind ones, the Indian pangolin having from eleven to thirteen rows of scales round the body, against from fifteen to eighteen in the Chinese species. On the other hand, the more slenderly built and longer tailed Malay pangolin differs from both the others in having the claws on the fore feet only slightly exceeding in length those of the hind limbs. In the Indian pangolin the length of the head and body is just over 2 feet, and that of the tail a foot and a half. The habits of all the three kinds are believed to be similar, although the Malay species is probably less of a burrower than the others. The Indian pangolin dwells either among the crevices and clefts of rocks, or in burrows of its own construction, such burrows extending to a depth of from 8 to 12 feet below the surface, and terminating

INDIAN PANGOLIN

AARD-VARKS OR ANT-BEARS IN THEIR NATIVE HAUNTS

in a large chamber, which may be as much as 6 feet in diameter. Here a pair of these animals take up their abode, and in the winter or early spring give birth to their young, which are one or two in number, and covered with soft scales at birth, although it does not appear to be ascertained whether they are born blind. When inhabited, the entrance to the burrow is stopped with earth ; and it is rarely that its occupants are seen abroad after sunrise. The food consists chiefly of termites or white ants, the pangolin tearing open the nests of these insects with its powerful claws and thrusting its long, glutinous tongue into their runs. The tongue is rapidly withdrawn with a swarm of white ants clinging to its surface.

In captivity pangolins eat finely chopped raw meat, hard-boiled eggs, and rice. Their stomachs have a somewhat gizzard-like structure, and frequently contain a few small pebbles, probably introduced to aid in triturating the food. In captivity pangolins drink freely by extending and withdrawing the tongue, but it is doubtful whether this habit is natural, as they are often found in places where there is no water. When irritated, pangolins give vent to a hissing sound, but at other times are believed to be silent.

AFRICAN PANGOLINS

There are four African species of pangolin, all characterised by the middle row of scales on the upper surface of the tail bifurcating at a short distance from the tip. They are also distinguished by the absence of any external conch to the ear and the lack of hairs growing between the scales, while in some the scales do not extend all the way down the outer surfaces of the limbs. Of the four species, the long-tailed pangolin (*M. macrura*) is easily recognised by

the great length of its tail, which is nearly twice as long as the body, and also by the absence of scales at the lower part of the outer surface of the fore limbs. Nearly allied is the white-bellied pangolin (*M. tricuspis*), distinguished by its larger and tricuspidate scales, and the white under parts.

The short-tailed pangolin (*M. temmincki*) is distinguished by its short and blunt tail, in which the under surface of the tip lacks the bare patch found in all the other species except the next ; the outer surfaces of the limbs being fully scaled. The giant pangolin (*M. gigantea*) is sufficiently distinguished from the last by its superior size.

It is remarkable that the remains of a closely allied species have been found in a cavern in Madras. The whole of the four African species inhabit the west coast, but the short-tailed species also extends to South Africa and ranges across the Continent to Zanzibar and Southern Somaliland.

In general habits African pangolins appear to be very similar to their Asiatic cousins ; but while the long-tailed and the white-bellied pangolins are partially arboreal, the other two are purely terrestrial. Most of the observations as to their habits have been made from captive specimens ; and in 1878 Mr. F. Holwood, in sending a young example of the short-tailed pangolin to the London Zoological Gardens, wrote that these pangolins " always appeared to burrow in hard or stony ground, and I saw them always in the daytime. The mother of the specimen I sent you lived three months in Zanzibar. She only fed at night, and remained curled up in a ball all day. She regularly retired to the dark corner of my harness-room at daylight, and left for the garden at sunset. There were very few ants, but she seemed to get plenty of insects. She burrowed at intervals all round the

871

garden walls, but this was evidently only trying to escape, as she never made a hole large enough to give cover." It may be remarked that, although the scales of this young pangolin were quite soft at birth, they had completely hardened by the second day.

Another observer relates how his pangolins would climb the somewhat roughly hewn square posts which supported a building, and sometimes roll up into a ball and throw themselves down, apparently without suffering any inconvenience from the fall.

THE ANT-BEAR OR AARD-VARK

THE name aard-vark, or earth-pig, is applied by the Boers of the Cape to the southern representative of the second family (*Orycteropodidæ*) of Old World edentates, which is confined to Africa; but to the British in Africa these animals are universally known as ant-bears. Remains of an extinct species have been discovered in the Pliocene deposits of the island of Samos, and those of another have been recorded from the Oligocene beds of France.

In appearance aard-varks are singularly ungraceful animals, specially characterised by the gradual passage of the tail into the body; a feature they possess in common with marsupials and reptiles. The body, which may be either almost naked or sparsely clad with bristly hairs, is heavy and ungainly (page 82); the head is greatly elongated, with a small tubular mouth, and somewhat pig-like snout; the ears are of enormous length, and the tail is thick, cylindrical, and tapering, and nearly equal in length to the body. The neck is very short, the fore quarters are short compared with the hind part of the body, and the back is much arched. The tongue is long and extensile, although not so completely worm-like as that of the pangolins, and the round nostrils are situated at the extremity of the truncated muzzle.

The fore limbs, which are rather short, but very powerful, have four toes, with moderate-sized, strong nails; and, in walking, the entire sole of the foot is applied to the ground. The hind feet have five toes of nearly equal size, each carrying a nail. The skin is of remarkable thickness, its general colour being usually yellowish brown, with a tinge of red on the back and sides, but on the head and under parts becoming light reddish yellow, and on the hind quarters, the root of the tail, and the limbs brown. There is, however, considerable local variation in colour, the hair of the back in one race being nearly white. A full-grown specimen measures a little over 6 feet in length.

The jaws are furnished with a number of well-developed teeth, preceded by milk teeth which do not cut the gum. In full-grown specimens there are usually five teeth on each side of both upper and lower jaws; but the total number developed is from eight to ten in the upper, and eight in the lower jaw, the anterior ones falling out as the animal attains maturity. When unworn, these teeth, which are of considerable size, have rounded summits, and are composed of a number of closely packed denticles, which by mutual pressure assume a polygonal form and are traversed by a series of radiating tubes; such a structure being unknown elsewhere in the whole mammalian class. The skull has a complete cheek arch, and the lower jaw is much less slender than in the pangolins.

Regarding the milk dentition and affinities of the ant-bear, Dr. R. Broom writes as follows: " In the skull of a newly born specimen I have been fortunate in finding a full set of milk teeth in both upper and lower jaws. In the upper are three minute but calcified

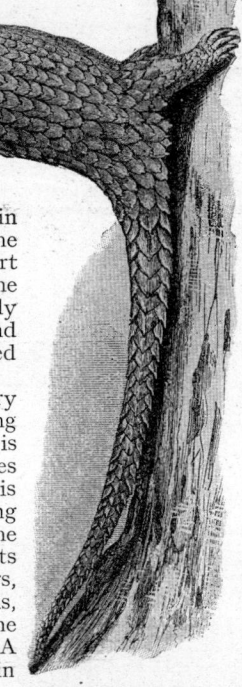

WHITE-BELLIED PANGOLIN IN CHARACTERISTIC ATTITUDE

incisors, one canine, and six premolars. Of these only the last five premolars probably cut the gum, and only the fourth and sixth are large enough to be functional to a slight extent. Succeeding teeth are found under the third, fourth, fifth, and sixth premolars, and possibly under the second; and beyond the sixth premolar there is evidence of at least four true molars. In the lower jaw there are also three minute calcified incisors, one minute canine, and six milk molars. Of these the second, third, fourth, fifth, and sixth milk molars probably cut the gum, and are slightly functional. The germs of replacing teeth are found in connection with all the milk molars except the first. Behind the last milk molar are evidences of five true molars. The dental formula of the ant-bear may thus be taken to be: $i. \frac{3}{3}, c. \frac{1}{1}, p.m. \frac{5}{5}, m. \frac{5}{5}$ or $\frac{6}{6}$. This dental formula is quite unlike that in any living mammal; but if we assume that the ancestor of the ant-bear had functional succeeding incisors and canines, it would have had a formula not unlike that found in many of the Mesozoic mammals. Dr. Elliot Smith suggests that the ant-bear may have branched off very early from the subungulate stem; while Professor Kitchen Parker was more impressed with the resemblances of the skull to those of marsupials and lower insectivores."

The single species of ant-bear (*Orycteropus afer*) ranges from the Cape to Somaliland, and is represented by local races, mainly distinguished by colour and the characters of the skull and teeth. These animals are essentially nocturnal and burrowing in their habits, and feed exclusively on termites and ants. In South Africa their deep burrows are constructed in the neighbourhood of the tall conical mounds formed by white ants, and, in the old days, before these animals were hunted for their skins, it used to be said that wherever white-ant hills were numerous there an ant-bear might be expected. Wherever these animals are abundant a number of half-formed holes are seen in the ground and on the sides of the ant-hills, which have been begun and abandoned.

Ant-bears spend the day asleep in their burrows, but may be seen abroad in the early morning. In a few minutes they can bury their large bodies, even when the ground is hard and sun-baked. In digging, they work with their fore feet, and throw out clods of earth between their hind legs. They are quick of hearing, and very shy, making off to their burrows at the slightest sound. The female gives birth during May or June to a single offspring, which is naked and flesh-coloured, and suckled for a long period.

ORDER X.   MARSUPIALIA

GENERAL SKETCH OF THE POUCHED MAMMALS

By R. LYDEKKER

THE whole of the mammals of which we have as yet treated are collectively characterised by certain peculiarities connected with the development of their young. In all of them the young are brought into the world in a more or less high state of development, due to the fact that during the greater portion of intra-uterine life the circulatory system of the fœtus is connected with that of the maternal parent by a special vascular organ termed the placenta; this placental connection between the blood-vessels of the parent and offspring allowing the blood of the latter to be oxygenated almost as completely as by breathing. On account of the development of this placenta all the foregoing orders of mammals are brigaded together into a single large group, known as Placentalia, or Monodelphia. On the other hand, in the mammals forming the order of marsupials with which we are now to deal, the young are born at a very early stage of development, and in an exceedingly imperfect and helpless condition, being, in fact, little more than animated lumps. In no instance is there a functional placental communication between the blood-vessels of the fœtus and the parent; and at birth the rudimentary young are transferred to the teats of the female, to which they adhere tightly for a long period, their lips being specially modified into a cylindrical sucking organ. In most cases the young thus suspended are protected by a fold of skin on the abdomen of the female, which forms a pouch in which the teats are contained.

Although there is no complete placenta, vestiges of such a structure are retained in the bandicoots; and it therefore appears probable that pouched mammals, or marsupials, are derived from the same stock as placentals, and have lost the placenta by disuse. They would thus seem to be a degraded rather than, as was once supposed, an ancestral group; this view being confirmed by their dentition. Since, however, the relationship of marsupials and placentals is a point upon which opinion is still somewhat divided, it must suffice to state that both groups may be included in the subclass Eutheria, of which placentals constitute the section Placentalia, or Monodelphia, and marsupials the section Implacentalia, or Didelphia.

In addition to the primary distinction of the absence of a functional placenta, pouched mammals present certain other more or less distinctive peculiarities. Mention has already been made of the presence of a pouch, or marsupium, in which the teats of the female are concealed; and to this it may be added that, with the single exception of the Tasmanian wolf, the front brim of the pelvis always has a pair of divergent splint-like bones projecting forwards in the form of

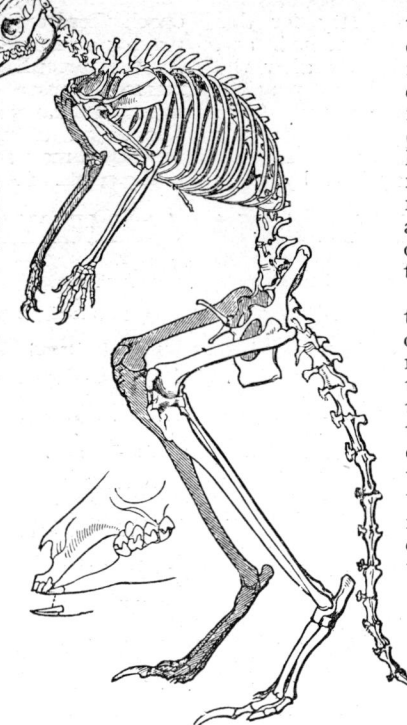

SKELETON AND DENTITION OF KANGAROO

the letter V. These so-called marsupial bones were originally considered to be for the purpose of affording support to the pouch, but this view is discredited by their presence in both sexes.

A peculiarity of the skull of nearly all pouched mammals is that the so-called angle, or lower posterior projection, of the lower jaw is more or less bent inwards, or inflected. This peculiarity, however, is not distinctive of the order, since it also occurs in some of the Insectivora. The skull of every marsupial is further characterised by the presence of larger or smaller vacuities, or unossified spaces, in the bony palate. As regards their brains, all pouched mammals display a low grade of organisation; the whole brain being small in proportion to the size of the body, while the foldings on the surface of its hemispheres are never of a very complex nature, and only developed at all in the largest members of the order. The reproductive organs of the female are likewise constructed after a lowly fashion; the oviducts always remaining perfectly separate from one another, and never uniting, as they do in so many placental mammals, to form a common chamber, or womb.

Certain peculiarities connected with the number and mode of replacement of the teeth also aid in distinguishing marsupials from other mammals. In the first place there may be more than three pairs of front, or incisor, teeth in the upper jaw; and in such cases the number of pairs of these teeth in the upper jaw always exceeds those in the lower by one. More important is the circumstance that only one tooth on each side of both the upper and lower jaw ever has a milk predecessor. This tooth corresponds, in my opinion, to the third, or last but one, premolar of the dog. The tooth behind this has no predecessor, and represents the last milk molar of other mammals. Behind this are the three true molars. With the exception of the replacing premolar, all the teeth in advance of the true molars appear to represent the milk series of the higher mammals, which are here permanently retained. This feature is another instance showing that modern marsupials are by no means primitive animals.

It should be added that most naturalists regard the replaced premolar as corresponding to the fourth, or last, premolar of the dog, and the tooth behind it as the first true molar. On this view, as in the figure on page 874, marsupials differ from those placentals with a full dentition in having three premolars and four molars, instead of four premolars and three molars.

The fact that the new-born young of the pouched mammals, when first transferred to the teats of the mother, are little more than mere animated lumps of flesh renders it imperative that some special arrangement should be made for their nutrition, as they are incapable of sucking by themselves. For this purpose the mammary gland of the female is overlain by certain specially developed muscles, the periodical contraction of which injects a supply of milk into the stomachs of the helpless young. In order to prevent the young marsupials from being choked during this injecting process, their throats are provided with an arrangement similar to that obtaining permanently in cetaceans. That is to say, the larynx, or upper terminal expansion of the windpipe, is prolonged upwards so as to extend into the hind aperture of the nostrils at the back of the palate ; and consequently there is a closed tube from the nostrils to the lungs, on each side of which the milk can flow without danger of choking the young animal.

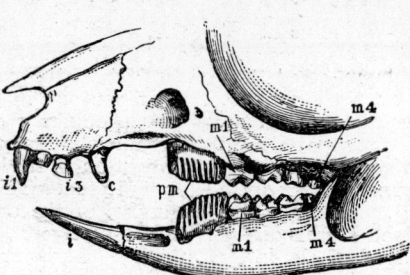

JAWS AND TEETH OF RUFOUS KANGAROO RAT

When there is no longer any necessity for this special arrangement, the larynx is shortened, and respiration and swallowing are carried on after the usual manner. It may be added that in pouched mammals the teats are confined to the region of the abdomen, and that the number of teats is frequently greater than that of the young. Such teats as have been in use may always be recognised by their elongation, owing to the weight of the young suspended from them.

With the exception of the true opossums and the genus *Cænolestes*, which are confined to America, and most numerously represented in the southern half of that continent, the living representatives of the order are restricted to Australia, New Guinea, and the adjacent islands so far west as Celebes and Lombok. Exclusive of egg-laying mammals, marsupials form almost the whole mammalian fauna of Australia, where the other native types are certain rodents and bats. In the more western islands marsupials, however, are mingled with placentals, thus showing that these islands have had a much closer connection with those of the Malay region than is the case with those farther to the east.

In the Tertiary period opossums were distributed over a large portion of Europe, and during the same epoch there existed in South America mammals displaying a marked resemblance to the Tasmanian wolf. In the preceding Mesozoic, or Secondary, period mammals more or less closely related to modern marsupials ranged over the greater part of the world. The origin of marsupials, like that of mammals generally, may some day be revealed by discoverers in the strata of Africa.   R. LYDEKKER

CLASSIFICATION OF MARSUPIALIA MENTIONED IN THIS WORK

GENUS 2
Extinct Giant Wombat—Phascolonus
FAMILY 4
Selvas—Epanorthidæ
GENUS
Selvas—Cænolestes
SPECIES
Ecuador selva ....Cænolestes fuliginosus
Colombian selva ....C. obscurus
EXTINCT SELVAS
Epanorthus
Abderites
FAMILY 5
Plagiaulacidæ (extinct)
Plagiaulax   Chirox
Ptilodus   Microlestes
Bolodon   Tritylodon
FAMILY 6
Bandicoots—Peramelidæ
GENUS 1
True Bandicoots—Perameles
SPECIES
Gunn's bandicoot ....Perameles gunni
Short-nosed bandicoot ....P. obesula
GENUS 2
Rabbit Bandicoots—Peragale
SPECIES
Rabbit bandicoot ....Peragale lagotis
White-tailed rabbit bandicoot ....P. leucura
Smaller rabbit bandicoot ....P. minor
GENUS 3
Pig-footed Bandicoot—Chœropus
SPECIES
Pig-footed bandicoot ..Chœropus castanotis

FAMILY 7
Carnivorous Australian Marsupials—Dasyuridæ
GENUS 1
Tasmanian Wolf—Thylacinus
SPECIES
Tasmanian wolf ....Thylacinus cynocephalus
GENUS 2
Tasmanian Devil—Sarcophilus
SPECIES
Tasmanian devil ....Sarcophilus ursinus
GENUS 3
Native Cats—Dasyurus
SPECIES
Spotted native cat ......Dasyurus viverrinus
Spot-tailed native cat ....D. maculatus
GENUS 4
Pouched Mice—Phascogale
SPECIES
Yellow-footed pouched mouse ....Phascogale
flavipes
Brush-tailed pouched mouse ..P. penicillata
GENUS 5
Narrow-footed Pouched Mouse—Sminthopsis
SPECIES
Narrow-footed pouched mouse ..Sminthopsis
murina
GENUS 6
Byrne's Pouched Mouse—Dasyuroides
SPECIES
Byrne's pouched mouse ..Dasyuroides byrnei
GENUS 7
Jerboa Pouched Mouse—Antechinomys
SPECIES
Jerboa pouched mouse..Antechinomys laniger

GENUS 8
Banded Ant-eater—Myrmecobius
SPECIES
Banded ant-eater ....Myrmecobius fasciatus
FAMILY 8
Pouched Mole—Notoryctidæ
GENUS
Pouched Mole—Notoryctes
SPECIES
Pouched mole ....Notoryctes typhlops
FAMILY 9
Typical, or Carnivorous, Opossums—Didelphyidæ
GENUS 1
True Opossums—Didelphys
SPECIES
Virginian opossum ....Didelphys marsupialis
Rat-tailed opossum ....D. nudicaudata
Thick-tailed opossum ......D. crassicaudata
Quica opossum ....D. opossum
Philander opossum ....D. philander
Woolly opossum ....D. lanigera
Mouse opossum ....D. murina
Three-striped opossum ....D. americana
Single-striped opossum ......D. unistriata
Shrew opossum ....D. sorex
GENUS 2
Water Opossum—Chironectes
SPECIES
Yapock ....Chironectes minima
EXTINCT CARNIVOROUS MARSUPIALS
Prothylacinus   Triconodon
Microbiotherium   Amphilestes
Amblotherium

THE KANGAROO TRIBE

THE survey of the pouched mammals may be begun with their most aberrant and specialised representatives, commonly known as kangaroos, wallabies, kangaroo rats, and the like; and it may be mentioned here that, whereas kangaroos are very frequently spoken of as typical marsupials, this is really very far from being the case. It is true that they conform in all essential characteristics to the marsupial type of structure; but they have been specially modified for a particular kind of progression—namely, leaping—which has profoundly modified their whole organisation, and rendered them some of the most specialised of all mammals. They retain, accordingly, little resemblance to what may properly be termed a typical, or generalised, marsupial, such as a bandicoot or the Tasmanian wolf.

Kangaroos belong to a group, or sub-order, of marsupials characterised by the adaptation of their teeth to a vegetable diet. The front, or incisor, teeth are never more than three in number on each side of the jaws, and are usually three in the upper and one in the lower jaw; while in all cases the innermost pair in each jaw is of large size and adapted for cutting. As a rule the upper canine teeth, or tusks, are small or wanting; and this invariably holds good for those of the lower jaw. As regards their molar teeth, these are invariably characterised by having broad, flattened crowns, surmounted either by tubercles or transverse ridges, and adapted for the trituration of vegetable substances.

The members of the kangaroo family (*Macropodidæ*) vary greatly in size and in the relative length of the

A GREAT WALLAROO

hind limbs, but are collectively characterised as follows. In the upper jaw there are three pairs of incisor teeth, with sharp and cutting edges; while the lower jaw is furnished with a large single pair inclining forwards, and sometimes biting against one another with a scissor-like action.

The upper canine, or tusk, if present at all, is of small size, while there is no corresponding lower tooth. In the adult the cheek teeth are five in number on each side, of which the first is a premolar and the second a persistent milk molar. In young animals, however, there are two milk molars in place of the premolar; the number of cheek teeth then being six on each side. The molar teeth may carry either a pair of transverse ridges or four blunt tubercles.

A characteristic feature of the family is to be found in the lower jaw, which has a deep pocket in the outer side of the hinder portion, communicating at its base by a large perforation with the canal on the inner side. In all the members of the family the fore limbs are short and feebly developed, with five complete digits. The hind limbs, on the contrary, are very powerful, and more or less elongated. Usually they have four toes, of which the one corresponding to the fourth in the typical series of five is much larger than any of the others, and terminates in a big claw. The outermost toe is considerably smaller, but still stout. The two toes on the inner side of the large one, corresponding to the second and third of the typical series, are, however, reduced to small slender rods, lying parallel to one another and enclosed in a common skin. These rudimentary digits are, of course, useless in progression, and their aborted condition is technically known as syndactylism.

The head, especially in the larger species, is small in proportion to the body, and tapers towards the muzzle. Generally the tail is long, cylindrical, and tapering, and passes more or less imperceptibly into the body; frequently it aids in supporting the body, and it may be prehensile. The female is provided with a large pouch, of which the aperture looks forwards.

All the members of the kangaroo family are purely vegetable-feeders; and most are confined to Australia and Tasmania, where, before the introduction of sheep and cattle, they took the place of the ruminants of other regions. They are divided into numerous genera, of which the first includes the true kangaroos and wallabies.

TYPICAL KANGAROOS

In the summer of 1770, when Captain Cook was refitting his vessel at the mouth of the Endeavour River, in New South Wales, a party of his crew who had landed to procure food brought back reports of a strange animal of large size, which sat upright on its hind limbs and tail, and progressed by a series of enormous leaps. Excitement among those on board was naturally raised to the highest pitch by this account—especially as a naturalist, Sir Joseph Banks, was a member of the expedition—and soon afterwards a specimen of the animal in question was killed. This was the species now known as the great grey kangaroo (*Macropus giganteus*), and was the first member of the family that came fully under European notice, although one of the smaller kinds from the Aru Islands had been partially made known so early as 1711.

The kangaroos and wallabies—names of native origin—which include the largest members of the family, are characterised by the great length and powerful development of the hind limbs as compared with the front pair, and the enormous size of the tail, which is regularly tapering, and evenly covered with fur from end to end. In the hind foot the claw of the fourth toe is enormously developed, and the first toe wanting.

The head is small, with an elongated and usually completely naked muzzle, and large upright ears. The females have four teats. The skull is characterised by its smooth and rounded contours, and the absence of any inflation in the bulla of the internal ear. The tusk in the upper jaw is minute, and shed at an early

period; and the upper incisor teeth are of nearly equal length, and form a regular open curve. The lower incisor teeth have sharp inner edges capable of cutting against one another in a scissor-like manner; and the crown of each of the molar teeth carries a pair of transverse ridges, which are nearly always connected by a longitudinal bridge.

Kangaroos and their smaller relatives the wallabies comprise more than twenty living species, as well as several which are extinct, and are found not only in Australia and New Guinea, but in some of the islands eastwards. While the larger species are as tall as a man, the smallest do not exceed the dimensions of a rabbit. They may be divided into three groups, distinguished by size, and partly also by colour.

Under the title of kangaroos may be included all the larger species, characterised by their uniform and sombre colouring, and large and massive skulls, in which the hind portion of the palate is well ossified. The best known of all is the aforesaid great grey kangaroo, the "boomer," "old man," or "forester" of the colonists, a full-grown male of which will measure 63 inches from the tip of the nose to the root of the tail, while the tail itself measures another 52 inches; the weight of the animal being about 200 pounds.

PARRY'S WALLABY

This species is of rather slender and graceful build, with soft woolly hair, greyish brown above, and nearly white beneath on the under parts and limbs, without any white markings on the face. It is further characterised by the middle of the muzzle being hairy between the nostrils, and also by the shortness from back to front of the permanent premolar tooth. It is an inhabitant of open plains, and found over the greater part of Australia and Tasmania.

On the other hand, the red kangaroo (*M. rufus*) and the antelopine kangaroo (*M. antilopinus*), together with certain allied species, are inhabitants of rocky districts, and have their muzzles completely naked, and the permanent premolar tooth of greater length from back to front. Their colours also may be more brilliant. The great red kangaroo (p. 938) is of slender build, with a reddish-coloured and very soft woolly fur, corresponding to the under fur of other species; the face having light markings and a black streak. This species inhabits South and Eastern Australia.

The antelopine kangaroo, from North Australia, is distinguished by its massive build and heavy, clumsy head, as well as by its short, coarse, straight, reddish hair, without under fur, and by the absence of face-markings. It is stated to attain a weight of from 120 to 170 pounds. Another well-known species is the wallaroo (*M. robustus*), from Queensland, New South Wales, and South Australia, in which the fur is long and thick, and of smoky grey colour; the build being also stout and heavy.

Kangaroos are exclusively vegetable-feeders, the larger kinds browsing solely on grass and other herbage, while many of the smaller wallabies also eat roots. Although, when feeding, kangaroos occasionally move about in an awkward manner on four feet, their habitual position is the upright one, when they are supported by the hind limbs aided by the tail; and the whole structure of their skeleton is modified to suit this posture; the bones of the lower leg (tibia and fibula) being immensely elongated, while the thigh bone (femur) is comparatively short, and the narrow pelvis set very obliquely to the axis of the backbone (page 873).

Consequently, when the animal is resting in the usual position, with the whole of the foot applied to the ground, the knee joint forms the summit of a solid support from which the whole body is suspended, as it were on pivots. The kangaroo can, however, raise itself so as to be supported only by the tips of the toes and the tail; and when in this position is enabled to take a wide survey of the country, and thus to obtain early warning of approaching danger.

When running, kangaroos spring from the ground in an erect position, propelled by their powerful hind legs and balanced by the tail, holding their short fore arm well into the chest after the manner of a runner. In this manner they bound lightly and easily along, clearing any obstacles, such as fallen trees, and even low fences, in their stride, which, it has been estimated, may be as much as ten yards. The long tail materially assists them in running, and its measured thumps may be heard on the ground long before the kangaroo itself appears in sight in the thick forest. It is stated that a wounded kangaroo often breaks a hind leg in struggling.

In general habits kangaroos much resemble sheep and deer. Timid and shy, their senses of sight, hearing, and smell are most acute; and, like hares, they appear to be unable to see an object directly in front of them when running. They are gregarious, and always to be met with in smaller or larger droves, which in former days used to comprise up to one hundred and fifty head, and averaged fifty or sixty. After the rutting season the old males often retire from the "mobs" to the thickest scrub. Each drove frequents a certain district, and has its own particular feeding-grounds.

The "mobs" do not appear to mix, and when the sportsman once obtains a knowledge of the country, he has no difficulty in planting himself for a

shot. Their favourite haunts are some open-timbered rise, and they have well-trodden paths from one ground to another. They feed early in the morning and at twilight, and also at night; but they lie up by day during the hot summer weather, in damp, thickly scrubbed gullies, and in winter on dry, sandy rises. Here, unless disturbed, they remain quiet for hours, and it is a pretty sight to watch them playing with each other, or quietly nibbling the young shrubs and grass, or basking in the sun half asleep on their sides. About Christmas-time the young ones leave their mothers and congregate in "mobs" by themselves.

When on the move, kangaroos invariably follow a leader; and, when once started, it is impossible to divert a drove from the direction they have taken. Except during the pairing season, when the males engage in fierce contests, they are as peaceful and harmless as sheep. When hard pressed, a kangaroo will take readily to the water, and there is an instance on record of one swimming across an arm of the sea two miles in width—half the distance being against a strong wind and current.

The principal food of kangaroos is the tender sprouts of shrubs and heather, quite as much as grass; but there is a small kind of spiky grass, called kangaroo grass, to which they are partial. At night they enter small bush enclosures, and nibble off the young blades of wheat, oats, and other crops. When feeding off the ground, they do not always use the fore paws as a support, but often merely crouch down. Occasionally they may be seen in the upright position, browsing from trees.

As regards breeding, it appears that in the great grey kangaroo the pairing season is either in January or February, although there is some irregularity in this respect. Only a single young is produced at a birth, after an exceedingly short period of gestation; and, when first transferred to the pouch of its mother, the length of the offspring is scarcely more than an inch. When the young kangaroo is sufficiently developed to move freely by itself, it becomes detached from the teat to which it at first adhered, but remains chiefly in the pouch till able to run by the side of its parent. Even then, when danger is near,

GREAT GREY KANGAROOS

it tumbles head-over-heels into the pouch for protection; and it is wonderful how quickly the female can pick up the "joey" when running at full speed, and thrust it into the pouch, with its face outside. There she carries it till hard pressed, when she casts it away to save herself. The "joeys" soon become strong runners, and by Christmas leave their parents and learn to shift for themselves.

WALLABIES

The red-necked wallaby (*M. ruficollis*) represents a group of large wallabies, or brush kangaroos, which includes species smaller and brighter-coloured than kangaroos, and distinguished by the more incomplete ossification of the hind part of the bony palate, and by the third incisor tooth of the upper jaw having a single distinct notch near the middle of the crown. All these species frequent dense scrub-jungle, known in Australia as " brush " ; and their leaping powers are nearly as great as those of the true kangaroos. The red-necked wallaby is one of the largest species, the length of the head and body being as much as 41 inches, and that of the tail 31 inches. It occurs in New South Wales and Victoria, but is represented in Tasmania by a smaller race known as Bennett's wallaby (*M. ruficollis bennetti*).

Other well-known species are the black-tailed wallaby (*M. ualabatus*), from New South Wales, Victoria, and Queensland ; Parry's wallaby (*M. parryi*), from mountain districts in Queensland and the north of New South Wales ; and the agile wallaby (*M. agilis*), of New Guinea, Queensland, and part of South Australia, distinguished from the rest by the uniform sandy colour of the short fur of the back, and by the presence of a distinct white stripe on the hips.

The " padamelon " wallaby (*M. thetidis*) of the colonists, which is very common in New South Wales and Victoria, and measures 26 inches from the muzzle to the root of the tail, is one of the best-known representatives of a group of small wallabies, several of which are not larger than a rabbit. All the species are lightly built, with perfectly naked muzzles, and the outer incisor tooth smaller than in the last group. Their hind feet are also relatively shorter ; and their jumping powers, therefore, probably less. This group has a wider distribution than either of the others, the Aru Island wallaby (*M. brunii*)—the earliest known member of the family—occurring in the islands from which it takes its name. Other well-known species are the rufous-bellied wallaby (*M. billardieri*), from South Australia, Victoria, and Tasmania, and the small short-tailed wallaby (*M. brachyurus*), from West Australia ; the latter being remarkable for the shortness of its tail and the small size of its ears.

ROCK WALLABIES

The yellow-rooted wallaby typifies a small group of medium-sized species collectively known as rock wallabies, characterised by the completely naked extremity of the muzzle, the shortness of the claw of the fourth hind toe, and also by the long cylindrical tail being thinner and more or less distinctly tufted at its tip than in other wallabies. None has any trace of a tusk in the upper jaw. The yellow-footed wallaby (*Petrogale xanthopus*) is the largest species, distinguished from the rest by its brilliant colouring, more especially the alternate brown and pale yellow rings on the tail.

The general colour of the long and silky fur is grey on the back, with a well-defined black streak running from between the long ears to the middle of the trunk,

the cheeks being marked by an oblique white stripe below the eye and a yellow spot above it. The ears are yellow externally, with their inner sides edged with white, except at the tips, and the sides of the body are marked by a pure white stripe from the elbow to the hip. The chin and under parts are also pure white, and there is likewise a white patch on the outer side of the knee, while the lower portions of the limbs, including the feet, are yellow. On the tail the rings occupy only the upper surface, the inferior aspect being uniformly yellowish. This species is restricted to South Australia.

The common brush-tailed wallaby (*P. penicillata*), from the coast districts of the eastern side of the island-continent, is more soberly coloured ; the general tint of the coarse hair being dull brown, tending to rufous on the hind quarters. In the male the length of the head and body reaches 28½ inches, and that of the tail, exclusive of the hair at the tip, 24 inches.

The remaining species are smaller, the north-western short-eared wallaby (*P. brachyotis*) being distinguished by the character from which it takes its name. All the rock wallabies are confined to continental Australia, and, as their name implies, frequent rocky districts, whereas the true wallabies are plain-dwelling animals.

Their tails lack the stiffness of those of the latter, and appear to be used rather in balancing the body when leaping than as a third support. The brush-tailed wallaby collects in large flocks, and forms regular well-beaten tracks on the mountain-sides.

PADAMELON WALLABY

SPUR-TAILED WALLABIES

Three species of wallaby differ from all other mammals, with the single exception of the lion, in having the extreme tip of the tail furnished with a horny spur, or nail, the use of which is unknown. They are further distinguished by the hairy muzzle, length and narrowness of the fourth toe of the hind foot, and the length of the tapering tail, on which the hair is short. The upper incisor teeth are relatively small, and decrease in size from the first to the third. They are all of moderate or small size, with short hair, and are some of the most graceful members of the family.

The spur-tailed wallaby (*Onychogale unguifera*) is of a fawn colour, and distinguished by the great length of the tail and the large size of its terminal nail ; the length of the head and body being 26 inches, and that of the tail an inch more. It is a rare species from North-Western and North Central Australia. The bridled wallaby (*O. frenata*) and the crescent wallaby (*O. lunata*) are smaller species, with relatively shorter tails ; the former inhabiting Eastern, and the latter, which is not larger than a rabbit, West and South Australia. All appear to frequent rocky and arid districts.

HARE WALLABIES

The hare wallabies, so called from their resemblance in size, and in some respects appearance, to a hare (page 882), are characterised by the muzzle being partially or completely covered with hair, the claw of the fourth

SOME TYPICAL KANGAROOS AND WALLABIES

BENNETT'S WALLABY   BLACK-TAILED WALLABY   BENNETT'S WALLABY

RED KANGAROO   GREAT WALLAROO

BLACK-TAILED WALLABY   GREAT WALLAROO   PARRY'S WALLABY

BLACK-TAILED WALLABY IN ITS NATIVE SCRUB
From a photograph by C. Grant Lane

toe of the hind foot long and not concealed by hair, and the tail rather short and evenly furred, without either a brush of hair or a spur at the tip. The skull is characterised by the shortness of the interval between the incisor and cheek teeth, and by the inflation of the auditory bulla on the inferior surface —the latter feature at once distinguishing the members of the group from the true wallabies. The upper tusk is always present, and the upper incisor teeth are small.

The hare wallaby (*Lagorchestes leporoides*) of South Australia and New South Wales measures 19½ inches to the root of the tail, and is clad in fur closely resembling that of the brown hare in colour. It is fairly abundant in the open country of the interior, more especially near the Murray River, and its habits are in many respects very similar to those of the hare.

The West Australian rufous wallaby (*L. hirsutus*), distinguished by the ruddy tinge of the hair on the rump and by the absence of a black patch on the elbow, appears to be very similar in its habits. In the north of the continent, and on some of the small adjacent islands, the genus is represented by the spectacled wallaby (*L. conspicillatus*), distinguished by its broader and heavier muzzle, shorter ears, the rufous tinge round the eyes, and the presence of two light bands on the flanks.

DORCA KANGAROOS

Müller's kangaroo (*Dorcopsis muelleri*) is one of a small group of Papuan species connecting the wallabies with the tree kangaroos. It is a medium-sized species, the length of the head and body being about four inches greater than in the brush-tailed wallaby. In the

dorca kangaroo (*D. luctuosa*) it is about as much less. These kangaroos differ from those hitherto noticed in that the hair on the nape of the neck is either completely or partially directed forwards, while the disproportion between the fore and hind limbs is much less marked. The large and broad muzzle is devoid of hairs, the ears are small, the tail has an almost naked tip, and the claws of the hind feet are not concealed by hair.

The teeth are distinguished by the great length, from front to back, of the permanent premolar in each jaw, which has a development similar to that which obtains in the potoroos. There is a well-developed upper tusk; and the molar teeth have low, rounded crowns, in which there is scarcely any trace of a longitudinal bridge connecting the two transverse ridges. Moreover, instead of converging at their extremities, the two series of cheek teeth run nearly, or quite, parallel. Müller's kangaroo has short, close, and glossy fur of a uniform chocolate brown, but with a white stripe on the front of the hips, and the fore arms and feet whitish. Externally it presents a remarkable resemblance to the Aru Island wallaby (*Macropus brunii*).

TREE KANGAROOS

In the dense tropical forests of New Guinea and the north of Queensland are found tree kangaroos; these being evidently specially modified types which have taken to an arboreal mode of life, and are in no way connected with the ancestral forms of the family. The tree kangaroos are easily recognised by the proportions of the two pairs of limbs to the body being normal; the length of the front pair falling only slightly short of that of the hind ones. The broad muzzle is only partially naked, and the hair of the nape, and in one species that of the back also, is directed forwards. In the hind feet the claws of the united second and third toes are nearly as large as those of the others, which are much curved. The tail is very long, and thickly furred. In the teeth, the permanent premolar is less elongated from front to back than in Müller's kangaroo and its relatives.

The dark forehead and tail-tip distinguish Bennett's tree kangaroo (*Dendrolagus bennettianus*), of Northern Australia (page 59). The black tree kangaroo of New Guinea (*D. ursinus*) is characterised by its black colour and whitish face; the length of the head and body of the female being 20½ inches, and that of the tail 23 inches. On the other hand, the brown tree kangaroo (*D. inustus*) of New Guinea and the Queensland tree kangaroo (*D. lumholtzi*) have the back greyish, and the face—and in the Queensland species the paws—black; while Doria's tree kangaroo (*D. dorianus*), of South-Eastern New Guinea, differs in having the fur of the back directed forwards. Other Papuan species have much yellow in their colour; the tail in one being banded with yellow and brown.

Comparatively little is known of any of the species in their native haunts, except that they spend most of their time in trees. Dr. F. H. Guillemard, who had on board ship two he had captured in New Guinea, writes that the tree kangaroo "is as yet a tyro in the art of climbing, performing this operation in the slowest and most awkward manner. Our pets, for instance, would take a full minute or more in ascending the back of a chair, but their hold is most secure, and if we wished to pull them off, we had considerable difficulty in doing so, so tightly do they cling." It is added that the tail, although not actually prehensile, is pressed against the branches in climbing, and appears to be of considerable assistance.

Of the Queensland species, locally known as the bungari, Dr. Carl Lumholtz, its discoverer, writes that it frequents the densest and most inaccessible

BLACK TREE KANGAROOS

portions of the highest mountain scrubs, where even the natives are scarcely able to penetrate. From the marks of its claws on the trees of the more open districts, the animal appears to have been once common there, but is now nearly exterminated. When disturbed, these kangaroos are stated to travel considerable distances, and to be most commonly seen abroad on moonlight nights. Two or three are often found sleeping in the same tree; and it seems that they

affect only one particular kind of tree, which grows to a considerable height. In rainy weather lower trees are selected.

Tree kangaroos feed largely on fruits and the birds'-nest fern, and will take leaps of from 40 to 60 feet to the ground. According to Messrs. Lucas and Le Souëf, " the vegetation at the altitudes which they frequent is almost invariably enveloped in moisture all night, just at the time when the animals are out feeding on it, so that they obtain probably nearly all the water they need with their food. In captivity they will drink large quantities of water."

BANDED WALLABY

The little banded wallaby (*Lagostrophus fasciatus*) of West Australia, which is about the size of a hare, and easily recognised by the dark transverse bands crossing the hind quarters, forms the single representative of a genus, and is specially characterised by the presence of long bristly hairs on the hind feet, which completely conceal the claws. The muzzle is naked, and the ears are small and rounded. The skull is characterised by its narrow muzzle and inflated auditory bulla; there is no tusk, the two series of upper incisor teeth meet in an angle, and the two halves of the lower jaw are welded together at their union.

These pretty little wallabies inhabit the scrub-jungle and the margins of swamps on the west coast of Australia and the small adjacent islands. On the islands they form tunnels beneath the dense bushes by gnawing off the lower branches on certain lines, and they can only be beaten out from their cover by the aid of dogs. On the mainland they are said to skulk in the open like hares.

KANGAROO RATS

As the name "kangaroo rat" clashes with one employed for a group of rodents, the attempt has been made to replace it by "rat kangaroo"; but, as is the case with all book names, the effort has proved a failure, and the animal must continue to be known by its colonial title.

All the members of the kangaroo family hitherto considered form a single sub-family (*Macropodinæ*), primarily characterised by the fact that the three incisor teeth of the upper jaw are of nearly equal height, while the tusk, or canine tooth, if present at all, is very minute. A second group or sub family

(*Hypsiprymnoinæ*) includes the kangaroo rats, or potoroos, none of which is larger than an ordinary rabbit. These are characterised by having the first incisor tooth on each side of the upper jaw considerably taller than either of the others, and narrow and curved in form, and by the presence of a rather large and blunted upper tusk.

Further characteristics are afforded by the permanent premolar tooth, which in the *Macropodinæ*, with the exception of Müller's kangaroo and its allies, is comparatively short from front to back, whereas in the group under consideration it is much elongated in this direction, and has a straight cutting edge, and its two surfaces generally marked by vertical grooves and ridges. Sometimes, moreover, this tooth may be bent slightly outwards, instead of forming a continuation of the line of the molars. The latter have blunt tubercles at their four angles, instead of complete transverse ridges ; and the last of the series is always smaller than the one in front of it.

KANGAROO RATS

The kangaroo rats are further distinguished by their narrow fore feet, in which the three middle toes are much longer than the other two, with long, narrow, and slightly curved claws ; whereas in the broader front paws of the preceding group the whole five toes are nearly equal in length, and have highly curved claws. All kangaroo rats have small rounded ears, and long furry tails, of which the extremity is partially prehensile in some of the species. Externally, kangaroo rats cannot well be distinguished in appearance from some of the smaller short-eared representatives of the preceding group ; and it is, accordingly, of prime importance that the foregoing distinctive characteristics should be understood. The group comprises several species, confined to Australia and Tasmania, and divided into four genera.

The typical, or common, kangaroo rat (*Hypsiprymnus*, or *Potoroüs tridactylus*) is characterised, in common with its immediate relatives, by the long and slender form of the head, the few (three or four) perpendicular ridges on the permanent premolar tooth in both jaws, the shortness of the foot,

HARE WALLABIES

the naked muzzle, and the rather large ears. In the skull the auditory bulla is somewhat swollen, and the unossified spaces in the palate are large.

This species, which is the largest of its genus, is confined to Eastern Australia and Tasmania, and is variable both in size and colour, the length being on the average about 15 inches, exclusive of the tail. It is specially characterised by the great elongation of the muzzle, and by the general colour of the coarse, long, and straight hair being dark grizzled greyish brown, with a more or less marked tinge of rufous.

The West Australian *H. gilberti* is a smaller but allied species, while *H. platyops*, from the same side of the continent, is still smaller, and has a broader and shorter muzzle.

Although the different groups of kangaroo rats vary to a certain extent in habits, all agree in being nocturnal, and in feeding not only on leaves, grass, and the like, but also on roots and bulbs, which are grubbed up with the fore paws. They generally frequent scrub-jungle, and get up before the sportsman after the manner of rabbits. Usually a single young is produced at a birth ; and, as appears to be the case with most marsupials, there is only one birth a year. In accordance with the reduced size of the hind feet, the leaping powers of the common kangaroo rat are less developed than those of the undermentioned species. It is stated, indeed, that although these animals habitually stand on their hind limbs alone, when running they employ both pairs of limbs in a kind of gallop. Moreover, they never kick out with their hind legs like kangaroos and wallabies.

The brush-tailed kangaroo rat and its kindred employ their prehensile tails in carrying grass and other substances for the construction of their nests, the extremity of the tail being curved downwards below the bundle. The nest is made in a hollow specially dug in the ground for its reception ; and as its upper surface is level with the herbage, only the practised eyes of the natives are able to detect it.

During the day either one or two of these tiny kangaroos occupy a nest, in which they completely conceal themselves by dragging herbage over the entrance. Here they remain till evening, when they sally forth in quest of food.

The rufous kangaroo rat may either form a somewhat similar nest beneath a fallen tree trunk, or under the hedge of some low bush, or may repose during the day in a seat among the herbage like the " form " of a hare.

BRUSH - TAILED KANGAROO RATS

The brush-tailed kangaroo rat (*Bettongia penicillata*) appears to be the commonest and most widely spread member of the group, and is one of several species having the following characteristics in common. The head is comparatively short and wide, with very small and rounded ears and a naked muzzle ; the foot is elongated, and the permanent premolar tooth has fourteen or fifteen slightly oblique ridges. The tail is thickly furred, with the hairs longer on the upper than on the lower surface, and somewhat prehensile. In the skull the auditory bulla is generally much swollen, and the unossified spaces in the palate are large.

HIPPOPOTAMUSES

"The hippopotamus is more essentially an aquatic animal than any other ungulate, the greater portion of its time being spent in the water, where its movements are far more rapid and natural than on land."

MALAY TAPIRS

"Owing to its retiring nature, the Malay tapir is seldom seen in its native haunts, and information as to its habits is consequently meagre. When taking to the water, it is said to plunge in and walk along the bottom, instead of swimming."

INDIAN RHINOCEROS

" The only sound that this rhinoceros utters is a peculiar grunt, repeated at frequent intervals during excitement. Its usual gait is a long swinging trot, although when disturbed it can break into an awkward but very rapid gallop."

ASIATIC WILD ASSES

"The voice of the Asiatic wild ass must be described as a bray, since it consists of a squealing inhalation, followed by a more guttural exhalation ; but these animals are remarkably silent and never noisy. The stifled and suppressed bray that they utter has no resemblance to the neigh of a horse."

This species, which is a somewhat smaller animal than the common kangaroo rat, is characterised by the great development of the tuft of hair on the upper surface of the end of the tail, of which the under side is brown. It inhabits nearly all Australia, but is replaced in Tasmania by the much larger jerboa kangaroo (*B. cuniculus*), in which the tail tuft is scarcely developed. Lesueur's kangaroo rat (*B. lesueuri*) is a South and West Australian species distinguished from the brush-tailed species by the small size of the tail tuft, which is almost always white at the tip. The plains kangaroo rat (*Caloprymnus campestris*) of South Australia differs in the naked portion of the muzzle extending somewhat less backwardly on the nose, and the absence of any crest or tuft of hair on the tail, and on these and other grounds it is made the type of a distinct genus.

RUFOUS KANGAROO RAT

The largest member of the group is the rufous kangaroo rat (*Æpyprymnus rufescens*) of New South Wales, distinguished from all the others by the partially hairy muzzle, and the unusually broad and short head, and evenly furred tail. The permanent premolar tooth in each jaw has a medium number (seven to eight) of vertical ridges; and the skull is characterised by the absence of any unossified spaces on the palate, and the unswollen auditory bulla. The head and body of this species may measure as much as 20 inches, and the tail about 4 inches less. The general colour of the long and soft fur is bright rusty red on the upper parts, more or less pencilled with white; but the under parts are dirty white, and the ears black.

MUSK KANGAROO

The rat-like species known as the musk kangaroo (*Hypsiprymnodon moschatus*) forms one of those connecting links so interesting to the evolutionist, but so extremely inconvenient to the systematic naturalist. This creature stands, indeed, almost exactly midway between the common kangaroo rat and the cuscuses, although the kangaroo-like structure of its lower jaw has led to its being placed in the present family.

The musk kangaroo is confined to Queensland, and is very nearly the size of a large rat, to which it also presents a general external resemblance. The body is clothed with close, crisp, velvety fur of a grizzled rusty orange grey colour, the orange tinge being strongest on the back, and almost disappearing on the lighter under parts. The head is sharply pointed, with rather large and nearly naked ears, and the tapering cylindrical black tail is likewise naked, but scaly. The relative proportions of the fore and hind limbs are not far removed from the ordinary mammalian type.

The fore paws are small, with five toes, each provided with a delicate claw; and the hind feet differ from those of all the other members of the family in having a first, or "great," toe in addition to the usual four. This first toe, which is clawless and opposable to the

others, is placed high up on the foot, near the heel; the second and third toes, as in all the other members of the family, are slender and united in a common skin. The teeth generally resemble those of the kangaroo rat, but the permanent premolar in each jaw is short from front to back, and bent outwards from the line of the other teeth in the manner characteristic of the Australian opossums.

Mr. P. Ramsay writes that the musk kangaroo "inhabits the dense and damp portions of the scrubs which fringe the rivers and clothe the sides of the coast range in certain districts. The animal is by no means rare, yet, from its retiring habits, and the dense nature of the parts frequented by it, it is at all times difficult to obtain. Its habits are chiefly diurnal, and its actions, when not disturbed, by no means ungraceful; it progresses in much the same way as the kangaroo rats, but procures its food by turning over the débris in the scrubs in search of insects, worms, and tuberose roots, frequently eating the palm-berries, which it holds in its fore paws after the manner of the phalangers, sitting up on its haunches, or sometimes digging, like the bandicoots. Seldom more than one or two are found together, unless accompanied by the young." In some instances, there are two young at birth, and the breeding season is during the rains, which last from February to May.

EXTINCT TYPES

In addition to those of several of the existing species of kangaroos, wallabies, and kangaroo rats, the caverns and superficial deposits of Australia contain numerous remains of kangaroos, or kangaroo-like types, some of which attained gigantic dimensions. One of these (*Macropus titan*) was allied to the great grey kangaroo, but of larger size; while others, as *M. brehus*, appear to have been gigantic wallabies, with skulls of as much as a foot in length. Other species, distinguished by their permanent premolar teeth, or the union of the two halves of the lower jaw, constitute extinct genera, named *Sthenurus*, *Procoptodon*, and the *Palorchestes*; the skull of the latter measuring 16 inches.

The gigantic extinct Australian marsupial *Diprotodon australis* is named from the presence at the extremity of the lower jaw of a pair of large, chisel-like teeth. In 1899, Dr. E. C. Stirling, of the Museum at Adelaide, obtained a number of its remains from the mud of Lake Cadibona, and from these the structure of the feet and the general form of the skeleton could be fully realised. These remains show that the diprotodon was certainly a strange beast, carrying a huge head, the jaws of which were armed with teeth approximating to the kangaroo type, and having the body very short, the front limbs longer than the hind pair, and the vertebral column much arched, and falling away towards the loins, behind which it terminated in a short tail. Another allied but somewhat smaller animal is the *Nototherium*, characterised by its extremely short skull; it appears to have been to some extent intermediate between kangaroos and wombats. The two species may be regarded as representing an extinct family, the *Diprotodontidæ*.

BRUSH-TAILED KANGAROO RAT

CUSCUSES AND HERBIVOROUS OPOSSUMS

THERE is considerable difficulty in finding a satisfactory popular designation for the members of the family *Phalangeridæ*, as the title "phalanger" generally used in zoology is one of the objectionable book names, while "opossum," which is the Australian name of several of its members, properly belongs to an American group. On the whole, it seems best to use the designation given above, the name phalanger being retained only for one small species differing markedly from all the rest.

The family includes a large number of small or medium-sized Australian marsupials of arboreal habits, which are so closely connected with the kangaroo tribe through the musk kangaroo as to render the distinction between the two families a matter of some difficulty.

All these animals are characterised by their thick, woolly coats; and, with the single exception of the koala, all have long tails, which are frequently endowed with the power of prehension. The fore and hind limbs, instead of presenting the disproportionate relative lengths characterising most of the kangaroos, are of the normal proportions; and the front paws are provided with five nearly equal-sized and clawed toes. The structure of the hind feet is essentially the same as in the musk kangaroo; that is to say, there is a nailless first toe which can be opposed to the others, while the second and third toes are slender and enclosed in a common skin; but whereas in the musk kangaroo the fourth toe is much longer and more powerful than all the others, in the cuscus tribe it is not much larger than the fifth. The whole group differs from kangaroos in the absence of any pit on the outer side of the hind portion of the lower jaw, and if there is any perforation in this portion of the jaw, it is extremely minute.

As regards the dentition, there are always three pairs of upper incisor teeth, of which the first is elongated, and likewise a well-developed tusk or canine; while in the lower jaw the single functional pair of incisors are large and pointed, although they lack the scissor-like action characterising those of the

A SPOTTED CUSCUS

In young animals there are three milk molars in advance of the first molar in each jaw; and between the first of these and the functional front teeth there occur several minute teeth in each jaw, variable in number and quite useless, which it is impossible to name correctly, several of these usually persisting throughout life. While some of the species are mainly or exclusively herbivorous, others are more or less omnivorous; and it is in this family alone among marsupials that species occur endowed with the power of spurious flight.

LONG-SNOUTED PHALANGER

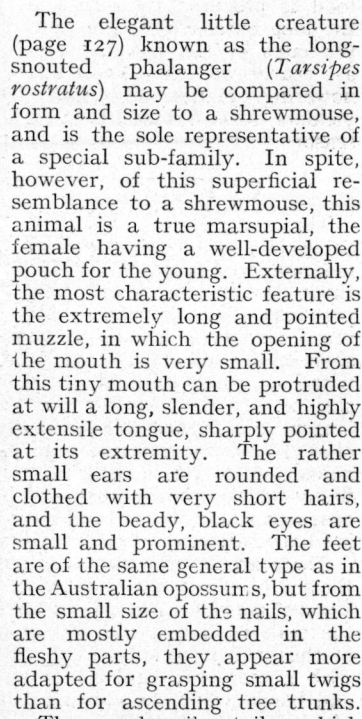

The elegant little creature (page 127) known as the long-snouted phalanger (*Tarsipes rostratus*) may be compared in form and size to a shrewmouse, and is the sole representative of a special sub-family. In spite, however, of this superficial resemblance to a shrewmouse, this animal is a true marsupial, the female having a well-developed pouch for the young. Externally, the most characteristic feature is the extremely long and pointed muzzle, in which the opening of the mouth is very small. From this tiny mouth can be protruded at will a long, slender, and highly extensile tongue, sharply pointed at its extremity. The rather small ears are rounded and clothed with very short hairs, and the beady, black eyes are small and prominent. The feet are of the same general type as in the Australian opossums, but from the small size of the nails, which are mostly embedded in the fleshy parts, they appear more adapted for grasping small twigs than for ascending tree trunks.

The prehensile tail, which slightly exceeds the length of the head and body, is cylindrical and tapering, with a scanty clothing of extremely short hairs. The fur is short, close, and somewhat coarse; and the colour, which is subject to considerable variation, is mainly grey, more or less suffused with rusty red above and yellow beneath. A black line runs from the head along the middle of the back to the root of the tail, and on each side of this are two greyish bands, bordered by a rusty brown stripe passing imper-

kangaroos. In the adults there are usually five functional cheek teeth, of which the last three are molars, and the first the permanent premolar. The premolar in each jaw has a tall cutting crown, set obliquely to the line of the molars; while the latter, of which the last may be absent, usually have blunt tubercles on their crowns, although they may be of a cutting type.

ceptibly into the rufous of the flanks. The upper part of the head is brown, passing into rufous on the sides of the face. Although the central pair of lower incisors is relatively large and well-developed, all the other teeth, of which the number is very variable, are simply conical, and placed at considerable intervals apart. This rudimentary condition of the teeth, together with the peculiar characters of the tongue and mouth, clearly indicate that this species is a very specialised member of the family.

The long-snouted phalanger is an inhabitant of West Australia, where it is known to the natives as the tait. Although in some districts stated to be very rare, in others it appears to be far from uncommon ; its favourite resort being low, scrubby bushes. It is strictly nocturnal, and constructs its nests in the taller plants and shrubs, among the branches of which it climbs in search of its favourite food, honey. This food is procured by thrusting the long extensile tongue into the cups of the flowers ; and as nearly all the Australian flowering plants are honey-yielders, it is obtainable at all seasons.

AUSTRALIAN OPOSSUM

CUSCUSES

The beautiful animals known as cuscuses are relatively large or medium-sized marsupials, with thick woolly coats and long prehensile tails, of which the terminal portion is completely naked. Their ears are short or of medium length, invariably covered externally with hair, which is sometimes found also on their inner surface. In the fore feet the toes are of nearly equal length, and furnished with long, stout, and curved claws ; and the soles of both fore and hind feet are naked and striated, with several large and ill-defined fleshy pads. The crowns of the molar teeth have four cusps, of which the outer pair in those of the upper jaw is somewhat compressed from side to side.

There are several species of cuscus, mostly of about the size of a large cat, the spotted cuscus (*Phalanger*, or *Cuscus*, *maculatus*) being by far the handsomest. In the male of this species the ground colour of the fur of the back is usually dirty yellowish white, marked with numerous irregular blotchings of reddish brown and black, while the chin and under parts are white, often tinged with yellow or red, and the head or limbs grey or reddish. There is, however, great individual variation, some specimens being almost uniformly grey or red. The smaller female is generally of a uniform grey and black above, and white beneath, although sometimes red. A much more sober-hued species is the black cuscus (*P. ursinus*), of Celebes, in which the fur is black or dark brown, with the exception of that on the inside of the ears, which is white.

Excepting the spotted species, which ranges to North Australia, the cuscuses are mainly confined to the islands of the Indo-Malay region, so far westward as Celebes. Only the spotted cuscus and one other species are ever found in New Guinea, and they are the sole Old World marsupials occurring to the westward of that island. The grey cuscus (*P. orientalis*), of Amboyna, Timor, and some of the smaller islands, was the first Australasian mammal known in Europe, having been discovered and described so early as 1611.

All the species of cuscus are dull and sleepy creatures by day, but become more active at night, their chief feeding time ; the comparatively large size of their eyes being in accordance with nocturnal habits. Dr. A. R. Wallace writes that these animals " live in trees, feeding upon the leaves, of which they devour large quantities. They move about slowly, and are difficult to kill, owing to the thickness of their fur, and their tenacity of life. A heavy charge of shot will often lodge in the skin and do them no harm, and even breaking the spine or piercing the brain will not kill them for some hours. The natives everywhere eat their flesh, and, as their motions are so slow, easily catch them by climbing, so that it is wonderful they have not been exterminated. It may be, however, that their dense woolly fur protects them from birds of prey, and the islands they live in are too thinly inhabited for man to be able to exterminate them."

These animals appear to be nowhere common, and in most parts of their habitat are very rare. In addition to leaves and fruit, they catch and eat birds and other small animals, and are reported to be more carnivorously inclined than any of the other members of the family. They frequent only forests containing large trees, and pass from the boughs of one tree to another after the manner of squirrels, sometimes swinging themselves by the tail in order to reach a branch otherwise inaccessible. There are four teats in the female's pouch, which usually contains from two to four young, and it is said that a female is never killed without at least one being in the pouch. So tightly do the young adhere to the nipples, that they cannot be torn away without causing blood to flow.

AUSTRALIAN OPOSSUM

The Australian opossum (*Trichosurus*, or *Phalangista*, *vulpecula*) is one of two Australian and Tasmanian species distinguished from the cuscuses by the character of the tail, which, instead of being tapering and naked for about half its length, is thickly covered with bushy hair up to its very tip ; this, together with a narrow line on the lower surface extending about a third of the length, being alone naked. The ears are more or less hairy behind, and there is also hair on the hind feet behind the heel. The relative lengths of the toes of the fore feet are somewhat different from those obtaining in the cuscuses ; and there is also a gland on the chest not found in the latter.

The opossum is one of the most abundant animals in Australia, being met with everywhere in forest regions, with the exception of Cape York peninsula, and is represented by a variety in Tasmania. Deriving its specific name from its resemblance in size and form to a small fox, it is especially characterised by its comparatively long and narrow ears, in which the length considerably exceeds the width. In the ordinary phase the colour of the soft and close fur is grey above, and yellowish white beneath, but the ears are white and the tail is black. In the larger and stouter built Tasmanian race, the fur is longer, and of a more decided brown or rufous colour, with little or no white on the ears. The short-eared opossum (*T. caninus*), of Queensland and New South Wales, comes very close to the latter race, but differs in its short and rounded ears.

While the common opossum inhabits forests, the short-eared species frequents scrub jungle, but in other respects the habits of the two are probably very similar, both being purely nocturnal creatures. During the daytime the common species lies securely curled up in some hole in a giant gum tree, but soon after sundown issues forth to prowl in search of food, and remains abroad until the laughing jackass begins its morning notes. Leaves—especially those of the peppermint gum—constitute its chief food, but the diet is occasionally varied with the flesh of a bird. In their movements among the forest trees, Australian opossums are very nimble, and much aided in their evolutions by their highly prehensile tails. They utter, especially during the pairing season, a loud, chattering cry, which echoes far through the woodland stillness. The female gives birth to one or two young, which are retained for a long period in the pouch, but afterwards cling to the back of their parent till able to shift for themselves.

YOUNG RING-TAILED OPOSSUM
Photo, C. Grant Lane

RING-TAILED OPOSSUMS

Very similar in appearance to the Australian opossum is the ring-tailed opossum (*Pseudochirus peregrinus*), which is the longest-known representative of a group of about a dozen species, characterised by the crescentic form of the cusps on their upper molar teeth. Externally they differ from the preceding group in the tail being tapering, and having shorter hair on its

terminal third and under surface than elsewhere, with the lower surface of the tip naked for a certain distance. The gland on the chest is absent, and the two inner toes of the front paw are very markedly opposable to the other three.

These opossums inhabit Australia, Tasmania, and New Guinea, and are divisible into two groups each containing five species. In the first group, which is confined to Tasmania and Australia, and may be represented by the Herbert River opossum (*P. herbertensis*), and the typical ring-tailed species discovered by Captain Cook, the ears are of medium length, and longer than broad, while the tail is tipped with white. In the second group, on the other hand, the ears are very short, and wider than long, while, with one exception, the tail is not white at the tip. The exceptional species is Archer's opossum (*P. archeri*), of Queensland, which is the only representative of the group found in New Guinea. Consequently, all the Australian members of the genus are distinguished from those of Papua by their white tail-tips. Forbes's opossum (*P. forbesi*) is a good example of the Papuan section of the group.

TAGUAN FLYING OPOSSUM

The flying representatives of the family known in Australia as flying squirrels, belong to three groups, severally allied to as many non-volant types. The largest of these forms is the great or taguan flying opossum (*Petauroides volans*), of Queensland and Victoria, which is the sole member of its genus, and appears to be nothing more than a crescent-toothed opossum which has acquired a flying membrane, having a decided resemblance to the ring-tailed opossum in the structure of its skull and teeth, while the tail, which is prehensile, is similarly naked on the under surface of the tip. The flying membrane extends from the wrist to the ankle, but is reduced to a narrow strip on the fore arm and lower leg.

In point of size this species may measure as much as 20 inches from the tip of the nose to the root of the tail, and is characterised by large and thickly-haired ears and long silky coat, the colour being

SQUIRREL FLYING OPOSSUM

blackish brown with white beneath.

STRIPED OPOSSUMS

The striped opossum (*Dactylopsila trivirgata*), ranging from New Guinea to Queensland, together with a second

Papuan species (*D. palpator*), represents a non-flying genus, agreeing with the two last in having the under surface of the tip of the tail naked, but distinguished by the fourth toe of the fore foot being much larger than any of the others. These opossums, which are of medium size, are distinguished from their kindred by the back being ornamented with broad longitudinal stripes of black and yellow. Although nothing definite is known as to their habits, it is probable that the elongated fourth digit of the fore paw is for the purpose of extracting insects and grubs from beneath the bark, or out of holes in trees.

SQUIRREL FLYING OPOSSUMS

The squirrel flying opossum (*Petaurus sciureus*) is the typical member of a group comprising two exclusively Australian species, and a third common to Australia and New Guinea; these being small or medium sized animals, allied to Leadbeater's opossum. They are distinguished from the preceding groups by the tail being evenly bushy to its extreme tip, without any naked portion, and not prehensile; while the flying membrane is broad, and extends from the outermost toe of the fore foot to the ankle. The squirrel flying opossum—the sugar squirrel of the colonists—is confined to Eastern Australia. The length of the head and body is about 9 inches, and that of the tail rather more. The ears are of medium length, the tail is extremely bushy, especially near its root, and the fur very soft.

The general colour is delicate ashy grey, but a longitudinal black band beginning near the nose runs down the back, to stop short of the root of the tail. The eyes are ringed with black, the ears are black at the base externally, but white at the hind angle; the cheeks are white, except for a black patch immediately below the ear, and the chin, under parts, and edges of the flying membrane are also white. The tip of the tail is black, and there is a black line on each side of the flying membrane internally to the white margin.

Of the habits of the yellow flying opossum (*P. australis*), from mountain districts in New South Wales and Victoria, Mr. J. Gould writes: "It is nocturnal in its habits, dwelling in holes and in the sprouts of the larger branches during the day, and displaying the greatest activity at night while running over the small leafy branches, frequently even to their very extremities, in search of insects and the newly-opened blossoms.

BROWN VARIETY OF RING-TAILED OPOSSUM
Photo, C. Grant Lane

SHORT-HEADED SPECIES OF SQUIRREL FLYING OPOSSUM
Photo, C. Grant Lane

"Its structure being ill-adapted for terrestrial habits, it seldom descends to the ground except for the purpose of passing a tree too distant to be reached by flight. When chased or forced to flight, it ascends to the highest branch and performs the most enormous leaps, sweeping from tree to tree with wonderful address; a slight ascent gives its body an impetus which, with the expansion of its membrane, enables it to pass to a considerable distance, always ascending a little at the extremity of the leap; by this ascent the animal is prevented from receiving the shock it would otherwise sustain."

Messrs. Lucas and Le Souëf state that a specimen kept in captivity "rested and slept on the top of the venetian blinds of one of the windows, but as evening came on he would wake and fly down for his milk and biscuit or sugar. 'Beauty,' as the children called him, would take his exercise by making flights from chair-back to chair-back, or from one of the children to another, alighting gently and without noise on head and shoulder. He never screamed, and never appeared to be in any way disconcerted if strangers, even a number of them, came into the room."

LEADBEATER'S OPOSSUM

Leadbeater's flying opossum (*Gymnobelideus leadbeateri*), which is rather smaller than the squirrel flying opossum, is of considerable interest as being apparently a representative of the parent form from which the latter species and its relatives were derived. This animal may, indeed, be concisely described as a flying opossum, *minus* the flying membrane. It is an inhabitant of Victoria, and measures about 6 inches in length.

DORMOUSE OPOSSUMS

The dormouse opossum (*Dromicia concinna*), together with a few allied species from West Australia, Tasmania, and New Guinea, somewhat resembles a dormouse in appearance, and is distinguished by the cylindrical mouse-like tail, covered with fur at the base, then scaly for the greater part of its length, but naked and prehensile at the tip. The length of the head and body may be less than $2\frac{1}{2}$ inches, and the tail slightly longer. All the species are nocturnal and arboreal in their habits; one being stated to conceal itself during the day beneath the loose bark of large gum trees. They feed upon honey and young shoots of grass and probably also insects.

PIGMY FLYING OPOSSUM

One of the smallest and most elegant of mammals is the exquisite creature known as the pigmy flying opossum (*Acrobates pygmæa*), in which the length of the head and body only slightly exceeds 2½ inches ; that of the tail being somewhat more. This species is distinguished from all those yet noticed by the long hairs on the tail being arranged in two opposite fringes, like the vanes of a feather. The build is extremely light and delicate, and the flying membrane very narrow, extending from the elbow to the flank, where it almost disappears, and thence to the knee, and the toes are furnished with expanded pads at their tips.

The fur is long, soft, and silky ; on the upper parts brownish grey, but on the margins of the flying membrane and beneath, together with the inner sides of the limbs, white. The teeth are sharp and apparently adapted for an insectivorous diet. In spite of its diminutive proportions, the female has a well-developed pouch containing four nipples, and it is difficult to imagine the minuteness which must necessarily characterise the newly-born young.

The pigmy flying opossum is confined to Queensland, New South Wales, and Victoria, and is reported to be abundant in the neighbourhood of Port Jackson. Its food consists of honey and insects ; and its agility in leaping from branch to branch is described as being little short of marvellous.

PEN-TAILED OPOSSUM

The little pen-tailed opossum (*Distæchurus pennatus*), of New Guinea, has precisely the same relation to the preceding species as is presented by Leadbeater's

THE KOALA

opossum to the members of the genus *Petaurus*, being, in fact, a pigmy flying opossum without the parachute. The foot pads, however, are wanting. The appearance of the animal is very dormouse-like ; the head being ornamented with stripes of white and dark brown, while the fur of the body is uniformly buff.

GIANT EXTINCT OPOSSUM

The superficial deposits of Australia have yielded evidence of the former existence in that country of a gigantic species of herbivorous opossum (*Thylacoleo carnifex*) far exceeding any of the living forms in

PIGMY FLYING OPOSSUM

point of size, and remarkable for the exceedingly specialised character of its dentition. The functional teeth are reduced to a pair of large incisors, and a single elongated cutting premolar on each side of both the upper and lower jaws ; the latter tooth evidently corresponding to the permanent premolar of the kangaroo rats. Such other teeth as remain are small, and of no functional importance. The skull is unique among marsupials in that the sockets of the eyes are completely surrounded by bone.

This giant herbivorous opossum received its technical names on the supposition that it was of purely carnivorous habits ; but, from the resemblance of its dentition to that of the existing members of the family, it seems probable that its diet was mainly of a vegetable nature, and may have comprised large fruits and roots, which would be easily sliced up by the powerful cutting premolars.

KOALA

The systematic position of the remarkable marsupials known to the colonists as the native bear and to the Australian natives as the koala (*Phascolarctus cinereus*), is a matter of some uncertainty. Formerly it was considered to represent a special subfamily (*Phascolarctinæ*) of the herbivorous opossums, but of late years it has been suggested that it is more probably a primitive type of wombat ; if removed from the herbivorous opossums to the wombats, a revision of the characters of each of these families will be necessary.

The koala, which measures about 24 inches in length, has been compared in size to a large poodle dog. It is a heavily-built animal, differing from the cuscuses and herbivorous opossums in the absence of any external tail, and also recognisable by its large, squared, and thickly-fringed ears. The fur is extremely thick, woolly, and moderately soft ; its colour on the upper parts being ashy grey, with a tinge of brown, but becoming yellowish white on the hind quarters and whitish on the under parts. All the feet are provided with long claws, and the two innermost toes of the fore feet are completely opposable to the remaining three.

A peculiarity of the koala is the possession of pouches in the cheeks for storing food, and the dentition differs from that of Australian opossums in the absence of the minute rudimentary teeth of some of the herbivorous opossums. The upper molar teeth have very short and broad crowns, somewhat resembling, in the structure of their tubercles, those of the ring-tailed opossum. In its internal organisation the koala approximates to the wombats.

The koala is confined to Eastern Australia, where it ranges from Queensland to Victoria. Like the Australian opossums, it is chiefly arboreal, moving awkwardly when on the ground, and when pursued always endeavouring to gain a tree with all possible speed. Usually its movements are comparatively slow and sluggish, and, although mainly nocturnal, it may not infrequently be seen abroad in the daytime. Koalas are generally found in pairs; and spend the day either on the tree tops or in hollow logs. They are purely herbivorous, and subsist chiefly on the leaves of the blue gum, although at night they descend to the ground in order to dig for roots. In the evenings these animals slowly creep along the boughs of the giant gums, many of the females often having a single cub perched on their backs. When irritated or disturbed, the koala utters a loud cry, variously described as a hoarse groan and a shrill yell.

WOMBATS

THE wombats of Australia and Tasmania, of which there are four existing species, all referable to the genus *Phascolomys*, constitute the last family (*Phascolomyidæ*) of Australian herbivorous marsupials. These animals are of considerable size, and characterised externally by their massive build, short and flattened heads, broad, flat backs, and extremely short and thick legs; their hind feet being plantigrade. Their ears are small or of moderate size, and more or less pointed, the eyes are small, and the tail is reduced to a mere stump. The fore feet have five toes, of which the first and fifth are considerably shorter than the remaining three, all being furnished with powerful and somewhat curved nails. In the hind feet the inner, or "great," toe resembles that of the Australian opossums in being unprovided with a nail, although it cannot be opposed to the rest; the others have strong curved nails and are of nearly equal length, but the second and third are relatively slender and partially united by skin, thus foreshadowing the "syndactylism" of the cuscuses and kangaroos.

The most distinctive feature of the wombats, however, is their dentition; the teeth, twenty-four in number, all growing uninterruptedly throughout life and never developing roots. The incisors, which are reduced to a single pair in each jaw, are exceedingly powerful chisel-shaped teeth, with enamel only on their front surfaces, thus resembling the incisors of rodents. The cheek teeth are five on each side, of which the first is separated by a long interval from the incisor. Each of the last four teeth is much curved, and consists of two triangular prisms; but the first of the cheek series comprises but one such prism. So far as their teeth are concerned, wombats strongly simulate rodents, to many of which they also approximate in habits. In appearance these marsupials, however, are curiously like diminutive bears.

Of the four species of the genus, the smallest is the Bass Strait wombat (*P. ursinus*), of the islands in Bass Strait, characterised by its small and somewhat rounded ears, the naked extremity of the muzzle, and the coarse and rough hair; the colour being uniform dark grizzled greyish brown. Nearly allied is the Tasmanian *P. tasmaniensis*. About one-fourth larger than the first named species is Mitchell's wombat (*P. mitchelli*), from New South Wales, Victoria, and South Australia, in which the length of the head and body is about 30 inches, while the colour may vary from yellow, through yellow mingled with black, to nearly pure black (page 128). . The fourth species is the hairy-nosed wombat (*P. latifrons*), from South Australia, intermediate in size between the first and third species, from which it differs by its longer and more pointed ears, hairy muzzle, and soft silky hair.

All four species seem to agree in their habits, and are exclusively herbivorous, living either in burrows

BASS STRAIT WOMBATS (LEFT) AND HAIRY-NOSED WOMBATS (RIGHT)

excavated by themselves, or in clefts and crannies of rocks. Like most marsupials, they are exclusively nocturnal; and their food consists of grass, other herbage, and roots. They walk with a peculiar shuffling gait, and utter either a hissing sound or a short grunt when irritated. In disposition they are shy and gentle, although their powerful incisor teeth are capable of inflicting severe bites.

In the superficial deposits of Australia are found remains of a giant extinct species (*Phascolonus gigas*) of the approximate size of a Malay tapir, and representing a genus by itself.

SELVAS

For want of a proper vernacular name of their own, certain rat-like South American marsupials may be called selvas (family *Epanorthidæ*) from the name of the estate on which one of them was discovered. There are two species, *Cænolestes fuliginosus* from Ecuador and *C. obscurus*, from Colombia; the former comparable in size to a mouse, and the latter to a rat.

Selvas are characterised by the long and narrow skull, which approximates to that of a bandicoot. There are four pairs of incisor teeth and a pair of canines in the upper jaw, and the lower jaw is furnished with a large forwardly-projecting pair of incisors, between which and the functional cheek teeth is a number of very small teeth representing the other incisors, canines, and earlier milk molars. The functional cheek teeth comprise three pairs of molars and one of milk molars, which are oblong, and four-cusped. The five-toed feet show no trace of syndactylism; the first toe being apparently slightly opposable to the rest. The tail is rat-like and partly prehensile at the tip.

In the character of their upper teeth selvas approximate to the second great group of marsupials—the polyprotodonts. They are nearly allied to a number of extinct marsupials, such as *Epanorthus* and *Abderites*, of which the remains are found in the middle Tertiary deposits of Patagonia.

When *Cænolestes* was first described it was referred to the diprotodont suborder, but it has been pointed out that the dental formula is identical with that of the Tasmanian wolf and the pouched mice, belonging to the polyprotodont section of the group; there being two pairs of small functionless lower incisors behind the large chisel-like pair. Further, there is a close general resemblance in bodily form between *Cænolestes* and the Australian pouched mice, on the one hand, and the American opossums on the other.

The skull also presents a marked similarity to that of the smaller Australasian polyprotodonts; while the rudimentary pouch is paralleled among the pouched mice and the smaller American opossums. Then, again, the fore and hind limbs are approximately equal in length, the two outer toes are fully developed and distinct, as in polyprotodonts, and the plantigrade feet, in the number and position of their pads and the short and clawless condition of the first hind toe, are exactly comparable with those of the pouched mice. These facts suggest that the resemblances in the dentition of *Cænolestes* to that of the Australian opossums is due to convergence and not to genetic affinity; for excepting tooth structure there appears to be no important character linking *Cænolestes* with the diprotodonts, while there are several which connect it with the polyprotodonts.

PRIMITIVE DIPROTODONTS

Many years ago a great controversy took place between the two English naturalists Dr. H. Falconer and Sir Richard Owen as to the affinities of a tiny extinct mammal known at that time merely by a few more or less imperfect specimens of the lower jaw, obtained from the so-called dirt-bed of the Purbeck beds near Swanage. These jaws are characterised by the presence, on each side, of a relatively large spear-like incisor, followed, after an interval, by several tall compressed teeth, whose cutting crowns are marked by conspicuous oblique grooves. From these oblique grooves Falconer gave to the animal to which the jaws belonged the name *Plagiaulax*. The last of these grooved teeth is considerably larger than those in front of it, and it is followed by a couple of lower and smaller teeth, which show a median groove flanked on each side by a row of cusps. It was suggested at the time that these obliquely-grooved teeth were premolars, while those behind them were true molars; and later discoveries have confirmed this interpretation.

Struck by the general resemblance of its dentition to that of the Australian kangaroo rats, Falconer came to the conclusion that *Plagiaulax* was a herbivorous marsupial more or less nearly akin to the living genus. This was disputed by Owen, who pointed out that when the jaw was horizontal, the condyle, or knob, by which it is articulated to the skull, lay below the plane of the cheek teeth. And since such a character is found in modern Carnivora, he argued that *Plagiaulax* must likewise have been carnivorous. Other naturalists, however, among them the late Sir William Flower, sided with Falconer.

Thus matters stood till 1881, when a last premolar tooth of the same general type as that of *Plagiaulax*, but relatively larger, was discovered in the lower Tertiary strata of North America and named *Ptilodus*. Afterwards more or less nearly complete lower jaws of the genus were obtained, some of which showed that the full dentition

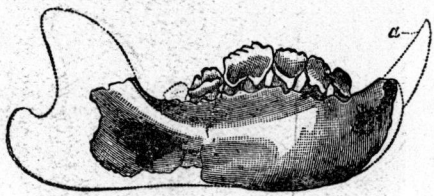

LOWER JAW OF PLAGIAULAX
The incisor is indicated by *a*, and the whole is greatly enlarged

included four pairs of premolars and two of molars. From the evidence of the American genus Professor Cope came to the conclusion that Falconer was right in referring the Dorsetshire mammal to the marsupials, and also in regarding it as a relative of the kangaroo rats. Subsequently, when the existence of temporary teeth in the duck-billed platypus of Australia was discovered, it was suggested that *Plagiaulax* and *Ptilodus*, along with a number of related extinct genera, were really members of the egg-laying, or monotreme group; but in 1909 Mr. J. W. Gidley announced the discovery of a nearly complete skeleton of *Ptilodus* in the lower Tertiary strata of Montana, and at the same time declared that both this genus and the English *Plagiaulax* are marsupials belonging to the same group as the modern Australian kangaroo rats. Nor is this all, for the new specimen made it clear that certain molars from the English Purbeck on which the supposed genus *Bolodon* had been founded, were the foremost cheek teeth of *Plagiaulax*, while somewhat similar American teeth described as *Chirox* were proved to belong to *Ptilodus*.

The new American specimen shows that the lower jaws of both *Plagiaulax* and *Ptilodus* were hung obliquely to the long axis of the skull, thereby enabling the large last premolar to bite against upper teeth of a lower and simpler type, and at the same time raising the condyle above the plane of the cheek teeth after the fashion which Owen pointed out to be characteristic of herbivorous mammals.

The genus *Microlestes* from the Trias of Europe and *Tritylodon* from the lower Jurassic of South Africa have cheek teeth approximating to those described as *Bolodon* and *Chirox*, and are probably, therefore, more or less nearly related to the *Plagiaulacidæ*. The diprodont affinities of these mammals are not accepted by Dr. R. Broom, who regards them as forming a group—the Multituberculata of uncertain position.

BANDICOOTS

With the exception of the selvas, the living members of the preceding families are characterised by the presence of not more than three pairs of upper incisor teeth, and by those of the lower jaw being reduced to a single functional pair of large size, which are inclined forwards. On account of this single pair of functional lower incisor teeth, they are collectively termed diprotodonts (Diprotodontia). The upper canine or tusk is small in all the group, and the corresponding lower tooth absent or represented by a rudiment. On the other hand, in the remaining families of the order the incisor teeth are of a more normal type; that is to say, they are numerous, and the innermost pair is not greatly developed at the expense of the others. The tusks are large and prominent; and while in the diprotodonts the molar teeth have broad and often squared crowns, surmounted by transverse ridges or blunt tubercles, those of the present group have sharp cusps, and are generally more or less triangular in form, thus indicating a partially or wholly carnivorous diet. On account of the number of their lower incisor teeth the name of polyprotodonts (Polyprotodontia) has been suggested for this second great group of the marsupials, which occupy the place in the order held by the Carnivora and Insectivora among placental mammals. Polyprotodonts are represented by the carnivorous opossums in America, and by three Australian families.

Bandicoots (family *Peramelidæ*) are small or medium-sized marsupials of fossorial habits, living either on insects or a mixed diet, and characterised by the structure of the hind feet. They have long and sharply-pointed noses, and the pouch is complete, with its opening directed towards the hind end of the body. In the fore feet the three middle toes, or two of them, are of nearly equal size and furnished with well-developed and somewhat curved claws, but the first and fifth toes are rudimentary or absent. The hind feet are constructed on the same type as in the kangaroos, the fourth toe being much larger than the others, while the second and third are small, slender, and united by skin, the first being rudimentary or wanting. The terminal bones of the larger toes in both feet are peculiar among marsupials in having their extremities cleft by a longitudinal slit, in the same manner as are those of the pangolins.

As regards their dentition, the bandicoots are characterised by having either four or five pairs of incisor teeth in the upper jaw, and three in the lower; while their upper cheek teeth are more squared than in the other families, with their cusps arranged in the form of a letter W. The similarity between the hind feet of the bandicoots and those of the kangaroos is a very remarkable feature, more especially if, as is now considered to be the case, this structure has been independently acquired in the two groups.

TYPICAL BANDICOOTS

Gunn's bandicoot (*Perameles gunni*), of Tasmania, may be taken as a well-known example of the typical genus, of which there are many species, all characterised by having the three middle toes of the fore foot large and functional, and the first and fifth present, although small and nailless; while on the hind foot there is also a rudiment of the first toe. The ears, although variable, are never of enormous length, and the tapering cylindrical tail is devoid of a crest of hairs near its extremity. The build is stout and clumsy, and there is no great disproportion between the fore and hind limbs. The various species inhabit Australia and Papua.

In Gunn's bandicoot the length of the head and body

RABBIT BANDICOOT   Photo, W. S. Berridge

is about 16 inches, and that of the tail 4 inches. It belongs to a group characterised by the ears being long and pointed, reaching as far as the eyes when turned forwards; and also by the hind half of the sole of the foot being covered with hairs. The fur is soft, and of a grizzled yellowish brown colour above, with four or more pale vertical bands, separated by dark brown intervals on the rump; the chin and under parts being white or yellowish white. The smaller short-nosed bandicoot (*P. obesula*), common to Australia and Tasmania, represents a second group, in which the ears are very short and rounded at the tip, the soles of the hind feet are naked, and the fur is intermingled with short spines. These two groups are closely connected by the Papuan representatives of the genus.

Bandicoots, which are the commonest of the Australian carnivorous marsupials, are detested on account of the damage they do. Consuming with equal gusto roots, bulbs, berries, fallen fruits, and other vegetable substances, as well as insects and worms, they are chiefly nocturnal, and pass the day either in holes or hollows or logs, to which retreats they at once fly when pursued. In addition to their burrows, some of the species construct nests.

RABBIT BANDICOOTS

Very different in appearance from the typical group is the rabbit bandicoot (*Peragale lagotis*), which, with two allied species, constitutes a genus distinguished by the enormous length of the ears, by the terminal half of the tail having a crest of long hairs on its upper surface, by the great relative length of the hind limbs, and by the absence of all trace of the inner toe. The molar teeth are curved, and in the typical species have longer roots and shorter crowns than in the true bandicoots. The rabbit bandicoot (page 128) is about the size of an ordinary rabbit, and clothed with fine silky hair of considerable length. The colour of the upper parts is pale grey, passing into rufous on the flanks, and becoming white beneath, the feet and the end of the tail being white.

The rare white-tailed rabbit bandicoot (*P. leucura*) is distinguished by the tail being wholly white instead of black in the middle. Its habitat is unknown. A third and smaller species (*P. minor*) inhabits the deserts of central Australia.

The rabbit bandicoot has disappeared from districts where it was formerly numerous, owing to " ringing " the timber and cultivation.

PIG-FOOTED BANDICOOT

A still more remarkable marsupial is the pig-footed bandicoot (*Chœropus castanotis*), a delicately built, rather small animal, measuring from 10 to 11 inches in length, exclusive of the short tail. It has long ears, and a short but sharp muzzle, naked at the tip, but its most characteristic features are to be found in its feet. In the fore limbs, which are much shorter than the hind pair, the functional toes are reduced to the second and third, these being furnished with short, symmetrical, and slightly curved claws ; while the first and fifth toes are absent, and the fourth is represented merely by a small rudiment. In the long and slender hind limbs the whole strength is concentrated in the long and stout fourth toe, the united second and third toes being very small, and the fourth altogether rudimentary.

The fur is coarse and straight, its colour on the head and body being a uniform grizzled grey, with a tinge of fawn, but the chin, chest, and under parts are white, and the feet pale grey or white, with a yellowish tinge. This animal inhabits the greater part of Australia, with the exception of the extreme north, north-east, and east ; its favourite haunts being open grassy plains, where it constructs nests like those of ordinary bandicoots.

CARNIVOROUS AUSTRALIAN MARSUPIALS

THE members of the dasyure family (*Dasyuridæ*) are distinguished from the bandicoots by having the second and third toes of the hind foot separate from one another, and as well developed as the fourth and fifth ; the first toe, if present at all, being small and without a claw. The dentition differs from that of most bandicoots in that there are four in place of five incisor teeth on each side of the upper jaw, both groups having three pairs of these teeth in the lower jaw.

In all the members of the family the fore and hind limbs are of approximately equal length, and the fore feet have five well-developed toes, all armed with claws. The tail, which may be either medium or long, is hairy, and without the power of prehension ; and the pouch, when present, opens downwards and forwards. In the more typical forms the incisor teeth are small, and the tusks large ; the number of cheek teeth being either six or seven on each side of both jaws. At the present day the family is confined to Australia, Tasmania, and New Guinea, although in the Tertiary period it may have been represented in South America. While the larger species are purely carnivorous, catching and killing their own prey, the smaller representatives of the family are mainly insect-eaters. In structure these animals are the most generalised of all marsupials.

TASMANIAN WOLF

The largest of the carnivorous marsupials is the one universally known in Australia as the Tasmanian wolf, although in works on natural history frequently referred to as the thylacine (*Thylacinus cynocephalus*). In appearance it is extraordinarily wolf-like, and the unscientific observer would probably at first sight regard it as a member of the canine family. Nevertheless, the female has a well-developed pouch, although marsupial bones are represented merely by cartilages. In size the Tasmanian wolf is rather smaller than a European wolf, from which it is distinguishable by the tapering and thinly haired tail passing almost imperceptibly into the body, as well as by the dark transverse stripes on the hind part of the back and loins, and the shortness and closeness of the fur. The ground colour of the fur is greyish brown, and the transverse bands are black. In the hind foot the first toe is

wanting ; and there are seven cheek teeth on each side of the jaws.

Tasmania is now the only habitat of this animal, although remains of a species near akin to the living one are met with in the superficial deposits of the mainland. Like most marsupials, the Tasmanian wolf is mainly nocturnal. Its favourite haunts are caverns and clefts of rocks among the deep glens of the mountains in the more remote districts of Tasmania, the settlers having nearly exterminated the animal from the more populated regions on account of the damage it inflicts on their flocks.

Writing of the Tasmanian wolf, Sir Ray Lankester observes that " few, if any, of the Australian mammals come so near in appearance to the corresponding unpouched mammals of the greater world as does the Tasmanian marsupial wolf to the ' true ' wolf. It has

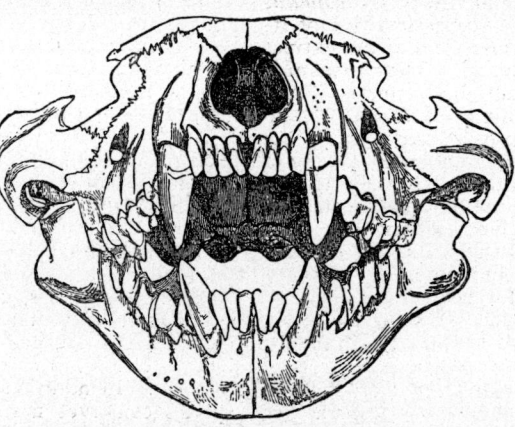

FRONT VIEW OF SKULL OF TASMANIAN DEVIL

been a matter of the greatest interest to naturalists and anatomists to compare these animals very closely. When this is done it is abundantly demonstrated that, though so much alike, they are really only parallel modifications of two ancestral stocks which differ in essential points of structure. The comparison of the skull, jaws, and teeth of the two animals is most instructive. In general shape they are wonderfully alike, but the bony palate is different, and the tympanic bony bulb is of different origin and relation. The other bones which build up the skull, and also the small proportions of the brain case, are in character more like those of other marsupials and not identical with those of the true wolf.

" The Tasmanian wolf not only differs from the common wolf in having a pouch to carry the young, but in important details of the viscera and of the bony structure and of the teeth—though the latter approach closely to the form of those of the wolf—the Tasmanian animal agrees with other marsupials, and not with extra-Australian placentals. It is a modification of the marsupial line of descent—parallel to or corresponding to the wolf in the extra-Australian series—but separated by immense ages of change from the common ancestor of both. The general features of the carnivorous wolf have been independently and gradually arrived at in the two different and completely separated stocks.

TASMANIAN WOLF

at the root of a tree. In its gait and movements it presents a considerable resemblance to a badger, or small bear. Except those which are too large to be attacked, living creatures of all kinds—whether vertebrate or invertebrate — form the prey of the Tasmanian devil; even sheep being destroyed in large numbers by these comparatively small marauders.

NATIVE CATS

On the mainland of Australia the carnivorous marsupials are represented by the so-called native cats, the largest of which is about equal in size to an ordinary cat. They have the same number of teeth as in the Tasmanian devil, but the cheek teeth are less massive and less powerful. The form of the body is also much longer and more slender, and the tail more elongated; while in all cases the body is profusely spotted with white, upon a grey or brown ground colour. The muzzle is sharp; the ears are long, narrow, and pointed; and the long tail is evenly and thickly furred. In some of the species there is a rudiment of the first toe of the hind foot.

Native cats, of which there are several species, are common to Australia, Tasmania, and New Guinea, the largest being the spot-tailed cat (*Dasyurus maculatus*) from Eastern and South-Eastern Australia, distinguished from the others by the tail being spotted as well as the body. The best-known species is the common spotted species (*D. viverrinus*), which inhabits both Australia and Tasmania. Native cats are arboreal animals, and in habits resemble the martens, of which they appear to take the place in Australasia. They feed on small

When one watches the Tasmanian wolf, one comes to the conclusion that it is stupid and of much lower intelligence than the common wolf. Its appearance, ways, and movements suggest the fancy that it is a kangaroo masquerading as a wolf, and not very successful in the part."

TASMANIAN DEVIL

Next in point of size to the Tasmanian wolf is the animal known as the Tasmanian devil (*Sarcophilus ursinus*), which is the sole living representative of its genus, although, like the former, it has an extinct cousin on the Australian mainland. The Tasmanian devil is an ugly and powerfully-built animal, with an excessively large head, terminating in a short and broad muzzle; its size being approximately that of a badger. The ears are large and rounded on the outer side, and the tail is of moderate length, and thickly, although evenly haired. The hind foot has no trace of the first toe; but, instead of being digitigrade, both fore and hind feet are markedly plantigrade. The fur of the head and body is thick and close, with a large quantity of under-fur, nearly equal in length to the straight fur. The fur is mainly black, or blackish brown; but there is a white collar, or patch, on the throat, and a variable number of white spots on the neck, shoulders, and rump. The incisor teeth differ from those of the Tasmanian wolf in that the outermost pair is not markedly larger than the others; while the cheek teeth are six instead of seven in number, on each side, and are closely packed together, in place of being separated from one another by intervals.

The Tasmanian devil is an even more exclusively nocturnal animal than its larger cousin, being almost blinded if exposed to the rays of the sun, and passing the day coiled up in some dark and secluded lair, which may be either a natural cave or cleft among the rocks, or a burrow excavated by its powerful claws

TASMANIAN DEVIL

mammals, birds and their eggs, and probably also lizards and insects, and are especially destructive to poultry.

POUCHED MICE

Far more numerous in species than the native cats are the pouched mice, the largest of which is not bigger than a good-sized rat. They are distinguishable by the

SPOTTED NATIVE CAT

absence of white spots on the fur, and the presence of an additional premolar in each jaw, bringing up the number of cheek teeth to seven on each side. The crowns of these teeth are more minutely cusped, and the canines relatively smaller than in the native cats. The muzzle is rather long and pointed, the ears are moderately rounded and nearly naked, and the feet short and broad; the hind foot always having a distinct, though nailless, first toe. The long tail is subject to considerable variation in the different species, being in some cases bushy, in others furnished with a crest of hair, and in others nearly naked. The pouch is rudimentary, and represented merely by a few loose folds of skin.

Probably these animals produce a larger number of young at a birth than does any other Australasian marsupial, seeing that in some species the number of teats may be as many as ten. There are more than a dozen species of the genus, distributed over Australia and New Guinea, and also ranging into the Aru Islands. The majority are distinguished by the absence of any stripe down the back, and mainly confined to Australia; but this stripe is present in the remaining species, which are exclusively Papuan.

YELLOW-FOOTED POUCHED MOUSE

The yellow-footed pouched mouse (*Phascogale flavipes*) is a small species, liable to considerable variation in point of size and colour, and inhabiting a large portion of Australia, although unknown in the island of Tasmania.

Belonging to a section of the first group characterised by the tail being evenly covered with short hair, in general appearance this species is a mouse-like creature,

with close and rather crisp fur, of which the prevailing colour is clear grey more or less suffused with yellow or rufous.

The under parts and the feet in the typical East Australian race are yellow, this colour sometimes deepening to rufous and spreading over the whole body; but the race inhabiting Western and Northern Australia differs in that the whole of the under parts and limbs are more or less nearly pure white instead of yellow.

BRUSH-TAILED POUCHED MOUSE

The brush-tailed pouched mouse (*P. penicillata*) is a larger species than the last, inhabiting the whole of Australia except the extreme north, although unknown in Tasmania. It belongs to a section of the unstriped group characterised by the extremity of the tail being evenly tufted on all sides; and is a more stoutly-built animal than the yellow-footed species, with short and coarse fur. The colour of the upper parts is pale grizzled grey, while the chin is white, and the lower surface of the body pale grey or white. The head is characterised by the large size of the ears, and the presence of a more or less indistinct black streak down the nose. These pretty little animals are arboreal and insectivorous in their habits; and appear to fill the place in Australia occupied in the Oriental region by the placental tree-shrews, which they much resemble in general habits. All seek their insect prey

BRUSH TAILED POUCHED MOUSE

by climbing the boughs of trees, and at least some make nests in the hollows of the trunks and branches.

NARROW-FOOTED POUCHED MICE

The tiny marsupial known as the narrow-footed pouched mouse (*Sminthopsis murina*), along with certain allied species, constitutes a genus differing from the last in the extreme narrowness of the hind foot, and also in the fact that the soles of the feet are covered with hair or granulated. This species measures $3\frac{1}{4}$ inches in length to the root of the tail; the length of the tail being a little less than 3 inches. The pouched mice of this genus are confined to Australia and Tasmania, and are terrestrial and insectivorous. In all the pouch is well developed, and the number of teats varies from eight to ten.

A pouched mouse from the deserts of Central Australia has been made the type of a distinct genus, under the name of *Dasyuroides byrnei*. It is closely allied to *Phascologale* and *Sminthopsis*, but exhibits some resemblance to the spotted native cats.

JERBOA POUCHED MOUSE

The last, and apparently the rarest, of the typical section of the family, is the jerboa pouched mouse (*Antechinomys laniger*), of South Queensland and New South Wales, which has much the appearance of a sharp-nosed jerboa, with very large oval ears, and a long tail, becoming bushy at the end. It is distinguished from the members of the genus *Sminthopsis* by the great elongation of the hind limbs, and the total absence of the first toe from the hind foot. Its form is very slender and graceful, and the soft and fine fur composed almost entirely of under-fur. The colour is pale grizzled grey, with the chin and feet pure white, and the hairs of the under parts grey at the base and white at the tips. The tail, of which the length considerably exceeds that of the head and body, is fawn-coloured. This pouched mouse inhabits open sandy districts, and is

YELLOW-FOOTED POUCHED MOUSE

(*Myrmecobius fasciatus*), which may be compared in size to a squirrel and differs from other members of the family in that there are no more than seven cheek teeth on each side of both jaws; and also in the tongue being elongated and cylindrical, and thus capable of being protruded a long distance from the mouth. The banded ant-eater takes its name from the broad transverse bars of white on the dark ground colour of the hind half of the back and loins; the general hue of the fur of the upper parts being dark chestnut red, with the under surface of the body white, and a dark line running from the ear through the eye towards the nose. The fur itself is of a somewhat coarse and bristly nature.

In form the animal is characterised by its long but broad head, and narrow, elongated muzzle, moderate-sized and somewhat pointed ears, long body, short limbs, and long, bushy tail. In the fore feet the first and fifth claws are considerably shorter than the others, and in the hind foot there is no external trace of the first toe.

The banded ant-eater is one of the few marsupials in which the female has no pouch; the young, when first born, being merely concealed by the long hair of the belly as they cling to the teats (four in number). The teeth are all small and mostly separated from one another by distinct intervals; those of the cheek series being either eight or nine in number on each side of both jaws, making a total of either fifty-two or fifty-six teeth—a greater number than in any other existing member of the order. In many of the above-mentioned points this creature differs widely from all other *Dasyuridæ*, and there is considerable justification for the view that it ought to constitute a family by itself. The banded ant-eater inhabits West and South

BANDED ANT-EATER

mainly, if not exclusively, terrestrial. It progresses by leaps like a jerboa, and is accompanied in its haunts by the placental jerboa mouse (*Conilurus*).

BANDED ANT-EATER

One of the most curious and most interesting of all Australian marsupials is the little banded ant-eater

Australia, and lives mainly on the ground, although it will sometimes ascend trees. Its nutriment consists entirely of insects, chiefly ants and termites, which are collected by the long extensile tongue; and its favourite haunts are sandy regions, where there are numerous hollow tree stems and ant hills.

The banded ant-eater was long supposed to be nearly

related to some of the extinct mammals of the Mesozoic period, but it has been suggested that the large number of its teeth is a degenerate, rather than a primitive, feature.

POUCHED MOLE

In bodily conformation the pouched mole (*Notoryctes typhlops*) is a mole-like creature, measuring about 5 inches in length, and covered with long soft silky hair of a light cream colour, deepening in parts to golden. There are no external ears, and the eyes are represented merely by small black dots buried in the skin. The nose and upper lip are protected by a peculiar quadrangular leathery shield, the use of which to a burrowing animal is sufficiently obvious. The short limbs, which are covered with hair down to the claws, are very remarkable in structure ; both pairs being of nearly equal length, powerfully made, and furnished with five toes. In the fore paws the third and fourth toes are enormously enlarged and furnished with large triangular claws of great power ; but in the hind pair the first toe is small and armed with a small claw, and the others decrease in size from the second to the fifth. The short, cylindrical, and stumpy tail is hard and leathery, and marked by a series of distinct rings. The pouch opens backwards, and contains two very small teats. The teeth are small and weak, and appear to be forty in number, of which three pairs in each jaw are incisors, and seven cheek teeth ; the molars having triangular three-cusped crowns, and much resembling those of the golden moles.

This mole appears to be a very rare and locally-distributed animal, restricted to the deserts of northern South Australia, lying to the northeast of Lake Eyre. Here it inhabits flats and hills of red sand, upon which grow porcupine grass (*Triodia*) and acacias. Dr. Stirling states that most of the specimens he obtained were " captured by the aboriginals, who, with their phenomenal powers of tracking, follow up their traces until they are caught. For this reason they can only be found with certainty after rain, which sets the surface of the sand and enables it to retain tracks that are immediately obliterated where it is dry and loose. Nor are they found except during warm weather, so that the short period of semi-tropical summer rains appears to be the favourable time for their capture."

" Perpetual burrowing seems to be the characteristic trait of this animal. On emerging from the sand, it travels on the surface for a few feet, at a slowish pace, with a peculiar sinuous motion, the belly much flattened against the ground, while it rests on the outsides of its fore paws, which are thus doubled in under it. It leaves behind it a peculiar sinuous triple track, the outer impressions, more or less interrupted, being caused by the feet, and the central continuous line by the tail, which seems to be pressed down in the rear. It enters the sand obliquely, and travels underground either for a few feet or for many yards, not apparently reaching a depth of more than two or three inches, for whilst underground its progress can often be detected by a slight cracking or moving of the surface over its position."

In the skin of the head certain curious modified groups of cells with a more or less definite arrangement have been detected, and similar cells are also found to exist in a modified patch of skin on the rump as well as in the region of the pouch. Although direct proof of the existence of nervous function is lacking, it seems probable that these modified cells represent some form of tactile sense organ, which would obviously be of very considerable value to a blind burrowing creature like the pouched mole. It is unfortunate that nothing is as yet known by naturalists with regard to the embryology and development of this remarkable and exceptionally interesting animal.

JERBOA POUCHED MICE

UNDER SURFACE OF POUCHED MOLE AND VIEWS OF FEET
1, Profile view of left fore foot ; 2, Inner aspect of same ; 3, Upper surface of left hind foot ; 4, Palmar surface of same.

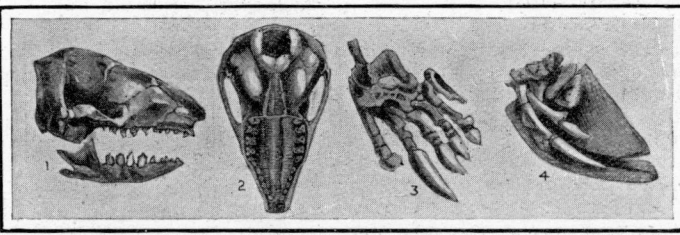

SKULL (1 AND 2) AND SKELETON OF THE HIND (3) AND FORE (4) FEET OF THE POUCHED MOLE

CARNIVOROUS OPOSSUMS

THE last family (*Didelphyidæ*) of existing marsupials is constituted by the typical carnivorous opossums now confined to America, although during the early portion of the Tertiary period they also ranged over Europe. Closely allied to the Australian spotted native cats, the American opossums are mainly distinguished by the hind foot having a well-developed inner toe, which, although nailless, is capable of being opposed to the other digits. They are further distinguished by the number of their incisor teeth, of which there are five pairs in the upper and three in the lower jaw. The tail is generally of considerable length, partially naked and prehensile at the extremity, and the feet are devoid of any hairy covering. Although complete in a few of the species, the pouch is either wanting, or represented merely by a couple of longitudinal folds in the skin of the abdomen, which partially conceal the numerous teats. As a rule, opossums may be compared in outward appearance to rats, although they have longer snouts, terminating in a perfectly naked muzzle, while in the larger species the body becomes proportionately stouter.

As regards habits, all opossums, with the exception of the water opossum, are arboreal, and omnivorous or insectivorous in their diet. They are nocturnal, and spend the day concealed either among the foliage of trees or in hollows in their trunks or boughs. Opossums take the place in South America of the Insectivora of the Old World. They are forest-loving animals, but a few are found on the pampas of Argentina, where they have adapted themselves to a terrestrial life. In those species in which the pouch is rudimentary or wanting, the young, after leaving the teats, are carried upon the back of their female parent, where they maintain their position by curling their tails round that of their mother, which is bent forwards for the purpose. Opossums are characteristic of Central and South America, only one out of about thirty species ranging into North America, where it extends as far north as the United States.

TRUE OPOSSUMS
VIRGINIAN OPOSSUM

In common with its allies of the same genus, the Virginian opossum (*Didelphys marsupialis*) is characterised by the absence of webbing between the toes, and its arboreal habits ; and is the only species found in the northern half of America. It is from three to five times the size of any other species, and characterised by its long, scaly, prehensile tail, and by the fur consisting of a mixture of long, bristle-like hairs and fine under fur. It may be compared in size to a cat, the length of the head and body reaching 22 inches in large specimens, and that of the tail 15 inches (page 58). It is, however, subject to great local variation both in size and colour, and is divisible into a number of local races, regarded by some naturalists as distinct species.

Inclusive of all these local forms, the range of this opossum extends from Paraguay and Argentina to New York. Despite its popular name the species is typically from Guiana and Venezuela, the northern race being distinguished as *D. m. virginiana*, and the one from Paraguay as *D. m. paraguayensis*, while there are other races in the intermediate area.

The colour of the fur varies locally through all the intermediate shades from black to white, while the hair on the face shows an equal amount of variation, the northern forms being almost wholly white in this region, while those from the south are darker, and often nearly black. In all cases the pouch is complete, but the number of teats ranges from five to thirteen.

In many parts of America this opossum is one of the commonest animals, and may be met with even in towns, where it lies concealed during the day in drains and other lurking places. Its diet is a mixed one comprising fruits, roots, birds and other small animals, eggs, and carrion ; and it is very destructive to poultry. With the aid of its prehensile tail, the opossum is one of the most expert of climbing mammals ; and when caught it has, in common with some of the other members of its genus, the habit of feigning death. Like so many marsupials, it is extremely tenacious of life. The young, which are born in the spring, and comprise from six to sixteen in a litter, remain in the pouch till they are about the size of a mouse, after which they venture abroad, although returning to its shelter for the purpose of being suckled or sheltering for a considerable time. The female exhibits the most marked attachment to her offspring, and endeavours by every means in her power to prevent her pouch from being opened.

PHILANDER OPOSSUM

RAT-TAILED OPOSSUM

The rat-tailed opossum (*Didelphys* [*Metachirus*] *nudicaudata*) is a well-known representative of the second group of the genus, which includes several medium sized species, characterised by their short, close fur being of one kind only, and the long tail, which in two of the species is naked, although in the thick-tailed opossum (*D. crassicaudata*) it is hairy nearly to its tip. Although in the two species above named the pouch is rudimentary or absent, it is well developed in the Quica opossum (*D. opossum*).

PHILANDER OPOSSUM

The philander (*Didelphys* [*Philander*] *philander*) and the woolly opossum (*D. lanigera*), which represent a second subgenus, are distinguishable from the members of the preceding group by the presence of a distinct brown streak running down the middle of the face. The pouch is represented merely by two longitudinal folds of skin. The philander attains a length of from 9½ to 11½ inches to the root of the tail ; the tail itself varying from 12½ to 15 inches. The fur is thick, soft and woolly, and of a dull yellowish or rufous grey colour, with the face pale grey, except for the dark brown streak down the forehead, and similar dark areas round the eyes; the under parts being some shade of yellow. This species is restricted to Guiana and Brazil, but is replaced in certain other parts of tropical South America by the somewhat larger woolly opossum. In both species the young, which may be a dozen in number, are carried on the back of the mother, and it is marvellous with what rapidity the females when thus loaded manage to climb trees.

MOUSE OPOSSUM

The elegant little mouse opossum (*Didelphys* [*Marmosa*] *murina*), ranging from Central Mexico to Brazil, may be taken as an example of the fourth group of the genus, in which all the species are small, with short, close hair, very long tails, and no dark streak down the middle of the face. The pouch is absent in all the group. In size this opossum may be compared to a house mouse; the colour of its fur is bright red. From their small size it may be inferred that they all live exclusively upon insects.

THREE-STRIPED OPOSSUM

Exclusive of a single species, the last group of the genus includes its smallest representatives, among which the three-striped opossum (*Didelphys americana*) of Brazil is conspicuous on account of its colouring. All the species which constitute this group are shrew-mouse-like creatures, easily recognised by their short and non-prehensile tails, which are less than half the length of the head and body. The three-striped species, which is by no means the smallest, measures from 4½ to 5¼ inches to the root of the tail; the length of the tail being rather less than 2½ inches. Its colour is reddish grey, with three black bands running down the back. Another species (*D. unistriata*) has a single dark line down the back, but in nearly all the others the colour is uniform. Smallest of all is the shrew opossum (*D. sorex*), from Rio Grande do Sul, in which the length of the head and body is less than 3 inches.

WATER OPOSSUM

The water opossum, or yapock (*Chironectes minima*), differs from the other members of the family in having the hind toes webbed, and in the presence of a large tubercle on the outer side of each forefoot, giving the appearance of a sixth digit. This species, which represents a genus by itself, ranges from Guatemala to Brazil, and is distinguished by its peculiar colouring and aquatic habits. The fur is short and close, and the long tail naked and scaly for the greater part of its length. The head and body measure about 14 inches in length, and the tail about 15½ inches. The ground colour of the fur is light grey, upon which is a blackish brown stripe running down the middle of the back, and expanding into large blotches on the shoulders, the middle of the back, the loins, and rump. The face has also blackish markings, with an imperfect whitish crescent above the eyes; and there is a certain amount

YAPOCK, OR WATER-OPOSSUM

of the dark tint on the outer surfaces of the limbs, the under parts being pure white. The female possesses a complete pouch. In habits the yapock closely resembles an otter, to which group of animals it was, indeed, referred by the earlier naturalists. Its food consists of crustaceans, small fishes, and the like.

EXTINCT CARNIVOROUS MARSUPIALS

For some years remains of a number of marsupial-like animals have been known from the Tertiary beds of Santa Cruz in Patagonia, but there has been considerable uncertainty as to whether some of these were true marsupials, or creodont carnivores. In the opinion of Mr. W. J. Sinclair, these marsupials are, in some instances, allied to Australian forms. One of the largest of these is *Prothylacinus patagonicus*, regarded by Mr. Sinclair as a relative of the Tasmanian wolf.

On the other hand, it is suggested that the living South American marsupials, here called selvas, and their extinct Patagonian relatives are not far removed from the ancestral type of the Australian opossums. The importance of this identification lies in the bearing it has on the evidence for a former land connection between South America and Australia. Mr. Sinclair considers himself justified in stating that the relationship between the extinct American and the living Australian types definitely establishes the reality of a former land connection between Australia and South America.

The Patagonian Miocene formation has also yielded remains of a number of species of small opossum-like marsupials, apparently representing a distinct family, the *Microbiotheriidæ*, typified by the genus *Microbiotherium*.

Jaws and teeth of small marsupial-like animals are also found in the Cretaceous and Jurassic formations of Europe and North America; but the imperfect condition of these remains render it very difficult to arrive at a satisfactory conclusion as to the affinities of the animals to which they belonged. They evidently indicate not only numerous genera, but also several distinct family types.

In the one known as *Triconodon*, from the English Purbeck beds, the molar teeth, of which there were four in the fully adult state, are characterised by carrying three compressed cones arranged in a line one before the other; while the premolars, three in number, were simpler. The groove seen on the inner side of the lower jaw corresponds to one found in the banded ant-eater and a few other living marsupials, but unknown in other mammals. In a second type, as represented by *Amphilestes* from the Stonesfield beds near Oxford, the cheek teeth were much more numerous, and the molars less unlike the premolars. In the molar teeth the front and hind cones were relatively smaller in proportion to the middle one than is the case in *Triconodon*; and in their number and form recall the living Australian banded ant-eater. A third type is represented by jaws from the Purbeck rocks of Dorsetshire, known as *Amblotherium*.

ORDER XI. MONOTREMATA
GENERAL CHARACTERISTICS OF THE EGG-LAYING MAMMALS
By R. LYDEKKER

THE Australasian mammals known as the platypus, or duckbill, and the echidnas differ from the other members of the class not only in certain important structural points, but also in their young being hatched from eggs laid by the female parent. In their structural differences and in their mode of reproduction, they resemble reptiles, although they agree with other mammals in that the young, when hatched, are suckled by milk secreted by the mother. Owing to these great differences, the egg-laying mammals, or monotremes, as they are technically termed, constitute not only a distinct order (Monotremata) in the class, but form a separate subclass known as the Prototheria, which is of equal value to the Eutheria, or the subclass comprising all other living mammals.

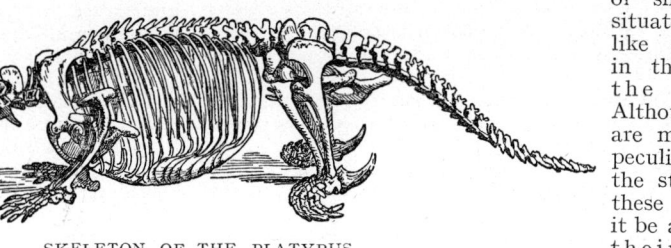
SKELETON OF THE PLATYPUS

These egg-laying mammals show no immediate relationship to birds, but exhibit many indications of close affinity with the extinct anomodont reptiles. The existing representatives of the group, however, are highly specialised types, widely different from the original ancestral types of the mammalian class, which may fairly be presumed to have once existed as members of the Prototheria. Such ancestral types were doubtless furnished with a full series of teeth of a simple type of structure, and it is possible that certain imperfectly known mammals from the earliest Secondary rocks may turn out to be such missing links.

In regard to the distinctive features of the egg-laying mammals as a subclass, they differ from all other members of the class in having only a single excretory aperture to the body, whence their name of Monotremata is derived. Then, again, in their skeleton the shoulder blade (scapula), instead of forming the sole support for the arm, is connected with the breast-bone (sternum) by another plate-like bone termed the coracoid, in advance of which is a third element, known as the precoracoid; the coracoid being always present in the lower vertebrates. Another resemblance to reptiles is found in the presence of a T-shaped bone overlying the breast bone and collar bones (clavicles), and known as the interclavicle; such interclavicle being similar to that of lizards and certain other reptiles, and unknown among higher mammals.

Another feature of these animals is connected with the milk glands, which, instead of opening by nipples or teats, communicate with the exterior by a number of small pores situated in a cup-like depressiom in the skin of the abdomen. Although there are many other peculiarities in the structure of these animals, if it be added that their temperature is markedly lower than that of other mammals, and that their brains are of an exceedingly low and simple type, while their young are produced from eggs, there will not be much difficulty in understanding why they are referred by naturalists to a distinct subclass. It may be added that their skeletons possess " marsupial " bones similar to those of the pouched mammals.

CLASSIFICATION OF MONOTREMATA
ORDER XI
EGG-LAYING MAMMALS—MONOTREMATA
FAMILY 1
Platypus or Duckbill—Ornithorhyncidæ
GENUS
Platypus—Ornithorhynchus
SPECIES

Platypus .... Ornithorhynchus anatinus

FAMILY 2
Spiny Ant-eaters—Echidnidæ
GENUS 1
Five-toed Echidna—Echidna
SPECIES

Five-toed echidna .... Echidna aculeata

GENUS 2
Three-toed Echidna—Proechidna
SPECIES

Three-toed echidna .... Proëchidna bruijnii

PLATYPUS OR DUCKBILL

THE platypus, or duckbill (*Ornithorhynchus anatinus*), derives its name from the duck-like bill forming the extremity of the head. In length the adult male measures from 18 to 20 inches from the tip of the beak to the extremity of the rather short tail (page 126). The muzzle is expanded and flattened, and has both the upper and lower jaws invested with a naked beak not unlike that of a duck, which, although hard and black in stuffed specimens, is probably soft and supple during life. This beak is bordered by a naked sensitive skin, forming a lappet-like fold at the base of the snout, and the nostrils are situated near its anterior extremity.

The depressed and oval-shaped body is covered with short, close, and somewhat mole-like fur, comprising both longer hairs and a woolly under-fur, of which the usual colour is deep brown, becoming paler underneath. There are no external conchs to the ears, and the eyes are small, and in the living state inconspicuous. The tail is broad and somewhat flattened, with a coat of coarse hairs, which on the under surface become more or less worn off in old individuals.

The short limbs have their feet—more especially the front pair—expanded and webbed for the purpose of swimming. Each foot has five complete toes furnished with strong nails; but while in the fore

T

feet the web extends considerably beyond the extremities of the nails, in the hind pair it reaches only to their bases.

The extension of the web of the fore feet might appear to be a hindrance in walking and burrowing, but this difficulty is avoided by the web being then folded back on the palm of the paw, although in almost all pictures, like the one annexed, the animal is represented when on land with the front webs fully expanded.

The nails of the fore foot are somewhat flattened and expanded, while those of the hind foot are longer, narrower, and much curved. To the heel of the male is affixed a long, horny spur (page 126), curving upwards and backwards, and nearly an inch in length ; a canal traversing this spur and opening near its summit is connected with a gland on the leg which secretes a poisonous fluid.

The tongue is small and non-extensile, and the cheeks are provided with pouches of considerable size, doubtless used for storing food. In fully adult specimens each jaw, in place of teeth, carries two pairs of horny plates, of which the more anterior are sharp and narrow, while those behind are broad and flattened. Between these plates the palate is thrown into a number of transverse wrinkles, like those in a duck. In young specimens, however, two or three pairs of cheek teeth may be observed in the upper, and two pairs in the lower jaw ; most of these teeth being broadly quadrangular in form, with two cusps on one side, separated by a hollow from a longitudinal crenulated ridge on the other. As these teeth are gradually worn away by the sand taken into the mouth with the food, the horny plates grow up beneath and around them, till they are eventually shed.

For a long time the number of teeth was supposed to be limited to three or four pairs in each jaw, but Messrs. Wilson and Hill have demonstrated that the set functionally developed originally consisted of five pairs. Of far more importance is their discovery that this functional series was preceded by a simpler series of milk teeth. It, therefore, follows that the platypus— and probably also its sole living relatives, the spiny ant-eaters, or echidnas—is descended from mammals, or half-mammals and half-reptiles, with a complete series of double teeth ; the toothless condition of the adults of both being a purely adaptive character.

The duckbill is restricted to Southern and Eastern Australia and Tasmania, where it used to be fairly common in places suited to it. Thoroughly aquatic in habits, and exclusively frequenting fresh waters, duck-bills are remarkably shy creatures, and rarely seen, except at evening, when they come up to the top of the water, and look like so many black bottles floating on the surface—sinking down immediately if alarmed. They will readily take a bait on a hook.

Although gregarious when in the water, these animals live in pairs in the burrows constructed in the banks ; their favourite haunts being where the streams expand into wide, still pools. In the banks of such sequestered spots are constructed their burrows (page 126) ; each of which usually has one entrance opening beneath the water, and another above the water-level, hidden among the herbage growing on the bank.

The burrow runs obliquely upwards from the water to a great distance—sometimes as much as fifty feet— into the bank ; and ends in a chamber, lined with grass and other substances, where the young are produced. Two eggs are laid at a time, enclosed in a strong, flexible, white shell, measuring about three-quarters of an inch in length, and two-thirds of that in diameter. They resemble the eggs of birds in the large size of their yolk, of which only a small portion goes to the formation of the embryo, while the remainder serves for its food. When first hatched, the young are blind and naked, with the beak very short, and its margins smooth and fleshy, thus forming a nearly circular mouth, well fitted to receive the milk ejected from the glands of the mother.

The duckbill feeds on various small aquatic animals such as insects, crustaceans, and worms, which it obtains by probing with its beak in the mud and sand near the banks ; the food being first stored in the capacious cheek pouches, and afterwards devoured at leisure. The large front paws are the chief agents in swimming and diving. Apparently these animals very seldom leave the water of their own will, except to enter their burrows ; and when on land move somewhat awkwardly, in a shuffling manner. When reposing in their nests, they curl themselves up in a ball-like fashion. The aborigines capture duckbills by digging holes with

PLATYPUS, OR DUCKBILL

sticks into the burrow from the ground above, at distances from one another, until they light upon the terminal chamber.   R. LYDEKKER

STORIES OF THE DUCKBILL

It is one of the dreams of zoologists to see an ornithorhyncus alive in an English collection of animals. It may figure in the zoological gardens of a future state, sharing accommodation with the adult gorilla and the okapi, the humming-bird, and other prizes dear to the naturalist, but unattainable, save in visions, in this life. The story of our mastery of the natural history of the duckbill constitutes one of the comedies of zoology. Travel in Australia and the neighbouring isles early brought to Europe the knowledge of the strange animal's existence, but its life-story none could accurately tell. The home of the animal was far from the haunts of men; only natives, who, in Australia, at any rate, are sometimes deplorably unreliable as naturalists, could track it. Those who were fortunate

FIVE-TOED ECHIDNA

enough to catch sight of the animal were so puzzled that they recorded their bewilderment in enduring terms—the " bird-billed, broad-footed puzzle " they called the beast.

The story that this animal with the body of an otter, or aquatic mole, was a mammal, and yet had the beak of a bird, and laid eggs, like an oviparous reptile, was, naturally, enough to stagger the imagination of sober naturalists. They did not believe in the beak; they doubted the webbed and clawed feet; least of all did they credit the story of the eggs. Many travellers' tales helped to swell the sum of mystery.

One good and meritorious seeker after truth had the fortune to capture an adult female and her two young ones. He kept an interesting record of their habits. " During the day," he wrote, " she (the mother) would remain quiet, huddling up with her young ones, but at night she became very restless and eager to escape. The little ones were as frolicsome as puppies, and apparently as fond of play, and many of their actions were not a little ludicrous. During the day they seemed to prefer a dark corner for repose, and generally resorted to the spot to which they had been accustomed, although they would change it on a sudden, apparently from caprice. They did not appear to like deep water, but enjoyed exceedingly a bathe in shallow water placed in one corner of the pan. They seldom remained more than ten or fifteen minutes in the water at one time. Though apparently nocturnal, or at least preferring the cool and dusky evening to the glare and heat of noon, their movements in this respect were so irregular as to furnish no grounds for a definite conclusion. They slept much, and it frequently happened

that one slept while the other was running about and this occurred at all periods of the day. They climbed with readiness to the summit of a bookcase, and thus, by means of their strong cutaneous muscles and of their claws, mounted with much expedition to the top. Their food consisted of bread soaked in water, chopped eggs, and meat minced very small, and they did not seem to prefer milk to water."

The observer whom we have quoted, could not entertain the idea that the duckbill was oviparous. Another writer, who knew his Australia particularly well, came upon a backwater of the Culgoa river which teemed with duckbills. He shot an adult male in the evening, and in the early morning killed an adult female. The former, though wounded, possessed sufficient vitality to enable him to test the story that the spur of the animal is used as a weapon of offence. It was supposed to emit a virulent poison, causing terrible suffering in the person struck by it. This poor beast, however, made no attempt to ply its weapon, any more than did one caught by the owner of the dam and young. The traveller whose experiences we are now relating, had the good fortune to mark out no fewer than five tunnels running from the water inland, made by duckbills, but he had not time to investigate them. On another occasion he bottled a couple of tiny duckbills in spirits, buried the bottle at the foot of a tree and— left it there to this day.

Our traveller was a sceptic of the sceptics after his own experience, and wrote, " The natives, in various parts of the country have exhibited their ignorance of the natural history of the platypus by asserting that the young are produced from *eggs* !"

The great denouement came in Canada. It was a year famous in the annals of the British Association, the first year in which that august body had met beyond the borders of the British Isles. The president of the Natural History Section for the year received in Montreal a cable from England announcing the illness of his son. He cabled for full particulars, then had to make a trip on the Canadian Pacific Railway. Upon his return he found a telegram awaiting him. Hoping that it might contain the news that their son was better, he placed it into the hands of his wife. She opened it, and instead of the details from home which she expected to find, she was confronted with the startling announcement :

" The duck-billed platypus is oviparous !"

The explanation was that the Royal Society had sent a special representative half-way round the world to study for himself the habits of the *Ornithorhyncus anatinus*. He had carried out careful investigations in Australia, and was able for the first time authoritatively to inform the world that this mysterious relic of ages long bygone really does, despite all its mammalian attributes, well and truly lay eggs. The great news had been cabled out to Canada to gladden the hearts of the devoted naturalists then and there assembled.

E. A. B.

ECHIDNAS

THE echidnas, or spiny ant-eaters, of which there are two species, representing as many genera, are widely different in appearance and structure from the duckbill, and have a more extensive distribution. Instead of mole-like fur, the echidnas have the upper surface of the head and body covered with a mixture of stiff hairs and short, thick spines. The head is rather small and rounded, and has a long, slender, beak-like snout, covered with skin, at the extremity of which are situated the small nostrils. There are no external conchs to the ears, but the eyes are of fair size. The opening of the mouth is very small, and the extensile tongue has the elongated cylindrical form characterising ant-eaters of all kinds. The skull is devoid of all traces of teeth, and remarkable for the slenderness of its lower jaw and its generally bird-like form. Although there is nothing corresponding to the horny plates of the mouth of the duckbill, both the palate and the tongue are thickly beset with small spines.

straight or slightly turned upwards. The smallest race inhabits Port Moresby, in New Guinea, and attains a length of about 14 inches ; its distinctive feature being the shortness of the spines on the back. The race from the Australian mainland is larger, and the spines are of great length. Larger than either of the others is the Tasmanian race, in which the length may be 19 inches ; the very short spines on the back are partially or completely hidden by the fur, the dark brown hue of which is frequently relieved by a white spot on the chest, and the beak is unusually short.

Echidnas are fossorial and mainly nocturnal animals frequenting rocky districts, and subsisting almost exclusively on ants. They are generally found in the mountains, and the three-toed species has been taken at an elevation of between three and four thousand feet. During the breeding season, which takes place at the beginning of the Australian winter, about May, the female develops a nursing-pouch on the under

FIVE-TOED ECHIDNA BURROWING

[Photo, C. Grant Lane

The body of the echidnas is remarkably broad and depressed, with a sharp line of division between the spine-covered area of the back and the hairy under parts. The tail is a mere stump, and the short and sturdy limbs are armed with enormously powerful claws, varying in number from three to five on each foot. Although the front feet are applied to the ground in the usual way, the hind feet, in walking, have the claws turned outwards and backwards. The males resemble those of the duckbill in having a hollow spur at the back of the hind foot, which is probably employed as a weapon in the contests between rival males during the breeding season. The brain of the echidnas differs from that of the duckbill in that the surface is extensively convoluted.

COMMON OR FIVE-TOED ECHIDNA

The common echidna (*Echidna aculeata*) is a variable species, inhabiting Australia, Tasmania, and New Guinea, and characterised by having five toes on each foot, all provided with claws ; those on the fore feet being broad, while the others are narrow and more curved (page 127). In length the beak is about equal to that of the remainder of the head ; and it is either

surface of her body, in which is deposited the single egg. It is ascertained that the female places the egg in the pouch by means of her beak ; and, when ready to hatch, the shell is broken by a heavy knob at the tip of the muzzle of the young. When the young one attains a certain size it is removed by the mother from the pouch, to which, however, it is from time to time returned for suckling.

THREE-TOED ECHIDNA

The three-toed echidna (*Proëchidna bruijnii*) of North-Western New Guinea, is larger than any of the races of the five-toed species, and usually has but three claws to each foot, although there is considerable variation in this respect, one specimen having five claws on the front and four on the hind feet. The beak is bent downwards, and attains a length equal to about double that of the rest of the head. The short spines are generally white, and the colour of the fur is dark brown or black, although the head may be almost white.

Remains of a large species of extinct echidna have been obtained from the superficial deposits of New South Wales, but otherwise nothing is known as to the past history of these animals.

END OF MAMMALIA

CLASS II. BIRDS
THEIR CHARACTERISTICS AND CLASSIFICATION
By R. LYDEKKER

IN many parts of the world a traveller may journey from one week's end to another without coming across a single wild mammal, but few indeed are the regions where bird life in some form will not present itself more or less abundantly to his gaze ; and in no country is this exuberance of birds more remarkable than in the British Islands. This abundance is largely due to the great majority of birds being diurnal in their habits, whereas most mammals are nocturnal ; but it is also in great part owing to the fact that birds are, as a rule, much more numerous, both as regards individuals and species. On this account alone birds have always aroused a widespread interest even among those who pay no particular attention to natural history ; and in addition to this, the beauty of their form, the gorgeous hues of their plumage, and their power of melodious song, combine to render them objects of universal admiration.

Then, again, the many interesting points connected with their habits, and more especially their conjugal affection and the care they bestow on their helpless young, have combined to aid in producing laudable enthusiasm for "our feathered friends." As a result of this world-wide popularity, the literature devoted to birds is far more extensive than that relating to any other group of animals of equal size ; and it may, perhaps, be questioned whether, in spite of their many undoubted claims, birds have not attracted rather more than their fair share of attention, for, after all, the members of the class are wonderfully alike in general structure, even its most divergent representatives presenting no approach to the differences distinguishing nearly allied mammalian orders. It is to a great extent owing to this remarkable structural uniformity that widely different views still exist with regard to the classification of birds.

Birds form a class in the Vertebrata ranking on the same level as the Mammalia, and technically known as Aves. All living birds, and, so far as is known, all fossil ones too, are sharply distinguished from every other animal by the possession of feathers, which correspond in structure to hairs, and are similarly developed from pits sunk in the superficial layer of the skin or epidermis. This is the grand characteristic of birds, most of their other peculiarities being shared by some of the other groups of vertebrates, either living or extinct.

Birds agree with mammals in having a four-chambered heart and hot blood, and also in that the blood is conveyed from the heart to the body by means of a single great artery or aorta ; but while in mammals this aorta passes over the left branch of the windpipe, or bronchus, in birds it crosses the right. In producing their young from eggs laid by the female parent, birds resemble not only the egg-laying mammals, but also most of the lower vertebrates.

All living members of the class possess two pairs of limbs, of which the hind pair is always adapted either for walking or swimming, while the first pair is generally specially modified for flight, although in the flightless species the wings, as the fore limbs are called, are small and more or less rudimentary. Except to a small degree in the penguins, the wings never subserve the purpose of walking, at least in the adult condition. The power of true flight, which is such an essential characteristic of the majority of birds, is found elsewhere in vertebrates only in bats among mammals, the extinct pterodactyles among reptiles, and possibly in flying fishes.

A special peculiarity of birds is the manner in which their whole structure is permeated by atmospheric air taken in through the windpipe. Whereas in most mammals the lungs are enclosed in complete sacs (pleura) and freely suspended in the cavity of the chest, in birds they are moulded to the form of the back of that cavity, while some of the great air tubes pass completely through them, and thus carry the air to all parts of the body. In most birds even the bones, which are hollow, are thus permeated by the air ; and in the dried state many or all of these show a small aperture (pneumatic foramen) by which the air tube enters. It is in consequence of this arrangement that it is impossible to kill a "winged" bird by compressing its windpipe, the process of respiration being carried on by means of the air entering at the broken end of the bone.

In addition to the hollow bones, birds also have a number of air sacs disposed beneath the skin, the position of which will be discussed later. Curiously enough, there appears to be no sort of relation between the power of flight of a bird and the degree of development of pneumaticity, as the aëration of the body and bones is called. The hornbills, for instance, which are poor and heavy fliers, have the whole of the bones, including the vertebræ, so hollowed that they are reduced to little more than shells, while in their not very distant cousin, the rapid flying swift, the aëration is reduced to a minimum.

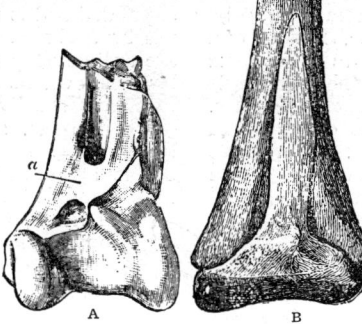

LOWER END OF LEFT FIBULA OF (A) CRANE AND (B) YOUNG OSTRICH
a, bony bridge over groove for tendons.

Among swimming birds a similar difference may be observed, the gannet having a remarkably pneumatic skeleton and large air sacs, while in the allied cormorants there are no air sacs, and the bones are but slightly or not at all pneumatic. According to the old theory, the heated air in the sacs and hollow bones makes the bird lighter than the medium in which it flies, and thus renders flight easy ; but, as has been well observed, the sight of an eagle flying off with a lamb ought to convince anyone that the saving of a fraction of an ounce cannot make the slightest difference to its flight. Moreover, the swallow has all the bones solid. That the air sacs aid to some extent in general respiration, and thus help in maintaining the high temperature of the blood in birds—reaching in some cases 112° F.— was long considered probable, but this cannot be the sole function ; and it has also been considered likely that during flight, when a bird's breathing must be rapid, they are the chief agents in maintaining an equable temperature of the system.

Mr. Bruno Müller, who has investigated the air sacs of pigeons with the view of deciding the function of these structures in birds generally, refuses to accept any of the older theories, and concludes that the air sacs, together with the air cavities in the bones, are not to be regarded as organs with any special function, but as a system of empty interspaces. "Their value lies in their emptiness, that is, in their containing nothing that offers resistance or has an appreciable weight. Flying is the highest form of locomotion, and as such is only possible to a body of high mechanical efficiency. Our most effective machines are by no means compact and solid, but composed of parts as strong as possible in themselves and arranged in the most appropriate manner. The interspaces between the parts are left empty and taken up by air. Birds, at the time they obtained the power of flight, became adapted to its mechanical requirements, and thereby similar to the efficient machines mentioned; they divested themselves of all superfluous material, filling the body space thus obtained with air sacs."

That one of the objects of the coat of feathers, which forms a most efficient insulator, is to assist in the maintenance of a uniform high temperature, cannot be doubted.

An important structural difference between mammals and birds is to be found in the absence in the latter of the partition or diaphragm, which in the former separates the cavity of the chest containing the heart and lungs from that of the abdomen. As the skeleton of birds affords many important characters, distinguishing the class from mammals, this portion of avian anatomy may be described in some detail. In the first place, the skull of a bird differs from that of a mammal in that it is attached to the first joint of the backbone by a single knob, or condyle, instead of by two such condyles. Secondly, each half of the lower jaw is composed of several distinct pieces instead of only one; and in place of the lower jaw articulating directly with what is known as the squamosal region of the brain case of the skull, it does so by the intervention of a separate bone, termed, from its form, the quadrate. In all existing birds both jaws are encased in horn, and are devoid of teeth, and the two halves of the lower jaw are completely soldered together by bone at their junction at the chin, technically known as the symphysis. Certain extinct birds, however, had a full series of teeth, and the two halves of the lower jaw separate; but these lived so long ago as the Chalk period.

As regards the backbone, all existing birds differ from mammals in that the bodies of the vertebræ, at least in the region of the neck, are articulated to one another by saddle-shaped surfaces, instead of by a cup-and-ball joint or two nearly flat surfaces; there is also no constancy in the number of joints in the neck in birds of different groups, so that in this respect the class presents a marked contrast to mammals, in which the number of vertebræ in the neck is nearly always seven. A further peculiarity is that a number of the vertebræ of the back, together with some of those of the tail, are solidly united with the proper sacrum, while the whole long series of welded vertebræ is firmly attached to the haunch bones of the pelvis.

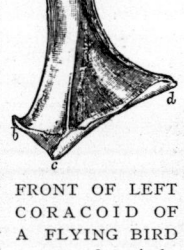

FRONT OF LEFT CORACOID OF A FLYING BIRD

a, process for articulation of furcula; *b, c, d*, surface for junction with breast bone.

In all living birds the bones of the tail are very few in number, and terminate in a triangular bone termed the ploughshare bone. It is to this region of the body that the tail feathers of a bird, commonly called the tail, are attached; although the so-called tail of a bird does not correspond with the tail of a mammal. In the earliest known birds, however, the tail was long, and composed of a number of vertebræ, each carrying a pair of feathers (p. 915). The pelvis of a bird is remarkable for the great elongation of the haunch bones, and also for the fact that the portion known as the pubis is directed backwards parallel with the element termed the ischium; the three elements being united together as in mammals, but, with two exceptions, differing from the condition obtaining in that class by the fact that neither the ischium nor the pubis unites with its fellow of the opposite side in the middle line. The cup in the pelvis for the head of the thigh bone is also peculiar in that it is always open at the base. The firm union of the haunch bones with such a large portion of the backbone is necessary to afford a solid basis of support for the rest of the skeleton in flight.

Equally essential is a solid union between the bones of the shoulder and the breast bone. Accordingly, as in the egg-laying mammals, the blade bone, or scapula, is connected with the breast bone, or sternum, by a coracoid, the scapula and coracoid thus jointly forming the cup for the articulation of the head of the arm bone, or humerus. Although in flightless birds the coracoid bone is short and broad, in other species it is more or less elongated; and in either case its lower expanded end is received in a groove on the summit of the breast bone. Usually the collar bones, or clavicles, are well developed, and united to form a V or U shaped bone, known as the "merry-thought," or furcula; this furcula generally articulating with a process on the coracoid bone, and also with the anterior end of the breast bone.

The breast bone in flying birds is provided with a strong keel in the middle of its inferior surface, in order to afford support for the powerful muscles moving the wing, but in flightless birds it is smooth and rounded. To the sides of the upper part of the breast bone are attached the lower segments of the ribs; the ribs themselves being few in number, and distinguished from those of mammals by the presence of oblique (uncinate) processes projecting from the hind border.

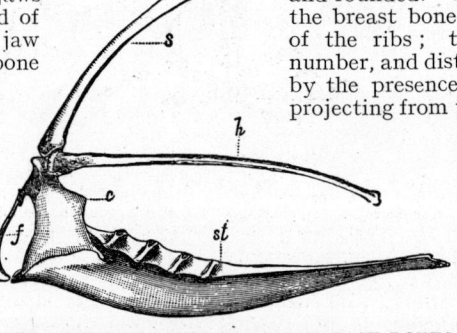

LEFT SIDE OF SHOULDER AND BREAST BONES OF A FLIGHTLESS BIRD

s, blade bone or scapula; *c*, coracoid; *h*, arm bone or humerus; *f*, furcula; *st*, breast bone or sternum.

With regard to the limbs, the bones of a bird's wing correspond generally to those of the arm or fore leg of a mammal; the arm bone or humerus having distinct condyles for the articulation of the bones of the fore arm (radius and ulna), and being sometimes furnished with a projecting process above the outermost of these two condyles. The two bones of the fore arm always remain separate from one another. In the wrist the numerous bones found in mammals, however, are reduced to two; and the metacarpus and hand are flattened and specially modified. Owing to this modification there are never more than three digits (fingers), which are usually without claws, although among recent birds two may be thus armed. The thumb, or first digit, is represented merely by one or two joints, and carries the so-called bastard wing; while the other two digits represent the index and middle fingers of the human hand. The respective metacarpals, or supporting bones of these digits, are united at their two ends so as to form a single bone, while the index finger has two flattened joints, and the third finger one.

In the hind limb there is a still wider departure from the mammalian type. The uppermost bone in a bird's leg is the thigh bone, or femur, below which comes the tibia, or larger bone of the lower leg, while on the outer side of this is a small splint representing the fibula. Below the tibia comes another long bone, terminating—except in the ostrich, where they are reduced to two—in three pulley-like surfaces, known as trochleæ, to which are articulated the toe bones. Obviously this third, or lowest, long bone corresponds to the metatarsus of a mammal, consisting, in fact, of the three middle metatarsals of the typical five-toed limb welded together, in the same manner as two such metatarsals are united in the hind limb of a ruminant mammal.

It may, therefore, be called either the metatarsus or the cannon bone, while that portion of the leg to which it belongs is often conveniently referred to as the shank. As regards the ankle, or tarsus, in the bird's leg, its upper bones have united to the lower end of the tibia ; while the lower row has joined the upper end of the cannon bone. The figure on page 907 exhibits the lower end of the tibia of an adult crane and of a young ostrich, and it will be seen that in the latter the upper ankle bone is still distinct, while in the former it has become completely united with the tibia.

A precisely similar state of things takes place in the formation of the cannon bone, which includes the lower row of the bones of the ankle ; and it will, therefore, be apparent that the tibia of a bird corresponds to the tibia, *plus* the upper half of the ankle, of a mammal ; while the cannon bone represents the metatarsus, *plus* the lower half of the ankle. Hence, while the ankle joint in a mammal occurs between the tibia and the upper row of ankle bones, in a bird it is placed between the upper and lower rows of the ankle. The bony bridge seen at *a* in the figure of the tibia of the crane, which is very commonly present in birds, acts as a pulley for the tendons of the muscles of the front of the leg which pass beneath. Such pulleys enable the fleshy portions of the muscles to be placed high up in the limb, and thus cause the centre of gravity of the body to be near the wings, an arrangement essential for flight.

In addition to the three toes articulating with the lower end of the cannon bone, most birds have another toe, corresponding to the first or great toe of the human foot, of which the metacarpal is loosely attached to a facet on the inner edge of the hind surface of the cannon bone. No bird has any trace of the fifth toe. The number of joints in each toe, in place of not exceeding three as in ordinary mammals, increases regularly from the first to the fourth toe.

Since the structure of the base of the skull is of

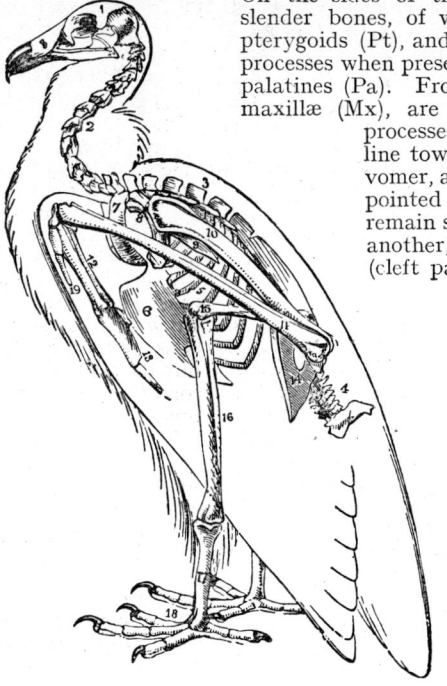

SKELETON OF VULTURE

1, head ; 2, neck ; 3, back ; 4, tail ; 5, ribs ; 6, breast bone ; 7, furcula ; 8, coracoid ; 9, scapula ; 10, humerus ; 11, ulna ; 12, metacarpus ; 13, phalanges ; 14, pelvis ; 15, femur ; 16, tibia ; 17, metatarsus or cannon bone ; 18, toes ; 19, thumb.

some importance in classification, a few words are necessary on this point. In the first place, the skull of a bird is characterised by the great size of the sockets for the eyes, which are separated from one another merely by a thin bony partition. The aperture for the nostrils may be either short and rounded, when the skull is said to be holorhinal, or they may form elongated slits, as in a pigeon, when the condition is termed schizorhinal. In all birds most of the component bones of the skull are completely united, without any trace of the original lines of division, in the adult state ; and in ornithology it is usual to apply the terms upper and lower mandible to the two halves of the beak.

With regard to the bones of the palate, the introduction of a number of technical terms is unavoidable. In the middle of the hind part of the lower surface of a bird's skull may be seen a pointed rod of bone, the sphenoidal rostrum, which may carry, (as in O of figure A on page 911) a pair of basipterygoid facets ; and in advance of this is a single or double bone, termed the vomer (Vo). On the sides of this central axis are two pairs of slender bones, of which the hind ones are termed pterygoids (Pt), and articulate with the basipterygoid processes when present ; while the front pair are named palatines (Pa). From the sides of the upper jaw, or maxillæ (Mx), are given off two maxillo-palatine processes (Mxp), projecting in the middle line towards the vomer. Now, when the vomer, as in the fowl and capercaillie (A), is pointed in front, while the maxillo-palatines remain separate both from it and from one another, the skull is said to be schizognathous (cleft palate). When, on the other hand, as in the duck (B), the maxillo-palatines unite in the middle line, so as to form a bridge in front of the vomer, the construction is termed desmognathous (bridged palate).

In a third modification, as exemplified in the raven (C) and all other perching birds, the maxillo-palatines, although extending beneath the vomer, do not unite either with that bone or with one another, while the vomer itself is expanded and abruptly truncated in front, this arrangement being termed ægithognathous (sparrow palate). Various minor modifications of these three types exist, but a little practice will render it easy to determine to which of the three any given skull conforms. A fourth modification, met with only among the ostrich-like birds and the South American tinamus, differs from the condition obtaining in all other birds, and is probably the most ancient type. Next to the ostrich modification, the most primitive type of palate is that of the game birds, and the most complex that of the ducks, owls, and certain other groups. This complex, or desmognathous, type of palate may have been acquired independently in two or more groups of birds.

Before leaving the subject of the skull, it may be mentioned that the outer coat or " white " of the eye of a bird contains a movable ring of overlapping bones surrounding the pupil and iris, which by their contraction or expansion are considered to alter the degree of convexity of the aqueous humour and cornea, and thus to render the eye focally adapted to the constantly varying distance of objects during flight.

When clothed with its feathers, the bodily form of an ordinary bird is the one best adapted for cleaving the air with the least possible resistance ; the head being more or less sharpened, the body gradually swelling to a point some distance in advance of the middle, and then as rapidly decreasing in girth, while the feathers are all directed from the head towards the tail. In those birds in which the neck is not unduly elongated the whole contour is spindle-shaped (fusiform) and may be compared to two cones placed base to base at the thickest part of the body. It is essential to the exigencies of flight that the centre of gravity should be on the lower aspect of the body, as nearly as possible immediately below the points of suspension by the wings ; and, in order to ensure this, there is the concentration of muscles and other organs in this region, to which allusion has been already made.

Not only are the fleshy portions of the muscles of the legs mainly confined to the upper portions of those limbs, but the muscles which elevate the wings are actually placed on the under instead of on the upper surface of the body. This is exemplified in the breast of a flying bird, such as the blackcock, in which the great superficial muscle known as the pectoralis major is for the purpose of depressing the wing ; while beneath this is a second muscle —the pectoralis minor—of which the function is to raise the wing bone, or humerus. This is effected by the muscle terminating in a tendon which passes through a pulley over the head of the scapula and coracoid, and is then attached to the upper surface of the humerus ; that bone being accordingly elevated when the muscle contracts. In a blackcock, the distinction between the pectoralis major and pectoralis minor is very easy to recognise, as the former muscle is red and the latter white. The same tendency to the concentration of structures is exhibited by the organ of voice (syrinx) of a bird being placed within the chest, where the windpipe divides into the two bronchi, instead of, as in mammals, immediately beneath the lower jaw.

An important external feature in birds is the frequent presence of a gland, termed the oil gland, on the upper surface of the rump, the function of which is to secrete oil for the lubrication of the feathers. This gland, which is most developed in aquatic birds, may be absent, and when present may be either naked at the summit, or crowned with a tuft of feathers. This gland is absolutely peculiar to birds ; and, as it does not appear to have been inherited from reptiles, those birds in which it is absent may belong to a group in which this organ was never developed.

Ornithologists have devised a number of terms to indicate the plumage of the different regions in the body of a bird, most of which are indicated in the diagram on page 912. The ears of all birds are unprovided with external conchs, merely opening flat on the sides of the head, usually a little behind and below the eyes. The eyes, which are in most cases placed laterally and near the middle of the head, are provided with a third eyelid, or nictitating membrane, which can be drawn obliquely like a shutter over the eyeball, while the proper eyelids remain open, as may be observed in a captive owl or eagle, when the glistening white nictitating membrane will be seen from time to time to sweep across the eye with extreme rapidity.

The beaks of birds have different terms applied to them, according to their relative length and form, such as fissirostral (split), dentirostral (notched),

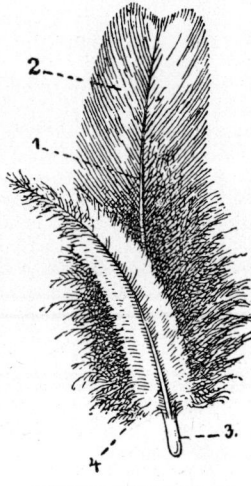

UNDER SURFACE OF CONTOUR FEATHER

1, shaft ; 2, vane ; 3, quill ; 4, after-shaft.

conirostral (conical), etc. A horny investment is also generally present on such portions of the lower parts of the legs as are devoid of feathers ; although in some cases, as in ducks, this is replaced by a more or less leathery skin. The horny covering of the metatarsus may consist of small scales, with their edges in apposition, as in the plovers, when it is said to be reticulate ; but frequently the front surface, as in game birds, has a number of broad over-lapping plates, when it is termed scutate. Occasionally each side is invested by a single greave-like plate meeting its fellow in a prominent ridge at the back.

In certain groups the horny sheath of the beak is composed of several separate pieces, which have received distinctive names ; and Dr. Einar Lönnberg has attempted to show that these elements of the bird's beak sheath really correspond with certain of the horny shields covering the fore part of the head in lizards and other reptiles. The heads of nearly all reptiles show a median unpaired horny shield on the muzzle known as the rostral, behind which on each side is a series of marginal labials, while these are represented in the lower jaw by an unpaired mental (chin) in front, and a series of infra-labials on the sides. There is generally also a single nasal shield pierced by the nostril, or two nasals adjacent to the latter. In ancestral reptiles there may have been, in addition to the paired nasals, a row of shields along the middle of the head, and a somewhat similar arrangement on the lower jaw. At the time that birds were provided with teeth, the horny covering of their beaks was probably of little moment, but when teeth were lost, the latter assumed a position of considerable importance in the economy.

As regards the correlation of the elements in the bird's beak sheath with the head scales of reptiles, Dr. Lönnberg finds that, as in the rhea and emeu, there is often present a median upper piece representing the rostral, and a lower element corresponding to the mental, while lateral pieces represent the labials and infra-labials. In the petrels, in which the different elements are very distinct, the rostral is represented by the powerful hook of the beak of the albatross, while the tubular shields enclosing the nostrils correspond to the nasals, and the lateral elements to the labials ; analogous identifications being made in the case of the lower jaw. Admitting these identifications, there will be little difficulty in naming the separate elements in the beak of the cormorant and the gannet ; while it will be equally obvious that the " nail " on the beak of the duck tribe represents the rostral shield in the upper mandible and the mental in the lower.

These elements are the most functionally important, and are, therefore, the most solid, the lateral elements tending to become softer, and thus approximating to a " cere." In hawks, owls, and parrots the hard part of the short beak seems to be formed almost entirely by the rostral and mental pieces, the lateral elements being in a state of degeneration and forming the " cere." In the game birds, again, the whole beak is practically formed by the above-named two elements, the lateral pieces having so completely degenerated that not even a cere is left, although traces of a few of them persist in the form of horny scales on the margins of the gape. Finally, in perching birds the beak likewise consists almost exclusively of the rostral above and the mental below, although remnants of the labials and infra-labials are present in the form of the yellow or orange band which so frequently borders the gape of the nestling. In this feature the perching birds proclaim their specialised position, the beak departing more widely from the primitive and presumed reptilian type than is the case in any other group.

As regards the plumage of birds, a feather in its complete state of development consists of a main stem, and a secondary stem, or aftershaft; but the latter is frequently wanting. The base of the main stem is formed by the hollow horny quill, the lower end of which is pointed and inserted into the skin. The upper part of the quill passes into the shaft, or rachis, at a point marked by a small aperture termed the upper umbilicus. The shaft is four-sided, elastic, pithy, and less horny than the quill, and gradually tapers at its extremity to a fine point. On each side of the shaft there are two webs, collectively forming the vane of the feather. Each web or half of the vane, one of which is generally considerably wider than the other, is composed of a series of flattened plates closely applied to one another, and diverging from the shaft at an open angle, each plate terminating in a point. These plates form the barbs, and they are held together by barbules, given off in the same manner as are the barbs from the stem, while the barbules may again give off hooklets (see page 922).

The aftershaft is, when fully developed, a miniature of the main stem, from which it is given off at the junction of the quill with the shaft. Such is the structure of a typical feather; but the soft feathers known as down have the stem short and weak, or even wanting, while the barbs are soft and not held together by fully-formed barbules and hooklets. Sometimes the ends of such feathers break up into powder, and they may then be spoken of as powder-down feathers. In another type of feather the vane is rudimentary, and the whole structure then becomes more or less hair-like; to such the term thread feathers is applicable. Finally, the feathers covering the body and concealing the underlying down are conveniently referred to as contour feathers.

Instead of being evenly distributed over the body of a bird, the feathers grow from certain well-defined tracts, between which are bare spaces. Although such tracts have received distinct names, and are of some importance in classification, it will suffice to mention their mere existence.

The tail feathers, very generally twelve in number, are termed rectrices, and are usually firm and fully developed. Above and below the rectrices are the upper and under tail coverts, as shown in the diagram on page 912. Although generally small and unimportant, in the peacock the upper tail coverts attain an extraordinary development, and constitute what is commonly designated the tail. Premising that the feathers clothing the shoulders are termed scapulars,

and those between them interscapulars, attention may be directed to the feathers of the wings. First of all is the little group of feathers forming the bastard wing, or alula, which are carried by the first digit, or thumb, and lie on the front border of the back of the wing. Next come the flight feathers, remiges, or quills, which arise from the bones of the arm and pinion (or hand, exclusive of the thumb), all these being strong, firm feathers, which give rise to the main contour of the wing.

Such of the remiges as take their origin from the pinion are termed primaries, while those attached to the fore arm (ulna) and upper arm (humerus) are entitled secondaries, though the remiges arising from the humerus used to be distinguished as tertiaries, and the term secondaries confined to those attached to the ulna. The primaries are the firmest and stiffest of the wing feathers, and are very generally either nine or ten in number. As the rectrices of the tail have tail coverts, so the remiges have wing coverts, both above and below [see page 922]. Of the upper wing coverts, the first are the primary coverts overlying the primaries; while the secondaries are overlain by three series, respectively known as the greater, median, and lesser upper secondary wing coverts, of which the greater coverts are the largest and the most important in classification. The under wing coverts, which are less important in classification, are likewise divided into a primary and secondary series.

When first hatched, birds are covered with some kind of down, very scanty in those which are reared in nests, but thick in all those able to run at the time of birth. The true feathers, however, are soon developed, those of the wings and tail being usually the first to make their appearance, and the rapidity with which feathers grow is one of the most remarkable features of birds. In order to preserve the plumage in good condition, it is essential that it should be renewed at least once a year. This renewal of the feathers is termed moulting, and often occurs twice during the year, while in the ptarmigan there are three moults. The chief moult usually takes place soon after the breeding season, but in those birds which have a special breeding plumage a second moult takes place previous to that period. In ducks the feathers developed after the main moult—the so-called eclipse plumage—are worn only for a very short period, and are soon succeeded by the breeding dress, which is in use for the greater part of the year. In the ptarmigan the third moult is for the assumption of the white winter dress. Usually the wing feathers are shed in pairs one after another, but among the ducks, which conceal themselves among water plants, and can thus protect themselves without flight, the shedding of all the wing feathers is frequently almost simultaneous.

Reference may be made in this place to what is known as parasitism among birds. Although the

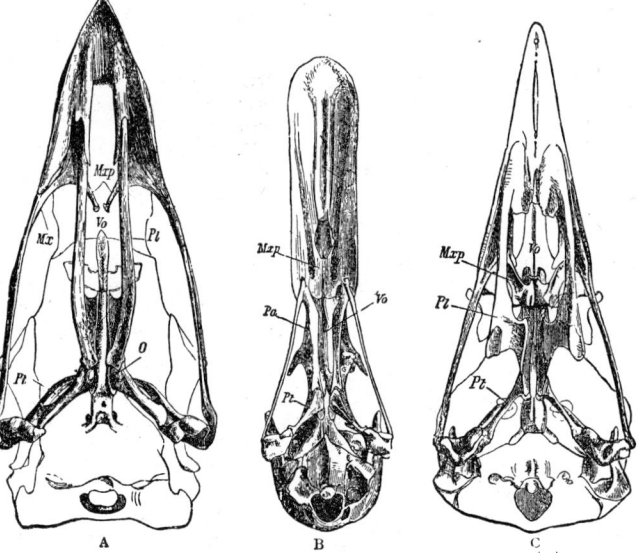

UNDER VIEW OF SKULL OF (A) CAPERCAILLIE, (B) DUCK, AND (C) RAVEN

Mx. maxillæ; Mxp, maxillo-palatine; Vo, vomer; Pa, palatine; Pt, pterygoid; O, basipterygoid facet.

European cuckoo is the most familiar example of a bird which deposits its eggs (singly) in the nests of other species, this parasitic habit is shared by a number of other kinds of cuckoos, some more or less nearly allied to the typical species, and others markedly distinct. Among the latter is the great spotted cuckoo of Southern Europe, which victimises magpies, blue magpies, and crows.

In the instance of magpies the resemblance of the eggs of the intruder to those of the rightful owner of the nest is remarkably close.

On the other hand, there are certain cuckoos, such as the coucal of Madagascar and the American black-billed cuckoo, which build nests and incubate a clutch of their own eggs, the nest in this instance being remarkably small for the size of the bird. Finally, in certain South American cuckoos, such as the ani and the guira, several hens combine to lay a clutch of eggs in one nest, in which they take turns at incubation.

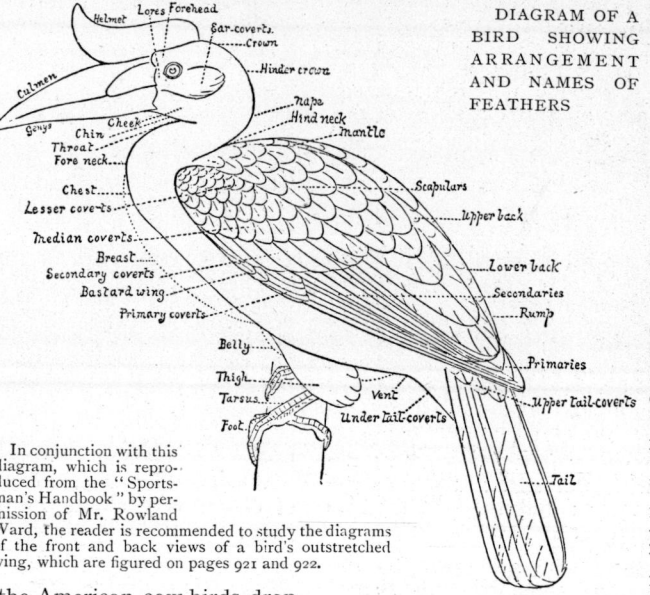

DIAGRAM OF A BIRD SHOWING ARRANGEMENT AND NAMES OF FEATHERS

In conjunction with this diagram, which is reproduced from the "Sportsman's Handbook" by permission of Mr. Rowland Ward, the reader is recommended to study the diagrams of the front and back views of a bird's outstretched wing, which are figured on pages 921 and 922.

The parasitic habit is, however, not restricted to the cuckoo family, for the American cow birds drop their eggs singly among those of tyrant birds and other species ; and the same is the case with the African honey-guides of the family Indicatoridæ.

In connection with the origin of the parasitic habit in cuckoos, it has been stated that one American species (*Coccyzus americanus*), which is generally in the habit of building a nest and hatching its own eggs, occasionally lays in the nests of other birds. Another instance of the beginning of this habit is afforded by the Indian hawk-cuckoos of the genus *Hierococcyx*, five species of which lay in the nests of babbling-thrushes, while the sixth is reported to make a nest of its own.

Although, from their power of flight and migratory habits, which are dealt with on pages 921-9, it might seem that birds would have no definite distributional areas, yet this is by no means the case ; and the zoological regions into which the world has been mapped out were originally defined from the various groups of birds by which they are inhabited. For instance, while the Eastern Holarctic region—that is to say, the greater part of Europe and Asia north of the line of the Himalaya—is characterised by the sole possession of capercaillie and its abundance of grouse, buntings, and the like, North America is the sole home of the turkey, and humming birds are mainly characteristic of South and Central America, as are birds of paradise, lyre birds, and cockatoos of the Australasian region. Many birds, especially some of the humming birds, have indeed a very local distribution ; and, as might have been expected, the various groups of flightless birds are now confined to particular continents and islands. The reader will gather many of the leading facts in connection with the geographical distribution in the course of the description of the various groups.

As regards their geological distribution, it may be mentioned that most of the birds from the Tertiary formations are more or less closely allied to existing types. In the antecedent Cretaceous (Chalk) epoch several, at least, of the birds were furnished with teeth, while in the still older Jurassic or Oolitic epoch the one definitely known bird (*Archæopteryx*) was not only furnished with teeth, but had a long tapering tail [page 915] and exhibited several other features indicative of reptilian affinity. While birds present no sort of relationship to mammals, they show manifest indications of being nearly allied to certain extinct groups of reptiles, but the nature of that relationship can be best indicated in the account of those groups.

On few subjects is there greater diversity of views among naturalists than with regard to the classification of birds ; scarcely any two ornithologists being in accord on this point. To a great extent this is owing to that structural uniformity among the members of the class to which reference has been already made, this rendering it almost impossible to determine what features should be regarded as of primary importance.

The following list shows the major groups, or orders, in which the great majority of birds may be arranged. Some species, indeed, do not lend themselves very readily to inclusion in any of these orders ; but, in place of forming special orders for their reception, such aberrant types may be noticed in connection with the groups to which they appear to exhibit most signs of relationship.

TABLE SHOWING THE ORDERS OF THE CLASS AVES

Order			
,,	i.	Perching Birds	Passeres
,,	ii.	Woodpeckers, Trogons, Hornbills, etc.	Picariæ
,,	iii.	Cuckoos and Turacos ..	Cuculi
,,	iv.	Parrots and Cockatoos ..	Psittaci
,,	v.	Owls	Striges
,,	vi.	Hawks, Eagles, and Vultures ..	Accipitres
,,	vii.	Cormorants, Gannets, and Pelicans	Steganopodes
,,	viii.	Ichthyornis (extinct) ..	Odontormæ
,,	ix.	Ducks, Geese, and Swans ..	Anseres
,,	x.	Flamingoes	Phænicopteri
,,	xi.	Screamers	Palamedeæ
,,	xii.	Herons, Storks, and Ibises ..	Herodiones
,,	xiii.	Cranes and Bustards ..	Alectorides
,,	xiv.	Plovers, Godwits, and Snipe ..	Limicolæ
,,	xv.	Gulls and Terns	Gaviæ
,,	xvi.	Auks	Alcæ
,,	xvii.	Petrels and Albatrosses ..	Tubinares
,,	xviii.	Penguins	Impennes
,,	xix.	Hesperornis (extinct) ..	Odontolcæ
,,	xx.	Grebes and Divers	Pygopodes
,,	xxi.	Coots and Rails	Fulicariæ
,,	xxii.	Pigeons	Columbæ
,,	xxiii.	Sand-grouse	Pterocletæ
,,	xxiv.	Game birds	Gallinæ
,,	xxv.	Tinamus	Crypturi
,,	xxvi.	Ostriches, Emeus, and Kiwis	Ratitæ
,,	xxvii.	Archæopteryx (extinct) ..	Saururæ

Although the various orders in this list indicate more or less nearly allied groups of birds, their mutual relationships—even if these were definitely known—cannot by any possibility be indicated in a linear series.

In the following summary of the various orders, reference may be made to alternative schemes of classification which have been proposed, and to presumed relationships between different groups.

As to the Passeres, or perching birds (i.), all naturalists are in practical agreement about the limitations and serial position of the group.

With regard to the Picariæ, or picarian birds (ii.), this group is equivalent to the Coraciiformes (roller-like) of Mr. A. H. Evans, with the exception of the exclusion of the owls (v.), which it is convenient to keep separate. An alternative scheme is to split up the picarian birds into (1) woodpeckers and toucans; (2) trogons; (3) swifts and humming birds; (4) nightjars; and (5) rollers, kingfishers, hornbills, etc.; and to intercalate the owls between Nos. 2 and 3. This scheme, however, has the disadvantage of increasing the number of orders.

The cuckoos (iii.) and the parrots (iv.) are brigaded together by Mr. Evans under the common title of Cuculiformes (cuckoo-like), but by Dr. Bowdler Sharpe are widely sundered.

The diurnal birds of prey (vi.) are divided by Dr. Sharpe into two orders—the hawk-like birds of the Old World, and the condors of the New; both being placed, as here, between the owls (v.) and the cormorant group (vii.). On the other hand, they are placed by Mr. Evans between the geese (ix.) and the tinamus (xxv.).

As regards the cormorant group (vii.), these are placed by Dr. Sharpe next the diurnal birds of prey, but by Mr. Evans with the flamingoes (x.) and herons, storks, and ibises (xii.) in a single group under the name of Ciconiiformes (stork-like).

The cranes and bustards (xiii.) are taken by Mr. Evans to include, under the name of crane-shaped birds, the rail tribe (xxi.), although the latter are widely sundered by Dr. Sharpe, who places them, as here, next the pigeons (xxii.).

The plovers, godwits, and snipe (xiv.), and gulls and terns (xv.), which are recognised by Dr. Sharpe as distinct orders, are brigaded by Mr. Evans with the auks (xvi.) and pigeons (xxii.) under the common title of Charadriiformes (plover-like).

All are agreed that the petrels and albatrosses (xvii.) form a perfectly distinct and natural group, although opinions differ as to its serial position; and much the same may be stated with regard to the grebes and divers (xx.) and penguins (xviii.). The pigeons (xxii.) are brigaded by Mr. Evans with the plover tribe, gulls, terns, and auks; and are placed by Mr. W. P. Pycraft next the Charadriiformes (plover-like), which he takes to include the three groups just named. On the other hand, they are located by Dr. Sharpe between the rail group (xxi.) and the game birds (xxiv.).

Nor are views less diverse with regard to the position of the tinamus (xxv.), which are placed by Dr. Sharpe, as here, but are included in the ostrich group by Mr. Pycraft; while by Mr. Evans they are located between the diurnal birds of prey (vi.) and the game birds (xxiv.); the two last-named groups being also placed in juxtaposition by Mr. Pycraft.

Passing on to the ostrich group (xxvi.), it may be mentioned that the loss of a keel, or carina, to the breast bone, or sternum, has been regarded as a feature of such importance as to justify the division of all existing birds into two primary sections, the Ratitæ (raft-breasted) on the one hand, and the Carinatæ (keel-breasted), comprising all the rest, on the other. It is, however, perfectly clear that the disappearance of the keel to the breast bone, accompanied by certain modifications in the relations of the bones of the shoulder girdle, is merely a result of the loss of flight, and therefore an adaptive rather than an original structural modification. Consequently, the ostrich group is entitled to little, if any, higher rank than the other orders of birds, although they differ from other living birds, with the exception of the tinamus, in the structure of the palate, and for the most part also in having only one condyle on the quadrate bone for the articulation of the lower jaw.

On the other hand, the extinct lizard-tailed birds (*Archæopteryx*) of the Jurassic period are so distinct from all other members of the class that they ought to form a group by themselves equivalent in value to one containing all the rest. For these two groups the names of Archæornithes (ancient birds) and Neornithes (modern birds) have been proposed. And to make the groups of birds correspond in some degree with those into which mammals are divided it has been suggested to regard the Archæornithes and Neornithes as orders, and the groups to which ordinal rank is generally accorded as sub-orders.

Summing up the results of the foregoing review, it seems that the division into Archæornithes and Neornithes, and the relegation of the ostrich group to the same rank as the other so-called orders, are practically the only points where the classification of birds is established on a firm basis. As regards the limitations and serial positions of most of the other orders scarcely any two naturalists are in complete accord.

The classification here adopted is, to a considerable extent, a compromise between extreme views, and will be found to agree in many important particulars with the one given by Dr. Sharpe in the "Hand-list of the Genera of Birds," published by the British Museum.

The number of existing species of birds being in all probability considerably over fifteen thousand—even when many of those commonly regarded as species are classed as races—it is obvious that the various groups must be treated more concisely than was possible with the mammals; and in many instances we need allude only to the families, without referring to the genera.

CUCKOO'S EGG IN A WHITETHROAT'S NEST

It may be noticed that in the course of this introduction practically nothing has been said as to the anatomy of the soft internal parts of birds, for which the reader must be referred to other works. It may, however, be mentioned that at the junction of the small with the large intestine most birds have a pair of blind appendages, or cœca, which vary greatly in relative length in the different groups, and are of considerable importance in classification.   R. LYDEKKER.

1. MOA 2. ÆPYORNIS AND ITS EGG 3. GREAT AUK 4. SOLITAIRE 5. DODO

THE PAST AND FUTURE OF BIRDS

By Prof. J. ARTHUR THOMSON

THE rock record, so far as we know it, shows that before the ages called Triassic—at the dawn of the Secondary or Mesozoic period—there were no back-boned animals of higher rank than reptiles. In other words, there were no birds or mammals upon the earth. The fossiliferous rocks that were laid down in the Triassic age contain a few very unsatisfactory remains of what were probably mammals, and the first known bird—*Archæopteryx*—occurred in the next series, which is known as Jurassic. In the same series remains of small mammals become more numerous and satisfactory. It may seem strange that remains of mammals should appear in the Triassic, and the first bird in the Jurassic, which is later; but, in the first place, the Triassic fossils ascribed to mammals are so very fragmentary that it is difficult to be sure that they are not reptilian; and, in the second place, birds and mammals are on quite different lines of evolution and not related to one another except in having a common ancestry in reptiles. For it was certainly from some ancient reptilian stock that the race of birds took origin. As there seems at first sight every possible antithesis, rather than any evidence of affinity between bird and reptile, it will be useful to consider the general arguments which lead to a belief in their close relationship.

STRUCTURAL RESEMBLANCES TO REPTILES

A bird is known by its feathers—such a contrast to the scales of reptiles, we are accustomed to say. But we have only to look at the foot of a bird to see that the legacy of scales is not lost. The horny bill which covers the bones of the beak is sometimes "compound"—that is to say, composed of many separable pieces, as in the albatross, and there is no doubt that these are comparable to the scales on the jaws of reptiles. It is interesting also to note that a puffin moults the outer covering of its bill-scales every year, which is much nearer to the moulting seen in reptiles than to the moulting of feathers. The little hardening of horn and lime at the tip of the bill of the unhatched chick—which is used in breaking the egg-shell, and is somewhat unfortunately named the egg-tooth—is seen in some reptiles as well. There is often a claw on the thumb of a bird's wing, and sometimes, as in the ostrich, on the first finger as well; in the young hoatzin (*Opisthocomus*) the claws on the thumb are unusually long, and are mobile enough to be used in scrambling.

FOSSIL REMAINS OF THE ARCHÆOPTERYX
Found in the lithographic stone of Erichstädt, Bavaria

Here, again, therefore, we have relics of reptilian ancestry.

The skull of an eagle is very different from that of a crocodile, but in both we see a single occipital condyle on which the skull moves, a complex mandible or lower jaw, made up of half-a-dozen bones on each side, an articulation of the lower jaw with the quadrate bone in the back part of the skull, a delicate rod of bone (the columella) passing from the drum to the inner ear, and so on, all of them features of some importance, and none of them to be seen in mammals. All of these point to the close alliance of birds and reptiles. In some other parts of the body the same relationship is indicated, but we have said enough to illustrate the anatomical section of the evidence which led Professor Huxley to unite birds and reptiles together as Sauropsida, in contrast to mammals, on the one hand, and amphibians and fishes (Ichthyopsida), on the other.

Birds and reptiles have the same type of egg, the true ovum, or egg-cell, becoming enormously dilated with yolk and surrounded by albumen and a shell. In both cases there is the same kind of egg-cleavage (partial and discoidal), and the early stages of embryonic development are closely alike. Indeed, in the case of the chick, it is not till the sixth day that definitely "avian" characters begin to appear. In other words, the embryo bird and the embryo reptile travel at first along parallel paths, and only gradually diverge.

Even after the divergence has begun, as seen, for instance, in the appearance of the initial stages of feathers, there is in the development of some of the bird's organs—for example, the heart—a gradual progress through stages closely similar to those seen in the organogenesis of reptiles. We may also notice that the membranes investing the embryo within the egg-shell are very closely similar in bird and reptile—the amnion forming a protective hood and the allantois securing respiration.

One of the most accomplished and original of embryologists, Professor W. K. Parker, gave, in 1868, a very vivid expression of his belief in the recapitulation of the past in the present. Speaking of his work on the development of the chick, he said, " Whilst at work I seemed to myself to have been endeavouring to decipher a palimpsest, and one not erased and written upon again just once, but five or six times over. Having erased, as it were, the characters of the culminating type—those of the gaudy Indian bird—I seemed to be amongst the sombre grouse; and then, towards incubation, the characters of the sandgrouse and hemipod stood out before me. Rubbing these away, in my downward work the form of the tinamou looked me in the face; then the aberrant ostrich seemed to be described in large archaic characters; a little while, and these faded into what could just be read off as pertaining to the sea turtle; whilst underlying the whole, the fish, in the simplest myxinoid form, could be traced in morphological hieroglyphics."

More than twenty years later, Parker described the development of the remarkable hoatzin (*Opisthocomus cristatus*), which has a paw-like hand, three clawed fingers, and a rudiment of a fourth, a wrist of numerous elements, and many other features suggestive of reptilian descent. Thus, from the general course of development as seen in the chick, and from particularly interesting cases like the hoatzin, Parker was convinced that the bird is "a transformed and, one might even say, a glorified reptile."

HISTORICAL EVIDENCE OF EVOLUTION OF BIRDS

In some cases—for example, horses, elephants, and crocodiles—the general pedigree of present-day forms is quite evident from the fossil series. Although it is rarely possible to make a linear series of types, in regard to which we can say T is derived from S, and S from R, and R from Q, the great steps of the descent are none the less clear. This cannot be said, however, in regard to birds. We know that they evolved from a reptilian stock, but we do not know from which. There are extinct forms—flying reptiles and toothed birds—which lessen the gap between modern reptiles and birds, but the precise line of ancestry is unknown.

There is, indeed, very little rock record of ancient birds, partly, perhaps, because they were less likely than terrestrial animals to be killed in crowds, partly, perhaps, because their dead bodies would be devoured as they lay on the ground or floated lightly on the water. When we remember the comparative rarity of dead birds, except in very hard winters or in the vicinity of shore-nets, we can understand why there are so few bird fossils. Doubtless, however, much remains to be discovered.

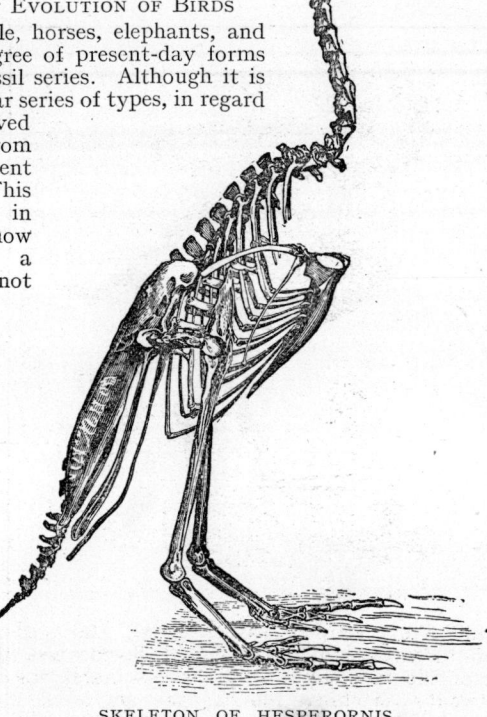

SKELETON OF HESPERORNIS

EVOLUTION OF THE BIRD TYPE

The threefold evidence, from structural resemblances, from similarities in early development, and from the occurrence of extinct types, leads to the conclusion that birds evolved from a reptilian stock. Great difficulties immediately arise when we try to get beyond this general statement, when we ask which reptilian stock has most affinity with birds, and when we ask what causes led, millions of years ago, to the evolution of the bird type.

In considering the origin of birds we are naturally led first of all to the extinct "flying dragons," or pterodactyles, which had the power of true flight; and it cannot be denied that among these quaint creatures we find many interesting resemblances to birds—especially in some features of the skull and pectoral girdle. The breastbone is keeled, the long bones are hollow, the brain seems to have presented avian characters, and so on.

On the other hand, when we turn to other parts of the pterodactyle, such as the backbone and the hip girdle, we find marked differences, and the organ of flight is so totally different that the theory of close affinity between pterodactyles and birds must be abandoned. The pterodactyle's wing is as far from a bird's as a bat's is; it consisted of an expansion of the skin stretched on the much elongated "little finger," and continued backwards to the hind legs and tail. It is probable that the resemblances between pterodactyles are in part the results of similar structural adaptations to similar habits; but it may also be that pterodactyles and birds evolved from a common ancestry.

Another reptilian stock that must be considered in connection with the pedigree of birds is that of the dinosaurs—extinct terrestial forms of great diversity of habit. Thus, some were quadrupeds, while others achieved the bipedal mode of progression, though perhaps they did not adopt it more habitually than kangaroos and jerboas. Especially among the bipedal dinosaurs we find approximation to birds in the hip girdle and in the hind leg, for instance, in the tendency to form what is technically called a tibio-tarsus, the fusion of the upper ankle bones to the lower end of the tibia.

Some of the dinosaurs had hollow bones, and there is something very suggestive in a form like *Compsognathus*, which stood about 2 feet high, and seems to have hopped about on its hind legs like a bird. On the other hand, it has to be admitted that no dinosaur shows any hint of an approach to a wing.

We may sum up thus: we feel sure that birds arose from some ancient reptilian or saurian stock, but we cannot, at present, be more precise as to the particular pedigree. Furthermore, while it is easy to ask by what steps and under what impulses birds evolved, it is at present impossible to answer. It is when we contemplate these "big lifts" in organic evolution that we feel that the theory has still a long way to evolve. To most naturalists it seems enough to say that the evolution was accomplished very gradually in the course of natural selection by the fostering of fit variations (including, perhaps, large mutations) and by the elimination of the disadvantageous. But this remains a vague formula. There is no doubt that many of the characteristics of birds are linked together as varied expressions of a big constitutional change. Thus, the incipient birds may be regarded as "fevered representatives of reptiles, progressing in the direction of greater and greater constitutional activity."

"Warm bloodedness," or the power of retaining a constant body temperature; high temperature, which is an index to the intensity of the chemical metabolism in the body; great development of the integumentary heat-retaining outgrowths—the feathers; enormous muscular development; a lightly-built skeleton; bipedal progression, and the associated strong and long hip girdle; the fore limbs turned into wings; the associated stiff back and strong shoulder girdle; the horny bill replacing heavy teeth, and, at the end of the long, flexible neck, doing the work of the lost hand; the splendidly developed heart; the lungs and their air-sacs, which effect internal perspiration (there being no external sweating and almost no water in the urine) and help to regulate the body temperature; the large brain; the keen senses of sight and hearing; the full, free life; the emotional development which is expressed in song and dance; the economisation of reproductivity rendered possible by the parental care—these and other characteristics are bound together in that bundle of adaptations which we call a bird. Thus, we may realise in detail what the transition from reptile to bird implies, but we are left wondering how the transition came about; "how the slow, cold-blooded, scaly beast ever became transformed into the quick, hot-blooded, feathered bird, the joy of creation."

THE OLDEST KNOWN BIRD

The lithographic stone of Bavaria has yielded two well-preserved skeletons of what is as yet the oldest known bird, *Archæopteryx* (p. 915). The grain of the stone is so fine that the impressions of the feathers are well seen, and most of the bones are clear except the breast bone. It was about the size of a crow, and probably arboreal; and many of its characters are not far from typical, such as the general shape of the skull, the merrythought, and the legs. In other respects, however, it was reptile-like, in having, for instance, teeth in both jaws, a long tail like a lizard, and three clawed fingers. A quite unique feature was the arrangement of the quill feathers of the tail in a double row—a pair to each of the twenty vertebræ. It was a strange, primitive creature, but when we consider characters like the skull, the wing, the merry-thought, and the legs, we see plainly that *Archæopteryx* could not have been the *first* bird, though it is the oldest of which we have any record.

PRIMITIVE TOOTHED BIRDS

The upper cretaceous rocks of Kansas have yielded some good skeletons of a very interesting toothed marine bird (*Hesperornis regalis*) which is often described as something like a swimming ostrich, though in many respects it seems to have much closer affinities with our modern grebes and divers (*Colymbidæ*). It stood about a yard high, and was perhaps twice as long; it was flightless, with rudimentary wings, and without a keel on its breast bone; it had powerful hind limbs suited for rapid swimming. For *Hesperornis* and its English representative *Enaliornis* the division Odontolcæ has been established in allusion to the fact

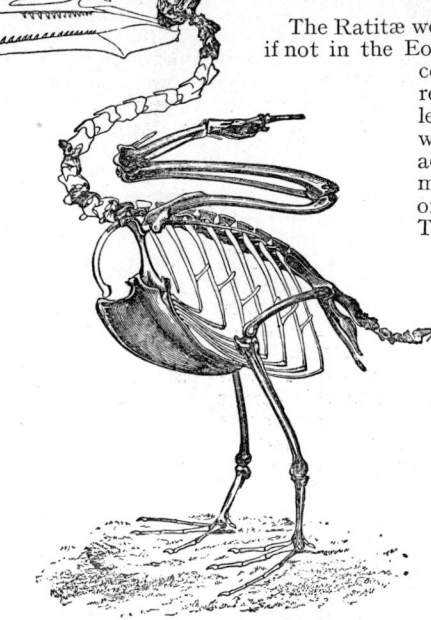

SKELETON OF ICHTHYORNIS

that the teeth are arranged in grooves. They probably represent, as Dr. A. Smith Woodward says, "an early specialised offshoot from the common ancestral type of the two great surviving orders."

THE TWO GREAT ORDERS

In the course of animal evolution there seems to have been a frequent bifurcation into more active and more sluggish types, and there is no doubt that a cleavage of this sort occurred very early in the evolution of birds. The one alternative is represented by the flying birds, or Carinatæ, and the running birds, or Ratitæ, the names referring to the conspicuous feature that the keel or carina on the breast bone of flying birds, which affords insertion to some of the muscles of flight, is not developed on the raft-like breast bone of running birds. There are, of course, a great many other differences, for the divergence of the two great orders, or divisions, was very thoroughgoing.

RUNNING BIRDS

The Ratitæ were established in the Miocene Ages, if not in the Eocene, and, though never very successful, they had a cosmopolitan representation. With their flightless, thoroughly terrestrial habits we may connect not only the character of the breast bone, but the more or less degenerate characters of the shoulder girdle and fore limb. The feathers of the adults have free barbs, and the barbules have no hooks. Their skull is of a type that never occurs among the flying birds with the single exception of the tinamou.

It is maintained by some authorities (see page 926) that the existing Ratitæ are descended from forms that could fly, but the evidence of this is not quite convincing. It seems not unlikely that they represent a primitive stock that never attained to flight, and they certainly carry marks of primitiveness in many different parts of their body. We may notice the absence of regularly arranged feather tracts, the absence of a ploughshare bone at the end of the tail, the absence or small size of hook-like (uncinate) processes on the ribs, the compound character of the horny bill, and the fact that the junctions, or sutures, of the skull bones remain for a long time distinct, whereas in flying birds they almost always disappear very early.

Professor W. K. Parker spoke of the Ratitæ as "overgrown, degenerate birds that were once on the right road for becoming flying fowl, but, through greediness or idleness, never reached the 'goal'—went back, indeed, and lost their sternal keel, and almost lost their unexercised wings." We may think of them as illustrating arrested development—the persistence of numerous primitive and also juvenile features.

The broad fact about them is that they have not been successful as compared with the Carinatæ. The giant *Æpyornis* of Madagascar has long since gone; the giant moas (*Dinornis*) of New Zealand have also disappeared; and there are only five living types—the African ostrich (*Struthio*), the South American ostrich (*Rhea*), the Australian emeu (*Dromæus*), the Austro-Malayan cassowaries (*Casuarius*), and the small kiwis (*Apteryx*) of

New Zealand. The persistence of two of these—the American ostrich and the kiwi—is seriously threatened. It seems as if flightless terrestrial birds were condemned in the struggle for existence as a sort of contradiction in terms.

CARINATE BIRDS

At the time when *Hesperornis* swam about in Cretaceous seas, there was another toothed bird, *Ichthyornis victor*, hardly less remarkable. It was a small bird, towards a foot in height, and delicately built ; it had a strong keel and well-developed wings. The teeth were fixed in distinct sockets and the vertebræ were biconcave—two very striking features, which point back to reptiles. Of its affinities, Mr. Pycraft says cautiously, " Ichthyornis may perhaps be, and generally is, regarded as the ancestral type of the present Steganopodes—the gannets, cormorants, pelicans, tropic and frigate birds."

The fossil record leads us to the conclusion that the running birds and the flying birds diverged at a very ancient date, and it is very striking that in Cretaceous times there should have existed such birds as *Hesperornis*, which is extremely specialised for aquatic life, and *Ichthyornis*, which, apart from its teeth and vertebræ, " had acquired all the characteristic peculiarities of the class Aves."

What, then, has happened among birds in the long interval of time since Cretaceous ages ? The general answer, we think, must be this—that there has been an extraordinary amount of specialised adaptation and of minutiose perfecting of detail, but no new departure of great importance.

It is not difficult to see the general reason for this, which an analogy may illustrate. When a piece of mechanism has become very complex, its range of evolutionary progress is restricted within narrow limits. It may be improved in detail in this corner and that, but it is not likely to undergo any great change. It is no longer open to any important modification in principle. The compound microscope of to-day, with its new glass and fine adjustments, is an improvement on that of fifty years ago, but there has been no fundamental change. When a highly evolved piece of mechanism seems to undergo a fundamental change, there is some discontinuity in the evolutionary process ; though the outer framework sometimes remains more or less the same there has been a thoroughgoing internal reorganisation in obedience to a new idea. The motor-bicycle is not an evolved ordinary bicycle, nor is a Zeppelin airship an evolved aeroplane.

Returning to the first known flying birds, we recognise that they were already exceedingly complex, with much of their constitution definitely adapted to the successful solution of a very difficult problem—that of flight. We can understand why they have not given rise to any other kind of creature, even in the course of millions of years. They have simply given rise to birds and birds, endlessly adapted to particular conditions of life.

It is among primitive undifferentiated types that we must look for important new departures. From an early date the bird's whole organisation was so thoroughly adapted for flight that no big change was possible, unless, indeed, at the risk, which the penguins

KIWI OR APTERYX

well illustrate, of losing the great secret of flight again. What has actually happened has been the evolution of of a large number of orders of which a list is given on page 912. And within these orders there has been an embarrassing detail of specialisation to particular haunts and habits.

EVOLUTIONARY POSSIBILITIES OPEN TO BIRDS

If we cannot expect birds to give origin to any different kind of creature, what other evolutionary changes are open ? As an answer we may state the following four directions in which evolution may trend. In the first place, what has been going on for untold ages may continue. There is the possibility of increasingly minute and specialised adaptation of structure. In the order of perching birds, or Passeres, there have evolved in the past hundreds of closely related species, each adapted to its own particular " niche of organic opportunity," and accordingly it may be that new species will go on appearing in this and in other orders. Secondly, there is the possibility of great increase in intelligence, of brain improvement, similar to that which marks off man from the other primates. In rooks, cranes, and parrots we get a glimpse of the intellectual possibilities of birds.

Thirdly, there is the possibility of larger changes in general constitution and habits, such as we see in burrowing birds, and this involves the risk of losing the secret of flight—a risk proportionate to the amount of divergence from the ordinary type. There is, lastly, also the possibility that the species of birds now existing may suffer reduction in numbers. In many cases this is already a probability, and we know that many birds that once flourished are now extinct. We shall briefly refer to birds that have disappeared or are disappearing.

EXTINCTION IN ANCIENT TIMES

Referring first for a moment to the fossil birds, we must recall the important distinction between " lost races," which have left no modern representatives, and the " extinct ancestors " of living birds. It may be that some of the Odontolcæ were ancestral to our modern divers, but there is no reason to believe that the highly specialised *Hesperornis* has any lineal descendants to-day. The same may be said of the giant Moas and *Æpyornis*. It is impossible to give any general answer to the question, " Why have these splendid types perished ? " except the familiar one, " Elimination in the struggle for existence," and this is apt to be somewhat platitudinarian in regard to distant ages whose conditions of life are very vaguely known. A pioneer like *Archæopteryx* was very far from being perfect as a flier, and the survival of birds that could not fly at all would be obviously imperilled when mammals appeared on the scene.

EXTINCTION IN RECENT TIMES

The dodo (*Didus ineptus*), a " ponderous pigeon," was found inhabiting Mauritius when that island was rediscovered by the Dutch at the end of the sixteenth century. " Clumsy, flightless, and defenceless, it soon succumbed, not so much to the human invaders of its realm as to the domestic beasts—especially hogs—which accompanied them " (Newton's " Dictionary of Birds," page 216). There is no evidence of its survival after 1681. There was an allied bird in the adjacent island of Réunion, and another, the solitaire, in Rodriquez, both of which disappeared with the dodo.

Besides the dodo, Mauritius has lost at least two parrots, a dove, a large coot, and a long-billed flightless Ralline bird called *Aphanapteryx ;* Réunion has lost a peculiar starling and other birds ; Rodriquez has lost an owl, a parrot, a dove, a heron, a rail, and, indeed, most of its original bird tenantry. The same is true of other islands, as reference to Newton's article "Extermination," in his " Dictionary of Birds," will show, but it is not within our present scope to pursue the subject further. It is enough to point out that there are several reasons why comparatively small islands afford so many instances of extermination : the advent of man and the introduction of new mammals must have a more pronounced effect in a circumscribed area ; fires are apt to bring about wholesale destruction ; and escape is more difficult than from a continent. For a flightless bird, like the dodo, escape from destruction was obviously impossible.

One of the best known of comparatively recent exterminations is that of the gare-fowl, or great auk (*Alca impennis*), a relative of our common guillemots and razor-bills. It used to be abundant in northern seas, especially round Newfoundland, and was much used as food by sailors, just as penguins are sometimes used to-day in the far south. Colony after colony seems to have dwindled, and the species seems to have become extinct about 1844, " in which year the last two examples known to have lived were taken on a rocky islet—one of a group called Fuglaskér, or Fowl-skerries, off the south-west point of Iceland."

The great auk was a truly British bird, though nowhere abundant. It used to breed on St. Kilda, where one of the last specimens was taken in 1821. Another, perhaps the very last, was captured alive in Waterford Harbour in 1834. The reason for its extermination must be found, on the one hand, in its reduced wings, which were useless for flight, in its apparent stupidity, in its localised breeding-grounds, and in its slow rate of reproduction ; and, on the other hand, in the fact that its feathers and its flesh were useful to man, who was, as in many other cases, short-sighted in his greedy persecution.

Another striking case is that of the Labrador duck, or pied duck (*Somateria labradoria*), which used to be extremely abundant on the North American Atlantic coast from the mouth of the St. Lawrence to New England, nesting, like its near relative, the eider-duck, on rocky islands, safe from most possibilities of molestation. There is no certain record of it since 1852.

Four skins and a few bones are all that remain of a fine cormorant from Bering Island, in the North Pacific ; perhaps a dozen museum specimens represent an interesting Nestor parrot (*N. productus*), from Phillip Island, off New Zealand ; half a dozen museums can boast a specimen of the mamo (*Drepanis pacifica*), of the Sandwich Islands, a victim to its gorgeous yellow feathers, which were used to decorate the state robes of the chiefs ; and we may close—without attempting to complete—the sad list, by noting that only one specimen is known of Latham's white-winged sandpiper. We have given instances enough to show how the list has been reduced within comparatively recent times.

CAUSES OF EXTERMINATION

In considering the causes of extermination we must in fairness remember that, altogether apart from ruthless persecution on man's part, birds may be forced to relinquish their old quarters because human habitations and cultivations encroach on wild nature. It seems that good forestry diminishes the number of birds in the woods. As the English fen-country was opened up and restricted the crane ceased to breed there, and the bustard became rarer on the downs as the arable land crept nearer.

Doubtless, in these two cases there was also persecution of the birds, especially at the breeding season, but the changes in the condition of the country must be borne in mind. As the indigenous pine-woods were more and more restricted in Scotland the capercaillie disappeared, probably by the end of the eighteenth century ; where it has been re-introduced and protected it has flourished and increased.

Another cause of extermination is game-preserving, for in its interests there has been a persistent and effective destruction of birds of prey. This is lamentable, not only because of the disappearance of

EMEUS

handsome and interesting birds, but also because their removal affords opportunity to mice and voles and other destructive pests. We must, of course, discriminate, as fuller knowledge may enable us to do before it is altogether too late, between species like the sparrow-hawk, which destroy large numbers of young birds (apart from game), and species like the kestrel, which keep chiefly to mice and the like.

Another factor making for extermination is the fashion of wearing the plumage of wild birds, as part of the dress, either for warmth, as in the case of feather boas and the like, or for decorative purposes. We must, of course, be precise in our judgment, finding nothing to be said against the use of feathers cut from ostriches, finding everything to be said against the use of "egrets," or so-called "ospreys"—tufts of filiform feathers which spring from the back of a white heron. "They are assumed only just before the breeding-season, and hence the procuring of them destroys the birds at a most critical moment."

It is a matter for deep regret that for various reasons the prosperity of many of our native birds, such as the chough, the raven, and many birds of prey, is at present markedly on the wane. Some, like the osprey and the marsh-harrier, are on the verge of extinction as indigenous species. Others, such as the kite, the sea eagle, and the ruff, have been arrested on the brink by the introduction of efficient protection. Not a few birds that were once native are now rare visitors; examples are the bittern, the great bustard, the avocet, the black-tailed godwit, and the black tern.

On the other hand, some species are increasing; the mistle-thrush, the hawfinch, the starling, and the tufted duck are instances of species that have greatly spread and multiplied as British-breeding birds. Not only from a zoological, but from an economic point of view, we cordially welcome what is being done in the way of judicious bird protection, not only by penal legislation, but positively by the establishment of "bird sanctuaries," and the like.

As Mr. C. William Beebe says in his admirable book entitled "The Bird": "Let us beware of needlessly destroying even one of the lives—so sublimely crowning the ages upon ages of evolving; and let us put forth all our efforts to save a threatened species from extinction; to give hearty aid to the last few individuals pitifully struggling to avoid absolute annihilation. The beauty and genius of a work of art may be reconceived, though its first material expression be destroyed; a vanished harmony may yet again inspire the composer; but when the last individual of a race of living beings breathes no more, another heaven and another earth must pass before such a one can be again."

REMARKABLE CHANGES NOW IN PROGRESS

Another evolutionary possibility is that the bird may make some big change in its habits; some constitutional change, arising mysteriously from within the germ, may lead to a change in the bird's manner of life. In the course of time this change of habit may come to be associated with a definite structural change which has been sifted out from among the continuous crop of "variations," because it was well

THE OWL PARROT
Photo, Lewis Medland

adapted to the survival of the particular kind of bird in the new ways it has adopted.

Sometimes, on the other hand, some progressive structural change in a particular organ, such as the bill, may lead the bird to seek out some slightly different mode of life, or kind of food, or habitat—some new niche which it fits better. By big changes in habit and in structure, probably begun millions of years ago when bird structure was less fixed than it is now, there may have arisen strange types like the penguins, and it is very interesting to inquire whether there are any hints of remarkable changes now in progress.

In illustration, we may refer to the well-known case of the kea parrot in New Zealand, which in the relatively short period since sheep-farming began in the colony has turned from its good old vegetarian ways to feeding on the fat above the kidneys of living sheep. This is a striking instance, but in not a few birds we find considerable plasticity as regards diet, and some of these may be hints of new departures whose significance will be plain to the ornithologist of the distant future. At the Antipodes there is a twilight-loving gull, whose food is said to consist exclusively of moths, and the herring-gulls in some parts of Britain are becoming more and more vegetarian.

A very remarkable and suggestive change seems to be in progress in the so-called steamer duck, found off the Falkland Islands. The young birds fly well, but as they become mature the power is lost. But the wings, too stiff to be of use in the air, are employed as paddles, and the steamer ducks move with great rapidity through the water, swimming quadrupedally. Some peculiarity of this sort may have been at the beginning of the penguin's evolution.

In the spotted tinamou of South America the state of affairs is hardly less remarkable. The bird can fly, but it has so little mastery of its flight, either as regards direction or height, that its imperfectly co-ordinated flight is in itself a danger.

We quote from Mr. Beebe another interesting case of peculiarity in flying power: "The wings of the owl parrot of New Zealand are of full size, but the muscles are so encased in fat that they are useless for flight. These parrots feed on ground mosses, and being nocturnal, and therefore having few enemies, their only use for wings is occasionally to sail gently to earth, like a flying squirrel, from the trees in the hollows of which they sometimes roost."

In considering the evolution of birds, it is important to realise that it is still going on. Although there may not be in the future any very sensational new departure, the raw materials of evolution are still being ceaselessly supplied. In 1871 Mr. J. A. Allen measured numerous individual representatives of some common species of American birds, and found that as regards important points, such as length of bill and length of wing, birds of the same sex and season, caught at the same place, on the same day, showed numerous variations, often large in extent. It is in all probability by the patient study of these presently occurring changes, and of those which go on among domesticated birds, that naturalists will eventually be able to throw light on what remains so largely an unread riddle—the evolution of birds.

J. A. THOMSON

THE FLIGHT OF BIRDS

By W. P. PYCRAFT

By a stretch of the fancy we may imagine that Nature only succeeded in fashioning flying creatures after a series of experiments, some of the more successful of which have been preserved for our instruction. At any rate, a number of animals other than birds have attained the power of travelling through space by means of parachutes, but only a few have attained the power of " flight," that is, of movement through space in any desired direction, and for more or less extensive distances. Among the higher orders the reptiles, birds, and bats, alone have achieved actual flight. Flying reptiles are represented by the extinct pterodactyles, flying mammals by the bats.

In all cases, as a matter of course, the fore limbs have become the organs of flight, and to this end have undergone extensive and quite unique transformation. In the pterodactyles, or flying dragons, for instance, the wing, as this modified limb is called, was formed by an extreme development of what answers to the little finger in man, between which and the body was stretched a thin sheet of skin. In the mammals a similar sheet of skin is stretched between four excessively long and delicate fingers and the body, the bones forming the palms of the hands being widely separated for the purpose (p. 297). But these wings differ in degree rather than in kind. Far otherwise is it with the birds, in which the flying membrane is represented by a number of elastic ribbon-like structures known as feathers, each perfectly separable from its neighbour.

But properly to appreciate the flight of birds, as distinct from that of animals or the butterfly and beetle, let us study a little more closely the bony framework of the wing in the several types to which reference has been made.

To begin with, the wings of all these vertebrate types are so many variants of a common plan — a five-fingered limb having digits of moderate length.

In the pterodactyle, the outermost digit was prodigiously elongated, while the remaining digits became extremely reduced in size, and were probably used only as hooks, or grasping organs, when the creature was resting. In the bat, the thumb alone is used hook-fashion, while the remaining fingers, greatly lengthened, and of marked slenderness, support the flying membrane. The apparent length of the fingers, however, is exaggerated by the fact that the metacarpal, or palm bones, instead of lying side by side, as in the human hand, embedded in the flesh, are widely separated, so as to bear their share in the extension of the wing membrane, which included also the hind limb and tail. Now compare these two membrane-supporting skeletons with the skeleton of the bird's wing.

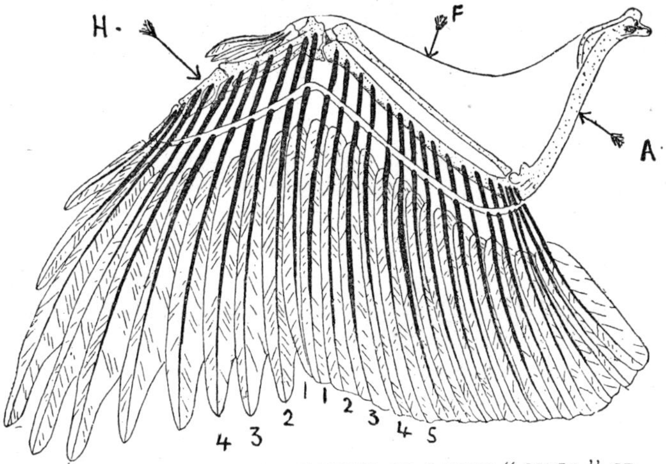

In the first place, a word as to the skeleton itself. As in the wings already examined, the wrist and hand are the parts that have undergone the greatest changes, as we have read on page 908. The thumb, greatly reduced, plays but a small part in flight, the stiff quills which it bears being used only in certain phases. Of the two remaining digits, the index or second finger is very long, while the third is exceedingly short. The bones of the palm and the thumb are fused or welded together, that of the thumb blending with that of the second finger, while that of the third digit is fused only at each end, leaving a space between.

Thus is formed a long, jointed rod, to which are bound a number of long, oar-shaped, elastic blades known as the quill feathers, and after the fashion shown in the figure. Above these is arranged a series of smaller feathers known as " coverts." Along the upper arm, in long-winged birds, is ranged a similar, but weaker, series of quill-like feathers, and these close up the space between the innermost quill feathers and the body during flight : the gap which would otherwise exist would render flight impossible.

While the number of the flight feathers of the hand, or *primaries*, is fairly constant, never exceeding twelve or falling below ten—though the tenth may be reduced to remarkably small proportions,—those of the forearm, or secondaries, range between forty, as in the albatross, and six, as in the humming birds. The feathers of the two series also differ markedly in their attachment, since the primaries are packed closely together at their bases, and are bound very tightly to the skeleton of the hand, while the secondaries are fairly widely spaced, and are by no means so strongly bound to the skeleton, though, in a number of larger-winged birds of powerful flight, the ulna develops a series of small bony papillæ corresponding in number with the quill feathers attached thereto by ligament.

In addition, however, to their relation to the skeleton, these quill feathers are further held in position by a more or less complicated arrangement of tendons lodged between a fold of skin known as the post-patagium, which runs from the tip of the finger to the elbow, and was possibly at one time much larger in extent. A similar, but more extensive, fold of skin extends between the wrist and the shoulder, and this is known as the prepatagium. It is of considerable importance in flight.

The fashion in which these quills fulfil the purpose of the continuous sheet of membrane seen in the bat and pterodactyle is worth noting. Each separate feather, then, is so placed that its free edge overlaps the middle of the feather next outside it, and so that

BIRD'S WING, SHOWING RELATION OF LARGE " QUILL " OR FLIGHT FEATHERS TO SKELETON

A, arm of which the humerus forms the support ; F, forearm which contains two supporting rods, radius and ulna, the latter forming the support for the large flight or quill-feathers known as secondaries, 1, 2, 3, 4, 5 ; H, hand, containing the bones representing the thumb and second and third fingers ; the thumb bears four small stiff quill-like feathers known as the bastard wing ; the second and third fingers support the flight feathers of the hand, marked 4, 3, 2, 1. The narrow white band of tendon through which the bases of the quills pass helps to keep the feathers in position [After Pycraft]

this free edge is directed outwards, towards the tip of the extended wing. As a consequence, on the under side of the wing the opposite arrangement prevails, the free edges of the feathers are directed towards the body. Owing to this arrangement, on the upstroke of the wing the air is driven between the feathers, and so reduces muscular effort, while in the down-stroke the separate feathers are forced one against another, providing a continuous surface as unyielding as that formed by the continuous membrane of the bat or pterodactyle. Thus the labour of flight is materially reduced without any loss of effectiveness. Moreover, when the wing membranes of the bat are seriously injured, flight becomes impossible for ever, but if more or fewer feathers of the bird's wing are damaged, flight is, at the most, but hindered until new feathers grow.

So much for the wing itself. Let us consider its relation to the body, and the machinery of motion. The wing is attached to a bony framework known as the shoulder-girdle, formed by a pair of flattened rods, or beams, known as the coracoids, a pair of scapulæ, or shoulder blades, and a merry-thought, and these are secured to the breast bone by the bases of the coracoids, while the breast bone in turn is fastened to the trunk by means of the ribs. The breast bone is peculiar in that it takes the form of an oblong plate of bone, along the under side of which there runs a deep median keel (carina), which plays a very important part indeed in flight.

In the most powerful fliers the keel is of great depth, and in birds which have lost the power of flight is absent. The importance of the depth of the keel will become manifest when it is remembered that it serves, with the plate of the breast bone, as a surface for the attachment of those muscles of flight whose function it is to depress the wing, and so lift and drive the body forwards. These are the breast muscles, which may weigh as much as one-fifth of the total weight of the body. They form the "flesh" of the breast in birds used for food. Into the names and number of the muscles employed in and essential to flight, and into the mechanism of flight, it is unnecessary to enter, for such information can be of little use to any save those versed in anatomy and the higher mathematics. But a brief survey of the main factors of flight will be helpful.

Firstly, birds, like all other flying creatures, are heavier than air, in which respect they differ from some human devices for travelling through space. Secondly,

OUTSTRETCHED WING SHOWING ARRANGEMENT OF FEATHERS

1, primaries; 2, secondaries; 3, major coverts of primaries; 4, major coverts of secondaries; 5, median coverts; 6, minor coverts; 7, marginal coverts; 8, remiges of bastard wing; 9, scapulas

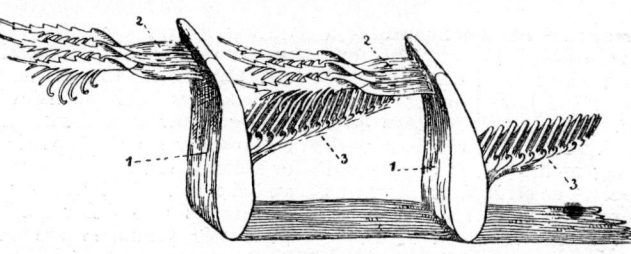

DIAGRAM SHOWING HOW A FEATHER'S BARBS ARE INTERLOCKED
1, section of barbs; 2 and 3, interlocking barbules   After Pycraft

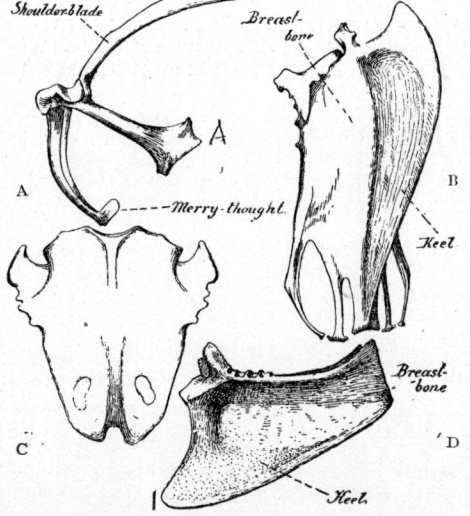

(A) shoulder girdle and (B) breast bone of Norfolk plover, (c) breast bone of rhea without keel, (D) breast bone of swift with deep keel

the shape of the body, and the clothing thereof, play a more important part than is generally realised. In the matter of form, the body during flight is spindle-shaped, tapering at both ends and beautifully rounded in contour, while the feathers, from their smoothness and closely-fitting character, offer the least possible resistance to motion. It is commonly supposed that the great air chambers, which it is well known birds possess, serve materially to reduce the weight of the body, much as gas floats a balloon. In point of fact, these chambers make no appreciable difference as weight-reducers, but they very decidedly aid the work of breathing and the regulation of the temperature, as we have already seen on page 907.

It is usually supposed that flight is performed by a simultaneous raising and depressing action of the wings, but this is by no means true. On the contrary, the wing in flight performs a number of extremely complicated movements, which have been severally analysed by Marey, Pettigrew, and Muybridge, and the complexities of these analyses can hardly be profitably discussed here. The accompanying illustration, however, will convey more to the general reader than a minute description. This much will become plain at a glance, that the flight of birds is not, as one would imagine from watching a gull, accomplished merely by a series of up and down flappings of the extended pinions. On the contrary, the wing when raised so that the tips point skywards, is then swung forwards and downwards so that the tips point far beyond the beak, and this downward movement serves both to lift and propel the body. The next phase is accompanied by a partial flexion of the pinion at the wrist joint, followed by a gradual extension as the wing is brought up for the next downward stroke. As a consequence the trajectory of the wing forms a figure of 8 curve, as has been demonstrated by experiment and instantaneous photographs.

The estimated speed of birds' flight has been grossly exaggerated, even by otherwise skilled observers. Herr Gätke, an ornithologist who spent many years in the study of migration, believed that the little Arctic blue-throat could leave Africa at dusk and arrive in Heligoland—his observatory—nine hours later, travelling during the short time no fewer than 1,600 miles, or about 180 miles an hour! Plovers and curlews, he calculated, were capable of travelling at the rate of 240 miles an hour!

As a matter of fact, few birds, if any, exceed, under favourable conditions, a speed of 80 miles an hour.

Birds make their best flight with a moderate wind behind them. When, however, the force increases to a gale, they fly rather at right-angles to the wind, since, the wind and the bird moving at the same velocity, the necessary support for the body is wanting, and the bird tends at once to descend. In rising, birds always turn head to wind for the sake of its lifting power. During heavy gales flight is performed as near the earth as possible, because the velocity of the wind increases with altitude. Mr. Headley made experiments as to this velocity during a blizzard. At 2 inches from the ground an anemometer registered a velocity of 515 feet per minute ; at 2 feet, 770 inches ; at 4 feet, 918 inches ; and at 7 feet 6 inches, 1,021 feet ! This accounts for the fact that on migration, during gales, birds fly only just above the surface of the water, while in good weather they travel at considerable altitudes.

The peculiar and very beautiful form of flight known as soaring is practised only by a few birds, such as eagles, vultures, storks, adjutants, and pelicans. Rising for the first hundred feet by rapid beats of the wing, the bird at last extends its pinions to the fullest, and proceeds to rise in a series of spirals to a height of from two to, it is said, six miles. This remarkable movement is apparently impossible in a dead calm, and is further believed to be dependent on upward currents of air. In mountainous regions such up-currents can readily be demonstrated, but this is by no means easy over vast plains ; yet here this form of flight is as commonly and as easily practised. Here the up-currents are supposed to be due to the ascent of heated air from the earth's surface.

GULLS IN FLIGHT AND ALIGHTING
Photograph by John Williamson

But be this as it may, the soaring seems to be due to the fact that during part of the circle the bird going with the wind slowly descends, when turning head to wind it is immediately lifted, the ascent being far greater than the slight descent which follows on turning with the wind ; but after the soaring process has begun, it is to be noted, the wings are held motionless, stiffly extended. The albatross similarly travels over enormous distances without moving the wings ; the flight is essentially that of soaring, the body, however, not being carried upwards, but being borne along more or less horizontally.

The past-masters in the art of soaring and gliding all share this peculiarity—they have the tips of the outermost primary, or hand quills, deeply emarginate— that is to say, the margin of the vane of the feathers, principally the hinder margin, becomes abruptly narrower than the rest of the feathers, as though its width had been reduced by half by the aid of a pair of scissors. Consequently, when the wing is fully extended, as in soaring, it seems to have a fringed appearance, the tips of the feathers being separated one from another by wide gaps. Thereby steadiness is obtained.

for wings which present a uniform surface are apt during such movements to collect the air in eddies under them, when, from slight movement, the air would escape at one margin, causing a momentary lack of balance (see the illustration on page 921).

These emarginated feathers may serve yet another purpose. At any rate, some remarkable observations on this point have been made by Mr. C. C. Trowbridge, an American naturalist. He contends, and seems to have proved, that these emarginate feathers, at any rate during gliding flight—and the recovery therefrom when the wings are partially flexed—such as many birds perform when riding on a descending stream of air, are suddenly placed in reverse order as to their overlap, which results in their interlocking one with another, forming thereby a rigid termination to the wing. There is certainly no mechanism by which this condition could be brought about, but it is argued that the feathers are thus thrown together by the action of the upward pressure of the air. Though much doubt has been cast on the correctness of these observations, the balance of evidence goes to show that this doubt is not justified. At any rate, in endeavouring to establish his point, Mr. Trowbridge shot a considerable number of hawks, while on migration, during the performance of this gliding flight — or "coasting," as he calls it — and in some 80 per cent. the birds fell dead with these feathers interlocked.

Nor is this all. The pressure of one feather against the emarginated edge of its neighbour next beyond, or outside it, caused a distinct notching of the vane of the feather, which did not disappear until some time after death, showing, it is held, that the pressure had been exerted for some considerable period. And a precisely similar notch could be produced at will in the dead bird's quills by placing them in the reversed position, and leaving them so locked for some time. After the pressure was removed the notch disappeared.

Though Mr. Trowbridge and a Japanese observer both maintain that this remarkable phase of flight is visible to the naked eye, this can only be the case after a very prolonged study. Photography may help. When soaring, at any rate, this interlocking almost certainly does not take place, as any may see who have the chance of watching birds in the field.

Some birds are enabled to hover over the same spot for a considerable time, as the kestrel, for instance, but during such movements the wings are kept in rapid vibration ; occasionally, however, the wings are held motionless, doubtless by virtue of up-currents of air.

Between the shape of the wing and the form of the flight there is a very close relation. Birds which of necessity pass much time on the wing, which perform long migrations, or which live by the capture of swiftly-moving prey, have long, pointed wings of fair width. The wings of falcons and gulls serve as good instances of such wings. In some birds, such as the swallows, the wings are conspicuously narrow in proportion to their length, and these relations reach an exaggerated form in the wings of the swift, on the one hand, and of the albatross, on the other, for therein the wings are of great length and extremely long and narrow. Though so alike in contour these wings contrast strongly one with another in their skeletal parts, for the swift has the shortest humerus of all birds, the albatross one of the longest. But the forearm of the albatross is also exceedingly long, while that of the swift is very short. Again, the hand of the swift is excessively long, while in the albatross it is relatively short. Both are birds of superb flight, spending indeed most of their time on the wing. Both are great exponents of the art of gliding, a gift which they share with the kite and a few other birds. By way of contrast we may take the heavy-bodied, short-winged grouse and partridge. Though capable of great speed for short distances these birds are, relatively speaking, poor fliers and drive the wings with immense speed.

That there is a direct relation between the length and shape of the wing and the power of flight is easily demonstrated. The owls afford a good illustration. The migratory long and short eared owls have long, pointed wings, the wood-haunting, sedentary tawny, or wood-owl has short, rounded wings; and this shortening and rounding off of the outer portion of the pinion increases as the power of flight declines. Compare, for example, the long, swallow-like wing of *Grandala caelicolor* and the short, round wing of the almost flightless *Zeledonia* —both members of the thrush tribe.

And this brings us to the relation between the development of the keel of the breast bone and flight. This keel, as we have said, serves for the attachment of the great breast muscles which have to perform the down-stroke of the wing, and hence the real work of flight. In proportion as these muscles decline so the keel becomes reduced, till in flight-less forms it is reduced to a mere ridge, as in the owl parrot, or is absent altogether as in the ostrich tribe. But in birds of powerful flight the size of the keel shows a considerable range of variation. In the swifts, which are among the best fliers, this keel attains its maximum in relation to the size of the sternum or breast bone, but in this bird, it is to be noted, the coracoids and arm and forearm are all excessively short.

In eagles the sternum is relatively short and wide, and the keel shallow, but the coracoids are long and set wide apart at their four ends, thus affording a lodgment for the muscles, which in the swift are attached to the great keel. In some birds, as in the gannets, which are also powerful fliers, the coracoids are also very long, and the keel is produced forwards beyond the body of the sternum, while posteriorly this keel soon dies out.

Again, in some powerful fliers the merrythought is fused with the coracoid on each side, and with the keel of the sternum, while the coracoids are fused with the sternal plate, as, for example, in the frigate bird. In the cranes this fusion takes place only between the merrythought, or furculum, and the sternal keel. In some birds, again, like the ducks, the breast bone is of great length and tolerably wide, while the coracoids are relatively short. But whatever direction these permutations and combinations may take, the accom-

modation for muscle is always large; on the other hand, in birds which fly little, this area is always restricted. The rails afford a good instance, for in them the keel is deep, but the sternal plate is excessively reduced in breadth, so much so as to form little more than a narrow ridge on each side of the keel. The tinamus present a similar remarkable reduction in the area of the sternal plate, while preserving a moderately deep keel, but these birds are also most indifferent fliers.

We may next deal with the carriage of the neck and legs during flight. Until comparatively recently it was universally believed that birds, at any rate with rare exceptions, carried the legs drawn up under the breast at this time. The exceptions to this rule were supposed to be formed by the long-legged type of birds, such as herons, storks, cranes, and the wading birds, or plover tribe. More careful study of this matter, however, has shown that, saving the perching birds, and probably species such as woodpeckers, rollers, hornbills, toucans, and the like, all fly with the legs held backwards close under the tail. In gulls this can plainly be seen owing to the contrast of the dark colour of the legs with the white plumage. But during severe cold it would seem that gulls—and perhaps other aquatic species—draw up the legs into the plumage of the breast till they are completely hidden, apparently for the sake of warmth.

In alighting the legs are suddenly thrown forward, as may be seen in watching pigeons, for instance. Birds of prey, such as falcons, similarly thrust the feet forward when within striking distance of their prey, the victim being killed by a sudden stab with the great hind claw.

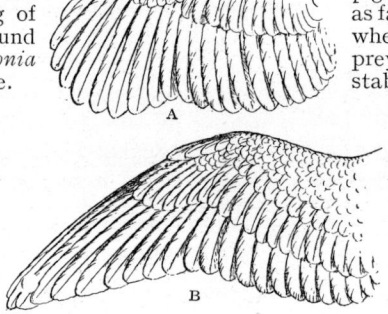

SHAPE OF WINGS OF (A) NON-MIGRATING OWL AND (B) MIGRATING OWL

The carriage of the neck in long-necked birds is no less peculiar, since some species — like ducks, geese, swans, storks, spoonbills, and flamingoes—fly with the neck stretched out to its fullest extent, while, on the other hand, herons and pelicans fly with the neck down as close up to the shoulders as can be. So far the reason for these striking differences remains entirely unaccounted for.

That the tail is by no means essential to flight is shown in the case of the grebes and tinamus, which, to all intents and purposes, are tailless, and of the rails, in which the tail is only feebly developed. The tail, however, does play some part as a rudder, as is shown by the fact that pigeons deprived of their tails, as at shooting matches, are unable to turn rapidly. But the chief function of the tail appears to be that of a brake when suddenly changing the course of flight, and when alighting. During this last motion the body is suddenly forced into a vertical position, while the wings and tail are spread to their fullest extent, and the legs are dropped and turned forwards. If these movements are not enough to avoid a jar on contact with the earth, the wings are given a sudden stroke, " backwater " fashion, when the bird alights like Mercury, and the wings are suddenly folded up.

" Getting off," steering, and alighting are phases of flight which have not received the attention they deserve. While some birds can, as it were, plunge into the air and get under way with incredible swiftness, others appear to leave terra firma only after considerable effort. This is specially true of long-winged, short-legged birds, like the swift, for example, which can only rise from a plane surface with great difficulty. The huge condor, one of the largest birds that fly, with an expanse of wing of 9 feet, must needs run a yard or

MALLARDS FLY WITH THEIR NECKS STRETCHED OUT

HERONS FLY WITH THEIR NECKS DRAWN IN TO THE BODY

two, flapping his huge pinions the while, till at last the wind lifts him. All birds prefer to rise head to the wind, and some *must* do so. Once on the way the course is steered not so much by the tail, as some suppose, as by an alteration of the balance of the body, the bird throwing itself over to the right or left side, as it desires to move in one or other direction.

Flight in regard to birds is usually regarded as a means of locomotion alone; but in not a few species more or less peculiar evolutions on the wing are largely indulged in during the critical time of courtship. The common snipe affords a striking example of this, for during this period both sexes apparently express their excitement by rapidly ascending to considerable heights, then as suddenly descending with a mighty downward rush, accompanied by very remarkable sounds likened to the bleating of a goat. These sounds are produced by the rush of air past the outer tail feathers, which have a peculiarly thickened, curved shaft, and are set out far apart from the rest of the tail, so as to act as strongly vibrating rods.

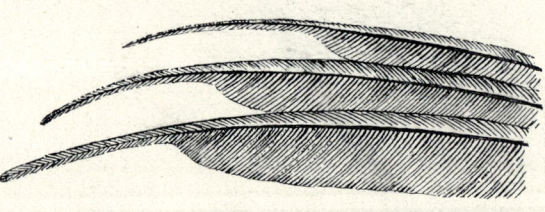

THE THREE OUTERMOST PRIMARIES OF A WING OF THE BLACK WATTLED GUAN THAT PRODUCE A WHISTLING SOUND

In the American woodcock the three outermost primaries differ noticeably from the rest of the series in being exceedingly narrow, shorter, and stiffer. Therewith they produce a strangely high-pitched whistling sound during their aerial courting. The black wattled guan of South America has the three outermost, and the sickle-winged guan the two outermost primaries similarly reduced to extremely narrow bands with stiff shafts for similar purposes; and the same is true of the piping guans. The black penelope of Central America, on the other hand, has no conspicuously modified feathers; yet by pitching rapidly downwards, with outstretched wings, it can produce a crashing, rushing noise like the falling of a tree! And similarly, one of the little black weaver birds of Africa, when courting, ascends into the air and with its wings makes a noise likened to the sound of a child's rattle, yet the wings show no peculiar structural modification.

In some of the little manakins of South America several of the secondary quills have the shafts curiously thickened and curved, the thickening increasing in successive feathers till a horny lump completes the series, and these birds make therewith a sharp sound like the cracking of a whip! These curious modifications of the wing feathers, and their accompaniments, are the more remarkable since some birds contrive to make sounds quite as loud and peculiar without developing any particular mechanism for the purpose.

The theme of flight would be incomplete without reference to birds in which this form of locomotion has been lost. It is surmised that the giant flightless birds, like the ostrich and the extinct moa and æpyornis, never possessed functional wings, that, in other words, the relatively minute fore limbs of these birds were to be regarded as *incipient* wings, and not, as is unquestionably the case, as degenerate *vestigial* wings. The mere fact that every grade of degeneration can be found, even to the absolute disappearance of the very smallest trace of a wing, as in some of the moas, where not even a vestige of the glenoid cavity remains in the shoulder girdle, is sufficient to demonstrate the truth of this contention. Else we must suppose the wings to have developed from nothing! And this would be to imply that the earliest birds were descendants of

creatures wherein the fore limb had disappeared, and in time reappeared in the form of a minute useless organ, such as is seen in the apteryx, and thence had continued to develop, attaining its climax in the wings of the eagle, condor, and albatross.

Flightlessness became possible only to birds that could procure abundance of food on the ground within a small area, free from raptorial enemies and extremes of climate. It might be thought that the decline of the wing would be so gradual that only in comparatively modern birds would it reach the vestigial stage. But this is by no means the case, though countless generations may have passed in reducing the wing to the stage of degeneracy seen in the apteryx or the emeu. Flightless birds, in which the wing has degenerated far more than in any living birds, existed long ages ago, and in one species, hesperornis, a gigantic toothed diver, only the stump of the humerus remained (p. 916). In the moas even this was lost. But the very nature of these vestiges is sufficient to show their true character, for they are, in every case, obviously degenerate wings, which at some earlier time, however, were functional, for in every essential particular they differ in no wise from functional wings which owe their peculiarities of structure solely to adaptation to the purposes of flight.

The wings of the ostrich tribe, furthermore, present two interesting features generally overlooked, features, by the way, which also tend to confirm the contention that the wings of these birds are degenerate organs of flight. In the first place, the wing of the rhea bears a striking resemblance to that of flying birds, even in the number of the primary quills, which are twelve in number, as in grebes and storks. In certain details as to the arrangement of the coverts it differs from that usually met with in the wing of the Neognathæ—the group which contains all existing birds other than the ostrich tribe, or Palæognathæ—though this arrangement recalls that of the owl's wing. In the ostrich, however, there are sixteen primary quills, and the arrangement of the coverts is less like that of typical wings, but then the wing, as a whole, is more degenerate than that of the rhea, as is manifest by the fact that the hand cannot be flexed at the wrist upon the forearm.

The second point concerns the rate of degeneration of the several segments of the wing. It would seem that this process of decay is at first gradual, the several segments of the limb preserving their relative proportionate lengths, but after a certain stage has been reached the digits decrease with greater rapidity. The arm and forearm retain their relative lengths yet longer, then the forearm enters upon a stage of rapid atrophy, and, finally, the arm itself vanishes. The rhea, emeu, apteryx, hesperornis, and moa afford a series of perfect gradations in this process of degeneration.

Finally, the ostrich, rhea, and apteryx are descendants of birds wherein the arm was of great length, while the emeu, cassowary, æpyornis, and moa belonged to types having a short arm.

That the rhea and ostrich have preserved relatively large wings, though useless as organs of flight, is due to the fact that they employ the wings partly as balancing organs and partly as sails when running. [For another view held as to the evolution of the flightless birds see page 917.] W. P. PYCRAFT

THE MIGRATION OF BIRDS

By A. LANDSBOROUGH THOMSON

THE phenomena of bird-migration have attracted attention from time immemorial, and have formed the subject of proverb and metaphor in the speech and literature of all peoples. And yet so much takes place altogether beyond our ken, that we are still very far indeed from a complete understanding of the facts, or a satisfactory solution to the great problems they suggest.

The fundamental fact of bird-migration is that many birds breeding in the colder parts of the world seek, on the approach of winter, " warmer lands and coasts that keep the sun." The return of summer sees them again on their way to their old haunts, and such evidence as we possess indicates that a return to the self-same place is the general rule.

A journey from colder to warmer countries is, as a rule, naturally one that is north to south in general trend. But this must not be pushed too far. In Northern Europe, for example, much migration takes place in a more markedly west to east direction—from the severe winter of Russia to the more temperate maritime countries, like our own, lying in almost the same latitudes. But migration as a whole may be said to take place from the arctic and temperate zones of the Northern Hemisphere to countries lying nearer the Equator in a more or less direct southerly line.

A corresponding state of affairs holds in the Southern Hemisphere. Many northern birds, however, migrate past the Equator and into high southern latitudes ; there they, of course, find summer while their own homes are in the grip of winter. These birds, therefore, seek not merely a milder winter within their own hemisphere, but keep perpetually on the summer side of the Equator. An extreme case is that of the Arctic tern, which is well-known as a breeding species in the northern summer from our own coasts to 82° N. lat. and was found " wintering " in the Antarctic summer in 74° 1' S. lat., by the Scottish expedition of 1902–4. So far as we know, this is " the greatest latitudinal range of any vertebrate animal."

Again, it is a fact of fundamental importance that the phenomena of migration are *orderly*. It is well-known, for instance, how punctually migrants arrive and depart with the recurrence of the seasons. And, so far as we can tell, the routes and destinations are equally fixed and according to law. The significance of this point we shall presently see.

Further, it must be noticed that there is no real difference between the migrations of the birds which we class respectively as " summer " and " winter visitors." The distinction is purely a local one. Thus the cuckoo is a winter visitor in the Mediterranean countries and the fieldfare a summer visitor in Scandinavia. Even within our own small area we have birds which have a different status in one part from that which they have in another. Thus the snow bunting is not only a well-known winter guest over the greater part of the British Isles, but also an uncommon summer bird in the Scottish Highlands.

Still more confusing are those numerous species which are found all the year round in a district, but are really migratory, the individuals changing with the season. Fluctuating numbers may betray the fact to careful observers, or the passage of the seeming " residents " may be noted at the lighthouses round our coasts. In northern latitudes true residents are not a numerous class.

Several minor characteristics of migration have very important bearings on the great problems. For instance, we find that most species are markedly gregarious at migration time, not only with their kind, but often with birds of other species. And yet old birds and young birds usually keep distinctly apart, while among the former the sexes may even be separated. In most cases concerning which we have much information, it appears that the young birds, only a few months or even weeks old, are the first to journey southwards in autumn. The reverse obtains in the familiar case of the cuckoo, and there are probably other exceptions. Individual exceptions naturally occur in all species.

Then we have the difficult question of the influence of weather conditions. That all the phenomena of migration must bear some relation to these seems evident, but how and to what extent we cannot say. Even the question of the conditions of wind and weather under which migration flight is usually performed still lacks a satisfactory answer. That great " rushes " of southward migration in our area frequently coincide with " favourable " winds, has misled certain writers, and induced them to dogmatise on the subject. But it has been shown that a direct connection is probably absent, migration and wind being both effects of certain atmospheric conditions further north. Under certain circumstances, the one may be produced without the other.

To generalise, local conditions can only be of secondary importance, and to find fundamental relations we must study the general conditions over the whole area affected by a particular movement, and, perhaps, especially the conditions at the starting point. Local conditions may, of course, influence the *aspect*

BIRDS RESTING ON A SHIP ON THEIR WAY SOUTH

927

of migration. In extreme cases they may perhaps render travelling impossible, but at other times they will only affect the habits, altitude, velocity, and so forth, of the migrants.

As regards habits we need only remark that the chief British movements are nocturnal. But this varies with species, locality, and other circumstances. It is on overclouded and misty nights that the lighthouse beams have their peculiar dazzling power.

As regards altitude, it may be said that migrants are generally to be seen flying at heights varying from a few feet to a few hundred feet above the sea or land. Enormous elevations are sometimes chosen, however, and some authorities have even claimed that these are normal. The view has also been put forward that migration flight has a quite peculiar and exceptional velocity. Of this, however, there is little or no proof. As to what length of flight is usually performed at a time we have no information.

The nature of the routes followed by migrants is another point on which our knowledge is sadly inadequate. At times migration seems to be concentrated in a narrow line—along a coast, for example. At others the birds move in broad waves across an area of land or sea.

We have seen that to class birds as "summer visitors" and "winter visitors," is to make a "distinction without a difference," when we are considering migration as a whole. But when we confine ourselves to a particular area, such as our own, the classification becomes rational.

The most important summer visitors to the British Isles are included in the following list : Ring-ousel, wheatear, whinchat, redstart, nightingale, nearly all our indigenous warblers, such as willow-wren, white-throat, flycatchers, swallows and martins, cuckoo, nightjar, wryneck, swift, turtle-dove, quail, landrail, common sandpiper, and tern. It is only exceptionally that any of these birds are found with us in winter, but there are other species which are in part summer visitors, but are also residents or even winter visitors as well, and are thus regularly found throughout the year in our islands. If we took the extreme north of Scotland by itself, the list of true summer visitors would include many species well known in winter in England. It will be noted that insectivorous birds bulk largely in the above list.

Our list of birds found only in winter is a short one—fieldfare, redwing, and various ducks and geese are the chief—but that is because most of our winter visitors are to some extent represented with us throughout the year. Their numbers, however, are temporarily augmented each autumn by vast hordes from Northern Europe. Members of the thrush, finch, lark, crow, duck, and plover families are predominant. Some of the last-named, among others, fall into the class of "birds of passage" which use our shores merely as a highway to and from more northern and more southern lands.

Under the rather unsatisfactory title of "partial migrants" may be classed most of the British species which do not come entirely under any of the above three heads. They may fall under more than one head in either of the ways already alluded to, or they may be birds which perform only local movements and migrations within our area.

The insignificant remainder are the true residents. Our information on the point is very far from complete, but we are more and more coming to believe that practically all our birds are migratory in some slight degree. Even the red grouse, a very pronounced type of a stationary species, may change its level with the seasons—a "vertical migration"! The general directions of the main migratory movements which affect our area may be briefly summarised, it being understood that the spring movements are just the reverse counterparts of the autumn movements mentioned. The great bulk of our winter visitors come to us across the North Sea. All along the eastern seaboard of Great Britain, from Shetland to Norfolk, the birds from Northern Europe arrive by south-westerly lines of flight. In the south-east of England those from Central Europe arrive in an almost due east to west direction. These, and the main emigration routes from the south coast of England, are the chief channels for the continual ebb and flow of British bird life. Many of the others are, nevertheless, of great importance, but cannot be detailed here.

As to the seasons at which migration takes place, April and May, September and October are the times of the chief British movements. But we have migration of some sort going on almost all the year round. A few very hardy species, such as geese, begin to move north as early as the end of February, and many others follow in March. On the other hand, our latest summer visitors, such as the swift, are not here in full force till well on in May.

Young birds of Arctic species and adult cuckoos may begin to move southwards before June is out, and the "autumn" movement is continued from that time onward into the winter, and even, in the case of some hardy species and under certain conditions, through December and into January. The turn of the migrational tide occurs in early February, and again in mid-June. Autumn migration is long-drawn out, and is apparently accomplished in a leisurely way. Business-like dispatch characterises the return movement, which is, partly for that reason, much the less evident of the two.

We have seen that the bare facts of migration are still very imperfectly known, but when we come to the theoretical questions of reasons and causes we realise the full measure of our ignorance. Partly from their

MAP SHOWING A TYPICAL MIGRATION IN EUROPE
A number of hooded crows caught at Rossitten during the migration time were marked with aluminium rings, and then liberated. Each cross on this map shows where one of these birds has been recovered. The entire migration of the hooded crows through Rossitten is thus mapped out

inherent difficulties, and partly from lack of data, these problems are as yet without very satisfactory solutions. We may, however, set down in brief some of the essential points.

In the first place, migration must have a reason—a good reason. It involves a great expenditure of energy and life, and would, therefore, soon succumb to the forces of natural selection had it not a satisfactory raison d'être. Cold, acting through food-supply rather than directly, is probably the chief factor in autumn. Shortened feeding hours may accentuate the difficulty for diurnal species.

The avoidance of the conditions indicated form good reasons for migration, but they cannot be considered as causes. Then, also, we must consider that migration begins before these conditions have made themselves appreciably felt. Further, migration is a regular, orderly, smooth-working, but yet complex phenomenon which can hardly be supposed to arise afresh each season. Everything, in fact, points to the existence of a deep inborn instinct. Forces which are insufficient to cause migration might readily stimulate a hereditary habit ; or the stimuli may come in another form, but that is an unsettled question.

Our main problem has thus become magnified by consideration, and is nothing more nor less than to discover the explanation of the origin of this instinctive habit. Two theories may be outlined.

The first supposes that high latitudes once enjoyed a temperate climate, and were inhabited by non-migratory birds. Then came the Great Ice Age, and forced these species, generation after generation, towards the Equator. At last the turn came, and the Polar ice-cap gradually receded, and the species as slowly spread after it towards their old homes. Each year, however, the now temporary return of winter stimulated an instinctive desire for the second home which had been established in the countries beyond the limits of the great glacial invasion. The routes followed by the individuals to-day are explained as the paths followed by the species during the glacial epoch. All this, we may say, is merely one form of the theory which ascribes the origin of the migratory habit to great climatic changes of past ages.

A second theory connects migration with food-supply. Overcrowding has caused species to extend their range along the lines of least resistance as regards food. The extension would naturally take place in spring, and the birds might be led into areas from which each winter would compel them to withdraw into the original area. In this way a regular smooth-working habit might be originated, and the routes of the species become those of the individuals. Where wide seas are now crossed, former land connections may not unreasonably be assumed.

A second class of problems also presents itself, a series of questions, which ask "How?" rather than "Why?" What is the mechanism of the whole thing? How, in fact, does it work? One question especially strikes deeply, "How the migrants find their way?" Against the obvious difficulties of the journey may perhaps be set great natural sense of direction—even a "magnetic sense," as some have supposed. But in the case of young birds migrating for the first time, and, as we have seen, unguided, there must be something more. Indeed, we seem to be driven to accept the answer that knowledge of route is part of the instinct—that it is, in fact, hereditary.

We may conclude by mentioning the various methods by which ornithologists hope to accumulate, in course of time, facts which may bring us much nearer to the heart of these mysteries.

First, we may consider the work of isolated observers in particular districts. Signs of migration are almost everywhere to be found,

STORKS ASSEMBLING FOR MIGRATION

but good opportunities for close observation are more rarely present. But when such exist much can be done. Thus, special stations like the island of Heligoland in the south-east corner of the North Sea ; Fair Isle, between Shetland and Orkney ; and Rossitten, on a narrow isthmus on the East Baltic, have yielded splendid results. There are obvious limits, however, to what may be learnt from isolated work of this nature.

The next logical step is to organise schemes of concerted observation at numerous stations over a large area. Two important inquiries on these lines have been carried out in this country. About twenty-five years ago a committee of the British Association arranged for a long series of observations at the lighthouses and lightships round the British coasts. The resulting reports are perhaps the most important contributions that have ever been made to the whole subject of migration. At the present time a committee of the British Ornithologists' Club are collecting records from observers all over England, inland as well as on the coasts. On different lines is the method of marking birds with rings made of aluminium or other metal, and inscribed with an address and an identifying number. A small proportion of birds are naturally heard of again, and the facts of the particular case may prove very insignificant. The method has only recently come into prominence, but it is to be welcomed as attacking the problem from a fresh aspect—that of the journeys and life-history of the individual bird.

The fuller employment of these methods of study is a matter for the future, and in the meantime we must confess that much mystery still surrounds the lives of the

"Wild birds that change
Their season in the night, and wail their way
From cloud to cloud down the long wind."

A. L. THOMSON

CONCERNING NESTS, EGGS, AND NESTLINGS

By W. P. PYCRAFT

In the building of the nursery a quite extraordinary diversity of skill and, if one may use such a term, preference, is displayed, for while some species are content with a slight depression in the bare earth, ready made or hastily scraped, others construct cradles of wonderful beauty and craftsmanship, and between the two extremes there exist innumerable gradations.

The earliest birds, like their immediate ancestors the reptiles, had small need of nests, because, being tree-dwellers, they deposited their eggs in the holes of decaying tree-trunks or in the crowns of disintegrating tree-ferns. As, with the course of time and the pressure of numbers, these ancestral types migrated to more open country, they sought caves, crevices in rocks and burrows in the ground ; and later, no doubt, many took to laying their eggs in the open and on the ground.

Of these last, many would find themselves forced into areas where the ground was cold and damp, and, to avoid this discomfort when brooding, would scrape together pieces of stick and other dead vegetation on which to rest. On such a platform the eggs were laid, and here the young enjoyed in turn the comfort originally designed by the parents for themselves. The less intelligent birds, breeding in the same neighbourhood and making no such provision, either died from cold or lost their offspring from the same cause. Hence, by this very simple process of selection, only those birds that had evolved the elements of nest-building would survive.

Many birds, even to-day, have not passed this stage. The nightjar makes no nest, but brooding on dry soil, no great need for a nest has arisen. Many of the plover tribe—and by this term we include the gulls and terns—breeding on sandy beaches, need no nest, for the rain soon drains away. Others, however—nesting in the same area, be it noted—pave some slight hollow with stones, or line it with grass and seaweed, while yet others construct quite passable nests. A colony of terns will illustrate all these stages.

How much of this workmanship is really due to "intelligence," and how much to a more or less variable degree of "instinct" in the right direction, it is difficult to determine. But evidence of intelligence is not strongly marked, since some birds will lay their eggs on a pavement of stones even when the underlying ground is of a highly porous nature. Here, at any rate, we have the material for selection to work on. Should the conditions change by any increase of wetness in the breeding area, the nest-builders alone would be left, and this in a very short time ; for the rest, either

NEST OF A REED WARBLER

in the adult, brooding stage, or as nestlings, would speedily be eliminated.

The habit of nest-building once fixed, it is easy to see how, on a return to arboreal nesting-sites, the more elaborate nests came into being. The pigeons are still very primitive builders, but the crows and birds of prey show an advance, for, through employing sticks, a more workmanlike cradle is fashioned.

From sticks we pass to the use of finer materials, and of a distinct lining of softly-woven texture—down, either vegetable or animal. Many birds, like the goldfinch and chaffinch, construct nests of remarkable beauty, the outside being largely woven of moss.

Others are still more skilled, and decorate the outside with lichens, held in place by spider webs. Thereby the cradle acquires so close a likeness to its surroundings as to be well-nigh invisible. Finally, we come to nests made entirely of the softest cotton down, so cunningly woven as to resemble felt ; the penduline tit and the humming birds afford cases in point.

Some birds—as among the thrush tribe—line their nests with rotten wood, moulded to form a basin-like cavity by an admixture of cow-dung and saliva. And here we stand at the parting of the ways in the evolution of mud-nests, on the one hand, and salivary nests on the other. How and why birds first came to use mud, we can hardly even conjecture, but at the present day a large number of birds use this material as a foundation for their nests. Some, as the house martin and swallow, employ it exclusively, cementing the particles together with saliva. The quaint flamingo is a mud-builder.

The little oven bird of South America is, perhaps, the most skilled architect of all in the use of this substance, for it builds a huge nest with tortuous chambers entirely of mud, a really extraordinary feat when one remembers that the edifice is built up of tiny beakfuls of earth, involving the labour of several weeks.

That the supply of saliva necessary for such architecture must be copious is self-evident. It is not surprising, then, to find that there are some birds which employ this and nothing else in the building of their nurseries. The edible swift achieves this feat, and their nests have from time immemorial been highly prized by the Chinese, who convert them into a soup. Over three and a half millions of these have been imported in a single year from Borneo. These much-prized nests are made only by one species of swift. Several nearly related species build similar nests, but mix feathers and grass with the hardened spittle, and thus render them unfit for commercial purposes.

TYPICAL NESTS OF BRITISH BIRDS

THE CHAFFINCH

THE KESTREL

THE CORMORANT

Photo, Bentley Beetham

GREBE'S FLOATING NEST

THE LAPWING

NESTS OF SOCIABLE WEAVERS

The hangnests affect a slightly different style of architecture, for, with similar materials, no less skilfully woven, they make a nest which looks like an enormously elongated Florence flask. But the strangest part is that some species, both of weaver birds and hangnests, build what may be called "normal," or typical, nests, and between these and the strange cradles just mentioned there are many intermediate stages.

The Indian fairy martin builds a mud nest which is tubular in structure and slightly swollen at the base. But this is affixed by its base to the face of some cliff or building, so that the tubular entrance projects several inches outwards, and at right angles to the vertical, or very nearly so.

Some of the humming birds build wonderful suspended nests. The pichincha hill-star, for instance, hangs its nursery from the bough of a tree by a slender rope, composed, like the rest of the nest, of wool and hair. The nest itself is oblong, and to preserve its balance, when one end happens to prove heavier than the other, little pellets of earth are used to adjust the error.

The reed warbler contrives to weave a marvellously compact nest between the stems of three or four reeds, lashing the nest and the reeds so that these look as though they had grown through its sides. Externally it is composed of dead reed leaves, and is lined with the feathery seed plumes thereof. The cup-shaped cavity is so deep that even when, by the fury of the wind, the reed bed is laid low, the eggs, or the chicks, rest snugly at the bottom.

During the construction of its nest the tailor bird exhibits a marvellous dexterity coupled with actions so complex that it is difficult to avoid regarding them as the outcome of reasoning. Selecting a suitable leaf, the bird proceeds to make a series of punctures along each edge, and then passing strands of cobweb through the holes, draws the margins together. This done, the resultant tubular cavity is lined with cotton down. During this process more holes are punched

The nest of the tree swift is probably the smallest made by any bird, relatively to its size. The total length of the builder is 9 inches, the width of the nest across the top is $1\frac{1}{4}$ inch. It is built of tiny pieces of bark, held together with saliva. The thickness of the nest wall is about one-eighth of an inch. These diminutive cradles are obviously too small to hold the sitting bird, but they are attached to the side of the branch of a tree, and level with its upper surface, so that the bird broods its single egg by sitting on the bough so that the belly rests upon the egg.

Salvin's swift builds a remarkable nest. This is composed entirely of wind-borne seeds cemented with saliva. It is a more elaborate structure than that of other swifts, since it is built with a false entrance, made apparently to deceive burglars in the shape of snakes.

Still more wonderful burglar-proof nests are those of the penduline tits. That of the Cape penduline tit, for example, is formed of cotton and seed down so interwoven as to resemble the finest felt carpet. Towards the upper end is a funnel-shaped opening, and below is a little pocket, used apparently as a roosting-place for the male, the mother and young sleeping in the larger compartment. When the birds go to roost they draw in the rims of the entrances and fasten them up, so that, if during the night some hungry snake begins fumbling for the aperture, the occupants may have due warning, and forcing their way through the back, escape in time.

As a rule, nests placed amid the branches of trees are lodged in the fork of a branch. Some, however, are suspended. The penduline tit's nests, just described, are of this sort, hanging down from the bough which supports them. The little gold-crest, among British birds, builds suspended nests. Still more remarkable are the nests of the weaver-birds and the American hangnests. The first-named weave a purse-shaped nest of long strips of palm leaves and grass, twisted and knotted together with the most amazing dexterity. Commonly the nest is suspended by a long rope of three twisted strands, and in many species the entrance is by way of a long, stocking-like opening on the under surface of the purse, rendering the admittance of snakes impossible.

NESTS OF CRESTED CASSIQUE AND BALTIMORE ORIOLE

through the leaf, and through these bits of the lining are thrust, thus helping still further to keep the edges of the leaf together. But, for safety's sake, the origina. stitches of cobweb are strengthened by strands of cotton, which, on being thrust through the several holes, fray out, giving the appearance of so many neatly-tied knots. Though these different stages seem to suggest something more than mere instinct, yet, on careful consideration, they do not indicate more skill than is necessary for the construction of the felted nest of the penduline tits or the marvellously woven nest of birds like the long-tailed titmouse and the chaffinch.

Birds in the matter of their nests, even when they build in colonies, manifest a very marked individualism. In such colonies, among some species, as the swallow-tails, the nests are often placed so close together as to touch one another. And thus is the way prepared for the evolution of compound nests, which present two forms. In one a number of birds combine to share the same nursery, a highly unsatisfactory arrangement, as might be supposed.

The black cuckoo, or ani, supplies a case in point. Herein a number of females join in the construction of a large nest, which, when completed, serves as the common depository of all the builders. Each bird apparently lays two eggs. Nor is this all, for these birds still further depart from precedent in depositing their eggs in two or three regular layers, with leaves between each, so that each stratum contains from four to six eggs. These, as is usual with their kind, are of a beautiful blue colour, but this is encrusted with a white chalky layer. Naturally, this gets scratched off at the sides, but it would seem that the chalk from each end of the egg is deliberately and carefully chipped off by these eccentric mothers, for what purpose none can say. Nesting in common begets a feeling of irresponsibility in regard to the young, and how the work of brooding and feeding is carried on is, so far, not clearly ascertained.

The weaver birds pursue a more excellent plan. Also very sociable, they contrive, however, to avoid the crazy tactics of the black cuckoos, and preserve all the essentials of privacy and independent action. Some species build in large communities, but keep their nests quite separate, and others, like the black weaver bird of Africa, collect a vast heap of sticks and twigs, in the centre of which they construct five or six grass-lined nurseries. If any damage be done to the colony, all join in the work of repairs ; and this same dwelling is restored and added to year after year. But, as is the rule with nests, they serve only as nurseries.

The sociable weaver birds introduce a new feature. These birds construct in some large tree a huge beehive-like mass of grass, which is honeycombed with tunnels, each leading into a cosy chamber lined with feathers. The aperture of each nest opens on the under side of the common roof. But, though primarily built to serve as nurseries, these chambers are occupied during the rest of the year as roosting-places

EDIBLE SWIFTS' NESTS

and shelter from tropical rains. Nests of this kind, made up of a cartload of grass and twigs, are conspicuous objects all over South Africa.

Nest-building skill becomes the more marvellous when we reflect that the bird's only tool is the beak. In some cases this seems well enough adapted for the work, but this cannot be said of all. Moreover, birds with very different beaks build nests of very similar materials, and often nests of rare beauty, such as the felt-work nests of the penduline tit and the felted work of the humming birds. In the case of birds which drive long tunnels into sandbanks this discrepancy is even more marked.

The little sand martin, for instance, is a marvellous engineer. For it has but the smallest of beaks, and the tiniest and feeblest of feet, yet it drives through the sand tunnels of many feet in length. The long, curved, pointed beak, like a pick of the bee-eater, appears much better fitted for this work ; yet, though successful enough in its boring operations, it suffers considerably at times from the labour demanded of it. There is, in short, no relation between the form of the beak and the nature of the nest ; nor is there any closer agreement between the form of the nest in nearly related birds. Thus the swallow builds a mud nest, the sand martin, with a beak precisely similar, bores holes in sandbanks. The petrels, for the most part, make their nurseries in the bowels

TAILOR BIRD MAKING NEST

of the earth; the lordly albatross, like the bizarre flamingo, builds a tower of mud and squats upon the top of it.

Nor is there any more order in the choice of site. Cormorants, gannets, herons, and the lordly eagles will, as occasion requires, build either on the ground or in the tree-tops. Ducks one regards as birds which breed in marshy ground, yet the golden-eye, like the woodpecker, prefers hollow trees; and this list might be extended indefinitely.

EGGS

As to eggs, though much might be written, yet little of first-rate importance remains to be said. On account of their diversity in colouring they appeal, unfortunately, largely to people in whom the "collecting" instinct is well developed. These know little of, and care less for, the problems which eggs present, and thus, in spite of the vast hordes of eggs that have been amassed by collectors of this type, scarcely anything, in comparison, has been added to our knowledge of eggs in particular or of the life histories of birds in general.

Originally, no doubt, all birds laid white eggs; this we may assume from our knowledge of the reptilian ancestry of birds. But it is difficult to trace the origin of the beautiful colouring which most eggs offer. In a large number of cases concealment from enemies was the guiding factor. Still, no bird, by desire, can affect the colour of its eggs. We must, therefore, suppose that colouring began with variations, and that a more or less gradual appearance of pigmentation took place in the white shells of eggs laid in exposed places. Any such toning down of a glaring white surface would help to hide the egg from the eyes of prowling egg-stealers, whether bird, beast, or reptile. Thus the strain of colour-producing birds would begin to dominate over those which continued to lay white eggs, since increased toll would be taken of the latter, accompanied in consequence by a corresponding decrease in the offspring reared.

Birds that still lay white eggs nest either in holes or in comparatively inaccessible places. Such as nest in holes, it has been contended, do so because their eggs are white and they seek to conceal them. Really, the reverse is the case. They lay white eggs because they lay in holes. The white shell being dimly visible in the dark, the bird on entering its nest can see the eggs and avoid crushing them. Coloured eggs under such conditions would likely be crushed when the brooding bird entered.

The colouring presents bewildering degrees of variety, yet withal, paradoxical as it may seem, a considerable sameness. Hence it is extremely difficult to identify eggs of unknown history. While the parent species are always distinguishable, the eggs are by no means equally so. If we were to hand the egg, say, of a redstart or thrush to an expert, asking him to name the species to which it belonged, and giving him no hint as to the country in which it was obtained, he would find the task hopeless. Of course, knowing it was obtained in Great Britain there would be no difficulty, but then locality and not colouring would be the determining factor.

Many ducks' eggs cannot be identified without the aid of the down. Some groups of birds, as the birds of prey, lay eggs of the most wonderful colouring, others white. Some eggs are encased in a thick layer of chalk, concealing vivid colours underneath, as in some of the cuckoos; others have a shell which rather resembles burnished metal or porcelain, as in the tinamus. No black eggs are known.

Finally, the eggs of most species show more or less variation, when they are multi-coloured. The guillemot is the best-known instance of this. Its eggs may be pure white, blue, red, or green, or marked with every conceivable variation in the matter of lines, spots, and blotches.

In shape, too, they vary, from the typical "egg-shaped" to cylindrical, pear-shaped, and spherical; while in the thickness of the shell they also display a lack of uniformity.

A COLONY OF NESTING ALBATROSSES

AFRICAN ELEPHANT

"The African elephant is a more decided tree-feeder than the Indian, and the destruction committed by a herd of such animals when feeding in a mimosa forest is extraordinary; they deliberately march forward, and uproot or break down every tree that excites their appetite."

935

X

UNAUS OR TWO-TOED SLOTHS

"Although by older naturalists sloths were regarded as ill-formed creatures destined to lead a miserable life on account of their misshapen limbs, no animals are in reality better adapted to their peculiar mode of existence"

GREAT ANT-EATER

"Although distributed over the whole of the tropical portions of South and Central America, great ant-eaters are nowhere common, and from their nocturnal habits seldom seen. They frequent either the low, wet lands bordering the rivers, or swampy forests, and are strictly terrestrial in habits."

RED KANGAROOS

"When running, kangaroos spring from the ground in an erect position, propelled by their powerful hind legs and balanced by the tail, holding their short forearms well into the chest, after the manner of a runner."

The number of eggs in a " clutch " also varies—that is to say, the full complement laid by any given species before brooding begins varies individually. For instance, in a clutch laid by this or that particular species the number may be determined sometimes by the relative abundance of food, sometimes by constitutional causes. But the number also varies as between different species. Guillemots, gannets, and auks, for instance, lay but one ; pigeons never exceed two ; the plover tribe four ; and so on. Some species, like the game birds, lay large clutches. The pheasant, for example, lays from 10 to 14 eggs, the partridge 10 to 20.

NESTLING BIRDS

There can be no doubt that the earliest birds were strictly arboreal in habit, and reared their young in nurseries amid the recesses of the forest. That these young were active from the moment of hatching scarcely admits of question, for, as we shall show, nestlings hatched in a helpless state represent a highly specialised phase of development. Moreover, the reptilian character of the earlier birds was, as might be supposed, more marked than in living birds, and these have been described as " glorified reptiles."

Happily, evidence is available which places the probability of this view beyond the reach of reasonable doubt. This evidence is drawn from three sources—from the facts derived from a study of the nestling of a remarkable South American bird, the hoatzin, from the nestlings of the game birds, and from fossils.

First of all, as to the hoatzin. This strange bird, which has its head-quarters along the banks of the Amazon, is generally regarded as an aberrant member of the gallinaceous birds; but it presents many puzzling and some remarkable anatomical characters which make its precise relationships difficult to determine. It is a bird of ex-

PARTRIDGE'S LARGE CLUTCH OF EGGS

tremely limited powers of flight, and is said never to alight on the ground. We are, however, concerned here rather with the early stages of post-embryonic development than with the adult.

The nestlings, then, are hatched in a rough nursery of sticks placed amid the boughs of some tree overhanging the water, but, unlike other nestlings hatched under similar conditions, they are ushered into the world in a relatively advanced stage of development, being clothed with a loose, red-coloured down, and capable of no small activity, climbing about the branches supporting the nest with marvellous agility. Though the feet are relatively of enormous size, the beak and wings are used as auxiliaries to locomotion, so that for a time these youngsters are quadrupedal.

As might be imagined, wings used at this tender age for such a purpose must display some peculiarities not met with in nestling birds as a rule. They are, in the first place, of considerable length, the hand being especially long in relation to the arm and forearm. Furthermore, the thumb and the index digit are very

" finger-like," having the under surface somewhat bulbous, thus affording increased sensitiveness to touch and a better grip. The hold, however, is still further improved by means of long claws. Thus equipped, climbing is necessarily an easy matter, but should one, by accident, fall into the water below, then it promptly strikes out and swims for the bank, clutching hold of the reeds and other vegetation, and thus by easy stages makes its way back to the nursery.

Long before the feathers appear on the body the quill feathers begin to sprout. But they display a very curious sequence of development, for those on the inner, wristwards, margin of the hand are the first to appear ; then those along the forearm (secondaries), the wristward feathers first, and finally those at the tip of the finger. What is the explanation of this unusual order ?

A little reflection will show that if all the hand quills (primaries) grew at the same rate, the outermost would soon render the wing absolutely useless as a climbing organ, for they would impede the grasp and the use of

GANNET'S SINGLE EGG
Photo, J. R. Adams

the claws. Consequently, not until the innermost primaries have attained a fan-shaped growth, and thus formed a wing area large enough to break the force of a fall, do the outer quills start to grow, when they develop rapidly. Simultaneously the claws become absorbed, and the forearm, growing more rapidly than the hand, soon reverses the original proportions, the hand becoming shorter than the forearm.

These facts, in themselves, would not carry us very far, but, coupled with what obtains among the nestlings of the game birds, they throw a surprising light on the developmental history of birds in general.

The facts in regard to the game birds are, in broad outline, a repetition of those sketched in the case of the hoatzin. But there are significant differences. Thus the thumb and finger do not display the thickened, sensitive under surface seen in the hoatzin, while the claws of the fingers are present only during embryonic life. The development of the quills in the region of the wrist before the appearance of those at the end of the finger is here, however, quite as conspicuous a feature ; and it is further to be noticed that this phase of development is greatly accelerated.

But for the facts yielded by the hoatzin this curious order in the development of the quills would have been unintelligible. I had indeed long and vainly tried to solve the riddle, till the nestling hoatzins were placed in my hands, and these gave me the key to the mystery. The answer to the riddle is shortly this : The wing of the nestling game birds is a survival of an earlier phase of existence, when these birds, like the hoatzin, were reared in arboreal nurseries. This explanation alone can account for such a curious arrest in the development of the outer quills. It is a phase which is slowly being obliterated, as is shown by the fact that the nail-bearing joint of the second digit fails to survive the embryonic stage.

But to complete the story of this strange history we must take the evidence of fossils, and this carries us back to the earliest known bird, archæopteryx. This, it is significant to note, was a strictly arboreal bird. Now, its wing recalls, in many respects, that presented by the early development stages of the wing in the hoatzin and the nestling game birds, inasmuch as the index finger projected considerably beyond the outermost primary. It differed from the wing of all existing species in that the third digit was fairly long, and was armed with a claw; but this is also true, at least occasionally, of the embryonic ostrich, while in the penguins this digit is always very long. Now, it is unlikely that these digits were used as climbing agents during the adult life of this archaic bird, save perhaps when moulting, when, we must assume, all the quills were shed at once, as in ducks, grebes, and rails.

At such times the temporarily useless wing could with advantage be used as a climbing organ; but it is more probable that the peculiar features of this adult wing were persistent post-embryonic characters, which have been preserved only in certain nestlings to-day. Therein the ordinary course of evolution is followed. That is to say, we must assume that this wing is the result of the transformation of an organ originally serving another purpose—probably climbing. Then it became a parachute in function, and, as such, served the immediate precursor of archæopteryx, and the nestling of archæopteryx.

FULMAR

Meanwhile, this organ was undergoing a series of progressive changes in the direction of a more perfect wing, and in proportion shed the characters belonging to earlier stages. But so much of the old order as served the purpose of the nestling has been maintained in a modified form, and has been handed on to the hoatzin, and, still further modified, to the game bird. The fact that the wing of the hoatzin during its embryonic development exhibits, as a passing phase, characters belonging to an earlier, more archaic stage, and that the game birds in turn develop during embryonic life characters seen only in nestling hoatzins, give this interpretation something more than probability.

Passing reference has been made to certain features of accelerated development in the wing of the game bird, and this must now be enlarged upon.

Enough has been said to show that the game birds are descended from an arboreal stock. The evidence of the wing surely establishes this. When migration was made to the new habitat, the activities of the young took on new phases. For, in the first place, some sort of adjustment to the new physical conditions was necessary; and, in the second, the animate environment was altogether changed, for new and formidable enemies had to be encountered and avoided.

The early development of the innermost primaries

BARN OWL

and outermost secondaries—an adaptation to an arboreal life for the sake of avoiding injury by falling from tree-tops—was now turned to account to afford a means of escape from pursuit by carnivores. Meeting with a measure of success, this device was improved upon by greatly accelerating the growth of the feathers, so that, within a few hours of hatching, flight over short distances became possible.

This curious succession of the quill feathers is certainly no comparatively recent adaptation to particular needs, but a survival carrying us back to the very dawn of avian evolution. And this view receives confirmation from the fact that the same order is found to obtain in the tinamus and in the rhea, one of the flightless ostriches. Similarly, we must remark, the claws in the wing are no mere relics of reptilian ancestry, but survivals from the earliest birds, wherein they were functional, as is seen in archæopteryx.

By way of contrast we may pass now to the ducks and their kin. In the nestling the wing shows no traces of the peculiar features just described. On the contrary, we meet here with a retardation of the wing. In the young pheasant the wing feathers have grown large enough to perform the office of flight, while the rest of the body is yet clothed in down. In the ducks, on the other hand, the reverse is the case. Not until the bird is more than half grown, and almost fully feathered, do the wings begin to show the slightest sign of feathers; they remain ridiculous-looking stumps embedded in the feathers of the flanks. The reason is not far to seek. The young of the game birds are surrounded by many dangers that can be avoided only by flight; the young duck escapes by swimming, or takes refuge in the dense reed clumps among which its early life is spent. Flight is unnecessary.

The next phase of development to be reviewed is that furnished by species which, having young of the active, or "nidifugous," type, breed either in large colonies or on the ledges of precipitous cliffs. The gulls and auks provide the most striking illustrations of this kind.

PIGEON

TYPICAL NESTLINGS
Photos, B. Beetham and J. T. Newman

The gulls, it must be remembered, are near akin to the plovers, the young of which enter the world endowed with an activity as marked as that displayed by the game birds or the young of the ducks. They resemble the young of the ducks, however, in this—that the wings develop late, though not so markedly as in ducks; escape from enemies is found after another fashion, of which more presently. The gull nestlings, as we have remarked, are of the active, or "nidifugous," type, but they depart from it in being exceedingly sluggish in habit; in fact, until able to fly they never leave the nest. The advantage of this will be evident when it is remembered that gulls breed either in large colonies or on precipitous cliffs.

In either case it is obvious that young of wandering and inquisitive habits would furnish an appalling death-rate. For, wandering about in a busy colony, they would never succeed either in finding the nest or their parents returning with food, while any tendency to explore on the part of nestlings hatched on the ledges of cliffs would be disastrous, since such ledges are often not more than a few inches in area, on the one side of which tower unscalable cliffs, and on the other yawns a greedy precipice hundreds of feet deep. On similar ledges the auks and guillemots contrive to rear their young also, and these are as inactive, till able to fly, as any young gulls.

Before attempting to explain how this inactivity has come to be, it will be best to follow up this phase of growth to its maximum development. The several further links in the chain are furnished by the steganopodous birds—gannets, cormorants, and pelicans; the stork tribe; the accipitrine birds—hawks and eagles; and the owls. Thence we pass to the coraciiform birds—parrots, cuckoos, bee-eaters, kingfishers, and a host more; and, finally, to the passerine, or perching, birds. Now, the steganopodous birds, such as the storks, accipitres, and owls, all agree in that the young during their sojourn in the nest are clothed in a thick, woolly covering of down, differing, it is to be remarked, from the down of active, "nidifugous" young in its greater length and softness.

The penguins appear to afford an exception to this rule, since they display considerable activity yet wear conspicuously woolly covering. But it must be remembered that these birds, at birth, are "nidicolous," and have a very long nestling

A COLONY OF GANNETS ON THE BASS ROCK
Photograph, J. T. Newman

period, since the down is not lost until the birds have attained nearly full growth—that is to say, until they are many months old. This down, then, is to be regarded as degenerate, its degradation proceeding hand in hand with the loss of activity.

Among the coraciiform birds only the parrots and the owls develop a really dense covering of down. Among the cuckoos the down is of an exceedingly degenerate character, more so than in pigeons. In the majority of this group the down is suppressed altogether, as in the kingfisher, for example. In the passerine birds a gradual series of down-reduction is traceable. The lyre birds stand at one end of the series, in having a thick, woolly coat; among others, as in the young bullfinch, this covering is moderately well developed.

The thrushes stand as types of nestlings in which the down is all but suppressed; only a few weak filaments, quite inadequate even to conceal the skin, remain; and in birds like the crows, for example,

even this has vanished, so that, until the feathers begin to appear, their young are absolutely naked.

We find, then, a series of insensible gradations between nidifugous and nidicolous birds, and between clothed (ptilopædic) and naked (dasypædic) birds, the one condition more or less intimately related to the others. How has the change from the active to the passive state been brought about? It has already been shown that the active is the most primitive condition, and that the more primitive birds were tree-dwellers, and reared their young in trees. We have seen, further, that in order to reduce the infant mortality caused by falls the growth of the outer wing quills was retarded, while the hand developed certain peculiarities converting it into a climbing organ. But this provision, it would seem, was not altogether a success, and in course of time became obsolete by the substitution of a process of "hobbling," resulting in nestlings rendered incapable of movement until fully able to fly.

Now, this "hobbling" process has been brought about by what we may call "premature" birth, enforced by a reduction in the amount of food-yolk in the egg, a process apparently caused by the action of natural selection.

The "eggs" of a bird, it must be borne in mind, contain, besides the germ destined to become the chick, a relatively enormous amount of food on which this chick is nourished. This food is the "yolk."

The greater the quantity of yolk the egg contains, the further will the development of the chick proceed before hatching takes place. The megapodes show this, for these birds lay relatively very big eggs, containing a large amount of yolk; so much so, that the chick passes through the downy stage within the shell, and emerges feathered. Now, in birds which lay eggs containing a relatively small amount of food yolk, like the crow tribe, for example, the chick is hatched blind, naked, and helpless; and between these two extremes are infinite gradations.

OSTRICH CHICKS

It cannot, of course, be supposed that birds can control the size of their eggs, but the circumstances of environment do this most effectually, and bring about a process of selection whereby birds with a tendency to lay smaller eggs than usual gained the ascendency by increase of numbers over those which had not this tendency. That is to say, this result took place when the nurseries were placed in situations dangerous to young birds of active habits, such as tree-tops and precipitous cliffs. For the more active birds would be the product of large and generously supplied eggs, the less active of small, sparsely fed chicks.

This process of selecting from smaller and smaller eggs has gone on until a stage has been reached when the chick has been reduced to the state of utter helplessness seen in so many nestlings to-day.

The passerine and coraciiform birds seem to have been the first to come under this environmental

EMEU CHICK

moulding force; and once the reduction has been made, be it noted, no return to the older state of things is possible. Hence we find many passerine birds, such as pipits, wagtails, larks, have young so helpless as young crows, though reared in nurseries placed on the ground. These several types have only comparatively recently taken to nesting on the ground, and hence the young bear the characters of young arboreal birds.

A similar process of reduction of food-yolk, with consequent evolution of "nidicolous" nestlings, has happened, apparently independently, in the case of several groups, and for varied reasons. In the gulls, for example, we find a half-way stage between the active young of the plovers and the entirely nidicolous condition seen in, say, petrels or cormorants.

Some of the terns and many of the heron and of the gannet tribes build either on ledges of precipitous cliffs or in high trees, and in either case very active young would be subjected to certain death, owing to falls on the part of the more venturesome chicks. Where, as we have pointed out, large breeding colonies on level ground are formed, restriction of movement on the part of the chicks effect an enormous saving of life. This is shown by the case of the adeliæ penguins, which breed in huge colonies and have nidifugous, or active, young. Here the death-rate is appalling, thousands of young dying of starvation owing to their inability to get fed, having strayed too far from the nest to be found by the parents returning with food.

The birds which lose their young are besieged on all sides by more fortunate, more vigorous chicks, and eventually, even while seeking their own offspring, are made to disgorge for the benefit of the importunate ones. Indeed, it is doubtful whether any of the older, more active birds are ever fed by their own parents. Hatched early, and gaining a good start, these, as soon as they begin to increase in numbers and activity, extracted more and more toll from parents returning from sea, and hence the late-hatched birds go on short commons, many, especially those congenitally weaker, eventually starving to death. The gulls, and other birds that breed in colonies, by reducing the amount of food within the egg, and so bringing about premature birth and its consequent enforced period of helplessness, have escaped this drain upon their ranks.

The megapodes, by vastly increasing the supply of food-yolk within the egg, have practically eliminated the nestling period altogether. These birds, it may be remarked, do not brood their eggs, but bury them in masses of decaying vegetable matter or in warm sand, and there leave them to hatch. How this strange state of things originated it is impossible to discover, but it is probably to be ascribed to some peculiar demand of the environment now long since passed away. But the parental instinct being now dulled, no return to the earlier and more normal fashion of brooding the eggs and feeding the chicks is possible. Hence, although the exciting cause may have gone, the effect remains.

COLORATION OF NESTLINGS

And now we must turn to the matter of the coloration of nestling birds, which presents some exceedingly interesting phases, divisible into two more or less distinct groups. The one embraces all that relates to the colouring of the body as a whole, and the relation thereof to the environment, while to the other belongs a number of curious facts, many of which are as yet inexplicable, but which have to do with the development of more or less brilliantly coloured areas on the head and in the mouth.

As to the coloration of the body as a whole, this, as in all the more primitive birds, takes the form of longitudinal stripes extending from the head, down the neck, and over the upper parts of the down-clad

PLOVER NESTLINGS
PROTECTIVE COLORATION IN NESTLINGS
Photo, J. Williamson

body. In the ostrich tribe this is seen to best advantage, more particularly in the emus, in which it is significant to note that the stripes—black on a white ground—on the neck display a tendency to break up into irregular spots or mottlings, and these mottlings are further traceable, during the first few days of life, on the beak and down the legs to the very toes! In the nearly allied cassowaries the head and neck are unicoloured, but the stripes—dark chocolate on a cream ground—are very strongly contrasted. In the rhea, similarly, the neck is unicoloured, while the stripes on the body are less conspicuous.

The ostrich affords a yet further contrast. Herein the neck is mottled, and these mottlings, as in other similar cases, are formed by the disintegration of continuous lines. The body feathers (down feathers), on the other hand, show no distinct pattern of coloration, but only a confused mottling of black and tawny colours, because these feathers have undergone a quite peculiar structural modification, since they take the form of crisp, glistening, narrow, horny bands, recalling in their texture shavings rather than feathers. In the game birds these stripes take the form of broad bands of chocolate on a buff ground—generally a median and two lateral bands.

The goose tribe, the rails, and the plovers also, it is to be noted, display this banded down-plumage in greater or less perfection. This peculiar colouring, indeed, disappears entirely in nestlings of a nidicolous, or helpless, type, leaving a uniform colouring of grey, buff, or white. Many nidifugous, or active, young similarly have a uniform colouring, or one relieved only by patches of white—the last traces of the originally striped livery.

In the plovers and gulls the several stages of degeneration of this striped plumage can be easily followed. In the Norfolk plover, or thicknee, the dark stripes are reduced to narrow streaks of black; in the nestling lapwing they are broken up altogether to form mottlings. In the gull tribe some of the terns are striped, but these, like most of the gulls, generally display a mottled plumage, though in many the earlier striped dress is readily traceable; but in the skuas all trace of markings of any kind is lost.

In the goose tribe—using this term in a wide sense—the striped dress is almost entirely suppressed, but it is almost perfectly retained in the cereopsis goose. The swans are unicoloured. The ducks have the upper parts dark with a patch before and behind the wing, the final relics of earlier stripes. In the rails the nestlings are commonly black, but in certain lights, in some species, faint traces of stripes are still visible.

It is not easy to discover what purpose these stripes serve. That they were originally protective, investing the wearer with a species of invisible mantle, and that in many cases they still serve this purpose seems probable enough. But it is curious that, while young grebes are striped, young coots and waterhens, living under precisely similar conditions, and often hatched and reared within a few yards of one another, are whole-coloured. If the grebe's dress is protective, why can the young coot and waterhen dispense with it?

It would seem that we must look to some deeper cause for an explanation of this mystery, especially since longitudinal stripes are so commonly, we might say so universally, developed during the early stages of post-embryonic growth. Larval fishes and newts are commonly striped, so also are young reptiles and many young mammals—for example, pigs and tapirs. Among invertebrates, caterpillars afford many examples.

But longitudinal stripes are not confined to immature animals, for many species among fishes, reptiles, birds, and mammals are so marked during adult life; and in these, it is to be noted, this livery is not assumed as a special adult livery, but is simply the persistent dress. In many other animals, as among deer and antelopes, the young are spotted, the adults uniformly coloured; but in others the spots are retained throughout life, or are displaced periodically by a unicoloured livery, as in the fallow deer, which loses its spots during the winter. In this case, as in many others, there is an obvious correlation between the spotted coat and the environment, which establishes the protective value of each of the two liveries without question. In other words, the spotted hide of summer is a device to secure invisibility, and thus a measure of protection from enemies. For these spots, when the animal is standing in the grateful shade of thickets during strong sunshine, exactly resemble the spots of light which fall on the surrounding foliage. In the winter, when the trees are bare and the play of sunlight on the ground is quite different, a spotted livery would be conspicuous, so the dull-hued whole-coloured dress is, for the season, worn instead.

SWAN AND CYGNETS

The striped livery of birds, then, may represent an ancestral *adult* livery or an ancestral immature dress, which is still useful during immaturity, and hence has been retained, passing over, in some cases where it still confers protection, into the adult plumage. The snipe is a case in point. This bird wears a markedly striped plumage, and it is certainly known that this affords a very considerable measure of protection. When threatened with danger, the snipe seeks to avoid it rather by trusting to its likeness to its environment than by flight, which is only resorted to when subterfuge no longer avails. During this period of "lying low" the bird thrusts the head down and the tail up, so that the body merges into its surroundings; and this largely because the long, straw-coloured stripes down the back now harmonise exactly with bits of dead reed, and so break up the solid appearance, which would at once make a conspicuous mark, by interrupting the continuity of the surrounding stems of reed and dead grass.

From such instances it would seem that we must conclude that the stripes of nestling birds are still useful when they are well developed. When they have begun to disintegrate and to form spots and mottlings, it may be that they are useful still, harmonising better with their particular surroundings than stripes would do,

And now we must proceed to the consideration of that other aspect of the coloration of nestling birds—that which concerns the development of more or less bright and conspicuously coloured areas on the head or in the mouth.

The young coot, for instance, has the head enlivened by curious fleshy filaments of a bright vermilion colour, though, be it noted, no red appears in the adult. The beak of the nestling waterhen, like that of the adult, is of a coral red; as a fledgling this is replaced by green, to yield to red in the adult. The crown of the head in the nestling great crested grebe bears a heart-shaped patch of vermilion red skin, though no such bare area appears in the adult. What can be the meaning of this red colouring?

The young of the water-rail—nearly related to the coot and waterhen—show no red during the nestling stage, though the down, like that of the nestling coot and waterhen, is black. Now, all these species may be met with in the same sheet of water. If the red serves any useful purpose in the coot and waterhen, why is it absent in the rail?

But, besides this external colouring, there are some curious facts in regard to the colouring of the mouth of nestling birds — facts which, until I drew attention to them, had received little or no notice from ornithologists. Only a few examples need be cited of their coloration. Let us take, first, the case of the Gouldian weaver finch. In the newly hatched nestling the gape is adorned after the most extraordinary fashion, since on either side there are developed three little balls, one of a beautiful cobalt blue, set between a pair of emerald green, and all displaying a lovely opalescence. But this is not all. Within the mouth, on the palate, appear five spots of jet black set off by a background of yellow, and a bar of black across the tongue. In another weaver finch similar beads of coral red are found at the gape, and similar spots and bars inside the mouth.

Many British birds, when in the nestling stage, have the mouth most gaily coloured, and often similarly marked with spots and bars of black. The hedge sparrow furnishes an example, having the inside of the mouth orange-coloured relieved by a black spot on each spur of the tongue, and a third across its middle. The skylark recalls the same scheme of colour, having two oval black spots on each side of the base of the tongue, and a third triangular bar at its tip.

The bearded tit is more conspicuously marked. In it the roof of the mouth is marked by four rows of pearly white conical "pegs"—two on either side of the middle line—set in a background of black spreading outwards into a rich carnelian red, the whole being framed in by lemon-yellow gape-wattles. As a rule, the inside of the mouth of nestling perching birds is either orange or lemon yellow, unrelieved by any other markings. In some species, however, other hues are met with. In the meadow pipit, for example, this lining of the mouth is of a deep pink; in the hawfinch, violet pink; in the chaffinch and bullfinch, violet red; in the greenfinch, crimson; and in the lesser redpoll, carmine.

What can be the meaning of this coloration? It has been suggested that the spots, at any rate, have a purpose, and that they serve as guide-marks to the parent when feeding. For it is to be noted that such markings appear most frequently among species which rear their young in dimly lighted nurseries, and hence any aids serving to pick out the open mouth from the encircling gloom would assist the parents in the task of feeding. This may be the correct interpretation, which is not invalidated by the fact that some birds so marked are reared in well-lighted nurseries. These may have been comparatively recently adopted, and in such case the spots, though no longer useful, might well remain, like many other characters no longer useful.

Many adult birds, however, have the lining of the mouth brilliantly coloured. In the kittiwake, for example, it is of a fine orange red, in the young only pinkish; in the shag and guillemot it is of a splendid gamboge, in the young pink. Now, among these birds the colour intensifies with age, and here, at any rate, its purpose seems to be to enhance the charms of courtship; for these birds during this critical period of life make the

SPOTTED CRAKE
AND NESTLINGS

most of these vivid hues, setting the mouth wide agape whenever they confront one another. Obviously, much patient observation remains to be done before this matter can be finally settled.

The list of characters peculiar to young birds is not yet exhausted, but only the more important of these call for mention. First comes the "egg-tooth." This is a small, conical, calcareous excrescence mounted upon the tip of the upper jaw, and is used by the chick to cut through the shell to obtain its release from the egg. In a few days after hatching it drops off, leaving no trace, save only among the ostrich tribe, wherein it is less conspicuous, and is later absorbed instead of falling off.

Some birds, like young woodpeckers, have a curious patch of horny, conical, wart-like structures on the "heel"—that is to say, on the under side of the ankle joint—and this seems to afford protection to the tender skin of this region during the early days of nursery life. Since these birds are reared not in a "nest," but at the bottom of some hole in a hollow tree, upon a bed of rotten wood, these hobnails in miniature may serve to protect the leg against the action of this decaying matter.

W. P. PYCRAFT

ORDER I. PASSERES
GENERAL CHARACTERISTICS OF PERCHING BIRDS

SONG THRUSH

THE order of Passeres, which includes by far the great majority of existing birds, and especially those popularly termed song birds, may be regarded as occupying a position analogous to that held by lizards among reptiles, and by the bony group among fishes, all its members being more or less specialised and highly organised. On this account the group is by general consent regarded as the highest in the class. All these birds are characterised by having the palate constructed on what is termed the ægithognathous modification. They are further distinguished by producing their young in a helpless and nearly naked condition, with merely a few patches of down scattered here and there over the body.

In the skeleton the slender metatarsus has its three nearly equal-sized condyles placed almost in the same transverse line; while the arm bone, or humerus, has a well-marked bifurcate process at the outer side of its lower end; and, as a minor character, the breast bone has but a single notch. The first toe is always present, and is mobile and directed backwards, in addition to being worked by a muscle independently of the other digits. A covering of feathers invests the legs as far down as the ankle joint. There are usually twelve feathers in the tail; while the primary quills of the wings vary from nine to ten, the latter being the usual complement among the typical members of the order.

With three exceptions, the perching birds of the Old World belong to a section characterised by having the intrinsic muscles of the syrinx, or organ of voice, attached to the cords of the open rings of the bronchial tube, and technically termed the acromyodi.

Although certain species of perching birds, such as the snow bunting and the sand martin, have a circumpolar distribution, numerous genera are restricted to the New World; while, in spite of the fact that many species, as well as families, range across the whole of the northern temperate parts of the Old World, from the British Isles to Japan, comparatively few families can be termed strictly cosmopolitan. For lustre of plumage and striking combinations of colour, the perching birds of the Indo-Malay region excel all others; but South America possesses a larger and more varied assortment of these birds. While the mocking birds, represented by closely allied species in both the northern and southern divisions of the New World, have the best claim to be considered the finest songsters in the entire order, in Europe it is probable that the blue thrush possesses the most beautiful notes of all the passerines.

R. LYDEKKER

CLASSIFICATION OF PERCHING BIRDS MENTIONED IN THIS WORK

ORDER I
Perching Birds—Passeres
FAMILY 1
Crow Tribe—Corvidae
GENUS 1
Crows—Corvus
SPECIES

Raven ....Coryus corax
African rook ....C. capensis
White-necked raven ....C. albicollis
Thick-billed raven ....C. crassirostris
White-bellied crow ....C. scapulatus
Crow ....C. corone
Hooded crow ....C. cornix
Indian hooded crow ....C. splendens
Fish crow ....C. ossifragus
Rook ....C. frugilegus
Siberian rook ....C. pastinator
Jackdaw ....C. monedula
Pallas's daw ....C. dauricus

GENUS 2
Nutcrackers—Nucifraga
SPECIES
Nutcracker ....Nucifraga caryocatactes
Clarke's crow ....N. columbiana

GENUS 3
Pies—Pica
SPECIES
Magpie ....Pica rustica
African magpie ....P. mauritanica
Californian magpie ....P. nuttalli

GENUS 4
Black Magpies—Platysmurus
SPECIES
Bornean black magpie ..Platysmurus aterrimus

GENUS 5
Short-tailed Magpies—Temnurus
SPECIES
Cochin China short-tailed magpie .. Temnurus
truncatus

GENUS 6
Azure-winged Magpies—Cyanopica
SPECIES
Azure-winged magpie ......Cyanopica cooki
Asiatic azure-winged magpie ....C. cyana

GENUS 7
Blue Magpies—Urocissa
SPECIES
Red-billed magpie ....Urocissa occipitalis
Chinese blue magpie ....U. sinensis

GENUS 8
Eastern Pies—Dendrocitta
SPECIES
Indian pie ....Dendrocitta rufa
Formosan pie ....D. formosana
Bayley's pie ....D. bayleyi
Himalayan pie ....D. himalayensis

GENUS 9
Jays—Garrulus
SPECIES
Jay ....Garrulus glandarius
Black-headed jay ....G. kynicki
Brandt's jay ....G. brandti
Syrian jay ....G. syriacus

GENUS 10
Siberian Jay—Perisoreus
SPECIES
Siberian jay ....Perisoreus infaustus

GENUS 11
Crested Jays—Cyanocitta
SPECIES
American blue jay ......Cyanocitta cristata
Mexican blue jay ....C. coronata
Central American jay ....C. yucatensis

GENUS 12
Urraca Jays—Cyanocorax
SPECIES
Brazilian urraca jay ....Cyanocorax chrysops
Pileated jay ....C. pileatus
Peruvian blue jay ....C. incasi

GENUS 13
Long-tailed Jays—Calocitta
SPECIES
Swainson's long-tailed jay ....Calocitta fumosa

GENUS 14
Green Jays—Xanthura
SPECIES
Green jay ....Xanthura luxuosa

GENUS 15
Choughs—Pyrrhocorax

SPECIES
Chough ....Pyrrhocorax graculus
Alpine chough ....P. alpinus

GENUS 16
Chough-Thrushes—Podoces
SPECIES
Pander's chough-thrush ....Podoces panderi
Henderson's chough-thrush ...P. hendersoni
Biddulph's chough-thrush ......P. biddulphi
Lesser chough-thrush ....P. humilis

GENUS 17
Huia—Heteralocha
SPECIES
Huia ....Heteralocha acutirostris

GENUS 18
Saddleback—Creadion
SPECIES
Saddleback ....Creadion carunculatus

GENUS 19
Callæas
SPECIES
Wilson's callæas ....C. wilsoni
Grey callæas ....Callæas cinerea

GENUS 20
Picathartes
GENUS 21
Struthideas—Struthidea
SPECIES
Grey struthidea ....Struthidea cinerea

GENUS 22
Corcorax
FAMILY 2
Paradise and Bower Birds—Paradiseidæ
GENUS 1
Seleucides
SPECIES
Twelve-wired bird of paradise ....Seleucides
ignotus

GENUS 2
Ptilornis
SPECIES
Scale-breasted bird of paradise ......Ptilornis
magnificus

GENUS 3
Epimachus
SPECIES
Long-tailed bird of paradise ......Epimachus
speciosus

GENUS 4
Drepanornis
SPECIES
Albertis bird of paradise . . Drepanornis albertisi
GENUS 5
Astrapia
SPECIES
Gorget bird of paradise . . . . Astrapia nigra
GENUS 6
Paradigalla
SPECIES
Wattled bird of paradise . . . . Paradigalla
carunculata
GENUS 7
Typical Birds of Paradise—Paradisea
SPECIES
Great bird of paradise . . . . Paradisea apoda
Lesser bird of paradise . . . . P. minor
Red bird of paradise . . . . P. rubra
GENUS 8
Cicinnurus
SPECIES
King bird of paradise . . . . . . Cicinnurus regius
GENUS 9
Schlegelia
SPECIES
Wilson's bird of paradise . . Schlegelia republica
GENUS 10
Diphyllodes
SPECIES
Magnificent bird of paradise . . . . . . Diphyllodes
magnifica
GENUS 11
Parotia
SPECIES
Six-plumed bird of paradise . . Parotia sexpennis
GENUS 12
Standard-wings—Semioptera
SPECIES
Wallace's standard-wing . . Semioptera wallacei
GENUS 13
Lophorhina
SPECIES
Superb bird of paradise . . Lophorhina superba
GENUS 14
Pteridophora
SPECIES
Albert's bird of paradise . . Pteridophora alberti
GENUS 15
Phonygammus
SPECIES
James's bird of paradise . . . . . . Phonygammus
jamesi
GENUS 16
Manucodia
SPECIES
Black Papuan paradise bird . . Manucodia atra
GENUS 17
Lycocorax
SPECIES
Moluccan bird of paradise . . . . Lycocorax
pyrrhopterus
GENUS 18
Bower Birds—Ptilorhynchus
SPECIES
Satin bower bird . . . . Ptilorhynchus viola
GENUS 19
Chlamydodera
SPECIES
Spotted bower bird . . Chlamydodera maculata
GENUS 20
Amblyornis
SPECIES
Gardener bird . . . . Amblyornis inornatus
GENUS 21
Prionodura
SPECIES
Newton's bower bird . . Prionodura newtoniana
GENUS 22
Queensland Bower Birds—Scenopœetes
SPECIES
Tooth-billed bower bird . . . . Scenopœetes
dentirostris
GENUS 23
Cat Birds—Æluredus
SPECIES
Australian cat bird . . . . Æluredus viridis

FAMILY 3
Starling Tribe—Sturnidæ
GENUS 1
Starlings—Strunus
SPECIES
Starling . . . . Sturnus vulgaris
Black, or Sardinian, starling . . . . . . S. unicolor
GENUS 2
Rosy Starling—Pastor
SPECIES
Rosy starling . . . . Pastor roseus
GENUS 3
Indian Mynas—Acridotheres
SPECIES
Indian myna . . . . Acridotheres tristis
Bengal myna . . . . A. ginginianus

GENUS 4
Silky Starlings—Poliopsar
SPECIES
Silky starling . . . . Poliopsar sericeus
GENUS 5
Pied Starling—Sturnopastor
SPECIES
Pied starling . . . . Sturnopastor contra
Wattled Starlings—Dilophus
SPECIES
Wattled starling . . . . . . Dilophus carunculatus
GENUS 7
Reunion Starling—Fregilupus
SPECIES
Crested pied starling . . . . Fregilupus varius
GENUS 8
Ox-peckers—Buphaga
SPECIES
Yellow-billed ox-pecker . . . . Buphaga africana
Red-billed ox-pecker . . . . . . B. erythrorhyncha

FAMILY 4
Glossy Starlings and Grackles—Eulabetidæ
GENUS 1
Long-tailed Glossy Starlings—Lamprotornis
SPECIES
Long-tailed glossy starling . . . . Lamprotornis
æneus
GENUS 2
Short-tailed Glossy Starlings—Lamprocolius
SPECIES
Green glossy starling . . Lamprocolius chalybeus
Superb glossy starling . . . . L. superbus
White-bellied glossy starling . . L. leucogaster
GENUS 3
Eastern Grackles—Eulabetes
SPECIES
Indian grackle . . . . Eulabetes intermedia
Malay grackle . . . . E. javanensis
South Indian grackle . . . . E. religiosa
Ceylonese grackle . . . . . . E. ptilogenys
GENUS 4
Asiatic Glossy Starlings—Calornis
SPECIES
Indian glossy starling . . . . . . Calornis calybeus

FAMILY 5
Drongos—Dicruridæ
GENUS 1
Drongos or King Crows—Dicrurus
SPECIES
Indian black drongo . . . . Dicrurus ater
GENUS 2
Australian Drongos—Chibia
SPECIES
Australian drongo . . . . Chibia bracteata
GENUS 3
Dissemuroides
GENUS 4
Dicranostreptus
GENUS 5
Racket-tailed Drongos—Bhringa
SPECIES
Lesser racket-tailed drongo . . . . Bhringa remifer
GENUS 6
Paradise Drongos—Dissemurus
GENUS 7
Buchanga
SPECIES
Japanese drongo . . . . Buchanga leucogenys
GENUS 8
Edolius
SPECIES
Malagasy drongo . . . . Edolius forficatus

FAMILY 6
Orioles—Oriolidæ
GENUS 1
Orioles—Oriolus
SPECIES
Golden oriole . . . . Oriolus galbula
Mango bird . . . . O. kundu
Green oriole . . . . O. viridis
GENUS 2
Sphecotheres
FAMILY 7
Troupial Tribe—Icteridæ
GENUS 1
Cassiques—Ostinops
SPECIES
Crested cassique . . . . Ostinops decumanus
GENUS 2
Cassicus
SPECIES
Yellow cassique . . . . Cassicus persicus
GENUS 3
Hangnests—Icterus
SPECIES
Baltimore oriole . . . . Icterus galbula
GENUS 4
Rice-Bird—Dolichonyx
SPECIES
Bobolink . . . . Dolichonyx oryzivorus

GENUS 5
Cow-Birds—Molothrus
SPECIES
Cow-bird . . . . Molothrus pecoris
Argentine cow-bird . . . . M. bonariensis
GENUS 6
Red-winged Blackbirds—Agelæus
SPECIES
Red-winged blackbird . . . . Agelæus phœnicurus
GENUS 7
Troupials—Quiscalus
SPECIES
Purple troupial . . . . Quiscalus versicolor
GENUS 8
Meadow Larks—Sturnella
SPECIES
Meadow lark . . . . Sturnella magna

FAMILY 8
Weaver Birds—Ploceidæ
GENUS 1
Ox-Birds—Textor
SPECIES
Ox-bird . . . . Textor albirostris
Red-billed black weaver . . . . T. niger
GENUS 2
White-headed Weavers—Dinemellia
SPECIES
White-headed weaver . . Dinemellia leucocephala
GENUS 3
True Weavers—Ploceus
SPECIES
Common weaver bird . . . . Ploceus baya
GENUS 4
Masked Weaver Birds—Hyphantornis
SPECIES
Masked weaver bird . . Hyphantornis larvatus
Abyssinian weaver bird . . . . H. galbula
Olive weaver bird . . . . H. capensis
GENUS 5
Vidua
SPECIES
Long-tailed whydah bird . . . . Vidua paradisea
GENUS 6
Bishop Birds—Pyromelana
SPECIES
Red bishop bird . . . . Pyromelana oryx
Black and yellow bishop bird . . . . . . P. capensis
GENUS 7
Sociable Weaver Birds—Philetærus
SPECIES
Sociable weaver bird . . . . Philetærus socius
GENUS 8
Cut-throat Finches—Amadina
SPECIES
Crimson-throated finch . . . . Amadina fasciata
Red-headed finch . . . . A. erythrocephala
GENUS 9
Java Sparrows—Munia
SPECIES
Java sparrow . . . . Munia oryzivora
Malagasy munia . . . . M. nana
Nutmeg bird . . . . M. punctulata
GENUS 10
Pœphila
SPECIES
Grass finch . . . . Pœphila mirabilis
GENUS 11
Waxbill Finches—Estrelda
SPECIES
Waxbill finch . . . . Estrelda cinerea
Amadavat . . . . E. amandava

FAMILY 9
Tanagers—Tanagridæ
GENUS 1
Violet Tanager—Euphonia
SPECIES
Violet tanager . . . . Euphonia violacea
GENUS 2
Scarlet Tanagers—Pyranga
SPECIES
Scarlet tanager . . . . Pyranga rubra
Crimson-headed tanager . . . . . . P. ludoviciana
GENUS 3
Calliste
SPECIES
Superb tanager . . . . Calliste thoracica
GENUS 4
Stephanophorus
SPECIES
White-capped tanager . . . . . . Stephanophorus
leucocephalus

FAMILY 10
Honey Creepers—Cœrebidæ
GENUS 1
Quit-quits—Certhiola
SPECIES
Banana quit . . . . Certhiola flaveola
GENUS 2
Cœreba
SPECIES
Yellow-winged sugar bird . . . . Cœreba cyanea

GENUS 3
Dacnis
SPECIES
Blue sugar bird .... Dacnis cyanea

GENUS 4
Chlorophanes
SPECIES
Black-headed sugar bird .. Chlorophanes spiza

FAMILY 11
Wood Warblers—Mniotiltidæ
GENUS 1
Green Warblers—Dendrœca
SPECIES
Black-throated green warbler..Dendrœca virens

GENUS 2
Typical Wood Warblers—Mniotilta
SPECIES
Black and white warbler .... Mniotilta varia

FAMILY 12
Finches and Buntings—Fringillidæ
GENUS 1
Greenfinches—Ligurinus
SPECIES
Greenfinch ....Ligurinus chloris
Algerian greenfinch ...... L. auranteiventris
Japanese greenfinch .... L. sinicus

GENUS 2
Hawfinches—Coccothraustes
SPECIES
Hawfinch .... Coccothraustes vulgaris
Black-tailed hawfinch .... C. melanurus
Hume's hawfinch .... C. humei

GENUS 3
Mycerobus
SPECIES
Black and yellow hawfinch ....Mycerobus melanoxanthus

GENUS 4
Rose-breasted Grosbeaks—Hadymeles
SPECIES
Rose-breasted grosbeak .... Hadymeles ludovicianus
Black-headed grosbeak .. H. melanocephalus

GENUS 5
Yellow-bellied Grosbeaks—Pheucticus
SPECIES
South American grosbeak ...... Pheucticus chrysogaster

GENUS 6
Blue Grosbeaks—Guiraca
SPECIES
Blue grosbeak ....Guiraca cœrulea
Brazilian blue grosbeak .... G. cyanea

GENUS 7
Orchard Finches—Phrygilus
SPECIES
Orchard finch .... Phrygilus finticeti

GENUS 8
Indigo Birds—Cyanospiza
SPECIES
Indigo bird .... Cyanospiza cyanea
Nonpareil finch .... C. ciris

GENUS 9
Cardinals—Cardinalis
SPECIES
Red cardinal .... Cardinalis virginianus

GENUS 10
Chaffinches—Fringilla
SPECIES
Chaffinch .... Fringilla cœlebs
Tintillon chaffinch .... F. tintillon
Teydean chaffinch .... F. teydea
Algerian chaffinch .... F. spodiogenia
Crested chaffinch .... F. cuculata
Brambling ....F. montifringilla

GENUS 11
Siskins—Carysomitris
SPECIES
Siskin .... Chrysomitris spinus
American siskin .... C. tristris
Black-throated siskin ...... C. magellanica
Yarrell's siskin .... C. yarrelli
Black-chinned siskin .... C. barbata
Crested siskin .... C. cuculata
Citril finch .... C. citrinella

GENUS 12
Sycalis
SPECIES
Jamaica yellow finch ...... Sycalis jamaicæ

GENUS 13
Goldfinches—Carduelis
SPECIES
Goldfinch .... Carduelis elegans
Buff-headed goldfinch .... C. caniceps

GENUS 14
Linnets—Linota
SPECIES
Linnet .... Linota cannabina
Mealy redpoll .... L. linaria
Lesser redpoll .... L. rufescens

GENUS 15
Snow Finches—Montifringilla
SPECIES
Snow finch .... Montifringilla nivalis

GENUS 16
Rock Sparrows—Petronia
European rock sparrow .... Petronia stulta

GENUS 17
Sparrows—Passer
SPECIES
Sparrow .... Passer domesticus
Tree sparrow .... P. montanus
Spanish sparrow .... P. hispaniolensis
Black-breasted sparrow ...... P. diffusus
Cape sparrow .... P. arcuatus
Alaris sparrow .... P. alaris
Grey-headed sparrow .... P. simplex
Yellow sparrow .... P. luteus
Golden sparrow .... P. euchlorus

GENUS 18
Serin Finches—Serinus
SPECIES
Serin finch .... Serinus hortulanus
Tristram's serin .... S. tristrami
Red-fronted serin .... S. rufifrons
Canary .... S. canarius

GENUS 19
Rose Finches—Carpodacus
SPECIES
Scarlet rose finch .... Carpodacus erythrinus
Purple finch .... C. purpureus
Severtzow's finch .... C. severtzowi
Caucasian finch .... C. rubicillus
Blood-stained rose finch .... C. hæmorrhous

GENUS 20
Desert Finches—Erythrospiza
SPECIES
Desert finch .... Erythrospiza githaginea
Mongolian desert finch .... E. mongolica

GENUS 21
Bullfinches—Pyrrhula
SPECIES
Bullfinch .... Pyrrhula europæa
Azores bullfinch .... P. marina
Brown bullfinch .... P. nepalensis
Red-headed bullfinch .... P. erythrocephala
Orange bullfinch .... P. aurantiaca

GENUS 22
Pine Grosbeaks—Pinicola
SPECIES
Pine grosbeak .... Pinicola enucleator

GENUS 23
Crossbills—Loxia
SPECIES
Crossbill .... Loxia curvirostra
Himalayan crossbill .... L. himalayana
Japanese crossbill .... L. japonica
White-winged crossbill .... L. leucoptera
Philippine crossbill .... L. luzoniensis

GENUS 24
Hæmatospiza
SPECIES
Nepalese scarlet finch .. Hæmatospiza sipahi

GENUS 25
Red-headed Rose Finches—Propyrrhula
SPECIES
Rose-headed rose finch .... Propyrrhula subhimalayensis

GENUS 26
Pyrrhospiza
SPECIES
Red-breasted rose finch ..Pyrrhospiza punicea

GENUS 27
Telespiza
SPECIES
Laysan finch .... Telespiza cantans

GENUS 28
Snow Buntings—Plectrophanes
SPECIES
Snow bunting .... Plectrophanes nivalis
Alaskan snow bunting ...... P. hyperboreus
Lapland bunting .... P. nivalis

GENUS 29
Typical Buntings—Emberiza
SPECIES
Reed bunting .... Emberiza shœniclus
Little bunting .... E. pusilla
Bunting .... E. miliaria
Black-headed bunting .... E. melanocephala
Yellow-breasted bunting .... E. aureola
Yellow bunting .... E. citrinella
Cirl bunting .... E. cirlus
Ortolan bunting .... E. hortulana
Meadow bunting .... E. cia

GENUS 30
Crested Buntings—Melophus
SPECIES
Crested bunting ...... Melophus melanicterus

GENUS 31
American Buntings—Euspiza
SPECIES
American bunting ...... Euspiza americana

GENUS 32
African Buntings—Fringillaria
SPECIES
Cape bunting .... Fringillaria capensis
Sahara bunting .... F. saharæ

GENUS 33
Zonotrichia
SPECIES
Sparrow bunting ...... Zonotrichia albicollis

GENUS 34
Snow Birds—Junco
SPECIES
Snow bird .... Junco hiemalis

GENUS 35
Spizella
SPECIES
Chirping sparrow .... Spizella socialis

GENUS 36
Ground Finches—Pipilo
SPECIES
Red-eyed ground finch..Pipilo erythropthalmus

GENUS 37
Indigo Birds—Cyanospiza
SPECIES
Indigo bird .... Cyanospiza cyanea

FAMILY 13
Larks—Alaudidæ
GENUS 1
Typical Larks—Alauda
SPECIES
Skylark .... Alauda arvensis
Indian skylark .... A. galgula
Thick-billed skylark .... A. crassirostris

GENUS 2
Woodlarks—Lullula
SPECIES
Woodlark .... Lullula arborea

GENUS 3
Crested Larks—Galerita
SPECIES
Crested lark .... Galerita cristata

GENUS 4
Desert Larks—Alæmon
SPECIES
Desert lark .... Alæmon desertorum

GENUS 5
Finch Larks—Ammomanes
SPECIES
African finch lark .... Ammomanes deserti

GENUS 6
Bush Larks—Mirafra
SPECIES
Madras bush lark .... Mirafra affinis

GENUS 7
Short-toed Larks—Calandrella
SPECIES
Short-toed lark .... Calandrella brachydactyla

GENUS 8
Calandra Larks—Melanocorypa
SPECIES
Calandra lark ......Melanocorypha calandra
Black lark ....M. yeltoniensis
White-winged lark ....M. sibirica
Chinese lark ....M. mongolica

GENUS 9
Rhamphocorys
SPECIES
Clotbey's lark ......Rhamphocorys clotbeyi

GENUS 10
Bullfinch Larks—Pyrrhulauda
SPECIES
White-headed bullfinch lark ....Pyrrhulauda verticollis

GENUS 11
Horned Larks—Otocorys
SPECIES
Horned lark .... Otocorys alpestris

FAMILY 14
Wagtails and Pipits—Motacillidæ
GENUS 1
Wagtails—Motacilla
SPECIES
White wagtail ....Motacilla alba
Pied wagtail ....M. lugubris
Grey wagtail ....M. melanope
Blue-headed wagtail ...... M. flava
Yellow wagtail ....M. raii
Yellow-headed wagtail ....M. citreola
Cape wagtail ....M. capensis

GENUS 2
Pipits—Anthus
SPECIES
Tree pipit .... Anthus trivialis
Meadow pipit ....A. pratensis
Richard's pipit ....A richardi
Tawny pipit ....A campestris
Yellow-breasted pipit ....A. chloris
Water pipit ....A. spipoletta
Red-throated pipit ....A. cervinus
Rock pipit ....A. obscurus

GENUS 3
Indian Pipits—Limonidromus
SPECIES
Brown Indian pipit ....Limonidromus indicus
GENUS 4
Grallina
SPECIES
Pied gralline ....Grallina australis
GENUS 5
Macronyx
SPECIES
Long-claw .... Macronyx crocea
Amelia long-claw .... M. ameliæ

FAMILY 15
Fork Tails—Henicuridæ
GENUS
Fork Tails—Henicurus
SPECIES
Scouler's fork tail .... Henicurus scouleri
Orange-crowned fork tail ...... H. ruficapillus
H. velatus
GENUS 2
Climacteris

FAMILY 16
Creepers—Certhiidæ
GENUS 1
Tree Creepers—Certhia
SPECIES
Tree creeper .... Certhia familiaris
GENUS 2
Wall Creepers—Tichodroma
SPECIES
Wall creeper ....Tichodroma muraria

FAMILY 17
Nuthatches—Sittidæ
GENUS
Nuthatches—Sitta
SPECIES
Nuthatch .... Sitta cæsia
White-bellied nuthatch .... S. europæa
Syrian nuthatch .... S. neumayeri
Canadian nuthatch ....S. canadensis
Pigmy nuthatch .... S. pygmæa

FAMILY 18
Honey-eaters—Meliphagidæ
GENUS 1
Tui—Prosthemadera
SPECIES
Tui or parson bird .... Prosthemadera
novæ-zealandiæ
GENUS 2
Stitch Bird—Pogornis
SPECIES
Stitch bird .... Pogornis cinctus
GENUS 3
Philemon
SPECIES
Four o'clock .... Philemon corniculatus
GENUS 4
Acrulocercus
SPECIES
Hawaiian honey-eater .. Acrulocercus nobilis
GENUS 5
Meliphaga
SPECIES
Warty-faced honey-eater ..Meliphaga phrygia
GENUS 6
Myzomela
SPECIES
Australian soldier bird .... Myzomela
sanguinolenta
GENUS 7
Acanthorynchus

FAMILY 19
Mamo Group—Drepanididæ
GENUS
Mamo—Drepanis
SPECIES
Mamo (extinct) ....Drepanis pacifica

FAMILY 20
White-eyes—Zosteropidæ
GENUS
White-eyes—Zosterops
SPECIES
Green-backed white-eye .... Zosterops gouldi

FAMILY 21
Sun-birds—Nectariniidæ
GENUS 1
Typical Sun-birds—Nectarinia
SPECIES
Malachite sun-bird ....Nectarinia famosa
Metallic sun-bird ....N. metallica
GENUS 2
Cinnyris
SPECIES
Syrian sun-bird .... Cinnyris osea
GENUS 3
Promerops
SPECIES
Long-tailed sun-bird ....Promerops caffer

GENUS 4
Arachnothera
SPECIES
Golden-cheeked sun-bird ......Arachnothera
chrysogenys

FAMILY 22
Flower-peckers—Dicæidæ
GENUS 1
Typical Flower-peckers—Dicæum
SPECIES
Scarlet-backed flower-pecker ....Dicæum
cruentatum
GENUS 2
Pardalotus
SPECIES
Diamond bird ....Pardalotus affinis
P. assimilis
GENUS 3
Melanocharis
SPECIES
Black flower-pecker ....Melanocharis unicolor

FAMILY 23
Titmice—Paridæ
GENUS 1
True Titmice—Parus
SPECIES
Great titmouse ....Parus major
Coal titmouse ....P. ater
Marsh titmouse ....P. palustris
Blue titmouse ....P. cœruleus
Azure titmouse ....P. cyaneus
Crested titmouse ....P. cristatus
GENUS 2
Long-tailed Titmice—Acredula
SPECIES
Long-tailed titmouse ....Acredula caudata
Macedonian long-tailed titmouse ....A. mace-
donica
Irby's long-tailed titmouse .... A. irbyi
Turkish long-tailed titmouse ..A. tephronotus
Caucasian long-tailed titmouse ...... A. major
GENUS 3
New Zealand Creeper—Certhiparus
SPECIES
New Zealand creeper ...... Certhiparus novæ-
zealandiæ

FAMILY 24
Bearded Tits—Panuridæ
GENUS
Bearded Tits—Panurus
SPECIES
Reed pheasant, or bearded tit.......Panurus
biarmicus

FAMILY 25
Shrikes—Laniidæ
GENUS 1
Shrike Tits—Falcunculus
SPECIES
White-bellied shrike tit ....Falcunculus leuco-
gaster
Southern shrike tit ....F. frontatus
GENUS 2
True Shrikes—Lanius
SPECIES
Great grey shrike .... Lanius excubitor
Lesser grey shrike ....L. minor
Red-backed shrike ....L. collurio
Woodchat shrike ....L. pomeranus
GENUS 3
Magpie Larks—Grallina
SPECIES
Magpie lark .... Grallina australis
GENUS 4
Wood Shrikes—Prionops
SPECIES
New Guinea wood shrike ...Prionops bruijni
GENUS 5
Helmet Bird—Euryceros
SPECIES
Malagasy helmet bird .... Euryceros prevosti
GENUS 6
Artamia
SPECIES
Malagasy two-coloured shrike ..Artamia bicolor
GENUS 7
Piping Crows—Gymnorhina
SPECIES
Black-backed piping crow .....Gymnorhina
tibicen
White-backed piping crow ......G. leuconota
G. dorsalis
Organ bird ....G. hyperleuca
GENUS 8
Minivets—Pericrocotus
SPECIES
Scarlet minivet ....Pericrocotus speciosus
GENUS 9
Cuckoo Shrikes—Campephaga

FAMILY 26
Waxwings—Ampelidæ
GENUS
Waxwings—Ampelis

SPECIES
Bohemian waxwing....... .. Ampelis garrulus
Japanese waxwing .... A. japponica
Cedar bird, or cherry bird ...... A. cedrorum

FAMILY 27
Greenlets—Vireonidæ

FAMILY 28
Wood Swallows—Artamidæ

FAMILY 29
Wrens—Troglodytidæ
GENUS 1
Typical Wrens—Troglodytes
SPECIES
Wren .... Troglodytes parvulus
Warbling Wrens—Cyphorhinus
SPECIES
Organ wren .... Cyphorhinus cantans
GENUS 3
Campylorhynchus
SPECIES
Cactus wren . Campylorhynchus brunneicapillus
FAMILY 30
Water Ouzels—Cinclidæ
GENUS
Water Ouzels—Cinclus
SPECIES
Water ouzel .... Cinclus aquaticus
Brown water ouzel .... C. asiaticus
Schulz's water ouzel .... C. schultzi

FAMILY 31
Mocking Birds—Mimidæ
GENUS 1
Mocking Birds—Mimus
SPECIES
Mocking bird .... Mimus polyglottus
Calandra .... M. modulator
GENUS 2
Cat Birds—Galeoscoptes
SPECIES
Cat bird .... Galeoscoptes carolinensis
FAMILY 32
Thrushes—Turdidæ
GENUS 1
True Thrushes—Turdus
SPECIES
Missel thrush .... Turdus viscivorus
Song thrush .... T. musicus
Redwing .... T. iliacus
Fieldfare .... T. pilaris
Père David's thrush .... T. auritus
Olive thrush .... T. gurneyi
Ground thrush .... T. guttata
Himalayan thrush .... T. monticola
Siberian thrush .... T. varius
New Zealand thrush .... T. crassirostris
Blackbird .... T. merula
Ring ouzel .... T. torquatus
GENUS 2
Rock Thrushes—Monticola
SPECIES
Rock thrush ....Monticola saxatilis
Blue rock thrush .... M. cyanus
GENUS 3
Bluebirds—Sialia
SPECIES
Bluebird .... Sialia sialis
GENUS 4
Wheatears—Saxicola
SPECIES
Wheatear .... Saxicola œnanthe
Russet wheatear .... S. melanoleuca
Isabelline wheatear .... S. isabellina
Desert wheatear .... S. deserti
GENUS 5
Chats—Pratincola
SPECIES
Mediterranean black chat . Pratincola variegata
Eastern black chat .... P. leucura
Whinchat .... P. rubetrus
Stonechat .... P. rubicola
GENUS 6
Forktails—Henicurus
GENUS 7
Redstarts—Ruticilla
SPECIES
Redstart .... Ruticilla phœnicurus
Black redstart .... R. titys
GENUS 8
Bluethroats—Cyanecula
SPECIES
Bluethroat .... Cyanecula suecica
Persian bluethroat .... C. discessa
Central Asian bluethroat .... C. abbotti
GENUS 9
Redbreasts—Erithacus
SPECIES
Redbreast .... Erithacus rubecula
GENUS 10
Rubythroats—Calliope
SPECIES
Rubythroat .... Calliope camchatkensis

THE CROW TRIBE

CONSPICUOUS in many cases by their black or pied plumage, often variegated with grey, and occasionally with brown, although some species, like the blue jays of South America, are much more gaudily coloured, the members of the crow family (*Corvidæ*) form a group which, while having few characters in common, is yet easy of recognition. Possessing a stout and generally large beak, without a distinct notch in the upper mandible, and usually straight, the crows have the chin angle, or union of the two branches of the lower jaw, almost always produced in front of the line of the nostrils, while the tongue is non-extensile. The toes are of the normal passerine type, but although the first toe is strong, it is inferior in length to the third. The nostrils are clear of the line of the forehead, and are protected by a number of stiff bristles reaching to the middle of the beak, which are, however, shed in the adult of the European rook. The wing always has ten primary quills, and the tail twelve feathers.

From titmice, which some naturalists believe to be nearly related to this family, the crow tribe may be distinguished by having the first primary quill longer than half the length of the second; while the plumage is more or less firm and glossy, and the length of the beak considerably greater than its depth. Both groups agree in that the plumage of the two sexes is alike and undergoes but one moult, which occurs in the autumn, and also in the fact that the plumage of the young is paler and duller than that of the adults.

The family has an almost world-wide range, although it is unrepresented in the islands lying between New Zealand and New Caledonia and Hawaii. Magpies, nutcrackers, and choughs are characteristic of the northern and central parts of the Old World. In America the family is poorly represented; South America having only a few jays of brilliant plumage, among which those of the genus *Xanthura* display beautiful blue feathers, associated with black or deeper blue markings.

In most cases the eggs are greenish, mottled with darker green, olive, or brownish, but they are pinkish with red spots in the South African *Heterocorax*, and may occasionally be so in other species.

THE RAVEN

The raven (*Corvus corax*) is the typical member of a genus distinguished by a stout compressed bill, straight at the base, arched towards the point, and sharp at the edges. The wings are long and graduated, and the tail is also more or less graduated; while the feet are powerful, with the metatarsus exceeding in length the middle toe. In the adult plumage black, more or less glossed with green or purple, decidedly predominates. Birds of this genus are found throughout the whole of Europe and Asia north of the line of the Himalaya, whence they range into North-Western India, Australia, North America, and Mexico.

THE RAVEN

The range of the raven includes the northern parts of both hemispheres. In Japan its place is occupied by a smaller and duller-coloured race, which also occurs in India, Ceylon, South China, and the islands of the Malay Archipelago. The raven thrives in a wide diversity of regions, ranging from Greenland to Spain and from Portugal to Palestine; and is an early breeder in the North of England, often repairing its nest while snow is lying on the mountain sides. Sometimes a raven's nest becomes swamped by rain and driving sleet to such a degree that the eggs are chilled and rendered useless; and when this happens the birds retire to some other haunt, in which the female lays a fresh clutch of eggs. The latter, usually four or five in number, but rarely six, are of a bluish green colour, blotched and spotted with dark olive brown, although a reddish variety is occasionally obtained (page 990).

Ravens perform valuable services as scavengers, and the damage they do to the game-preserver is comparatively small, although shepherds have only too good reason to complain of the injuries inflicted by these birds on the ewes when dropping their lambs, as they readily attack any defenceless animal such as a weak lamb or a feeble fawn. ·

AFRICAN CROWS

In Africa the genus is represented by the black African rook (*C. capensis*) ; the white-necked raven (*C. albicollis*), which is brown and black with a conspicuous white collar ; the thick-billed raven (*C. crassirostris*) ; and the white-bellied crow (*C. scapulatus*). The last-named is a handsome bird, not larger than the European crow, and recognisable by its black and white or parti-coloured plumage. It obtains much of its food about the high roads, and nests in trees or in the recesses of rocks, where it lays five or six light blue eggs, profusely spotted with brown. Occasionally it will approach the haunts of men, but at other times is shy and retiring, especially when breeding.

The thick-billed raven is of the size of the European species, from which it differs in the depth of the beak and the white patch at the back of the head.

EUROPEAN CROWS

In Europe there are two kinds of crow, the carrion, or black, crow (*Corvus corone*), and the grey, hooded, or Royston crow (*C. cornix*) ; the former being a summer visitor to South-West Europe, while the latter is commoner in the north-east. In certain districts, notably in those parts of Scotland which both frequent during summer, the two interbreed ; and in Eastern Siberia this interbreeding is carried to an extraordinary extent, the hybrid offspring of the original stocks apparently proving fertile for several generations in the valley of the Yenisei. This is the more remarkable because both forms possess a well-defined distribution,

THICK-BILLED RAVEN

to all intents and purposes identical. While, however, the carrion crow lives chiefly in wooded valleys, nesting in isolated pairs, and harrying the nests of other birds, the hooded crow frequents the wildest coasts of Western Europe, ranging from the northern islands that fringe the continent to the forest regions of Central Russia, and rearing its young with equal success on the ground, in the top of a tree, or on the face of a frowning precipice. The nest of the hooded crow is often a cumbrous collection of heather roots, sticks, and seaweed, lined with softer substances well felted together. The eggs, which vary from four to six in a clutch, are greenish in ground colour, blotched with dark olive brown (page 990).

The so-called hooded crow of India (*C. splendens*) differs from the European species in its inferior size and the lustre of its darker feathers. It is extremely bold and confiding. The North American fish crow (*C. ossifragus*) displays decidedly maritime habits.

ROOKS

Although commonly miscalled crow, the rook (*Corvus frugilegus*), which is one of the best known and most familiar of European birds, is really a very distinct species. The sooty plumage differs from that of its eastern representative, the Siberian rook (*C. pastinator*), chiefly in having a bluish purple in lieu of a reddish purple gloss. The Siberian bird to a large extent retains the feathers around the beak, which are generally shed by the European species as it reaches maturity. Like many members of the family, the rook is an early breeder, nesting sometimes in shrubs or even on the roofs of houses, but chiefly in tall trees, often in the midst of crowded streets. The young are mainly reared on noxious insects in their various stages, on field-mice, and waste substances.

In the autumn rooks band together to plunder cornfields ; and they also do much mischief to young turnips, often tearing up thousands of newly planted

WHITE-BELLIED CROW

and only occasionally overlap one another in the breeding season. Many naturalists, indeed, consider that the carrion crow is only a black phase of the hooded crow, which has lost the dun-coloured portions of the plumage peculiar to the latter in both sexes and at all ages ; and the flight and notes of the two are

seedlings, while in severe weather they attack the roots of turnips, or devour such small birds as have become too enfeebled by want of food to elude their enemies. During the greater part of the year they are gregarious, and many of their established "rookeries" contain myriads of birds every night. Their sagacity enables them to evade the various forms of destruction which reduce the numbers of other birds, and, as they are extremely long-lived, their increase is very rapid. Though less easily reconciled to captivity than others of the family, rooks form lively and amusing pets.

THE JACKDAW

The too familiar daw or jackdaw (*Corvus monedula*) is distinguished from the rook and the crow by its smaller size, less powerful beak, and slaty grey collar, the remainder of the plumage being black in the typical western bird, which is replaced in Northern Asia and Japan by Pallas's daw (*C. dauricus*), distinguished by a broad collar of ashy white and a white belly. The daw, which is distributed locally throughout temperate Europe, is very abundant in parts of Algeria, where it is highly gregarious even in the breeding season, associating in colonies in low cliffs, and nesting in the holes and recesses formed by weathering.

Elsewhere single pairs sometimes appropriate disused rooks' nests, which they adapt to their own purposes. Not the least remarkable of the many idiosyncrasies of this bird is the readiness with which it contents itself with every variety of nesting site, rearing its young as happily in a disused rabbit-hole as in the belfry of a church. The nest is often a cumbrous pile of sticks, carefully lined with hair, wool, or other soft material. The eggs vary from four to six, and are bluish green spotted with grey and brown (p. 990).

WHITE ROOKS

The jackdaws frequenting the islands on the coast of Galicia breed in holes under stones, and follow droves of pigs to secure the insects these animals turn up when grubbing in the soil. While the pigs turn up the ground, the jackdaws may be seen perching on their backs, waiting their own opportunity. During drought jackdaws often commit serious depredations on pheasant coops, in consequence of the earthworms, on which they largely subsist, having retired from the surface to secure moisture at a greater depth. These birds do not appear to make the migratory journeys of rooks and hooded crows, being of a somewhat sedentary character, as evinced by the attachment they display for favourite nesting sites. A black variety of the European jackdaw, in which the grey collar has become suppressed, has been

WHITE RAVEN
Photographed in the London Zoological Gardens

regarded by some naturalists as a valid species. Although these are rare, white jackdaws are not very uncommon, while specimens of a uniform silver grey occur from time to time, although less frequently than white or pied examples.

NUTCRACKERS

The nutcracker (*Nucifraga caryocatactes*) is a member of a small group of species, three of which share its partiality for nuts and other fruits. The American representative is the so-called Clarke's crow (*N. columbiana*), a plain grey-coloured bird with glossy black wings, most of the secondaries broadly tipped with white, and the tail white, with the exception of the black middle pair of feathers. This species inhabits the coniferous woods of western North America, nesting in high pines in the mountains.

The nutcrackers of the Old World, and farther north in the plains, resemble their plain-coloured relative in the possession of a long, straight, pointed beak, and a black and white tail, always conspicuous in flight, long wings, and nostrils covered with bristly feathers, while they exhibit in a special degree a general similarity of colouring among themselves, all being chocolate brown, more or less spotted with white. Two of these species frequent the middle ranges of the Himalaya, where they are resident throughout the year in forests of pine and cedar.

The typical European species, which inhabits the northern and central portions of Europe and Northern Asia, ranging into Northern China and Japan, is in evidence during many months of the year, sometimes approaching the neighbourhood of human dwellings in search of food, but in the breeding season becoming shy and cautious, so that its whereabouts are difficult to ascertain. The difficulty of discovering the position of its nest is enhanced by the nutcracker being one of the very earliest birds to breed, the pine forests in which it usually nests, often several thousand feet above sea-level, being frequently deep in snow at the time when the quest takes place. The eggs are usually laid in March, and are pale bluish white in ground colour, thickly spotted with olive brown. The young are easily reared by hand if supplied with a sufficient variety of food, and exhibit a marked predilection for insects.

Mr. Howard Saunders gives the following description of the habits of the nutcracker, as observed in the Prättigäu: "Between September 14 and 18 this species was quite common among the hazel-bushes, and the top of a low wall within five minutes' walk above the village where I was staying was a favourite anvil on which to hammer the nuts, their shells lying thick around. Every few minutes a bird might be seen flitting along the hillsides—its widely spread tail feathers displaying the white spots on their tips—with a somewhat dipping flight, less laboured than that of the jay. Often alighting on a sloping patch of sward, the nutcracker would draw itself up till its neck seemed unnaturally elongated, then give a few skips, and, taking a short flight, make a furious attack on a bush, tearing off a whole cluster of nuts. This was sometimes rejected, after a comically critical examination, and another cluster would be torn off, after which the bird would fly up to some tolerably wide branch of a fir, and hammer the nuts energetically to free them from their shucks, pausing to look up as if for admiration. Then it

1. ROOK   2. GREY CROW   3. JACKDAW   4. MAGPIE   5. RAVEN

would hop rapidly up the branches—as if on the rungs of a ladder—to the top of the tree, dash away across a ravine, settle on a bush, and be lost to view for a time, returning with its crop quite distended with nuts.

"One of the notes of this bird is a peculiar 'gurre, gurre'; but it has another, like a sprung rattle. A nutcracker which lived in captivity for six years had a sweet, low, delicate, warbling song, uttered only when everything was perfectly quiet." These handsome but noisy birds are occasional visitors to Great Britain.

MAGPIES

While all the members of the magpie group are characterised by the stout and compressed beak, sharp at the edges and arched towards the tip, short and rounded wings, strong feet, and long, graduated tail, the more typical species are distinguished by the black and white plumage, although many of their Oriental representatives are gorgeously coloured.

The European magpie (*Pica rustica*) ranges over the more northern portions of the Old World, from Britain to Northern China and Formosa, and also occurs in the western districts of the United States. On the other hand, the African magpie (*P. mauritanica*) is peculiar to North-Western Africa, although certain Spanish specimens tend to bridge over the differences of colour distinguishing the typical representatives of the two forms, and thus indicate that they are probably races of a single species.

Familiar enough in many parts of the British Islands, magpies in the north of Europe may be seen hunting for insects on the roofs of cottages; but elsewhere they lead a wandering life, feeding on carrion, small birds, and such other animal food as they can obtain. Breeding in a variety of situations—frequently in tall poplars, but at other times in low bushes or hedges—they construct domed nests of dry branches, securely protected by projecting thorns. Even in China, where they nest in February, their choice of a site for building is quite as varied as in Europe, their nests having been seen on the poles in front of a mandarin's house and in the crown of a cocoanut palm. The eggs, from five to seven in number, are bluish white with greenish brown or brownish spots (page 990).

The aforesaid North African magpie is distinguished by the presence of a naked patch of blue skin behind the eye; while in the Californian magpie (*P. nuttalli*) this spot and the beak are bright yellow. As representatives of distinct genera, mention may be made of the black magpie (*Platysmurus aterrimus*) of Borneo, and the short-tailed magpie (*Temnurus truncatus*) of Cochin China, both characterised by their sable plumage.

AZURE-WINGED MAGPIE

The azure-winged magpie (*Cyanopica cooki*), on account of certain differences, is regarded as representing a separate genus, and is one of the handsomest of European birds. In colour the head and upper part of the neck are coal-black, the back and mantle brownish grey, the throat greyish white, the under parts pale fawn grey, and the wings and tail light greenish blue. This bird has a remarkable geographical distribution; the typical azure-winged magpie being confined to certain districts of Spain and Portugal, where it is far from common, and very local, breeding in small colonies, and resorting to districts where evergreen oaks are abundant. Unknown elsewhere in Europe, it is replaced in China and Japan by an almost identical bird (*C. cyana*), distinguished by its superior size and generally greyer tone of colour. Such an instance of discontinuous distribution is scarcely paralleled in the perching birds. In disposition the azure-winged pie is an active and intelligent bird, building a nest very like that of the jay.

BLUE MAGPIES

The red-billed magpie (*Urocissa occipitalis*) is taken as a well-known representative of the group of blue magpies, collectively distinguished by the nostrils being covered with soft plumes instead of stiff bristles, and situated near the base of the beak. They further differ from ordinary magpies in having the beak either red or yellow, but never black, and are all characterised by the predominance of azure blue in the plumage. Unlike the true magpies, they build open nests. One species is found in Formosa, China, and Burma, and two others inhabit the Himalaya and Nepal. The Chinese blue magpie (*U. sinensis*), which inhabits the hills of Eastern China, sometimes extending its range into the more wooded portions of the plains, is described as a noisy bird, possessing a great variety of notes, and wandering about the wooded hillsides in large parties, composed exclusively of members of its own kind. The upper parts are lavender brown, slightly shaded with bluish purple, while the wings are dull azure, brighter on the quills, the primaries being spotted with white; the tail is azure blue, broadly tipped with white; the head and throat are black, all the feathers of the fore part of the crown being tipped with lavender grey; and the under surface of the body is light grey.

The red-billed species extends through the Himalaya, from the north-west to Nepal, where it is chiefly confined to the outer ranges. It lives in small parties, containing from two or three to half a dozen birds, and breeds from March to July. The open nest, which is built at a variable elevation above the ground, is formed of twigs and branches, and lined with fine roots.

The eggs, which vary in number from three to five, are similar in colour to those of the European magpie. When feeding, these birds are generally on the ground. The head, neck, and breast of the red-billed magpie are black; a large patch on the nape is white; the back, scapulars, and rump are purplish blue, the wings brown,

JACKDAWS

the first primaries edged with blue, the tail broadly tipped with white, and the lower parts white tinged with purple.

EASTERN PIES

The genus *Dendrocitta* has been founded for the reception of a group of eastern pies generally resembling the European magpie, but distinguished by the short curved beak and a colouring of mingled chestnut and black. One species inhabits Formosa, another (*D. bayleyi*) is peculiar to the Andaman Islands, a third (*D. himalayensis*) is found in the Himalaya and Assam, and there are several others, of which the most generally distributed is the Indian tree-pie (*D. rufa.*) This is abundant in well-wooded districts, especially in the plains, and in the more northern parts of the country may be seen in pairs and small parties in every grove and garden, and about every village. It builds a large nest of sticks, usually in some lofty tree, and lays three or four eggs of a light greenish fawn colour, usually indistinctly blotched with brown.

These magpies prey upon insects, small birds, and even bats, but at times feed principally upon fruits. In the adult the upper parts are orange brown, shading off into a brighter orange buff on the lower parts of the back and rump, the wings black, the tail feathers grey, with black tips, the lores and throat blackish, and the rest of the under parts orange buff.

Tree-pies seldom descend to the ground, and utter a series of clear metallic notes, well known to those who have camped in Indian jungles.

YOUNG JACKDAWS

NUTCRACKER

forest fruits. Nevertheless, when dwelling in woods bordering gardens, they are frequently tempted forth during its season to plunder the fruit. Not content, however, with a vegetable diet, the jays rifle and destroy the nests of the smaller birds, consuming both eggs and callow young alike; while they also destroy a considerable number of pheasants' eggs and chickens. In consequence of these thieving propensities they are cordially detested by gamekeepers, who seize every opportunity for shooting them, and in many districts of England these handsome but mischievous birds have become scarce.

The jay flies with an undulating and somewhat heavy motion, accompanied by much flapping of the wings, and takes only short flights from tree to tree, although when on migration it can fly for long distances. Unlike the preceding members of the family, when on the ground, jays progress by hopping instead of walking. In their movements, when perching, they are lively and apparently self-conscious, the head being continually turned from side to side, the crest alternately raised and depressed, and the wings and tail in motion.

SIBERIAN JAY

A characteristic bird of the more northern parts of the Old World is the Siberian jay (*Perisoreus infaustus*), typifying a second genus distinguished by the possession of a soft fluffy plumage, well adapted to protect its owner from the rigour of an Arctic winter. The adult bird has the crown and nape sooty brown, gradually fading in tinge as it joins the colour of the back; the upper parts being dull lead-grey, washed with reddish brown, and the rump and tail bright foxy red, excepting the middle tail feathers. The chin, throat, and breast are grey, and the under parts and flanks bright rufous.

The Siberian jay breeds early in the year, building its nest close to the stem of a pine or fir tree, and forming it principally of grey lichens closely interwoven with dry fir twigs, a few of its own feathers and those of the

JAYS

Under the title of jays may be included a group of several genera of closely allied members of the present family, in all of which the wings are relatively short, and the tail more than three-fourths the length of the wing. In the typical genus the short and compressed beak is shorter than the head; the nostrils are placed at the base of the beak and hidden by stiff, forwardly directed feathers, while the feathers of the crown of the head are long and erectile. The majority of the species have white upper tail coverts, and the wings barred with light blue, the general colour of the body plumage being fawn red. Chiefly frequenting woods, where their presence is revealed by their harsh, discordant cries, jays are omnivorous, living on almost every description of animal and vegetable substance, but changing their diet according to the season.

The typical jays of the genus *Garrulus* are principally inhabitants of the northern and temperate regions of the Old World, although one species is found in Burma, a second is peculiar to Algeria, and a third is confined to Japan. The European jay (*G. glandarius*) ranges throughout Europe from Northern Russia and Scandinavia to Spain and Italy, but is replaced in Asia Minor by the black-headed jay (*G. kynicki*), while in Eastern Russia its place is taken by Brandt's jay (*G. brandti*), and in Syria by *G. syriacus*. Shunning open country, the jay frequents large woods, where it often nests at only a moderate elevation above the ground, laying usually six eggs, of a greyish white colour speckled with brown.

Although shy birds, never dwelling in the open country and seldom seen on the ground, the jays are thoroughly arboreal in their habits, and, as their Latin name implies, are specially fond of acorns and other

YOUNG MAGPIES

THE MAGPIE

ptarmigan being inserted here and there, as also stalks of dry grass. The eggs vary from three to five, and are dirty white, blotched with purplish grey and brown.

CRESTED JAYS

In North America the present group is represented by the well-known blue jay (*Cyanocitta cristata*), the typical member of a small genus characterised by the tall erectile crest on the crown of the head. This handsome bird is smoky grey on the back, passing on the rump and upper tail coverts into cobalt blue, which also extends to the lower parts, while the sides of the head are bluish white bordered behind with black, the wings blue with white patches and black bars, and the tail blue with transverse black bars.

"The blue jay," writes Mr. W. Dutcher "has an extensive range, being found in Eastern North America as far north as 52° N., and, casually, a little further; it extends westwards to about 100° W. in Assiniboia, and south to about 97° W. in Northern Texas. It breeds throughout its range, but in winter most northern birds move southwards. In Florida, and along the Gulf Coast to South-Eastern Texas, there is a slightly smaller race, but the ordinary observer will not be able to note any difference. The nesting places vary very greatly as to the kind of trees selected and the position in the tree. Sites may be found in conifers and also in deciduous trees, and even in shrubbery. The nest is usually bulky, but compactly built of twigs, bark, moss, leaves, and various other materials. A set of eggs varies from four to six, the colour is greenish or buffy, irregularly spotted with shades of brown or lavender."

In Mexico the group is represented by the still bluer Mexican blue jay (*C. coronata*), and a third species, *C. yucatensis*, inhabits Central America.

URRACA AND OTHER JAYS

The Brazilian urraca jay (*Cyanocorax chrysops*) is a well-known representative of a Central and South American genus also distinguished from the typical jays by the greater prevalence of blue. In colour it is black above, glossed with purple, the feathers of the crown forming a crest; the nape is greyish blue, deepening into purple on the hind part of the neck; above the eye is a blue spot, and the under surface is a creamy yellow.

This jay is an abundant bird in Paraguay, where it is as familiar and as inquisitive as is the magpie in England, not even hesitating to enter the houses of the inhabitants. Not ranging into the still colder regions of Argentina, this bird seems to suffer in Uruguay from the cold during winter, and at that season it is by no means uncommon to see a party of from ten to twenty huddled together in the most sheltered part of a tree, to obtain protection from the wind. If the tree or bush be small, and the best space limited, it may happen that some of the birds will perch on the backs of their fellows, and thus form a regular pyramid.

THE JAY

Like most gregarious pies and jays, when the flock is on the move, one bird flies off first, followed soon by another, and then by a third, till the whole party is on the wing. As a rule, the nest is built in a tall and thorny tree, and, though strongly constructed, so coarsely is it made that the eggs can always be seen from below, and sometimes actually fall through the chinks. With a blue ground colour, and a chalky incrustation, the eggs are generally six or seven in number, although upwards of fourteen have been taken from a single nest.

Other species of the same genus are the so-called pileated jay (*C. pileatus*) of Argentina, and the Peruvian blue jay (*C. incasi*) of Colombia. *Calocitta* is a nearly allied genus typified by Swainson's long-tailed jay (*C. fumosa*) of Central America. Lastly, there is the green jay (*Xanthura luxuosa*) of Southern Texas and Mexico, characterised by its general green colour, black and blue head, and yellow under parts, which represents another genus.

RED-BILLED MAGPIES

CHOUGHS

The chough, or Cornish chough (*Pyrrhocorax graculus*), along with the allied Alpine species, although agreeing with the crows in general form and sable plumage, differs in the long and pointed wings, as well as in the comparatively slender and longer beak. Unlike crows, these birds have the shank of the leg smooth, and the feet and beak brightly coloured. Of the two species, the Cornish, or red-billed, chough ranges from Eastern Europe to China and Eastern Siberia, being no less at home in the deserts of Ladak than on the cliffs of the English coast. Formerly this species was a comparatively common bird on the western coasts of Great Britain and Ireland; nor was it entirely a coast-loving one, since individual pairs nested in the recesses of limestone precipices inland, such as Whitbarrow Scaur in Westmorland. Of late years, however, the chough has decreased in numbers in most of its strongholds, largely owing to human interference; although there is some reason to suppose that its extermination may be partially accounted for by the special predilection of the peregrine falcon for its flesh.

The chough nests in spring, breeding principally among the precipices of dizzy cliffs and headlands, but occasionally it rears its young among the broken pinnacles of some ruined cathedral. The eggs are white in ground colour, streaked with brown and grey. The Isle of Man was formerly a great stronghold of the species, and when Sir William Jardine visited that island in 1827 he found the "red-legged crows" most abundant. Even in Britain the chough occasionally wanders from its maritime haunts; and in Ladak it dwells in the very heart of Asia. Not the least interesting feature in the life-history of this bird is the constancy with which individual pairs endeavour to rear their young for many successive years in the same nesting-places.

Among the Alps and other mountain ranges of Central Europe the red-billed chough is in many cases replaced by the Alpine chough (*P. alpinus*), which has

SIBERIAN JAY

woods, when it happens to fly from one high tree to another. The old birds, as a rule, respond to the call note in a low, tremulous whistle or whimper, and

MALE AND FEMALE HUIA BIRDS

almost immediately after- wards answer the summons in person, coming down noiselessly, and almost with the rapidity of an arrow."

The huia builds its nest in hollow trees, lining it with coarse grasses and bits of coarse herbaceous plants, twined into a basin-like form. The eggs are in some cases of a very delicate stone grey, inclining to greyish white, without any markings except at the larger end, where there are some scattered rounded spots of dark purple, grey and brown; but other specimens are pure white, without any trace of markings. With the exception of a broad band of white at the tip of the rounded tail, the whole of the plumage is black, with a green metallic gloss. Both sexes are adorned with large, rounded wattles, of a rich orange colour in the living bird. The beak is ivory white, darkening into blackish grey at the base. The young differ from the adults in having the entire plumage of a duller black, and the terminal bar washed with rufous. It may be added that, in the superficial deposits of the North Island, re- mains of the huia have been found in association with those of the extinct moas.

SADDLEBACK

Another peculiar New Zealand genus is represented by the saddleback (*Creadion carun- culatus*), which takes its name from having the back, rump, and tail coverts chestnut; the rest of the plumage being black, and the gape having small red or yellow wattles. The genus *Callæas*, with two species, the one with the wattles wholly blue (*C. Wilsoni*), and the other blue and orange (*C. cinerea*), is also from New Zealand, where these birds inhabit the lower hill forests.

The West African *Picathartes*—a slaty grey bird, with brown quills, white under parts, and a bare, yellow head, displaying a black mark behind the eyes—may also be provisionally placed in the neighbourhood of the huia.

GREY STRUTHIDEA

Considerable uncertainty obtains with regard to the systematic posi- tion of the curious bird known as the grey struthidea (*Struthidea cinerea*), which is confined to the rocky hill ridges of Southern and Eastern Australia, and may be provisionally associated with the crow tribe. The two sexes are so nearly identical in size and colour that they can only be distinguished by dissection. This species differs from many other Aus- tralian birds by the sombre colour of its dress, which is absolutely identical in the two sexes, and so inconspicuous as to be little likely to attract atten- tion. The general colour both above and below is grey, each feather being tipped with lighter grey; but the wings are brown, and the tail is glossy black, with a greenish lustre on the outer webs of its feathers.

The short beak is strongly arched, apparently for the purpose of cracking the seeds of the cones of a tree to which this bird constantly resorts. The eggs are four in number, and are white in colour, blotched with reddish brown and grey; the nest is of mud, thickly lined with fine grass. *Corcorax melanor-*

GREY STRUTHIDEA

hamphus is an allied Australian bird, distinguished by the black plumage, with white on the wings. It haunts forests and the neighbourhood of water.

Like most gregarious pies and jays, when the flock is on the move, one bird flies off first, followed soon by another, and then by a third, till the whole party is on the wing. As a rule, the nest is built in a tall and thorny tree, and, though strongly constructed, so coarsely is it made that the eggs can always be seen from below, and sometimes actually fall through the chinks. With a blue ground colour, and a chalky incrustation, the eggs are generally six or seven in number, although upwards of fourteen have been taken from a single nest.

Other species of the same genus are the so-called pileated jay (*C. pileatus*) of Argentina, and the Peruvian blue jay (*C. incasi*) of Colombia. *Calocitta* is a nearly allied genus typified by Swainson's long-tailed jay (*C. fumosa*) of Central America. Lastly, there is the green jay (*Xanthura luxuosa*) of Southern Texas and Mexico, characterised by its general green colour, black and blue head, and yellow under parts, which represents another genus.

RED-BILLED MAGPIES

CHOUGHS

The chough, or Cornish chough (*Pyrrhocorax graculus*), along with the allied Alpine species, although agreeing with the crows in general form and sable plumage, differs in the long and pointed wings, as well as in the comparatively slender and longer beak. Unlike crows, these birds have the shank of the leg smooth, and the feet and beak brightly coloured. Of the two species, the Cornish, or red-billed, chough ranges from Eastern Europe to China and Eastern Siberia, being no less at home in the deserts of Ladak than on the cliffs of the English coast. Formerly this species was a comparatively common bird on the western coasts of Great Britain and Ireland; nor was it entirely a coast-loving one, since individual pairs nested in the recesses of limestone precipices inland, such as Whitbarrow Scaur in Westmorland. Of late years, however, the chough has decreased in numbers in most of its strongholds, largely owing to human interference; although there is some reason to suppose that its extermination may be partially accounted for by the special predilection of the peregrine falcon for its flesh.

The chough nests in spring, breeding principally among the precipices of dizzy cliffs and headlands, but occasionally it rears its young among the broken pinnacles of some ruined cathedral. The eggs are white in ground colour, streaked with brown and grey. The Isle of Man was formerly a great stronghold of the species, and when Sir William Jardine visited that island in 1827 he found the "red-legged crows" most abundant. Even in Britain the chough occasionally wanders from its maritime haunts; and in Ladak it dwells in the very heart of Asia. Not the least interesting feature in the life-history of this bird is the constancy with which individual pairs endeavour to rear their young for many successive years in the same nesting-places.

Among the Alps and other mountain ranges of Central Europe the red-billed chough is in many cases replaced by the Alpine chough (*P. alpinus*), which has

SIBERIAN JAY

URRACA JAY

parts being clear grey, the wings white, with black at the base and at the tip, the tail glossy purplish black, the throat whitish, with a large black patch on the fore part of the neck, and the lower parts vinaceous, fading into white.

Of the other species, *P. hendersoni* and *P. biddulphi* have the crown of the head black, marked with white spots in the former, while *P. humilis* is brown, with the nape and under parts whitish.

HUIA BIRD

Among a number of strange types of bird life peculiar to New Zealand, one of the most bizarre is the huia bird (*Heteralocha acutirostris*), which by some naturalists has been referred to the hoopoes, and by others to the present family; while others, again, believe its relations to be most intimate with the starlings. A strange difference is found between the beaks of the two sexes, that of the male being rather short, straight, and acutely pointed, with the sides compressed, and the nostrils at its base, while that of the female is long, curved, and slender, the difference being so great that the two sexes were at first regarded as distinct species. The wings are long and rounded.

The huia has an extremely restricted habitat, being confined to certain mountain ranges, with their divergent spurs, and the intervening wooded valleys. The Maori, who prize the bird very highly for its tail feathers, which are used as a badge of mourning, state that, unlike other species which have diminished and become more confined in their range, the huia has from time immemorial been limited to its present haunts.

Sir W. Buller, who comments on the readiness with which the huia becomes reconciled to the loss of its liberty, received in 1864 a pair of these birds from a native in exchange for a valuable stone. They were

a yellow instead of a red beak, and is somewhat smaller in dimensions. The Alpine chough is the characteristic representative of the crow tribe in the mountains of Switzerland, as it also is of the Apennines; and its lively chatter, breaking suddenly on vast and silent solitudes, recalls the familiar jackdaw. This chough nests amongst the crags of its native precipices; the eggs being four or five in number, and in colour white, varied with dirty yellow mottlings. Both species of chough utter a ringing metallic note, quite different from the "caw" of the crows, and resembling the syllables "chough-chough."

CHOUGH THRUSHES

Pander's chough thrush (*Podoces panderi*) is the typical representative of a small but interesting group of birds of somewhat doubtful affinity, though perhaps not distantly related to the choughs. From the latter the chough thrushes are distinguished by the relative shortness of their wings, which fall short of the tip of the tail by more than the length of the metatarsus; and they are further distinguished by their peculiar style of colour and their inferior size. Comparatively little is known of the habits of the chough thrushes, which are found only in certain parts of Central Asia.

All the species known to science inhabit desert regions and sterile plains; and of these the first discovered was Pander's chough thrush, whose home is the lower Oxus and the inaccessible deserts of Turkestan. It is not a gregarious species, nor does it congregate with other kinds of birds, living for the most part in couples, which presumably pair for life, and constantly associate, subsisting upon the insects and other food to be found in the vicinity of their favourite sandhills. This species is a handsome and attractive bird, the upper

MEXICAN BLUE JAY

fully adult, and had been caught in the following simple fashion. Attracting the birds by an imitation of their cry to the place where he lay concealed, the native, with the aid of a long rod, slipped a running knot over the head of the female and secured her. The male, emboldened by the loss of his mate, suffered himself to be easily caught in the same manner.

When these birds were liberated in a large room, writes their owner, " it was amusing to notice their treatment of the hu-hu. This grub, the larva of a large nocturnal beetle, which constitutes their principal food, infests all decayed timber, attaining at maturity the size of a man's little finger. Like all grubs of its kind, it is furnished with a horned head and horny mandibles. On offering one of these to the huia, he would seize it in the middle, and, at once transferring it to his perch, and placing one foot firmly upon it, would tear off the hard parts, and then, throwing the grub upwards to secure it lengthwise in his bill, swallow it whole.

" For the first few days these birds were comparatively quiet, remaining stationary on their perch as soon as their hunger was appeased, but they after-

PANDER'S CHOUGH THRUSH

wards became more lively and active, indulging in play with each other, and seldom remaining more than a few moments in one position. I sent to the woods for a small branched tree, and placed it in the centre of the room, the floor of which was spread with sand and gravel. It was most interesting to watch these graceful birds hopping from branch to branch, occasionally spreading their tail into a broad fan, displaying themselves in a variety of natural attitudes, and then meeting to caress each other with their ivory bills, uttering at the same time a low, affectionate twitter.

" But what interested me most of all was the manner in which the birds assisted each other in their search for food, because it appeared to explain the use, in the economy of nature, of the differently formed bills in the two sexes. To divert the birds, I introduced a log of decayed wood infested with the hu-hu grub. They at once attacked it, carefully probing the softer parts with their bills, and then vigorously assailing them, scooping out the decayed wood till the larva or pupa was visible, when it was carefully drawn from its cell, treated in the way above described, and then swallowed. The very different development of the mandibles in the two sexes enabled them to perform separate offices. The male always attacked the more decayed portions of the wood, chiselling out his prey after the manner of some woodpeckers, while the female probed with her long, pliant bill the other cells, where the hardness of the surrounding parts resisted the chisel of her mate. Sometimes I observed the male remove the decayed portion without being able to reach the grub, when the female would at once come to his aid and accomplished with her long, slender bill what he had failed to do. I noticed, however, that the female always appropriated to her own use the morsels thus obtained.

" The huia never leaves the shade of the forest, and moves along the ground, or from tree to tree, with remarkable celerity, by a series of bounds or jumps. In its flight it never rises, like other birds, above the tree-tops, except in the depths of the

CHOUGHS

woods, when it happens to fly from one high tree to another. The old birds, as a rule, respond to the call note in a low, tremulous whistle or whimper, and

MALE AND FEMALE HUIA BIRDS

almost immediately after- wards answer the summons in person, coming down noiselessly, and almost with the rapidity of an arrow."

The huia builds its nest in hollow trees, lining it with coarse grasses and bits of coarse herbaceous plants, twined into a basin-like form. The eggs are in some cases of a very delicate stone grey, inclining to greyish white, without any markings except at the larger end, where there are some scattered rounded spots of dark purple, grey and brown; but other specimens are pure white, without any trace of markings. With the exception of a broad band of white at the tip of the rounded tail, the whole of the plumage is black, with a green metallic gloss. Both sexes are adorned with large, rounded wattles, of a rich orange colour in the living bird. The beak is ivory white, darkening into blackish grey at the base. The young differ from the adults in having the entire plumage of a duller black, and the terminal bar washed with rufous. It may be added that, in the superficial deposits of the North Island, remains of the huia have been found in association with those of the extinct moas.

SADDLEBACK

Another peculiar New Zealand genus is represented by the saddleback (*Creadion carunculatus*), which takes its name from having the back, rump, and tail coverts chestnut; the rest of the plumage being black, and the gape having small red or yellow wattles. The genus *Callæas*, with two species, the one with the wattles wholly blue (*C. Wilsoni*), and the other blue and orange (*C. cinerea*), is also from New Zealand, where these birds inhabit the lower hill forests.

The West African *Picathartes*—a slaty grey bird, with brown quills, white under parts, and a bare, yellow head, displaying a black mark behind the eyes—may also be provisionally placed in the neighbourhood of the huia.

GREY STRUTHIDEA

Considerable uncertainty obtains with regard to the systematic position of the curious bird known as the grey struthidea (*Struthidea cinerea*), which is confined to the rocky hill ridges of Southern and Eastern Australia, and may be provisionally associated with the crow tribe. The two sexes are so nearly identical in size and colour that they can only be distinguished by dissection. This species differs from many other Australian birds by the sombre colour of its dress, which is absolutely identical in the two sexes, and so inconspicuous as to be little likely to attract attention. The general colour both above and below is grey, each feather being tipped with lighter grey; but the wings are brown, and the tail is glossy black, with a greenish lustre on the outer webs of its feathers.

The short beak is strongly arched, apparently for the purpose of cracking the seeds of the cones of a tree to which this bird constantly resorts. The eggs are four in number, and are white in colour, blotched with reddish brown and grey; the nest is of mud, thickly lined with fine grass. *Corcorax melanor-*

GREY STRUTHIDEA

hamphus is an allied Australian bird, distinguished by the black plumage, with white on the wings. It haunts forests and the neighbourhood of water.

BIRDS OF PARADISE AND BOWER BIRDS

In spite of their gorgeous plumage, which seems to run riot in the way of exuberance and eccentricity, the birds of paradise (family *Paradiseidæ*) may be regarded as near allies of the crow tribe, from which they are distinguished by the abnormal structure of the toes; the outermost or fourth of these being inferior in length to the third, which is longer than the second; while the first is very large, and equal to or longer than the third. The birds of paradise may be divided into two groups, in the first of which the beak is short and more or less stout, with its culmen shorter than the metatarsus; while in the second it is long and slender, with the culmen longer than the metatarsus.

These birds, which are represented by fully fifty species, are almost wholly confined to New Guinea and the adjacent Papuan Islands, especially the Aru group, although one genus is found in the Moluccas, while three genera extend to North Australia. Although the females are at best plain and ordinary-looking birds, often of a uniform chocolate colour, the adult males of all the species are characterised by an extraordinary development of plumage, quite unparalleled in any other group (p. 987). "In several species," writes Dr. A. R. Wallace, "large tufts of delicate, bright-coloured feathers spring from each side of the body beneath the wings, forming trains, or fans, or shields; and the middle feathers of the tail are often elongated into wires, twisted into fantastic shapes, or adorned with the most brilliant metallic tints. In another set of species these accessory plumes spring from the head, the back, or the shoulders; while the intensity of colour and of metallic lustre displayed by their plumage is not to be equalled by any other birds, except, perhaps, the humming birds, and is not surpassed even by these."

Although comparatively little is known in regard to the habits of these lovely birds, it appears that as regards food they are omnivorous, feeding on fruits and insects, and showing a marked preference for figs, grasshoppers, locusts, leaf-insects, and caterpillars. While the long-tailed species are purely arboreal, some of the short-tailed kinds, like the six-plumed bird of paradise, are frequently seen on the ground, and in all cases the cocks are fond of assembling for mutual display. The six-plumed and magnificent species have dancing-grounds, carefully cleared, on which they disport themselves, while the raggiana has a special tree to which the males resort for their nuptial display, but the other species use for this purpose any tree that may be convenient. Probably many of the rarer species lay only a single egg; but in the case of other

GREAT BIRD OF PARADISE

kinds the eggs, which recall those of some of the rails in appearance, are two in number, and laid in a nest built high up in the tree-tops.

The eggs of the Empress Augusta paradise bird have a pale pinkish buff ground colour, upon which are streaks and spots of reddish brown and grey. Several of the species have a very small distributional area, but in no case is the range more restricted than in the red bird of paradise, which is confined to the small island of Waigiu, at the north-western extremity of New Guinea, in which it replaces the members of the genus to which it belongs found in the other islands.

TWELVE-WIRED BIRD OF PARADISE

Beginning with the second of the two groups referred to above, or the one in which the beak is relatively long and slender, the beautiful twelve-wired bird of paradise (*Seleucides ignotus*), the sole representative of its genus, may be taken as the first example of the family. Having a short, squared tail, much inferior in length to the body, this bird is distinguished by the absence of a shield of metallic plumes on the throat and fore part of the neck, and still more so by the feathers of the flanks, which are yellowish like those of the breast, being expanded and their shafts elongated into six pairs of bare wire-like bristles, bent forwards in a bold curve.

As regards plumage, the head is covered with short velvety feathers of a purplish bronze colour, while the breast appears at first nearly black, but in different lights shows various metallic tints, especially green and purple, the outer edges of the feathers being margined with emerald green. The whole of the back and shoulders is rich bronzy green, the closed wings and tail are of the most brilliant violet purple, and the whole plumage has a delicate silky gloss. Posteriorly to the fore portion of the breast, the whole of the under parts are of a rich buff yellow, the same tint characterising the plumes of the flank feathers, which extend about an inch and a half beyond the tail. The total length of the bird (page 57) is about twelve inches, of which two inches are taken up by the compressed beak. The female, although less sombre than in some members of the group, has none of the bright plumes of her partner, being bright chestnut red above, with the crown of the head and back of the neck brown, and the under parts buffy brown, irregularly barred with blackish brown.

Inhabiting the island of Salwatti and the north-western parts of New Guinea, the twelve-wired bird of paradise, according to Dr. Wallace, "frequents flowering trees, especially sago palms and pandanus,

RED BIRD OF PARADISE

a splendid opalescent blue, but its chief ornament is the group of broad feathers arising in a fan-like manner from the sides of the breast, which are dilated at their extremities, and banded with vivid blue and green. The beak is long and curved, and the feet are black. In total length this bird measures between 3 and 4 feet, and is an inhabitant of the mountains of New Guinea, sometimes found near the coast.

ALBERTIS' BIRD OF PARADISE

The third of these genera is represented by Albertis' bird of paradise (*Drepanornis albertisi*), which differs from all the rest in its long, slender, sickle-shaped beak, downy plumage, moderately long and graduated tail, and in having the flank feathers developed into a brown, fan-like shield. "Above the beak," writes its discoverer, Mr. Albertis, "are two tufts, or horns, formed of small feathers deeply marked with green and copper-coloured reflections. The long feathers which grow from the sides of the breast are, when closed, grey, shot with a violet tint; but when spread they form almost a semicircle round the body, and in certain lights shine like gold, in others, like fire. Long feathers of a greyish violet colour grow from the sides, their edges being of a metallic violet lustre. "The upper parts of the wing and tail feathers are of a darkish yellow, as are those of the back, but sometimes of a still darker hue. The feathers of the throat are black, shading off into olive colour; those of the breast of a greyish purple, with an olive band; the abdomen is white. The beak is black, the eyes chestnut, and the feet dark lead colour. When the bird raises the long feathers on his sides and breast, they form two semicircles, and he presents as extraordinary and beautiful sight as one could behold." The female of this Papuan species is chestnut above and yellower beneath.

GORGET BIRD OF PARADISE

A native of the mountains of the interior of New Guinea, the gorget bird of paradise (*Astrapia nigra*) is the first representative of the short-beaked, or typical, group of the family (page 57). Having a long and graduated tail, of which the central plumes are not elongated into wire-like shafts, it is especially distinguished by the thick feathering of the lores and angle of the beak, by the presence of an erect frill surrounding the head, and another frill of a golden coppery tint round the throat.

In the adult male the general colour of the upper parts is velvety black, with a purplish gloss; the two long central tail-feathers are glossed with purple, the frill round the head is golden green, the feathers of the throat are steely black, with the above-mentioned gorget of brilliant copper, a ruff of black plumes springs from the shield on the neck, the flanks are dusky black, and the under parts velvety grass green.

An allied genus is represented by the wattled paradise bird (*Paradigalla carunculata*) of New Guinea, distinguished by the lores having an erect orange-yellow wattle, while another of azure blue hangs from each angle of the beak; the tail being shorter than the body, and the head and throat devoid of frills. The plumage is black, with brilliant reflections of green and bronze on the upper parts.

sucking the flowers, round and beneath which its unusually large and powerful feet enable it to cling. Its motions are very rapid. It seldom rests more than a few moments on one tree, after which it flies off, and with great swiftness, to another. It has a loud, shrill cry, to be heard a long way off, consisting of '*cah, cah*,' repeated five or six times in a descending scale, and at the last note it generally flies away. The males are quite solitary in their habits, although, perhaps, they assemble at certain times like the true paradise birds."

RIFLE BIRDS

Three other genera of paradise birds are included in the long-beaked group—namely, *Ptilornis*, *Epimachus* and *Drepanornis*; the members of the first of the three being inhabitants of Northern Australia and New Guinea, where they are commonly known as rifle birds. While agreeing with the twelve-wired paradise bird in the relative proportions of the tail, they differ in having a conspicuous shield of metallic plumes, occupying the throat and fore part of the neck, as well as in the absence of the "wires." The scale-breasted bird of paradise (*Ptilornis magnificus*) is the Papuan representative of this genus, and is characterised by the shield of stiff, metallic green feathers on the breast, and a small tuft of somewhat hairy plumes on the sides of the same; the back and wings being velvety black, faintly glossed with purple.

LONG-TAILED BIRD OF PARADISE

The long-tailed bird of paradise (*Epimachus speciosus*), together with an allied Papuan species, represents the second of the three genera, sufficiently distinguished by the great elongation of the graduated tail, which is much longer than the body. Resembling the twelve-wired species in its dark, velvety plumage, glossed with purple and bronze, this bird has the tail, which exceeds two feet in length, tinted above with

GREAT BIRD OF PARADISE

The typical member of the family is the great bird of paradise (*Paradisea apoda*), the first known representative of the group, which derives its specific name from having been described by Linnæus from a skin prepared in Papuan fashion, with the wings and feet cut off. The genus, which is represented by several species from Papua and the Aru and other islands, is characterised by the production of the central pair of tail feathers into extremely long, horny, wire-like shafts, the absence of a shield on the back, and the elongation of the flank plumes into two huge bunches of feathers reaching far beyond the tail.

The great bird of paradise of the Aru Islands (pages 961 and 987), which is the largest representative of the genus, measuring from 15 to 18 inches in total length, is described by Dr. Wallace as follows: " The body, wings, and tail are of a rich coffee brown, which deepens on the breast to a blackish violet or purple brown. The whole of the top of the head and neck is of an exceedingly delicate straw yellow, the feathers being short and close set, so as to resemble plush or velvet ; the lower part of the throat up to the eye is clothed with scaly feathers of an emerald green colour, with a rich metallic gloss, and velvety plumes of a still deeper green extend in a broad band across the forehead and chin as far as the eye, which is bright yellow. The beak is pale lead blue, and the feet, which are rather large, and very strongly and well formed, are of a pale ashy pink.

" The two middle feathers of the tail have no webs, except a very small one at the base and at the extreme tip, forming wire-like cirrhi, which spread out in an elegant double curve, and vary from 24 to 30 inches in length. From each side of the body, beneath the wings, springs a dense tuft of long and delicate plumes, sometimes 2 feet in length, of the most intense golden orange colour, and very glossy, but changing towards the tips into a pale brown. This tuft of plumes can be elevated and spread out at pleasure, so as almost to conceal the body of the bird."

In the female the ornamental plumes are wanting and the colour is a uniform coffee brown. The lesser bird of paradise (*P. minor*), from New Guinea, and several of the adjacent islands, although considerably smaller, is very similar in general characteristics.

RED BIRD OF PARADISE

On the other hand, the red bird of paradise (*P. rubra*), inhabiting the islands of Waigiu, Ghemien, and Batanta, is a very distinct type. Measuring from 13 to 14 inches in length, it has the flank plumes shorter, and of a rich crimson hue, while in structure they are rigid, with the tips horny and nearly white. The forehead, sides of the head, and the whole throat are brilliant metallic green, with the plumes of a velvety texture, the sides of the neck and entire mantle bright golden yellow, deepening into orange on the sides of the mantle and the middle of the back ; the rump is straw yellow, the two middle tail-feathers form slender shafts 21 inches in

WILSON'S BIRD OF PARADISE

length, of a metallic horny structure ; the wing coverts are golden yellow, and the primaries ruddy chestnut, while the breast is deep purplish chestnut. The female and young have the sides of the head and forehead purplish brown, the hind part of the head, neck, and mantle straw yellow, deepening into orange, and the remainder of the upper surface, including the wings and tail, chestnut brown, as are the lower parts.

Thoroughly arboreal in their habits, the gorgeous birds of this genus live both upon insects and fruit, and occasionally may be seen running along the lower boughs of trees almost like woodpeckers, with the long black filaments of the tail hanging gracefully down on each side. In motion throughout the day, they are active and vigorous, and while small flocks of females and immature males are constantly met with, the adult cocks are less commonly seen, although their presence near by is revealed by their loud and harsh cries.

At certain seasons the adult males flock together in a selected tree for the purpose of a display, forming what the natives term dancing parties. " On one of these trees," writes Dr. Wallace, " a dozen or twenty full-plumaged male birds assemble together, raise up their wings, stretch out their necks, and elevate their exquisite plumes, keeping them in a continual vibration. Between whiles they fly across from branch to branch in a state of great excitement, so that the whole tree is filled with waving plumes in every variety of attitude and motion." When thus assembled, the birds are shot with blunt-headed arrows by the natives, who climb silently into the " play-tree," and seat themselves in some convenient fork. From continual persecution to supply the European market with skins, the great bird of paradise has greatly diminished in numbers.

KING BIRD OF PARADISE

The beautiful little king bird of paradise (*Cicinnurus regius*), from New Guinea and the adjacent islands, forms the type of a distinct genus, distinguished by the flank plumes not extending beyond the tail, the presence of a large tuft of fan-like plumes on each side of the breast, and by the racket-like shape of the long middle pair of tail feathers. Measuring only about 6½ inches in length, this lovely species has the head, throat, upper parts, wings, and tail red, the fan-like plumes on the sides purplish, tipped with green, a green gorget below the red of the throat, and the rest of the under parts white (page 987).

WILSON'S BIRD OF PARADISE

One of the strangest and most bizarre members of a remarkable family is Wilson's bird of paradise (*Schlegelia respublica*), a Papuan species representing a genus by itself, although nearly related to the genus *Diphyllodes*, typified by the magnificent paradise bird (*D. magnifica*). This group is distinguished from the preceding by the presence of a shield of feathers on the back, and the absence of elongated flank plumes ; while from the allied genus (*Rhipidornis*) both differ in having no fan-shaped shield of feathers springing from each side of the breast. In the magnificent paradise bird and its congeners the head is thickly feathered, but in Wilson's species the whole head, with the exception of a few narrow tracts of feathers, is bare.

In describing this remarkable species, Dr. F. H. H. Guillemard writes that " behind the head a ruff of canary-coloured feathers stands erect above the scarlet back and wings. The breast is covered by a shield of glossy green plumes, which towards the throat are marked with metallic green and violet spots of extraordinary beauty. The two central feathers of the tail, prolonged for five or six inches beyond the others, cross one another, and are curved into a circle of bright steely purple. But the chief peculiarity of the bird is the head, which is bald from the vertex backwards, the bare skin being of the brightest imaginable hue. The bizarre effect thus produced is still further heightened by two fine feathers, which, running lengthways and from side to side, form a dark cross upon the brilliant azure background." The bird is of small size, and is confined to Waigiu and Batanta Islands, where it appears to be very locally distributed, frequenting forests of no great height, at an elevation of some eight hundred feet above the sea.

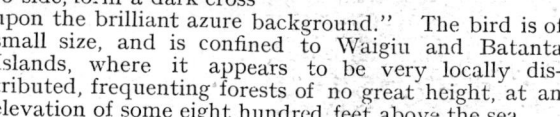

HEAD OF SIX-PLUMED BIRD OF PARADISE

SIX-PLUMED BIRD OF PARADISE

Another strange and beautiful representative of a group in which all are lovely beyond description is the six-plumed bird of paradise (*Parotia sexpennis*) of New Guinea, the only known member of its genus. In common with the remaining members of the family, this bird has a short tail, without any elongation of the central pair of feathers, but is specially characterised by three pairs of long, racket-like feathers springing from the sides of the head. With the exception of a vivid steel green bar across the crown of the head, and a tuft of silvery feathers at the base of the beak, together with a green and bronze gorget on the breast, the plumage is almost entirely black, the tuft of silvery feathers on the beak being capable of erection or depression at will.

For many years this splendid species was known only by skins badly prepared by the natives, but eventually it was observed in the living state by Mr. Albertis, who writes as follows of his first sight of it in its native haunts : " After standing still for some moments in the middle of the little glade, the beautiful bird peered about to see if all was safe, and then he began to move the long feathers of his head, six in number, from which his name is derived, and to raise and lower a small tuft of white feathers above his beak, which shone in the

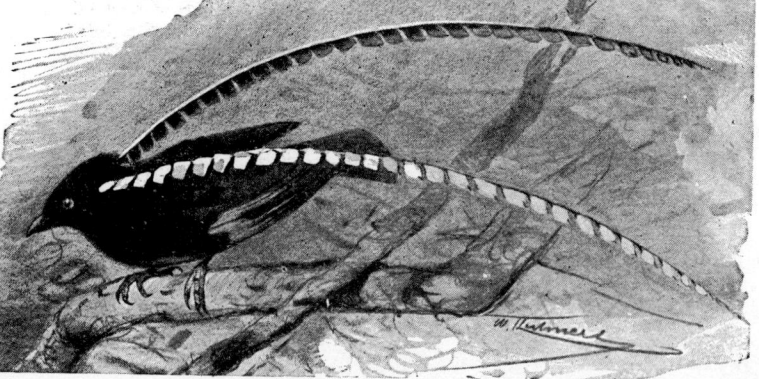

ALBERTIS' PARADISE BIRD

rays of the sun like burnished silver; he also raised and lowered the crest of stiff feathers, almost like scales, and glittering like bits of bright metal, with which his neck was adorned. He spread and contracted the long feathers on his sides in a way that made him appear now larger and again smaller than his real size, and, jumping first on one side and then on the other, he placed himself proudly in an attitude of combat, as though he imagined himself fighting with some invisible foe. All this time he was uttering a curious note, as though calling on someone to admire his beauty, or perhaps challenging an enemy." From this account it appears that the species is much less arboreal in its habits than are the other members of the family.

STANDARD-WING

Even more remarkable than the last is the standard-wing (*Semioptera wallacei*), from the islands of Batchian and Gilolo, which also forms a genus by itself, and is characterised by the absence of long, thread-like plumes on the head, and the presence of two long projecting feathers from each wing, which are capable of being erected at the pleasure of their owner. This bird is generally of a delicate olive brown colour, deepening to a kind of bronze olive in the middle of the back, and changing to a delicate ash violet with metallic reflections on the crown of the head ; the feathers covering the nostrils and extending half-way down the beak being loose and upwardly curved. On the breast the scale-like feathers are margined with a rich metallic bluish green, and the same colour embraces the throat and sides of the neck, along with the long, pointed plumes rising from the sides of the breast. The two long, projecting white feathers springing from near the bend of the wings are fully 6 inches in length, and are spread out at right angles to the wings whenever the bird is excited. The beak is horny olive, the iris deep olive, and the foot bright orange. In total length the bird measures eleven inches.

The standard-wing, which resembles the rest of its tribe in being in constant motion, frequents the lower boughs of the forest trees, flying from branch to branch, clinging to the twigs, and even to the smooth and vertical trunks almost as easily as a woodpecker. It continually utters a harsh, croaking note, somewhat intermediate between that of the great paradise bird and the king bird of paradise. The males at short intervals open and flutter their wings, erect the long shoulder feathers, and spread out the elegant green breast shields. It is noteworthy that the race of this species from Gilolo differs somewhat in colouring and the conformation of the plumes from the one inhabiting

Batchian, so that an expert is at once able to say from which of the two islands any specimen was obtained.

SUPERB BIRD OF PARADISE

The acme of strange plumal adornment—which in all these cases is probably developed to attract the admiration and attention of the female, since it can have no other conceivable object—seems to be attained by the superb bird of paradise (*Lophorhina superba*), which is chiefly characterised by the presence of an enormous erectile forked shield of velvety black feathers, arising from the nape of the neck, but when in repose lying flat on the back. So strange and apparently incongruous is this shield that it might suggest to the beholder that the tail of some other bird had been stuck on to the skin, were it not that its feathers are of a different type.

The ground colour of the plumage is of the deepest black, with bronze reflections on the neck, while the feathers of the head are metallic green and blue. Spreading over the breast is a shield composed of narrow and rather stiff feathers, which extends in a pointed form along each side, and is emarginate in the middle. In colour this is bluish green, with a satiny sheen : the back shield, on the other hand, being velvety black, with reflections of bronze and purple, and its outermost feathers exceeding the primaries of the wing in length.

The enormous crest, as it appears displayed during the courtship of the female, is not only raised, but spread widely out in a fan-like manner, while the chest shield is similarly expanded, so that the head of the bird forms the centre of an irregular circle of feathers of velvety black and emerald, completely concealing the rest of the body when viewed from the front.

OTHER BIRDS OF PARADISE

Of the remaining genera of the family, one of the most remarkable is Albert's bird of paradise (*Pteridophora alberti*), characterised by the presence of a long streamer, twice the length of the body, behind each eye. The plumage is black, with olive on the rump, and ochre below ; the head and neck carrying long plumes. Each of the long streamers bears on its outer side between thirty and forty squared enamel-like lobes, light blue above and dusky below. In *Phonygammus jamesi*, of New Guinea and North Australia, the general colour is purplish violet, with the head, elongate neck plumes, under parts, and occipital tufts bluish green. The genus *Manucodia*, of North Australia and the adjacent Papuan Islands, and *Lycocorax*, of the Moluccan and Papuan Islands, are of special interest in connecting the other members of the family with the crows and bower birds. *Manucodia atra* is steel green and black with purple reflections. *Lycocorax pyrrhopterus*, which is greenish black with brown wings, being remarkably crow-like.

SATIN BOWER BIRDS

The group of Australian species collectively known as bower birds may be included in the family of birds of paradise, which they serve in some degree to connect with the starlings. While the so-called regent bird approximates to the birds of paradise in the nature of the feathers on the head, and the gorgeous colouring of its plumage, the true bower birds are more thrush-like in appearance. The group is mainly peculiar to Australia, although one Australian genus extends to the Papuan Islands, and another genus (*Amblyornis*), with a single species, inhabits New Guinea only.

They all have the base of the beak fully feathered, and the foot of the normal passerine type. In the position of the flexure of the lower half of the beak, immediately below the aperture of the nostrils, the skull resembles that of the birds of paradise ; but in a slight backward projection of the hind extremity of the mandible, it approximates to starlings, in which the projection is more developed and the flexure further back.

SATIN BOWER BIRDS

Bower birds take their name from their habit of constructing playing-grounds, or "runs." The species of the genera *Ptilorhynchus* and *Chlamydodera* adorn their bowers chiefly with bones, next to which come shells, stones, berries, and fragments of metal ; but *Priono dura* uses flowers alone, and thus approaches the Papuan gardener bird, while the tooth-billed *Scenopœetes* forms a connecting link, in the matter of habits, between the more typical bower birds and the cat birds. In place of constructing a bower, the tooth-billed species merely clears a space, which it decorates with leaves, usually placed with the under surface uppermost, but cat birds neither build a bower nor clear a space. Special attention may be directed to the bowers of Newton's bower bird (*Priono-dura newtoniana*), some of which are stated to be more than 8 feet in height, and decorated with flowers, generally orchids. At the larger bowers males alone are usually seen during the nesting season, as the females are engaged elsewhere.

The satin bower bird (*Ptilorhynchus viola*) is the type of a genus characterised by the short, convex, and laterally compressed beak, in which the nostrils are basal and concealed by the silky feathers of the forehead ; the wings being pointed, the tail somewhat rounded, and the feet stout and furnished with moderately long claws. These bower birds belong to the eastern and northern districts of Australia.

The localities frequented by the satin bower birds are the luxuriant and thickly foliaged bush country stretching along the coast of New South Wales. Their "runs" are used as playing-houses, and constructed in avenue form of pieces of stick or grass and adorned with stones, bright-coloured shells, and even bleached bones, as well as the blue tail feathers of certain parakeets. This is a stationary species, but roams from one part of the district to another in search of food. It appears to have particular times in the day for feeding, and when thus engaged may be approached within a few feet, although at other times the old males are shy and watchful.

In autumn these bower birds associate in small flocks, and may often be seen on the ground near the sides of the rivers. The plumage of the adult male is deep, shining blue black, closely resembling satin, with the exception of the wings and tail, which are of a deep velvety black. In the female the upper parts are greyish green; the under surface being similar, but lighter and washed with yellow, and having each feather with a crescentic dark brown mark near the extremity. Young males closely resemble the females. There are other species of the genus.

SPOTTED BOWER BIRD

The spotted bower bird (*Chlamydodera maculata*) and its immediate relatives differ from the preceding group in having the nostrils exposed, instead of completely hidden by silky plumes, while from an allied species they are distinguished by the nostrils being oval in shape, and overhung by a membrane behind, as well as by the longer and more slender beak.

In colour the upper parts of the spotted bower birds are deep brown, as are also the wings and tail; each feather of the back and rump, as well as the scapularies, being tipped with a large buff patch, while the under parts are greyish white. The male is ornamented with a broad crest of rose pink, which is wanting in his partner. Much similarity exists between the habits of the satin bower bird and those of the spotted bower bird.

The latter species is, however, extremely shy, and would often escape notice were it not for the harsh, grating note with which it receives the intrusion of a stranger into its haunts. When disturbed, it takes to the topmost branches of the loftiest trees, and frequently flies off to another neighbourhood. In the interior of New South Wales the bowers, or runs, of this bird may be situated either on the plains studded with small trees, or in the bushes clothing the lower hills, and are considerably longer and more avenue-like than those of the satin bower bird, being in many instances 3 feet in length. "They are outwardly," writes Mr. J. Gould, "built of twigs and beautifully lined with tall grasses, so disposed that their heads nearly meet; the decorations are very profuse, and consist of bivalve shells, crania of small mammalia, and other bones bleached by exposure to the rays of the sun or from the camp fires of the natives. Evident

PLAYGROUND OF SPOTTED BOWER BIRD
Photo. C. Grant Lane

indications of high instinct are manifest throughout the whole of the bower and decorations formed by this species, particularly in the manner in which the stones are placed within the bower, apparently to keep the grasses with which it is lined fixed firmly in their places. These stones diverge from the mouth of the run on each side so as to form little paths, while the immense collection of decorative materials is placed in a heap before the entrance of the avenue, the arrangement being the same at both ends.

"In some of the larger bowers, which had evidently been resorted to for many years, I have seen half a bushel of bones, shells, etc., at each of the entrances. I frequently found these structures at a considerable distance from the rivers, from the borders of which they could alone have procured the shells and small, round, pebbly stones; their collection and transportation must therefore be a task of great labour. I fully ascertained that these runs, like those of the satin bower bird, formed the rendezvous of many individuals."

GARDENER BIRD

In the peculiar Papuan gardener bird (*Amblyornis inornatus*) the beak is less elevated than in the other genera, and the nostrils are completely concealed. The bird is remarkable for building a kind of hut-like structure, fronted with what may be termed a garden, which displays a striking appreciation of beauty in its mode of arrangement. The hut, which is always placed at the foot of a large tree, is some two feet in height, and formed of the stems of orchids, radiating and sloping from a central support, and roofed with a mass of moss, while round it runs a gallery. One side of the hut is left open, and in front of this is the garden, decorated with bright-coloured berries and flowers, which are removed as soon as they wither. All "bowers" have nothing to do with nesting, and appear to be erected solely for the amusement of the birds.

OTHER GENERA

Among other genera may be mentioned *Æluredus*, as represented by the Australian cat bird (*Æ. viridis*), which, instead of building a bower, merely clears a space of ground, occasionally as much as 8 feet in diameter.

In colour this species is bright green, washed with blue on the back, and ornamented with white markings on the nape, wings, tail, and under parts, the latter being yellowish. In other species, however, the head is chiefly black or brown, and others, again, have the throat white with black markings. Other members of the family, such as *Parotia lawesi* and the above-named *Scenopœetes dentirostris*, also make open playing-grounds.

STARLINGS, ROSY STARLINGS, GRACKLES, AND DRONGOS

STARLING TRIBE

THE European starling is the typical representative of a group of birds (family *Sturnidæ*) characterised by the presence in the wing of nine primary quills, and of twelve tail feathers; while the beak is generally, though not invariably, slender and curved. The nostrils are clear of the line of the forehead; but the length of the metatarsus is variable. The members of this and the next family are believed to connect the crows and birds of paradise with the troupials.

Members of the family are found throughout the Eastern Hemisphere, with the exception of New Zealand.

In the typical genus *Sturnus* the beak is as long as the head, and blunt at the tip and depressed, with its edges quite smooth; the wings are long and pointed, and the tail is short and squared. The members of the genus principally inhabit the temperate regions of Europe and Asia, as well as Northern Africa.

THE STARLING

Breeding commonly in most parts of temperate Europe, although more rarely in the north than in the central districts of the Continent, the starling (*Sturnus vulgaris*) is one of the most adaptive of birds, in consequence of which its range is steadily increasing, especially in the British Isles, in which its numbers have augmented of late years to an extraordinary extent.

So long as the starling contented itself with nesting locally in the pigeon-houses of farms and in hollow trees, little was to be said against so charming a bird; and there can be no doubt that it merits some degree of protection, since it works assiduously to destroy the larvæ of injurious insects.

At the same time, account should be taken of the heavy loss which fruit-growers sustain from the inroads of hordes of hungry starlings; the extraordinary numbers of these birds which visit orchards of ripe fruit almost defying description. Recently the starling has developed a special fondness for ripe pears and apples, and does not altogether disdain wild fruit, even the berries of the rowan, or mountain ash, being much to its taste. When feeding on grass lands, in company with thrushes, the starling is apt to play the part of a bully, robbing gentler neighbours of their fairly earned subsistence.

STARLING'S NEST

GROUP OF YOUNG STARLINGS

In addition to being a vocalist of no mean order, the starling is a first-class mimic, and delights in reproducing the call-notes of the skylark, goldfinch, wagtail, and other small birds. It does not, however, confine its attention to reproducing the notes of other birds; any sound that strikes its fancy being rehearsed time after time, until the sharpest expert might be deceived.

The starling nests in April, and the young usually fly about the end of May; many pairs rearing two broods of young in a season. Some pairs nest in the recesses of sea-caves in company with rock-doves and black guillemots, others rear their broods in the interior of old stone walls, and others, again, inhabit and enlarge the burrows of sand-martins in some perpendicular cliff, but by far the greater number nest in or near human habitations. In some districts the fledged young gather together in dense flocks as early as July; and with the advance of autumn young and old congregate at their favourite roosts in prodigious numbers, feeding during the day in widely different localities, but flocking together at their accustomed rendezvous before nightfall. Myriads of starlings migrate along the British coasts in spring and autumn, where they frequently make their appearance at one or other of the lighthouses. Many that have bred in Northern Britain winter in the English midland counties, where they frequent half-flooded meadows and other attractive haunts.

The male in summer has the plumage black, brilliantly shot with purple green and steel-blue, the feathers of the nape and upper parts generally being tipped with buff in the form of triangular spots. After the autumnal moult the plumage is profusely spotted with buff, especially on the lower parts, but in the spring many of these spots become obsolete. The plumage of the young is uniform dull brownish grey.

Starlings have been introduced into Australia and New Zealand, where they do an enormous amount of damage to orchards.

SARDINIAN STARLING

In Southern Europe the spotted starling is replaced by the black, or Sardinian, starling (*S. unicolor*), which is abundant in some parts of Spain and in Portugal. It is a very restless bird, often seen flying up and down in small flocks; and although some reside in the Peninsula

and conspicuous crest, reaching to the upper part of the back. One of the most beautiful of European birds, the rose-coloured starling (*Pastor roseus*) has its winter home in India, from which country, however, it is absent during the breeding season. Occasionally wandering so far north as the west of Scotland, this bird is very erratic in its habits, and many years have passed since it has been seen in any considerable numbers in the British Islands. In the summer of 1875 vast numbers visited Villafranca, near Verona; a small flock making its appearance on June 3, and alighting on the high, ruined walls within the castle, and being followed in about half an hour by another flock of about one hundred. Towards evening appeared many thousands of these starlings, which, joining with first-comers, stopped till dusk, when they dispersed in numerous troops over the open country.

On the following day from twelve to fourteen thousand rosy starlings arrived and took possession of the castle; driving away by force of superior numbers the common starlings, pigeons, and all other birds that nested in the ruins, and proceeding to fill every available hole and fissure. About June 17 the birds began to lay their eggs, which are uniform with

THE STARLING

all through the year, the bulk of the black starlings which breed in Spain appear to pass the winter in Algeria, where they feed on the fruit of date palms. This starling nests both under the eaves of outhouses and in crevices of rocks. Its nesting habits are said to be identical with those of the common starling, and the egg is of a similar pale blue colour. The black starling has the entire plumage black, glossed with purple without any spots whatever; the smaller feathers being very long and tapering.

ROSY STARLING

The single representative of the genus *Pastor* differs from the typical starlings in having the head furnished with a long

ROSY STARLING

a greenish tinge. The young were hatched about July 10, and were fed exclusively upon locusts, the old birds foraging in the country in flights of from ten to twenty, or even forty, and returning in the same united fashion to their offspring.

The rosy starling is one of the most sociable and most cheerful of birds. "Always busy and restless," writes Mr. de Betta, "it may be seen running here and there, accompanying every movement with its cries. The song of the male is a continual chatter, mixed with harsh and disagreeable sounds; both one and the other begin in the early morning, continuing for a length of time, and renewed at intervals after feeding. The males, always at strife, may be seen pursuing one another and exchanging blows with their bills while in the most curious attitudes, and with their long black crests elevated and expanded. They exhibit great affection for the hen birds, which, never leaving the nest during the period of incubation, are protected and fed by them with all assiduity."

These birds not infrequently associate with ordinary starlings, and retain their vivacious character even in captivity, in which state they form some of the most charming of aviary birds, darting to and fro on rapid flights or singing from their perches. The male in summer plumage has the head, crest, wings, and tail black, with a blue or violet gloss, and the back and breast are a beautiful rose-colour, suffused with brown in the winter plumage. The young are uniform light greyish brown above, with the wings and tail dark brown edged with buff, and the throat and lower parts dull buff white.

YELLOW-BILLED OX-PECKERS

RED-BILLED OX-PECKERS

INDIAN MYNAS

Among numerous other members of the family, mention must be made of the well-known Indian myna, or maina (*Acridotheres tristis*), the typical representative of an Oriental genus characterised by the long and curling plumes in the region of the nostrils and forehead, the long, pointed feathers of the crown, and the presence of a large patch of bare skin behind and below each eye.

The general colour of the myna is black, with the under parts brownish, and what is known as a vinous tinge on the secondary quills and wing-coverts, the primaries brown for the greater part of their length, and white tips to the black tail feathers, with the exception of the middle pair. In striking contrast to this generally sable livery is the bright yellow of the beak and ear-patches.

This species inhabits the whole of India and some of the neighbouring countries, and is for the most part, like its relatives, a ground bird; it breeds in hollow trees, hedges, and holes in banks, and possesses a variety of notes, some of an agreeable nature and others decidedly the reverse. The Bengal myna (*A. ginginianus*) is distinguished by the axillaries and under wing-coverts being buff instead of white. Nearly allied is the silky starling (*Poliopsar sericeus*), a well-known representative of an Oriental genus with several species. All these birds are insectivorous, and take their generic name from their partiality for locusts.

The pied starling (*Sturnopastor contra*) of India, as well as the African wattled starling (*Dilophus carunculatus*), likewise belong to this group. Mention may also be made of the handsome crested pied starling (*Fregilupus varius*) of the island of Réunion, near Mauritius, exterminated about the middle of the nineteenth century.

OX-PECKERS

The yellow-billed ox-pecker (*Buphaga africana*), which ranges from Senegambia to Damaraland and the Transvaal, is the typical representative of a group of

SUPERB GLOSSY STARLING

African birds characterised by their habit of frequenting the backs of cattle and other large animals for the sake of feeding on the ticks and insects to be found in such situations. From Natal to Abyssinia this species is replaced by the red-billed *B. erythrorhyncha*. Ox-peckers are not very unlike starlings in general appearance, but are distinguished by the beak being stout, broad at the base, and nearly straight, with the nostrils bare.

The wings are long, with the first quill very short, and the second nearly equal in length to the third; the tail is long, broad, and wedge-shaped; and the feet are strong, and furnished with sharp, curved claws, by means of which the birds retain their hold on the slippery skin of buffaloes.

These birds fly in small parties of six or eight, and have a somewhat laboured flight; they may be observed climbing over the oxen in a team, much as a woodpecker climbs a tree; and the cattle for the most part enjoy the operation of being freed from the ticks and other pests with which they are infested. On the first arrival of a flock of these birds, however, the oxen are apt to be alarmed, and start off as if they had been attacked by gadflies. It must not be supposed that these birds confine their attention to cattle, since they perform the same offices for rhinoceroses, elephants, antelopes, and probably almost all the larger African mammals.

Although not loud, the notes of the ox-peckers are harsh and grating; and are always uttered when a flock approaches cattle to feed. In the red-billed species the colour of the upper parts is greyish brown, the wings are black, the tail is brown, the throat is grey, the under parts are pale fulvous, and the beak is red.

GLOSSY STARLINGS AND GRACKLES

Unlike true starlings and their allies, which have no trace of bristles at the rictus of the gape, and lay uniformly coloured eggs, the members of the present African and Asiatic family (*Eulabetidæ*) possess such bristles, and lay spotted eggs. They are, moreover, mainly or entirely arboreal, instead of hunting for a large portion of their food on the ground.

The most beautiful of all the starling-like birds are undoubtedly the African glossy starlings, which are neatly built birds, with the beak strong, of moderate length, compressed, swollen at the base, and notched, and the nostrils situated about the middle. The wings are large, the feet are long and strong, the tail is of variable length, and the plumage is remarkable for its brilliant gloss, being generally adorned with shades of bluish green, violet, purple, or copper.

Such species of the African glossy starlings as have long, graduated tails are included in the genus *Lamprotornis*, while those in which the tail is short and squared are classed as *Lamprocolius*.

The glossy starlings are gregarious birds, ranging all over Africa, and feeding on vegetable as well as animal substances. Uttering harsh, clamorous notes, they are rapid in their flight and lively in their movements; and though generally dwelling high up in the branches of the forest trees, descend at times to pick up insects and other food on the ground. From the retiring habits of most of the species, they are seldom seen; and they either build in holes of trees, or make large cup-shaped nests, in which are laid five or six spotted eggs.

LONG-TAILED GLOSSY STARLING

The typical long-tailed species (*Lamprotornis æneus*) is a denizen of the west of Africa, although also ranging into the southern, eastern, and central districts of that continent. Measuring about 20 inches in total length, of which two-thirds are occupied by the long, graduated tail, this bird has the head, chin, and upper part of the throat black, with a golden lustre, the upper parts

INDIAN GRACKLE

and wings dark metallic green, the upper wing-coverts ornamented with small black spots, the middle of the throat, as well as the upper tail-coverts, tail, and under parts, dark purple violet, marked with darker cross bands, and the middle of the breast is copper-red. The upper wing-coverts have black spots. The iris of the eye is yellow, and the beak and feet are black. Feeding largely upon insects, these birds are more terrestrial in their habits than many others of the group.

SHORT-TAILED GLOSSY STARLINGS

The green glossy starling (*Lamprocolius chalybeus*), an inhabitant of North-Eastern Africa, is a good example of the second genus of the group. With the exception of a spot in the region of the ear and the under wing-coverts, the whole plumage is steely bluish green, but each of the secondaries and the feathers of the upper wing-coverts is marked at the end with a round blackish spot. Such is the wonderful shimmer of the plumage, which is similar in both sexes, that it shows totally different tints according to the light in which it is viewed, so that it can scarcely be described in words. The reader should refer to the coloured plate on page 988, on which is a representation of this species, together with the long-tailed species and the one mentioned below, namely, the superb glossy starling. In the young of the short-tailed species only the upper parts are metallic green, the under parts being dark brownish grey, devoid of lustre.

Although typically an inhabitant of Abyssinia, this beautiful bird ranges into Senegambia, and frequents alike thickly wooded river valleys and high mountains, ascending in Abyssinia to an elevation of some ten thousand feet. While generally going about in pairs, in the breeding season these starlings congregate in small flocks, and both in flight and habit resemble the European starling.

The superb glossy starling (*L. superbus*) is a native of East Africa, and easily recognised by the white band across the chest, the mantle being steel-green, and the upper part of the head and neck black.

WHITE-BELLIED STARLING

Here also may be mentioned the pretty little white-bellied starling (*L. leucogaster*), which differs considerably in colouring from the foregoing species. The

SOUTHERN GRACKLE

upper parts and the throat as far as the breast are purplish blue, and with a wonderful violet shimmer in certain lights, but the remainder of the under parts is white, and the wings blackish brown, with a violet tinge; the whole of the darker portion of the plumage being shot with a coppery lustre.

The white-bellied starling is distributed over Central Africa, and extends northwards into Abyssinia and Western Arabia. A truly arboreal species, it is found both on the plains and in the mountains, associating in parties of from six to twenty individuals; its habits being very similar to those of the other members of the group.

INDIAN GRACKLES

Strikingly handsome birds are the grackles, or hill mynas, of the Malay countries and India, easily distinguished by their black plumage and the presence of fleshy wattles, frequently accompanied by patches of bare skin, on the sides of the head. The beak is thick, high, curved, and shorter than the head, the feathers of the crown are short and inwardly curved, with a kind of parting down the middle of the head, the wings rather blunt, the tail short and nearly squared, and the feet strong.

In the Indian grackle (*Eulabetes intermedia*) the whole plumage is glossy black, with the exception of a patch of white at the base of most of the primaries; the wattles are naked, being rich yellow, the beak orange yellow, and the legs and feet citron yellow. The total length of the adult is about ten inches. Young birds have a dull black plumage, and are devoid of wattles.

From the nearly allied Malay grackle (*E. javanensis*) this species is distinguished by the fact that the patch of bare skin below the eye is united with the one behind the eye; while both differ from the South Indian grackle (*E. religiosa*) by the absence of a pair of these bare patches on the nape of the neck. The last-named species is common to

BLACK INDIAN DRONGO

I A

Southern Indian and Ceylon, but Ceylon has also a species of its own (*E. ptilogenys*), characterised by the absence of bare patches on the sides of the head.

The Indian grackles, which are either resident in one spot throughout the year or only locally migratory, are chiefly confined to the large forests of India and Ceylon ; the southern species breeding from March to October, and generally laying only a pair of eggs, deposited in holes in trees. Its food consists entirely of various fruits, obtained among the higher branches of forest trees. All the different species of grackles learn to whistle and talk when in captivity, and as they are excellent mimics are much prized by the natives of India as cage-birds.

ASIATIC GLOSSY STARLINGS

The Asiatic glossy starlings of the genus *Calornis* differ from grackles in having no wattles ; their plumage is highly glossy ; the beak is short, with the culmen curved ; the nostrils are small and round ; the wing is long and sharp ; and the tail of moderate length, and graduated. It is difficult to decide how nearly related these birds are to the African glossy starlings, although there appear to be important differences between some members of the two groups.

The range of the genus extends from South-Eastern Asia to Australia ; the Indian glossy starling (*Calornis calybeïus*) being the only representative in the country from which it takes its name. The whole plumage is black, with a brilliant green gloss on the greater portion.

DRONGOS

The drongos, or king crows, of South-Eastern Asia, Australasia, and Africa, form an easily recognised family (*Dicruridæ*), which may be provisionally placed here, although some naturalists consider that its affinities are rather with the creepers, while others class it with the shrikes. Their black plumage and deeply forked tail of ten feathers serve at once to distinguish drongos from all other members of the order. The edges of both mandibles are smooth, with a single notch in the upper one ; the wing has ten primary quills ; and the nostrils are clear of the line of the forehead.

Both sexes are alike ; and the young differ from their parents only by their plumage being paler. Several of the species have the head crested, and there are always bristles at the base of the beak. Entirely insectivorous, the drongos are habitually upon the wing, darting from a tree to catch an insect and returning speedily to the same or another perch ; and they are also fairly endowed with vocal powers.

Since these birds are so much alike in general characters, there is considerable difficulty in defining the genera and species. In addition to the typical genus *Dicrurus*, as

represented by the Indian black drongo, or king crow (*D. ater*), ranging from Afghanistan to China, and several other species, no fewer than six genera of the family are recognised as natives of India. Two species, which may be included in the type genus, are found in South Africa, while Australia has but a single representative, *Chibia bracteata*.

INDIAN BLACK DRONGO

The black drongo, which has the entire plumage deep black, with a steel-blue gloss, but the under tail-coverts generally tipped with white, is one of the most familiar of Indian birds, both in the hills and the plains, selecting the most exposed and most barren

LESSER RACKET-TAILED DRONGO

tree or a post for its perching-place. The nest, which is usually placed in a thickly leafed bough, is composed of fine twigs and grass, covered externally with cobwebs. Usually four, although occasionally five in number, the eggs may be either uniformly pure white, or salmon - colour with brownish spots. Not infrequently this bird may be observed perched on the back of cattle searching for insects.

In the genus *Chibia* the outermost pair of tail feathers are somewhat elongated and turned up at the tips ; in *Dissemuroides* they are still more elongated and distinctly turned up at the tips ; while in *Dicranostreptus* the elongation is much greater, and the feathers are so twisted as to face one another.

A further modification is displayed by the racket-tailed drongos (*Bhringa*) and paradise drongos (*Dissemurus*), in both of which these feathers have long, bare shafts, with racket-like terminal expansions, as is shown in the Indian lesser racket-tailed drongo (*Bhringa remifer*). The paradise drongos have an exceedingly elegant flight, and a not unpleasing note. One member of the group, *Buchanga leucogenys*, is reported to reach Japan ; Madagascar has *Edolius forficatus*, and the range of the family extends to the New Ireland group of islands in the South Pacific.

ORIOLES

THE orioles (family *Oriolidæ*) comprise a number of brightly coloured birds, from the temperate and tropical portions of the Old World, in which the bill is as long as the head, and gently curved to the tip, where it is notched. The head is never crested; the wings are long, with the first three quills equally graduated, and the third and fourth longest; the tail is moderate and rounded; and the toes are free at the base, and have long, curved claws. The nostrils are bare, and well in front of the base of the beak; this character, along with the presence of twelve tail feathers, at once distinguishing them from the drongos. Brilliant yellow generally adorns the plumage of the male orioles, but in other cases the lower parts are variegated with rich crimson.

Orioles are fruit-eating birds, and frequent forest trees in preference to smaller covert. They are divided into two genera, of which *Oriolus* has the lores feathered, while in *Sphecotheres* they are naked. These birds inhabit the temperate parts of Europe, the whole of Africa, India, China, the Indo-Malay countries, and Australia.

MALE GOLDEN ORIOLE

GOLDEN ORIOLE

The golden oriole (*O. galbula*) visits Northern Europe in spring, at which time these birds may be observed migrating in small numbers, when both sexes journey in company. At this season they are silent and anxious to escape notice, although, as they arrive before the beech trees which clothe the mountain sides in the north of Spain have unfolded their leaves, they have some difficulty in concealing their brilliant plumage among the bare twigs. The oriole on the Continent reaches its nesting haunts about the end of April, and at once claims its own peculiar area of forest. Each pair confines itself to a certain portion of a wood, the intrusion of a strange male into the haunts of a pair of breeding birds being sure to result in a fight.

Although the golden oriole is shy and retiring in Europe, its cousin, the mango bird (*O. kundu*), is by no means so in India, where it often perches on a tree immediately over the tent of the traveller, and pours out its flute-like notes. In addition to these tones, both sexes have a cat-like call. The nest is usually placed on a bough, and the young are attended with remarkable care by the parents. Although feeding mainly upon insects, which are often captured on the ground, the golden oriole during the fruit season takes toll of the orchard.

The range of this oriole includes the whole of Europe, except the extreme north, as well as Persia and other parts of South-Western Asia; and in winter this species visits South Africa. The bright colour of the male golden oriole renders it peculiarly liable to be attacked by the sparrowhawk; and, in such a contingency, the oriole does not trust to its thrush-like flight to enable it to elude its tormentor in the open, but on the earliest opportunity seeks refuge in the densest thickets. The oriole forms a good cage-bird, although old birds are not easily reconciled to the loss of their freedom, and are apt to pine away. Young birds, on the other hand, are easily tamed.

The adult male of this species is rich golden yellow above; the wings are black, with the primary coverts broadly edged with yellow, which forms a conspicuous spot; the tail is black, tipped with yellow, the outer feathers having more yellow than black; and the entire under surface is golden yellow. The female differs from the male in having the back and scapulars tinged with green.

In both sexes the eyes are black. The mango bird is distinguished by the presence of a black streak behind each eye. Other species have the head or nape black.

GREEN ORIOLE

Among the numerous other species of the genus, mention may be made of the green oriole (*O. viridis*) of New South Wales, which frequents orchards and gardens, where it fills the summer air with its melodious notes. This oriole may often be seen perched on some shady tree, with its head thrown back, showing to perfection its mottled breast, singing in a low tone, and imitating the notes of many birds, such as the black magpie.

While feeding, it frequently utters a harsh guttural sort of squeak but during the breeding season, which begins at the end of September and ends in January, it confines itself to a monotonous although melodious cry, the first part of which is quickly repeated, and ends in a lower note.

This oriole builds a cup-shaped nest, principally composed of shreds of the bark of a species of gum tree, strongly woven together and lined with leaves or grass and hair; this generally being suspended between a fork at the extreme end of some horizontal bough, often in an exposed situation. The eggs vary in ground colour from cream to dull white or very light brown, minutely dotted and blotched with umber and blackish brown. Green orioles feed principally on berries and wild fruits, particularly figs, although they sometimes capture insects on the wing. In the adult male the beak is dull yellowish olive above; the wings and tail are brown washed with grey; part of the throat is dull olive; the fore neck greyish; and the breast and sides of the body are white, washed with olive yellow, each feather having a dark central streak. The sexes when adult are almost identical in colour, but the male has the olive of the upper parts of a deeper tint than the female.

GREEN ORIOLE

TROUPIALS

To a certain extent intermediate in structure between crows and finches, and agreeing with starlings in the general structure of the skull, and especially the backward prolongation of the hind extremity of the lower half of the beak, the large assemblage of American birds collectively known as troupials (family *Icteridæ*) may be regarded as the New World representatives of the starlings of the Old World, although, so far as habits are concerned, there is not any very marked signs of affinity between the two families. Distinguished by the length and slenderness of the beak, which in most cases equals the head in length, these birds generally possess pointed wings, which have never more than nine primaries; they have strong feet, and chiefly black plumage. Among the numerous genera only a few need be selected for notice.

Troupials congregate in flocks, after the manner of starlings, and many of them build the long, pendent, bottle-like nests from which the name of one group is derived. The family may be divided into three groups, the first comprising the rice-birds and cow-birds, the second the hangnests, and the third the troupials.

CASSIQUES

As a well-known representative of the first sub-family (*Cassiqinæ*), mention may be made of the South American crested cassique (*Ostinops decumanus*), near akin to which is the yellow cassique (*Cassicus persicus*), also a South American species. The sub-family to which these genera belong is characterised by the naked, exposed nostrils and the presence of a shield on the forehead at the base of the beak.

The crested cassique is characterised by the small crest from which it takes its name; and while the general colour of the upper parts is deep black, with the feathers of the mantle and shoulders shaded with brown and the upper and lower tail coverts chestnut, the five outermost pairs of tail feathers are brilliant citron yellow. This bird constructs a nest of a curiously elongated shape.

BALTIMORE ORIOLE

The typical member of the whole family is the so-called Baltimore oriole (*Icterus galbula*), which represents the true hangnests, ranging from North and Central America to Southern Brazil and Bolivia. Together with an allied genus, containing one species, this bird and its allies form a second sub-family (*Icterinæ*), in which the nostrils are partially covered by a membrane, while the culmen of the beak is more or less incurved, and there is no shield on the forehead; the metatarsus being short, the feet adapted for perching, and the tail rounded. As a rule, the plumage is bright orange and yellow, relieved with black and white; the sexes being in some cases alike, and in others very dissimilar.

Unlike the members of the preceding sub-family, these hangnests are thoroughly arboreal in their habits, and while the majority construct pendent nests like those of the cassiques, others appear to build open cup-shaped nests. The eggs are bluish or pinkish white, spotted with purple and red.

Baltimore orioles, which are natives of the United States, build in large companies, the males generally arriving first at the breeding places, where they are soon joined by their partners. The nest is wider and less elongated than that of the crested cassique. On a single tree sometimes so many as forty nests may be observed; and during November they will be found to contain both eggs and young birds. All the numerous species of the genus *Icterus* are good songsters, the notes of the Baltimore oriole being especially melodious.

Miss M. O. Wright observes that the nest "is not only from twenty feet above the ground upward, but is suspended from a forked branch that is at once tough yet so slender that no marauding cat would dare venture to it. This pensile nest is diligently woven of grasses, twine, vegetable fibre, horsehair, bits of worsted, or anything manageable, and varies much in size and shape, as if the matter of individual taste entered somewhat into this matter. It is fairly well proven that situation enters largely into this matter, and that nests in wild regions, where birds of prey, etc., abound, are smaller at the top and have a more decided neck than those in the trees of home lawns and orchards. Of the many nests that I

CRESTED CASSIQUES AND THEIR NESTS

have found and handled or else observed closely with a glass, the majority have been quite open at the top, and the only one with a narrow and funnel-like opening came from a wayside elm on the edge of a dense wood.

"The female seems to be weaver-in-chief, using both claw and bill, though I have seen the male carry material to her. It is asserted that orioles will weave gaily-coloured worsteds into their nests. This I very much doubt, or, if they do, I believe it is for lack of something more suitable. I have repeatedly fastened vari-coloured bunches of soft linen twine, carpet thread, flosses, and the like, under the bark of trees frequented by orioles, and, with one exception, it has been the more sombre tints that were selected."

BOBOLINK

Another well-known bird in the United States is the bobolink (*Dolichonyx oryzivorus*), or rice-bird, which belongs to another sub-family (*Agelæinæ*) differing from the last by the straight culmen of the beak and the elongated metatarsus; the genus *Dolichonyx* being specially characterised by the short, conical beak, the long, pointed wings, the rigid, acuminate feathers of the tail, and the stout and long-clawed feet. An inhabitant of North America, where it is especially common in the States, this well-known bird winters in Central America and the West Indies, returning northwards in vast flocks along the Atlantic coast in spring, when the males are in nearly full breeding plumage, and are thus very conspicuous as they flock to the meadows and orchards

"Their number," writes Dr. Elliott Coues, "seems out of all proportion to that of the females, but this is probably due to the silent and more retiring ways of the latter sex. They really pass through, in the vernal migration, quite rapidly, though they do not appear to be at all in a hurry, as we see them by day. They throw themselves in a field, scatter on the ground feeding, and at the slightest alarm, or in mere wantonness, suddenly fly *en masse* to the nearest tree, fence, or bush, and begin to sing, producing an indescribable medley, hushed in an instant, only to be resumed.

Sometimes the bobolinks sing as merrily, though with less concerted action, while they are rambling in the grass. Their daytime leisure for song and food is easily explained; for they migrate at this season almost entirely by night. Every night in early May, as we walk the streets, we can hear the mellow, metallic clinking coming down through the darkness, from birds passing high overhead, and sounding clearer in the stillness. By the middle of May they have all passed; a few, it is stated, linger to breed south of New England, but the main body passes on, spreading over that portion of the Union and the neighbouring British provinces, occupying in pairs almost every meadow. The change of plumage is completed before the return movement is made."

Millions return on their southern journey late in the summer and during September. They are now songless, but have a comfortable, self-satisfied "chink," befitting such fat and abandoned gourmands as they

RED-WINGED BLACKBIRD

are, thronging in countless hordes the wild rice tracts and the grain fields. So they go until the first cold snap, that sends them into winter quarters at once. The bobolink nests upon the ground, making a rude and flimsy structure of dried grass, which is artfully concealed. The hen lays four or five eggs, bluish white in ground colour, blotched and spotted with dark chocolate.

The male in the breeding season has the head and lower parts black, the hind neck buff, the scapulars,

THE COW-BIRD

rump, and upper tail coverts ashy white, the interscapulars streaked with black, buff, and ashy, and the outer quills edged with a yellowish tint. The nuptial garb just described is, however, unlike the plain plumage worn by both sexes after the breeding season, when the colour is yellowish brown above and brownish yellow below, the crown and back being conspicuously streaked with black, and the wings and tail blackish.

COW-BIRDS

Nearly allied to the last are the cow-birds, characterised by the short, conical beak, long and pointed wings, slightly rounded tail, and strong feet. In the majority of the species black is the prevailing colour, being sometimes lustrous, with bronzed reflections. The cowbirds are mainly a South American genus, although the typical species (*Molothrus pecoris*) is only too well known in the United States. Some of the species seize upon the nests of other birds, and having driven away the rightful possessors, proceed to rear their own young in their new home. The majority, however, are more truly parasitical, depositing their eggs in other birds' nests, and leaving the strangers to hatch and rear their offspring.

The common cow-bird of the United States is a polygamous species, the sexes never mating, and their association being merely a herding together in quest for food. "In the west," writes Dr. Coues, "every waggon-train passing over the prairies in summer is attended by flocks of these birds; every compound or stock corral, permanent or temporary, is besieged by the busy birds, eager to glean subsistence from the wasted forage. Their familiarity in these circumstances is surprising. Perpetually wandering about the feet of the draught animals, or perching upon their backs, they become so accustomed to man's presence that they will hardly get out of the way. I have even known a young bird suffer itself to be taken in the hand, and it is no uncommon thing to have the birds fluttering within a few feet of one's head. The animals appear rather to like the birds, and allow them to perch in a row upon their backbones, doubtless finding the scratching of their feet a comfortable sensation, to say nothing of the riddance from insect parasites."

The cow-bird's foster-parents are numerous, notably the summer yellow-bird, the Maryland yellow-throat,

PURPLE TROUPIAL

and the red-eyed vireo. It is rare to find more than two eggs of this cow-bird in a single nest, although as many as five have been found together. In colour the eggs are white, speckled with brown. The adult of the common cow-bird is lustrous greenish black, with blue and purple reflections ; the head and neck being deep wood brown, with some purplish lustre. The female is dull coloured, of a nearly uniform greyish brown above, and paler beneath.

Writing of a South African member of the genus, Mr. W. H. Hudson observes that the male of the "screaming cow-bird of La Plata, when perched, emits a hollow sounding note that swells at the end into a sharp metallic ring, almost bell-like ; this is uttered with wings and tail depressed, the whole plumage being puffed out as in a strutting turkey-cock, while the bird hops briskly up and down on its perch as if dancing. The bell-like note of the male is followed by an impetuous scream from the female, and the dance ends.

"Another species, the common Argentine cow-bird (*M. bonariensis*) of La Plata, when courting, puffs out his rich violet plumage, and, with wings vibrating, emits a succession of deep internal notes, followed by a set song in clear, ringing tones ; and then, suddenly taking wing, he flies straight away, close to the surface, fluttering like a moth, and at a distance of twenty to thirty yards turns and flies in a wide circle round the female, singing loudly all the time, hedging her in with melody as it were."

RED-WINGED BLACKBIRD

Another genus is typified by the unmistakable species commonly known in the United States as the red-winged blackbird (*Agelæus phœnicurus*), although often termed by naturalists the red-shouldered starling. In this bird and its immediate relatives the beak is about as long as the head, stout at the base, and tapering rapidly to an acute point ; while the wings are pointed and the tail is broad. Black, associated with red or

yellow, is the predominating colour of the males, but the females are more soberly attired. Several species are found in Central and Southern America, while others are peculiar to the United States.

The red-winged blackbird is commonly distributed throughout temperate North America, and is especially abundant among the marshy tracts of the Eastern States. It nests in reeds and bushes near the ground or in a tussock of grass, building a bulky nest of coarse, fibrous materials, such as strips of rushes or marsh grass. The eggs are pale blue, dotted and blotched with dark markings.

In autumn this bird becomes highly gregarious, thronging in the grain fields, where it does much mischief. The male is lustrous black, with the lesser wing coverts scarlet, broadly bordered with brownish yellow, but the female is blackish brown above with pale streaks, and below whitish with many dusky streaks. Young males at first resemble females, but are larger, and generally suffused with buff.

Miss Wright states that "as a nest-builder, the redwing (as it is often called) shows much of the weaver's skill of its oriole cousins, though the material they work with is of coarser texture, being fastened firmly to low bushes or reeds and woven of grass and the split leaves of reeds and flags, all nicely lined with soft grasses or various vegetable fibres. Often the nest is suspended between three or four reeds, and so firmly knit that it resembles one of the four-legged work-baskets that belonged to the 'mother's room' of our youth. The pale blue eggs of the redwing are particularly noticeable from the character of the markings that thickly cover the larger end, for they seem the work of a sharp scratching pen dipped in purplish black ink and held by an aimless human hand, rather than the distribution of natural pigment."

PURPLE TROUPIAL

Omitting mention of several genera, the next species for notice is the purple troupial (*Quiscalus versicolor*), representing a genus of the third sub-family, whose members enjoy a variety of names, such as crow-blackbirds, grackles, and boat-tails. As the first two of these are liable to lead to confusion, it is better to adopt the French name of troupials, which is also taken as the designation of the family to which they belong. In these birds the beak is equal in length to the head, and somewhat crow-like in shape ; the wings are relatively short, the tail is of varying length, and the feet are long.

The purple troupial is a native of the Atlantic States, the other species being more southern in their distribution. It is a migratory, gregarious bird of very general distribution, building in a tree or bush, and making a large nest, usually of mud. The eggs are green or blue in ground colour, variegated with dark brown and purple markings.

These birds at times inflict great injury upon the crops, much to the annoyance of the agriculturist, but also consume large quantities of injurious insects. They have a propensity for destroying the eggs of other birds, especially those of the American robin or migratory thrush, lurking about the robin's vicinity until the parents are away, and then pouncing on the nest, seizing an egg or young one, and hastily retreating.

The adult male is black above and below, variously glossed with green, purple, blue, violet, and bronze ; the female is similar, but her tints are more subdued. It should be added that some writers divide the family into five groups, one of which is typified by the so-called meadow lark (*Sturnella magna*) of the United States.

WEAVERS, TANAGERS, HONEY CREEPERS, WOOD WARBLERS

WEAVER BIRDS

THE weaver birds (family *Ploceidæ*), which derive their name from the extraordinary textile nests they construct, comprise a large group very abundant in Africa, and represented by many genera in South-Eastern Asia and Australia. While very similar to the finches in external appearance, they differ in having ten primary quills in the wings, and also in the fact that some of them undergo a partial moult in spring. Resembling troupials to a certain extent in the structure of their nests, they differ both from those birds and the starlings in having no backward prolongation of the hind extremity of the lower half of the beak. The beak itself is strong and conical, with the culmen projecting on to the forehead and arched at the tip, and the nostrils pierced within the line of the forehead or close to it, while the space between the nostril and the edge of the beak is greater than that between the former and the culmen; there is never any distinct notch in the margin of the beak. The wings are somewhat rounded, with the first primary quill very short, and the legs and toes are stout and strongly scaled.

The family may be divided into two sub-families—namely, the typical weaver birds, or *Ploceinæ*, in which the first primary of the wing is nearly as long as the metatarsus, and there is a spring moult; and the whydah birds and their allies, or *Viduinæ*, in which the first primary is much shorter than the metatarsus, and the only moult is autumnal.

OX-BIRD

The ox-bird (*Textor albirostris*) of Western Africa is a well-known member of a small African genus belonging to the first sub-family, and characterised by the rather long, conical, and laterally compressed beak, the somewhat rounded wings reaching a little below the base of the tail, and having the second primary quill only a little shorter than the third and fourth, which are the longest, the tail of moderate length and somewhat rounded, and the claws strong and curved. The ox-bird itself may be recognised by its nearly uniform shining black plumage, with the bases of the contour feathers white, yellow beak, with its tips and edges bluish, and blackish grey feet.

RED-BILLED BLACK WEAVER

An allied species known as the red-billed black weaver (*T. niger*) inhabits the Transvaal, Damaraland, and the lake regions, and is readily distinguished by the feature from which it takes its name. It is a large finch-like and very noisy bird, gregarious in its habits, and breeding in colonies, the members of which construct many nests in a single tree. The nests consist externally of an immense mass of dried grass, twigs, and sticks, in which are to be found from four to six separate nests or holes of an oval form, composed of grass only, but united to each other by intricate masses of sticks defying the ingress of any intruder except a small snake. In each of these separate holes are laid three or four eggs like sparrows' eggs, but much larger.

Curiously enough, the birds roost in nests which are used year after year, any injury to the structure being at once repaired by all the members of the community. These birds frequent herds of buffaloes, perching on the backs of the animals in search of the parasitical insects which infest the hides; but, like other members of the family, they also feed on berries and seeds, as well as on insects. The general colour of the adult male is black, with the first half of each wing feather white; but young birds have some whitish patches on the neck and breast.

WHITE-BEAKED WEAVER

The white-beaked weaver (*Dinemellia leucocephala*), which represents another genus, is a comparatively small species inhabiting Central Africa and Abyssinia. Like other members of the family, it is absent from dense forests, preferring to dwell upon grass lands in the more open portions of the country. It is by choice somewhat gregarious, taking up its abode on rough meadow lands, and seeking out the neighbourhood of cattle. Although a true weaver, it does not construct so neat a nest as most of its allies. The adult male has the head and under parts white, the back, wings, and tail chocolate brown, and the rump and tail-coverts scarlet.

TRUE WEAVER BIRDS

Nearly allied to the last are the true weaver birds, forming the typical representatives of a comparatively

NESTS OF WEAVER BIRDS IN GERMAN EAST AFRICA

small group common to East and West Africa and the Indo-Malay region, exclusive of the Philippine Islands. Unlike all the preceding genera, in which it is flattened at the base and sometimes crested, the present and allied genera have the culmen of the beak rounded at the base ; the true weaver birds being specially dis-

WHITE-HEADED WEAVER AND OX-BIRD

tinguished by the rounded and exposed nostrils, and the claw of the first toe very strong and highly curved. The genus *Ploceus* is confined to India and the Malay countries, where it is typically represented by the common weaver bird, or baya (*P. baya*) of India and Ceylon, which, like its relatives, constructs long flask-shaped nests, with a tubular entrance, and lays pure white eggs.

MASKED WEAVER BIRD

The masked weaver bird (*Hyphantornis larvatus*) of Abyssinia may be taken as a representative of an exclusively African genus, with over thirty species, distinguished from the last by the exposed oval nostrils being partly reached by the plumes at the base, and also shut in by a horny membrane. The masked species may be recognised by the scarlet iris of the eye, the black beak, and greyish black legs. It is reported to lay pale bluish green eggs, with a few violet brown spots at the larger end.

ABYSSINIAN AND OLIVE WEAVER BIRDS

An allied species from the same district is the Abyssinia weaver bird (*H. galbula*), in which the iris is orange brown, the beak black—except in the breeding plumage of the male, when it becomes horn-coloured—and the legs flesh-coloured. A third kind is the olive weaver bird (*H. capensis*) of South Africa, which generally lives in flocks, and is more numerous in the Transvaal than in Natal. These birds are fond of sucking the honey from the scarlet flowers of the Cape broom. The nest is constructed of coarse grasses, and formed somewhat in the shape of a chemist's retort, with the neck cut short and the aperture downwards, while across the entrance is a kind of bar to prevent the eggs from falling out. This nest is lined with the soft flowering heads of grass, which furnish a warm bed for the young ; and the eggs are of a beautiful, spotless green colour.

These weavers become very tame in confinement, and, if supplied with cotton or thread, will weave it most

industriously into the bars of the cage, forming a dense mass impossible to unravel. This work they perform entirely with their beaks, clinging the while to the sides of the cage with their powerful claws. They have a loud churring cry. The adult has the crown of the head and the sides of the neck gamboge yellow ; the nape, back, and rump lemon yellow ; the back of the neck and shoulders greenish yellow ; the wing feathers dark purplish brown edged with yellow ; the tail olive brown tinted with yellow ; and the throat and lower parts saffron yellow.

PARADISE WHYDAH BIRDS

The exclusively African group of long-tailed and strikingly coloured birds collectively known as paradise whydahs represents the second sub-family, the distinctive characters of which have been already indicated. The paradise whydah birds, of which there are several species, may be taken to include all those in which the two middle pairs of tail feathers of the males are greatly elongated, although they are frequently subdivided into distinct genera, according as some or all of these feathers are attenuated and wire-like.

The long-tailed whydah bird (*Vidua paradisea*) is an inhabitant of South Africa, where it frequents swampy ground and the long reeds about ponds. Its flight is feeble ; and in the breeding season especially, when the male has assumed its nuptial livery and long tail feathers, the flight is so laboured that the native children constantly run these birds down. They are unable to fly against the wind, and in rainy weather can hardly be got to move out of the thick bushes in which they conceal themselves. The Kafir children stretch bird-limed lines across the fields of millet and Kafir corn, and take great numbers of the males owing to their tails becoming entangled in the lines.

These birds build their nests in long grass close to the ground, generally placing them in tussocks of herbage, to the blades and stalks of which they are roughly

ABYSSINIAN AND MASKED WEAVER BIRDS

joined. The nest itself is rather a rough structure, composed of fine grass lined with the seed-ends ; the opening is at the side. The average number of females is stated to be fifteen to one male. The long tail worn by the male in the breeding season does not appear to be an inconvenience, the birds never seeming to enjoy themselves so much as during a high wind, in which they show off to advantage, spreading their tails out like a fan. The male in nuptial plumage is of a general glossy black; the long feathers of the shoulders are fulvous and brilliant crimson, and the tail is enormously developed. The female plumage is pale yellowish brown, but the wing feathers are black with pale yellowish brown edges.

BISHOP BIRDS

Nearly the whole of the remaining genera of the sub-family have the tail shorter than the wing; and among them are the gorgeously coloured bishop birds of Africa, in which the tail is squared, with the two middle feathers not markedly produced beyond the rest, and the feathering of the body soft and velvety. There is a distinct winter and summer plumage, in the latter of which a frill is developed round the neck.

Among the handsomest of the group is the red bishop bird, or red Kafir finch (*Pyromelana oryx*), of Cape Colony, Natal, and the Transvaal, a bird of social habits, gathering in immense flocks both in winter and summer; the flocks during the latter season apparently consisting almost entirely of males in their gaudy red and black plumage. The red bishop bird breeds in September, constructing its nest of fine grass and suspending it among reeds by the rivers. The eggs are pure light blue. In winter the flocks of bishop birds do much damage to the grain fields. The species is imported into Europe as a cage-bird. The adult male in nuptial plumage has the upper parts, throat, and vent brilliant scarlet, the wings and tail brown, and the forehead, cheeks, and chin black. After the breeding season is over the male assumes the brown plumage of the female.

Another common bird throughout Cape Colony is the black and yellow bishop bird (*P. capensis*), affecting alike the loneliest swamps and the homesteads of farmers. It breeds in the neighbourhood of water, constructing its nest of strong grasses and suspending it between the stalks of two or three reeds. The eggs are very pale green, thickly marked with dark greenish brown blotches and spots. This bishop bird generally lives in small companies in the open fields, and feeds chiefly upon grass seeds. The adult male has the head and upper parts rich velvety black, the rump and shoulders brilliant yellow, and the wings brown.

SOCIABLE WEAVER BIRD

The sociable weaver bird (*Philetærus socius*) typifies another exclusively African group, the members of

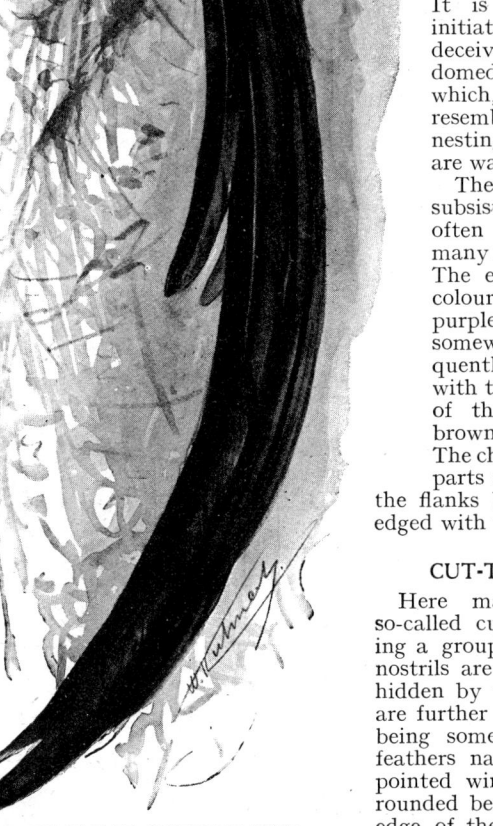

LONG-TAILED WHYDAH BIRD

which differ from bishop birds in having the plumage similar throughout the year, and no frill round the neck, while they are distinguished from several allied forms by the nostrils being clearly exposed and placed well in front of the plumes at the base of the beak, and also by the small size of the bastard primary. Among the representatives of the genus the best known is the common species of the interior of South Africa. This bird congregates in flocks, many pairs incubating their eggs under the same roof, which is composed of whole cartloads of grass piled on a branch of a camel-thorn tree in one enormous mass of an irregular umbrella shape, looking like a miniature haystack and almost solid, but with the under surface, which is nearly flat, honeycombed with little cavities. These serve not only as places for incubation, but also as a refuge against rain and wind.

The nests probably last for a great number of years, and are constantly being repaired by their active little inhabitants. It is curious that even the initiated eye is constantly being deceived by these peculiar domed-topped structures, which, at a distance, closely resemble native huts. The nesting chambers themselves are warmly lined with feathers.

The sociable weaver bird subsists chiefly upon seeds, and often feeds in company with many members of its own kind. The eggs are drab in ground colour, closely speckled with purple grey. The males are somewhat pugnacious, frequently indulging in fights with their rivals. The plumage of the adult males is drab brown above, edged with grey. The chin is black, and the under parts are pale isabelline brown, the flanks being varied with black, edged with whitish.

CUT-THROAT FINCHES

Here may be mentioned the so-called cut-throat finches, including a group of genera in which the nostrils are more or less completely hidden by the nasal plumes. They are further distinguished by the tail being somewhat elongated and its feathers narrow, as well as by the pointed wing and the swollen and rounded beak, in which the cutting edge of the upper half is festooned near the base. The genus *Amadina* includes several Australian and African species, one of the latter (*A. fasciata*) having the throat marked by a crimson band extending to the ear-coverts. This species ranges from Western into Central Africa, and is represented in South Africa by the red-headed finch (*A. erythrocephala*), in which the colour of the whole of the head and throat is red.

JAVA SPARROW

The Java sparrow (*Munia oryzivora*) and its relatives, often collectively termed munias, are distinguished from their allies by having—besides other points—the middle tail feathers produced and pointed, while the whole tail is wedge-shaped. The beak, which is most strongly developed in the Java sparrow, is strong, swollen, and rounded, the wings are moderately long, and the tail is graduated and rounded at the extremity. Some thirty species of munias are known, ranging through the Indian region to New Guinea and Timor, while a few inhabit Africa, and *M. nana* represents the group in Madagascar. The Java sparrow has long been domesticated, and a white variety developed, which presents a striking appearance, owing to the contrast between the pure white plumage and the pink beak. In Java and some other parts of Asia these birds are regarded as pests on account of the ravages they inflict on growing fields of rice.

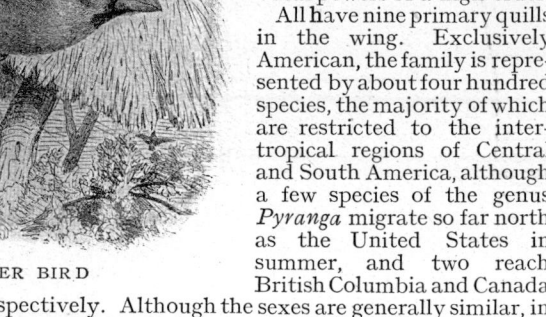

SOCIABLE WEAVER BIRD

The nest is constructed of dry grass or other available materials, and the eggs are white. The adult male has the crown of the head black, the cheeks pure white, the upper and lower parts, including the wings, uniform slate grey, and the rump and tail black. Some individuals have a song of considerable sweetness, but the usual note of this species is unattractive.

This bird has been introduced into Zanzibar, Mauritius, and Réunion, as well as Madras and Tenasserim. Another well-known species is the Indian nutmeg, or cowry, bird (*M. punctulata*), of which the colour is brown, with white streaks above and spots beneath, the rump yellow, and the middle of the under parts white. An allied group includes the grass finches, among which *Pœphila mirabilis* shows a perfect medley of bright colours.

WAXBILL FINCHES

The waxbill finches have the tail longer than the wing, the inner secondaries so elongated as to equal the primaries in length, the beak curved, and the nostrils entirely hidden by plumelets. As typically represented by the common waxbill finch (*Estrelda cinerea*), they take their name from the prevalence of scarlet in their coloration. The more typical members of the group are African and Arabian, but other species, such as the amadavat finch (*E.

JAVA SPARROWS

amandava*), occur in India and others in Australia. They have been introduced into Madagascar.

TANAGERS

Numerous both as regards species and genera, and brilliant in colour, the tanagers (family *Tanagridæ*) have been not inaptly described as tooth-billed finches, on account of the conical, finch-like beak, triangular at the base and notched near the tip. The notch in the beak, however, is scarcely apparent, or even obsolete in some of the genera, while in others it is greatly developed. Tanagers, which are chiefly remarkable for their gay colours, feed more upon fruits and insects than is the case with finches, while some members of the group possess vocal powers of a high order.

All have nine primary quills in the wing. Exclusively American, the family is represented by about four hundred species, the majority of which are restricted to the intertropical regions of Central and South America, although a few species of the genus *Pyranga* migrate so far north as the United States in summer, and two reach British Columbia and Canada respectively. Although the sexes are generally similar, in some cases, as in *Pyranga* and *Rhamphocœlus*, the female may be duller than, or even quite different from, her mate. The smallest species are included in the genus *Euphonia*, and the largest in *Pitylus* and *Saltator*.

VIOLET TANAGER

Of the six sub-families into which the family has been divided, the violet tanager (*Euphonia violacea*) and its allies constitute the typical representatives of the second. In this group the beak is short, swollen at the base, but not very much broadened; and the hooked upper half of the beak usually has two or three slight serrations behind the terminal notch. The wings are moderate, with the first three primaries longer than the rest, and nearly equal in length, and both the tail and metatarsus are short. The violet tanager is a lovely little bird, with a rapid flight, frequenting the very tops of the trees in which it dwells, its soft, tuneful note often denoting its presence before the musician itself is seen. The large nest is spherical in shape, and built of dry grass, the finer stems of creepers, and tufts of cotton. The interior is lined with tufts of grass. From three to four eggs are laid in a clutch, reddish yellow in colour, marked with small brown spots. The song of this tanager consists of a succession of pleasing notes, softly poured forth and long sustained. The violet tanager feeds on ripe fruit, preferring soft kinds, such as bananas, and plundering gardens so eagerly as sometimes to strip a whole tree. It flourishes as a cage-bird if supplied with plenty of space, fed upon an adequate variety of fruits, and kept in a warm room. The adult male has the upper parts violet the forehead and lower parts pure yellow, and the tail feathers steel-blue above and dark beneath. The female lacks the ornamental colours of her partner, being dull olive green above and yellowish grey below.

SCARLET & TYPICAL TANAGERS

The splendid scarlet tanager (*Pyranga rubra*, or *P. erythromelas*) belongs to the typical subfamily, in which the beak is more lengthened and more awl-like than in the last, with a single terminal notch, which may be obsolete; and both the tail and metatarsus are long. Of some two hundred species included in the sub-family, the typical tanagers (*Tanagra*) have the plumage blue and yellow; while in the allied *Pyranga* scarlet generally predominates in males.

Writing of the typical scarlet tanager in the United States, Mr. Nuttall observes that "this splendid and transient resident, accompanying fine weather in all his wanderings, arrives from his winter station in tropical America from the beginning to the middle of May, and extends his migrations probably to Nova Scotia as well as Canada. With the shy, unsocial, and suspicious habits of his gaudy fraternity, he takes up his abode in the deepest recesses of the forest, where, timidly flitting from observation, he darts from tree to tree like a flashing meteor. A gaudy sylph, conscious of his brilliance and the exposure to which it subjects him, he seems to avoid remark, and is only solicitous to be known to his humble mate, and hid from all besides. He therefore rarely approaches the habitations of men, unless, perhaps, the skirts of the orchard, where he sometimes, however, builds his nest, and takes a taste of the early and inviting, though forbidden, cherries."

The nest is built on the horizontal branch of some shady forest tree, constructed of stems of dry weeds, or slender fir twigs loosely framed together, lined with slender roots and wiry stems, the whole nest being so loosely welded as to admit the light between the interstices. The eggs are dull blue, spotted with two or three shades of brown or purple. The female scarlet tanager is a devoted parent, and shows great maternal solicitude for the safety of her young. Even the male of this species has been known to follow one of his brood for half a mile, feeding it with insects through the wires of the cage in which it was confined.

The scarlet tanager is the "red-bird" of Americans. Unfortunately, its crimson body, contrasting with black wings and tail, makes it only too conspicuous an object, the never-failing bait to the greed of the dealer in bird skins. The adult male is uniform scarlet above, with the wings and tail pure black; but the female is far less exposed to danger than her mate, being clear olive green above, and below greenish yellow, with the wings and tail dusky, glossed with green. Adult males often show abnormal colouring, the body being yellow, orange, or flame-colour, or red patches appearing on the wings.

Mr. W. Dutcher observes that this tanager "arrives at its summer home early in May, and starts on its southward journey in the autumn, late in September or early in October. As the tanagers migrate by night, many of them become the victims of lighthouses, and thus give accurate records of migration dates, especially in the southward migration. It is of singular interest that the mortality occasioned by the light-stations is many times as great in the autumn as it is in the spring. What the reason for this difference is has not yet been discovered, although it may in some measure be accounted for by the fact that in autumn there is thicker and mistier weather than in the spring."

CRIMSON-HEADED TANAGER

Another gorgeously coloured representative of the tanagers is the crimson-headed tanager (*P. ludoviciana*) of the western United States and Mexico. In Southern Colorado this tanager may be met with in small numbers among cotton woods along the streams, at an elevation of about seven thousand feet, and much more abundantly among the pines, up to nine thousand feet, and even ten thousand feet, above sea-level. It is common in Southern Arizona, and lingers on the Gila River as late as the middle of October. Writing of this species, Mr. Henshaw observes that "it is busy the whole time gleaning from among the pines and spruces the larger

VIOLET TANAGERS

SUPERB TANAGER

beetles and insects which infest them, and generally keeps well up among the higher branches, whence it makes its presence known by occasional bursts of melody."

Dr. George Suckley gave the following account of this species : " The beautiful Louisiana tanager is quite abundant in certain seasons in the vicinity of Fort Steilacoom. The favourite habitat of the species, in those localities where I have observed it, is among the tall, red fir trees belonging to that magnificent species *Abies douglasi*. They seemingly prefer the edges of the forest, rarely retiring to its depths unless for concealment when alarmed. In early summer, at Fort Steilacoom, they may be seen during the middle of the day sunning themselves in the firs, occasionally darting from one of these trees to another, or to some of the neighbouring white oaks on the prairies. Later in the season they may be seen actively flying about in quest of insect food for their young. Both sexes during the breeding season are much less shy; the males during the daytime frequently sitting on some low limb, rendering the scene joyous with their delightful melody."

The eggs of this crimson-headed tanager are green, sparingly dotted with dark purplish brown.

BLUE AND YELLOW TANAGERS

The superb tanager (*Calliste*, or *Calospiza*, *thoracica*), of South America, may be cited as an example of the blue and yellow group; the genus *Calliste* being closely allied to the above-mentioned *Tanagra*, of which, indeed, it may be regarded as a sub-genus. To describe such a lovely bird in words is almost impossible, and it must suffice to mention that this species and its kindred display a beautiful mixture of blue, green, olive, yellow, red, etc., arranged in perfect harmony.

WHITE-CAPPED TANAGER

One of the loveliest members of the family is the white-capped tanager (*Stephanophorus leucocephalus*), a summer visitor to Argentina, where, writes Mr. W. H. Hudson, " it makes its appearance in spring in the woods bordering on the Plata River, and is usually seen singly or in pairs. The nest is built in a tree ten or twelve feet from the ground, and is somewhat shallow and lined with soft dry grass. The female lays four eggs, white and spotted with red. During incubation the male sits concealed in the thick foliage close by, amusing itself by the hour with singing, its performance consisting of chattering disconnected notes, uttered in so low a tone as to make one fancy that the bird is merely trying to recall some melody it has forgotten, or endeavouring to construct a new one by jerking out a variety of sounds at random. The bird never gets beyond this unsatisfactory stage, however, and must be admired for its exquisite beauty alone."

BANANA QUIT

An old naturalist named this species the " blue white-headed beautiful," and the term was justified, for the entire plumage of both sexes is a lovely deep cornflower blue, surmounted by a cap of silvery white feathers ; a crimson spot ornamenting the forehead, looking like a drop of blood. The head is surmounted by a short crest, as it is in the allied genus *Eucometis*.

Among the other genera, *Phlogothraupis* and most species of *Rhamphocœlus* and *Calochœtes* resemble *Pyranga* in the prevalence of red or red and black. On the other hand, *Buthraupis* and *Iridornis* are blue or purplish black and yellow, while *Procnias* and *Pseudodacnis* are blue and black, and *Spindalis* and *Lanio* orange or yellow, with black and white, *Lamprospiza* and *Cissopis* being wholly black and white.

HONEY CREEPERS

The honey creepers (family *Cœrebidæ*), which constitute a small group of species, are allied to the true warblers, some of the latter possessing the deeply bifid, pencillate tongue once supposed to be peculiar to the present group. Unlike the creepers of the Old World, honey creepers have soft-feathered, squared tails. They are almost wholly confined to the tropical parts of South America, only a single species ranging so far north as Florida, but are most numerously represented in the West Indian Islands.

BANANA QUIT

As a well-known member of the family, special reference may be made to the West Indian banana quit (*Certhiola flaveola*). The birds of the genus to which this species belongs have the beak rather shorter than the head, stout at the base, but tapering rapidly to the extremely acute tip, and the whole beak much curved ; the wings are long, but the tail is short and rounded.

Scarcely larger than an average-sized humming bird, the banana quit is often seen in company with certain members of that group, probing the same flowers and for the same purpose, but in a very different manner.

" Instead of hovering in front of each blossom, a task for which its short wings would be utterly incompetent, the banana quit," writes Mr. P. H. Gosse, " alights on the tree, and proceeds in the most business-like manner to peep into the flowers, hopping actively from twig to twig, and throwing the body into all positions, often clinging by the feet with the back downwards, the better to reach the interior of a blossom with its curved beak and pencilled tongue. The minute insects always found in the interior of flowers are the objects of its search and the reward of its perseverance.

" Unsuspectingly familiar, these birds often resort to the blossoming shrubs of gardens and yards. A large moringa tree, that is profusely set all the year through with fragrant spikes of bloom, is a favourite resort of both these and the humming birds. One within a few feet of my window is, while I write, being actively scrutinised by two active little creatures, that pursue their examination with a zeal perfectly undisturbed by my looking on, while the same blossoms are rifled on one side by a minute humming bird, and on the other by that gorgeous butterfly *Urania sloaneus*—an interesting association.

The quit often utters a soft sibilant note as it peeps about.

"The nest of the bird is very frequently, perhaps usually, built in those low trees and bushes from whose twigs depend the paper nests of the brown wasps, and in close contiguity with them. The grass quits are said to manifest the same predilection; it is a singular exercise of instinct, almost of reason, for the object is doubtless the defence afforded by the presence of the formidable insect, but upon what terms the league of amity is contracted between the neighbours I am ignorant. It is in the months of May, June, and July that the creeper performs the business of incubation. On May 4 I observed a banana quit with a bit of silk cotton in her beak, and on searching found a nest just begun in a sage bush. The structure, though but a skeleton, was evidently about to be a dome, and so far was constructed of silk cotton. Since then I have seen several completed nests. One before me is in the form of a globe, with a small opening below the side. The walls are very thick, composed of dry grass, intermixed irregularly with down."

The eggs are greenish white, speckled with reddish at the larger end. In colour the upper parts of this species are dark brown, with a conspicuous white eyebrow, the breast and the rest of the under parts being a bright yellow. These birds take their name of quit, or quit-quit, from their note.

SUGAR BIRDS

The typical genus *Cœreba* is well represented in South America by the yellow-winged sugar bird (*C. cyanea*); while the blue sugar bird (*Dacnis cayanea*), which is likewise South American, typifies a third genus. Mention may likewise be made of the black-headed sugar bird (*Chlorophanes spiza*) of Brazil, as well as of the genus *Certhidea*, on account of its being confined to the Galapagos Islands.

In flight and habits the quit-quits and sugar birds are very like titmice, although they seldom associate in companies. The colouring is often sombre, being a mixture of black, grey, or purplish, with white or chestnut; but in some species brilliant blue, purple, or green is prevalent, with the quills black, or with patches of yellow, chestnut, and more rarely scarlet.

THE WOOD WARBLERS

The American family of birds known as wood warblers (*Mniotiltidæ*) is probably more or less closely related to the *Cœrebidæ*, among which they are placed

by some naturalists. The black-throated green warbler (*Dendrœca virens*) may be selected as a well-known example of a widely spread genus. Small in build, the numerous species of this large group have the beak of variable size, conical in shape, and provided with bristles at the gape, while the wings are long and pointed, the first and second primaries being the longest. The

BLACK-THROATED GREEN WARBLER

metatarsus is long, and the claws are rather small and much curved. The colour of the tail feathers affords a good clue to any member of this genus, since it will be found that these are almost invariably blotched with white.

Of thirty-five reputed species of this genus of wood warblers, twenty-six have been ascribed to North America, one of the best known being the summer yellow-bird of the United States, an abundant and familiar denizen of parks and orchards; while another is the lovely orange-breasted Blackburn's warbler, of which Dr. Elliott Coues writes that "there is nothing to compare with the exquisite hue of this Promethean torch."

The black-throated green warbler, which annually arrives in the eastern parts of the United States early in May, nests chiefly in fir woods, building in the oblique fork of a bough, generally at some distance from the ground, the nest being constructed of a variety of materials, such as vegetable fibres and dry stems, lined with finer grass, horsehair, and feathers.

The eggs are white, variegated with purplish spots. The plaintive and prolonged song of the male is generally uttered among pine trees. As a straggler, this bird has occurred in the island of Heligoland. The adult male has the upper parts olive green, yellower on the rump, the forehead and sides of the head bright yellow, the chin, breast, and throat jet black, the abdomen white, and the wings and tail dusky, the former being barred with whitish.

The typical genus *Mniotilta* is specially characterised by the great length of the toes, the most familiar species being the black and white warbler (*M. varia*). Some of the genera have very limited range, *Leucospiza* being restricted to the islands of St. Vincent and St. Lucia, and *Teretistris* to Cuba.

FINCHES AND BUNTINGS

THE finches (family *Fringillidæ*) and buntings comprise a large number of genera of small, hard-billed, seed-eating birds, distributed over the northern and temperate regions of both the Eastern and Western Hemispheres, although unknown in Australia. They are characterised by the smooth edges of the beak, the doubly plated hind surface of the metatarsus, the presence of nine primary quills, of which the first and second are approximately equal in length, and by the fact that the secondary quills extend to about three-quarters the length of the wing. The tail has twelve feathers; the beak is more or less conical in shape, with the nostrils pierced close to the line of the forehead and near the culmen, and the bristles at the gape are few and short. The lower half of the beak has no backward prolongation behind the quadrate bone. In the nestling the plumage is variable; and the sexes are generally unlike. The family is closely related to the tanagers and weaver birds, and may be divided, from the characters of the skull and beak, into three sub-families.

GREENFINCHES

The greenfinch (*Ligurinus chloris*) is a member of the first sub-family, *Coccothraustinæ*, in which a general stoutness of beak is accompanied by great relative depth of its lower half. Many of the species, such as the evening grosbeak of North America, are noticeable for the beauty of their colouring. The members of the group are inhabitants of the northern regions of both the Old and New Worlds, but some extend so far south as India.

In the greenfinch and its immediate relatives the beak is moderately stout and rather acute, with the distance between the nostrils equal to the depth of the lower half of the mandible. Green and yellow predominate in the plumage. Greenfinches inhabit the whole of Europe, as well as North-West Africa, Palestine, and Turkestan, and are also represented in Eastern Siberia, Japan, and China. The European species frequents gardens and small plantations, especially during summer, when its monotonous song is heard at intervals throughout the day. Despite this monotony, the song has some soft and plaintive notes, and although the bird is usually devoid of imitative talent, it has been known to reproduce the song of the canary.

Generally, the greenfinch is a late breeder, eggs sometimes being found so late as September. The nest is a coarse, untidy structure of fibrous roots, moss, and wool, lined with finer roots, horsehair, and a few feathers. The eggs are white, spotted with reddish brown and grey. The greenfinch not infrequently pairs with the canary in confinement, and in a wild state occasionally mates with the goldfinch, the hybrids resulting from the latter cross resembling the greenfinch in shape and colour, but the head and wings showing goldfinch blood. It will also interbreed with the linnet, and in confinement has produced offspring by pairing with

YOUNG GREENFINCHES

the bullfinch and twite. During autumn greenfinches range the fields in large flocks, feeding on the seeds of charlock and other weeds. The male is olive yellow above, overshaded with ashy grey, and yellow on the under surface. The South European race is smaller and brighter than the one breeding in the British Isles and Northern Europe. In North Africa the group is represented by the Algerian greenfinch (*L. auranteiventris*), and there is also a Japanese species (*L. sinicus*).

HAWFINCHES

In striking contrast to the gaudy livery of the greenfinch is the somewhat Quaker-like dress of that shy and retiring bird the hawfinch (*Coccothraustes vulgaris*). The distinctive feature of this bird is the large and heavy beak, furnished internally with a special

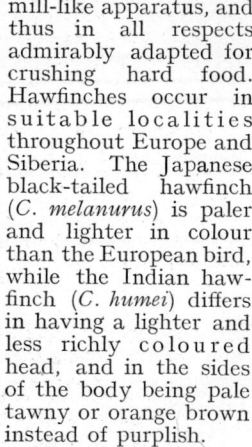

mill-like apparatus, and thus in all respects admirably adapted for crushing hard food. Hawfinches occur in suitable localities throughout Europe and Siberia. The Japanese black-tailed hawfinch (*C. melanurus*) is paler and lighter in colour than the European bird, while the Indian hawfinch (*C. humei*) differs in having a lighter and less richly coloured head, and in the sides of the body being pale tawny or orange brown instead of purplish.

The hawfinch is a well-known bird in many parts of Europe, locally distributed over England, although rarely visiting Scotland, and uncommon in Ireland. It frequents the skirts of forests, especially where hornbeam flourishes, since it feeds on the seeds of that tree. Seldom seen in open country, it resides in gardens and orchards, especially during the summer months, and may be recognised by its rapid and undulating flight. The male should be seen in bright sunshine if his beauty of plumage is to be appreciated, the light burnishing up the deep-brown back and blue-black wings.

The hawfinch is a shy bird and seldom courts attention; when alarmed, its first action is to crouch close to the branch upon which it happens to be perching, so as, if possible, to escape unnoticed. Mr. Seebohm remarks that the "hawfinch is not much of a songster. It has few notes, which can scarcely be called more than a low chatter. There is nothing very striking in its performance, but when several are twittering away together the general effect is very pleasant. Its call note is said to resemble the well-known 'zh' of the greenfinch. The hawfinch pairs about the middle of April, and its nest is rarely built before the trees are in full foliage. The site of the nest differs considerably. A favourite place is in the apple or pear trees in an orchard, or in an old whitethorn, often in quite an exposed situation, and when it breeds in woods it sometimes selects a hornbeam, and less frequently a holly.

"The hawfinch does not often breed in shrubberies, and its nest is somewhat rarely placed in evergreen trees, but it has been found amongst ivy. It will also breed in tall oak trees, and occasionally nests in fir trees and plantations. Sometimes the nest is only a few feet from the ground, while at others it is as much as forty feet. Building is usually begun by the latter end of April or early in May, and sometimes several nests will be found in the same plantation. " The nest is a very beautiful piece of handiwork, similar to that of the bullfinch, on an enlarged scale. The outside is invariably made of twigs, frequently intermixed with lichens, and sometimes with dry plants, and the cup is formed of dry grasses lined with fine roots, and often a little hair. As a rule, it is very flat, and somewhat bulky, and the cup is generally shallow and neatly finished. The eggs vary from four to six in number, and are usually laid about the second week in May, sometimes earlier. There are two very distinct types. The usual one is pale olive or bluish green in ground colour, streaked with dark olive brown, and having a few spots of the same colour on the surface, and with underlying markings of greyish brown ; the second differs in having the ground colour buff, and the underlying spots more inclined to violet grey."

In winter the hawfinch sometimes conquers its shyness sufficiently to approach houses, and even to partake of crumbs thrown upon the lawn, although only in hard weather, when driven to extremities. The injuries inflicted by these birds on the garden are compensated by the destruction of noxious insects, their food during the early months of summer consisting principally of caterpillars. The colour of the adult

GREENFINCH

male is chocolate brown above, with a broad collar of ash grey separating the crown of the head from the mantle ; the lower part of the back, rump, and upper tail coverts are cinnamon brown ; the wings black, glossed with steel blue at the end of the square-shaped inner primaries and outer secondaries ; the primaries have a large spot of white about the middle of the inner web ; the tail feathers are blackish, edged with brown, the outer ones being tipped with white on the inner web ; the throat is black, and the lower parts are purplish brown. The black-and-yellow hawfinch (*Mycerobus melanoxanthus*) of Northern India represents a distinct generic type.

ROSE-BREASTED GROSBEAK

The rose-breasted grosbeak (*Hadymeles* [or *Zamelodia*] *ludovicianus*) is a well-known representative of an American group in which the beak is very heavy, with its lower half as deep as the upper, the wing longer than the tail and pointed, the secondaries falling short of the primaries by more than the length of the metatarsus, and the feet short and stout. These birds are found in North America generally, ranging throughout Central America to Colombia, Ecuador, and the Antilles.

The rose-breasted grosbeak of the United States has a handsome plumage and charming song. Dr. Elliott Coues gives the following account of its habits : " I have nowhere found this beautiful bird more abundant than along the Red River of the North, and there may be no locality where its nidification and breeding habits can be studied to greater advantage. On entering the belt of noble timber that borders the river in June, we are sure to be saluted with the rich, rolling song of the rose-breasted male ; and, as we

HAWFINCH

penetrate into the deeper recesses, pressing through the stubborn luxuriance of vegetation into the little shady glades that the bird loves so well, we may catch a glimpse of the shy and retiring female darting into concealment, disturbed by our approach. She is almost sure to be followed the next moment by her ardent spouse, solicitous for her safety, and bent on reassuring her by his presence and caresses.

"Sometimes during this month, as we enter a grove of saplings, and glance carefully overhead, we may see the nest placed but a few feet from the ground in the fork of a limb. The female, alarmed, will flutter away stealthily, and we may not catch another glimpse of her nor of her mate, even though we hear them both anxiously consulting together at a little distance. The nest is not such an elegant affair as might be desired; it is, in fact, bulky and nude, if not actually slovenly. It is formed entirely of the long, slender tortuous stems of woody climbers and similar stout rootlets; the base and outer walls being very loosely interlaced, the inner more compactly woven, with a tolerably firm brim of circularly disposed fibres. Sometimes there is a little horse-hair lining, oftener not. The eggs are of a light and rather pale green colour. profusely speckled with dull reddish brown."

The summer range of this grosbeak extends to Labrador. The general colour of the adult male is black above; the lower part of the back and rump is pure white, slightly mottled with black tips; the wings are black, with the secondaries tipped with white; the tail feathers black, the three outer ones marked with white on the inner web; the crown of the head, lores, the sides of the neck, and throat are also black; the fore neck and chest show a large patch of rose colour, extending in a line down the centre of the breast; the breast and flanks are white, the thighs spotted with black; and the under wing coverts rose colour. This beautiful dress is only gradually acquired, three years being needed for the assumption of the perfect adult male plumage. The black-headed grosbeak (H. melanocephalus) is a well-known Mexican species.

OTHER GENERA

The South American yellow-bellied grosbeak (Pheucticus chrysogaster) belongs to a distinct generic type; another genus being represented by the blue grosbeak (Guiraca cærulea) of North America, the Brazilian blue grosbeak (G. cyanea), and other species. There are many other allied American birds, belonging to several generic types, such as the orchard finch (Phrygilus finticeti) of Chile, and the North American indigo bird (Cyanospiza cyanea) and nonpareil finch (C. ciris).

RED CARDINAL

Apart from its brilliant livery, that gorgeous bird the red cardinal (Cardinalis virginianus) is characterised by the large, stout, pointed, and conical beak; the short and rounded wings; the tail longer than the wings, and rounded; and the long crest. This bird and its immediate relatives present an instance, not very common among birds, of a group in which the males are nearly all alike, so that the specific characters depend upon the females. There can, however, be no doubt about the differences in the latter; although the males differ from one another mainly in intensity of colour, and to a slight extent in size. The most brilliant forms appear to be those from tropical localities.

Red cardinals are found in the United States, ranging south into Mexico and British Honduras, one of the best known being the typical species, often called the Virginian nightin-gale. This cardinal inhabits by choice thickets, tangle, and undergrowth of all kinds, whence issue its rich, rolling, whistling notes, while the brightly clad per-former eludes observa-tion by his shyness, vigilance, and activity.

RED CARDINAL AND ROSE-BREASTED GROSBEAK

The nest, built loosely of bark strips, twigs, leaves, and grasses, is placed in a vine or low, thick tree, in which the female lays eggs recalling in some cases those of a night-hawk, in colouring at least, while others are more like those of the rose-breasted gros-beak in the pattern of markings. While the ground colour was white in fifty cases noticed, the spotting was of every shade of brown, from pale reddish to heavy chocolate. The markings, however, are usually rather dark, with variations of purplish brown or stone grey.

The typical form of the Virginian nightingale ranges westwards from the Eastern United States to Kansas, Nebraska, Indian Territory, and Texas, where it may be either stationary or slightly migratory. A smaller form found in Eastern Mexico is a deeper red, approach-ing rich rosy scarlet. The Californian race has a larger beak than the type, and is rather smaller in size, the black mask on the face not being continued across the forehead.

In Western Mexico is a race similar to the last, but smaller, and of a much more rosy red, the crest feathers being elongated and stiffened. The adult male of the typical form is deep scarlet vermilion or rosy red above, with the forehead, chin, and upper part of the throat black; the wings dusky, externally rosy, and the under surface rich vermilion. The female is dull ochre brown above; with the long, crested feathers, wings, and tail dull vermilion, and the under parts buff, washed with vermilion.

GREAT BIRD OF PARADISE AND KING BIRD OF PARADISE
"Although comparatively little is known in regard to the habits of these lovely birds, it appears that as regards food they are omnivorous, feeding on fruits and insects, and showing a marked preference for figs, grasshoppers, locusts, leaf-insects, and caterpillars."

I B

GLOSSY STARLINGS

"The glossy starlings are gregarious birds, ranging all over Africa, and feeding on vegetable as well as animal substances. Uttering harsh clamorous notes, they are rapid in their flight and lively in their movements; and though generally dwelling high up in the branches of the forest trees, descend at times to pick up insects and other food on the ground."

WEAVER BIRDS

"The weaver birds derive their name from the extraordinary textile nests they construct. While very similar to the finches in external appearance, they differ in having ten primary quills in the wings, and also in the fact that some of them undergo a partial moult in spring."

THE EGGS AND NESTS OF THE BEST-KNOWN BRITISH BIRDS

A key to this plate is given on the opposite page

CHAFFINCHES

The chaffinch (*Fringilla cœlebs*) is the typical representative of the true finches, which collectively constitute the sub-family *Fringillinœ*. These true finches are distinguished from the grosbeak group by their less powerful beaks and different form of the skull; but, although the beak is variously modified to meet their manner of life, these birds possess many characteristics in common. They are principally natives of temperate climates.

Chaffinches have rather long, slender, conical beaks, and the first primary so small as to seem wanting; the rest of these feathers varying in length. The tail is moderately long and decidedly forked. These finches inhabit Europe generally, as well as Western Siberia, Persia, Turkestan, Madeira, and the Canaries and Azores.

The European chaffinch is abundant in most parts of Europe, being in some districts even more plentiful than the house sparrow, nesting in close proximity to dwelling-houses. In winter chaffinches consort in large flocks, which break up at the close of the cold weather; in early spring they begin to pair, when the male birds are no longer tolerant of the society of their fellows, but exhibit a high degree of jealousy towards rivals. The nest (pages 931 and 990) is usually built in a tree—frequently on the small boughs springing from the trunk —or hedge, and when in the former situation its grey trimming harmonises with the colour of the bark.

It has been remarked that the chaffinch varies the structure of its nest according to the locality which it happens to frequent. In country districts, away from the dust and smoke near cities and large towns, the nest is a model in its way for neatness and compactness of form; but in less favourable situations, where the building materials are not so fresh, it is slovenly. A large series of nests will give ample proof of this, some being composed of moss closely interwoven, others of lichens laced all over with spiders' webs, while those obtained in the outskirts of cities are built of straws, pieces of paper, and bits of blackened moss.

A nest taken in Finland was built in a birch tree, and neatly ornamented with pieces of yellow and grey lichen and small bits of birch bark, so as to resemble a portion of the tree itself; while it was carefully lined with soft moss and bits of down and wool, through which some fine roots showed every here and there. A nest found in Denmark was decorated all over the outside with small pieces of newspaper. The eggs are generally purplish grey in ground colour, washed with green, and blotched and spotted with dark red; but perfectly blue, unspotted eggs occasionally occur.

The chaffinch feeds during the spring and summer months principally upon insects; but at other times seeds form a large portion of its nutriment. It is to a large extent a bird of passage, moving from one part of the country to another, according to the supply of food and the condition of the weather.

The young birds frequently associate as early as the middle of July, the sexes then being hardly distinguishable.

The chaffinch is a fairly early nester, the eggs usually hatching during the last days of May. On the Continent the chaffinch is abundant on mountain ranges of moderate elevation, as in Central France and the Black Forest. In Switzerland it is common about the summer chalets, descending into the plains before severe weather sets in. The male in summer has the upper parts and scapulars chestnut brown, the wing coverts white, or black tipped with white, the quills black margined with pale olive yellow, the inner primaries white at the base, the secondaries also white at the base, forming a band with white tips to the grey coverts, the forehead black, the crown slaty blue, the chin and breast pale purplish red, and the lower parts purplish white. The female is ashy brown above washed with olive yellow, the wings being conspicuously pied with white, and the lower parts ashy brown.

TINTILLON CHAFFINCH

The tintillon chaffinch (*F. tintillon*) is peculiar to Teneriffe, where it inhabits the dreary heights of the Peak and surrounding plateaus. It frequents the pine forests, feeding on the seeds of the pines, breaking the cone with its powerful beak in order to get at its contents. The note is plaintive and often repeated, and bears some resemblance to that of the serin finch. It is a somewhat rare species, occurring on the lower grounds only when driven by a heavy fall of snow from its usual haunts. The adult male has the entire upper parts rich dark grey; the wings and tail black, edged with slate blue; and the under parts blue, fading into dull white on the abdomen. In the female the blue garb of the male is replaced by dull greyish brown.

The Teydean chaffinch (*F. teydea*) is more widely spread in the Canaries; and Algeria likewise possesses a species of its own (*F. spodiogenia*). A very distinct bird is the crested chaffinch (*F. cuculata*), which takes its name from the production of the feathers of the crown into a distinct crest.

KEY TO THE PLATE ON THE OPPOSITE PAGE

Labels on the plate: ROBIN'S NEST, LANDRAIL, BULLFINCH'S NEST, WILLOW WREN, STARLING, MOORHEN, SKY LARK, GOLDEN EAGLE, REDPOLL, CORMORANT, WOOD LARK, LINNET, KINGFISHER, HERON, SWALLOW, MISSEL-THRUSH, CARRION-CROW, KESTREL, SPARROW-HAWK, SEA-GULL, SONG-THRUSH, REED-WARBLER, CRESTED WREN, NIGHTINGALE, STONECHAT, GREAT TIT, ROOK, RAVEN, BLACKBIRD, CHINCHAT, BLUE TIT, WAGTAIL, MEADOW-PIPIT, GOLDFINCH, HAWFINCH, LAPWING, MAGPIE, JACKDAW, HEDGESPARROW, ROBIN, NIGHTJAR, BLACKCAP, WREN, SPOTTED FLYCATCHER, YELLOW BUNTING, TREE-PIPIT, CHAFFINCH'S NEST, WREN'S NEST

THE BRAMBLING

A member of the same genus as the chaffinch is the brambling (*F. montifringilla*), which breeds in the forest regions of the Arctic Circle, whence it journeys to winter in Southern Europe, Persia, and India. In Siberia, according to Dr. Radde, the brambling remains occasionally during the summer. On May 16, 1859, he found it not far from Tunkinsk; while on July 14, 1855, he met with a family, the young birds of which were fledged. Only a few visit the high steppes of Dauria in spring. On August 15 he saw only a few males, on the 16th only a female, but on the 26th large flocks, consisting of young birds of both sexes, arrived. On the 30th they increased in numbers and frequented a garden. Later, when the night frosts set in, they took refuge in the high reeds round the ponds; and there they remained till September 11, although large flocks were wanting, and only stragglers were seen up to September 15.

Usually the brambling lays a larger number of eggs than any other finch, seldom fewer than six, or, more generally, seven ; and when compelled to leave its

THE CHAFFINCH

nest to seek food, or for any other purpose, the bird is in the habit of covering its eggs, which are laid late in May or early in June. Bramblings generally build in birches or spruces, close to the main stem, and about six or seven yards from the ground. The nest is constructed like that of the chaffinch, but, as a rule, with more moss. The eggs closely resemble those of the latter species, but the colour is greyish brown, instead of greyish blue, with smaller spots. The nest is composed of green moss and fine, dried grass, interwoven with cobwebs, externally decorated with flat pieces of white lichen and thin threads of birch bark, and lined with fine wool and feathers of the willow grouse.

During the autumn considerable numbers of bramblings cross the North Sea to winter in the British Isles, their arrival being usually heralded by the reiteration of their harsh call note. They frequent stubble fields and farmyards in common with chaffinches, greenfinches, and sparrows, but prefer to subsist upon beech mast.

The adult male in breeding plumage has the colour above blue black, generally with few sandy margins to the feathers, the lower part of the back and rump white, the wing coverts orange rufous tipped with white, and the wing quills black, with pale yellow edges to the outer and white bases to the inner primaries. The tail feathers are black, with the outer pair broadly white for more than half the outer web, the crown and sides of the face black, the throat and breast pale orange rufous, and the flanks spotted with black.

SISKINS

The siskin (*Chrysomitris spinus*) is the typical representative of a number of small finches characterised by a long and acute beak, long wings, short,

deeply-forked tail, and the predominance of green and yellow in their plumage. All are highly gregarious in their habits. They belong to both the Old and New Worlds, having representatives in Abyssinia, the Himalaya, Siberia, the United States, and especially South America, where several species are found in Chile, Bolivia, Ecuador, and other countries. From Japan to the British Isles the siskin is found in suitable localities, breeding chiefly in the northern part of its range.

During the breeding season the cocks are restless and lively, singing nearly all day, generally while on the wing. The nest is very like that of the goldfinch, but not so neat. Although only occasionally nesting in England, the siskin breeds regularly in Scotland, and has been recorded as breeding in Ireland. In winter it frequents alder groves, living in flocks, and searching the catkins for their seeds ; and it may be seen feeding on thistle heads and the seeds of wild grasses. It occasionally pairs with the lesser redpoll and goldfinch in confinement. The general colour of the male siskin is yellowish green above, with the rump bright yellow ; the quills are blackish, the primaries being edged with bright yellow ; the tail feathers blackish, edged with yellow, and all but the middle feathers yellow at the base ; the chin is black, and the throat and breast are bright yellow. In the Himalaya this species is replaced by the closely allied *C. spinoides*.

AMERICAN GOLDFINCH

In the United States the group is represented by the yellow bird or American goldfinch (*C. tristis*), also common in many parts of Canada. It is a lively, graceful species, full of vivacity, and leads a social life, roving about in small communities. Even in the breeding season these birds are partial to the company of their fellows, and fly in flocks between their nests and their favourite feeding grounds, where they consume the seeds of various wild plants. After the breeding season, the family parties unite permanently, and wander over the prairies in search of weedy places where they can find

THE BRAMBLING

subsistence. The adult male in summer is bright golden yellow above and below ; the crown and wings being black, the great coverts tipped with white, and the tail black spotted with white. In September the general plumage changes to pale flaxen brown above, and whitish brown below.

" The nesting site," writes Mr. W. Dutcher, " may be in an evergreen or deciduous bush or tree, and the nest may be built only a few feet from the ground or at considerable height, where it is saddled on or attached to a forked twig. The nest itself is an exquisite piece of bird architecture, compactly built of dried grasses, leaves, and shreds of bark, the outside being embellished with lichens, which Audubon says are attached by saliva. The inside of the nest is lined with the softest plant down. The mother bird is the builder of this tasteful home, her handsome consort, during the nest-building time, devoting most of his efforts to singing to cheer his industrious mate. After the four to six bluish white eggs have been laid the singing partner has more work to do, for he has to feed his brooding wife. His frequent visits are always announced with a sweet conversational song, which he seems able to give even though his bill is filled with weeds."

In Brazil the group is represented by the black-throated siskin (*C. magellanica*) and Yarrell's siskin (*C. yarrelli*), in Chile by the black-chinned siskin (*C. barbata*), and in Venezuela and Trinidad by the crested siskin (*C. cuculata*), a species easily recognised, not only by the feature from which it takes its name, but also by the light band ascending from the breast to divide the head from the neck.

CITRIL FINCH

Another member of the siskin group is the citril finch (*C. citrinella*), which is an inhabitant of the Tirol, many parts of Switzerland, Greece, and other districts in the south of Europe. Avoiding the plains, this bird generally nests among pine forests, as far as possible from human habitations. In the Jura a nest of this finch was found high up in a spruce fir at the extreme end of a branch. This nest, which contained several feathers of the nutcracker, was cup-shaped, and constructed chiefly of dry grass stems, moss, and thistle down, woven together with fine roots and hair, lined with thistle down and feathers. A second nest contained no feathers, being lined entirely with thistle down;

CRESTED SISKIN

while a third was lined entirely with hair, with very little thistle-down used in its construction. The eggs are greenish blue in ground colour, speckled with reddish-grey and blood red. The citril finch is a favourite among continental bird-fanciers, being easily tamed, and occasionally hybridising with other finches in captivity.

Although it passes the summer among the mountain forests, it descends from the higher grounds during severe weather. It is valued as a cage bird, principally on account of its loud, pleasant song, sometimes compared to that of the canary. The adult male in breeding plumage has the general colour

THE SISKIN

above dull olive green, with dusky shaft streaks to the feathers; the rump and upper tail coverts are brighter yellow, the nape and sides of the throat ashy grey, the wings and tail dusky brown, edged with ashy yellow and the crown of the head, as well as the feathers round the eye, the fore part of the cheeks, and the throat and chest olive yellow.

YELLOW FINCHES

Nearly allied to the siskins are the Tropical American yellow finches of the genus *Sycalis*, of which the Jamaica yellow finch (*S. jamaicæ*) is a good example. These are small yellow or yellowish birds with exposed nostrils, moderate or somewhat long and rather pointed wings, an emarginate, or doubly rounded, tail rather shorter than the wings, and the shank, or metatarsus, not larger than the middle toe and its claw. One of the species (*S. pelzelni*) is noteworthy on account of its habit of making use of the nests of other birds.

GOLDFINCHES

The goldfinch (*Carduelis elegans*) is an unmistakable and familiar bird, with its red cheeks and yellow feathers in the wing. As regards affinities, it appears to be connected, on the one hand, with the siskins—from which, however, it differs widely in habits—and, on the other, with the hawfinches. The range of this bird includes the greater part of Europe, along with North Africa, and extends eastwards to Persia and Turkestan. Further east its place is taken by the buff-headed goldfinch (*C. caniceps*) of Central Asia, easily recognised by wanting the black hood and white ear tufts of the European species. In Britain goldfinches are far less common than formerly. To a certain extent this may be due to netting, but probably

JAMAICA YELLOW FINCH

of greenfinches in search of food. The linnet is frequently white or pied, but the most beautiful variety is of a cinnamon brown, which harmonises with the rose-coloured breast. The male is warm reddish brown above, with the forehead, fore neck, and chest crimson, and the breast and other parts dull buffy white.

MEALY AND LESSER REDPOLLS

The two species of redpoll —namely, the mealy redpoll (*L. linaria*) and the lesser redpoll (*L. rufescens*) — are so nearly related that they have been regarded as varieties of one and the same bird. The former is widely distributed in Northern Europe, but the latter is chiefly confined as a breeding species to the British Isles and certain parts of the Alps, though it has also nested in Heligoland. The lesser redpoll is an early breeder, selecting a variety of trees to contain its nest, including alder, hazel, crab, birch, willow, and walnut.

As many as five nests have been seen at once in a single hawthorn hedge. The height from the ground at which the nest is placed varies from four to twenty feet; and the composition of the nest also varies, the exterior generally consisting of moss and dried grass, with a lining of beautiful down from the catkin of the willow; but in some cases composed of dead fir twigs, and in others of hawthorn. The mealy redpoll is light brown above, with dark middles to the feathers; the forehead being dark crimson, while the throat and breast are suffused with rosy pink, especially in the breeding season. The lesser redpoll differs in being smaller and of a more reddish colour. The sexes are generally

a more potent element has been the breaking up of the waste and fallow lands which formed the favourite haunts of these birds. Of late years, however, there has been a tendency to an increase in their numbers.

Thistles and other plants of the order *Compositæ* are especially affected by goldfinches, which cling to the stems in order to feed on the seeds. The majority of these birds leave Britain in the autumn, to return in spring, when they build a neatly-constructed and carefully-hidden nest, often at no great height from the ground. The eggs are greenish, mottled with rufous (page 990). On account of the beauty of their plumage, coupled with their possession of a pleasing song, goldfinches have always been great favourites as cage birds. The so-called American goldfinch is mentioned above

LINNETS AND REDPOLLS

The group of excellent songsters typified by the linnet (*Linota cannabina*) is characterised by the hard and conical beak, the somewhat pointed wing, the rather long and forked tail, the short metatarsus, and the stout toes. They are also distinguished by their nearly uniform brown or whitish brown plumage, associated to some small extent with pale crimson. Chiefly found in the northern part of the Old World, they are also represented in the Arctic portions of North America.

The typical linnet inhabits most parts of Europe, being common from Spain eastwards to Central Asia, although assuming brighter plumage in Turkestan and other distant parts of its range. In England it frequents commons covered with gorse, in which the nest is often placed; although sometimes it nests in a hedge or small tree. Generally an early breeder, the young may sometimes be seen in the nest so late as August. These birds build a loose, untidy nest of fine twigs and fibres lined with hair, wool, and sometimes a few feathers, in which are laid from four to six eggs of a greenish white ground colour, blotched with red (page 990).

After the breeding season linnets range through the fields in vast flocks, often composed almost exclusively of one sex. As autumn advances, many that have been bred in England cross the sea to other countries, while others, again, join company with bands

THE LINNET

alike, but the female does not assume the rosy tint upon the breast.

SNOW FINCHES

The birds known as snow finches form a small group possessing the characteristic make of typical finches, but with the long wings falling short of the tail by less than the length of the metatarsus. Chocolate or reddish brown predominates in the plumage of this group, often associated with rose colour, but the type of the genus is conspicuously pied with white. Snow finches are chiefly found in the mountains of Central Asia, but some species range over the northern parts of Siberia, Japan, and Northern China. The best known is the snow finch (*Montifringilla nivalis*) of the mountains of Southern Europe, and ranging eastwards to Palestine, but replaced in Persia, Turkestan, and Afghanistan by the eastern snow finch.

The snow finch breeds in the highest regions of the mountain ranges of Central Europe, adapting its habits to the desolate regions in which it passes the summer. Mr. Scott Wilson gives the following account of its habits; " It was observed at a greater height than any other Alpine bird. At the foot of the Lammern glacier, 7,600 feet high, we found it breeding at the summit of the Furka Pass, as well as at the Gemmi. It lays about the end of May or the beginning of June, at a time when the ground in these Alpine regions is entirely covered with snow, from which cause I suppose it is obliged to place its nest under the roofs of buildings, or, where there are no buildings, in rocks which do not hold the snow, the former not only affording them a

GOLDFINCHES · · · · · · · · · Photo. C. Reid

dry nesting place, but one which also protects the nest from the storms of snow and sleet, which have by no means ceased to fall by the end of May. A nest obtained on the Furka is principally made of dry grass stalks, intermingled with which are tufts of hair, wool, leaves, shavings of wood, and a few feathers. The inside walls are lined with ptarmigan's feathers, both white and brown, these being woven together very compactly with horsehair, and in another nest with strands of green worsted. The bottom of the nest is not lined with feathers. The outside diameter, which is nearly round, is $8\frac{1}{4}$ inches ; the inside diameter, $3\frac{1}{2}$ inches ; thus the inside cup is small in proportion. The eggs are pure white, and from three to five in number.''

In winter snow finches descend from the Alpine regions to the lower valleys. The snow finch is a beautiful bird, rather larger than the greenfinch or sparrow, with long wings, in which the primary quills are much longer than the rest, as in some other birds of airy and graceful flight. The strong contrast of jet black and purest white in the plumage—notably in the tail, which has two black feathers in the middle, while the rest are as white as snow—makes the bird conspicuous at a long distance, and a more striking object than the browner snow bunting, which occasionally strays from the north to the Alps.

There are few more beautiful sights than the wheelings and whirlings of a flock of snow finches, with their white feathers glistening in the sun one moment, while the next the black ones will show clear against the snow. The adult snow finch has the upper parts brown, with light edgings to the feathers, the hind part of the neck and sides of the neck ashy grey, the wings and tail black and white, some of the feathers being edged with brown, and the lower parts white throughout.

ROCK SPARROWS

The rock sparrow (*Petronia stulta*) and its relatives resemble sparrows in structure and habits, but differ in the stronger beak and longer wings. Unlike the latter, however, the females have no distinct plumage of their own, but resemble more or less closely the male. Rock sparrows inhabit Southern and Central Europe, whence they extend eastwards into Central Asia and Siberia, as well as Northern China. One species is found in India as a winter visitor, while two are resident in Africa.

YOUNG LINNETS

The European rock sparrow is a native of certain districts of Spain and Portugal and the south of France, as well as Greece and Palestine. Its habits resemble those of the sparrow, but it is generally a very shy bird, flying away on the approach of danger, and constantly keeping a good look-out. It builds in the ruins of old castles and crevices of rocks, constructing

GROUP OF YOUNG SPARROWS

a large, untidy nest, composed of stems of grass and plant fibres, lined with hair, feathers, and other materials. In a clutch there are two or three eggs, which are white, streaked and spotted with ash-grey and brown. The parents wait assiduously upon the young, and manifest the greatest distress if the safety of their progeny be endangered. In autumn these birds gather into flocks, and some migrate from their higher breeding grounds. The flight is rapid and well-sustained, and the usual note a harsh chirrup.

Although partial to fruit, rock sparrows feed principally upon insects during the summer months, but visit stubble fields in autumn. Upon the approach of winter they often consort with other small birds, and frequent roads and even villages. The general colour of the male is brown above, the mantle and back being broadly streaked with black, with a whitish brown spot at the tip of the outer webs of the feathers; the crown is light brown in the centre, bordered with dark brown, and followed by a broad whitish brown eyebrow; the wings and tail are blackish brown; the cheeks, throat, and under surfaces pale ashy brown; and the lower part of the throat is marked with a patch of pale yellow.

SPARROWS

The genus *Passer* contains the sparrow and its immediate relatives, which are represented over the greater part of the Old World, and characterised by both sexes exhibiting a peculiar pattern upon the outer web of the first primaries. The beak is stout and short, and the wings fall short of the tail by more than the length of the metatarsus. Originally absent from the New World, sparrows have been introduced into the United States, where the common species has become a serious pest, its injurious character becoming more and more appreciated as the species spreads. The group is indigenous to the greater part of the Old World, excepting Australia and the Moluccan Islands.

HOUSE SPARROW

The house sparrow (*P. domesticus*), which nests only too numerously in many country districts, is essentially a dweller among men, and produces many broods in a season. The eggs are greenish white, blotched or spotted with ashy grey and dusky brown.

It is generally supposed that sparrows feed largely on insects, and there is no doubt that in many districts this is the case for a considerable part of the year; but in autumn they band together in flocks, and, leaving their haunts in the towns, join their country brethren in anticipating the farmer's harvest. Only practical men are aware of the enormous injury annually inflicted on farm produce by the hordes of sparrows which ravage the cornfields. Nor is their mischief limited to assailing standing crops of grain. On the contrary, they inflict considerable injury upon gardeners by pecking up freshly-sown seeds. They destroy green peas quite as effectually as do hawfinches, and are in many other respects most undesirable neighbours. In America the introduction of the sparrow has proved disastrous to many of the indigenous birds, which have been driven from their proper haunts by the intruder. Even in remote districts of the Highlands of Scotland sparrows are gaining ground every year, and taking the place of other birds.

The sparrow builds a cumbrous nest of straw, hay, dry grass, rags, or any other material that comes handy, this being often placed in a water-spout, a chink of a wall, the thatch of a barn, or the frieze of a building. Occasionally it is situated in an open tree or hedgerow, but the nest is them domed as a protection against the weather, and is almost always profusely lined with feathers. Taking great pains to maintain their plumage in good condition, sparrows not only indulge in frequent baths, like most of the finch tribe, but in summer show a partiality for dusting their feathers in lark-fashion.

They exhibit some variation of plumage; all the birds in a brood being occasionally spotted with white, or at any rate cream-coloured; while cocks are frequently variegated with white, more especially on the quill

THE SPARROW

feathers. The adult cock in summer has the plumage of the upper parts chestnut, streaked with black on the mantle and back, the primaries blackish, edged with pale rufous, the median coverts black, tipped with white, forming a wing bar, the tail feathers dusky brown, the crown of the head and nape ashy grey, with a broad streak of chestnut extending downwards from the upper part of the eye, the cheeks ashy white, the throat and fore neck black, the sides of the breast brownish ash, and the under parts white. The female is dull brown, lacking the black gorget of the other sex.

TREE SPARROW

The haunts of the tree sparrow (*P. montanus*) are more remote from human dwellings than are those of its cousin. Sometimes, it is true, a pair or two of these birds may take up their abode in some old wall beside a cottage or farmhouse, but trees are their favourite resorts. Not infrequently tree sparrows build under old nests of rooks, the nest being less bulky and untidy than that of the house sparrow. The eggs are bluish white in ground colour, blotched and spotted or suffused with hair-brown. Sometimes tree sparrows nest in the crevices of a chalk cliff, and a colony has been found established under the iron girders of a railway bridge.

In its movements the tree sparrow is more graceful than is the common species; its chirp is more musical and shriller,

1, ROCK SPARROW ; 2, SPANISH SPARROW ; 3, HOUSE SPARROW ; 4, TREE SPARROW

while it also possesses a short but pleasing song. Instead of courting observation, the tree sparrow shuns publicity, and its flight is more rapid than that of the house sparrow. The adult is fawn-coloured above, the feathers of the mantle having ashy edgings and broad black streaks ; the lesser wing coverts are uniform chestnut, the medium wing coverts black, with broad white tips forming a wing bar, the chin black, the cheeks white, spotted with black, and the under parts ashy.

SPANISH SPARROW

The Spanish sparrow (*P. hispaniolensis*) replaces the English bird in many parts of the Mediterranean region, including Sardinia, Corsica, Sicily, and Malta, where it nests in the walls of houses and the crevices of rocks. It is abundant in Algeria, especially among reeds in salt marshes. Mr. O. Salvin observes that in the Atlas it " is found in great numbers during the breeding season among the tamarisk thickets on the Chemoria and in the high sedge at Zana. The Arabs destroy the eggs, nest, and young wherever they find them, as the numbers of these birds do much damage to the crops of corn. The nests are placed as thickly as they can stand, the whole colony, consisting of perhaps one hundred pairs, occupying only five or six trees. The noise and ceaseless chattering proceeding from one of these sparrow towns can easily be imagined, and, guided by the sound alone, one may walk directly to the spot for a considerable distance."

The egg of the Spanish sparrow is somewhat smaller than that of the house sparrow, white in ground colour, blotched and streaked with dark grey. The male has the crown and nape dark chestnut, the back black, streaked with cream colour, the cheeks and eye stripe white, the lesser wing coverts chestnut, tipped with white, and the throat and upper part of the breast black. The female is dull brown.

BLACK-BREASTED SPARROW

In South Africa the black-breasted sparrow (*P. diffusus*) takes up its abode near dwellings. In some districts these sparrows build their nests in low, thorny bushes, but they are equally partial to holes in walls and the eaves of thatched roofs. The nest is a large, loose structure, consisting of sticks, straws, and feathers lined with wool ; the eggs being light green in ground colour, blotched with brown. Having all the pert ways of its European relative, the black-breasted sparrow is partial to corn, but also consumes insects. The adult male has the crown, throat, and breast black, the back of the head and neck brown, the back and rump rufous, a white eye stripe running backwards from above the eye, the wings and tail brown, and the lower parts dirty white.

A second South African species, *P. arcuatus*, is commonly called the Cape sparrow, and a third kind, *P. alaris*, the alaris sparrow. West Africa is the home of the grey-headed sparrow (*P. simplex*), the place of which is taken on the opposite side of the continent by the yellow *P. luteus*. In Arabia the group is represented by the golden sparrow (*P. euchlorus*).

SERIN FINCHES

The serin finch (*Serinus hortulanus*) is the typical representative of an Old World group characterised by the hard, conical beak, with the upper half slightly exceeding the lower in length, the wings moderate in length, the tail rather deeply forked, the metatarsus slender, and scutellate in front, and the toes short. Yellow usually predominates in the plumage, the females generally having the flanks striated with dark brown. Out of about a score of species, the majority are peculiar to Africa, and of these the greater number to the southern portion of that continent.

The typical serin ranges through Central and Southern Europe to Asia Minor, Palestine, and Egypt; Tristram's serin (*S. tristrami*) inhabits Palestine; while the red-fronted serin (*S. rufifrons*) is found in the Caucasus and Turkestan. The serin is partial to orchards and gardens, and winters in Southern Europe and North Africa, visiting Central Europe in summer.

Its nest is a neat structure, generally placed at the extremity of a bough, composed of vegetable fibres, moss, and fine stems, lined with feathers and sometimes a little horsehair. Although it prefers fruit trees to beech, oak, or alder, the serin sometimes nests in fir trees in walled gardens. On the Continent it frequents the foot of the mountains skirting the plains, but does not affect the plains themselves; neither is it found in the mountains, where it is replaced by the citril finch. It is usually met with in orchards, gardens, and vineyards, frequently in gardens surrounded by houses.

The serin may easily be recognised by its call note and flight. The former somewhat resembles that of the canary, but may be distinguished by anyone who has heard both. Its song is poor, and lacks both depth and melody, being merely a continuous twittering warble, generally uttered, it would seem, as the bird is seated on the topmost spray of some tree, usually a fruit tree. The flight is exceedingly swift, and may be compared to that of a sand martin, which it far more nearly resembles than that of any other finch.

This bird sometimes sings whilst on the wing; that is to say, it will fly up from the spray on which it has been seated like a tree pipit, and continue its song during the short time it is in the air. It feeds chiefly on seeds of different kinds, seeds of grass and those of various wild plants and weeds, chiefly such as are oily; and it appears always to shell the seeds and discard the husks before swallowing them. It seeks food in fields, gardens, and especially in vineyards, where it is usually found. The nest is a very compact structure, carefully made, and neatly shaped, built of fine roots and grass bents, and neatly lined with feathers and horsehair. The eggs vary from four to five in number, and are blotched with dark reddish brown.

SERIN FINCH AND NEST

When migrating in the north of Spain, these birds do not seem to travel in large flocks, but rather in small parties, sometimes even singly, though the latter are presumably only stragglers from the main detachment of the migrating host. The serin is among the small birds netted in the environs of Paris. Occasionally it straggles to the south coast of Great Britain, where it has been taken on the southern shores on several occasions, especially in the neighbourhood of Brighton, these visits generally taking place in the spring.

The plumage of the male is pale brown above, with dark middles to the feathers; the forehead and nape are yellow, the lower part of the back and rump bright yellow, the cheeks ashy grey, the quills blackish or dusky brown, edged with yellow, the throat and breast yellow, and the sides of the body and flanks ashy brown, washed with yellow and streaked with black.

THE CANARY

Although found in most of the islands from which it takes its name, the canary (*Serinus canarius*) is specially abundant in Las Palmas, where it may be seen in great flocks throughout the breeding season. In Teneriffe it begins breeding near the coast in January, while in the high mountains it nests in June and July, ascending to its elevated haunts in the end of May; the nest being generally placed in an evergreen tree or shrub. The eggs are bluish green in ground colour, and spotted with reddish brown. The song of the wild male is sweet and powerful, but does not possess the variety of notes heard from cage birds.

The male has the upper parts ashy brown washed with yellow and streaked with blackish brown, the forehead, rump, and lower parts yellow, and the sides ashy streaked with black. The domesticated bird, which in some cases has been crossed with the greenfinch, exhibits considerable variation in the colour of the plumage, and in some breeds has developed a kind of crest or topknot.

ROSE FINCHES

The scarlet rose finch (*Carpodacus erythrinus*) is the typical representative of a group of finches common to both hemispheres, and characterised by the beak being of proportionately smaller dimensions than in the pine grosbeak, to which these birds are nearly related. The side of the beak is convex, and the culmen moderately curved, the wings are long and pointed, the tail is much shorter than the wings, and considerably forked, and the feet are small and weak. The males are remarkable for their crimson plumage, but the females and young males are plain-coloured.

Rose finches are found in North-Eastern and Eastern Asia, Asia Minor, Palestine, the Indian region, and China, one species breeding so far west as Pomerania; and although the majority belong to the Old World, a few are peculiar to North America, one of which closely resembles an Old World kind.

In regard to the typical species, Dr. Taczanowski observes that in Poland these birds "first appear about May 15, and after a few days are found at their regular nesting places. They arrive singly, and take up their habitation in bushes near water in the middle of fields and marshes; nowhere numerous, they are generally rather rare. The males announce their arrival by a characteristic song, which is easily recognised even at a great distance. They are very restless, whereas the female, on the other hand, is quiet. When singing, the male usually perches on the top of a tree or bush, always in full view, and during the short intervals of the song utters a deep, clear whistle. After about a quarter of an hour of repose it reappears in full view and recommences its song. In singing, it raises the feathers of its crown and throat, and in the sun looks much more beautiful than it really is. The food consists chiefly of the various seeds of trees and bushes, tender buds, etc. These finches seldom feed on seeds of plants, but sometimes resort to the fields to pick up hemp seed. They are not often seen on the ground, and only go there in search of materials for the nest.

"The latter is placed on small bushes, generally on thorns, wild rose trees, hawthorns, and among hops. In form it resembles that of *Sylvia cinerea*, and is constructed of fine, elastic, dry bents, particularly of ranunculus and hop, clover, and umbelliferous plants. The interior is formed of delicate, dry roots and shoots of plants, often interlaced with a few horse-hairs or other coarse hairs. The nest is loosely constructed and the exterior almost carelessly, but it is regular and neat in the inside and in form almost semicircular. It is placed in a fork of the bush without being fastened to the branches, and is always well hidden in the foliage. The general complement of eggs is five, rarely four or six. They are slightly elongated, slender, oval, or sometimes almost pyriform. In colour they are of a beautiful blue green, almost like the eggs of the song thrush, and are marked with spots of reddish black, more numerous at the larger end and but few on the rest of the surface. In general character they resemble those of the bullfinch, but are less in size, and the ground colour is more intense and pure, while at the same time the spots are deeper.

"During the period of incubation, and when the young are still small, the male sings continually, but in different places and often far off, although it frequently returns to the vicinity of the nest. When any person approaches, it calls exactly like a canary, and the female uses the same alarm note. As soon as the young begin to be feathered, the male ceases his song and becomes as shy as the female. When they leave the nest, the whole family conceal themselves in the foliage, and it is very difficult to get sight of them, and they remain thus until they leave. In Siberia they are common, and remain longer there than in Poland. They nest in young conifers."

Although never varied, the song is sometimes repeated twice in rapid succession, and when it is heard, the bird may usually be seen perched conspicuously on the top of a bush or low tree. The marshy forest banks of the great Siberian rivers are favourite resorts of this bird; and in the Baltic provinces, where it is common, and in the valley of the Upper Volga it frequents willows and other low trees in marshy districts. In winter it ranges over the plains of India, sometimes in large flocks, but more generally in small parties, frequenting alike groves, gardens, and jungles. In Gilgit it breeds at an elevation of ten thousand feet above the sea, eggs having been obtained there in the second half of July.

In Central and Western Europe the scarlet finch is only known as a rare straggler, generally on the autumnal migration, and as such it has occurred in the British Isles. The colour of the adult male is dark brown above washed with rosy or pale crimson; the wings and tail are dark brown, the lower part of the back and rump are dull rosy, the crown of the head is dull crimson, the cheeks, throat, and breast are bright crimson, and the centre of the breast and under parts dull white, slightly washed with crimson; Indian specimens, as a rule, are much more brilliant than those obtained in Northern Europe. The female, on the other hand, lacks

THE CANARY

bright colours, being olive brown above, with the lower part of the back and rump olive brown, the wing coverts dark brown, edged with olive and tipped with yellowish white, so as to form a double wing bar; the wing quills and tail dark brown, edged with olive, the throat dull white streaked with brown, the fore neck and breast ochrey buff, with dusky centres to the feathers, the under parts white, and the sides of the body and flanks brown with dusky stripes.

PURPLE FINCH

In the United States the group is represented by the so-called purple finch (*C. purpureus*). This bird,

SCARLET ROSE FINCH AND SIBERIAN LONG-TAILED FINCH

with both halves much curved, the wings very long, reaching within a third of an inch of the end of the tail, when closed, and the metatarsus comparatively long. The plumage of both sexes is grey or brown, suffused with pink (p. 1039). The desert finch, the western representative of the genus, is found in the Canaries, the Sahara, and Egypt, extending eastwards through Afghanistan and Baluchistan to the Punjab, while the Mongolian desert finch (*E. mongolica*) inhabits the deserts of Central Asia, extending eastwards into Western China. The typical desert finch is an inhabitant of the most sterile regions.

Its song in the Canaries has been described by Dr. Bolle, who writes that " it is always ringing like silver bells through the still desert, or the almost imperceptible chords of a harmonium played by unseen hands. Again it changes, and this time its notes resemble the deep croak of the green frog of the Canaries, but less coarse, hastily repeated one after another. The desert finch does not appear frequently on the steep, rocky hills. It is much more partial to the black lava streams of the desert, which, full of gaping rents and chasms, hardly permit a blade of grass to become green. They feed entirely, or almost so, on the seeds either of grasses, which are found like a mealy kind of bread in their stomachs when killed, or the oily seed of composite and cruciferous plants, which they shell, like other finches, by moving them most carefully backwards and forwards between the mandibles of their strong beaks.

" In Fuertaventura the moras, as they are called there, build in crevices under large overhanging stones upon the ground. The nest has a tolerably strong texture, and is woven with coarse desert grass and lined with feathers, mostly of the ostrich and bustard, as well as the wool of the camel and hair of the goat. The number of eggs is from three to five ; they are pale sea green, with small spots and points of reddish brown. The desert finch occasionally strays from its southern home into the Mediterranean region." The adult male

observes Miss M. O. Wright, " is not purple, but, when in full plumage, washed with a rich raspberry red, deepest on the breast, crown, and rump, light breast, brownish back, wings, and tail, is one of the notable members of the family. Its bill is heavy and round, approaching in size those of the grosbeaks, while in body it ranks with song and house sparrows. Besides having a heavy bill that suggests the grosbeak, it has a way of bristling the feathers of its crown that sometimes gives it the aggressive mien of the cardinal ; while its clinking call-note and way of flying in scattered flocks, and the fact that it winters in the United States, cause it to be sometimes mistaken in the distance for one of the crossbills.

" One would think that, with its rich colouring and the fact that it is a winter resident in many parts of its range, this finch would be a well-known bird ; yet many people who have a fair knowledge of common birds do not seem to know it. Perhaps this is because the females and immature birds, wearing grey and brown stripes, look so very much like their sparrow kin that the rosy-vested bird that sings in the trees, where his colours cannot be seen unless you are directly under him, escapes unnoticed. The change of the young male finch from his northern plain garb to the full crimson costume is interesting, as it is deliberate, taking two seasons, the rosy flush not appearing until the end of the second year."

In Central Asia the group is represented by *C. severtzowi*, and in the Caucasus by *C. rubicillus*. The above-mentioned American *C. purpureus* appears closely allied to the Siberian species, but the Mexican bloodstained rose finch (*C. hæmorrhous*) is very distinct. Nearly allied to this genus are the long-tailed finches (*Uracus*), inhabiting Eastern Siberia and Manchuria.

DESERT FINCHES

The desert finch (*Erythrospiza githaginea*) is a member of an allied group characterised by the beak being short and much arched,

DESERT FINCHES

in the breeding season has the upper parts, including the crown, ashy grey, the forehead, cheeks, rump, and lower parts rose pink, and the wings and tail brown, edged with rose pink. The female is similar, but with duller tints.

BULLFINCHES

Bullfinches form an Old World group, most of the members of which are distinguished by the large head, short, swollen beak, sharp wings, and squared or slightly forked tail. Although the two sexes differ considerably in colour, both combine a white rump with black wings and tail. The bullfinch (*Pyrrhula europæa*) is typically a native of Northern Europe and Siberia, the Central European and British bird being a small and duller-coloured race.

The Azores possess a bullfinch (*P. marina*) which has almost entirely lost the bright colours adorning the males of the other members of the genus ; and another plain-coloured species is the brown bullfinch (*P. nepalensis*), of the Himalaya, whose range apparently overlaps that of yet another Himalayan species, the red-headed bullfinch (*P. erythrocephala*). The orange bullfinch (*P. aurantiaca*) is found in Kashmir and the adjoining territories. During the summer the habits of the bullfinch are shy and retiring, but in the spring this bird appears commonly in gardens, where it commits serious ravages upon the buds of fruit trees.

There can be little doubt that bullfinches pair for life ; and it may be noticed that these birds are of an affectionate disposition, the cock being rarely absent from its mate at any time of the year. Generally beginning to build about the middle of May in ordinary seasons, the bullfinch may lay a full clutch of eggs as early as the middle of April ; the nest, which is placed in a low tree or bush, seldom at a greater

HEN BULLFINCH ON NEST

height than five feet from the ground, being composed of slender twigs, flat and shallow in form, but firmly woven together, and lined with root fibres (page 990). The eggs vary from four to six in number, and are greenish blue in ground colour, speckled and spotted with purplish grey, and dark purplish markings. Two or even three broods of young are sometimes reared in a season, in which the male sex largely predominates ; indeed, there are cases where all the young in a brood have been of this sex. When the young leave the nest, they live with their parents in family parties, searching the hedgerows for the berries of privet and other shrubs. In the breeding season the cock bullfinch is a pugnacious bird, always ready to do battle with any intruder who may venture into his territory.

The bullfinch is not migratory to any large extent, although it wanders considerable distances when pressed by hunger. In England it is seldom that more than nine or ten are seen in a flock, but in Southern Sweden the typical form wanders about in large droves, sometimes composed exclusively of cocks. Generally feeding almost entirely on wild seeds, fruit-buds, and berries, in severe weather the bullfinch devours the seeds of the plantain. The flight is usually low and undulating ; but at times these birds may be seen flying at a considerable elevation, and alighting on the tops of the tallest forest trees.

The natural song is feeble and without pretension ; not that this species is devoid of musical taste, for the young cocks, if untrained, essay to sing their natural notes when about four weeks old, but rather that the bird stands in need of a tutor, by whose patience its capacity for reproducing a lively air may be turned to practical account. Germans bestow great pains on teaching bullfinches, and are content to turn out only a limited number of really accomplished birds. The call note is low and plaintive, and one of the most familiar of the varied sounds that from time to time break the silence of English woodlands.

The plumage is subject to considerable variation, even in a wild state ; one of the most remarkable varieties being creamy dun colour, contrasting strongly with the jetty black crown, wings, and tail. The cock sometimes combines a rosy breast with upper parts of snowy whiteness. Typically the adult male is bluish grey above, with the crown, wings, and tail glossy black, the rump white, and the lower parts pale vermilion, of varying shade. In the female the breast is chocolate brown.

THE BULLFINCH

PINE GROSBEAK

A near relative of the bullfinch, the pine grosbeak (*Pinicola enucleator*) is an inhabitant of the pine woods of the northern regions of both the Eastern and Western Hemispheres. It is remarkable for variation in the time of the assumption of the adult dress, there being little doubt that cocks have bred while in the immature plumage. The wings and tail are of moderate length, the latter being distinctly forked; and the feet are small, the metatarsus not exceeding the third toe in length. The sexes are easily distinguished by the crimson red plumage of the adult male, although immature cocks cannot thus be distinguished.

Mr. Seebohm observes that " pine grosbeaks arrive at their breeding grounds in small flocks in April, and continue to be gregarious until summer comes, when they disperse for the purpose of building their nests. They appear to be somewhat shy and retiring birds, because they do not frequent the roads like the bullfinches, the snow buntings, and the mealy redpolls. But this is by no means the case; they confine themselves principally to the woods, where they are not difficult to approach, even when the sportsman is obliged to hunt them in snowshoes, six feet long, to support his weight upon the untrodden surface.

" In the large pine forests they prefer the banks of the rivers or the outskirts of some open place, and may often escape detection from the habit of frequenting the tops of trees. Within the Arctic Circle many of the trees are small, and on the hilly ground they are scattered in small clumps, or sometimes in isolated trees, the drooping boughs of the spruce firs looking very graceful on the white snow. In places like these the pine grosbeak may often be seen perched conspicuously on the top of a spruce fir, twenty or thirty feet from the ground, but looking so much like the last spike of the tree as frequently to escape notice.

" The call note is a plaintive single note, somewhat like that of the bullfinch, but incapable of being expressed on paper. The song is very melodious, no very loud or long, but flute-like. The flight is undulating and powerful. The breeding season is said to be the end of May or beginning of June. The nests are generally placed in a spruce fir tree ten or twelve feet from the ground, on a thick branch close to the main stem. The nest is made on the same model as that of the hawfinch and bullfinch, but of coarser materials. The outside is a framework of slender fir twigs; and the inside, which projects above the outside, is composed of roots of fine grass, and a lichen which grows upon the branches of the trees, and might easily be mistaken for hair. The number of eggs varies from three to four. The ground colour is pale greenish blue, boldly spotted, principally at the larger end, with surface spots varying from rich brown to almost black, and with underlying spots of greyer brown."

The general colour of the adult male is rosy crimson, with ashy bases to the feathers, the wings and tail being dusky brown, with the feathers edged with rose colour. The female has the upper parts ashy grey, the crown of the head and sides of the face golden olive yellow, spreading on to the mantle, and the throat and under surface ashy grey, washed with golden olive.

CROSSBILLS

Crossbills are unmistakable birds on account of the crossing of the tips of the two halves of the beak. In general conformation the beak is hard, strong, and thick at the base, with the lower half curving upwards, and its point crossing that of the upper one; a structural conformation enabling these birds to extract with facility the seeds deeply buried beneath

PINE GROSBEAK

the overlapping scales of the fir cones on which they feed.

This peculiar structure is, however, developed only in the adult, young birds in the nest having the beak of normal conformation. As regards other characters, crossbills have the wings long and pointed, and the tail forked and relatively short in proportion to the wings.

The males are gaily attired in scarlet, crimson, and orange plumage, but green and yellow are the predominating hues of the females. Crossbills inhabit the pine forests of both the Old and New Worlds, extending from Siberia to the Himalaya in the Eastern Hemisphere, and in the Western ranging from Arctic North America into Mexico.

When wandering through the pine forests of Northern Scotland or Western Norway the cry of the crossbill (*Loxia curvirostra*) often greets the traveller from amongst the fir cones, directing his attention to the bright plumaged birds skilfully extracting the seeds of the conifers, whilst hanging gracefully in every variety of attitude.

In regard to nesting habits, Mr. Ussher remarks that in March a crossbill was observed carrying twigs to the top of a Scots fir, in which the nest was discovered, although it could only be seen from the ground by a person standing immediately below it and looking straight up through the tree against the sky. " This tree is the outer one of a group, and bare of living branches to within a short distance of its top, which consists of a mass of green, bending over from the west winds, in the midst of which the nest was built among the thick tufts. The finder saw the crossbills visit it frequently with building materials; and several times I saw the birds fly to and from it, and recognised the male by his redness. This pair probably reared their young in safety, for, on May 10, a pair of crossbills were seen feeding their young on larch trees in the vicinity of this nest. A second nest was subsequently discovered, which was in the top of a Scots fir about two hundred and fifty yards from the first. It was built in the fork formed by several small lateral branches with the leader, which at that point takes a bend; and the nest, which is small for so large a bird, might easily be mistaken from the ground for a knot or enlargement of the crooked leader. It was placed in a perfect little cluster or bower of smaller branches; and was composed externally of fine dead twigs of larch and Scots fir, and within them of green moss, interwoven with wool, a few horsehairs, and flakes of finer bark. The birds used not to cease their call notes while flying to a neighbouring tree and thence into the nesting-tree; and the call of the female was heard apparently coming from the nest itself. It was like the syllables '*yep yep*,' or '*yup yup*,' while that of the male is much sharper, like '*gip gip*.'

" In a young bird taken from this nest the points of the mandibles were straight, not crossed, but the edges of the upper one overlapped the lower on both sides. The down was all gone, and the plumage exhibited dark spots on a lighter ground both on the upper and under surfaces. It was replaced in the tree, from which it must have afterwards fallen, for a nestling was found in the adjoining field and placed in a cage near the nesting tree, where the old crossbills, which had other young in the tree, continued to feed

pair of crossbills, when excited, used often to attract another pair—the male a red one—which frequented the neighbouring trees, and which on such occasions would join their neighbours in the excitement; their nest was discovered by the birds being seen carrying building materials to it. They picked up bits of hay off the ground, not heeding the observer standing near them."

Although the crossbill resides permanently in many parts of its range, in certain years great flights visit the British Isles, and take up their abode in parts of the country planted with belts of fir trees, as was the case in 1888 and 1909. Sometimes large flocks appear on their journey across the North Sea, and in June, 1888, crossbills visited Heligoland in flights, varying from ten to fifty birds. Hawthorns in the gardens were then crowded with these birds, and on some days there must have been hundreds dispersed among the foliage.

In the full plumage the adult male is pale vermilion above, the feathers having dusky bases; the crown of the head is pale vermilion, like the back and under surface, the primaries and tail feathers are dark brown, and the lower part of the abdomen, the sides of the body and the flanks ashy brown washed with vermilion. After the first moult the tints become more orange and more uniform, but the flanks are striped, and there are also more or less striped feathers on other portions of the body. It is now conclusively proved that the bright colours of the male are gradually assumed, and that it takes two or even three moults before the full red plumage is acquired.

The plumage of the female differs from that of the male in being olive yellow where the latter is red; the head, the lower part of the back, and the rump are much brighter than the mantle, which is dusky brown, while the under surface of the body is yellow, with ashy bases to the feathers.

From the typical species the Himalayan crossbill (*L. himalayana*) is distinguished by its small size, but the Japanese *L. japonica* is large, while the white-winged American *L. leucoptera* is again small. The range of the Himalayan bird extends from Sikkim to North-Western China and Tibet. Another species (*L. luzoniensis*) inhabits the Philippines. Writing of the American red crossbill (*L. curvirostra minor*) and the white-winged species, Dr. Elliott Coues observes that " both are birds of the most strongly marked originality of character, and it is never safe to predict what they may or may not be found about. Their most remarkable habit is that of breeding in winter, or very early in spring, when one would think it impossible that their callow young could endure the rigour of the season. They are most devoted parents, seeming entirely insensible of danger in defence of their homes.

" These birds are much attached to pine woods, the seeds of the conifers furnishing them abundant food, of a kind that their curiously shaped bills enable them to secure with great ease and address. From their summer resorts in the depth of evergreen woods the crossbills come flocking in the autumn to all other parts of New England and beyond, generally associated with pine grosbeaks and redpolls, always gentle, unsuspicious, and apparently quite at their ease. They are not so common, however, as the red crossbills, and both species take such freaks in deciding their course of action that their appearance can never be relied upon. It need surprise no one to come upon a pair of crossbills breeding anywhere in New England, for they seem to be independent of weather or season.

THE CROSSBILL

it often in the presence of observers. In the meantime it became accustomed to feed on bruised hemp-seed when it was removed to the house, where it soon became full-grown, and tame. The notes of the last

"Their diet is not so exclusive as many suppose; the birds may sometimes be seen helping themselves to decayed garden fru ts. They have been observed feeding on the seeds of beach-grass, and their stomachs have been found filled with canker-worms. The eggs of this species resemble those of the purple finch, and are probably indistinguishable from those of the red crossbill. Both species of crossbills have a chattering or rattling note, usually uttered as they fly, but their true song is seldom heard south of their nesting grounds."

SCARLET FINCH

Nearly allied to the crossbills is the scarlet finch (*Hæmatospiza sipahi*), from the mountains of Nepal and Sikkim, distinguished by the very strong and stout beak being of normal form. The cock of this species is red, while the hen is green; a remarkable feature of both sexes being the white of the bases of the feathers of the head and neck, which are seen conspicuously when the plumage is at all ruffled. The wing is of considerable length, reaching beyond the middle of the tail. The scarlet finch is an inhabitant of both forest and bushy districts, and utters a loud, whistling note

RED-HEADED AND RED-BREASTED ROSE FINCHES

The Oriental genera *Propyrrhula* and *Pyrrhospiza*, intermediate between the crossbills and rose finches, are among the most interesting of the remaining members of the sub-family. The red-headed rose finch (*Propyrrhula sub-himalayensis*) is found in the more open parts of the woods in North-Western India. The male has a brownish crimson body, with bright crimson forehead, cheeks, and throat, the brown wings and tail having reddish margins; the female is not unlike the female of the scarlet finch, but much yellower in colour.

The female of the red-breasted rose finch (*Pyrrhospiza punicea*) is almost exactly like those of the genus *Carpodacus*, but the male is easily distinguishable, being brownish, with crimson forehead, throat, and breast, the crown black like the back, and light brown margins to the feathers. The horn-brown bill is stouter and shorter than that of the red-headed rose finch, but of much the same shape as that of the scarlet finch.

The red-breasted rose finch is a Himalayan bird, ranging from Kashmir to Tibet and Western China at elevations of from ten to seventeen thousand feet. The nest is built of coarse grass, and contains greenish brown spotted eggs. Closely allied is *P. humei*, which is also found in the Himalaya, and has the head and breast rosy instead of crimson, while the brown of the back is pale.

LAYSAN FINCH

The genus *Telespiza* is characterised by the beak being short and much arched, with the upper half showing a tendency to cross the lower, as in the crossbill; the wings are of moderate length, reaching to

about the end of the basal third of the tail feathers; the tail is slightly forked, and the feet are remarkably large and strong. The single species (*T. cantans*) is peculiar to the island of Laysan, in the Pacific. These birds, when first discovered, were common among the scrubby bushes covering the surface of their island home, where they were so excessively tame and unsophisticated that their capture with the hand was an easy matter.

This finch has a clear, metallic note, which may be rendered "chwit, chwee." In the adult the head and sides of the face are olive green, shading behind into dark chestnut brown on the back, where each feather has the centre black; the rump and upper tail coverts chestnut brown; the primaries black, edged with yellowish; the tail black, having each feather edged with greenish yellow, and the throat and breast bright greenish yellow, passing into white on the under parts.

SNOW BUNTINGS

The snow bunting (*Plectrophanes nivalis*) may be taken as the first representative of the buntings, sub-family *Emberizinæ*, distinguished from the finch section by the fact that the cutting edges of the upper and lower halves of the beak are not in contact throughout their length, forming a gap about midway between the gape and the tip. The palate is furnished with a hard, horny knob. In a few species the claw of the first toe is elongated like that of a lark. The great majority of the buntings belong to the northern parts of the Old World, although some inhabit Central Asia or reside permanently in India, many having an extensive range. The snow bunting supports life further north than any other small bird.

SNOW BUNTING

In this species the beak is small and conical, the wings are very long and pointed, the tail is moderate and slightly forked, and the claw of the first toe straight and elongated. The snow bunting is common to nearly all the northern portions of the world, and occasionally strays on migration into Central and even Southern Europe; in Alaska it is represented by the closely allied *P. hyperboreus*.

Although many snow buntings pass the entire year on certain Scottish mountains, it was not until the summer of 1885 that several parties of these birds were observed in Sutherland, and not till the following year that a nest was taken in the north of Scotland containing the only eggs of the species discovered up to that time on the mainland of Great Britain. The finder was searching for ptarmigan on the mountains between Sutherland and Caithness, and while descending recognised the call note of the snow bunting, and reached the nest, which contained five richly-coloured eggs, and was composed of bents and moss, lined with a few ptarmigan's feathers, and one or two small pieces of wool. Since then several nests have been found in Scotland.

Considerable numbers of snow buntings pass the summer in the Färoes, where on the southerly islands they are restricted to the mountain tops, although on the northerly ones they frequent the lower ground in small colonies. Throughout Iceland the species is perhaps the commonest of small birds, a pair or more being established in nearly every convenient locality, even among the most desolate lava streams, and it breeds there almost on the sea level as well as up to the snow line. As is shown by the accumulation of old materials, the birds commonly use the same nest-hole more than once. The eggs vary from four to six in number, and are white in ground colour, more or less tinged with pale greenish blue, splashed with dull lilac, and spotted with brownish red.

The adult male has the crown ruddy brownish black, the scapulars black, edged with reddish brown, the primaries black, the secondaries white, the outer ones being marked on both edges with black, the central tail feathers black tipped with white, the under tail feathers white streaked with black on the outer edges, a rusty band across the breast and the lower parts white. In summer the light tips to the feathers of the upper parts are shed, and the bird then appears to be black and white, black predominating (page 1040).

LAPLAND BUNTING

On account of its greatly elongated hind toe, the Lapland bunting (*Plectrophanes nivalis*), together with two nearly allied North American species, or races, is often assigned to a genus (*Calcarius*) distinct from the one typified by the snow bunting. This is a widely-spread Old World species, inhabiting the high northern regions during summer, and migrating southwards to more congenial winter quarters before the arrival of frost and snow in its northern home.

In summer this bird frequents the fell-mosses of Norway and Sweden, especially such as are covered with grass and willow scrub and are situated below the snow region. Not inhabiting the high mountains on which the snow bunting breeds, it prefers the upland swamps, and in Northern Europe seeks the swampiest ground it can find, so long as there are tussocks of dry grass full of flowers where it can breed. If there be also a few stunted willows or birches upon which it can perch, so much the better. The nest is nearly always placed in some hole in a side of the little mounds or tussocks abounding on the marshy parts of the tundra, and is composed of dry grass and roots, and profusely lined with feathers. The eggs vary from pale grey to pale brown in ground colour, and are streaked with dark brown with underlying blotches of brown. Nests of this species in Norway are often built of dry grass and lined with feathers; particularly those of snipe. The newly-hatched young are clothed with dark down.

The sweet and musical song is usually poured forth when the bird is in the air, soaring like a lark, and continued until it alights on a grassy knoll or stunted bush. The female has almost as rich a song as the male. Formerly the Lapland bunting rarely straggled

LAPLAND BUNTINGS

so far westwards as the British Isles during its autumnal migration, but nowadays it not only breeds nearer than it used, but small numbers visit the southern shores of England yearly. Before 1892 the Lapland bunting had been captured most frequently in Kent, more particularly near Dover, but in the autumn of that year great numbers visited Eastern and Southern England, the first arrivals being observed in Norfolk during September, and these being soon followed by large flocks. Numbers were also obtained during the winter of 1892–3 on the downs near Brighton, and the species has occurred in equal abundance in Northumberland. Lapland buntings become tame sooner than do snow buntings, while their notes are more silvery.

The male Lapland bunting in breeding plumage has the entire head, throat, and upper part of the breast black; a rich chestnut collar reaches from behind the head on to the back; and the upper parts are brownish black margined with buff and white (page 1040). The female differs in having light margins to the feathers of the head, throat, and flanks, while the feathers of the chin and upper throat are buffish white, with half-concealed black bases. After the autumnal moult all the feathers have light edges. Males of the year closely resemble adult females, but differ in having no black centres to the feathers on the nape.

TYPICAL BUNTINGS

The genus *Emberiza* includes the typical buntings, all of which are crestless, and have forked tails; the bill being hard, short, and conical, the first primary small, and the fourth or fifth commonly the longest in the wing, and considerably longer than the next, while the metatarsus is covered with scales in front and on the sides with an entire plate forming a sharp ridge behind. These buntings are represented by numerous species from the temperate and northern parts of Europe and Asia, as well as from North Africa and India.

REED BUNTING

The reed bunting, or reed sparrow (*E. schœniclus*) frequents swampy ground over almost the whole of the continent of Europe, from the south of Spain to the North Cape. Among the osier beds of the Thames and its tributaries it forms a conspicuous object in summer, as it chants its snatches of song from some prominent position by the waterside. The female builds her nest among rushes or long grass on the side of a bank, or in a dense tussock of the morass which forms her home, not infrequently amid white tufts of cotton grass. The eggs are drab in ground colour, streaked with black and dark purple. The young, like those of certain other species which nest upon the ground, frequently leave their nest before they can fly, trusting to their protective colours to secure their safety.

Resident in some districts, these buntings are in others partial migrants, a considerable number passing the winter in the British Isles, where they occasionally seek shelter in woods at a distance from their usual aquatic haunts. Their food consists of seeds of water plants, small molluscs, and insects, but occasionally they feed in stubble fields. The reed bunting is gregarious, and fond of associating in small or even large flocks during winter and spring.

The colour of the adult male in the breeding season is rufous, with broad black middles to the feathers of the back; the wing coverts are chestnut; the primaries blackish, edged with rufous; the tail feathers dark brown, but the two outer ones edged with white; the crown of the head and sides of the face and ear-coverts black, separated from the back by a broad band of white, which forms a collar joining the white sides of the head; the throat black, and the remainder of the under surface are white, streaked with black on the sides of the body (p. 1040).

LITTLE BUNTING

Among the Arctic birds from time to time straying into Western Europe during their seasonal migrations may be mentioned the little bunting (*E. pusilla*). Near Archangel it is very common in summer, although local in its choice of nesting grounds. Its low, sweet song is comparable to that of a warbler rather than of a bunting, and the bird frequents pine woods and mixed timber. Mr. Seebohm, who found this bunting abundant on the Yenisei, states that its quiet song was constantly heard before the snow had sufficiently melted to make the forest penetrable. The first nest was found on June 23, on the south bank of the Kurayika, a tributary of the Yenisei, and contained five eggs.

The nest was nothing but a hole made in the dead leaves, grass, and moss, copiously and carefully lined with fine dead grass. A second nest was taken in the forest on the opposite bank of the river on June 29, containing three eggs, and was in a similar position to the first. On June 30 was found a third nest, containing five eggs, slightly incubated; this nest was lined with reindeer-hair. On July 6, a few miles further down the river, yet another nest was discovered,

containing six eggs; it was similar to the last, but rather more sparingly lined with reindeer-hair. In each case the tameness of the bird was very noticeable.

The eggs in the first nest were almost exact miniatures of those of the corn bunting. The ground colour was pale grey, with bold twisted blotches and irregular round spots of very dark grey, and equally large underlying shell-markings of paler grey. The eggs in the second nest were redder, being brown rather than grey, but the markings were similar.

The adult male in breeding dress has the upper parts rufous brown, with broad black middles to the feathers, the centre of the crown purplish chestnut, with a broad black streak on each side, forming a band, and an eyebrow stripe, the lores, sides of face, ear coverts, and throat purplish chestnut. The remainder of the lower parts are dull white, the lower portion of the throat, fore neck, and breast, as well as the sides of the body, being streaked with black. The adult female scarcely differs from the male, although not so bright-coloured.

TRUE BUNTING

The true bunting, or corn bunting (*E. miliaria*), is abundant in many parts of Europe, from Southern Spain to the Hebrides, but being to a large extent dependent upon grain crops for its existence, its distribution varies with that cereal. Sometimes it frequents the pastures, uttering its droning song from the top of a tall hedge-row tree; but more often it resorts to arable fields, where it utters its short song from a clod of earth, a clump of dock, a stone wall, or turf dyke.

Generally these buntings feed partially on insects, but in autumn and midwinter subsist almost entirely on grain. The nest is a loose structure, built on the ground in a tuft of rough herbage, and constructed of dry bents and pieces of moss, lined with finer stems of grass and sometimes a little hair. The eggs vary greatly in colouring, being either white or buff in ground colour, blotched and streaked with purplish brown, grey, and pale brown. The normal colour is dull brown above, streaked with darker brown; the under parts being buffish white, and the breast and flanks streaked with black (p. 1040).

BLACK-HEADED BUNTING

South-Eastern Europe is the home of the handsome black-headed bunting (*E. melanocephala*), which but rarely strays into Western Europe, though it has been

REED BUNTING

obtained repeatedly in Heligoland, and on a few occasions in Great Britain. In Greece and Turkey, on the other hand, it is a common summer bird. Dr. Lindermayer gives the following account of its habits : " This bunting arrives always in the last five days of April in Greece, and, like other migrants, appears everywhere at once, so that the flats near the sea, which are covered with vines and other creepers, and also places where the olive trees are scattered about, are alive with this lovely and melodious bird. It is peculiarly partial to vineyards, where it builds on the vines, pomegranates, thorns, or almond trees.

" Its nest is always formed of dried straws, and is carefully made and lined with horsehair. Five eggs are the usual complement, and these are pale sea-green, covered with scattered dark brown spots, though sometimes quite unspotted. I have received hundreds of nests, and often found them myself, as they are not difficult to discover, the bird not being at all shy, and only leaving the nest when approached within a distance of about a yard. I have often known the female to lay afresh after her eggs have been removed. During the breeding season the male sits near the nest, on a branch or a tree top, and continually serenades its mate with its sweet song. If scared away, even by a shot, it retreats to the nearest tree and continues its song."

This species much resembles the corn bunting in general habits, often sitting on the top of a bush or low tree and pouring forth its simple notes, or flying from one elevated part to another with its legs dangling down. The adult male at breeding time has the crown and sides of the head black, the entire back and scapulars chestnut, the primaries and tail feathers brown, the whole under surface, as well as the sides of the neck, rich canary yellow, and the sides of the breast and flanks chestnut. The female is a dull-plumaged bird by comparison with her brilliant mate, having the upper parts nearly uniform brown, but the under surface yellow, with ashy margins to the breast feathers, and the flanks tinged with ash colour.

YELLOW-BREASTED BUNTING

The yellow-breasted bunting (E. aureola) is distributed over the northern parts of the Old World from Russia to the Pacific, and has even strayed so far west as Heligoland, and been captured also in Italy. It is one of the commonest birds in Eastern Siberia, where it frequents the valleys, particularly on the plains and where bushes abound. It perches on the top of a plant or bush, and there sings continually, its song being short and often interrupted, but sweet. The peasants regard it as the best songster in Dauria ; but that is a matter of taste, for many others sing better. These birds arrive on their breeding ground about the middle of May, and begin building early in June, although most of them only begin breeding late in that month.

The nests are placed on the ground and constructed of dry bents, lined with horsehair. The female sits hard, and will permit anyone to approach quite close ; while, when driven off her eggs, she keeps flying about with the male closely in attendance, perching every now and then on the neighbouring bushes, and uttering a note like that of the whinchat. The eggs generally resemble those of the reed bunting, but the ground colour is tinged with greenish.

In the neighbourhood of Archangel the yellow-breasted bunting frequents swampy meadows, or marshes overgrown with birches and willows. The colour of the male is deep chestnut, with the forehead, sides of the face, and upper part of the throat jet black, and the under surface of the body bright yellow, except the chest, which is banded by a zone of chestnut. The female is greyish brown, like a hen-sparrow, above, the lower parts being pale yellow, striped on the flanks with dark brown.

YELLOW BUNTING, OR YELLOW HAMMER

The yellow bunting, or yellow hammer (E. citrinella), is common in Northern Europe, extending eastwards into Siberia, and frequenting alike the more cultivated valleys of Norway and the south of Europe. It may be seen on almost every hedge-row in many parts of England, and is very partial to telegraph wires as a perch. Standing on the highest twig, the cock may be heard incessantly pouring out his monotonous song, and during the breeding season his notes strike the ear from early morn till late in the evening. As twilight sets in, the yellow bunting may still be heard, and it is perhaps the last bird to cease its song, with the exception of the corn bunting,

ORTOLAN AND BLACK-HEADED BUNTINGS

which sings till dusk. The yellow bunting generally nests upon some bank, occasionally in a furze bush. The eggs are white, scribbled over with fine, hairlike markings (page 990). In autumn yellow buntings collect in flocks, feeding on blackberries and other wild fruits, as well as on grain in the open fields. As the season advances they seek the neighbourhood of homesteads, and search for worms and other insects on heaps of manure.

Although the yellow bunting is supposed to be a resident species in Great Britain, there can be no doubt that it is only a summer visitant in its more northern breeding grounds. Large numbers sometimes occur on migration in Heligoland. The male has the head and throat bright yellow, the back brown, inclined to rufous, with dark middles to all the feathers ; the wings and tail are blackish brown, the outer tail feathers having the inner webs partly white (page 1040). In winter the plumage is rendered more dingy by tawny edgings to the feathers. The female is greyish brown above, with the lower part of the back, the rump, and upper tail coverts pale cinnamon, the under parts citron yellow, and the upper portion of the breast mottled with brown and tinged with olive green.

CIRL BUNTING

Closely allied to the last, but more elegant in colouring, is the cirl bunting (*E. cirlus*), which is sparingly distributed throughout Central Europe, being in some districts even more common than the yellow bunting, although generally taking rank as a scarce bird. English ornithologists know it best as a resident in the southern counties, particularly in the west, but it has nested so far north as Yorkshire. It is numerous in North Devon, around Barnstaple especially, where it is a shyer bird than the yellow bunting, and fond of concealing itself in spring and summer in thick hedges. In spring, and again in autumn, the cock may often be seen perched on the branch of a hedgerow elm, whence it delivers its unpretending song.

In Germany the cirl bunting is migratory, leaving its northern habitat in November, perhaps even much earlier, wintering far to the south and returning in April. It frequents the same kind of places as the yellow bunting, such as the bushy banks of streams, meadows, and hedges, small groves, and mountainous districts in the neighbourhood of fields and gardens. In many other respects the cirl bunting resembles the yellow bunting. In spring it prefers to take up its position in a high and open place on the tops of trees, but later in the season is found lower down, and always likes to hide in dense thickets. It hops a good deal upon the ground, is by no means shy, and when disturbed soon settles on the nearest low bush. In flight it resembles its relative, and is equally quarrelsome, and at times as restless. These buntings eat both insects and seeds. The song bears some resemblance to that of the lesser redpoll and lesser whitethroat, but still more closely resembles that of the yellow bunting, although never ending with the long-drawn note characteristic of the latter.

The cirl bunting breeds early, nesting in positions similar to those adopted by the yellow bunting, and constructing its nest on a bank or amongst briars and brambles, usually at no great distance from the ground. The nest is built of dry roots and grasses, lined with fine roots and a little hair. The eggs are bluish white in ground colour, streaked and blotched with dark brown, two clutches being usually laid in a season.

The song of the male begins early in the year, and is continued through August and September. In hard weather cirl buntings associate with other birds, such as larks, in the open fields. In confinement the cirl bunting is a shy species, very difficult to tame.

In colour the cirl bunting bears some resemblance to the yellow bunting, but the male is distinguished by the fact that the head and nape are olive green, and the rump and upper tail coverts olive green streaked with

MEADOW BUNTING AND CIRL BUNTING

dusky, while one bright stripe extends above and another below the eye. The wings and tail are similar to those of the yellow bunting, but the lesser wing coverts olive green instead of chestnut. The throat is dull black, below which is a broad patch of yellow, and a zone of olive green extends across the breast, shading into chestnut. The hen may be distinguished from the female yellow bunting by the head showing no trace of yellow, the bright yellow under parts, and the olive instead of chestnut rump and upper tail coverts.

THE ORTOLAN

The far-famed ortolan (*E. hortulana*) is a relative of the cirl bunting, and, like that species, more common in Southern Europe than further north. The tameness of the ortolan buntings in Spain is so great that they will forage for the worms which form part of their food while visitors are sitting on the grass close by. They often resort to the edges of thickets and the skirts of fir woods, and their song somewhat resembles that of the yellow bunting. In Sweden they sing both during the day and throughout the light nights of the Arctic summer.

The nests, which are invariably placed upon the ground, and generally in the open fields, are built of dry grass or roots, lined with fine fibres or hair. The eggs vary from bluish white to pale salmon colour, spotted and blotched with rich purple brown. It is remarkable that a bird so common on the Continent should be so rare in Britain. It breeds on the mountains in the pine regions both of Greece and Asia Minor. In Siberia its plaintive, monotonous song may be heard as the bird sits on the branch of a tree or a hedge close to a village; and in the wilder districts of Norway the species is by no means uncommon in the trees by the roadside. It is not a shy bird, and frequently remains a long time on the same twig, generally near the top of the tree, especially in the evening, when its song harmonises with the stillness of the outskirts of the village.

These birds leave Europe in September, arriving in North Africa in large flocks. On their way south numbers are caught in nets and fattened for the table, many being sent to England from Holland and Belgium alive. The adult male has the head grey, tinged with greenish yellow, a ring of feathers round the eyes and throat pale citron yellow, the general colour of the upper parts reddish brown, with black streaks to the feathers of the mantle and back, the eyelid white, the fore neck and chest dusky greenish olive, and the remainder of the under parts reddish cinnamon.

MEADOW BUNTING

The meadow bunting (*E. cia*) is met with locally in Central Europe, frequenting chiefly mountain valleys such as those of many parts of France. Each pair

NEST AND EGGS OF YELLOW BUNTING

Photo, C. Reid

generally occupies its own particular district, and, while the females incubate their eggs, the males rehearse their songs perched in a prominent position on the top of a bush. The nest is made of dry stalks and moss, lined with horsehair and wool. This bunting is numerous in the neighbourhood of Barcelona, where it frequents the cactus hedges, flying when disturbed from plant to plant, and often perching on the top of the cactuses and uttering its call note, " zi, zi, zi."

This species chiefly affects hill sides and barren dry places where only a few stunted bushes are scattered, but in some parts of Europe has been found frequenting vineyards. It feeds on various seeds of wild plants and to some extent on insects. The eggs are distinguished by their continuous markings, which appear as if made by a pen without removing it from the surface. In colour they are pale grey, marked with blackish brown lines. The adult male has the head and neck bluish grey, with two black bands along the sides of the crown, and two others passing through the eye, forming a moustache, the upper parts bright russet, streaked with black, the rump chestnut red, the throat white, the neck and chest delicate bluish grey, and the rest of the under parts russet red. In the female the head, nape, and body are varied with black and russet, the rump and under tail coverts bright russet, the front of the neck and chest shaded with dull grey and spotted with brown, and the flanks of a deeper russet, more or less spotted with brown.

CRESTED AND OTHER BUNTINGS

There are several genera more or less closely allied to the true buntings, which need only be incidentally mentioned. Among these, the crested bunting (*Melophus melanicteris*) of the Himalaya, India, Burma, and China, is the only representative of a genus characterised by the presence of a crest on the head,

larger in the male than in the female. The tail is less forked than in the true buntings, and the sexes differ in colour, although both display a considerable amount of red on the wings and tail. This bunting is solitary in its habits, and generally found on rocky hills and the banks of streams.

The American bunting (*Euspiza americana*) represents a second genus, and the Cape bunting (*Fringillaria capensis*) and Sahara bunting (*F. saharæ*) a third, which is exclusively African and contains numerous species. The sparrow bunting, or white-eyebrowed finch (*Zonotrichia albicollis*), of Mexico, belonging to a group of genera in which the tail is longer than the wing, differs from the true buntings in the exposed nostrils, which are protected by covers, and is specially characterised by the spotted back and sparrow-like form. The genus, which includes numerous species, is exclusively American.

Among other well-known North American members of the family—each representing a genus by itself — may be mentioned the snow bird (*Junco hiemalis*), the chipping sparrow (*Spizella socialis*), and the red-eyed ground finch (*Pipilo erythrophthalmus*).

The indigo bird (*Cyanospiza cyanea*) is another familiar North American species. In

SPARROW BUNTING

the female the upper parts are ashy brown without stripes, the under parts greyish white washed and faintly streaked with dull brown. It is difficult to describe the plumage of the male, for to use simply the term indigo blue is as inadequate as to say that a bit of water that looks blue while in shadow is of the same colour when it ripples out into full sunlight and catches a dozen reflections from foliage and sky. A merely technical description would read: Front of head and chin rich indigo blue, growing lighter and greener on back and under parts ; wings dusky brown, with blue edges to coverts, tail feathers also blue-edged ; bill and feet dark, general shape rounded and canary-like.

LARKS

REPRESENTED by fully a hundred species, arranged under several generic heads, the larks (*Alaridiæ*) are mainly confined to the Old World, although the shore larks (*Otocorys*) range into North America and the West Indies. Some of the more highly specialised forms are peculiar to desert regions, and are adapted

THE SKYLARK

to their environment both in structure and protective coloration. The shape of the beak varies too much in different genera to be of value as a diagnostic character, but the feet are very characteristic. The metatarsus, for instance, is invariably scutellated, and as blunt behind as in front; that is to say, it is covered with two series of plates behind and before, which meet on the inner surface. Other characters are the very long straight claw of the first toe, the long, pointed wings, and the lengthened inner secondary wing feathers. Except for a notch in the upper one, the edges of both mandibles are perfectly smooth.

SKYLARK

In common with the other members of its genus, the lark, or skylark (*Alauda arvensis*), is distinguished by having the first of the ten primaries very small, while the second, third, and fourth are nearly equal, although the third is somewhat the longest; the secondaries are comparatively long, and the tail is moderate and slightly forked. The beak is rather slender, long, arched, and slightly compressed, with plumelets covering the nostrils. Skylarks are principally found in the temperate portions of Europe and Siberia, although extending southwards into China and the plains of India.

The skylark is one of the most common of European birds, nesting in the British Isles, which are visited by myriads from the Continent in autumn and winter. So abundant are these birds that they constitute an article of commerce, and on the Sussex downs extraordinary numbers were formerly netted. Sentiment has never failed to recognise the exceeding beauty of the notes of the lark, which surpass those of all other British birds except the nightingale. Frequenting heaths and pasture lands, and most abundant in open country, during the winter the skylark is a gregarious species, and on a sharp, frosty mornings hundreds may be observed congregating in a single field, flying restlessly, with low, warbling call notes to their companions. The salt marshes bordering many parts of the British coasts are specially adapted to their habits.

Generally skylarks place their simple nests in tussocks of coarse grass, lining them with fine grass. The young are exposed to the attacks of ground vermin, owing to being reared on the ground, but are screened from enemies by the highly protective character of their first plumage, which is spotted with buff, and assimilates to the colour of dried grasses even more closely than do the darker tints of the adult. In the breeding season larks are singularly fearless, the parents of a young brood often allowing a stranger to approach within a very few yards before taking wing.

Young birds reared from the nest become much attached to their owners, and readily acquire the notes of any bird under whose tuition they may be placed. Such birds, however, as are captured adult and in open weather, are apt to pine for the loss of liberty; but those caught when snow is lying on the ground are more susceptible of domestication, and soon begin to sing. The eggs (page 990) are white, thickly blotched and freckled with brown and grey. Young birds may be found in the nest at any time from April to September. Skylarks do not wash, but delight in cleansing their plumage by dusting their feathers in dry earth, this being done in order to remove ticks or other parasites. On migration skylarks often appear at lighthouses in dense hordes, and vast numbers are killed in Heligoland. Although the song is principally uttered during spring and summer, larks often sing in snatches in November.

The food of the skylark consists of oats, wheat, barley, and the seeds of wild plants, together with such insects as it meets with in the ploughed fields. The adult has the upper parts brown, tinged more or less with rufous, many of the feathers having dark middles; the wings are dark brown, the primaries being narrowly edged with white on the outer webs; the tail is brown, with the exception of the outer feathers, which are nearly all white; the throat and breast are buff, streaked with brown; and the rest of the under surface is creamy white. Both sexes are alike.

The range of the skylark extends from the Färoes to the Kurile Islands; in winter the species wanders

CRESTED LARK

as far south and east as North Africa, Persia, and the Punjab. In India it is replaced by the nearly allied *A. galgula*, and in North Africa by the thick-billed lark (*A. crassirostris*).

WOODLARK

The woodlark (*Lullula arborea*), which is placed in a genus apart, may be readily distinguished from the skylark by its shorter tail, more distinctly marked breast, and the presence of a distinct light streak over the eye and ear coverts, while its size is considerably smaller. Unlike the skylark, which frequents open country, the woodlark prefers fields that border upon woods. In localities where the soil is sandy and partially covered with second growth, it is generally numerous, but does not frequent dense forest. In habits it is lively and sprightly, fond of the society of its congeners, and not quarrelsome, although more shy than the skylark. Frequenting the ground more commonly than is supposed, it only perches occasionally on branches when singing, and seeks its food almost always on the ground, where it runs with celerity and ease. It roosts on the ground in open places close to woods, under weeds or grass, or in weed-covered furrows, and retires early to rest.

Being more affected by cold than is the skylark, it migrates earlier southwards than the former. The woodlark's song is sweet and flute-like, more melancholy than that of the skylark, and generally uttered from the top of a tree, or on the wing. The bird rises to some height before beginning, then ascends higher and higher, throwing itself from side to side, hovers and floats in the air, and when the song is ended drops with closed wings to the ground again. Woodlarks sing not only in the morning and evening, but at other times, especially at night.

The woodlark constantly builds upon the ground, usually in a tuft of grass, or in a depression of the earth, sheltered by a low bush. Made of stems of grass and moss, and lined with hair and wool or fine bents, the nest is more compact than that of the skylark. The eggs are generally white, finely flecked, and blotched with brown and purplish markings, sometimes arranged in a zone (page 990).

Very local in the British Isles, especially in the breeding season, when it is chiefly found in the southern and western counties, particularly Devonshire, the woodlark is common in Southern Norway and Sweden, and extends eastwards through Central Russia, ranging

DESERT LARK

south to Spain, Morocco, and Egypt. The plumage of the adult is brown above, each feather being striped with dark brown and edged with rufous; a broad, yellowish white stripe extends from each eye to the nape, forming an irregular collar; the rump and upper tail coverts are greyish brown; and the tail is dark

THE WOODLARK

brown, with the middle pair of feathers much lighter than the others, while the outer pair are dirty white towards the tip, and their outer webs bordered with white.

CRESTED LARKS

The crested lark (*Galerita cristata*) and its relatives are sufficiently distinguished from both the foregoing by the presence on the head of a crest composed of a few long feathers springing from the centre of the crown. The common species is a partial resident in the Continent, and a rare, accidental visitor to the shores of Great Britain. In spring it may be seen in the north of Spain travelling in flocks, which generally frequent the ploughed fields in preference to grass lands. These large flocks are relatively wild; but on other occasions the crested lark is confiding and fearless, and in the neighbourhood of villages and inhabited places one of the most unsuspicious birds.

In Southern Germany and Hungary, where it is common, it may be seen on the high roads and in the streets of small towns and villages pecking about almost as tamely as a sparrow. These larks appear, indeed, partial to inhabited places, and frequent high roads in preference to fields. In different parts of Europe they are resident or migratory according as the locality is suitable or not for winter quarters, but in most districts are partial migrants. In Germany, Dr. Naumann writes that " they leave their northern haunts in the winter, which they spend in smaller or larger companies in milder climates. Many winter on the Maine and Rhine, and in Franconia and Thuringia, arriving in October and November, and disappearing at the beginning of spring. In Northern Germany these larks are resident or partially migratory, these latter rambling in pairs or small companies from place to place, and arriving in winter where they are not observed in summer, but seldom remain there long. The time of migration is in November and December. Old pairs remain year after year at the same breeding place. They migrate from the one inhabited place

AFRICAN FINCH LARK

to the other in the daytime, generally in the forenoon, and fly at a considerable altitude."

The song of the crested lark is sweeter and in some respects more pleasing than that of the skylark. This lark nests upon the ground in any small depression of the soil or behind a clod of earth; the nest being loosely and simply constructed of stems of dry grass and fine roots, sometimes lined with a little horsehair. The eggs, which are greyish white, marked with dark or light brown and grey, may be found from the middle of April until the middle of July. The crested lark is a favourite cage bird in Germany, and may be seen from time to time exposed in the Paris bird market. The upper parts are brown, the feathers of the neck and back having dark middles fringed with buff; the crest is conspicuous, and consists of nine or ten narrow feathers, blackish brown in colour, edged with buff; the lower parts are creamy white, the sides of the throat spotted with blackish brown, and the feathers of the breast and flanks streaked with dark brown.

DESERT LARK

In the desert lark (*Alæmon desertorum*) the beak is very long and slender, gently curved in its terminal half, the nostrils are fully exposed to view, the first of the ten primaries of the wing is short, although longer than the primary coverts. The toes and claws are very short, the latter being stout. The plumage is the same in both sexes.

A native of the deserts of Arabia and Northern Africa, this species extends eastwards into Afghanistan and Western India, where it is sparsely distributed throughout the desolate wastes in which it makes its home, living in pairs, each enjoying the run of its own territory. The song of the male is often uttered in the breeding season, but is short and unpretentious. Breeding in May and June, when it makes a small nest of dried grass on the sand, the desert lark lays greyish white eggs, marked with yellowish brown.

In many birds the plumage serves the purposes of concealment from enemies; and the desert lark, like other species that haunt deserts, is coloured a pale sandy grey, with ashy tinge on the forehead and upper tail coverts. The first primaries are black, with white bases, the tail feathers black margined with fulvous, the two middle feathers being sandy brown, broadly edged with very bright fulvous; a black streak, with a white band

above and beneath a second, passes through the lores; a black band runs backwards from the eye; the chin and throat are white, as is the abdomen; but the fore neck and breast are pale fulvous, spotted with black (page 1039).

FINCH LARKS AND BUSH LARKS

Another genus (*Ammomanes*) belonging to the group with ten primaries to the wings is formed by the finch larks, of which one species is the African finch lark (*A. deserti*), while other species inhabit India. Having the first primary long, as in the preceding genus, these larks are specially distinguished by the thick beak being much shorter than the head, and the nostrils concealed by plumelets. They inhabit open arid plains, from which they rise singing into the air for a short distance, and then suddenly drop.

There are several other genera of the group, such as the Asiatic bush larks (*Mirafra*), which may be distinguished from the finch larks by the open nostrils; a well-known species being the Madras bush lark (*M. affinis*) of Southern India.

SHORT-TOED LARKS

The short-toed lark (*Calandrella brachydactyla*) and its relatives are inferior in size to most of the family, and have the beak short and stout, with the upper half arched, while there are only nine primaries in the wing, of which the first is long and reaches to the tip. The inner secondaries are lengthened and reach to the end of the primaries, or nearly so; the tail is rather long and slightly forked, and the slightly curved claws are very short. Several species of short-toed larks inhabit Europe and Northern Asia, and others are found in India. The European short-toed lark is common in Southern Spain and Malta during summer, frequenting the wild parts, where the song of the cock may be often heard while the hen is sitting.

Ranging eastwards to Turkestan, in winter this lark visits India. Its mode of ascending in the air differs from that of the skylark, consisting of a succession of jerks. Their food consists almost exclusively of small seeds, the husks of which they break with their beaks; but it may be presumed that insects are supplied to the young. On the ground this lark runs quickly, and it is especially fond of grovelling in sand. When at large, it never perches on shrubs or bushes, though in confinement, like the skylark, it will readily take to a perch. The

CALANDRA LARK

cock has a lively song, uttered while on the wing both in the morning and evening, but seldom in the middle of the day.

The nest is formed of a few bits of grass collected in a depression of the ground, often a horse's footprint ; and the eggs, four or five in number, are white, generally minutely freckled with pale hair brown. The adult has the upper parts sandy grey, with dark middles to the feathers ; the wings and tail are blackish brown, some of the feathers being margined with buff ; the sides of the head are marked with blackish brown, a creamy white stripe extending over and behind the eye ; on each side of the upper part of the breast is a blackish brown patch ; and the under parts generally are white washed with buff. Individuals vary in tint, some being more rufous or grey than others.

CALANDRA LARKS

The calandra lark typifies a small assemblage of large, stout-billed larks, characterised by patches of black feathers on each side of the breast. The wing, which is very long, reaching nearly to the tip of the tail, has ten primaries, the first being very minute ; and the claw of the first toe is long and straight. This group, which is confined to the Old World, is most common in Southern Europe, Algeria, Egypt, Nubia, and India ; the Eastern representative of the Western bird inhabiting Northern China.

The calandra (*Melanocorypha calandra*), which is one of the finest of European songsters, in appearance somewhat recalls the corn bunting. It is a heavily built bird, and rather similar to the latter in shape, but does not dangle its legs in the air when flying. A permanent resident in the South of France and Spain, as well as in parts of Italy and in Greece, the calandra is also common in Turkey. Mr. G. F. Mathew states that the male on beginning his song " springs from the ground, and, with a graceful undulating motion, describes a series of large circles until he rises to an immense height ; his song is then clear and beautiful, but at close quarters it is piercing and unpleasant. The call note is loud and harsh, and somewhat similar to that of the corn bunting."

The calandra lark nests in a depression of the ground, often at a depth of three or four inches ; the nest being a careless structure built of grass stems. The eggs are dull grey, blotched with brown and pale amber, with underlying markings of grey and light brown. The adult is greyish brown above, with dark middles to the feathers ; the under surface is white tinged with fulvous, and streaked finely with dark brown. The distinguishing character of this species is a large patch of black adorning the sides of the neck.

BLACK LARK

The black lark (*M. yeltoniensis*) inhabits the steppes of Central Asia, migrating westwards into Southern Russia in autumn and winter. After rearing their

SHORT-TOED, BLACK, AND WHITE-WINGED LARKS

progeny, these larks congregate, especially in August, and wander over the brackish places of the desert throughout the whole autumn, especially in the region of the salt Lake Yelton. In mid-winter, when the snow covers the land, they approach towns. In summer, when on the ground, the black lark utters a feeble piping, generally singing from a hillock, but its song is not powerful. The nest is merely a slight hollow in the ground, lined with a few vegetable fibres, moss, and dried grass. The female lays four bluish eggs, spotted with yellow, some time between the end of April and the end of July. The colour of the black lark varies at different seasons ; the plumage of the male being black in spring, with the feathers of the back, rump, and breast edged with light sandy, but these markings become almost completely obsolete in the height of summer. The colour of the female is sandy brown, the lores and eye stripe being whitish, the wings and tail dark brown, edged with sandy ; the under parts white tinged with buff, the upper portion of the breast mottled with brown, and the flanks striated.

WHITE-WINGED LARK

The white-winged lark (*M. sibirica*) is a Siberian representative of the calandra, which has occasionally wandered into Western Europe ; its home is the steppes of Eastern Russia, whence it extends eastwards as far as the Yenisei. Arriving on its breeding grounds in Russia in the spring much later than the skylark, it affects grassy and open districts ; and when singing, often soars aloft, but does not ascend so high as the skylark. It pairs about the middle of May, and builds its nest of grass upon the ground, the four or more eggs being greyish white, closely marked with dull brown.

The adult male in summer has the upper parts rich brown, bordered with russet, which becomes lighter on the nape. The crown, lesser wing coverts and upper tail coverts are brilliant red russet, which gives the bird a marked and distinct character; the primaries are dark brown, the first white on the inner web, and becoming almost entirely so in the middle; the tail feathers are brown edged with white on the inner webs, the throat and sides of the neck spotted with brown and russet, and the under parts white. The female is similar, but duller and less pure in tint. Yet another member of the group is the Chinese lark (*M. mongolica*).

Clotbey's lark (*Rhamphocorys clotbeyi*), which takes its name from the large size of the beak, is an Algerian species, representing a distinct genus. Allied to this is the South African white-headed bullfinch lark (*Pyrrhulauda verticollis*)

SHORE LARKS

The shore lark (*Otocorys alpestris*) and its kindred are distinguished by a tuft of feathers springing from each side of the crown of the head of the adult males; the beak is rather short and slightly arched, the nostrils densely covered by plumes, the wings long, and the claw of the first toe straight, and about as long as the toe itself. These birds are remarkable for the constancy of the pattern of their plumage; yellow and black being usually associated with purplish brown. The genus is represented in the New World, the northern parts of which possess several species, one of the number at least being virtually identical with the shore lark of Europe. The latter appears to inhabit the whole of the northern parts of Europe and Siberia, and other species are found in the Himalaya and adjoining plateaus, two of the number being peculiar to very high altitudes.

The shore lark breeds on the fields and tundras of Northern Europe, extending southwards into Central Norway. Formerly the species was regarded as a rare straggler to the coast of Great Britain, but it is now known that considerable numbers annually cross the North Sea to winter on the eastern shores of England. Certain spots are frequented by these birds year after year, where they feed chiefly on the seeds of marine plants. For many years the horned, or shore larks which visited Britain were almost exclusively cocks; but females have latterly been taken, although not in the same proportion as males. The shore larks which winter on the British coast rarely wander inland, although they sometimes migrate across England from the Yorkshire coast to that of Lancashire. They arrive during the latter months of the year, and remain until the end of February, or even the middle of March.

Mr. Seebohm writes that "the shore lark is as much a bird of the tundra as the snow bunting and the Lapland bunting, but it breeds at a lower latitude than the former species, and is almost as abundant as the latter, although more local. It avoids the marshy districts, and confines itself to dry sandy plains or rocky hills, though it comes down to the mud shores of the rivers to drink. It is one of the earliest of the small birds to arrive at its breeding grounds. The snow bunting and the mealy redpoll arrive first, and may be seen running about on the snow some weeks before the ice breaks up; but as soon as the thaw begins in earnest a batch of small birds arrive, among which is certain to be the shore lark. During migration the shore lark is a gregarious bird, and though the first flocks consisted of shore larks only, as soon as the Lapland buntings began to arrive, they seemed to be on the best of terms together, and the later flocks usually consisted of both species. Flocks of pipits were migrating about the same time, and it was very striking to contrast the wildness of these birds with the tameness of the shore larks. The shore lark often sings on the ground, and when apparently too busy feeding to mount in the air for the purpose will occasionally utter snatches of song.

SHORE LARKS

"At their breeding places they sing continually, mounting up into the air like a skylark, and singing their charming song as they sail about with wings and tail expanded. The song is very melodious, though short, and among its few variations a long drawn-out note often occurs, which resembles much the song of the corn bunting. The bird often remains some time in the air, and sings its little song several times over before it descends. It will also sing from the roof of the wooden houses. Its call note is loud and clear, but scarcely capable of being expressed by a word.

"In Lapland the shore lark lays its eggs from the middle of May to the middle of June, but in Siberia not before the latter date. The nest is always built on the ground, generally in some slight hollow. I found one in Finmark in the middle of a mountain pass, in the hollow formed by the foot of a horse in the soft mud which the sun had afterwards hardened. Others were among stones on the bare ground, and one under the shelter of some rushes in the grass. The nest is loosely made of dry grass and stalks; and the inside, which is rather deep, is lined with willow down or reindeer-hair. Four is the usual number of eggs, but very often only three are laid, and sometimes as many as five. They may be said to be characteristic larks' eggs, and only differ from those of the skylark by their more olive shade of colour."

The adult male shore lark in breeding plumage has the forehead and a stripe over each eye, the chin, and upper part of the throat pale yellow, the crown and tufts of the head, the lores, and a band across the lower part of the neck black, the upper parts purplish brown, and the under parts dirty white. The female is similar, but all her colours are duller, a remark which applies also to the male birds of the year. In winter plumage the shore lark lacks the purplish tint characterising the breeding plumage. The young have the whole of the upper plumage dark brown spotted with dull yellow; the throat being pale yellow streaked with black, and the lower parts dull white.

WAGTAILS AND PIPITS, AND FORK TAILS

WAGTAILS AND PIPITS

THE members of this family (*Motacillidæ*) form a group of slender-bodied birds, characterised by the more or less slender and slightly-notched beak, adapted to an insectivorous diet; the presence of nine primaries in the wing, which is usually elongated and pointed, with the inner secondaries reaching nearly to the end of the primaries; a metatarsus of considerable although variable length, and a tail which is either long or medium.

WAGTAILS

Wagtails are distinguished from pipits by their proportionately longer tails and legs, and also by their gay colours, in which yellow usually predominates; they are migratory, and perform long and arduous journeys to and from their breeding grounds. Wagtails are chiefly inhabitants of the Old World, especially the northern portions of Europe and Asia, but are also represented in North America by two species in Alaska, although not in the eastern portions of that continent.

WHITE AND PIED WAGTAILS

The white wagtail (*Motacilla alba*) and its congeners are small, elegantly-shaped birds, noticeable on account of their habit of running over grass in pursuit of insects. The beak is slender, nearly straight, and very slightly notched at the tip; the wings are moderate, the first three primaries being about equal and longest, and the inner secondaries very long; the tail consists of twelve long narrow feathers; and the metatarsus is long and slender. The white wagtail is found throughout Northern Europe, extending so far east as the Yenisei, and wintering in North Africa; while an allied species is found in Persia; and a third breeds in Northern China, and winters in Burma. Several species of the genus *Motacilla* occur in South Africa; and no fewer than thirteen visit India during winter, at least one of which is a permanent resident in that country.

The white wagtail is a common summer visitor to the northern and central portions of Europe, where it frequents parks and gardens, and may be seen running on the roads in pursuit of insects. In Portugal its provincial name signifies "washerwoman," the term having been suggested by the custom of the local laundresses of wading into the streams to cleanse the clothes on a stone. The English name of "dish washer," applied to the pied species, is somewhat analogous. The white wagtail is partial to the neighbourhood of old buildings and outhouses, often nesting in such situations, and in Switzerland seeking the mountain chalets and cowsheds, in search of the insects to be found in the neighbourhood of domesticated animals. The nest may be either among the roots of a tree, or in a bank by the river-side, or occasionally on a shelf in some outbuilding.

In Siberia the white wagtail is one of the first of the soft-billed birds to arrive in the Arctic Circle in any numbers. This species nests two or three times in the season, rearing four or five young ones in a brood; the nest being built of dry stems of grass, moss, and fibres, closely worked together and neatly lined with wool, hair, and often feathers. The eggs are white, spotted and speckled with greyish brown (p. 990). When the young leave the nest, they live for some weeks with their parents, haunting garden lawns and meadow lands in search of food. The flight of the adult is rapid and undulating, the call note loud and sibilant, and the song somewhat pleasing, although far from powerful. The white wagtail sometimes migrates in large parties, and is fond of roosting in reeds. All the movements of this bird are elegant and rapid, perhaps even more so than those of the closely-allied pied wagtail (*M. lugubris*), so well known in the British Islands as a summer visitor.

The adult male of the white wagtail in the breeding season has the forehead and sides of the head white, the crown, back of the head, and nape black, the back, rump, and upper tail coverts pearl grey, the primaries and wing coverts dusky black, edged with greyish white; the tail black and white; the chin and throat black; and the lower parts pure white.

GREY WAGTAIL

Like the white and pied species, the grey wagtail (*M. melanope*) is essentially a water bird. Although most common in Central Europe, it is a summer visitant to and partial resident in the British Isles, where it shuns the neighbourhood of sluggish, turbid rivers, and is fond of wading in the shallows of streams and running over the rocks rising out of their beds. Nesting year after year in the same place, the grey wagtail is a very early breeder, full complements of eggs being laid early in April; and it breeds twice in a season, the second brood being generally fully fledged about the middle of July.

The nest is placed in a variety of situations, often in the recesses of some loose stone wall or mossy shelf of rock overhanging running water; while a hole in a wooden bridge is occasionally selected. It is built of dry stems of grass and a few roots, usually lined with horsehair; six white eggs, suffused with pale brown or olive, being laid in a clutch. The grey wagtail has a pretty song, often uttered from the top of a willow or other river-side tree. The cocks are very jealous, each choosing his own territory from which every intruder is ousted. Even when the members of the first brood are fledged, and searching for food in company with their parents, the old cocks are always on their guard against the possible intrusion of a stranger, whose approach is invariably heralded with a challenge to

WHITE WAGTAIL

combat. The adult male in summer has the crown and upper parts slaty grey, the upper tail coverts greenish yellow, a white stripe above the eye and another beneath the lore, the chin and throat black, and the lower parts bright yellow. In winter the chin and throat are dirty white, the breast dull buff, and the under parts greyish white tinged with yellow.

BLUE-HEADED WAGTAIL

The blue-headed species (*M. flava*) represents a group of wagtails which frequent meadows and cornfields rather than the neighbourhood of water. This species is well known in most parts of Europe, though but a chance summer visitor to the British Isles, where, however, it has nested. Its flight is swift, graceful, and undulating, often accompanied by a call note which may be heard at a considerable distance. This species nests in meadow lands, generally in a tuft of grass or a tussock of rushes, but sometimes a number of pairs breeds together in a single field. The nest is built of dry stems of grass and scraps of moss, lined with fine bents and hair; the eggs being yellowish white in ground colour, mottled and clouded with pale brown.

When the eggs are hatched, the old birds wait upon their offspring, and continue to watch over their safety long after they are fledged. These birds are exceedingly fond of the neighbourhood of horses, running in and out between the feet of the animals with singular unconcern. The upper parts yellowish green, the forehead, crown, and lores slaty blue, set off to great advantage by the white eye stripe, the under parts being pure yellow. In the female, the crown of the head is greenish brown instead of blue, the eye stripe less pure, and the under parts duller yellow. Nearly allied to the blue-headed species is the yellow wagtail (*M.raii*), a common, although local, British bird in summer.

YELLOW-HEADED WAGTAIL

Another species is the yellow-headed wagtail (*M. citreola*), a native of Siberia and Eastern Russia, wintering in most parts of India, and apparently finding its westward summer limits in the valleys of the Petchora and Volga. It breeds in Kashmir, where the nests are placed under clods in ploughed fields. The proper home of this beautiful bird, however, is among the dreary tundras of the far north, where it has been observed on alder bushes in the neighbourhood of flooded lands on the banks of the Petchora. There it breeds in June, and its habits resemble those of other yellow wagtails, its light, dainty form assimilating closely to that of the blue-headed and yellow species. The adult male in summer has the entire head, neck,

BLUE-HEADED WAGTAIL

The adult male has the forehead, crown,

YELLOW-HEADED WAGTAIL

and under parts deep yellow, and the upper plumage ashy grey tinged with bluish.

CAPE WAGTAIL

European wagtails are replaced in South Africa by several allied species, among which the Cape wagtail (*M. capensis*) frequents crowded cities no less than outlying farmhouses, being everywhere protected, in recognition of its charming ways. Like their European cousins, these birds consort much with cattle, for the sake of the small flies found about those animals, and also frequent the sea beach to procure flies bred in putrefying seaweed. The cup-shaped nest of dry grass lined with cows' hair and fur is generally constructed in the side of a bank or a crevice of a stone wall, but is sometimes built under a projecting stone or overhanging root on the bank of a stream. The eggs are brownish cream, freckled with brown.

The Cape wagtail has the dipping flight peculiar to the genus, and like other wagtails is fond of seeking its food on the margins of muddy streams. Its song is seldom uttered. Sometimes it is seen in flocks, especially when the birds are gathering to roost in some favourite tree; at other times it lives chiefly in pairs, preying upon insects, which it takes both upon the ground and on the wing.

The adult male has the head and hind part of the neck ashy grey, the eye stripe, cheeks, and throat white, the upper parts brown washed with olive, and the tail feathers blackish brown, with the exception of the outer ones, which are chiefly white; a black crescentic band crosses the neck, the breast and under parts are yellowish white, and the sides of the body brown.

PIPITS

The members of the extensive group of pipits differ as a rule from the wagtails in the colour of their plumage, which is generally brown on the upper parts, with the individual feathers light-edged and streaked with black, and the under parts buff, whitish, or rufous, with triangular bluish spots. There are, however, indications of a transition in the matter of colour between the two groups, the Indian bird known as *Limonidromus indicus* being practically a brown wagtail, while the yellow-breasted pipit (*Anthus chloris*), which takes its name from the yellow patch on the chest, is a pipit showing an approach to the wagtail type of colouring.

Pipits differ from larks in having the nostrils devoid of feathers, although some show the same long hind toe. With the exception of being unknown in the islands of the South Pacific, they have an almost cosmopolitan distribution. In the New World, however, they are comparatively rare, North America possessing only two out of some forty species, while there are but few in South America, one of which is confined to the Andes. Although the tree pipit (*Anthus trivialis*) is by no means unknown in the north of Europe, it is far commoner in the British Isles and the centre of the Continent.

TREE PIPITS

Tree pipits migrate in flocks, although in the nesting season each couple selects its own breeding area. The song is melodious, its notes bearing a strong resemblance to those of the canary. Sometimes this pipit sings on the ground, threading its way through the grass and pouring forth in snatches a volume of melody. More often the song is uttered while the bird is perching on one of the larger branches of a tall tree by the roadside, or when on the wing.

Mr. Seebohm writes that in early spring the tree pipit may be seen taking short flights, as he "springs up from the topmost twig of some branch and mounts nearly perpendicularly into the air, warbling his pretty song.

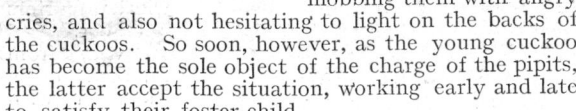

YOUNG PIED WAGTAILS

He soon begins to hover in the air, and, as if fatigued by his recent journey, almost immediately descends with tail and wings extended like a parachute, and at last finishes his song on the ground, in a tree, or on a wall. His downward course is in a semi-spiral curve, and he alights where the curve of his flight would make a tangent to the surface of the ground. All this time he has been singing melodiously, the clear, rich, joyous notes following each other in rapid succession, until, as he reaches his perch, he concludes his song with several long-drawn notes expressive of almost impatient anxiety."

These pipits nest upon the ground, often upon a bank skirting the edge of a wood ; the nest being always well concealed, and built of dry stems of grass and moss, lined with fine bents and hair. At times several pairs breed on a single strip of moorland, although this is unusual. The eggs vary greatly in colour, but the most usual type is white so closely suffused with deep brown as to be almost entirely of that colour (page 990). The young birds leave the nest early, and soon become independent of their parents. In autumn these pipits flock together, and many are captured by the birdcatchers. The upper parts of the tree pipit are brown, the feathers having dark middles, and the lower parts buffish white profusely spotted with dark brown.

MEADOW PIPIT

On the waste moorlands of Western Europe the meadow pipit (*A. pratensis*) generally replaces the tree pipit, and finds a congenial abode among peat bogs and dreary wastes only redeemed from ugliness by strips of cotton grass. A partial resident in most of its haunts, many individuals merely shifting from the higher grounds to the plains before the arrival of winter, the meadow pipit loves rough, marshy ground and treeless wastes of heather, rearing its young in the most remote and most forbidding solitudes. The song is inferior in compass to that of the tree pipit, which is chanted on the wing.

Meadow pipits breed on rough ground and undrained meadows, building slight nests of dried stems of grass, often in tussocks of herbage, sometimes but little above tide mark on the beach. The eggs are white, closely mottled with brown or brownish grey (page 990). The cuckoo is exceedingly fond of depositing her eggs in the meadow pipit's nest ; and a pair of these birds may at times be seen endeavouring to drive one of these undesirable visitors from their vicinity. It is often assumed that the cuckoo finds a willing dupe in the meadow pipit, but such is not the case in actual fact. When cuckoos first arrive in England, and begin to pair and lay, meadow pipits assail the strangers with persistency, mobbing them with angry cries, and also not hesitating to light on the backs of the cuckoos. So soon, however, as the young cuckoo has become the sole object of the charge of the pipits, the latter accept the situation, working early and late to satisfy their foster-child.

A small, pale-coloured race of the species inhabits Madeira. In colour the meadow pipit is olive brown above, with dark middles to the feathers, often tinged with olive green ; the under parts being buffish white, thickly streaked with dark brown.

RICHARD'S PIPIT

The large species known as Richard's pipit (*A. richardi*) breeds in Northern Siberia, whence stragglers often wander to Britain during autumn and winter. Mr. Seebohm found this pipit "exceedingly abundant in the meadows on the banks of the Yenisei, near Yenisaik. The country is almost a dead flat for miles, and intersected with half-dried-up river-beds and chains of swampy lakes, full of tall sedges and reeds and water plants of various kinds, and half-concealed by willow bushes and alders, whilst far away in the distance the horizon is bounded on every side by the forest. These oases of grass in the boundless forest are the paradise of Richard's pipit. The birds arrive about the

MEADOW PIPIT

middle of May, and build their nests on the ground in the grass. They usually choose a hollow in the meadows, such as the footprint of a cow or horse in the soft earth. The first nest is made in the first half of June, and frequently a second brood is reared, the eggs being laid in the second half of July.

"The nests are said to be very difficult to find. The male keeps watch, and, on the approach of danger, gives the alarm to the female, who leaves the nest and runs along the ground for some distance, when she rises and joins the male in endeavouring to entice the intruder from the nest with anxious cries. If their little manœuvres are successful, the female drops to the ground and runs back to the nest through the grass. In this district the nest of Richard's pipit is the one

RICHARD'S PIPIT AND
WATER PIPIT

usually selected by the cuckoo in which to deposit her eggs. They leave for their winter quarters late in September."

The eggs vary from four to six, some being profusely spotted with minute specks and blotches of greenish brown on a pale greenish white ground colour, while in others the spots are reddish brown upon a pinkish white ground. In the adult male the upper parts are nearly uniform brown, and the under parts buffish white, darkest on the breast, which is streaked with dark brown. So far as colour is concerned, the sexes are identical. Richard's pipit may always be known by the long metatarsus and greatly developed claw of the first toe.

TAWNY PIPIT

The haunts of the tawny pipit (*A. campestris*) are chiefly in desert regions, at least through a large portion of its range. In Europe it is chiefly known as a summer visitor to certain favoured districts, such as the sierras of Spain and Portugal, the sand dunes of the Baltic coast, and sparingly on high ground in Central France. It is a shy and wary species, even on the breeding ground. In Greece, where it is the only pipit that nests, it is very common and frequents the open plains, being especially abundant on the undulating prairie country, half-rock and half-grass and heath, between Athens and Marathon. It runs on the ground with great agility, and has a restless zigzag flight, which appears less undulating than that of the meadow pipit. The nest is sometimes under a bush, sometimes beneath a tuft of dense herbage or the shelter of a clod of earth ; although it may be in the open plain among the growing crops, or near the dry bed of a stream on a bank beside a stone. It is made of dry grass, often mixed with stems of coarse herbage or straws and roots, and lined with horsehair. The eggs are white, profusely spotted with reddish brown and underlying spots of grey.

The tawny pipit migrates from its breeding ground in August, at which season it has occasionally been captured in the British Isles and Heligoland. The adult male is nearly uniform brown above; the wings

and tail being conspicuously edged with buff, while the chin is buffish white, and the lower parts buffish slightly streaked with brown on the breast.

As occasional visitors to the British Islands, brief reference may be made to two other members of the genus—namely, the water pipit (*A. spipoletta*) and the red-throated pipit (*A. cervinus*). The rock pipit (*A. obscurus*), on the other hand, is a regular native of Britain, where it frequents rocky coasts.

PIED GRALLINE

Of the other generic types included in the family, reference may be made to the pied gralline (*Grallina australis*) of Australia; and also to the members of the genus *Macronyx*, some of which are much more brilliantly coloured than the pipits, while all, such as *M. crocæ* and *M. ameliæ*, present a remarkable resemblance to the genus *Sturnella*. Nor is this all, for certain species of *Macronyx* seem to imitate particular kinds of the other genera.

FORK TAILS

Although by some naturalists the curious birds known as fork tails are grouped with the redstarts, the opinion is very generally held that they are entitled to rank as a family by themselves (*Henicuridæ*), of which the affinities are with the *Motacillidæ*. In appearance they are not unlike pied wagtails, from which they are distinguished by the long and deeply-forked tail, although this feature does not occur in *Henicurus scouleri*, in which the tail is short and squared. Another difference is the presence of ten primary quills. The stout, straight, and generally elongated beak is furnished with a number of bristles at the gape, and the long metatarsus is not covered with large shields.

The distribution of the one genus included in the family is somewhat peculiar, extending from the hills

TAWNY PIPIT

of Southern and Western China and the Himalaya to Burma and the Malay Islands, while one species is found in Samarcand. The orange chestnut crown distinguishes *Henicurus ruficapillus*, while *H. velatus* is equally well characterised by its brown head. The eggs are greenish white, irregularly blotched with brown.

CREEPERS, NUTHATCHES, HONEY-EATERS, AND MAMOS

CREEPERS

THE elegant tree creepers, or, strictly, creepers, form a small group (family *Certhiidæ*), of which the members are specially adapted to pursue their prey, comprising spiders and insects, on the surface of cliffs or the trunks of trees, the majority being small, plain-coloured birds, typified by the European tree creeper. The beak is generally long, slender, sharp, and curved downwards, although shorter and straighter in the genus *Climacteris*. Bristles at the gape of the beak and on the nostrils are wanting. The wings include ten primaries, and the tail consists of twelve stout and pointed feathers, often stiffened to aid climbing. Generally the tail is squared, although graduated in the typical genus. The claws are long and curved.

The *Certhiidæ* are widely spread over the northern regions of both the Eastern and Western Hemispheres; several species also inhabiting the Indian and African regions, while others are peculiar to Australasia. Some difference of opinion prevails as to the serial position of the family, certain naturalists placing it next the quit-quits (*Cœrebidæ*), and following on with the honeypeckers (*Dicæidæ*), although all admit a certain kinship with the nuthatches.

EUROPEAN AND INDIAN TREE CREEPERS

The common European tree creeper (*Certhia familiaris*) is the typical representative of a genus characterised by the graduated tail, of which the feathers are stiff and pointed. The Indian spotted-grey creeper, which represents a second genus *Salpornis*) with (soft tail feathers, is remarkable for building an open cup-shaped nest upon a branch.

WALL CREEPER

Another genus has been formed for the reception of the beautiful wall creeper (*Tichodroma muraria*), which passes its active existence in traversing the surfaces of precipices in pursuit of the spiders and flies on which it feeds. The long, slender, and almost straight beak is most admirably adapted for probing the interstices and cracks which usually constitute the haunts of its prey. The wings are large and rounded, like those of a butterfly, thus affording an easy support as the bird half-flies, half-flits about the precipices in which it makes its home. The tail is slightly rounded, and composed of twelve feathers, the metatarsus is smooth, and the claws are sharp and curved.

Residing in the mountain ranges of Europe, and ranging eastwards into Central Asia, the wall creeper is found throughout the Himalaya, although only as a winter visitor. It occasionally straggles to Great Britain. In summer it makes its home among precipitous rocks, either in rugged ravines or on the faces of cliffs.

Its flight almost recalls that of a large butterfly, as the bird makes its way from one crevice to another, hanging momentarily with expanded wings in one spot, thence shuffling upwards for a foot or two, and then suddenly darting off to explore another corner of the rocks, ever in restless motion, save when it creeps to roost in some secure fissure. The wall creeper nests from April till June, depositing four or five pure white eggs, sparsely speckled with red, in a nest built of straw, grass, and moss, intermingled with wool and feathers. The Australasian genus *Climacteris*, already mentioned on account of its relatively short and straight beak, is also peculiar in habits, being to a great extent a ground bird instead of a climber. Its eggs are pinkish.

TREE CREEPER

NUTHATCHES

Although related in some degree to the creepers, nuthatches (family *Sittidæ*) are probably much more nearly allied to titmice. They are stoutly-built birds, with short, squared tails, and long, pointed wings. The edges of both halves of the beak are smooth, or the upper one slightly notched; the hind surface of the metatarsus is smooth, and covered with two entire longitudinal plates; the wing has ten primaries; the nostrils are clear of the line of the forehead, and overhung by some hairs; bristles are usually present at the gape of the beak; there are twelve tail feathers; and the first and second toes are of very unequal lengths. In all the members of the group there is but one annual moult, and the plumage of the nestling resembles that of the female; while in most cases the colouring is different in the two sexes.

With the exception of South America and Africa south of the Sahara, nuthatches are very generally distributed, extending to Australasia. They are small climbing birds, with the first toe greatly developed, and the second proportionately shortened, and feed both on insects and nuts. They nest in the holes of trees or the crevices of rocks, often reducing the size of the aperture of the hole by building it up with mud; and they are not migratory.

In addition to the type genus, the family is represented by the Australian and Papuan genus *Sitella*, and by the Malagasy *Hypositta*, as well as by the Indo-Malay genera *Dendrophila* and *Callisitta*, and the Papuan *Daphœnositta*. The typical genus *Sitta* itself has a very wide distribution, and is characterised by the slaty blue colour of the plumage.

EUROPEAN NUTHATCHES

Abundant in many parts of Central and Southern Europe, as it is in England, the European nuthatch (*Sitta cæsia*) invariably indicates its whereabouts by its call note, which in spring resounds through the beech woods, so generally frequented by these interesting birds. Nuthatches pair at the close of winter, and choose for their nesting a hole in some hollow tree, plastering up the entrance with clay, and only leaving a small orifice through which they pass to the nest; the interior of the latter being lined with dry beech leaves. The eggs are white, spotted with bright red; and the young, when fledged, live for a time with their parents, but soon become independent and wander through the woods in company with titmice and other small birds. If a nuthatch be watched, it will be found that although it sometimes perches across a bough like an ordinary singing bird, when feeding it generally runs up and down the trunk of old trees somewhat like a woodpecker.

The call note is a loud "twet, twet," which may be compared to the words "fetch it," "fetch it," but this cry must not be confused with the spring whistle of the male. If encouraged, it becomes a tame and confiding bird, laying aside much of its fear of man. In winter nuthatches approach dwelling-houses and willingly partake of scraps of food with tits. In summer they feed chiefly on insects, but in autumn subsist more on nuts and beechmast. Few sights are prettier than to watch a nuthatch opening nuts; the bird swinging its body freely forward as it brings down its long bill with accuracy on the right part of the shell.

Nuthatches are decidedly pugnacious, and if two males are placed in the same cage in the breeding season, the probability is that the stronger bird will kill its rival. The devotion which paired birds show to one another is a marked trait in the character of the nuthatch. The adult male has the upper parts slaty blue; a black line passes from the base of the bill through the eye to the nape; the wings and tail are slaty blue, the outer tail feathers showing, when open, white edges; the flanks are bright chestnut red, and the lower parts buffy white. A variety with a black throat and crown has been recorded. In Northern Europe the common species is replaced by the white-bellied nuthatch (*S. europœa*).

SYRIAN NUTHATCH

The Syrian nuthatch (*S. neumayeri*), which might well be called the rock nuthatch, as its habits in Southern Europe differ in a remarkable way from those of its congeners, builds its nest of earth, small stones, and the like, placing it on the face of a rock, and constructing a round, funnel-shaped entrance an inch or more in length. Mr. Seebohm, who found this nuthatch building in the crags near Smyrna, gives the following account of its breeding habits : "The nest of this bird is a very curious structure. A recess in the rock is selected, and a funnel made of mud and little bits of dry grass is built in front of it. It is quite an important affair; the base is frequently twenty-four inches in circumference, and the walls vary in thickness from half an inch to an inch and a half. The tube of the funnel, which, of course, serves for the ingress and egress of the bird, is about four inches long, with an internal diameter of an inch and a quarter at the entrance.

WALL CREEPER

"The outside of the nest is carefully made to resemble the appearance of the rock against which it is built. One which I brought home with me is curiously corrugated or granulated, to imitate the calcareous deposits on the inside of the cave where I found it. The nest is warmly lined with goats' wool, thistledown, and all sorts of soft materials.

"As might be expected in a bird which remains in its summer home during the winter, it is an early breeder, laying its eggs about the middle of April; and it would not appear to breed a second time in the year, as all the nests I found in June were empty. The number of eggs varies from six to ten. They are very beautiful, well marked, and unlike any other egg with which I am acquainted. The typical egg is about the size of that of the wryneck, but rather wider and flatter at the top and straighter at the sides. It has the same pearly white ground colour, spotted with large rust-coloured blotches."

This nuthatch seems to confine itself entirely to rocks, and never alights on the trunk of a tree. The adult male has the entire upper parts leaden blue; a black stripe passes through the eye; the quills are bluish brown, edged with russet; the tail is blackish brown, with the outer feathers tipped with russet; and the throat and lower parts are white, tinged with russet on the flanks and abdomen.

CANADIAN AND PIGMY NUTHATCHES

The nuthatches of North America differ from their European cousins in that they never plaster up the entrance hole to the nest. In Canada the genus is represented by *S. canadensis*. More widely distributed is the pigmy nuthatch (*S. pygmæa*), which roams through the woods in flocks composed of its own kind, occasionally joining company with tits and warblers. As many as twenty or thirty may sometimes be seen together, calling incessantly to one another. They feed partly on the tiny insects which they find lurking in the crevices of bark, and partly on the seeds of fir trees. Their notes are very varied. The eggs of this nuthatch are deposited in the hole of a tree, which is sometimes lined and sometimes left bare ; the eggs being pinkish white dotted with reddish. The young birds leave the nest in June.

The pigmy nuthatch is a delicately-built bird, with more of the habits and voice of the Canadian than of the white-breasted species ; a similarity extending to the colour of the tail, and the half warbler-like movements of the bird at certain times. It is very active and incessantly on the move, creeping over the trunks and limbs of the pines tapping here and there like a woodpecker, and far louder than do other nuthatches. The adult has the upper parts ashy blue, the top of the head and sides to below the eyes olive brown bordered with black, the tail feathers blackish spotted with white, except the two middle ones, which are blue, and the under parts varying from buffish white to rich rusty.

The Indian members of the group sometimes plaster up the entrances of their nests. Of the Australian nuthatches it must suffice to observe that they are distinguished by their thin piping voices, their funnel-shaped nests, which are built in forks or on branches, and their greenish or bluish white eggs, with blackish, grey, or lilac markings.

HONEY-EATERS

Distinguished from all the families

TUI OR
PARSON BIRD

A PAIR OF NUTHATCHES

hitherto noticed by the long extensile tongue, which is frayed out at the top and at the sides into a number of filaments, and thereby most admirably adapted for extracting the honey upon which they subsist from the flowers of gum and other trees of the Australasian forests, the honey-eaters form a large and interesting group (family *Meliphagidæ*). In all of them the beak is long and slender, with the upper half curved, but there are no bristles at the gape ; the feet are generally large, and the wings of moderate length. The group is confined to Australasia and the islands of the South Pacific, extending so far westwards as the island of Bali, near Java. Although the group comprises many genera, only a few need be mentioned.

Except in two genera (in one of which it is straight), the beak is long and curved, with the base wide and the culmen prominent ; the upper half being nearly always notched and serrated. The family is divided into the two sub-families *Meliphaginæ* and *Myzomelinæ*, in the former of which the sexes are, in most cases, coloured alike.

TUI OR PARSON BIRD

One of the most interesting members of the family is the New Zealand species known to the Maori as the tui and to Europeans in those islands as the parson bird (*Prosthemadera novæ-zealandiæ*). It is characterised by the long, slender, and somewhat curved beak, broad at the base, and long and broad tail. The sole representative of its genus, this bird is found on both the main islands of New Zealand, where it is one of the most abundant of the indigenous species.

Sir Walter Buller writes that in a state of nature, the tui, or parson bird, is even more lively and more active than in captivity. "It is incessantly on the move, pausing only to utter its joyous notes. The early morning is the period devoted to melody, and the tuis then perform in concert, gladdening the woods with their wild ecstasy. When engaged in song the tui puffs out the feathers of his body, distends his throat, opens wide his beak, with the tongue raised and slightly protruded, and gesticulates with his head as he pours forth the wild harmony of his soul. A pair may often be observed scarcely a foot apart on the same branch performing in concert, for both sexes sing.

"The notes are rich and varied, now resembling the striking together of metallic rods, then a long-drawn sigh, a warble, and a sob, followed by a note of great sweetness like the touch on the high stop of an organ. One of its finest notes is a clear silvery toll followed by a pause, and then another toll, the performance lasting sometimes an hour or more. This is generally heard at the close of the day, or just before the bird betakes itself to roost for the night. I have, however, on one or two occasions heard a sweet 'tui' toll long after the shadows of darkness had settled down upon the forests, and all other sounds were hushed. At other times it may be heard uttering a sweet warbling note, followed by a sneeze, after that a pause, then a sharp cry of 'tu-whit, tu-whit, ooo,' a pause again, and then its warbling note with variations, very soft and liquid, but ending abruptly in a sound like the breaking of glass."

The species derives its name of parson bird from its talking powers, being a regular mimic when in captivity, in which state it feeds on ripe berries, flies, and other insects, and the honey of certain wild blossoms. The nest, which is built in the fork of a bushy shrub, usually only a few feet from the ground, is a large structure, composed chiefly of sprays or dried twigs, intermixed with coarse moss, and lined with fine grasses. The eggs are generally white, finely spotted with red or brown. This bird builds twice in the year, the first nest being found in August. The newly-hatched young are almost entirely bare, but the feathers soon appear, and grow.h is rapid.

The adult male has the general colour shining metallic green, with bluish purple reflections on the shoulders, rump, and upper tail coverts; the middle of the back and scapulars bronze brown; the primaries and tail feathers metallic green; the hind part of the neck ornamented with a collar of soft plumes, showing a white line down the centre; and the lower part of the breast metallic green, changing into purplish blue. The sides and abdomen are blackish brown, and the throat is ornamented with two tufts of white filamentous feathers.

STITCH BIRD

The so-called stitch bird (*Pogonornis cinctus*), which also belongs to the meliphagine sub-family, is characterised by the beak being of moderate size and much compressed and slender, and the gape furnished with slender bristles; the wings are moderate, with the fourth quill the longest; the tail is

HONEY EATER

forked, and the metatarsus long, robust, and covered in front with transverse scales. Although formerly abundant in the southern parts of the North Island of New Zealand, this bird was never found in the South Island.

The stitch bird is remarkable for the bright plumage of the male, and is, therefore, an exception to the type of colouring characteristic of the sub-family. On account of its brilliant plumage the bird has been almost completely exterminated by the natives, in order that the chiefs might wear the canary yellow feathers from the wings in their gorgeous feather robes. Always a shy and retiring species, when disturbed by the report of a gun, this bird flies to a neighbouring tree with a light and graceful movement of the wing; but when descending to a lower station adopts a different manner of flight, elevating the tail almost to a right angle with the body, and scarcely moving the wings.

The male erects the tail and spreads the ear tufts when excited or alarmed, but the female habitually carries the tail perfectly erect and the wings drooping. The male utters at short intervals, and with startling energy, a melodious whistling call of three notes, but at other times produces a sharp, clicking sound, like the striking of two quartz stones together.

The nest is a slight, shallow structure, built of sprays and fibres, lined with fine grass and cow-hair. The egg is yellowish white, thickly spotted with pale rufous. The adult male has the head, neck, upper part of the back, wings, and tail black; a tuft of snow-white feathers is present on both sides of the head; a band of rich canary yellow crosses the back of the neck; and the under parts are light greyish brown. The female is plain brown. The stitch bird takes its name from its note; and the same is the case with the bird commonly called "four o'clock," or "pimlico" (*Philemon corniculatus*).

The members of the Hawaiian genus *Acrulocercus*, as typified by *A. nobilis*, are black or brownish birds, mostly with yellow axillary tufts and under tail coverts, called by the natives "o-o," from their harsh, double cry. The typical genus of the family, as represented by the warty-faced honey eater (*Meliphaga phrygia*), includes yellow and black birds, spotted and barred beneath.

The second sub-family comprises the Australian soldier bird (*Myzomela sanguinolenta*) and its immediate relatives, conspicuous for the most part on account of the sharp contrast of the deep black and brilliant scarlet of their plumage. To the same section belongs the "cobbler's awl" (*Acanthorhynchus*) and its allies, in which the prevailing colours are brown chestnut, black, and white.

MAMO TRIBE

Special interest attaches to a family (*Drepanididæ*) of exclusively Hawaiian birds typified by the now extinct mamo (*Drepanis pacifica*), on account of the fact that from the feathers of the latter were made the yellow cloaks worn by Sandwich Island chieftains in the time of Captain Cook. The numerous genera of this family present so much variation that it is difficult to find characters common to all. In most cases, however, the partially tubular tongue is frayed out into a brush; and the beak is not serrated and devoid of bristles at the gape, although the nostrils may have a cover.

In the mamo itself the beak was long, slender, and curved, but in the allied *Heterorhynchus* it is usually straight, with the lower portion only half as long as the upper; while in *Loxops* it is twisted to one side. The feathers of the back, flank, or axilla are generally fluffy. The mamo was mainly black, with the rump, upper and under tail coverts, and the bend of the wing golden yellow. An enormous number of mamo skins was employed in the construction of a coat, which took many years to make, and was handed down from father to son for generations.

WHITE-EYES, SUN BIRDS, AND FLOWER PECKERS

WHITE-EYES

THE so-called white-eyes (family *Zosteropidæ*), which take their name from the general presence of a white ring round each eye, are represented by the single genus *Zosterops*, and are characterised by having the beak curved, slender, and pointed, and the nostrils covered by a large membrane, while the eye is surrounded by a characteristic circle of small white feathers. The tongue is capable of being extended to a great length, and is cleft at the tip, in some cases with each half broken up into numerous stiff horny fibres, so as to form a brush. The wing has ten primaries, but the first is very minute; and the tail is short and squared. About a dozen species of white-eye are found in Madagascar and the Mascarene Islands, and these are divided into a green-backed and a grey-backed group, and several respectively inhabit India and Australia; Japan also possesses a species, and some occur in Africa.

GREEN-BACKED WHITE-EYE

Taking as an example the green-backed white-eye (*Z. gouldi*) of Australia, it may be mentioned that as this bird is partial to garden fruit, particularly figs and grapes, it abounds in all gardens where those fruits are cultivated, being in some localities as numerous as sparrows in England. Besides feeding on fruits, it catches flies while on the wing, after the manner of the true flycatchers. Its note is a single plaintive one, several times repeated, and its flight is irregular and of short duration.

The breeding season begins in August and ends in November; during the earlier part of the season the nests contain only two eggs, but in those built in October and November the number is increased to three, and rarely to four. The nest is a small, compact structure, formed of dried wiry grasses bound together with the hairy tendrils of small plants and wool, the inside being lined with very minute fibrous roots. The eggs are greenish blue, without spots or markings. In South Australia the green-backed white-eye is replaced by the grey-backed species, which frequents gardens, building its nest and rearing its young in shrubs and rose trees bordering the walks. This bird makes a very neat nest, and its eggs are of a beautiful pale blue. The green-backed white-eye has the crown and upper parts olive green, the wings and tail brown edged with olive green, the throat and under tail coverts light greenish yellow, and the breast and lower parts grey tinged with brown. In habits these birds resemble the honeysuckers, from which they differ in their uniformly blue eggs.

SUN BIRDS

The sun birds form a tropical family (*Nectariniidæ*) corresponding in the Old World to the humming-birds of the New. They are characterised by the long, slender, curved beak, with the sides compressed nearly to the tip, which is acute, devoid of bristles at the gape, and in most cases with both the upper and the lower half finely serrated for the terminal third of their length; the wings are of moderate size, and consist of ten primaries, the tail is more or less elongated, with the middle feathers sometimes prolonged beyond the rest; the metatarsus is usually short, and the toes are of moderate size with the claws curved and sharp. In colour the two sexes are very different, the males having bright metallic tints in the plumage, while the females are dull. Most numerously represented in the African continent, the sun birds are fairly plentiful in the Indian region, and also occur in Australasia. In India they are commonly miscalled humming-birds.

LONG-TAILED
SUN BIRD

In the members of the typical genus *Nectarinia* the beak is long, curved, and acute, the wings are moderate and rounded, the tail broad and slightly rounded, with the middle feathers lengthened and narrowed, and the metatarsus short, and covered in front with very broad scales. The majority of these sun birds are found in Africa, but the Australian sun bird represents the genus in Australasia.

MALACHITE SUN BIRD

One of the best known of the South African species is the malachite sun bird (*N. fumosa*), noted for its partiality to the blossoms of the aloe, among which it finds an abundance of its insect food; although it also feeds on the sugary juice extracted from blossoms by means of its long, brush-tipped tongue. It has a shrill and not unpleasing, although short, song.

The male is very combative, and when pursuing a rival utters a piercing scream; if two males meet, a fight is sure to ensue, to the great detriment of the beautiful tail feathers. The males lose their beauty in the winter season, and young birds are just like adult females. The domed nest, which, built of cobwebs, lichens, and dry leaves, is usually suspended on the outside of a bush, or the branch of a tree; the eggs, two in number, are dull greyish brown minutely mottled all over.

In Natal this sun bird frequents the open country, feeding on the nectar of the various kinds of aloes, and also on that of some species of lilies, which are numerous in many of the valleys.

The adult male has the plumage for the most part a shining malachite green, with the tufts of the breast brilliant yellow; the two middle tail feathers are prolonged three inches beyond the rest, and the wings and tail are blackish. The female is dull brown tinged with green above, and greenish yellow beneath.

METALLIC SUN BIRD

The lovely metallic sun bird (*N. metallica*) inhabits Equatorial Africa, living in pairs wherever the mimosa is abundant. During the heat of the day its actions become most animated, and at noon, when all other birds seek rest and shelter from the parching heat, the cock flies from blossom to blossom, accompanied by its faithful mate. Standing beneath a mimosa tree in full flower, an observer may hear the quick whirring flight of the bird as it alights on the branches of the thorn bushes, and begins to probe the blossoms in search of honey and the insects to be met with in such situations. It feeds also on flies and other winged insects, which it takes in flight; and as soon as a male has exhausted the contents of the blossoms of one tree, it darts off to another, always followed by its mate.

The male is much devoted to its companion, which it frequently entertains with a lively song; and is jealous of an intruder, darting angrily against any stray cock that may happen to invade its territory, and promptly expelling it from the neighbourhood. The nest is suspended in the centre of a mimosa tree, and built of the down of plants and cobwebs; the eggs being reddish white in ground colour, variegated with dark grey and violet. The adult male is brilliant green above, with the addition of a violet gorget; the wings and tail being bluish black, and the under parts bright yellow. The

MALE AND FEMALE OF METALLIC SUN BIRD

female is olive brown above, and sulphur yellow beneath.

From India species of the family extend westwards into Baluchistan and Persia, where they are represented by a species of the abundant Indian genus *Cinnyris*, and also into the Muscat district of Arabia and Palestine, the species found in the latter country being *C. osea*. Generally the eggs, two or three in number, are greenish or brownish grey, marked with dots or spots varying from purplish to dusky, but in the South African long-tailed sun bird (*Promerops caffer*)—representing a genus of which the inclusion in the family is only provisional—the eggs are cream-coloured, with wavy lines or blotches of purple, thus resembling those of the buntings. The long-tailed sun bird is one of the most striking members of the whole group, the three middle pairs of tail feathers being greatly elongated. The genus to which this splendid bird belongs, like *Chalcoparia*, is further characterised by the absence of serration at the tip of the beak. The genus *Neodrepanis* is specially distinguished by the great curvature of the beak, as well as by the bluish wattles around the eyes of the cock, while the golden-cheeked sun bird (*Arachnothera chrysogenys*) takes its name from the naked lores.

FLOWER PECKERS

The flower peckers form a group (family *Dicæidæ*) of small and mostly gaily-coloured species, distributed over the whole of the Indo-Malay and a part of the Australian region, and nearly allied to the sun birds, from which they are distinguished by the beak being usually short and triangular, instead of long, slender,

and cylindrical. In the genus *Prionochilus* the beak is rather short and stout, but in *Pholidornis* it becomes long and slender. Whereas all the sun birds have ten primary quills to the wing, in the flower peckers the number of these feathers may be either ten or nine; in all cases the tail is short, and the metatarsus is never elongated. In the majority of the species the two sexes differ markedly in plumage, although in a few they are alike, and in all instances the young resemble the adult females. None of these birds migrates even locally; while all are remarkable for the beauty of their nests, which are frequently suspended from branches and pear-like in form.

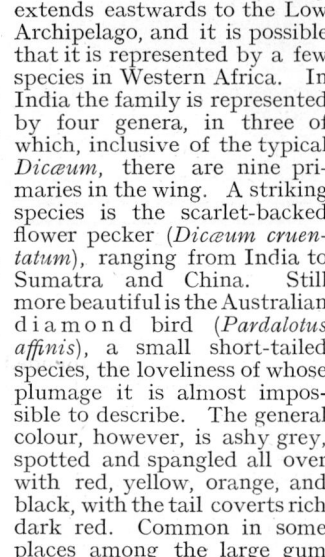

From Australia the family extends eastwards to the Low Archipelago, and it is possible that it is represented by a few species in Western Africa. In India the family is represented by four genera, in three of which, inclusive of the typical *Dicæum*, there are nine primaries in the wing. A striking species is the scarlet-backed flower pecker (*Dicæum cruentatum*), ranging from India to Sumatra and China. Still more beautiful is the Australian diamond bird (*Pardalotus affinis*), a small short-tailed species, the loveliness of whose plumage it is almost impossible to describe. The general colour, however, is ashy grey, spotted and spangled all over with red, yellow, orange, and black, with the tail coverts rich dark red. Common in some places among the large gum trees of the deep forest, this bird has a remarkably loud call note, which can be heard for long distances. It is generally only a summer visitor to Victoria, although occasionally seen there during the winter; it nests in hollow logs, or more rarely in a hole in the ground, and not infrequently makes use of the deserted nests of swallows.

Mr. Robert Hall gives the following interesting account of the nesting habits of one of the Australian diamond birds, namely, *Pardalotus assimilis*. In common with some of their kindred, these birds make their nests at the end of a tunnel drilled by themselves in a bank. "The nest is made to fit in a cavity with a domed ceiling, excavated in the hard subsoil at the end of the tunnel. This tunnel is ten inches long, and is drilled with a slight upward tendency, as is usual in most ground-boring birds. The nest entrance is two feet below the surface of the ground, and in a creek bank some nine feet above a stream." Both sexes take part in the drilling operations, one excavating while the other removes the rubbish.

The species of *Dicæum* and the allied genus *Prionochilus* build domed, pear-shaped nests, in which are laid from two to four eggs. In the former genus, as in the family generally, the eggs are white; but in those of *Prionochilus* the colour is redder, with brownish or purplish blotches. In habits these birds much resemble tits; their food consisting of insects, spiders, fruits, seeds, and perhaps honey. They generally go about in flocks, and utter a low whistle. The black flower pecker (*Melanocharis unicolor*) is remarkable on account of the uniformly sable hue of the plumage.

TITMICE AND BEARDED TITS

TITMICE

ALTHOUGH occasionally classed with the crows—from which they may be distinguished by the first primary quill never exceeding half the length of the second, and being generally shorter still—the titmice are evidently allied to the nuthatches, on the one hand, and perhaps to the honey-eaters, on the other. They constitute a considerable group (family *Paridæ*) of small, agile birds, obtaining their food on trees, and living principally upon insects. All are very much alike, and have a short, conical, and entire beak, about one-third the length of the head, with the bristles at the gape short, and those covering the nostrils, although likewise short, straight and thick. The wing, which contains ten primaries, is weak and rounded, and the metatarsus covered with long, greave-like shields.

Thoroughly arboreal in their mode of life, seldom descending to the ground, and often going about in parties of three or four, the titmice are chiefly denizens of the Old World, some inhabiting the forest regions of Northern Europe and Asia, while others are indigenous to the Himalaya, and others peculiar to North America, while there is also one genus in New Zealand.

Titmice are great foes of insects, and are therefore, for the most part, welcome in gardens, where, however, they do considerable damage to pears.

TYPICAL TITMICE

The more typical members of the family are specially characterised by the rounded tail, in which the outer pair of feathers falls short of the tip by the length of the claw of the first toe. These birds are distributed over a large portion of the world, and are numerously represented in Europe, while four are denizens of the Indian region. They are also common in North America. The beak is generally strong and conical, and well adapted to extract insects from their hiding-places in the bark of trees, while the wings are somewhat rounded, and the tail is comparatively short.

GREAT TITMOUSE

The great titmouse (*Parus major*) is common in the northern parts of the Old World, living in companies which haunt woods and gardens during the greater part of the year. In England it is resident, frequenting in summer woods and large gardens, where its food, which at that season consists almost exclusively of insects, is abundant. In winter these tits associate in family parties, and either wander about wherever there are trees, in company with creepers and other small birds, seeking for insects in the bark of trees, or remain in the neighbourhood of inhabited places to feed upon such refuse as they can find. They are fond of picking bones, and by hanging bones in trees can readily be attracted to gardens.

Mr. Dresser writes that " when hunting after insects, etc., in trees, they appear to examine every part most carefully, moving along and round the branches, now clinging head-downwards, now moving along the limbs of the tree almost like a creeper, or clinging to the end of a small branch, examining carefully a bud to see if any insect is harboured therein. This is done in a most business-like, quiet manner, and only now and then a low call, 'ze,' is uttered; but, when taking a short flight from tree to tree or bush to bush, they utter their cheerful loud note."

The great titmouse has a variety of notes, some of which are harsh and unmelodious ; the song being inconsiderable but characteristic. Building early in spring, it places its nest in all sorts of situations, even in the roots of an elm a foot below the ground. Most nests, however, are placed in holes in trees, sometimes in the deserted nest of hornets, and some have been found in garden pumps, flower-pots, and other unlikely places. Probably one of the most extraordinary nests, so far as situation is concerned, ever discovered was built in a rough corner cupboard, fixed at one end of a hut erected in a plantation for the use of a game-keeper. In the centre of the cupboard was a single shelf, and the door being kept shut, the pair of titmice could only obtain access through a small hole in the woodwork above, and through this opening the large amount of material employed in the construction of the nest must have been introduced.

GREAT TITMICE

The eggs of this species are white, blotched with bright red (page 990). The birds frequently rear two broods in the same nest in the course of a summer. In the adult male the crown of the head and the sides of the neck and throat are glossy black, the sides of the face white, the back yellowish green, the lower part of the back, wings, tail, and upper tail coverts slaty grey, and the under parts bright yellow with a black median stripe.

COAL TITMOUSE

An inhabitant of the fir woods of Central and Northern Europe, the coal titmouse (*P. ater*) breeds early in the year, generally in a hole in a wall or chink in some rotten tree-stump ; the nest being lined with fine roots, moss, hair, and feathers. The eggs are white, spotted and blotched with red. A nest of this species has been found in the burrow of a sand martin. The British coal titmouse is distinguished from the Continental race by the fact that the back is olive brown instead of slaty blue. Nevertheless, some specimens of coal titmouse obtained in the north of Scotland are intermediate between the British and Continental races. The adult male of the typical

In the adult the whole of the head is snowy white, the hind part of the neck is deep black, the sides of the back and scapulas vinous red, the wings and tail black and white, and the under parts whitish tinged with pink. All these titmice are sometimes referred to under the name of *Ægithalus*, in place of *Acredula*.

NEW ZEALAND CREEPER

In New Zealand the family is represented by a species locally known as creeper (*Certhiparus novæ zealandiæ*). The genus is characterised by the moderate-sized curved and compressed beak, the moderate and rounded wings, the long and rounded tail, and broad shields on the front of the comparatively long shank, or metatarsus. The single species is confined to the wooded portions of the South Island, where it frequents low undergrowth and the outskirts of bush in which insect life is abundant. During severe seasons it has been known to leave the shelter of the bush for sheep stations, flitting about the meat stores, and picking off morsels of fat from the bones and skins of the carcases. Its ordinary food consists of minute beetles and other insects.

The New Zealand creeper breeds late in the southern summer, the young being sometimes found in the nest in December. The eggs are white, spotted with brown and purple. The nest is rounded, and not unlike a large pear in shape. In structure it is composed of dry vegetable fibres, fragments of wool, moss, spiders' webs, and other soft materials closely felted together. The entrance is placed on the side about one-third the distance from the top, and is perfectly round with smoothened edges, the interior being lined with soft white feathers. The adult male of this tit-mouse has the upper parts bright cinereous brown, inclining to rufous ; the quills of the wing are light brown ; the tail is pale rufous, the sides of the head and nape are grey, and the throat, breast, and under parts rufous white.

BEARDED TITS

The bearded tit (*Panurus biarmicus*), best known, perhaps, by its Norfolk name of reed pheasant, is so distant from the titmice that it represents a family by itself, *Panuridæ* ; and it is even a question whether it is not more nearly related to the finches than to the titmice, from which latter it is broadly distinguished by its colouring. Among the more important characteristics of the genus are the short, sub-conical beak, the minute first primary quill of the wing, the long and graduated tail, the long shank, and the comparatively stout feet ; although the most distinctive character is the elongation of the feathers of the sides of the throat into a moustache.

The bearded tit is peculiar to Central and Northern Europe in its typical form, being replaced in Central Asia by a paler variety. Throughout its range it haunts large reed beds and marshes. Norfolk was formerly its home, and a few pairs still breed in some of the more favoured parts of the Broads. Mr. Stevenson states that when shooting in winter he has more than once observed the arrival of a flock from some neighbouring Broad, their presence overhead being indicated by the clear ringing of their silvery notes uttered preparatory to their pitching into the nearest reed bed ; and in autumn, after roosting in small parties on the reeds, they will fly up simultaneously soon after sunrise, swarming for a while like a flock of bees, and uttering in full chorus their pretty song, disperse themselves over the reed beds for their morning meal.

Delicate as these birds appear, they may be found during the sharpest frosts, when snipe have left the half-frozen waters for upland springs and drains, still busy among the reed stems as lively and musical as ever. The same writer also states that he has often found the nests completed by the end of the first week of April. These are generally placed among the reed stems close to the edge of the water, supported on the loose herbage forming the foundation of the reed beds, but never in any way suspended ; they are constructed

BEARDED TIT OR REED PHEASANT

of the dead stems of sedges and reeds, intermixed with a few pieces of grass, and invariably lined with the tops of reeds.

The eggs are pure white, sprinkled all over with small, purplish red spots. The food of these birds during winter is principally the seeds of the reed, and so intent are they in searching for these that they have been taken with a bird-limed twig attached to the end of a fishing-rod. When alarmed by a sudden noise or the passing of a hawk, they utter shrill notes and hide among the thick bottom of the reeds, but soon resume their station, climbing the upright stems with the utmost facility. Their movements are not unlike those of long-tailed titmice, and these birds may often be seen hanging with their heads downwards and turning themselves into curious attitudes. Their food is not entirely reed seed, but includes insects and their larvæ, and the young snails of different kinds which are numerous at the bottom of the reeds.

In Holland many bearded tits are captured, chiefly during the early part of October, when the old birds go on foraging expeditions, accompanied by the young ones, to the number of six or seven in a flock. They are then caught by means of nets laid among the reeds, while decoy birds are placed at a short distance. The adult male has the head clear bluish grey, the lores and moustache stripe black, the back rich fawn colour, the primaries brown edged with white, the tail feathers deep rusty red, the throat and upper part of the breast greyish white, and the sides of the body fawn. The female is greyish fawn above and greyish white beneath.

TITMICE AND BEARDED TITS

TITMICE

ALTHOUGH occasionally classed with the crows—from which they may be distinguished by the first primary quill never exceeding half the length of the second, and being generally shorter still—the titmice are evidently allied to the nuthatches, on the one hand, and perhaps to the honey-eaters, on the other. They constitute a considerable group (family *Paridæ*) of small, agile birds, obtaining their food on trees, and living principally upon insects. All are very much alike, and have a short, conical, and entire beak, about one-third the length of the head, with the bristles at the gape short, and those covering the nostrils, although likewise short, straight and thick. The wing, which contains ten primaries, is weak and rounded, and the metatarsus covered with long, greave-like shields.

Thoroughly arboreal in their mode of life, seldom descending to the ground, and often going about in parties of three or four, the titmice are chiefly denizens of the Old World, some inhabiting the forest regions of Northern Europe and Asia, while others are indigenous to the Himalaya, and others peculiar to North America, while there is also one genus in New Zealand.

Titmice are great foes of insects, and are therefore, for the most part, welcome in gardens, where, however, they do considerable damage to pears.

TYPICAL TITMICE

The more typical members of the family are specially characterised by the rounded tail, in which the outer pair of feathers falls short of the tip by the length of the claw of the first toe. These birds are distributed over a large portion of the world, and are numerously represented in Europe, while are four denizens of the Indian region. They are also common in North America. The beak is generally strong and conical, and well adapted to extract insects from their hiding-places in the bark of trees, while the wings are somewhat rounded, and the tail is comparatively short.

GREAT TITMOUSE

The great titmouse (*Parus major*) is common in the northern parts of the Old World, living in companies which haunt woods and gardens during the greater part of the year. In England it is resident, frequenting in summer woods and large gardens, where its food, which at that season consists almost exclusively of insects, is abundant. In winter these tits associate in family parties, and either wander about wherever there are trees, in company with creepers and other small birds, seeking for insects in the bark of trees, or remain in the neighbourhood of inhabited places to feed upon such refuse as they can find. They are fond of picking bones, and by hanging bones in trees can readily be attracted to gardens.

Mr. Dresser writes that "when hunting after insects, etc., in trees, they appear to examine every part most carefully, moving along and round the branches, now clinging head-downwards, now moving along the limbs of the tree almost like a creeper, or clinging to the end of a small branch, examining carefully a bud to see if any insect is harboured therein. This is done in a most business-like, quiet manner, and only now and then a low call, 'ze,' is uttered; but, when taking a short flight from tree to tree or bush to bush, they utter their cheerful loud note."

The great titmouse has a variety of notes, some of which are harsh and unmelodious; the song being inconsiderable but characteristic. Building early in spring, it places its nest in all sorts of situations, even in the roots of an elm a foot below the ground. Most nests, however, are placed in holes in trees, sometimes in the deserted nest of hornets, and some have been found in garden pumps, flower-pots, and other unlikely places. Probably one of the most extraordinary nests, so far as situation is concerned, ever discovered was built in a rough corner cupboard, fixed at one end of a hut erected in a plantation for the use of a gamekeeper. In the centre of the cupboard was a single shelf, and the door being kept shut, the pair of titmice could only obtain access through a small hole in the woodwork above, and through this opening the large amount of material employed in the construction of the nest must have been introduced.

The eggs of this species are white, blotched with bright red (page 990). The birds frequently rear two broods in the same nest in the course of a summer. In the adult male the crown of the head and the sides of the neck and throat are glossy black, the sides of the face white, the back yellowish green, the lower part of the back, wings, tail, and upper tail coverts slaty grey, and the under parts bright yellow with a black median stripe.

COAL TITMOUSE

An inhabitant of the fir woods of Central and Northern Europe, the coal titmouse (*P. ater*) breeds early in the year, generally in a hole in a wall or chink in some rotten tree-stump; the nest being lined with fine roots, moss, hair, and feathers. The eggs are white, spotted and blotched with red. A nest of this species has been found in the burrow of a sand martin. The British coal titmouse is distinguished from the Continental race by the fact that the back is olive brown instead of slaty blue. Nevertheless, some specimens of coal titmouse obtained in the north of Scotland are intermediate between the British and Continental races. The adult male of the typical

GREAT TITMICE

Continental race has the crown black, with a distinct white patch on the nape, the sides of the head white, the upper parts slate blue, the throat black, the centre of the body whitish, and the flanks buff.

MARSH TITMOUSE

Generally frequenting gardens, orchards, and woods near swampy ground, the marsh titmouse (*P. palustris*)

CRESTED TITMOUSE

displays a marked partiality for rabbit's fur as a nesting material. One nest taken from a hole in a birch tree was compact, cup-shaped, smooth out and in, and mainly composed of this substance, interwoven on the inner side with minute chips of dried grasses, and on the outer side with fine moss. The eggs are pure white, dotted with red. In the adult the crown is glossy black, the sides of the neck are white, the back greyish brown, the throat black, the wings and tail greyish brown, and the breast white tinged with buff.

BLUE TITMOUSE

The blue titmouse (*P. cœruleus*) is common in most parts of Europe, frequenting gardens, orchards, and the neighbourhood of houses, and often exhibiting its antics in full view of any passer-by. Its laughing call note is well known to most persons living in the country. The blue titmouse often nests in a hole upon the ground, while a pair has been known to rear a brood in the steeple of a church; in many cases the same site is used year after year. The hen sits very close upon its eggs, which, like those of other tits, are white spotted with pale red (page 990). Both the present species and the great titmouse are migratory in habit, crossing the North Sea upon their journeys, and sometimes venturing into the heart of London. The forehead is white, the crown, back of the neck, and collar are bright blue, the back yellowish green, the wings and tail blue, the throat dusky black, and the under parts pure yellow.

AZURE TITMOUSE

Another member of the family that calls for notice on account of the beauty of its plumage is the azure titmouse (*P. cyaneus*) of Siberia, which occasionally wanders into Europe, having been captured more than once in the neighbourhood of the Russian capital. This titmouse breeds in holes in old trees, especially willows, sometimes making use of a deserted woodpecker's nest. The nest is composed of the fur of the mountain hare and squirrel, with a few pieces of slender grass. The female lays ten or eleven eggs, which are white, spotted with dull red at the larger end.

The adult male has the head snowy white, appearing in life as if powdered over with blue, the back pale bluish grey, the upper tail coverts Prussian blue tipped with white, the wings greyish brown, with the base of the inner web white, and the outer web Prussian blue, and the long tail bright Prussian blue, with the exception of the outer feathers, which are white, as are the lower parts.

CRESTED TITMOUSE

Although frequently referred to a genus by itself, the crested titmouse (*P. cristatus*) of Northern Europe may well be included in the genus *Parus*, the presence of a head crest not being a feature of much importance. In common with several other species, these titmice constitute the sub-genus *Lophophanes*, distinguished from an allied sub-genus (*Macrolophus*) by the tail being squared or slightly forked instead of rounded, and also by the absence of the black abdominal band found in the last-named group. The home of the crested titmouse is in large pine forests, or extensive stretches of beech wood and mixed timber. It is a shy and retiring species, not courting observation, like many of its cousins, but shunning the haunts of men even in winter, and in spring met with in small droves, in pairs, and even singly.

Any person who has trained his ear to recognise the cries of birds will soon become familiar with the liquid call-note, " prrit " or " chrrit " of this species, which may often be heard before the tiny musician has revealed its whereabouts. The crested titmouse has also a pretty little song, generally uttered when a male is pursuing one of its companions in mock anger.

Writing of these birds a well-known observer states: " I have generally seen them in the top boughs of the firs,

MARSH TITMOUSE AND COAL TITMOUSE

but they frequently come on to the ground, apparently to pick up a seed that may drop from the fir-cones; at any rate, you see them fly down, look in the grass, and fly up again immediately. They appear to remain in families, as you seldom see a single one. As a rule, they prefer the rotten stem of a fir, about twelve or fourteen feet high, and bore a hole in the tree from two feet to eight feet above the ground. I have also found the nest in old stumps of very large trees within six inches of the ground. Their nidification is therefore more like that of the coal titmouse in that respect."

In Rhenish Prussia the crested titmouse lays in the deserted nests of the crow, magpie, or squirrel, as well as in hollow trees, the nest being made of moss, wool, and feathers. The eggs are white, spotted all over with bright red. When the pairing season is over, crested titmice associate with tree-creepers, goldcrests, and other titmice to scour the woods in search of food, themselves leading the van. They do not work the branches minutely as other titmice do, preferring to range more widely.

The crested titmouse takes its name from an elongated crest, which is often raised. The forehead and the sides of the head are white, mottled slightly with grey, the feathers of the crown black edged with white, the cheeks and side of the head white, the throat deep black, the upper parts greyish brown, so that the bird appears sombre while upon the wing, and the lower parts fulvous.

LONG-TAILED TITMICE

Agreeing with the more typical members of the genus *Parus* in the absence of a head crest, the long-tailed titmouse (*Acredula caudata*) and its relatives are sufficiently distinguished by the elongation of the appendage from which they take their name. The typical Continental race of the species inhabits the northern districts of Europe and occurs also in many parts of Germany, its range somewhat overlapping that of the British race (*A. c. rosea*), which extends through France, Germany, and Italy to the Balkan Peninsula. In Switzerland the long-tailed titmouse ranges up the mountains to an elevation of five thousand feet.

It would be difficult to name a more sociable or confiding species, for this titmouse lives in flocks during the greater part of the year, and roves about with its fellows in quest of the small insects, especially certain grubs found in the catkins of willows, which form its subsistence. Flying in an undulating fashion, and exhibiting a rather peculiar appearance on the wing, as it flits from tree to tree, uttering its loud and shrill call note almost without cessation, this titmouse builds a beautiful nest composed of mosses, interwoven with wool and feathers, and exquisitely trimmed on the exterior with grey and white lichens, the interior of the structure being copiously lined with a variety of soft feathers.

A peculiarly shaped nest of this species taken in Denmark resembled in shape a plain honey-jar, placed horizontally on the upper part of a long cleft between two large branches, to the base of which a pouch twice or three times as long as the jar itself was attached perpendicularly, filling up the face of the fork between the branches, the entrance hole being the mouth of the jar. The nest was built of moss closely covered with pieces of lichen.

LONG-TAILED TITMICE

An early breeder, this titmouse lays from ten to fourteen white eggs, spotted with red, the young being sometimes hatched as early as the month of April, and both old birds participating in the labours of incubation. These titmice have been kept in confinement for no less a period than two years, the method of treatment being to confine them between large double windows where ivy was growing, on the leaves of which were numbers of plant-lice. On these the freshly caught titmice fed, and by degrees got accustomed to confinement, and would take ants' eggs and other food.

More than a dozen species, or races, of the genus are known, among which may be mentioned the Macedonian long-tailed titmouse (*A. macedonica*), which resembles the British long-tailed titmouse, but has a black chin and black, instead of white, lores. Irby's long-tailed titmouse (*A. irbyi*) inhabits Spain and Italy; and closely allied to it is the Turkish *A. tephronotus*; this bird resembling Irby's titmouse in having the centre of the back grey and not black, but differing in the presence of a large blackish patch on the centre of the throat.

A sixth species (*A. major*), inhabiting the northern slopes of the Caucasus, has the forehead pale brownish, and the sides of the crown brown instead of black.

In the adult the whole of the head is snowy white, the hind part of the neck is deep black, the sides of the back and scapulas vinous red, the wings and tail black and white, and the under parts whitish tinged with pink. All these titmice are sometimes referred to under the name of *Ægithalus*, in place of *Acredula*.

NEW ZEALAND CREEPER

In New Zealand the family is represented by a species locally known as creeper (*Certhiparus novæ zealandiæ*). The genus is characterised by the moderate-sized curved and compressed beak, the moderate and rounded wings, the long and rounded tail, and broad shields on the front of, the comparatively long shank, or metatarsus. The single species is confined to the wooded portions of the South Island, where it frequents low undergrowth and the outskirts of bush in which insect life is abundant. During severe seasons it has been known to leave the shelter of the bush for sheep stations, flitting about the meat stores, and picking off morsels of fat from the bones and skins of the carcases. Its ordinary food consists of minute beetles and other insects.

The New Zealand creeper breeds late in the southern summer, the young being sometimes found in the nest in December. The eggs are white, spotted with brown and purple. The nest is rounded, and not unlike a large pear in shape. In structure it is composed of dry vegetable fibres, fragments of wool, moss, spiders' webs, and other soft materials closely felted together. The entrance is placed on the side about one-third the distance from the top, and is perfectly round with smoothened edges, the interior being lined with soft white feathers. The adult male of this tit-mouse has the upper parts bright cinereous brown, inclining to rufous; the quills of the wing are light brown; the tail is pale rufous, the sides of the head and nape are grey, and the throat, breast, and under parts rufous white.

BEARDED TITS

The bearded tit (*Panurus biarmicus*), best known, perhaps, by its Norfolk name of reed pheasant, is so distant from the titmice that it represents a family by itself, *Panuridæ*; and it is even a question whether it is not more nearly related to the finches than to the titmice, from which latter it is broadly distinguished by its colouring. Among the more important characteristics of the genus are the short, sub-conical beak, the minute first primary quill of the wing, the long and graduated tail, the long shank, and the comparatively stout feet; although the most distinctive character is the elongation of the feathers of the sides of the throat into a moustache.

The bearded tit is peculiar to Central and Northern Europe in its typical form, being replaced in Central Asia by a paler variety. Throughout its range it haunts large reed beds and marshes. Norfolk was formerly its home, and a few pairs still breed in some of the more favoured parts of the Broads. Mr. Stevenson states that when shooting in winter he has more than once observed the arrival of a flock from some neighbouring Broad, their presence overhead being indicated by the clear ringing of their silvery notes uttered preparatory to their pitching into the nearest reed bed; and in autumn, after roosting in small parties on the reeds, they will fly up simultaneously soon after sunrise, swarming for a while like a flock of bees, and uttering in full chorus their pretty song, disperse themselves over the reed beds for their morning meal.

Delicate as these birds appear, they may be found during the sharpest frosts, when snipe have left the half-frozen waters for upland springs and drains, still busy among the reed stems as lively and musical as ever. The same writer also states that he has often found the nests completed by the end of the first week of April. These are generally placed among the reed stems close to the edge of the water, supported on the loose herbage forming the foundation of the reed beds, but never in any way suspended; they are constructed

BEARDED TIT OR REED PHEASANT

of the dead stems of sedges and reeds, intermixed with a few pieces of grass, and invariably lined with the tops of reeds.

The eggs are pure white, sprinkled all over with small, purplish red spots. The food of these birds during winter is principally the seeds of the reed, and so intent are they in searching for these that they have been taken with a bird-limed twig attached to the end of a fishing-rod. When alarmed by a sudden noise or the passing of a hawk, they utter shrill notes and hide among the thick bottom of the reeds, but soon resume their station, climbing the upright stems with the utmost facility. Their movements are not unlike those of long-tailed titmice, and these birds may often be seen hanging with their heads downwards and turning themselves into curious attitudes. Their food is not entirely reed seed, but includes insects and their larvæ, and the young snails of different kinds which are numerous at the bottom of the reeds.

In Holland many bearded tits are captured, chiefly during the early part of October, when the old birds go on foraging expeditions, accompanied by the young ones, to the number of six or seven in a flock. They are then caught by means of nets laid among the reeds, while decoy birds are placed at a short distance. The adult male has the head clear bluish grey, the lores and moustache stripe black, the back rich fawn colour, the primaries brown edged with white, the tail feathers deep rusty red, the throat and upper part of the breast greyish white, and the sides of the body fawn. The female is greyish fawn above and greyish white beneath.

SHRIKES

THE members of the shrike tribe (family *Laniidæ*) form a somewhat variable group, here taken to embrace such different forms as the gay-coloured minivets (*Pericrocotus*) of Asia, the cuckoo-shrikes (*Campephaga*), the wood shrikes (*Prionops*), and the Indian pied shrikes (*Hemipus*), while the Australian so-called piping crows, and certain allied types, are likewise included in the family. In the more typical forms the edges of both halves of the beak are either smooth, or the upper one is simply notched or toothed, or both together ; the hind surface of the metatarsus is smooth and covered with two longitudinal plates ; the wing has ten primaries ; the tongue is of ordinary form ; the nostrils are clear of the line of the forehead, and more or less overhung with bristles ; and there are twelve tail feathers. The plumage of the nestling is cross-barred, and there appears to be only an autumnal moult.

The family comprises a large number of genera, and, with the exception of South America, has a world-wide distribution, although most numerous in Africa. With the flycatchers the family is connected by the genus *Pachycephala*, with the bulbuls by *Neolestes*, and perhaps with the crow tribe by the aforesaid piping crows ((*Gymnorhina*) and their allies. By some naturalists the cuckoo shrikes are made the type of a separate family (*Campephagidæ*).

SHRIKE TITS

For want of a better name, the birds composing the genus *Falcunculus* have been described as shrike tits. In some degree they combine the form of a shrike with

SOUTHERN SHRIKE TIT

the habits of a woodpecker ; they possess strong toothed beaks, with which they are able to tear off pieces of rotten wood, and even the bark of gum trees, in search of food, and the head is surmounted by a crest of feathers. Inhabiting the larger branches of trees, and resembling titmice in many of their habits, these birds, when attacked by an enemy, defend themselves with ferocity. All are exclusively Australian, the white-bellied shrike tit (*F. leucogaster*) being a native of West Australia, while the southern shrike tit (*F. frontatus*) inhabits South Australia and New South Wales.

The southern shrike tit is an active and sprightly bird, feeding chiefly on insects, which are obtained either among the foliage of trees or under the bark of the larger branches and trunks. In procuring these the bird exhibits great dexterity, stripping off the bark with its powerful beak. While searching the branches for food it frequently erects its crest, and no bird of its size possesses greater strength in its beak, or is capable of inflicting severer wounds. Its song consists only of a few piping notes. In the male the crest is black, the sides of the head are white, divided by a black line, the back, shoulders, and wing coverts are olive, the primaries, secondaries, and tail are blackish brown margined with grey, the two outer tail feathers and the tips of the remainder are white, the throat is black, and the under parts are bright yellow.

An allied genus is *Pachycephala*, which forms the type of a sub-family, the members of which extend from Polynesia and Australia to the Malay Islands and Tasmania.

TYPICAL SHRIKES

In the typical shrikes (genus *Lanius*) the beak is curved, large, compressed, and hooked and toothed, and thus adapted to tear the flesh of the small mammals and birds upon which these shrikes often prey. The wings are moderate in length, and comparatively powerful, while the tail is generally much longer than the wings, and graduated, with the middle feathers the longest. The relatively strong metatarsus and toes are of assistance in enabling the shrikes to retain hold of beetles and other insects. The typical shrikes constitute a sub-family (*Laniinæ*), ranging over the greater part of the world, except Australasia and South America, there being two representatives in North America.

GREAT GREY SHRIKE

The great grey shrike (*L. excubitor*) inhabits Western and Central Europe, being replaced eastwards chiefly by a single-barred species, which extends through Asia, merging into the great northern shrike of North America. The brightly coloured shrikes belong chiefly to Africa.

The great grey shrike, which frequents the skirts of forests in summer, is a shy and retiring species when unmolested, but, when it has lost its nest or young, becomes most vociferous. It builds in a variety of situations, occasionally in the top of a Scots fir ; while a nest has been observed in Finmark in a birch tree on a sterile terrace. In Central Europe large forest oaks are most frequently chosen by this species for its nest, the tree selected being always on the edge of a belt of timber, never in the centre of a big wood. The nest itself is generally placed at the apex of a forked bough a long way out from the main trunk, built on a knot in the fork, at an elevation of some thirty-five or forty feet ; it is a bulky structure composed of fine twigs interlaced with a few stout straws, bents, and fibres. Within, it is quilted with a profusion of soft substances, feathers of the pheasant and buzzard, a little of the white fur from the belly of a hare, and some of the shed coat of the roebuck, wool, or any convenient substitute. The eggs are greenish white in ground colour, blotched with olive green, wood brown, and dull lilac. The female is most assiduous in the care she bestows upon her young, and exhibits distress and consternation if she imagines their safety is endangered.

To a large extent migratory in its habits, this species does not breed in the British Isles, although considerable numbers visit England and Scotland in the fall of

GREAT GREY AND RED-BACKED SHRIKES

rocks. It breeds early in June, and the nests found in Slavonia are built in acacia trees; in size they are as large as those of the blackbird, and chiefly composed of chickweed, freshly plucked feathers, and wool. Some contain as many as six eggs, which are bluish green in ground colour, spotted and blotched with greenish brown. This shrike feeds principally on beetles, butterflies, grasshoppers, and other insects. Its flight, like that of its congeners, is undulating, but easy and comparatively noiseless, the bird skimming through the air like a partridge for a moment or two before it alights on some perch, on to which it drops with a scuffle of the wings.

The song is a not unmusical chatter, something like the twitter of the swallow or starling, but louder and mixed with some harsher notes. The bird, however, has a variety of cries, some very harsh, which are probably alarm notes, and others somewhat plaintive. In the adult the forehead, lores, and ear coverts are deep black, the crown of the head and upper parts are pearl grey, the wings are black, the primaries having white bases which form a single white wing-bar, the tail is black and white, and the under parts are white tinged with reddish buff.

RED-BACKED SHRIKE

The red-backed shrike (*L. coilurio*) is another migratory species, spending many months of the year beneath the burning rays of an African sun, and returning northwards in spring to rear a family in its haunts in Central Europe or the British Isles. Those that visit England—for in Scotland the bird is very rare—apparently journey to their summer quarters by way of the valley of the Rhine. The red-backed shrike arrives somewhat later than the majority of summer migrants. Each pair becomes established in a certain area, which it rarely if ever leaves, the male being conspicuous as he perches on some tall spray of hawthorn. Apparently, this shrike never nests in a tree, and seems invariably to build in a hedge or low bush, the nest, although this is exceptional, being at times placed in a tiny bush barely eighteen inches from the ground. The nest is composed of dry stalks and moss, lined with fibrous roots and a little

the year. They have occurred in Heligoland as early as the middle of August, and while a few pass yearly along favourite flight lines, in certain years their numbers are increased tenfold. Those that winter in England for the most part lead lives of solitude, frequenting a particular beat of country for a week or two at a time, during which the familiar outline of the butcher bird, as the species is commonly called, may be detected perching upon the top of a leafless tree, watching incessantly for field-mice, shrewmice, and small birds. The flight is sometimes high and sometimes low, but constantly undulating. With the arrival of spring the great grey shrike in England moves eastwards to the coast, from which it takes its departure in March and April, though an occasional straggler is sometimes reported as having been seen during the summer.

In common with other butcher birds, this shrike is in the habit of impaling the carcases of its prey on thorns, in order to facilitate the flaying of the bird or small mammal, and to provide a larder. In the adult cock the upper parts are nearly uniform slaty grey, the lores, cheeks, and ear coverts are black, the wings are black with white bases to the quills, the graduated tail is black and white, and the under parts are pure white, often finely barred with crescentic grey markings.

LESSER GREY SHRIKE

The lesser grey shrike (*L. minor*) is a migratory species, wintering in Africa and passing the summer in Central and Southern Europe, Asia Minor, and Persia. In Eastern Europe this shrike frequents the outskirts of civilisation, where trees and bushes of various kinds struggle for existence among the broken

LESSER GREY SHRIKE

hair; the eggs vary, being sometimes yellowish white with markings of olive and lilac, and at others salmon-coloured marked with light red.

No sooner has this shrike reared its young than it prepares to leave Britain, hurrying south in advance of many other summer birds to moult in the heat of a tropical winter. So long as it remains in England it always exhibits the same alert character—vigilant, resourceful, ready to anticipate danger. It is a bird of rapid flight and considerable agility, and when about to seize a smaller bird shoots forward like an arrow, rarely missing the quarry. It will swoop upon a humble-bee, and impale the unfortunate insect with perfect deftness upon the sharpest thorn available.

Although the red-backed shrike is content to feed upon insects, it has been known to attack a lizard, and is partial to small birds, field-mice and frogs, and sometimes, like the great grey shrike, attacks the decoys of bird-catchers. The adult male has the head, back, and sides of the neck bluish grey, the middle of the back and scapulars dull brick-red, the wings dull black edged with rufous, the tail black and white, the forehead, lores, and ear coverts black, the chin white, and the under parts rose colour. The female is brownish grey above, with a reddish brown tail, the under parts being dull white, closely barred with transverse brown markings.

WOODCHAT SHRIKE, MASKED SHRIKE, AND HOODED SHRIKE

WOODCHAT SHRIKE

The woodchat shrike (*L.* [*Phoneus*] *pomeranus*) is rather rare in many parts of its summer quarters in Central Europe, although the commonest of all shrikes in Portugal. Preferring to nest amid extensive orchards, it is absent from forest land, and frequents sunny valleys and the gentle slopes of low hills commanding a southern aspect rather than more elevated and exposed situations. A trained eye soon learns to recognise the woodchat at a considerable distance, owing to the fact that this bird, true to the watchful character of its congeners, perches, at least during migration, in a bush, with its white breast facing the quarter from which the approach of danger is apprehended.

The flight is strong and undulating. During migration these shrikes travel in the wake of their fellow wanderers, and, although two days may often interrupt the migration, when this is resumed it will be found that they have adhered to the line taken by the advance guard. In Eastern Algeria they breed in numbers on the hillsides, constructing their nests almost entirely of the stalks of one species of small grey flower. As a rule, the eggs are bluish grey in ground colour, spotted and blotched with dark grey and brown. Captive specimens will eat not only insects, but small frogs, and, in default of thorns, will hang their prey on the crossbars of their cage.

In the adult male the crown of the head and lower part of the neck are bright chestnut, the forehead and ear coverts black, the scapulars and rump pure white, the wings and tail black and white, and the lower parts white, slightly tinged with buffish red.

MAGPIE LARKS

As an example of the sub-family *Prionopinæ*—raised by some naturalists to the rank of a distinct family—reference may be made to the black and

RED-BACKED SHRIKE

AUSTRALIAN MAGPIE LARK

Neolestes, display yellow and green, while in *Laniarius* these colours are mixed with red.

It is unnecessary to name other genera, but it may be added that while some naturalists include in this group the Malagasy genera *Vanga* and *Artamia*, others place them and certain other genera from the same island in a family by themselves, far away from the shrike tribe. The typical species (*Artamia bicolor*) of the second genus has the plumage cobalt blue, except on the hind and underparts, where it is white, thus forming a striking contrast.

PIPING CROWS

The Australian piping crows, locally known as magpies, typify another sub-family, the *Gymnorhininæ*, whose range extends westwards to Borneo. These birds are easily recognised by their pied plumage, white beaks, and peculiar whistling notes. Four species are commonly recognised, of which the most typical representatives are the black-backed piping crow (*Gymnorhina tibicen*), universally distributed over Australia, the white-backed piping crow (*G. leuconota*), restricted to South Australia, *G. dorsalis* of Western Australia, and *G. hyperleuca*, or *organica*, known to the colonists as the organ bird, peculiar to Tasmania. The last pours from the branch of a dead tree a succession of the strangest notes that can be imagined, much resembling the sound of a hand-organ out of tune; it is easily tamed, and can be taught to whistle various tunes as well as articulate words.

The black-backed species is bold and showy, enlivening and ornamenting lawns and gardens by its presence, and with the slightest protection from molestation becoming so tame and familiar that it approaches close to dwellings, perching around them and the stock-yards in small families of from six to ten. It prefers cleared lands, or open plains skirted by belts of timber, so that the interior of the country is more favourable to its habits than the neighbourhood of the coast. Its lively and intelligent habits and fine vocal powers render it a favourite cagebird both at home and abroad. The crown, back, and under parts are black, and the nape, wing coverts, and upper and under tail coverts white. Insectivorous in their habits, piping crows live chiefly on grasshoppers, of which they consume enormous quantities.

white Australian bird locally known as the magpie lark (*Grallina australis*); another member of the same genus (*G. bruijni*) inhabiting New Guinea. The sub-family, however, is typified by the wood shrikes of the genus *Prionops*, which are characterised by the presence of a frontal tuft of feathers overhanging the nostrils and fleshy wattles round the eyes. Some of the members of the group are dull-coloured birds, although in others there are bright patches of chestnut or yellowish, while yet others are black and white or even wholly black.

The magpie larks and the Indian pied shrikes of the genus *Hemipus* represent the black and white section, the former being running birds, with somewhat the habits of larks on the ground, but with a slow, heavy flight. They utter a whistling cry, and build mud-nests on low boughs.

MALAGASY HELMET BIRD

In this neighbourhood should probably also come the remarkable Malagasy helmet bird (*Euryceros*, or *Ærocharis*, *prevosti*), distinguished by its purplish black and chestnut plumage, and compressed, swollen, and hooked beak. It is sometimes regarded as representing a family by itself.

Another sub-family, the *Malaconotinæ*, contains a number of genera, for the most part, or entirely—for there are different opinions as to the limits of the group—confined to Africa, and typically represented by *Malaconotus*. In these birds the beak is generally shorter than in the other groups, and the scutes on the metatarsus tend to coalesce to a greater extent. Black, white, and chestnut form the prevailing tints of the plumage, although some forms, such as

ORGAN BIRD

The breeding season begins in August and lasts till January, during which each pair nests twice. The round and open nest is formed of twigs and leaves, with a softer lining; the three or four eggs are bluish white, often with a reddish tinge, marked with large blotches of brownish red or light chestnut brown. It is noteworthy that, although these birds seem always to thrive in captivity, yet their vocal powers in that state vary considerably some specimens pouring forth the full song, while others sing only in a subdued undertone.

Mr. Robert Hall states that, as a rule, these birds mate for life, and if one of a pair be killed a new partner is secured in one of two ways. If the survivor be a female, a new mate is found for her by the parents of another brood in the neighbourhood. On the other hand, a bereaved male has to find a new companion in the best way he can, and generally effects this by driving away the male of a pair, calling in the assistance of another bird of his own sex if his own exertions are insufficient, the female meanwhile remaining passive until the contest is settled one way or another. What becomes of the vanquished rival in such cases is not stated.

Young birds mate in Victoria during May, and on such occasions several families assemble on neutral ground, for each pair of these birds has normally a territory of its own. The members of the assemblage at the beginning of the proceedings keep up a constant chorus of piping and warbling for several days, after which the old birds retire, when the young males continue the process of selecting their partners—a matter usually accomplished without quarrels. Directly this is finished the old birds reappear on the scene, and drive the young couples to a distance from the parental domains, which they are not permitted to revisit. *Strepera* is an allied Australian genus, while the nearly related *Cracticus* occurs also in New Guinea, and *Pityriasis* represents the group in Borneo.

MINIVETS AND CUCKOO SHRIKES

The handsome scarlet minivet (*Pericrocotus speciosus*) and its numerous Indian relatives, together with the cuckoo shrikes (*Campephaga* and *Graculus*), form a group in regard to whose serial position some difference of opinion obtains. They have been included in the *Laniidæ*, but they are now regarded by many naturalists as representing a family by themselves, the *Campephagidæ*. Whether their affinities are with the shrikes or with the flycatchers and crows is indeed still a matter of uncertainty. The range of the group

INDIAN SCARLET MINIVET

extends from India and Africa to Australia, while a few outlying forms occur in North-Eastern Asia.

There are few absolutely characteristic and easily recognisable features which can be formulated of the group as a whole. It may be mentioned, however, that the plumage is soft, with stiff shafts to the feathers of the lower part of the beak, and that the nostrils are concealed by feathers, while bristles at the gape of the beak are absent. The tail is more or less elongated, and the beak generally stout, although there is considerable variation in these respects. The maximum stoutness of beak is found in *Artamides*.

The cuckoo shrikes differ from the minivets in having the tail moderately instead of greatly graduated, the outer feathers being three-quarters instead of less than half the entire length.

The minivets, on the other hand, are peculiar to India and Eastern Asia ; the Siberian species, inhabiting Manchuria in summer, and migrating through China to winter in the Philippine Islands and the Malay Peninsula, being the hardiest of the family. This bird is grey above and white below, but the majority of minivets are gaudy in their attire, scarlet and yellow predominating in their plumage, or at least in that of the male, the females being less gorgeous.

The brilliantly coloured Indian scarlet minivet, like other members of its genus, is arboreal in habits, and lives in family parties, which fly briskly about the branches of trees in active pursuit of insect prey. The call note is lively, and frequently repeated. Breeding in April, this minivet constructs a beautiful cup-shaped nest of moss trimmed with lichens, placed in a slender branch. The eggs are greyish white, marked with brown and inky purple. The adult male has the whole head, back, and scapulars glossy black, the lower surface from behind the throat, together with the rump and upper tail coverts vivid scarlet, the wings black, barred with scarlet, and the tail scarlet, except the middle pair of feathers, which are black.

BLACK-BACKED PIPING CROWS

WAXWINGS, GREENLETS, AND WOOD SWALLOWS

WAXWINGS

THE waxwings (family *Ampelidæ*), together with the American family of the greenlets (*Vireonidæ*) and the wood-swallows (*Artamidæ*), may be conveniently placed between the shrikes, on the one hand, and the thrushes and warblers, on the other. Containing only five genera, with not more than some ten species, the waxwings and their relatives are characterised by the usually short and slightly hooked beak, broad at the gape, long wings, and short legs as well as by the soft and silky plumage.

The typical waxwings are inhabitants of the northern half of both hemispheres, and form a single genus, *Ampelis*, in which the metatarsus is short, the feet are weak, and the inner quills of the wings are tipped with curious red horny appendages compared to pieces of sealing-wax. The Bohemian waxwing (*A. garrulus*) inhabits the northern parts of both the Old and New World; the Japanese waxwing (*A. japponica*) breeds in South-Eastern Siberia, and winters in Japan, China, and Formosa; while a third species, the cedar bird (*A. cedrorum*), is peculiar to North America. The Bohemian waxwing breeds in Finland, Lapland, and other Arctic countries.

Writing of his nest-hunting experiences, Mr. Dresser states that, after finding a tree in which a waxwing built, "I climbed up to the nest, which was in the fork between the main stem and the first branch, and not above nine or ten feet from the ground. The moment I touched it the young ones, five in number, flew out. I jumped down, and made a cut at the largest with my cap, and secured him. Directly the young one which I had caught began to cry out several waxwings flew from the neighbouring thicket, all, however, keeping out of gunshot, except two, which came close round me, and both of which I shot. I then sat down and imitated as well as I could the call of the old birds.

"I was soon rewarded for my trouble by a young one coming out of a blueberry bush close by, and calling lustily. I then climbed up again and took the nest away carefully, so as to preserve the shape, and to my great delight found one egg in it. We hunted for several hours in the higher part of the island for another nest, but, although we saw about nine old birds, we didn't succeed in finding another nest."

The eggs of the waxwing are pale blue, ornamented with purplish underlying markings and black overlying surface spots. In some seasons large numbers of waxwings cross the North Sea to winter in the British Isles, where, unfortunately, their pretty plumage and strange appearance attract the attention of the gunner. In habits the waxwing is confiding and tame, though much less so in spring and summer than in winter.

"At the latter season of the year," writes Mr. Dresser, "I used to see large flocks in Southern Finland, usually frequenting the mountain ash trees, and very often seen in the gardens quite in the centre of the towns. So tame are they that, when fired at and one or two killed, the remainder will only fly to a short distance, and soon return to the same tree again. The flocks are often very large; and I have known of more than twenty specimens having been killed at one shot; I once killed as many as fourteen at a shot off a large mountain ash tree, on which a flock was perched picking off the berries.

"It is a peculiarly silent bird; and I watched a flock for some time without hearing any of them utter a sound. The only note I have heard is a low plaintive whistle, from which, I imagine, it is called by the Finns by the name of tilhi, as this gives some idea of the sound of its call note. When frightened or suddenly disturbed, the same note is uttered, but is then shriller and louder in tone. The bird sits very erect, and carries its crest so that it is distinctly seen; when frightened, it at once raises its crest, slightly spreading it.

"A flock busy feeding on a rowan tree, especially if the ground and tree are covered with snow, is a most pleasing sight; and I have often sat and watched them from a window close to which was a small mountain ash, to which they often came to feed on the berries, which, having large clusters, like bunches of coral beads, formed a rich contrast to the pure white snow."

THE WAXWING

Waxwings in confinement are somewhat inactive. Occasionally, it is true, they will hop restlessly from perch to perch, or even take a brisk fly around the aviary; but for the most part they prefer to sit on some favourite perch, now and then uttering a short succession of running notes. They feed somewhat greedily, and show a preference for dried currants. In winter small flocks of waxwings may often be seen in Sweden, flying hither and thither at a considerable height, and presenting somewhat the appearance of starlings from their long wings and comparatively short tails.

The adult male has the upper parts light greyish brown, the forehead and crest reddish chestnut, a broad black streak through and above the eye from the base of the beak, the primaries blackish, with the outer web towards the tip white on the outer feathers and yellow on the inner ones, and the inner web broadly tipped with white; the secondaries are blackish grey, tipped with red wax-like appendages, the tail is grey at the base, black towards the tip, and terminated by a broad bar of yellow; the throat is black, and the under parts purplish red.

CEDAR BIRD

The cedar bird, or cherry bird (*A. cedrorum*), a smaller and less beautifully coloured species than the Bohemian waxwing, is common in the gardens and orchards of the United States. It breeds somewhat late, generally building in an orchard or garden; the nest is placed in a bough, or on a limb of the tree, and built of coarse, dry stalks of grass, lined with very fine stems of the same. The eggs are bluish white, thickly marked with blackish spots. The young are at first fed upon insects, but, as they advance, berries become their chief diet. The cry of the young birds for food is loud and incessant.

The cedar bird flocks in July and August, and betakes itself to regions where whortleberries are plentiful. In October these birds descend to the lower parts of the country, to feed on the berries of the red cedar, thirty or forty individuals being sometimes seen fluttering among the branches of one small cedar, plucking off the berries. In the fall and beginning of summer the cedar bird becomes extremely fat, for which reason it was formerly esteemed for the table. In the adult the head, neck, breast, upper part of the back, and wing coverts are purplish cinnamon, shading into ash on the rump; the forehead, lores, and eye stripe are black, the wings slaty grey, with the inner feathers tipped with red horny appendages, and the tail is grey, tipped with yellow.

The other genera of the family are *Phænoptila*, *Dulus*, *Phænopepla*, and *Ptilogenys*; the last characterised by the elongation of the middle tail feathers.

GREENLETS

A group of small and active American birds, ranging from Nova Scotia and Winnipeg to Argentina, take their name of greenlets (family *Vireonidæ*) from the prevalent colour of their plumage, which varies from green or olive to grey on the upper parts, with the crown of the head black, brown, reddish, or ashy, and from whitish to yellowish grey below. Both halves of the beak, which may be either depressed or compressed, are notched, and there are bristles at the gape. Except in the typical genus, the shank, or metatarsus, is comparatively short and stout, and the three front toes are partially united at their bases. The form of the wing is variable, but the tail is usually short and squared, with the feathers narrow, although in *Neochloe* it is rounded. As a rule, the colour of the two sexes varies. The genera include *Vireo*, *Vireolanius*, *Vireosylvia*, *Lanivireo*, *Neochloe*, and *Hylophilus*, two of these names indicating the presumed relationship of the family to the shrikes.

Greenlets are essentially wood birds, seldom descending to the ground, and capturing insects on the wing, somewhat after the manner of flycatchers. They have a loud, flute-like note which, in one example, is said to resemble the words "Whip Tom Kelly." The nests are composed of bark, lichen, spiders' webs, etc., generally fixed in forks; and the eggs are white, usually spotted with brown or purplish.

WOOD SWALLOWS

Much more uncertainty prevails with regard to the systematic position of the wood swallows (family *Artamidæ*), which are mainly an Indo-Australian group, although the genus *Pseudochelidon* is also met with in West Africa. These essentially woodland birds derive their name from their resemblance, so far as many of their habits are concerned, to swallows. They feed largely on insects, which they capture on the wing, but will also collect and eat grubs and seeds on the ground. At times they may be seen to dart through the air like swifts, but on other occasions to poise themselves with scarcely a movement of the wings.

Some of the Australian species have the strange habit of collecting and hanging in great masses from the boughs of trees. The nests are always built in trees, but vary in position; the eggs, which may be from two to four in number, vary from white to greenish or flesh colour, spotted or streaked with darker markings. The note of these birds is a swallowlike chirrup.

The two sexes scarcely differ in colouring. In the typical genus, *Artamus*, as in most of the other forms, the beak is long and slightly curved, with a wide gape, but in *Pseudochelidon* it is broad throughout. The wings are long, the tail is short, and in some cases slightly emarginate, and the metatarsus is likewise short.

BOHEMIAN WAXWINGS

WRENS, WATER OUZELS, AND MOCKING BIRDS

WRENS

THE wrens form a group of very small birds (family *Troglodytidæ*) showing a considerable variety of shape among fully one hundred representatives. They are characterised by a moderate·or slender beak, either straight or slightly curved; narrow or broadly oval and exposed nostrils, wings short and generally rounded, and a tail of variable length, often rounded, and frequently carried over the back. These birds are most abundantly represented in South America, but have their typical representatives both in North America and the northern parts of the Old World. Certain

THE WREN

forms inhabit the Himalaya and Tibet, and others are natives of Patagonia and North-West America. Out of a large number of generic types reference can be made to three only.

TYPICAL WRENS

The European wren and its congeners are characterised by a beak of moderate size, pointed, and slightly curved; very short and rounded wings, and the tail comparatively short and rounded. The feet are strong for so small a bird, and the metatarsus is comparatively long.

Typically European, the wren (*Troglodytes parvulus*) is represented in the Kurile Islands by a race remarkable for its long beak, while the Japanese wren is darker and more rufous on the under parts than the British bird. It seems, however, that in the colour of the upper parts the various forms of wrens completely intergrade, so that it is impossible to draw a line anywhere between the palest desert forms from Algeria and Turkestan and the darkest tropical forms from Kashmir and Sikkim. A pale phase of the wren inhabits even the desolate Bering Island.

The wren is one of the most familiar of European birds, its sweet, ringing song being heard at almost every season of the year, not excepting frosty weather. These birds build domed nests, varying in material with the situation, but often made of green moss studded with lichen on the outside. The numerous eggs are white, finely spotted with red (page 990). Wrens have the peculiar habit of building nests not required for purposes of incubation. It is probable that they are intended as houses of refuge during cold or inclement weather. These birds appear to be very susceptible

of cold; and during the winter an entire family will creep into a convenient hole, and by huddling close together retain as much heat as possible. The eggless nests are commonly termed "cocks' nests." The wren rears several broods in a season, and the old birds attend their offspring with the utmost assiduity.

The adult cock has the upper parts reddish brown, banded, except on the head, with numerous blackish brown bars, the eyebrow stripe dull white, and the under parts white varied with rufous. In Iceland and the Färoes the ordinary form is replaced by the northern wren (*T. borealis*), which is larger, darker, and has the under parts more strongly barred.

WARBLING WRENS

Although the European wren is not much of a musician, some of the South American representatives of the family are renowned for their powers of song. Among them stands pre-eminent the so-called organ bird, or warbling wren (*Cyphorhinus cantans*), of the forests of Amazonia. "When its singular notes strike the ear for the first time," writes Mr. H. W. Bates, "the impression cannot be resisted that they are produced by a human voice; some musical boy must be gathering fruits in the thicket, and singing a few notes to cheer himself. The tones become more fluty and plaintive; they are now those of a flageolet, and, notwithstanding the utter impossibility of the thing, one is for a moment convinced that someone is playing that instrument. . . . It is the only songster that makes an impression on the natives, who sometimes rest their paddles whilst travelling in their small canoes along the shady bypaths, as if struck by the mysterious sound."

CACTUS WRENS

All the numerous species included in this group are characterised by the stout, compressed beak, the broad wings, the graduated and fan-shaped tail, and the strong and much curved claws of the feet. Although the majority of the group are inhabitants of Central and South America, the true cactus wren (*Campylorhynchus brunneicapillus*) is found in California and Texas. Of the habits of this wren, Dr. Elliott Coues gives the following description, observing that in "the most arid and desolate regions of the south-west, where the cacti flourish with wonderful luxuriance, covering the impoverished tracts of volcanic débris with a kind of vegetation only less ugly and forbidding than the very scoria, this wren makes its home and places its nests on every hand in the thorny embrace of the repulsive vegetation. True to the instincts and traditions of the wren family, it builds a bulky and conspicuous domicile; and when many are breeding together the structures become as noticeable as the nests which a colony of marsh wrens build in the heart of the swaying reeds. But it is not a globular mass of material, nor yet a cup; it is like a purse or pouch, and also peculiar in its position, for such nests are usually pensile.

"In the present case the nest resembles a flattened flask—more exactly, it is like the nursing-bottle with which all mothers are familiar, and this is laid horizontally on its flat side in the crutch of a cactus. It is constructed of grasses and small twigs woven or matted together, and lined with feathers. Including the covered way, or neck of the bottle, leading to the nest proper, the structure is some 10 or 12 inches long, and rather more than half as much in breadth. The bird appears to be an early breeder, and has been found preparing to build nests about San Diego so early as February 26. The eggs are white, but so thickly flecked with small, salmon-coloured spots that a rich cast of this tint is given to the whole surface."

WATER OUZELS

The water ouzels, or dippers, as they are called in books, but not by country people, form a small group (family *Cinclidæ*) apparently allied to the thrushes, but specially adapted to a semi-aquatic life. Looking somewhat like overgrown wrens, they may be recognised by the narrow, straight beak, slightly bent and notched, very short and rounded wings, a short and broad tail, a long and smooth metatarsus, and the long claws. The sexes are alike ; and the young, unlike the adults, are always spotted on the lower surface. The plumage is close and dense, and the body covered with down.

Water ouzels frequent the beds of clear streams in the northern parts of both hemispheres ; but three species exist in South America, one of the latter being Schulz's water ouzel (*Cinclus schultzi*), a dark grey bird with a pretty rufous throat, but similar in size and shape to the European species. The whole of the known species are included in the typical genus *Cinclus*. The mountain streams of Europe are all frequented by one or other form of the white-breasted water ouzels, which agree in habits wherever they are found ; favourite haunts of the typical species being the streams of North Wales.

The typical water ouzel (*Cinclus aquaticus*) of Western Europe is a very early breeder, building at the end of winter, sometimes in the branches or the roots of a tree, but generally beneath a bridge or overhanging rock. The nest is constructed of fine stems of grass, lined with dead leaves, and enclosed in a beautifully

WATER OUZEL

formed case of green moss, the eggs being pure white. Although these birds delight in frosty weather, their song may be heard at any season. The adult has the under parts slate grey, the head brown, the chin, throat, and upper portion of the breast pure white, and the

rest of the lower parts chestnut brown, varying much in intensity.

The European species is replaced in the Himalaya by the brown water ouzel (*C. asiaticus*), found at elevations from one to fourteen thousand feet, according to the season. This species lays at very different periods, according to elevation, sometimes nesting so early as December. The nests take the form of large

MOCKING BIRD

balls of moss, wedged into clefts of moss and fern-covered rocks, the one half under a little cascade, the other about a foot above the water's edge in the side of a rock standing in the midst of a broad, deep stream. The eggs are pure white, similar to those of the European water ouzel, but smaller. In the adult male the entire plumage is chocolate brown, with the edges of the feathers somewhat paler in places; the eyelids are covered with white feathers, and the wings and tail are dark brown.

MOCKING BIRDS

The American group typified by the well-known mocking bird (*Mimus polyglottus*) of the United States is regarded by some naturalists as forming merely a sub-family of the thrush tribe, and by others as entitled to rank as a separate family (*Mimidæ*). These birds are perhaps related to the wrens and the thrushes. All the members of the group are renowned for their vocal and mimetic powers. The typical species ranges from the United States to Mexico and the West Indies. In South America it is represented by the calandra (*M. modulator*), which ranges so far south as Argentina, and (*M. triurus*), the second of these being alone endowed with " mocking " powers.

The cat bird (*Galeoscoptes carolinensis*) takes its name from its habit of uttering screams, cluckings, and whistling cries, in addition to which it has a not unpleasing song. Other genera are *Oreoscoptes, Harporhynchus* (thrashers), *Dinacobius, Melanoptila*, and *Melanotis*. The members of the two latter lay blue eggs, but those of the thrashers are very variable in colour, while those of the mocking birds are generally greenish blue marked with brown and purplish. While the notes of the typical mocking bird range from an imitation of the scream of the eagle to the cries of domesticated animals, a peculiar mewing kind of cry is uttered by *Melanoptila*.

In their mode of flight all these birds are decidedly thrushlike, and they are active and graceful in their general movements ; their food comprises both insects, frequently captured in the air, and fruits.

THE THRUSH TRIBE

THE members of the large and important thrush tribe and their apparent relatives the warblers collectively form a group characterised by the beak being slender but rather depressed, and variously modified in the different groups, and the wings comparatively long and slender, with ten primary quills; the tail feathers being either ten, twelve, or fourteen in number. Although variable, the feet are generally slender and the metatarsus is elongated; while the nostrils are free from hairs. The members of the thrush tribe (*Turdidæ*) are specially distinguished by the spotted or mottled first plumage of the nestlings, the family including ring ouzels, chats, robins, redstarts, and hedge sparrows. There is but one complete moult in the year, the number of tail feathers is never less than twelve, the metatarsus is smooth behind, and bristles are present at the gape. Many of the species are migratory; and the range of the family is practically worldwide. These birds appear to be the most primitive and least specialised representatives of all the typical Passeres.

THRUSHES AND BLACKBIRDS

The thrushes and their immediate allies constitute a group (*Turdus*) whose members are more frugivorous in their tastes than the chats. Blackbirds and thrushes spend a large proportion of their time on the ground, more especially in open meadowlands, searching for worms and slugs. All possess fine vocal powers; and all build cup-shaped nests, usually composed in part of mud. In the typical, or spotted, thrushes the beak is of moderate size, decurved and notched near the extremity; the wings and tail are long, the latter slightly graduated; there is no pattern on the undeside of the wing; and the metatarsus is longer than the fourth toe. The feathers of the throat and breast are more or less spotted at all ages. These thrushes are most abundant in South America, which is the home of more than twenty species. Many breed in North America, but only five nest in Europe and Northern Asia—namely, Père David's thrush (*Turdus auritus*) of Sze-chuen, and the first four species described below. Several are peculiar to Africa, among them being the olive thrush (*T. gurneyi*) of the Transvaal, an allied bird (*T. guttatus*) from Natal, and the South African thrush, the last uttering a peculiar half song, half call, as if it were troubled with a cold.

MISSEL THRUSH

The missel thrush (*Turdus viscivorus*) is found in nearly every part of Europe at one or other season of the year, breeding in the northern regions and wintering partially in the southern lands. This bird enormously increased its breeding range in the British Isles during the nineteenth century.

In autumn and winter it is shy and retiring, hunting the open fields in flocks, which exercise extreme vigilance over their common safety. Although it feeds principally on worms and berries in the winter, its common name is derived from its fondness for the berries of the mistletoe, which are rejected by the majority of small birds, even when pressed by hunger. The missel thrush pairs early in the season, and the nest is generally placed in some conspicuous position. In districts where magpies are numerous, this species often builds its nest in a bush or low tree close to a cottage, as though recognising a certain protection in the neighbourhood of man.

The nest is constructed of stems of dry grass, moss, and vegetable fibres, often trimmed externally with grey lichens, the eggs being greyish green in ground colour, spotted with chocolate [page 990]. During the breeding season the missel thrush exercises a watchful surveillance over the orchard or garden in which its nest is built, boldly mobbing jackdaws, and even larger intruders, if they attempt to rob its belongings. The old birds display much devotion to their young, and will permit of a very close approach whilst feeding them. When the young are fledged, they gather into family parties, which scour the country in search of new feeding-grounds. The song of the stormcock, as the bird is frequently called, can be heard to

MISSEL THRUSH

the best advantage on a stormy day in spring, when the singer sends forth its loud, sonorous notes as though in defiance of the elements. A migratory species, and often snared on its return journey through Central Europe, the missel thrush is not so subject to abnormal variations of plumage as is the song thrush. The adult male is greyish brown above, washed with golden on the rump; the sides of the neck are greyish brown, streaked with darker brown; in the tail the greater part of the outermost feathers is greyish white, closely speckled with black.

THE THRUSH

The thrush, or song thrush (*T. musicus*), although by no means averse from the presence of man, is as much at home among the surf-beaten rocks of the Hebrides as in the parks and orchards of the south of England. Breeding early in the year, or rather beginning to do so, it rears several broods during the season. Most nests are built of stems of grass and fibrous roots, interwoven with mosses and lined with clay, but they are occasionally constructed of bright green moss.

DESERT FINCHES AND DESERT LARKS

"The typical desert finch is an inhabitant of the most sterile regions. . . . In many birds the plumage serves the purpose of concealment from enemies; and the desert lark, like other species that haunt deserts, is coloured a pale sandy grey, with ashy tinge on the forehead and upper tail coverts"

1. REED BUNTING; 2. YELLOW BUNTING; 3. TRUE BUNTING; 4. LAPLAND BUNTING; 5. SNOW BUNTING

"The great majority of the buntings belong to the northern parts of the Old World, although some inhabit Central Asia or reside permanently in India, many having an extensive range   The snow bunting supports life further north than any other small bird."

WHEATEAR, STONECHAT, AND WHINCHAT

"Resembling flycatchers in their mode of taking insects, wheatears and chats differ from other small birds by their frequent vibration of the tail when perching and running. . . . . The white patch at the root of the tail of the wheatear is probably a 'recognition mark,' for the purpose of guiding the members of a flock when following their leader."

WATER OUZEL, PIED WAGTAILS, AND YELLOW WAGTAILS

"The mountain streams of Europe are all frequented by one or another form of the white-breasted water ouzels, which agree in habits wherever they are found, favourite haunts of the typical species being the streams of North Wales."

Very generally the nests of the song thrush are placed in a hedge or low shrub, sometimes in a niche in an ivied wall, sometimes in a fruit tree. Such thrushes as rear their young amid the treeless straths of the north of Scotland build their nests upon the ledges of convenient boulders of rock, well sheltered from the weather. The eggs are bright blue, spotted with dark brown (page 990). The song of the thrush is generally poured forth from the bough of a tree; but in Scotland these birds often sing from the roofs of houses, and even from grassy knolls on the hillside.

The food of the thrush consists principally of earth-worms and insects; and this bird confers a great benefit upon the gardener by its warfare against snails. Near the sea it feeds in the winter on whelks and other molluscs, which it obtains on rocks when the tide has begun to ebb. On the other hand, it consumes a great deal of ripe fruit. In Norway it is a special favourite, and holds a similar place in Scandinavian poetry to that which the nightingale occupies in the songs of other countries.

GROUP OF YOUNG THRUSHES

The adult male is dark brown above, tinted with golden brown, the throat is buff, and the under parts are golden or buffish white, closely spotted with brown. The thrushes which breed in the Hebrides are of a greyer colour than more southern birds.

THE REDWING

The most delightful song to be heard in the solitudes of the forests of Northern Europe is that of the redwing (*T. iliacus*), which generally chants its flute-like melody from the top of a fir. Never nesting in colonies, the redwing appears to seek the society of the fieldfare, since a pair of redwings is sure to be found wherever a colony of the latter species exists. In the eastern part of Norway redwings build in bushes and low trees, but in the barren, treeless portions of the west coast of Norway, like the song thrush in the Hebrides, they modify their habits to suit their surroundings, and the nest is often placed on the ground, between stones, on fences, or in stunted birch trees. Redwings, like other thrushes, show great anxiety if their nest be approached, snapping their beaks, and uttering a mournful cry. The eggs are pale bluish green, profusely covered with greenish brown markings.

In the fall of the year redwings unite in large flocks, and many cross the North Sea to the British Isles and Germany, migrating chiefly at night, when they may be heard passing over the housetops, calling

THRUSH ON NEST

at frequent intervals to their companions. The redwing is not a very hardy species, suffering severely in protracted frost, even while other birds are able to retain sound condition. The explanation of this is that it subsists on worms and other insects rather than on berries. The adult is olive brown above, with a broad line of buffish white passing over the eye, the under parts white, streaked with brown, and the flanks and under wing coverts bright rufous

THE FIELDFARE

The fieldfare (*T. pilaris*), which is the most abundant of the northern thrushes, alike in the pine-clad valleys and in the regions of birch, breeds in colonies, the nests being placed in firs and birches at various elevations, some being as much as 15 feet from the ground. They are built of long, dry, fine grass, with a coating of mud or clay between the outer and inner layers of that material. A fieldfare once nested in a milk-pail inside a dairy, and successfully reared its young; and a nest has been found in a hollow top of a rotten stump, not a foot above the ground. When an intruder approaches the nest, the old birds fly round, uttering loud, harsh cries, and thus attract attention to the whereabouts of their treasure.

The eggs resemble those of the blackbird, being bluish green in ground colour, speckled and blotched with reddish brown. The young are fairly tame when they first leave the nest, but soon become shy and wary even on their nesting grounds. It is possible that their shyness or boldness may depend on the extent to which the birds are molested.

Myriads of fieldfares annually cross the North Sea to winter in the British Isles and Central Europe. In the adult male the head and hind part of the neck are ashy grey, the feathers of the crown having dark middles, the back and wing coverts rich chestnut brown, the wings and tail blackish brown, the eyebrows whitish, and the under parts rich ochre, thickly spotted with black.

The Himalayan *T. monticola*, with two allied species, represents the sub-genus *Zoothera*; the Siberian *T. varius* and about a dozen other species constitute the Indo-Malay and Australasian sub-genus *Oreocichla*; *T. [Turnagra] crassirostris* and another species represent the genus in New Zealand; while the South African ground thrush (*T. guttata*) and a number of other African and Oriental species form the sub-genus *Geocichla*, a few of which have fourteen tail feathers.

BLACKBIRDS

Another sub-genus (*Merula*) is formed by the black-birds and ring ouzels, which, however, are essentially thrushes in all structural characters, and differ from the foregoing chiefly in the fact that the plumage of the adult male is more or less widely distinct from that of the female, in a number of species the male being black or slate grey. Many of the species referred to in this group are peculiar to South America; others inhabit Australia, and yet others are found in the Indo-Malay region. Many inhabit Northern Asia, and two are well-known European birds.

Although the blackbird (*T. merula*) does not usually inhabit the more northern parts of Europe, it breeds in most districts of this region, migrating from colder countries before the approach of winter. It is resident throughout the year in the south of Spain, Algeria, and the Canaries. During the summer black-birds frequent gardens and orchards, nesting in shrubs and hedges, sometimes upon the ground.

The nest is composed of grass-stalks and mosses, together with dead leaves, and, under pressure of circumstances, can be completed in a couple of days, the female alone working at the structure. The eggs are bluish green in ground colour, closely freckled with light brown (page 990). Although the song lacks the compass and variety of that of the song thrush, it is, nevertheless, powerful and well sustained. The black-bird is specially liable to sport white feathers, especially in the case of the male, the tendency to such variations having been proved to be hereditary. In the adult male the plumage is uniform black throughout, but

THRUSH AND FIELDFARE

the female is dusky olive brown above, and reddish brown on the under parts.

RING OUZEL

The ring ouzel (*T. torquatus*) is a mountain-loving species, spending the summer among the heaths and pine forests of the hills of Central and Northern Europe. In Northern Europe the cocks arrive on the breeding ground in April and May, and the females soon after-wards join their partners. Generally nesting in some wild solitude, and building in the rocks that overhang mountain streams, especially where the ground is covered with heather, the ring ouzel is shy and wary, and rarely permits close approach to the nest. In Switzerland, however, a fir tree is the more common site for the nest, which is always built of dry grass and heather, and lined with fine stems. The eggs are blue, finely spotted with reddish brown. The young occasionally fly as early as the beginning of June.

All through the early summer ring ouzels live among the sheep on the hillside, but when the fruit ripens in autumn they approach the neighbourhood of orchards and gardens, and feast on the crops. They are especially partial to cherries, though when the berries of the mountain ash ripen, ring ouzels gorge themselves to repletion, so that they become fat and in high condition before they leave the shores of Europe to seek a more genial climate in Northern Africa.

Flying strongly and direct, ring ouzels utter a song which is both sweet and powerful, and audible at a great distance, although inferior to that of the black-bird. The harsh, chuckling notes which this bird utters when its haunts are invaded cannot well be confused with those of any other bird. Ring ouzels which breed in the Swiss forests frequent the vineyards by the lakes in autumn to feed on the grapes. During migration ring ouzels are sometimes found with black-birds and thrushes at lighthouses. The adult male, in breeding plumage, has the upper surface blackish brown, the wings brown with whitish edgings, most of the feathers of the under surface with pale grey margins, and a broad, conspicuous white gorget across the breast.

ROCK THRUSHES

The representatives of this small group are charac-terised by the stout, straight beak, arched towards its extremity, the moderately long wings, and short and even tail. The legs are stout, long, and well adapted to progression over irregular surfaces. Rock thrushes are peculiar to the Old World, three species inhabiting South Africa, and a fourth Abyssinia; while two breed in the Himalaya, one of which extends eastwards into Western China. The two best-known species, the blue thrush and the rock thrush of Western Europe, range from Northern China to Spain and Italy.

THE ROCK THRUSH

The common or true rock thrush (*Monticola saxatilis*) is a summer visitant to the more barren portions of the principal mountain ranges of Central Europe and Siberia, but does not reach the Far North in its annual wanderings. Like its cousin the blue rock thrush, it is partial to rocky gorges among hills and regions far removed from human habitation, except for the presence of a shepherd's hut or farm. It is a shy and wary species, constantly vibrating its tail like a red-start, and migrating in flocks to its breeding ground, where it begins to nest in May.

The nest is generally built in a precipitous position among crags of rock, often close to a waterfall, although sometimes in holes in stone walls surrounding vineyards. The nest is composed of fine roots, moss, and dried herbs; and the eggs are pure light blue, without spots.

THE ROCK THRUSH

The blue thrush is a well-known bird at Rome, Malta, and many other European resorts of tourists. Everywhere it frequents rocks, ruins, and old walls, pouring forth its delicious music in solitary wastes. The adult male is dull blue above and below, with a silvery wash on the head and breast, while the under parts of the body are dull blue. The female differs from the male in being greyish brown above, tinted with blue, and reddish buff on the lower parts.

BLUEBIRDS

Its sky-blue plumage, associated with chestnut, renders the bluebird (*Sialia sialis*) unmistakable from all other North American birds, except its immediate relatives of the same continent, in some of which the colour is wholly azure. In all the members of this strictly American group the beak is straight and compressed, notched near the extremity ; while the wings are pointed and much longer than the tail, which is slightly forked ; the feet being stout and short and adapted for perching. No more charming bird is to be found in the United States than the bluebird, or blue robin, which breeds as far north as Southern Canada, and passes the winter in great numbers in the Southern United States. It is one of the first birds to arrive in the States in spring, preceding the swallows and many other species ; indeed, it is occasionally observed so early as January and February in its summer home. The male is a cheery songster, and all his movements are characterised by grace and energy.

Miss Mabel Osgood gives the following picturesque account of the habits of this species : " Before more than the first notes of the spring song have sounded in the distance, bluebirds are to be seen by twos and threes about the edges of old orchards along open roads, where the skirting trees have crumbled or decaying knot-holes have left tempting nooks for the tree-trunk birds, with which the bluebird may be classed. For, though he takes kindly to a bird-box, or a convenient hole in fence-post, telegraph-pole, or outbuilding, a

In Italy the young are often reared from the nest by hand, and are much prized as cage-birds ; the song of the rock thrush being extremely beautiful, though not so fine as that of the blue rock thrush, which is in the first rank of European feathered songsters.

Although the rock thrush is a local and even rare bird in most parts of its range, and does not ordinarily migrate further north than Central France, stragglers have wandered to Great Britain and Heligoland. The food of the rock thrush consists principally of beetles and other insects, but the bird shares the fondness of its congeners for wild berries and garden fruits. In the adult male the head and neck are ashy blue, the scapulars are blackish, slightly washed with blue, the centre of the back is pure white, the tail and upper tail coverts are light red, the entire throat is ashy blue, and the rest of the under parts are rufous orange.

BLUE ROCK THRUSH

The blue rock thrush (*M. cyanus*) is found chiefly in the countries bordering the Mediterranean, and is a wild, shy bird of solitary disposition, resident in single pairs in rocky districts. This bird appears to be the "sparrow that sitteth alone upon the housetop." Colonel Irby writes that " a pair nested in a hole outside the wall of my stables at Gibraltar, in June, 1869. Five eggs were laid, which were hatched about the 20th. The nest was of small dried roots, and was very scanty. When the young were hatched, I broke through the wall from the inside of the stable to the nest, making the hole large enough to admit a small cage, in which I placed the nest and young ; over the inside hole I then hung an old coat, so as to shut out the light from the inside, cutting a small slit in the coat, through which I used to watch the old birds feeding their young within six inches. Both birds fed them at intervals of not more than five minutes. The food consisted entirely of centipedes, with now and then a large spider or bluebottle-fly by way of change. Two of the five young died in the cage, from the old birds not being able to get at them. Of the other three, only one attained maturity, living till October."

THRUSH AND RING OUZEL

MALE AND FEMALE WHEATEARS

chestnut, and the lower parts white ; while the female is blue, mixed and obscured with reddish brown.

WHEATEARS

Occupying an intermediate position between the thrush group (*Turdinæ*) and the robins, the wheatear and its relatives the chats form a second subfamily (*Saxicolinæ*) characterised by the beak with well-developed bristles at the gape, the wing pointed and equal in length to the tail, and the metatarsus and foot adapted to desert-loving habits. Resembling flycatchers in their mode of taking insects, wheatears and chats differ from other small birds by their frequent vibration of the tail when perching and running.

Wheatears are most strongly represented on the African continent, several species inhabiting North Africa, while others are peculiar to the south of the continent, and yet others inhabit Abyssinia and Nubia. Eight belong to Europe, while four species breed in Persia, and another four in Turkestan. Wheatears have a straight beak, broadest at the base and slightly curved towards the extremity ; the legs and beak are black, and the metatarsus is not scutellated. The bastard primary feather is small, and the wings are comparatively flat and pointed. In the more typical species, the rump, upper tail coverts, and the base of the tail are pure white in both sexes ; the tail consisting of twelve feathers of nearly equal length.

The russet wheatear (*Saxicola melanoleucas*) breeds in Russia, Transcaspia, and Palestine ; the western form summering in Morocco, Algiers, Spain, and the south of France. The isabelline wheatear (*S. isabellinus*) breeds in Asia Minor, South Russia, and Siberia, and has been obtained in Madagascar ; while the Indian desert wheatear (*S. deserti*) passes in the cultivated districts of Turkestan, and winters in North-West and Central India and Northern Africa.

The wheatear (*Saxicola œnanthe*) is one of the earliest of the many migrants that traverses the length and breadth of Europe, and is well known in most parts of the British Isles, where it arrives in March and April. The wheatear is both a moorland and maritime species ; many may be seen on Scots grouse moors or sheep farms in the north of England, and some remain very late in the ploughed fields

tree-hole must have been his first home, and consequently he has a strong feeling in its favour.

" As with many other species of migrant birds, the male is the first to arrive ; and he does not seem to be particularly interested in house-hunting until the coming of the female, when the courtship begins without delay, and the delicate purling song and the low two-syllabled answer of the female are heard in every orchard. The building of the nest is not an important function, merely the gathering of a few whisps and straws, with some chance feathers for lining. It seems to be shared by both parents, as are the duties of hatching and feeding the young. The eggs vary in number, six being the maximum, and they are not specially attractive, being so pale a blue that it is better to call them bluish white. Two broods are usually raised each year, though three are said to be not uncommon ; for bluebirds are active during a long season, and, while the first nest is made before the middle of April, last year a brood left the box over my rose arbour on September 12, though I do not know whether this was a belated or a prolonged family arrangement.

" As parents the bluebirds are tireless, both in supplying the nest with insect food and attending to its sanitation ; the wastage being taken away and dropped at a distance from the nest at almost unbelievably short intervals, proving the wonderful rapidity of digestion and the immense amount of labour required to supply the mill inside the little speckled throats with grist. The young bluebirds are spotted thickly on throat and back, after the manner of the throat of their cousin, the robin ; or, rather, the back feathers are spotted, the breast feathers having dusky edges, giving a speckled effect."

The food of the nestling bluebird consists of insects and other invertebrates, but the adults vary their diet at all seasons with berries and small fruits. In autumn and early winter, cedar and honeysuckle berries, the grape-like cluster of fruit of the poison ivy, together with bittersweet and catbrier berries, are alike consumed. The adult male has the head and upper parts deep azure blue, the throat, breast, and sides of the body

THE STONECHAT

of the English midland counties. Numberless pairs spend the summer months playing about the rabbit-holes which line the sand-banks on the coast in many districts of Britain.

The wheatear builds its nest in a variety of situations; sometimes in a loose heap of stones, sometimes in a rabbit-hole or beneath a heap of dried peats. The eggs are light blue. The song consists of some very sweet notes, generally uttered on the wing. These birds leave the British shores chiefly in August and September, although some begin their journey in July, while other belated stragglers linger into early winter. The range of the wheatear is very extensive, embracing, according to season, a great part of Asia north of the Himalaya (including Gilgit), Africa, and North America. The adult male in the breeding season has the crown and most of the upper parts greyish blue, the lores and ear coverts black, the upper tail coverts pure white and constantly displayed, the tail black and white, and the throat and under parts buffish white (p. 1041).

The white patch at the root of the tail of the wheatear is probably a "recognition mark," for the purpose of guiding the members of a flock when following their leader.

CHATS

The chats, which are also an Old World group, differ from the wheatears in the broader beak and the more numerous and stouter bristles at the gape. A well-known Mediterranean species is the black chat (*Pratincola variegatus*), inhabiting the rocky districts of Spain, Italy, North-West Africa, Persia, and Central Asia, but replaced by the eastern black chat (*P. leucurus*) in India and Burma. Partially resident in its breeding grounds, it is only a summer migrant to many districts, and is essentially a bird of desolate mountains, which it enlivens with its active movements. It is a shy, cautious bird, avoiding the haunts of men; and as, even when wounded, it generally manages to creep into some deep fissure to die, it is difficult to secure. Brehm states that the male black chat often "either dances about on a precipice or a stone, or runs up the precipice, spreading its tail and wings like a blackcock, nods its head, turns sharp round, rises singing into the air like a tree pipit, and then gradually sinks with outspread wings to the ground, where it finishes the last strophes of its song in the neighbourhood of the female bird, which quite silently watches the antics of her mate. In all its comical postures it knows how to show its

THE WHINCHAT

GROUP OF YOUNG WHINCHATS

beautiful white tail to the best advantage. If there are any trees or prickly pear bushes in the mountains, it will also repose on them during the intervals of its dance and song; otherwise it selects the most prominent positions for its resting-places."

The black chat builds about the middle or end of April, placing its nest in a hole or fissure in the rocks, frequently in a precipitous situation. The nest is large, loosely constructed of dry stalks of grass and the finer stems of various wild plants, and lined with soft fibres and hair. The eggs are pale light blue, with a zone of pale reddish spots round the larger end. The song of the black chat is wild and sweet, and has been compared, when heard in autumn, to that of the blue thrush, although not so loud and clear, and generally concluding with a peculiar churring sound, resembling that of the black redstart.

The adult male in the breeding season has the entire plumage of the upper and lower parts of the body sooty black, with the exception of the rump and upper tail coverts, which are pure white. The two middle tail feathers are black, and the remainder white, broadly tipped with black; while the under tail coverts are pure white. The female is a duller bird than her mate, being blackish brown instead of sooty black.

WHINCHAT

The whinchat (*P. rubetrus*) winters in Africa, extending its range further north than the stonechat in the breeding season. Passing through Spain in April, it makes its way to the Arctic Circle by the end of May; one of the principal routes by which its spring journey is accomplished lying along the valley of the Rhine, where the species is extremely abundant. The whinchat loves the neighbourhood of meadows, from which the song of the male may often be heard resounding, while his mate is engaged in the duties of incubation. The call note is loud and monotonous, representing the word "utik." The nest, usually placed on the ground and adroitly concealed, contains eggs of a bluish green colour, often spotted with fine specks of reddish brown (page 990). When the young are fledged, they live in a family party with the old birds, which exhibit the greatest anxiety for the safety of their progeny.

REDBREASTS

The redbreast, or robin (*Erithacus rubecula*), whose range includes the greater part of Europe, is a universal favourite. It breeds alike in gardens and shrubberies and in the middle of lonely woods, and constructs its nest of dry leaves, moss, and dead grass, lined with a little hair. The eggs are white, blotched and streaked with light red (page 990). When the young birds are fledged, they flit about gardens and outhouses gathering a variety of insects. Many migrate in autumn, while others linger to utter their silvery notes during the dead months of the year, drawing near cottages and farmhouses at the approach of frost.

In colour the plumage is olive brown above, tinted with grey, with the neck, forehead, and throat bright orange, the breast red, and the remainder of the lower parts olive brown. The red breast, unlike the throat patch of the bluethroat, is common to the adults of both sexes, but is lacking in young birds, which are spotted. The robin of the Canary Islands has been described as a distinct species (*E. superbus*), and names have also been given to the robins of the Caucasus, Siberia, and Japan.

RUBYTHROATS

Another beautiful species is the rubythroat (*Calliope camchatkensis*), which makes its summer home in the extreme north of Russia and Siberia, breeding among the tundras of the Arctic Circle, after the ice and snow have thawed and disappeared. Mr. Seebohm writes that the song of the rubythroat " is very fine, decidedly more melodious than that of the bluethroat, and very little inferior to that of the nightingale. When first I heard him sing I thought I was listening to a nightingale ; he had his back towards me when I shot him, and I was astonished to pick up a bird with a scarlet throat. The feathers were as glossy as silk, and when I skinned him I thought I had rarely, if ever, seen so beautiful a warbler."

The rubythroat appears in the south of Siberia as early as the beginning of April. Its nest is said to be a slight structure, and the eggs are olive grey. It is a bird of shy and solitary habits, frequenting thickets and close cover and obtaining its food chiefly upon the ground. The brilliant colour of the throat disappears in captivity. The rubythroat winters in the Philippine Islands, South China, Burma, and Northern and Central India, occasionally straying into Europe. The adult male has the upper parts uniform olive brown, the eye stripe and cheeks white, the chin and

THE REDBREAST

throat glossy scarlet, and the breast ash grey shading into buffish grey. Three other Central Asiatic species have received names.

NIGHTINGALES

The nightingale (*Daulias luscinia*) is celebrated in Western Europe as an incomparable songster, and has from all times enjoyed just reputation for the perfecttion of its vocal powers. Wintering in Africa, it reaches its summer home in the British Isles about the middle of April, the males being the first to arrive. Its range in the British Isles is somewhat circumscribed, and it does not breed north of Yorkshire. The nest is a loose structure of stems of grass and dry leaves, generally raised a little from the ground by a deposit of dead twigs, and screened from observation by a profusion of wild brambles or nettles ; the eggs being uniform olive brown or coffee-coloured (page 990).

The female, though shy, is much devoted to her charge, and will allow a stranger to stand close beside her without exhibiting her agitation further than by a slight movement of the head. The nightingale is easily trapped, and was formerly an object of eager pursuit among birdcatchers, who used to imitate its note in order to lead it to the trap, baited with a live insect. When the young are hatched, both parents become absorbed in catering for their progeny.

The song is chiefly heard during the night, simply because other birds are then comparatively silent, but the nightingale sings with great power even during the middle of the day. The male has the upper parts russet brown shading into chestnut on the upper tail coverts and tail, and the lower parts buffish white shading into greyish white on the breast and flanks.

In the east of Europe the western nightingale is replaced by a somewhat larger bird (*D. philomela*), which has a distinct song, differing from that of its congener in its greater volume and inferior perfection. This bird breeds generally in thickets near water, and builds a similar nest to that of the western species. The eastern nightingale differs from the western species in being more olive brown in colour, especially on the upper tail coverts, in having a more pointed wing and a smaller bastard primary, and being slightly spotted or streaked on the breast with grey. A third species is the Persian nightingale (*D. golzi* or *D. hafizi*),

DHYAL BIRD

of the English midland counties. Numberless pairs spend the summer months playing about the rabbit-holes which line the sand-banks on the coast in many districts of Britain.

The wheatear builds its nest in a variety of situations; sometimes in a loose heap of stones, sometimes in a rabbit-hole or beneath a heap of dried peats. The eggs are light blue. The song consists of some very sweet notes, generally uttered on the wing. These birds leave the British shores chiefly in August and September, although some begin their journey in July, while other belated stragglers linger into early winter. The range of the wheatear is very extensive, embracing, according to season, a great part of Asia north of the Himalaya (including Gilgit), Africa, and North America. The adult male in the breeding season has the crown and most of the upper parts greyish blue, the lores and ear coverts black, the upper tail coverts pure white and constantly displayed, the tail black and white, and the throat and under parts buffish white (p. 1041).

The white patch at the root of the tail of the wheatear is probably a "recognition mark," for the purpose of guiding the members of a flock when following their leader.

CHATS

The chats, which are also an Old World group, differ from the wheatears in the broader beak and the more numerous and stouter bristles at the gape. A well-known Mediterranean species is the black chat (*Pratincola variegatus*), inhabiting the rocky districts of Spain, Italy, North-West Africa, Persia, and Central Asia, but replaced by the eastern black chat (*P. leucurus*) in India and Burma. Partially resident in its breeding grounds, it is only a summer migrant to many districts, and is essentially a bird of desolate mountains, which it enlivens with its active movements. It is a shy, cautious bird, avoiding the haunts of men; and as, even when wounded, it generally manages to creep into some deep fissure to die, it is difficult to secure. Brehm states that the male black chat often "either dances about on a precipice or a stone, or runs up the precipice, spreading its tail and wings like a blackcock, nods its head, turns sharp round, rises singing into the air like a tree pipit, and then gradually sinks with outspread wings to the ground, where it finishes the last strophes of its song in the neighbourhood of the female bird, which quite silently watches the antics of her mate. In all its comical postures it knows how to show its

GROUP OF YOUNG WHINCHATS

beautiful white tail to the best advantage. If there are any trees or prickly pear bushes in the mountains, it will also repose on them during the intervals of its dance and song; otherwise it selects the most prominent positions for its resting-places."

The black chat builds about the middle or end of April, placing its nest in a hole or fissure in the rocks, frequently in a precipitous situation. The nest is large, loosely constructed of dry stalks of grass and the finer stems of various wild plants, and lined with soft fibres and hair. The eggs are pale light blue, with a zone of pale reddish spots round the larger end. The song of the black chat is wild and sweet, and has been compared, when heard in autumn, to that of the blue thrush, although not so loud and clear, and generally concluding with a peculiar churring sound, resembling that of the black redstart.

The adult male in the breeding season has the entire plumage of the upper and lower parts of the body sooty black, with the exception of the rump and upper tail coverts, which are pure white. The two middle tail feathers are black, and the remainder white, broadly tipped with black; while the under tail coverts are pure white. The female is a duller bird than her mate, being blackish brown instead of sooty black.

WHINCHAT

The whinchat (*P. rubetrus*) winters in Africa, extending its range further north than the stonechat in the breeding season. Passing through Spain in April, it makes its way to the Arctic Circle by the end of May; one of the principal routes by which its spring journey is accomplished lying along the valley of the Rhine, where the species is extremely abundant. The whinchat loves the neighbourhood of meadows, from which the song of the male may often be heard resounding, while his mate is engaged in the duties of incubation. The call note is loud and monotonous, representing the word "utik." The nest, usually placed on the ground and adroitly concealed, contains eggs of a bluish green colour, often spotted with fine specks of reddish brown (page 990). When the young are fledged, they live in a family party with the old birds, which exhibit the greatest anxiety for the safety of their progeny.

THE WHINCHAT

Subsisting on insects, and especially beetles, the whinchat is very partial to warm, sunny situations, especially if they are well bushed and command a southerly aspect. It leaves its home in Central and Northern Europe in August and September, rarely, if ever, delaying its departure into late autumn. The adult male has the crown and upper parts blackish brown, many of the feathers having light buff edges. The tail is white, banded with blackish brown for the terminal half, and the throat and under parts are pale fawn, varying in intensity. A conspicuous white eyebrow stripe is also present (page 1041).

STONECHAT

The stonechat (*P. rubicola*) is found throughout Central and several parts of Northern Europe, being a resident in many places, while to others it is but a summer or winter migrant. During the summer generally to be found on common lands, chalk downs, or other open places, the stonechat is an early breeder, nesting in April, and concealing its choice of a site with much care. In Oxfordshire stonechats seem partial to aquatic situations, one male having haunted a ditch beside the Isis for months during one winter; and they have been known to build at the bottom of a hedge adjoining a flooded meadow.

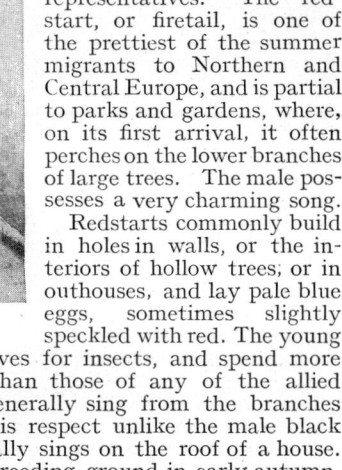

The stonechat builds a nest of moss and dried grass, lined with feathers and hair; the eggs being pale greenish blue, finely spotted with reddish brown (page 990). This bird has a short but rather pretty song, and is somewhat noisy when its haunts are invaded. The adult male in summer has the head and back glossy black, with a white collar; the tail is blackish brown, with light buff outer webs to the outer feathers, and the under parts rufous, but varying somewhat in different individuals (page 1041). The female is browner than her mate. This group of the genus is represented by several species in India, where they are commonly known as bush-chats.

FORKTAILS

The redstarts and robins represent another subfamily (*Ruticillinæ*), differing mainly from the chats in their habits; these birds being terrestrial, and capturing their insect prey on the ground, instead of flying from a perch and returning thereto, after the manner of flycatchers. They have a slender, compressed beak, a long metatarsus, and feet well adapted for running; and the majority of the species are denizens of Europe and Asia, north of and including the Himalaya. Possibly the Indian forktails should be placed near the *Ruticillinæ* as a separate subfamily, *Henicurinæ*, but many naturalists refer them to a family by themselves, *Henicuridæ*.

They are small birds, having the appearance of pied wagtails, but differing from these in possessing a forked tail and ten primaries, together with a coarse beak. Usually the beak is almost as large as the head, stout and straight; bristles are well developed at the gape; the wing is large, the first primary being about half the length of the second; and the tail is much longer than the wing, and deeply forked, its outer feathers being one-third longer than the innermost pair. Forktails

(*Henicurus*) are chiefly found in the Himalaya, and generally in the neighbourhood of mountain streams, but they also range into Tenasserim. All are solitary in their habits, and move their tails incessantly up and down after the manner of wagtails, and are in the habit of perching on rocks or bare branches near the ground.

REDSTARTS

That striking bird the redstart (*Ruticilla phœnicurus*) typifies a genus exclusively confined to Europe, Northern Africa, and Asia north of the Himalaya, the members of which are characterised by the short, slender, black beak, with finely developed bristles at the gape, and the black and smooth legs; while most of them have the rump and tail red. In Europe the group has half a dozen representatives. The redstart, or firetail, is one of the prettiest of the summer migrants to Northern and Central Europe, and is partial to parks and gardens, where, on its first arrival, it often perches on the lower branches of large trees. The male possesses a very charming song.

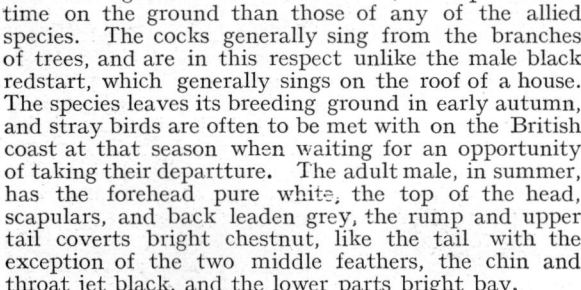

THE REDSTART

Redstarts commonly build in holes in walls, or the interiors of hollow trees; or in outhouses, and lay pale blue eggs, sometimes slightly speckled with red. The young hunt among dead leaves for insects, and spend more time on the ground than those of any of the allied species. The cocks generally sing from the branches of trees, and are in this respect unlike the male black redstart, which generally sings on the roof of a house. The species leaves its breeding ground in early autumn, and stray birds are often to be met with on the British coast at that season when waiting for an opportunity of taking their departture. The adult male, in summer, has the forehead pure white, the top of the head, scapulars, and back leaden grey, the rump and upper tail coverts bright chestnut, like the tail with the exception of the two middle feathers, the chin and throat jet black, and the lower parts bright bay.

BLACK REDSTART

Very distinct is the black redstart (*R. titys*), a well-known bird in many parts of Central Europe, and frequently seen in large cities. In Switzerland it breeds chiefly about the chalets on the mountains, attaching itself to the neighbourhood of farm buildings, and obtaining most of its food around the outhouses. In Germany it is a common garden bird, dwelling near human habitations and chanting its notes from the gable of a roof. It begins to sing very early in the morning, and continues until late in the evening; no bird being more self-conscious or more frequently seen in a prominent position. The males are pugnacious and desperately jealous of rivals, although they do not so readily fight as do redbreasts.

The nest is built of stems of grass, moss, and dry leaves lined with hair and feathers, and the white eggs are five or six in number. The female sits closely during incubation, and when the young first leave the nest the old birds continue their devotion and cater with unremitting industry. The greater part of their food consists of flies, at least during the finest period of summer ; and when they leave the nest the young birds catch midges on their own account. The young of the first brood generally have to be independent of the female parent early, because, as soon as they are qualified to quit the mother, she lays a fresh clutch of eggs ; and it falls, therefore, to the male chiefly to feed the fledged young of the first brood, and his practice is to take them to the top of a stone wall, or some other sunny place within view of his favourite point of observation, and gradually leave them to shift for themselves. The young that are reared late in autumn have a harder struggle for existence, especially in Switzerland, where the weather often breaks up in August.

Black redstarts like fine weather, and in stormy seasons become somewhat disconsolate and sit moping with their feathers puffed out. When the season for migration arrives, this redstart loses its domesticated habits, becoming shy and unobtrusive, and setting forth on its journey with energy. Although never breeding in the British Isles, many of these birds annually visit the south-western parts of England during autumn, and even pass the winter under the shelter of cliffs or in the vicinity of houses. They arrive in Devonshire in parties of two or three in the autumn, while those that winter in England assemble again in March on the coast for departure.

The plumage of the adult male is dark bluish grey above, with a conspicuous white patch on the wings ; the forehead and throat are black ; the tail is chestnut, tipped with blackish brown, except the two middle feathers, which are blackish brown throughout ; and the breast and lower parts are slate grey. The female and young males have the upper parts brownish grey, and lack the black throat of the adult male ; the males of the year breeding in this grey plumage.

BLUETHROATS

One of the loveliest members of the whole group is the bluethroat (*Cyanecula suecica*), which derives its name from the bright blue patch marked with a central spot of chestnut red on the throat. The Arctic bluethroat, as this bird is frequently called, twice annually crosses the length and breadth of Europe, but is so seldom noticed on migration through Central Europe as to have given rise to suggestions of impossible distances conjectured to have been accomplished without rest. This bird reaches its northern breeding grounds at the end of May, and takes up its residence in willow swamps and other damp situations.

Its song has been compared by Mr. Seebohm to that of several other birds. " His first attempts at singing are harsh and grating, like the notes of the sedge-warbler, or the still harsher notes of the white-throat ; these are followed by several variations in a

louder and rather more melodious tone, repeated over and over again somewhat in the fashion of the song thrush. After this you might fancy that the little songster was trying to mimic the various alarm notes of all the birds he can remember ; the ' chiz-zit,' of the wagtail, the ' tip-tip-tip ' of the blackbird, and especially the ' whit-whit ' of the chaffinch. As he improves in voice he sings louder and longer, until at last he almost approaches the nightingale in the richness of the melody that he pours forth.

" Sometimes he will sing as he flies upwards, descending with expanded wings and tail to alight on the highest bough of some low tree, almost exactly as the tree pipit does in the meadows of England. When the females have arrived, there comes at the end of his song the most metallic notes I have ever heard a bird utter. It is a sort of ' ting ting,' resembling the sound produced by striking a suspended bar of steel with another piece of the same metal. The female appears to shun the open far more carefully than her mate ; and while he will be perched upon a topmost spray, gladdening the whole air around him with his varied tuneful melody, she will remain in the undergrowth beneath him gliding hither and thither more like a mouse than a bird through the branches."

The nest of the bluethroat is well concealed in the side of a tussock of grass and lined with fine roots and hair ; and the eggs are olive-coloured. When the young leave the nest, they forage for insects in the undergrowth, peering at a stranger with the wistfulness of young robins, to which they bear some resemblance in their actions. In Spain the bluethroat is to be met with in dry situations, but only when the birds are on migration ; and this is probably true of its occurrence in the arid districts of Ladak. Bluethroats arrive in flocks in Heligoland, both in May and early autumn. There they are chiefly to be found in the potato-fields in autumn, while in spring they frequent gooseberry and currant bushes

On the Norfolk coast the bluethroat is well known as a September visitor, and has even appeared in considerable numbers when weather-stayed. In the adult male the upper parts are brown, with a conspicuous white or buff eyebrow stripe, the throat and upper part of the breast metallic cobalt blue, with a large

BLUE-THROATED AND RUBY-THROATED WARBLERS

central spot of chestnut, a band of black succeeding the blue, bordered by another band of chestnut, while the rest of the under parts are buffish white.

The bluethroat breeding in Europe south of the Baltic has been described as a distinct species (*C. wolfi* or *C. leucocyana*), on account of the central spot in the blue throat patch being white, if present at all, but it is, perhaps, preferably regarded as a local race.

The bluethroats of Persia and Transcaspia (*C. discessa*), and of Central Asia (*C. abbotti*) have also been regarded as separate species.

REDBREASTS

The redbreast, or robin (*Erithacus rubecula*), whose range includes the greater part of Europe, is a universal favourite. It breeds alike in gardens and shrubberies and in the middle of lonely woods, and constructs its nest of dry leaves, moss, and dead grass, lined with a little hair. The eggs are white, blotched and streaked with light red (page 990). When the young birds are fledged, they flit about gardens and outhouses gathering a variety of insects. Many migrate in autumn, while others linger to utter their silvery notes during the dead months of the year, drawing near cottages and farmhouses at the approach of frost.

In colour the plumage is olive brown above, tinted with grey, with the neck, forehead, and throat bright orange, the breast red, and the remainder of the lower parts olive brown. The red breast, unlike the throat patch of the bluethroat, is common to the adults of both sexes, but is lacking in young birds, which are spotted. The robin of the Canary Islands has been described as a distinct species (*E. superbus*), and names have also been given to the robins of the Caucasus, Siberia, and Japan.

RUBYTHROATS

Another beautiful species is the rubythroat (*Calliope camchatkensis*), which makes its summer home in the extreme north of Russia and Siberia, breeding among the tundras of the Arctic Circle, after the ice and snow have thawed and disappeared. Mr. Seebohm writes that the song of the rubythroat " is very fine, decidedly more melodious than that of the bluethroat, and very little inferior to that of the nightingale. When first I heard him sing I thought I was listening to a nightingale ; he had his back towards me when I shot him, and I was astonished to pick up a bird with a scarlet throat. The feathers were as glossy as silk, and when I skinned him I thought I had rarely, if ever, seen so beautiful a warbler."

The rubythroat appears in the south of Siberia as early as the beginning of April. Its nest is said to be a slight structure, and the eggs are olive grey. It is a bird of shy and solitary habits, frequenting thickets and close cover and obtaining its food chiefly upon the ground. The brilliant colour of the throat disappears in captivity. The rubythroat winters in the Philippine

DHYAL BIRD

Islands, South China, Burma, and Northern and Central India, occasionally straying into Europe. The adult male has the upper parts uniform olive brown, the eye stripe and cheeks white, the chin and

THE REDBREAST

throat glossy scarlet, and the breast ash grey shading into buffish grey. Three other Central Asiatic species have received names.

NIGHTINGALES

The nightingale (*Daulias luscinia*) is celebrated in Western Europe as an incomparable songster, and has from all times enjoyed just reputation for the perfection of its vocal powers. Wintering in Africa, it reaches its summer home in the British Isles about the middle of April, the males being the first to arrive. Its range in the British Isles is somewhat circumscribed, and it does not breed north of Yorkshire. The nest is a loose structure of stems of grass and dry leaves, generally raised a little from the ground by a deposit of dead twigs, and screened from observation by a profusion of wild brambles or nettles ; the eggs being uniform olive brown or coffee-coloured (page 990).

The female, though shy, is much devoted to her charge, and will allow a stranger to stand close beside her without exhibiting her agitation further than by a slight movement of the head. The nightingale is easily trapped, and was formerly an object of eager pursuit among birdcatchers, who used to imitate its note in order to lead it to the trap, baited with a live insect. When the young are hatched, both parents become absorbed in catering for their progeny.

The song is chiefly heard during the night, simply because other birds are then comparatively silent, but the nightingale sings with great power even during the middle of the day. The male has the upper parts russet brown shading into chestnut on the upper tail coverts and tail, and the lower parts buffish white shading into greyish white on the breast and flanks.

In the east of Europe the western nightingale is replaced by a somewhat larger bird (*D. philomela*), which has a distinct song, differing from that of its congener in its greater volume and inferior perfection. This bird breeds generally in thickets near water, and builds a similar nest to that of the western species. The eastern nightingale differs from the western species in being more olive brown in colour, especially on the upper tail coverts, in having a more pointed wing and a smaller bastard primary, and being slightly spotted or streaked on the breast with grey. A third species is the Persian nightingale (*D. golzi* or *D. hafizi*), ranging from the Caucasus to Central Asia; and two African species have also been named.

NEW ZEALAND ROBINS

The birds locally termed in New Zealand robins are characterised by the straight, slender beak, furnished

THE NIGHTINGALE

with bristles at the gape; the wings moderate, extending to half the length of the tail, and rounded; and the tail is broad and even, with the feathers sharply cut off at the tips. The metatarsus is very long and slender. This genus is confined to New Zealand and the Chatham Islands; the species peculiar to the later group of islands being entirely black. Of the habits of the North Island robin (*Miro australis*), which is confined to the gloomy forests of the interior of the North Island, the following description is given by Sir Walter Buller: "As the popular name implies, it is naturally a tame bird, and in little-frequented parts of the country it is so fearless and unsuspicious of man that it will approach within a yard of the traveller, and sometimes will even perch on his head or shoulder. It is a favourite companion of the lonesome woodcutter, enlivening him with its cheerful notes, and when, sitting on a log, he partakes of his humble meal, it hops about his feet, like the traditional robin, to pick up the crumbs. Like its namesake in the old country, moreover, it is noisy, active, and cheerful.

"Its note is generally the first to herald the dawn, while it is the last to be hushed when evening shades bring gloom into the forest. But there is this noticeable difference between the morning and the evening performance: the former consists of a scale of notes, beginning very high and running down to a low key, uttered in quick succession and with all the energy of a challenge to the rest of the feathered tribe. The evening performance is merely a short, chirping note, quickly repeated, and with rather a melancholy sound; three or four of them will sometimes join in a chirping chorus, and continue it until the shades of evening twilight have deepened into night. It lives almost entirely on small insects, and the worms and grubs that are to be found among decaying leaves and other vegetable matter on the surface of the ground in every part of the woods. Its nature is pugnacious, and in the pairing season the male birds often engage in sharp encounters with each other."

The North Island robin nests in October and November. The nest is generally against the bole of a tree at a moderate height from the ground, built of coarse moss, lined with fern hair and vegetable fibres. The eggs are creamy white in ground colour, thickly freckled, and speckled with purple and brown. This charming little bird has become comparatively rare, though the robin found in the South Island (*M. albifrons*) is still fairly abundant. In the adult male, the upper parts are dull ashy grey, with whitish shafts to the feathers, the wings dark brown, with white bases to the secondaries, the tail feathers dusky brown margined with ash, the throat, breast, and sides of the body hoary grey, and the abdomen white. Some naturalists, it may be mentioned, place the New Zealand robins among the flycatchers.

DHYAL BIRDS

Next on the list is a small group of birds closely related to the redstarts and robins, but distinguished from all other members of this subfamily by the black and white tail, equal in length to the wing, and considerably graduated. Peculiar to the Old World, these birds are most abundant in the Indo-Malay region, the finest songster amongst them being the white-browed warbler (*Copsychus inexpectatus*, or *albospecularis*) of Madagascar, the notes of which rival those of the sweetest European birds. The Indian dhyal bird (*Copsychus solaris*) is a widely-spread species resident in Ceylon and Southern China, but replaced in the Malay countries by the allied *C. musicus*, by *C. mindanensis* in the Philippines, and in the Seychelles by *C. seychellarum*.

The Indian species is a common and familiar bird throughout its range, exhibiting a confiding and friendly disposition, like the European redbreast. The cocks are highly pugnacious in the breeding season, and engage in frequent combats with their rivals. The nest is a rough structure, built in a hole of a tree, in an old stump or crevice of a wall. The nesting holes of the barbets and woodpeckers are often utilised by the dhyal bird. The male has a pleasing song, not unlike that of the redbreast, but of greater compass. The adult male has the head, neck, breast, and upper parts glossy black, the wings and tail black, varied with white, and the abdomen and under tail coverts white. In the female the upper parts are uniform dark brown, glossed

INDIAN SHAMA

with bluish, the throat and breast dark grey, and the wings and tail dark brown varied with white.

SHAMAS

The shamas (*Cittocincla*) are closely related in structure to the dhyal birds, but are distinguished by the proportionally greater length of the tail, which considerably exceeds the wing in this respect. Shamas are shy and retiring birds, avoiding the neighbourhood of houses, and obtaining their food in the woods and jungle. The black shama (*C. nigra*), inhabiting the Malay region, is a skulking species, haunting the dense covert near to the coast. Another kind (*C. cebuensis*) is a native of the Philippines, while the Andaman shama (*C. albiventris*) is peculiar to the islands from which it takes its name. The best known is the Indian shama (*C. macrura*), a permanent resident in the plains of India, and a timid but graceful bird, much sought after by Indian birdcatchers, on account of its beautiful song.

The shama nests from April to June, retiring into the depths of the jungle and constructing its nest of grass and dead leaves in the hollow end of the broken branch of a tree. The eggs are greenish marked with reddish brown, and vary in number from three to four. The adult male has the head, breast, back, and the wing coverts black, the rump and upper tail coverts white, the tail feathers black and black and white, and the abdomen and under tail coverts bright chestnut. The glossy black and chestnut colour of the male are replaced in the female by dark brown and pale rufous.

HEDGE-SPARROWS

Some diversity of opinion still prevails among naturalists as to the proper serial position of such a familiar bird as the hedge-sparrow, which has no relationship to the typical sparrows. It is sometimes placed next the rock thrushes, in the subfamily *Turdinæ*, but it will also be found classed in a separate subfamily (*Accentorinæ*), or even in a distinct family, These birds possess a fairly strong beak, broad at the base, with a nearly straight culmen, about half the length of the head, long and pointed wings, and nearly square tail. The legs and feet are strong, and generally adapted to progression over rocks and rough surfaces; while the plumage is dark brown, varied with rufous. Distributed over Europe, North Africa, and Asia north of the Himalayas as far east as Japan, these birds usually inhabit mountain ranges, although frequenting bushes and scrub.

ALPINE ACCENTOR

Common among the mountains of Europe, the Alpine accentor (*Accentor collaris*) inhabits the Pyrenees and Alps, occasionally wandering far from its usual haunts, and reaching the British Isles and Heligoland. It begins to build in May; the nest is round, somewhat shallow, fairly compact, and composed mainly of dry grass stems and very small pieces of moss, the inside being lined entirely with the same kind of moss and the small white feathers of the ptarmigan. The eggs are light greenish blue and unspotted. The adult male has the head and neck grey, the upper parts dark brown, with light brown edges to the feathers, the wing coverts tipped with white, the throat white spotted with black, and the breast and under tail coverts dark grey, shading into rich chestnut on the flanks.

THE HEDGE-SPARROW

Although generally nesting in the vicinity of dwelling houses, the hedge-sparrow (*A. modularis*), which is very widely distributed in Europe, may be found in Spain in the depths of forests. Its cheery song is often uttered from the top of a small shrub or spray of hawthorn; and being an early breeder, its eggs are often laid before the leaves of the hedges have sufficiently expanded to save them from being chilled by heavy showers of rain. The nest, built of fine roots and moss, is placed in the shelter of a hedge on a bank, under a hawthorn bush, or in the side of an ivied wall, and generally contains four or five blue unspotted eggs (page 990).

ALPINE ACCENTOR

The young, when first hatched, are invested with black down, but they feather rapidly. In the Hebrides, the hedge-sparrow nests by the sides of streams, adapting its existence to a moorland life. During winter this bird obtains most of its subsistence in gardens, and may often be seen stealing in and out among the growing plants like a mouse. Its call note is loud but monotonous.

The hedge-sparrow is very subject to variation of plumage, specimens being often seen prettily pied with white, sometimes symmetrically arranged, while pure white specimens are occasionally met with. The adult has the head and sides of the neck bluish grey—purest in the breeding season—the wings and tail dusky brown, the back reddish brown, streaked with darker brown, the chin and throat grey, and the lower parts white. Altogether, about nineteen representatives of the genus are known, the hedge-sparrow and its immediate relatives forming the subgenus *Tharrhaleus*.

THE WARBLER TRIBE

OPINIONS are somewhat divided as to the proper position of the warblers. By some naturalists they are included in the thrush tribe, to which they present many affinities; but, on the other hand, they are also related to the flycatchers, to which some of the genera we have included among the thrush group are also related. The fact is, that it is impossible to classify perching birds in a linear series; and as a matter of convenience it is advisable to rank the warblers as a family by themselves (*Sylviidæ*), which ought properly to come between the *Turdidæ* and *Muscicapidæ*.

Warblers are mostly birds of small size and plain-coloured plumage. More insectivorous in their habits than thrushes, and also more migratory in their movements, they usually have slender beaks adapted to the capture of insects. The wings are variable in size, and the feet slender. The young of the warblers, unlike those of the thrush tribe, do not differ materially from the adults in colour. This group of birds, in common with the *Ruticillinæ*, is of most universal distribution, but so preponderates in the Eastern Hemisphere that they may be regarded as an Old World assemblage only meagrely represented in North America.

WHITETHROATS

The whitethroat (*Sylvia cinerea*), which is the typical representative of the whole group, belongs to a genus in which the beak is relatively slender, with a rounded upper half, and its lower half paler at the base than elsewhere; the first primary quill is much shorter than the second; yellow is absent from the feathers of the axillary region; there are only three bristles on each side of the gape, and the beak is shorter than the middle front toe and claw.

The whitethroat is one of the most abundant of summer birds throughout Europe, arriving in its breeding haunts in April, and speedily beginning to make its simple nest of dry stems of grass and flowering plants, lined with finer bents and sometimes a little horsehair. The eggs are white, mottled with olive green specks. The male sings noisily upon the wing, generally starting from the top of a hawthorn hedge, and then slowly descending, with the tail at an angle to the body. It may frequently be seen picking small moths off the blossoms of the gorse, as it flits actively from one plant to another, and utters a harsh croak. In the adult male the upper parts are greyish brown, the wing coverts and innermost secondaries edged with chestnut, the outer tail feathers margined with white, and the lower parts buffish white.

LESSER WHITETHROAT

The lesser whitethroat (*S. curruca*) is a scarcer bird than the last, but its pretty song may be heard in hedgerows and bushes in many parts of Europe. The

LESSER AND COMMON WHITETHROATS

nest, which is placed in a bush or shrub, is firmly built of strong bents, and lined with finer bents, fibres, and horsehair; the eggs being white, spotted with olive brown. The lesser whitethroat frequents gardens, on account of its fondness for fruit, which is specially manifested when raspberries become ripe. It becomes very tame in confinement, when it will eat pears and other fruits with avidity. The adult male has the upper parts slaty grey, suffused with brown on the back, the wings and tail brown and conspicuous.

ALPINE WARBLER

The alpine warbler (*S. subalpina*) has a wide range, inhabiting the whole of the Mediterranean region, as well as North Africa and the Canaries. It is an active bird building a globe-shaped nest of stems of grass, lined with fine fibres in thick bushes, and situated from three to five feet above the ground. The eggs are greenish white, finely spotted with brown. The adult male has the upper parts slate grey, the wings brown with pale edges, the tail brown with more or less white on the outer feathers, and the throat and breast chestnut, shading into paler chestnut on the flanks and to nearly white in the centre of the breast.

SPECTACLED WARBLER

The spectacled warbler (*S. conspicillata*) is another Mediterranean species, resident in some parts of its habitat, and in others a summer visitant. A migrant in the north of Spain, it is there somewhat shy and retiring, flitting about the roadside in a furtive, uneasy fashion, and quite solitary. This species builds its nest in a small bush about a foot from the ground, and the eggs are white, blotched with green. The short, sweet song has been compared to that of the goldfinch.

In the adult male the upper parts pass from slate grey on the crown to greyish chestnut on the centre of the back; the wings are dark brown, edged with chestnut, the tail feathers dark brown, the outer ones partially pied, and the chin is white, fading into slate grey on the throat, which again fades into purplish red on the breast and flanks.

SARDINIAN WARBLER

Another South European warbler is the pretty black-headed Sardinian warbler (*S.* [*Meloziphilus*] *sarda*), an active, restless species, partial to the neighbourhood of undergrowth. It builds in a branch of a tree, generally at a small distance from the ground; and constructs its nest of blades of grass and roots lined with fine bents. The eggs are greenish white blotched at the larger end with greenish grey. This warbler is common in the pine woods around Cannes; as also in the gardens near the sea; and its habits have been compared to those of the whitethroat.

The male sings from a bush, and then darts off in a jerking flight into the air still singing; while the old birds, like the blackcap, simulate the appearance of being injured when they find their young endangered, trailing their wings in the dust and exhibiting the greatest distress. The song is not unlike that of a garden warbler, but more intermittent. In the adult male the upper parts are slate grey above, shading into black on the nape, head, and ear coverts, the wings dark brown edged with grey, the tail dark grey tipped with white, and the throat white fading into greyish white.

ORPHEUS WARBLER

The Orpheus warbler (*S. orpheus*) is one of the larger representatives of the group in Europe, which it visits in April, not continuing its journey north of the Baltic. Mr. Seebohm writes that "the song is louder than that of the blackcap, but I thought it somewhat harsher. Its alarm note is very loud, as loud as that of the blackbird. In the Parnassus I found it very common, and obtained thirteen nests between May 3 and 21. They were easy to find in the bushes which were scattered over the rocky ground above the region of the olive and the vine; but when we got into the pine region they disappeared. My friend Captain Verner informs me that he has found nests of this bird in Spain placed near the summit of young cork trees, about twelve feet from the ground. The nest is a tolerably substantial one and deep, composed of dry grass and leafy stalks of plants. Inside it is built of finer grasses, and lined sparingly with thistledown or the flower of the cotton grass. . . . The ground colour of the eggs of the Orpheus warbler is white, sometimes faintly tinted with grey and sometimes tinted with brown. . . . The colour of the overlying spots varies from olive brown to nearly black."

The Orpheus warbler is a large form of the blackcap, and decidedly more elegant in shape than that species. The adult male has the crown sooty black, the general colour of the upper parts dull slate grey, the wings and tail brown, and the under parts white shading into grey upon the breast and flanks.

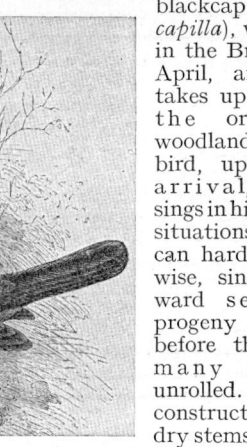

RUFOUS AND ORPHEUS WARBLERS

GARDEN WARBLER

A more skulking species than the last is the garden warbler (*S. hortensis*), which arrives in its summer haunts in Europe about the same date as the blackcap. Being rather a retiring bird, it is often overlooked, although to a musical ear it may be recognised by its sweet song, generally poured forth from the centre of some thick bush or other covert. The nest is of dry stems and moss, lined with fibres and a few hairs, and the eggs are greenish white blotched with grey and olive brown. The garden warbler is partial to fruit, but does not strip the berries from elder bushes in the same way as the blackcap does. The adult male has the upper parts olive brown, darker and greyer on the wings and tail, and the under parts greyish white.

THE BLACKCAP

Among the sweetest songsters that visit the gardens and shrubberies of Europe is the slim and attractive blackcap (*S. atricapilla*), which arrives in the British Isles in April, and at once takes up its abode in the orchards and woodlands. The male bird, upon its first arrival, frequently sings in highly exposed situations; indeed, it can hardly do otherwise, since in backward seasons its progeny are hatched before the leaves of many trees have unrolled. The female constructs her nest of dry stems of grass and fibres, lining it with fine roots and hair; the eggs being generally yellowish brown, clouded with a darker colour (page 990).

The song is rich and well sustained, and from the fine quality of its notes the bird has been termed the Norfolk nightingale. The blackcap is a most anxious parent, exhibiting lively distress if the safety of the young be menaced. The young feather rapidly and leave the nest proportionately earlier than do many other birds. In July the song of the blackcap becomes soft and subdued, and the bird then sings in close covert, shunning notoriety.

THE BLACKCAP

In the cock of the typical race the forehead and crown are pure black, the upper parts bluish grey, suffused with olive brown, the wings and tail brown, and the lower surface bluish grey. The female, in which the cap is rusty red, sings sweetly in captivity, although less powerfully than her mate. In the Canaries there occurs a curious variety of this species, in which the black of the cap extends over the nape and shoulders as well as round the throat.

BARRED WARBLER

The barred warbler (*S. nisoria*) arrives in its summer quarters in Europe somewhat later than the majority of migrants, and takes up its abode chiefly in gardens; constructing a bulky nest, more compact than that of most warblers, of roots and dry stems neatly lined with horsehair or fibres. The nest is generally built in a thorn-bush not far from the ground, and the eggs are buffish white spotted with brown and ash colour. The barred warbler is shy and skulking in its habits, and even in confinement retains its shyness, although this does not extend to birds reared from the nest. The adult male has the upper parts brownish grey, and the under parts greyish white, finely barred with brown.

DARTFORD WARBLER

The Dartford warbler (*S.* [*Meloziphilus*] *undata*) is a resident but local bird in the temperate parts of Europe, breeding also in the mountains of Algeria. It is a small, retiring species, fond of thick covert, and used to be tolerably common even in the neighbourhood of London until exterminated by several severe winters. A correspondent, writing in 1883, stated that : " I have taken several hundreds of eggs of the Dartford warbler within a few miles of Brighton, but the birds were all exterminated in a recent severe winter. I have not heard of any since, though formerly we could find a dozen pairs within a few miles. I have taken the eggs of a single pair three or four times in a season. If the nest contained three eggs when I first robbed it, the next clutch usually contained five eggs, but if it contained four eggs the first time the second laying usually consisted of the same number."

The Dartford warbler builds a very slight nest, composed of dry stalks, and lined with finer stems added to a little wool. The nest is usually extremely difficult to find, and can only be discovered by patient observation of the old birds. Mr. Newman often observed the Dartford warbler in the neighbourhood of Godalming, and has left the following sketch of its winter habits : " When the leaves are off the trees, and the chill winter winds have driven the summer birds to the olive gardens of Spain or across the Strait, the furze wren is in the height of its enjoyment. I have seen them by dozens skipping about the furze, lighting for a moment upon the very point of the sprigs, and instantly diving out of sight again, singing out their angry, impatient ditty, for ever the same. They prefer those places where the furze is very thick, high, and difficult to get in."

The egg of the Dartford warbler is white or buff in ground colour, suffused with olive or reddish brown. The song of the male is lively and often uttered upon the wing. The nestlings begin to sing as soon as they assume the adult plumage. In the adult male the general colour is very dark sooty brown, shading into slate grey on the head, the tail dark grey, with the outer feathers tipped with white, the under parts chestnut brown, shading into white on the centre of the belly, white tips to the feathers of the chin and upper part of the throat, and the under tail coverts grey tipped with white.

WOOD WRENS

The wood wren (*Phylloscopus sibilator*) is the typical representative of a group of small warblers differing from *Sylvia* by the supplemental bristles in front of those of the gape being stronger and more numerous, and the beak shorter and stouter. The genus includes the chiff-chaff (*P. minor*), willow wren (*P. trochilus*), yellow browed warbler (*P.* [*Reguloides*] *superciliosus*), etc. Of these, the yellow-browed warbler passes the summer in North Siberia, where Mr. Seebohm discovered the nest and eggs, of which he gives the following account : " As we were walking along, a little bird started up, and began persistently to utter the alarm note of the yellow-browed warbler, which I had learned in Heligoland. As it kept flying round from tree to tree, we came to the conclusion that it had a nest near. We searched for some time unsuccessfully, and then retired to a short distance and sat down upon a tree trunk to watch. The bird was very uneasy, but continually came back to a birch tree, frequently making several short flights towards the ground, as if anxious to go into its nest, but dare not whilst we were in sight. This went on for about half an hour, when we came to the conclusion that the treasure we were in search of must be within a few yards of the birch tree, and we resumed the search. In less than five minutes I found the nest, with six eggs. It was built in a slight tuft of grass, moss, and bilberries, semi-domed exactly like the nests of the willow-warbler. It was composed of dry grass and moss ends lined with reindeer-hair. The eggs were very similar in colour to those of the willow warbler but rather more spotted and smaller."

This warbler occasionally straggles to Europe on the autumnal migration. The adult male has the upper parts olive green, a well-defined narrow greenish yellow eye-stripe, the wing coverts are tipped with yellow, forming two bars across the wings, the wing quills and tail brown, and the lower parts white suffused with yellowish green.

TREE WARBLERS

As an example of a small genus differing from *Sylvia* by the length of the beak from the gape exceeding, instead of falling short of, the third toe and its claw, may be mentioned the tree warbler (*Hypolais icterina*) ; one other species of the genus, the western *H. polyglotta*, of South-West Europe and North Africa, being known. Annually visiting temperate Europe south of the Baltic, the tree warbler is a graceful, slender bird, and on its first arrival may be observed flitting actively about the lower branches of trees and bushes in quest of insect prey.

Although in colour this warbler bears some resemblance to the willow wrens, it does not form a dome to its nest like those birds, nor does it build near the ground,

WILLOW WREN

BARRED AND GARDEN WARBLERS

On the contrary, its pretty nest is made of dry stems of grass interwoven with moss, wool, and other materials, placed in a small tree, generally eight or ten feet from the ground. The eggs are brownish pink, spotted with dark purplish brown.

Mr. Seebohm gives the following description of the song of this warbler : "Perhaps, on the whole, the song of the common tree warbler comes nearest to that of the marsh warbler, but often it reminds you strongly of the sedge warbler. At other times you may trace a fancied resemblance to the chirping of the sparrow, the scolding of the whitethroat, or the scream of the swift." The adult male in spring is olive green above, with the wings and tail brown, and the under parts uniformly of a beautiful and delicate yellow. The female is rather duller.

REED WRENS

Yet another genus of warblers is represented by the reed warbler, or reed wren, and its allies, and is distinguished from all the foregoing by the feathers of the forehead being short and rounded, instead of disintegrated and with elongated shafts. Moreover, there are no hairs or bristles on the forehead, with the exception of the ordinary ones at the gape. In this particular genus of the group, the first primary quill of the wing is much less than one-third the length of the second, while the bristles are strongly developed, and the tail is but slightly graduated.

The reed wren (*Acrocephalus streperus*) is an annual visitor to most parts of temperate Europe, arriving in April and May, and taking up its abode in extensive morasses. The nest is a singularly beautiful structure ; one has been found which was composed of delicate green moss, while another from Romney Marsh was almost entirely built of sheep's wool. The eggs are greenish white in ground colour, clouded or freckled with dark olive (page 990). The song of this warbler is rich and much varied. The adult male in spring has the upper parts rufous brown, most pronounced on the rump and upper tail coverts, the chin and throat dull white, and the breast and flanks pale buff.

SEDGE WARBLER

The sedge bird, or sedge warbler (*A. phragmitis*), is common in many parts of Europe, arriving in April from North Africa, and speedily taking up its residence in some suitable haunt, generally a scrub near the waterside. It departs again for the south in September, wintering in

SEDGE BIRD

Africa. Its song is loud and varied, and often delivered during the stillness of a summer night.

The nest is a slight structure of dry stems without any lining, or of dry stems and a little green moss, lined with the feathers of the gadwall ; and the eggs are yellowish brown. The adult male in spring has the upper parts rusty russet brown, with dark centres to the feathers, the eye stripe buffish white, the wings and tail brown, and the under parts buffish white.

The marsh warbler (*A. palustris*) is another member of this group.

GRASSHOPPER WARBLER GROUP

Nearly allied to the last, the grasshopper warbler and its relatives, of which there are some nine species, may be distinguished by the smaller development of the bristles at the gape, as well as by the more markedly graduated tail, in which the outermost feathers are less than three-fourths the total length. The grasshopper warbler (*Locustella nævia*), which derives its name from its peculiar chirping notes, is a regular but local summer visitant to Europe, arriving in Britain in April in small flocks, which soon break up, each pair taking up its residence either on a heath on the margin of large woods or in the bottom of a deep hedge. On its first arrival the hedges are bare or nearly so, a condition that facilitates the observation of the movements of this shy bird. Both the male and female sing, but most of the ventriloquising efforts proceed from the former.

The grasshopper warbler sings its song principally during the early hours of the day and shortly before dusk, although it would be a mistake to suppose that it does not sing at other times, for it often chants lustily in the middle of the day. The nest is cunningly concealed in thick herbage ; the best plan to discover its whereabouts being to visit the spot which the birds are known to frequent shortly before sunset. If every likely corner be explored with the aid of a stick, the female will almost certainly be detected in the act of slipping off her eggs, creeping away through the undergrowth with the stealth and rapidity of a mouse. The eggs are pinkish white, freckled with darker reddish brown.

TREE WARBLERS

The adult male has the upper parts olive brown with dark middles to the feathers, and the chin and centre of the belly white, shading into buffish brown on the breast and flanks.

RIVER WARBLER

Among the finest of songsters is the river warbler (*L. fluviatilis*) of Eastern Europe, which spends the summer on the shore of the Elbe, the Danube, and other large rivers, where it frequents thickets and dense undergrowth, building a cup-shaped nest of dry stems. The eggs are greyish white, spotted with reddish brown. The song for which the river warbler is famed has been compared to the chirping of grasshoppers. During the early hours of the day the bird sometimes sings in exposed situations, but in ordinary circumstances skulks in almost impenetrable thickets. Both sexes have the upper parts uniformly dark olive brown with a scarcely perceptible eye stripe, and the under parts greyish brown, shading into white on the throat and belly.

REED WARBLER

SAVI'S AND FAN-TAILED WARBLERS

One of the rarer European warblers is the obscurely-coloured Savi's warbler (*L. luscinoides*), which breeds in Holland, building a nest of blades of dry sedge firmly interwoven, which cannot well be mistaken for that of any other bird. The eggs are white, sprinkled with ashy brown spots. In the Rhone marshes this bird may be observed running up and down the reeds, occasionally uttering a curious cry, which has been compared to that of a tree frog. The male has the upper parts uniform russet brown, and the under parts pale buffish brown, shading into nearly white on the centre of the throat and belly.

Another member of this group is the fan-tailed warbler (*L. lanceolata*), which is one of the smallest of European warblers, easily recognised by its curved beak and fan-shaped tail. It ranges from Eastern Europe to Siberia, and visits India, Burma, and China in winter.

CETTI'S WARBLERS

Cetti's warbler (*Cettia cettii*) may be taken as the best-known European representative of another large group of genera differing from all the foregoing in having only ten in place of twelve tail feathers. This warbler holds a high position among the song birds of Southern Europe, and passes the summer in the Mediterranean region, inhabiting close and impenetrable covert during its sojourn. It builds its nest of dry stems and blades of grass in the neighbourhood of water, and the eggs are brilliant red, without spots. In some

GRASSHOPPER WARBLER

parts of its range Cetti's warbler is resident throughout the year. It sings in every month, and it is somewhat startling in winter to hear a loud and abrupt burst of song, resembling that of a nightingale, from a thick bush.

The adult male has the upper parts rich russet brown, the eye stripe greyish white, but indistinct, the wings and tail dark russet brown, and the chin and throat white, shading into ashy grey on the sides of the breast, and into brownish grey on the flanks and upper tail coverts.

The other member of the genus is the Eastern Cetti's warbler (*C. orientalis*), ranging from Palestine to Central Asia, and visiting North-Western India in winter.

PHEASANT-TAILED WARBLERS

On account of the remarkable structure of its tail, attention may be directed to the Australian pheasant-tailed warbler (*Stipiturus malacurus*), distinguished by the elongation and peculiar structure of the three middle pairs of tail feathers. It belongs to the same section as the last, and is one of two species restricted to Australia.

GOLDCRESTS AND FIRECRESTS

While some naturalists refer the goldcrests and firecrests to a distinct family (*Regulidæ*), it is simpler to include them in the same group as the warblers, to which they are evidently allied. In addition to their small size, the golden-crested wrens, or goldcrests, are characterised by the straight and slender beak, which is compressed towards the point, where it is notched. The basally-placed nostrils are covered by a single bristly feather, and there are numerous bristles at the gape. The rather long wings have the first primary nearly half the length of the second, which is somewhat shorter than the third, and this in turn is exceeded in length by the fourth and fifth. The tail, which has twelve feathers, is slightly forked; the legs are long and slender, with elongated claws.

THE GOLDCREST

An inhabitant of the pine forests of Europe, the typical species, *Regulus cristatus*, is a hardy bird, contriving to obtain subsistence when others are famishing with hunger. During summer it haunts gardens and the skirts of woods, building its beautiful little nest on the under surface of a conifer at varying distances from the ground; the nest itself—an exquisite structure, chiefly of the softest moss and lined with the

PHEASANT-TAILED WARBLER

among the slender twigs, sometimes with head down, and sometimes with the feet upwards, but the most curious part of the performance is when they come to the end of the twig and examine the under surface of the leaves at its extremity. As they have nothing to stand upon, they flutter more like bees than birds from leaf to leaf, with their little wings beating rapidly all the time.

The male has the forehead buff, the crest bright orange, bordered with black on each side, two other black stripes passing through the eye and from the base of the beak downwards, the upper parts olive green varied with gold on the sides of the neck, and the under parts dull buffish white.

THE RUBYCREST

The rubycrest, or golden-crowned kinglet (*R. calendula*), is a well-known bird in the United States, returning from the far north, in which it breeds, in September, when it presses gradually southwards into all the Southern States, a few continuing their journey into South America. Dr. Elliott Coues gives the

most delicate of feathers—being sometimes finished as early as the middle of March, while fresh eggs may be taken in the middle of July; considerable latitude thus existing in the breeding season.

The brooding female is never long away from her eggs, and, even if disturbed, only flits anxiously about the tree which contains the nest, uttering a low, troubled cry so long as she is conscious of being under observation. If surveillance be removed, she slips hastily on to her eggs, and probably remains in the nest, trusting to the decorative skill with which she has adorned its exterior to render her detection difficult. The eggs are white, suffused with reddish buff. When a brood of young goldcrests is going to roost, a scramble takes place for the warmest place, all roosting in a row, and each endeavouring to get an inside position.

Although many of the goldcrests haunting English hedgerows in winter have been bred in the country, the largest proportion congregating in the coverts at that season are birds which have crossed the North Sea, thousands annually arriving upon the East Coast, often much exhausted by their travels. The adult male has the forehead olive green, the crest bright yellow or orange, banded by a black stripe on each side, the upper parts olive green tinged with yellow, the wings dark brown edged with greenish yellow, and the lower parts greyish olive. The female has the crest pale yellow instead of orange, and all her tints are more obscure than those of her partner.

THE FIRECREST

Although much more local than the goldcrest, the firecrest (*R. ignicapillus*) is fairly common in the pine forests of many parts of Europe, often frequenting bushes and scrub as well as the larger branches of trees. Pairing by the middle of April, this bird generally indicates its whereabouts by its shrill call note, which is louder and less tremulous than that of the goldcrest.

The firecrest builds a similar nest to that of the goldcrest, but the eggs are of a warmer colour. It is a partial migrant, crossing the North Sea in autumn, but only in small numbers. These birds climb in and out

CETTI'S AND FAN-TAILED WARBLERS

following description of its habits : " To observe the manners of the rubycrest, one need only repair at the right season to the nearest thicket, coppice, or piece of shrubbery. These are its favourite resorts, especially in autumn and winter, though sometimes, more particularly in spring, it appears to be more ambitious, and its slight form may be almost lost among the branches of the taller trees. We shall most likely find it not alone but in straggling troops, which keep up a sort of companionship with each other as well as with different birds, though each individual seems to be absorbed in its particular business.

"We hear the slender, wiry note, and see the little creatures skipping nimbly about the smaller branches in endlessly varied attitudes, peering in the crevices of the bark for their minute insect food, taking short nervous flights from one bough to another, twitching their wings as they alight, and always too busy to pay attention to what may be going on around them."

The rubycrest builds a tiny nest consisting of a mass of hair and feathers mixed with moss and some short bits of straw ; commonly breeding in the heavy pine and spruce forests on the mountains of Colorado and Arizona. The male has a rich scarlet crest, the upper parts greenish olive, the wings and tail dusky, and the under parts yellowish white.

Mr. W. Brewster describes the breeding habits of this species as follows, stating that one particular nest " was placed in a slender spruce on the south side, within two feet of the top of the tree, and at least sixty feet above the ground, suspended among fine, pendent twigs about two inches below a short, horizontal branch, some twelve inches out from the

GOLDEN-CRESTED WREN OR GOLDCREST

main stem, and an equal distance from the end of the branch. The tree stood near the upper edge of a narrow strip of dry, rather open woods, bordered on one side by a road, and on the other by an extensive sphagnum swamp.

" The outside of the nest was composed chiefly of green mosses prettily diversified with greyish lichens, the general tone of the colouring, however, matching that of the surrounding spruce foliage. The interior, at the bottom, was lined with delicate strips of inner bark and rootlets. Near the top were feathers of the ruffed grouse, hermit thrush, and oven-bird, arranged with the points of the quills down, the tips rising slightly above the rim and curving inwards, so as to form a screen for the eggs. The second nest was closely canopied by the spruce foliage, under which it was suspended, leaving hardly enough room for the parents to enter.

" The ground colour of the eggs varies from cream white to a deep muddy cream colour. Over this are varied markings of pale wood-brown, these, in turn, being the background for sharper markings of lavender. In both nests the eggs were too numerous to find room on the bottom of the nest, and were piled in two layers.

" These nests were found by watching the birds while building ; a task of no little difficulty in dense spruce woods, where the light was dim, even at noon. Moreover, the movements of this little architect were erratic and puzzling to the last degree. We finally found that her almost invariable custom was to approach the nest by short flights and devious courses, and, on reaching it, to dash in, deposit and arrange her load in from two to four seconds, and at once dart off in search for more."

The total number of species of the genus *Regulus* recognised was fourteen, of which one ranges so far south as the Azores, while a second inhabits the island of Madeira, and a third is found in Mexico. Northwards the genus is represented in Alaska by the species known as *R. grinelli*.

YELLOW-BROWED WARBLER AND FIRECREST

FLYCATCHERS

ALL the flycatchers (*Muscicapidæ*) are insectivorous in habit, and, like chats, pursue their prey in short flights from a perch, to which they return after the capture. They display much variety in form and plumage, some species being for the most part plain and homely coloured, while others, such as the Indian paradise flycatchers (*Terpsiphone*), almost vie with the birds from which they take the first half of their name in the bright colouring of their plumage and the elongation of the middle tail feathers of the male.

As a group, flycatchers may be best recognised by the mottled plumage of the nestling, and the presence of numerous hairs, distinct from the bristles at the gape, stretching from the forehead over the nostrils. There are, however, many connecting links between the most specialised flycatchers, with their flattened beaks, and the more warbler-like forms. With smooth, simply notched beak, ten primaries, and twelve tail feathers, they all have feebly developed legs and feet, which prevent them from walking on the ground, and thus serve to differentiate them from the more typical members of the thrush family. They are affiliated to the thrush tribe, especially the chats, by the spotted plumage of the young and the numerous bristles near the gape in the adults; and some groups, such as *Miro* and *Henicurus*, which have been included in the *Turdidæ*, might perhaps be better placed in or near this family. Flycatchers are abundant in the tropical regions of the Old World, but are unknown in America.

TYPICAL FLYCATCHERS

In the typical flycatchers (*Muscicapa*), of which there is a considerable number of species, with a wide distribution in the Old World, the tail is considerably shorter than the wing, the second primary quill is equal in length to the fifth, and the wings, when closed, do not reach beyond the middle of the tail.

SPOTTED OR GREY FLYCATCHER

Among the commonest of European summer birds is the spotted or grey flycatcher (*Muscicapa griseola*), which, however, does not reach its haunts until later in the spring than the majority of small migrants, not being met with even in Spain until the latter part of April, and being still later in the more northern parts of its habitat. Unlike most English migratory songsters, this flycatcher may be met with throughout the summer in the London parks, although its sombre plumage and habit of perching up high on trees render it far from conspicuous. Variously placed, the nest of this species may be situated on an ivy-clad wall, in the middle of a shrub, or on wooded rocks overhanging rivers, while it has been found in the hole of a tree, in a flower-basket hanging at a window, and even in an empty cup. It is made of moss, grass, and horsehair, and the eggs are white, much blotched and suffused with light red (page 990).

Although not disdaining larger insects, the parent birds feed their offspring chiefly on flies, caught in the manner characteristic of the group. In the adult cock the plumage of the upper parts is uniform brown, with dark middle lines to the feathers of the crown of the head; the wings and tail are likewise brown; while the sides of the head and under parts are dull white, the breast being streaked with grey.

PIED FLYCATCHER

Spending the summer in Central and Northern Europe, and passing on migration through the Spanish peninsula in April, the pied flycatcher (*M. atricapilla*) associates its presence in many lands with scenes of picturesque beauty. The male possesses a sweet song, which begins like that of the great titmouse and then passes into a sweet strain suggestive of that of the redstart. The constancy with which a pair of pied flycatchers will return to the same nesting-hole during a period of several successive years is one of the most remarkable traits in its character.

The nest is sometimes built in a chink of a stone wall or ruined building; the stump of a felled tree often supplies a convenient hole, while sometimes a nest may be found in a birch tree at from four to seven feet from the ground. A couple may occupy a fissure in a dead limb of a Scots fir, or the nest may be in the hollow branch of an ash tree, while a decayed thorn-bush sometimes holds a nest for several seasons. The nest, which is only slightly put together, is composed almost entirely of small fibrous roots and dried grass, always lined with a little hair, and generally a few decayed leaves on the outside. The eggs, which vary from five to six or even seven, are pale green, and so closely resemble those of the redstart that it is frequently difficult to distinguish them apart.

The males, soon after their arrival, frequently perch for a considerable time on a branch of a decayed tree, constantly repeating their lively song between their sallies in pursuit of passing insects, but the females are somewhat coy and rather shun the other sex. Pied flycatchers are birds of strong passion, and fight for the possession of their female companions, but paired couples are devotedly attached. So long as the hen is sitting on her eggs, her mate caters to supply her appetite with constant activity; and when the young are hatched, the old birds are devoted to them, the female feeding them at more frequent intervals than does her companion. While the call note of the male somewhat resembles the sound produced by clattering together two pebbles, the female has a cry like that of a hen chaffinch. Individuals breeding in districts where woodpeckers are common frequently adopt the deserted holes of the latter for their own nests.

WHITE-COLLARED FLYCATCHER

Pied flycatchers rarely spend more than three months at their breeding grounds, and long before the trees in England have begun to change from green to red and orange slip quietly away, almost unnoticed, to seek an asylum on the southern side of the Mediterranean. In Switzerland, however, and other parts of Central Europe, they are more loth to bid farewell to the scene of their summer life; and in the former country may often be seen poised on the lower branches of walnut trees. In summer they obtain much of their prey on the ground, and after capturing a victim usually alight on a fresh perch.

The plumage of the male in the breeding season is black above, with here and there a shade of brown; although specimens seem to be unknown in which the black plumage is entirely unsullied by a brown tinge. The wings are dark brown, with the primaries white at the base of the outer web; the tail is black and white, and the forehead is white, as are the cheeks and under surface.

WHITE-COLLARED FLYCATCHER

Another well-known species is the white-collared flycatcher (*M. collaris*), which visits the south of Europe in considerable numbers, but is always local. Like the pied flycatcher, it frequents the neighbourhood of old timber, and builds its nest in hollow trees; the eggs being greenish blue. The song is distinct from that of the pied flycatcher, as is also the call note, which is a sharp, disagreeable whistle.

It is possible, however, that the two species interbreed, since the form found in the Caucasus is intermediate between the white-collared and the pied flycatcher. The adult male is black above, with the lower part of the back and rump ashy grey, the wing feathers black with white bases, the tail black edged with white on the outer webs, the forehead white, a white collar completely encircling the hind part of the neck, and the throat and lower parts pure white.

RED-BREASTED FLYCATCHER

Mention may also be made of the red-breasted flycatcher (*M. parva*) as a summer visitant to Eastern Europe, and occasionally wandering into the western part of the continent. Always a rare local bird, though frequently overlooked, and occasionally straggling to the shores of the British Isles on autumnal migration, it breeds in beech forests, constructing its nest in some natural cavity, or between a bunch of small twigs and the main stem. The nest is built almost entirely of moss, with a little lichen and hairs; and the eggs are pale bluish green in ground colour, freckled with reddish and greyish brown.

The song is simple and unpretentious, but the actions of the bird are full of life and energy. The adult male has the upper parts ashy brown, the two middle tail feathers dark brown, and the remainder for the greater part white, the cheeks, throat, and fore part of the neck clear orange, and the rest of the under surface white.

PARADISE FLYCATCHERS

Commonplace and devoid of anything striking in their plumage, the typical flycatchers agree with a large assemblage of genera in having the tail considerably shorter than the wing; but there is a much more beautiful, although smaller, group of genera, in which the tail equals or exceeds the wing in length. From their allies the paradise flycatchers are distinguished

SPOTTED AND PIED FLYCATCHERS

by the crested head and the great length of the middle pair of tail feathers. The beak is very large, much depressed, and swollen, with numerous long and coarse bristles at the gape. Distributed all over India and the adjacent regions, the paradise flycatchers have the sexes almost or completely alike for the first two years, when the prevailing colour of the plumage is chestnut. This dress is never changed by the hen birds; but some time after the second autumn the cocks assume a beautiful white plumage, and it thus happens that in some cases both members of a pair may be breeding in the chestnut dress, instead of the male being far more gorgeous than his partner.

Writing of the Indian paradise flycatcher (*Terpsiphone paradisi*), whose range extends from Ceylon to Kashmir, Dr. Leith Adams observes that, in the plains of India, " its singularly attractive plumage can scarcely escape observation. The adult male has a blue head and white body, with two of the tail feathers prolonged for upwards of eight inches beyond the tip; those in the female scarcely extending beyond a quarter of an inch. The young birds are chestnut. The paradise flycatcher does not possess great power of flight, except when hunting for insects; then its movements are quick." The five eggs laid by the hen are pink spotted with brownish red.

FANTAIL FLYCATCHERS

As another interesting group, special mention may be made of the fantail flycatchers, which, while differing from the members of the preceding genus in the absence of a crest on the head, are distinguished from the other crestless forms of the group by the length of the tail considerably exceeding that of the wing. Possessing a short depressed beak, broad at the base, with the culmen arched, and the upper half notched, these birds have the nostrils oval, basal, and nearly covered by bristles at the gape; while the tail is ample and rounded, and the feet are moderate and slender. Full of life and energy, hopping merrily from bough to bough, the fantails construct beautiful little nests covered with cobwebs.

Between forty and fifty species of fantails are known, inhabiting the Indo-Malay and Australian regions, and ranging to Tasmania and the islands of the Malay Archipelago. Layard's fantail (*Rhipidura layardi*), for instance, inhabits the Fiji group, while the white-bellied fantail (*R. albiventris*) is found in the islands of the Philippine Archipelago, and the sooty fantail (*R. flabellifera*) is peculiar to New Zealand. The white-browed fantail (*R. albifrontata*) ranges from Ceylon to the Himalaya, while various species inhabit Tenasserim, Siam, Cochin China, and the Malay Peninsula.

WHITE-BROWED FANTAIL

One of the best known of the Indian fantails is the white-browed species, which breeds all over the plains of

India, sometimes nesting in a bush but generally in a mango tree. The nest is cup-shaped and deep, framed by fine stems of grass, and lined with fine grass roots and a little hair, the exterior being coated with cobwebs. It is generally placed on the upper surface of a nearly horizontal bough; and the eggs are white, with many minute brown specks, and a fine zone of greyish brown at the larger end. This fantail rears two broods in a season.

The adult male has the crown, lores, and ear coverts black, the forehead white, the wings and upper parts ashy brown, the cheeks and throat black, tipped with white, the sides of the breast black, and the remainder of the lower parts white.

WHITE-THROATED FANTAIL

In the wooded tracts of the lower Himalayan ranges, the white-throated fantail (*R. albicollis*) is to be seen in summer, generally frequenting a thickly wooded country; it is very partial to mango trees, darting out occasionally with a tumbling flight as if falling and suddenly returning to its perch. It keeps up an almost incessant snapping sound with the beak as it hawks about the tree for insects, and indulges occasionally in a not unpleasing little song.

The nest is built in some slender, upright fork, and composed of dry stems and blades of grass, with here and there fragments of vegetable fibre, and entirely coated with cobwebs, while in form it resembles an inverted cone and is comparatively solid. The eggs are slightly smaller than those of the white-browed species, wanting in gloss, and of a very pale fawn or greyish white ground colour, with an irregular zone of grey specks and spots.

The adult male is smoky black above with a white eye-stripe, the wings are browner than the back, the two middle tail feathers are black, the remainder broadly tipped with white, a dull patch of white extends across the lower throat, and the rest of the under surface is slate black.

RED-BREASTED FLYCATCHER

BLACK FANTAIL

One of the tamest and most familiar of Australian birds is the little black fantail (*R. motacilloides*), which passes much of its time on the ground, where it runs and darts with the utmost celerity, and when skirting a stream with tail erect and shaking from side to side presents an appearance very similar to that of the pied wagtails. The movements of the tails of the two birds, however, are very different, that of the European being perpendicular, while that of the Australian is a kind of lateral swing. The song, which consists of a few loud and shrill notes, is continually poured forth throughout the entire night, especially if it be moonlight; and the flight is at times gracefully undulating, but always of very short duration.

This bird begins to build in September, often placing its beautiful cup-shaped nest on a branch overhanging the water. Sometimes it nests on the upper side of a fallen branch without the slightest shelter from the sun and rain, and at an elevation of only three or four feet from the ground. The nest consists of dried grasses,

strips of bark, and roots firmly matted together, and covered over with cobwebs, so that the entire nest looks like an excrescence of the wood; it is lined with fine grass, roots, or feathers.

The eggs are dull greenish white, blotched and spotted with blackish and chestnut brown. The old birds are very tame at the nest, and will even perch upon it while the eggs are being removed, uttering a peculiar cry.

The adult male has the upper parts black, the great wing coverts brown, as are the primaries, the tail black, as are the sides of the face, throat, and sides of the breast, and the remainder of the lower surface white.

BLUE WRENS

Perhaps the most gorgeously coloured members of the family are the so-called blue wrens of Australia, which are small, long-tailed birds, taking their popular name from the prevalence of purple and azure in their plumage. All show more or less of black on the nape and breast, but the extent of this, as well as of the blue, varies according to the species. In one kind (*Malurus elizabethæ*) all the upper parts, with the exception of the greater part of the wings, are blue and black; but in *M. assimilis* the hind part of the back is violet purple, and the black does not extend on to the wings, which are partly chestnut and partly brownish fawn.

GREY WARBLER

The grey warbler (*Gerygone flaviventris*) and its relatives are selected for notice on account of their relations with the cuckoos of the country. These birds, which are common to New Zealand, Australia, New Guinea, and the neighbouring islands, are characterised by the slender, compressed, and slightly curved beak, the long and somewhat rounded tail, and the long, thin shank, or metatarsus. Among them, the grey warbler acts the part of foster-parent to the young of the two species of cuckoos found in New Zealand. It is a bird of sombre plumage and unobtrusive habits, but utters at short intervals a note of much sweetness; it is common in every part of New Zealand, where it appears to be as much at home in the woods as in the open scrub. Its food consists of small insects, which it obtains in the leafy tops of forest trees as well as in the dense foliage of thick bushes.

The grey warbler is remarkable for the form of its nest, which is a domed structure, belonging to one of two types—the bottle-shaped nest with a porch entrance, and the pear-shaped form without a porch. The materials used in nest-building are dry moss, grass, vegetable fibres, and spider-webs. The eggs are white, often spotted with red. The grey warbler is an attentive parent to the young of the cuckoos which are foisted upon it, and probably owes its preservation to the fact that it builds a pensile nest, out of the reach of rats and other vermin.

The adult male is olive brown above, with the sides of the neck dark ashy grey, the tail feathers ashy brown, shaded with black, and the throat, breast, and sides grey.

SWALLOWS

Furnished with a short, wide, and deeply-cleft beak, of which the gape is very broad, and the mouth opening extends to about the line of the eye, swallows (family *Hirundinidæ*) and their relatives have the wings much elongated, and comparatively narrow, consisting of only nine primaries, of which the two outer ones are about equal in length, although the inner ones decrease, and he secondaries are very short. The feet are small, weak, and imperfectly adapted for progression; while the tail consists of twelve feathers, and is generally forked. As a family, swallows are cosmopolitan, some species entering the Arctic Circle, the typical species having strayed to Spitzbergen and Novaya Zemlya.

Although there has been some difference of opinion among naturalists with regard to the serial position of the swallow tribe, there seems little doubt that the nearest relations of these birds are the flycatchers, and the two groups are accordingly placed in sequence.

SWALLOWS

The swallow, or chimney swallow, as it is often called, (*Hirundo rustica*) typifies a genus characterised by the short, depressed beak, very long wings and tail, and the great elongation of the outer tail feathers of the adult. The plumage is purplish above, correlated with a more or less perfect zone on the breast. Swallows construct their nests of fine clay, carefully welded into a compact mass, and lined with feathers.

Africa is the home of many remarkable swallows, and it is in that continent that the members of the genus seem to reach their largest dimensions, the great African mosque swallow (*H. senegalensis*) measuring upwards of nine inches in length, while Monteiro's swallow (*H. monteiri*) is nearly as large. The elongation of the outer tail feathers is most marked in the wire-tailed swallow (*H. smithi*), in which the shafts are produced as much as seven inches. This species inhabits India and some parts of Africa. Sclater's swallow (*H. sclateri*) is a lovely green and white bird inhabiting San Domingo.

Unless interfered with, the swallows that come to England build their mud nests in the same corners during many successive years, the nest being generally placed in a situation which affords some support; nests in trees are very rare. The nest is lined with feathers and dry grass; and the first brood will leave it as a rule during the last days of June, while the second broods are able to fly before August has expired. Some birds even rear late broods during October, but the struggle for existence

SWALLOW AND NEST

among the young has then become very severe. The swallow lays from four to six eggs, white in ground colour, and spotted with brown and grey (page 990). After their first flight, young swallows return for several nights to the nest for shelter. The male swallow in summer has the forehead and throat chestnut, a band on the breast, and the upper parts steel blue, glossed with purple; the tail feathers spotted with white, and the under parts pink or white.

RED-RUMPED SWALLOW

Another species that may be mentioned is the red-rumped swallow (*H. rufula*), which spends the summer in the eastern portion of the Mediterranean, whence it extends eastwards to the Himalaya and Turkestan. Many red-rumped swallows breed in Greece, inhabiting the mountain ranges of that country. In Palestine this species nests in caves, although the birds do not consort in colonies; the arches of the monastery on Mount Carmel being a favourite breeding place. The nest is a beautiful structure built of the same materials as that of the martin; the eggs being four in number, and pure white in colour.

This swallow is common in warm, sheltered valleys in the highest parts of the vine regions of Greece and Asia Minor, where it may often be seen hawking for insects in company with ordinary swallows and martins. It cannot, however, be mistaken for either of the species, as it has the long, forked tail of the swallows in addition to the white rump of the martin; and may also be distinguished by its note, which is lower than that of the swallow. The nests are built of mud, and are similar to those of the martin, although having a curious funnel at the top, so that the whole structure recalls a chemist's retort. The adult male is purplish blue above, with the feathers of the upper part of the back streaked with white; the rump is pale rufous, merging into creamy white on the upper tail coverts, the tail feathers are blackish, glossed with dull blue, and the under parts cinnamon buff.

RED-BELLIED SWALLOW

In the United States the genus is represented by the red-bellied, or barn swallow (*H. erythrogaster*), characterised by the pale rufous of the under parts posteriorly to the red throat patch. This species is found not only in all parts of North America, but in Alaska and Greenland as well, and it breeds in the greater part of its range where suitable sites are to be

RED-RUMPED SWALLOW AND CRAG MARTINS

Northern Asia, building its nests in crowded rows under the eaves of houses, and also rearing its young among the crags of limestone precipices. Blakiston's martin (*C. dasypus*) is a well-known Japanese species, which passes the winter in Borneo.

EUROPEAN MARTIN

No bird is better known in Northern Europe than the black and white martin (*C. urbica*), which usually arrives during early spring. The birds which come to Britain are not the first migrants of their race ; for martins have been found nesting in Southern Europe in the middle of April, at a time when many of their companions are still migrating in squads.

Most people, from long observation, have come to believe that the martin never builds its nest in any position except against the side of some building ; but it is a bird which adapts its habits in the breeding season to whatever locality it may resort to. For example, in Norway martins breed in the crags of river banks or nest in precipitous cliffs, as they also do in certain other parts of Europe. Martins generally build their nests during May, but frequently find their labours frustrated by the intrusion of sparrows, which oust the rightful owners from their domiciles. The nest is lined with feathers, and the eggs are pure white.

The British Isles, it may be mentioned, lie directly in the line of many birds when migrating from their breeding grounds in Northern Europe to their winter quarters in Africa ; the birds that breed in the north of Europe naturally nesting later than those which breed further south. Consequently, these northerners, or at least a proportion of their number, chiefly young birds, make their appearance in the British Isles in November almost as a matter of course ; and it is, therefore, only natural to expect that a few young martins tarry in England until the beginning of winter. Like the swallow, the martin is subject to some variation of plumage, although albinos are much rarer than among swallows.

This species is the most gregarious of all European members of the swallow tribe, and may often be seen clustering in hundreds on the roofs of houses. The adult male has the crown and sides of the head, back, and wing coverts rich bluish black, the rump and central upper tail coverts white, the wings and tail dull black, and the chin and lower parts dull white. The sexes are identical in colour, although the adults are very unlike their sooty brown young.

SAND MARTINS

The slender, plain-coloured sand martins of the genus *Cotile*, or *Clivaria*, are distinguished by the small depressed beak, broadest at the base, the wings long in proportion to the tail, which is slightly forked, and the feet small and slender. The metatarsus is bare, except for a tuft of feathers at its base. Sand martins are pre-eminently gregarious in the nesting season ; the best known and most widely distributed member of the genus being the European species (*C. riparia*), which extends its range to Northern Asia and North America. The Indian species (*C. sinensis*) is resident throughout the northern portions of the Indian Empire ; while Cowan's sand martin (*C. cowani*) is peculiar to the island of Madagascar, several species also inhabiting Africa.

EUROPEAN SAND MARTIN

The European sand martin arrives in the northern parts of its breeding range a week or two before the

found. Miss M. O. Wright describes the habits of this bird as follows : "During the nesting season the food flight of the barn swallow is incessant, and, as the birds are of a sociable nature, they often go out in groups when in search of food, their happy twittering song when on the wing being one of the sounds we should miss sadly. In addition to killing myriads of mosquitoes and their kin, flies are taken, small beetles, and several species of winged ants.

"Everyone who, on a cloudy day or late in the afternoon, has stood by a millpond or other large body of forest water, must have noticed these swallows skimming low over the water, taking the gnats that swarm there, upon wings that never tire. It was often the habit of boys, idle and worse, to throw sticks and other missiles at these low-flying birds, to see how many they could kill—this game being played in the nesting as well as the flocking season. This sort of thing is, of course, mere wanton cruelty, as there can be no pretence of eating the birds. Be the cause what it may, this swallow is decreasing rapidly in Southern Connecticut, and one day in spring, in a drive of twenty miles through the farming country, where there was a fair proportion of old-fashioned weathered barns, I saw only three small colonies of the birds."

MARTINS

Martins form a group in some of the members of which the tail is forked, while in others it is squared ; but all have the same short, broad beak and deep gape as the swallows, correlated with great length of wing and weak feet. The feathers of the rump are always white, and all the species have the metatarsus and toes feathered. Of this widely-distributed genus, one species (*Chelidon*, or *Chelidonaria*, *cashmiriensis*) is indigenous to the Himalaya and Central Asia, while another, the Siberian martin (*C. lagopus*) breeds in

swallow, and may be seen in sheltered situations during the last days of March, frequently hawking flies under the crags that overhang salmon rivers. It soon proceeds to the nesting grounds, and begins to tunnel the chamber intended to contain its eggs in a sandy bank, gravel pit, or railway cutting ; although sometimes it digs a hole in the bank of a small stream, or even burrows in a heap of sawdust. The male is a somewhat jealous bird, and often indulges in a struggle with its rivals. The eggs, which are pure white without spots, are laid in a hole lined with stems of grass and feathers. When the young are able to fly, they join the company of swallows and martins, and are constantly to be found by the river-side. The sand martin leaves its summer quarters earlier than its congeners, and its movements are less extended. The upper parts of the sand martin are uniform brown, as is the band on the breast ; the lower parts being dull white.

CRAG MARTIN

The species known as the crag martin (C. [*Ptyono-progne*] *rupestris*) spends the summer among the mountain ranges of Central and Southern Europe ; as a rule frequenting rocks and old ruins, and nesting in inaccessible places in March, the nests being often placed in the roofs of caverns in the rocks. In the Eastern Pyrenees the crag martin builds under the eaves of the houses in the centre of the towns, the nests being large structures of mud, quite open at the top, and lined with feathers. The eggs are white, profusely spotted with pale greyish brown. The general colour of the adult bird is light ashy brown above, with the under parts creamy buff, and the tail feathers dark brown, but the middle and outer pairs conspicuously spotted with white.

TREE SWALLOWS

A nearly allied American species, the white-bellied or tree swallow (*Iridoprogne*, or *Tachycincta*, *bicolor*) represents an exclusively New World genus. On this species Miss Wright records the following observations : "The nest, or rather hole-lining, is made of dried grass and a few feathers, put together without the plaster used by the barn swallow, and the half-dozen eggs are paper white, like those of the woodpeckers.

SWALLOW AND MARTIN

This total absence of colour in the eggs of some notable tree-trunk nesters is one of the arguments used by the holders of the colour-protection theory—being in a hole the eggs do not need the protection of colour to conceal them. The tree swallow is a notable insect eater, and has many attractive domesticated habits. "It is not in the nesting season, but in the long period of the autumn migration, that we are most familiar with it. Indeed, this event, spread as it is from July to late October, is one of the great spectacular features of bird life ; for, though the large flocks are made up of both barn and bank and cliff swallows, the tree swallows are greatly in the majority. By day these swallows skim over the meadows and country at large with a wide, circling flight, easy to distinguish from the more angular course of the barn swallow. Toward night they gather either in the marsh reeds or in the low bushes of some region of ponds, or the backwater of rivers, where they roost, coming forth again in clouds at dawn."

PURPLE MARTINS

The *Hirundinidæ* have been divided into two groups, according to the character of the outer primary quill. The majority of genera belong to the smooth-winged group ; but the purple martins (*Progne*) of America typify the rough-winged group, in which the outer margin of the first primary presents a serrated edge in the adult males. The purple martins are birds of robust and elegant form, with long and stout beaks, broad at the base, long and pointed wings, and much-forked tails. Although they are most numerous in Brazil and the adjoining states of South America, one species summers in the United States, and

SAND MARTINS AND PURPLE MARTIN

another is a native of Patagonia. Darwin's purple martin (*P. concolor*) is confined to the Galapagos Islands; while the Caribbean purple martin (*P. dominicensis*) is peculiar to the West Indies. There is a number of other species, the total recognised in 1901 being no less than forty.

The common purple martin (*P. purpurea*), which is one of the most familiar of North American birds, enters the southern borders of the United States as early as February, and gradually extends its range over the country, the highest latitudes being reached only in the middle or end of May. In its habits the purple martin differs from most of its congeners in its predilection for nesting in cavities in hollow trees, such as the deserted holes of woodpeckers; this being especially the case in the Western United States. The nest cavity is lined with fine stems of grass, leaves, and small twigs, quilted with feathers and other soft substances; and the eggs are pure white. Several pairs of birds often occupy the same nest, and the majority of couples are double-brooded. Purple martins leave their summer home in August to retreat to the interior of South America. The adult male has the entire body of a lustrous steel blue, and the wings and tail bluish black. The female is dark greyish brown, but has the head and back glossed with blue.

BABBLERS AND BULBULS

BABBLERS

THIS family (*Timeliidæ*), of which the serial position and extent are somewhat uncertain, contains a large assemblage of birds, of which the majority agree in possessing short and rounded wings, adapted to fit the body, a loose and fluffy plumage, and large and powerful legs and feet. The beak is variously modified, but always adapted to an insectivorous diet, and is furnished with bristles at the gape. The females and young are never spotted.

The babblers are confined to the Old World, where they are most numerously represented in India and the neighbouring countries, though their distribution through the tropical parts of the Eastern Hemisphere is very extensive. The laughing thrushes (*Trochalopterum*) of the Himalaya and Southern China are well-known representatives of this group, as are the true babblers (*Argya*), which wander in flocks all over the plains of India and Burma, and are also represented in North Africa and Syria. Six genera, among them *Crossleyia* and *Oxylabes*, are confined to Madagascar. The scimitar-babblers form an important section of the family, highly characteristic of tropical Asia, and distinguished by their long curved bills.

The typical member of the family is the babbling thrush (*Timelia maculata*), which takes its name from its general thrush-like appearance and the spotted breast of the male.

ABYSSINIAN BABBLER

The Abyssinian babbler (*Crateropus leucopygius*) may be taken as a well-known representative of an important group characterised by the fairly stout beak, of which the upper half is distinctly arched; the wings are short and rounded, and the metatarsus, toes, and claws remarkably strong. The style of colouring is plain; in fact, devoid of gorgeous tints. Several species of these babblers are found in Africa, while others are peculiar to the Indian region; the species inhabiting the forests of Abyssinia frequents dense scrub on the slopes of the mountains. A social species, and rarely found without companions of its own kind, it principally lives in flocks of ten or a dozen individuals, which seek their food in company. The flight is laboured, the bird generally rising but little above the ground in passing from one bush to another. It is a lively, noisy species, like all its congeners, and readily announces its whereabouts by its busy chattering. The upper parts in the adult are dark umber brown above; the sides of the head and chin and tail coverts are white, and the lower parts are umber brown edged with much paler brown.

GREEN BULBULS AND HILL-ROBINS

The green bulbuls and so-called hill-robins constitute a sub-family group (*Liotrichinæ*) in which the sexes are unlike, the plumage is brilliant in colour, and the eggs are generally spotted; while as regards habits, the birds themselves are entirely arboreal, and either solitary or associating in small family parties. The green bulbuls are characterised by the slender, curved beak, equalling the head in length, with the tip notched, and the nostrils oval; the wing is rounded, the tail short and square, and the foot short and weak. The members of this group are restricted to Southern and South-Eastern Asia, several species occurring within the Indian Empire.

One of the best known is the gold-fronted green bulbul (*Chloropsis aurifrons*), which feeds on insects picked off the surfaces of leaves, and is exceedingly difficult to detect amid a profusion of foliage, since its bright, grass green plumage harmonises closely with the leaves. It lives in pairs or singly, and

ABYSSINIAN BABBLER

ranges over a considerable portion of Bengal and the adjacent provinces, as well as Burma and the spurs of the Himalaya.

The cock has a sweet song, and is also an excellent mimic of the notes of other birds. The forehead and front of the crown are orange yellow, the ear coverts and lower part of the throat are black, and the chin and upper part of the throat are purplish blue, a yellow collar passes round the black of the throat, and the remainder of the plumage is bright green.

RED-BILLED HILL-ROBIN

The red-billed hill-robin of India (*Liothrix lutea*) is the typical representative of the subfamily, and is a mountain species, with the feathers of the slightly forked tail curved outwards.

STRAIGHT-CLAWS

Certain remarkable Australian birds may be noticed here, although their serial position is open to some doubt. The group, of which there are several species, such as the spiny-tailed (*Orthonyx spinicauda*) and yellow-headed straight-claw (*O. ochrocephalus*), is characterised by the short and straight beak, in which the culmen is arched, the moderate and rounded wings, with the first four quills graduated and shorter than the fifth, and the long tail, in which the feathers are broad, and furnished with soft webs, but with stiff, rigid shafts terminating in naked points. The feet are very large and strong.

Inhabiting South and Eastern Australia, the common species frequents remote situations in the bush, rapidly traversing the surface of moss-covered stones and the fallen trunks of trees in search of food. It never climbs, and is solitary in its habits, seldom more than two being seen together. Its oft-repeated cry of "cri, cri, cri, crite," betrays its presence, when its native haunts, the most retired forests, are visited. Its food consists of insects and wood bugs. The eggs are white and large in proportion to the size of the bird. The situation of the nest is the side of a slanting rock, the entrance being level with the surface.

The adult male has the head and upper parts reddish brown, the wings brown, the coverts largely tipped with grey, the primaries crossed with grey at the base, the tips of the secondaries tipped with dark brownish grey, the tail dark brown, the sides of the head and neck dark grey, the throat and chest white, separated from the grey of the sides of the neck by a crescent-shaped

black mark, and the flanks and under tail coverts grey, stained with reddish brown. The female differs from her mate in having the throat rich rusty red instead of white.

CROW-TITS

With the babblers may likewise be classed the so-called crow-tits, of the genera *Conostoma, Paradoxornis, Suthora, etc.,* which are restricted to the mountains of North-Eastern India and China. In all these birds the young are similar in plumage to the adults, there are ten primaries in the wings, and the nostrils are completely hidden by thick bristles. As these characters are also common to the crows and tits, some naturalists regard these birds as very nearly related to those families. In those species of which the breeding habits are known the nests are cup-shaped and placed in trees, and the eggs have a light-coloured ground, with yellowish brown and purple markings.

BULBULS

The bulbuls, of which there are several genera, form a family (*Pycnonotidæ*) presenting the following characters : The sexes are alike, the metatarsus is very short, and never exceeds the length of the middle toe and its claw, the wing is rounded and moderately long, and the gape is generally furnished with some hairs. As regards habits and the colour of their eggs, bulbuls resemble green bulbuls. While many of them have a more or less largely developed crest, those of the typical genus, *Pycnonotus,* are practically crestless. They are further characterised by having the beak of moderate size with the culmen curved and the sides compressed to the tip ; the gape furnished with a few short, weak bristles ; the nostrils basal and placed in a groove ; the wings moderate and rounded ; the tail fairly long and rounded, and the feet terminating in strong claws.

Among the species, the Syrian bulbul (*Pycnonotus nigricans*) is very common in Syria, Arabia, Cyprus, and Rhodes, also visiting the Cyclades ; while the white-vented bulbul (*P. arsinoë*), considered the finest songster of all the family, frequents the mimosa groves of Northern Africa. The latter species is abundant in

SYRIAN AND WHITE-VENTED BULBULS

the Fayum province of Egypt, where it is partial to apricots, and sings in the palm trees. In South Africa the red-eyebrowed bulbul (*P. capensis*), the knif-kop of the colonists, is well known for its partiality to figs and grapes.

AMERICAN FLYCATCHERS AND CHATTERERS

AMERICAN FLYCATCHERS

ALL the members of the passerine order hitherto described are characterised by having the muscles of the syrinx, or organ of voice, attached to the ends of the half-rings of cartilage forming the windpipe; such muscles being generally of a very complex type. Hence these birds are termed the Acromyodi. In those remaining for consideration, on the other hand, these muscles are simple, and frequently consist of only a single pair, and are attached to the middle of the half-rings of the windpipe; and they are accordingly known as the Mesomyodi. Since none of them possesses the high vocal powers of the first group, they are often spoken of as the songless perching birds. As their name implies, the members of the first family of this group, or *Tyrannidæ*, are exclusively confined to the New World, where they are represented by fully four hundred species, the majority of which are South American.

SULPHUR TYRANT BIRD

Insectivorous in habits, the typical members of the family have the beak broadest at the base, from which it tapers to a fine point, the upper half being slightly notched, and the nostrils basal and overhung, although not concealed, by bristles. The wing has ten primaries, and the tail, which is generally nearly even, although sometimes forked, is composed of twelve feathers. The metatarsus is relatively short, and the foot weak. The range of these birds extends from the Arctic regions to Tierra del Fuego.

THE KING BIRD

The king bird, or bee martin (*Tyrannus pipiri*), is well known in the United States for the audacity with which it attacks crows, owls, and hawks, and drives them away from the neighbourhood of its nest; a party of king birds having even been known to harass a swallow-tailed kite, which eventually struck down one of its tormentors before it sailed away.

THE FIRE-EYE

The king bird builds a conspicuous nest, usually choosing an isolated tree, often in an exposed situation; the nest itself being constructed of vegetable fibres and twigs, lined with horsehair, fine roots, and grasses. The eggs are rosy white in ground colour, spotted and blotched with purple and reddish brown. Not possessing a true song, the king bird merely utters a monotonous sucession of twitterings.

This species owes its name of "bee-bird" to its fondness for bees, but this is somewhat of a misnomer, since it destroys a thousand noxious insects for every bee it eats. It feeds largely on winged insects, and its flight, when in pursuit of these, is accomplished by rapid vibrations of the wings, the birds seeming to float in the air after the manner of a swallow. The king bird arrives in its summer haunts in April and May, and prolongs its sojourn until September, when it migrates south. The male has the crown flame colour, the upper parts blackish ash, the wings dusky, edged with whitish, the tail black, tipped with white, and the lower parts pure white, except the breast, which is shaded with grey.

BIENTEVEO TYRANT

A well-known South American representative of the group is the bienteveo tyrant (*T. sulfuratus*), in regard to which Mr. W. H. Hudson writes that in Buenos Aires "the bienteveo is found in every orchard and plantation; it is familiar with man, and invariably greets his approach with loud notes especially with a powerful three-syllabled cry, in which people fancy there is a resemblance to the words, 'Biente-veo' ('I see you well'); while its big head and beak and strongly contrasted colours, especially the black and white head stripes, seem to give it a wonderfully knowing look as it turns its head from side to side to examine any intruder. It is a loud-voiced, garrulous bird, and has a great range of sounds, from grating screams to long clear, almost mellow, call notes.

"It has one pretty habit which brings out strongly the pleasant feature in its character. The male and female are greatly attached; they do not go afield to hunt in company like the short-winged tyrant, but separate to meet again at intervals during the day. One of a couple (say the female) returns to the trees where they are accustomed to meet, and after a time, becoming impatient or anxious at the delay of her consort, utters a very long clear call note. He is, perhaps, a quarter of a mile away, watching for a frog beside a pool, or beating harrier-like over a thistle bed, but he hears the note and presently responds with one of equal power. Then, perhaps, for half an hour, at intervals of half a minute, the birds answer each other, though the powerful call of the one must interfere with its hunting. At length he returns; then the two birds perch close together, with their yellow bosoms almost touching, crests elevated, and, beating the branch with their wings, scream their loudest notes in concert, a confused jubilant noise that rings through the whole plantation."

As regards nesting, the bienteveo is unlike the majority of tyrant birds, which build small and shallow nests; whereas this species constructs a very elaborate domed nest, which sometimes takes weeks to complete.

It is placed in a tree without any attempt at conceal-ment, and composed of a variety of soft materials, especially wool. The eggs are cream-coloured, spotted with chocolate and purple, chiefly at the larger end.

The bienteveo preys chiefly on large insects, such as beetles, which it invariably beats against its perch before swallowing, but sometimes carries off the callow young of other birds from their nests. It is also fond of fishing in shallow pools for tadpoles and small fishes, while occasionally it enters slaughter-houses in search of pickings ; and it is quite common to see a bienteveo waiting on a butcher's cart in hopes of securing some titbit. In autumn it feeds largely on ripe grapes, figs, and other fruit. The adult has the head black, with a large yellow crest and white eye stripe, the upper parts brown, the wings and tail brown edged with rufous, and the lower parts sulphur yellow.

ANT-BIRDS

To the members of an exclu-sively South American group the name of ant-bird (*Formicivora*) is commonly applied, on account of the nature of their food. In these birds the beak is sharp and conical, with the upper half hooked, and the wings moderate, with the fourth feather the longest. The tail is fairly long and rounded, and the feet are furnished with long toes, adapted to walking, the claws being short and narrow.

All the ant-birds are inhabit-ants of the forests of Brazil, a well-known species being the fire-eye (*F. domicella*) which fre-quents dense portions of the primeval scrub, creeping about the bushes, and rarely venturing into the open. This bird, which has a pleasing, warbling note, feeds upon a variety of insects ; and its fondness for ants induces it to lay aside its usually cautious and retiring habits, and at times many individuals assemble to devour those insects in wood-pecker-fashion. The adult male is nearly all black, with the plumage set off to great advan-tage by white wing coverts and the fiery red iris of the eye, from which this species takes its name.

KITE-TAILED TYRANT BIRDS

The most striking members of the family are the kite-tailed tyrant birds (*Milvulus forficatus*) of Texas, Mexico, and Costa Rica, and the allied *M. tyrannus*, whose range extends from Mexico to Argentina. These two species constitute a genus readily distinguished by the long and deeply-forked tail. In size they are somewhat smaller than thrushes. The kite-tailed tyrant bird is characterised by the crown of the head being grey, the flanks pale rose colour, and the almost equality in length of the two elongated pairs of outer tail feathers. On the other hand, in the typical *M. tyrannus* the crown of the head is black, the flanks are white, and the outermost pair of tail feathers is much larger than the adjacent pair. In habits these birds much resemble flycatchers, the typical species having, indeed, been

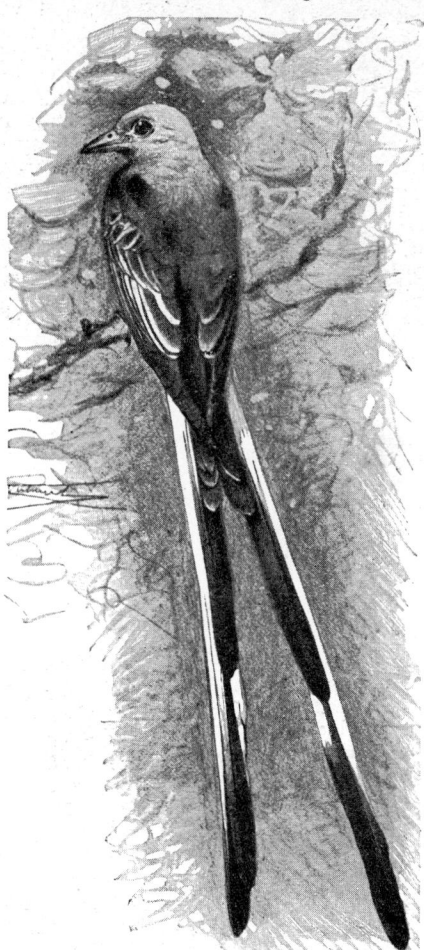

KITE-TAILED TYRANT BIRD

described by Linnæus as a member of that group under the name of *Muscicapa tyrannus*.

CHATTERERS

Some of the most gorgeous birds of South America are to be found in the family of chatterers (*Cotingidæ*), which is remarkable for the variations of plumage exhibited by certain of its representatives. Chatterers usually have the beak arched, broad at the gape, and adapted to a frugivorous diet, the wings being generally of moderate length, although sometimes reaching almost to the extremity of the tail. The metatarsus is stout, and covered with large shields in front.

The greater number of the chatterers are inhabitants of the vast equatorial region of the Amazon, frequenting the interior of the forests, and leading an arboreal life ; one of the loveliest being the Pompadour chatterer (*Xipholena pompadora*), so named after the famous Frenchwoman to whom this and other specimens of birds were being sent when the ship that bore them from Cayenne fell a prize to a British cruiser.

UMBRELLA BIRDS

The singular bird for which the genus *Cephalopterus* was established has a stout, robust beak, with a strongly-arched upper half, the nostrils open and longitudinal in shape, the wings long, and the tail rounded. The umbrella bird takes, however, its name from its curious crest, composed of straight, elevated feathers, the extremities of which curve outwards and form an elegant line of drooping plumes. The sides of the neck are naked, but long feathers spring from beneath the throat and from the sides of the neck, to form a loose lappet.

Confined in its range to the forests of the plains of the Upper Amazon, the umbrella bird (*C. ornatus*) is a shy, retiring species, living in the higher branches of forest trees, where it readily obtains the wild fruits upon which it chiefly subsists. It has been seen by very few naturalists in its native wilds, but no doubt exists regarding its peculiar vocal powers. Mr. H. W. Bates, for instance, writes : " The Indian name of this strange creature is uirá mimbéu, or fife bird, in allusion to the tone of its voice. We had the good luck, after remaining quiet for a short time, to hear its performance. It drew itself up on its perch, spread widely the umbrella-formed crest, dilated and waved its glossy breast lappet, and then, in giving vent to its loud piping note, bowed its head slowly forwards. The nest of the umbrella bird is built of small branches, placed in the top of a tall tree."

The eggs are white, and two in number. In flight the helmet or crest is depressed, and the lappet placed close to the body. The plumage of the male is deep black throughout, the lappet being glossed with steel blue. The female has only the rudiments of the crest and lappet, and is altogether duller-coloured than the male. In the allied *C. penduliger* the lappet, or wattle, on the throat is extraordinarily elongated;

THE UMBRELLA BIRD

while in *C. glabricollis* there is a large patch of bare orange-coloured skin on the throat, with a terminal tuft on the red projecting outgrowth.

BELL-BIRDS

Long known to travellers in consequence of their remarkable vocal powers so closely resembling the ringing of a bell as to have suggested for them their popular appellation, two of the four known species of bell-birds have the plumage pure unspotted white, in which respect they are unique among the chatterers. All the bell-birds have a moderately-curved beak, broad at the base and deeply cleft; the wings extend to the end of the upper tail coverts, the metatarsus is strong and scutellated, and the toes are short and strong.

The brown-headed bell-bird (*Chasmorhynchus variegatus*) is found in Venezuela, while the snowy bell bird (*C. niveus*) inhabits the forests of Surinam, Cayenne, and Demerara, and the bare-throated bell bird (*C. nudicollis*) is a native of Brazil. Of the last-named species the following account has been given by Dr. P. L. Sclater: " This bell-bird was first made known to science by the French naturalist Viellot, in 1815, from specimens in the collection of the Jardin des Plantes at Paris. But the best and, in fact, only good account of it in a state of nature is one given by that excellent and observing naturalist, Prince Maximilian of Neuwied, who states that this remarkable bird is one of the most singular creatures in the fauna of the wooded coast region of Brazil, and attracts the stranger's notice as well as by its brilliant white plumage as by its clear-ringing voice.

" It seems to be very generally distributed throughout the woods, resorting especially to the thickest and most secluded parts of them. Hence it resulted that the prince and his party during their expeditions in the vicinity of Rio de Janeiro became well acquainted with its singular notes some time before they obtained specimens of the producer of them. Prince Maximilian describes these notes as resembling the sound of a clear-ringing-bell, sometimes repeated at intervals, sometimes following each other in quick succession. In the latter case they are more like the sound produced by a blacksmith when he strikes a piece of steel upon an anvil, whence the bird has obtained its Portuguese name of ferreiro (smith). The song is heard at all hours of the day, and when, as often happens, several of these birds are in the same neighbourhood, and begin singing against and answering one another, a most wonderful vocal concert is the result."

Of this extraordinary bird a living specimen was first acquired for the aviaries of the Zoological Society of London in May, 1867. Shortly after its arrival it began its song, and continued to pour forth its peculiar notes at intervals of more or less frequency for several weeks. These notes have been described by an accurate observer : " The first note is a loud, harsh, and somewhat grating noise ; this is followed by six or eight fine, clear, metallic, ringing notes, with an interval of about a second between each. The resemblance of these to the sound of an anvil is most extraordinary. The clear metallic ring, repeated at about the same rate that a blacksmith strikes upon the anvil, is so perfect that many persons on hearing it are unwilling to believe the sound could be produced by the delicate organs forming the vocal apparatus of so small a bird. So

WHITE-HEADED BELL BIRD

admirable is the imitation that, when the first bell-bird reached the Zoological Gardens its clear, ringing note was mistaken by one of the officials for the sound of a blacksmith ringing on an anvil, and inquiry was made by him as to the work that was going on."

In the adult male of the bare-throated bell-bird the plumage is pure white throughout, the space round the eyes and throat being covered with a naked skin, which is only sparingly invested with minute black feathers and becomes of a fine green in the breeding season. The female has a blackish head and the upper parts dull green, while beneath it is yellowish, varied with green. The allied snowy bell-bird differs by having a single spiral, erectile, wattle-like projection, only sparsely covered with feathers. The brown-headed species, on the other hand, has a brown head, black wings, and a bare warty throat, while the white-headed species (*C. tricarunculatus*), of Central America, has the head and neck white and the rest of the plumage chestnut; this extraordinary bird being further distinguished by carrying three long, whip-like, erectile processes on the head, one at the base of the upper surface of the beak and the other two at the angles of the gape.

COTINGAS

The cotingas (*Cotinga*), or typical chatterers, form a group of small species distinguished from their near allies the bell-birds by the brilliancy of the colouring of the males. In the more typical species of the group the beak is depressed, broad at the base, and narrowed towards the extremity, with the upper half slightly arched, while the wings are of moderate size and pointed, the metatarsus is short, and the toes are stout and furnished with fine claws. Cotingas inhabit the forests of Southern Brazil; the banded species (*C. cincta*) being a bird of solitary habits, which keeps to the topmost branches of trees, and generally resides in dense forest, though at times approaching cultivated grounds in search of food. It feeds upon a variety of fruits, which its wide gape enables it to swallow with ease. The adult male has the upper parts and the band across the breast full ultramarine blue, and the under parts deep plum-colour.

BARE-THROATED BELL-BIRDS

COCKS OF THE ROCK

Another sub-family of the chatterers is typified by the relatively large bird known as the cock of the rock

THE COCK OF THE ROCK

(*Rupicola croceus*). This and two allied species are remarkable for their brilliant colouring, especially as regards the males, in which orange red predominates. In these birds the beak is of moderate size, curving towards the extremity, with the upper half as wide as it is high, compressed at the base, and notched at the point. The nostrils are oval and hidden by the feathers of the elevated crest; the wings are short and rounded, with the fourth and fifth quills the longest; the tail is of variable length; the metatarsus is partially invested with feathers; and the feet are large and strong. This typical species inhabits Guiana and the lower countries of the Amazon, but farther westwards it is replaced by the Peruvian cock of the rock (*R. peruvianus*); and a third species (*R. sanguinolentus*) inhabits Ecuador.

Although in confinement the cock of the rock is indolent, such is not its character in its native wilds. Sometimes a score assemble in the neighbourhood of an open space, where they become intent on watching the performance of the males. While the dance is in progress the cock becomes absorbed in the performance of his task; he hops upwards, accompanying his movements with peculiar steps, swaying his head, and extending his wings; the exhibition being continued until the performer becomes tired, when he gives a cry, and retires, leaving other birds to continue the entertainment. In the typical species the adult male is almost wholly of a brilliant orange colour, while he is also adorned with a helmet-like crest. The female lacks the brilliant colouring of the other sex, being almost entirely of a more or less uniform reddish brown.

Two allied birds from Amazonia, Guiana, and Ecuador, respectively known as *Phœnicocercus carnifex* and *P. nigricollis*, are the only other representatives of the subfamily *Rupicolinæ*.

MANAKINS, PLANT-CUTTERS, BROADBILLS, AND PITTAS

MANAKINS

FORMERLY classed with the chatterers, the gorgeous little Central and South American birds known as manakins are now allowed to rank as a family by themselves (*Pipridæ*). They are even more brilliant in colour than the cotingas, showing the most splendid tints of blue, crimson, scarlet, orange, or yellow in combination with chestnut, deep black, black and white, or olive green. Among their most obvious

BLACK-HEADED MANAKIN

characteristics are the short beak and feeble feet, with the fourth toe of the latter united to the third for a part of its length. A few species are crested ; and the tail is very short in the majority of species, although in others the middle feathers are much elongated.

Although the white-headed manakin (*Pipra leucocilla*) has a wide distribution, ranging from the valley of the Amazon to the Isthmus of Panama, the majority of the species are confined to Brazil. Among them, the black-headed manakin (*Pipra manacus*), which is spread over a large portion of South America, is a lively, active, restless species, generally to be seen in motion. Making its home in the dense scrub of primeval forests, avoiding large trees, and flitting through the bushes at a short distance from the ground with a short but swift flight, it is a bird of social disposition, rarely found solitary. The most curious fact about this manakin and certain of its allies is the circumstance that the wings are modified by the thickening of their shafts so as to produce a loud noise, which has been compared to the whirr of a spinning wheel. The adult has the crown of the head, the middle of the back, the wings, and tail black, the rump grey, and the neck and under parts white. All manakins are essentially birds of the forest, and feed on fruits and berries.

PLANT-CUTTERS

The tropical American birds commonly known as plant-cutters (family *Phytotomidæ*) were formerly placed by naturalists between the finches and the horn-bills ; but are now known to be nearly related to the chatterers. They have the wings relatively short, and the tail long and even, but their most marked characteristic is the short, compressed beak, the cutting-margins of which are minutely notched like the blade of a saw. The whole of these thick-beaked birds are peculiar to the temperate regions of South America, being found in Chile, Bolivia, and Argentina, where they are represented by four species, all included in the typical genus *Phytotoma*.

The typical Chilian plant-cutter (*P. rara*) takes its name from its destructive habit of feeding on plants, which it cuts down, often wantonly, with its powerful beak. This bird builds in lofty trees, but the nests are frequently destroyed in consequence of their owners' mischievous habits. It is a plain-coloured bird, dull grey, both above and below, with the wings and tail blackish, and the coverts tipped with white. Its voice is harsh and grating.

A common bird in Patagonia is the red-breasted plant-cutter (*P. rutila*), generally found alone, but sometimes associating in small flocks. The bright red breast of the male gives it a gay appearance among the dull-plumaged species that people the thickets of Patagonia. These birds build slight nests of fine twigs, lined with fibres, and generally placed in thorn bushes ; the eggs being bluish green in ground colour, with brownish flecks. The male has the upper parts dull grey, with the tips of the tail feathers and a wing bar white, and the forehead and under surface deep brick red. The female is yellowish grey above, with obscure mottlings, while the breast and under parts are buff with dark spots.

BROADBILLS

Deriving their name from, and readily distinguished by, the enormous breadth of their beaks, the broad-bills (family *Eurylæmidæ*), which are for the most part bright-coloured birds, are the eastern representatives of the chatterers of the New World. They are birds of fairly powerful make, with the upper half of the beak dilated at its base, the tip abruptly hooked, the wings rather short, and the tail short and rounded. Although they may be the survivors of a once extensive group, at the present day they have a very limited distribution, ranging from the lower spurs of the Himalaya, through Burma and Siam, to Sumatra, Borneo, and Java.

Several generic types of these birds are now recognised, among which those included in *Eurylæmus* have the beak broader than the head, with the lower half very thin, particularly at the base, the nostrils basal, the primaries slightly graduated, the tail short and rounded, and the feet moderately strong. These broadbills are found in the forests of tropical India, as well as those of Sumatra and the Malay Peninsula.

SUMATRAN BROADBILL

Among the species, the Javan broadbill (*Eurylæmus javanicus*) is a native of the eastern extremity of the island from which it takes its name, where it frequents the banks of rivers and lakes, feeding on worms and insects. It seems partial to the neighbourhood of water, building its nest in its aquatic haunts, often overhanging a pool, and is generally found in situations difficult of access, clothed with extensive forests, and intersected with marshes and rivers. The plumage of the head, sides of the neck, and under parts is violet, varying in intensity. The forehead is nearly black, the upper part of the neck is brown, the wings are deep blackish brown, varied with yellow, the tail coverts are yellow, with the bases of the feathers black, the middle tail feathers are wholly black, and the outer ones black, marked by a white transverse band near the extremity. The Sumatra species (*E. [Corydon] sumatranus*) is regarded by some naturalists as representing a genus by itself.

PITTAS

The pittas, or Old World ant-thrushes (family *Pittidæ*), are distinguished by the structure of the syrinx and the form of the wing, the first primary quill of the latter being of large size instead of being nearly suppressed, as in other passerines with ten primaries. Pittas are birds of lovely plumage, with blue and crimson prevalent in many of the species, and are most abundant in the forests of the Malay Archipelago, especially the islands of Borneo and Sumatra. The blue-naped pitta (*Pitta [Hydrornis] nepalensis*), for instance, inhabits the Himalaya from Nepal to Assam; while the fulvous pitta (*P. [H.] oatesi*) is found in the ever-green forests of the hills of Pegu, and Sumatra and Borneo are the home of the great pitta (*P. venusta*). The rainbow pitta (*P. iris*) of Australia is a beautiful bird, golden green above, with bright metallic blue shoulders, velvety black head and throat, and crimson abdomen, but the Malay pittas are the most gorgeous of the family. A single species of this group (*P. angolensis*) is found in Western Africa.

TYPICAL PITTAS

The typical pittas (*Pitta*) have no crests of elongated feathers, but are plain headed, with a strong, thrush-like, gradually curved beak, and wings of moderate size, in which the first and second quills are but slightly graduated. The tail is very short, and almost hidden by the coverts, but may be broad and rounded or narrow and pointed. The feet are very long and adapted to a terrestrial life, pittas passing most of their existence on the ground in the midst of dense jungle, and rarely flying long distances, except on migration, although their flight is strong and well sustained. Pittas may be regarded as the most characteristic birds of Borneo, where six species are found, three of the number being peculiar to the island. In regard to Ussher's pitta (*P. ussheri*) of that island, it has been stated that when the bright scarlet breast is turned towards the observer, the bird is not easily distinguished from the scarlet fruits and bright red dead leaves which carpet the forests. The bird when alarmed, however, generally

INDIAN PITTA

keeps its dark back towards the intruder, when it is still more difficult to detect in the dusky shades of the forest.

The Indian pitta (*P. brachyura*), which ranges from the lower slopes of the Himalaya to Ceylon, is the most common in forest regions in the Central Provinces, where it breeds in July and August, building a huge globular nest of twigs and leaves on the ground or in a low branch. Few Indian eggs are more beautiful than those of this species; they are glossy white, marked with maroon and purple.

The Indian pitta is a taciturn bird, though possessing a fine loud whistling note, and appears to be a migratory visitor to Ceylon, arriving from the north with the snipe. Although this pitta is a local migrant, being found in the southern part of its range in winter and in the central and northern portions in the hot weather and rains, yet a certain number are constant residents in all parts of the range suited to the habits of the species.

During its sojourn in Ceylon the Indian pitta is shy and wary, resorting chiefly to tangled brakes and ill-kept native gardens. It rarely alights on a tree, and is oftenest seen alone, though three or four individuals are sometimes met with in company. Its food consists of beetles and other insects.

In the adult the forehead, crown, and lower parts are tawny; a broad, median band extends from the forehead to the nape; the back, scapulars, and upper part of the rump are green; the lower portion of the rump, upper tail coverts, and lesser wing coverts are pale blue; there is a broad, black band over the eyes; the primaries are black tipped with grey; the tail is black tipped with dull blue; the chin and throat are white, and the abdomen and under tail coverts are crimson.

The blue pitta (*P. cyanea*), of Bhutan, Arracan, Pegu, Tenasserim, and Siam, is a bird of considerable beauty, though far inferior in lustre to many of the Malay species of the genus. Like other members of the family, it lives principally in dense scrub and jungle, obtaining its insect prey on the ground. It begins to build its nest in the month of May, making a large, globular structure of dry leaves and twigs, placed on the ground, and lined with fine twigs and grass roots. The eggs are white marked with various shades of purple. The adult male has the forehead and crown greenish grey, changing to red, and giving place entirely to red on the nape, where the feathers are long and form a crest; the upper parts and tail are blue, the primaries brown, with a white basal patch, the lores and a broad streak from the eye to the nape black, the chin and throat whitish, and the lower parts light blue barred with black.

Nearly allied to the pittas are two curious Malagasy birds, *Philepitta jala* and *P. schlegeli*, which alone represent the family *Philepittidæ*. They are easily recognisable by the presence of a bare ring round the eye, furnished in the male with an upright green wattle-like growth. Another family, the *Xenicidæ*, is formed by three New Zealand birds, two referable to the genus *Xenicus* and the third to the allied *Traversia*.

WOOD-HEWERS AND LYRE-BIRDS

WOOD-HEWERS

THE so-called wood-hewers (family *Dendrocolaptidæ*) are in the main brown-coloured birds, with the long or moderate and laterally compressed beak rather strong, straight, or curved, the third, fourth, and fifth quills of the wing the longest, the tail feathers stiff, pointed, and often of a ferruginous colour, and the claws of the feet much curved. Over two hundred species of these birds are known, ranging from Mexico to Patagonia; thirteen of the genera being confined to the high Andes and south temperate America, while fourteen are restricted to the tropical parts of South America. A single species inhabits the Falkland Isles. But vast as this assemblage is, it will suffice to mention the oven-birds, spine-tails, and the sickle-beaked wood-hewers.

OVEN-BIRDS

On account of the remarkable character of their nests, special interest attaches to the oven-birds, which are characterised by the beak being shorter than the head, laterally compressed and pointed, with the upper half slightly curved, the wings moderate, the tail consisting of twelve feathers, and the feet strong and adapted to terrestrial progression. The members of this genus range all over South America, eighteen species being restricted to the temperate regions.

A well-known species in Paraguay, Uruguay, and Argentina is the red oven-bird (*Furnarius rufus*), which enjoys a wide popularity on account of its familiarity with man, its loud ringing voice, and the wonderful mud nest which it prefers to build near human habitations, often on a projecting beam of the roof of the house itself. In favourable seasons oven-birds begin building in the autumn, and the work is resumed during the winter whenever there is a spell of mild, wet weather; the material used being mud, with the addition of horse-hair or fibrous roots, which make the structure harder, and prevent it from cracking. When finished, the structure is shaped outwardly like a baker's oven, only with a deeper and narrower entrance. It is always placed very conspicuously, and with the entrance facing a building if one be near, or, if at the roadside, looking towards the road.

When the structure has assumed the globular form, with only a narrow opening, the wall on one side is curved inwards, reaching from the floor to the dome, and at the inner extremity an aperture is left to admit the bird to the interior, or second chamber, in which the eggs are laid. The interior is lined with dry and soft grass, upon which five white, pear-shaped eggs are laid. The oven is a foot or more in diameter, and sometimes very massive, weighing eight or nine pounds, and so strong that, unless loosened by the swaying of the branch, it often remains unharmed for two or three years.

The birds incubate by turns, and when one returns from the feeding grounds, it sings its loud notes, on which the sitting bird rushes forth to join the chorus, and then flies away, the other taking its place on the eggs. The young are exceedingly garrulous, and when only half-fledged may be heard practising trills and duets in their secure oven in shrill, tremulous voices, which change to the usual hunger-cries of young birds when the parent enters with food. After leaving the nest, the old and young birds live for two or three months together, only one brood being raised in each year. A new oven is built every year, and occasionally a second may be built on the top of the first, when this has been placed advantageously, as on a projection and against a wall.

A somewhat curious circumstance occurred at the house of a neighbour of Mr. W. H. Hudson at Buenos Aires one spring. "A pair of oven-birds built their oven on a beam-end projecting from the wall of a rancho. One morning one of the birds was found caught in a steel trap placed the evening before for rats, and both of its legs were crushed above the knee.

"On being liberated, it flew up to and entered the oven, where it bled to death, no doubt, for it did not come out again. Its mate remained two or three days, calling incessantly, but there were no other birds of its kind in the place, and it eventually disappeared. Three days later it returned with a new mate, and immediately the two birds began carrying pellets of mud to the oven, with which they plastered up the entrance. Afterwards they built a second oven, using the sepulchre of the dead bird for its foundation, and here they reared their young.

"My neighbour, an old native, had watched the birds from the time the first oven was begun, feeling greatly interested in their diligent ways, and thinking their presence at his house a good omen; and it was not strange that, after witnessing the entombment of one that died, he was more convinced than ever that the little house-builders are pious birds."

BROWN-FRONTED SPINE-TAIL AND RED OVEN-BIRD

BRAZILIAN SICKLE-BEAK

The plumage of this oven-bird is earthy brown above, with a slight reddish tinge ; the breast and flanks are pale sandy brown, and the upper tail coverts and tail bright reddish brown. There is no difference in the colour of the sexes.

SPINE-TAILS

Near akin to oven-birds are the spine-tails, distinguished by the short straight laterally compressed beak, the wings very short and much rounded, with the primaries scarcely exceeding the inner secondaries, the tail broad, with the shafts of the feathers rather rigid and the tips pointed, and the feet very large and furnished with slender claws. The white-throated spine-tail (*Synallaxis spixi*), like its congener the brown-fronted species (*S. frontalis*), is a summer visitor to Buenos Aires ; its arrival in spring being easily recognised by the utterance of its harsh persistent, cat-like note, which is remarkably strong for so small a bird, and is reiterated for half an hour at a time with only intervals of a few seconds. The nest, which often contains a barrowful of material, and is placed in a low thorn bush, sometimes only two or three feet above the ground, is an oblong structure of sticks twelve or fourteen inches in depth, with

the entrance near the top, and reached by a tubular passage made of slender sticks six or seven inches long. From the top of the nest a crooked passage leads to the cavity near the bottom, which is lined with a little fine grass ; upon this being laid nine pear-shaped, bluish white eggs. The nest is often entered through a long tube, built at a point about halfway up the side, and formed by the interlocking of thorny twigs ; and although the diameter of the passage is only large enough to admit the old birds one at a time, yet they pass out with ease and rapidity.

In Colombia this spine-tail varies the form of its nest, making it as large as that of a magpie, and roofing the top with a mass of large leaves to protect it from the heavy rains. The adult bird has the forehead grey, the crown of the head and upper wing coverts pale chestnut, the sides of the head, neck, back, and tail pale earthy brown, the primaries olive brown, and the lower parts white, tinged with brown.

SICKLE-BEAKED WOOD-HEWERS

The oven-birds and the spine-tails respectively constitute two distinct sub-families of wood-hewers ; and a third sub-family (*Dendrocolaptinæ*) includes the typical genus *Dendrocolaptes* and the sickle-beaks (*Xiphorhynchus*), remarkable on account of the great length and strong curvature of the beak. There are nearly a dozen representatives of the second genus, among which the Brazilian *X. procurvus* is a well-known species.

LYRE-BIRDS

The last representatives of the order of perching birds that will be mentioned here are the aberrant lyre-birds (family *Menuridæ*) of Australia, where they are represented by three species, all included in the genus *Menura*, of which the typical form is the lyre-bird of New South Wales (*M. superba*). Altogether abnormal in their structure, these remarkable and highly specialised birds can scarcely be assigned to either of the two great groups into which the passerines are divided, and must accordingly be regarded as

LYRE-BIRDS DANCING

Photo : C. Grant Lane

standing to a great extent by themselves. Of very large size, lyre-birds are specially characterised by the great development of the tail feathers of the male, which assume a lyrate form, the majority being devoid of hooklets, and thus having the webs formed of separate plumules. The general colour of the plumage is brown; but while in the typical species the large pair of outer tail feathers has reddish brown transverse bars on a light ground, in Prince Albert's lyre-bird (*M. alberti*) these feathers are uniformly coloured.

The lyre-birds are remarkable for their power of imitating the cries and songs of other birds, this faculty being most developed in the species last mentioned; and they are also peculiar in making playing grounds somewhat similar to those of some of the bower-birds.

In the case of Prince Albert's lyre-bird, each bird appears to have its own walk or boundary, and never to infringe on the others' grounds, as these birds may be heard day after day in the same place, and seldom nearer than a quarter of a mile to each other. When singing, they spread their tails over their heads like a peacock, and droop their wings to the ground, and at the same time scratch and peck up the earth. They sing mornings and evenings, and more so in winter than at any other time. The young cocks do not sing until they get their full tails, which apparently is not until the fourth year; the two middle curved feathers being the last to appear. Feeding upon small insects, and more especially beetles, they begin nesting in May, the eggs being laid in June, and the young hatched in the following month. The nest is constructed of small sticks, interwoven with moss and fibres of roots, and internally is lined with the skeleton leaves of the parasitical tree fern, which in texture resemble horsehair; the whole structure being roofed in, and entered by an aperture on one side. A single egg is laid, which is of a very dark colour, looking almost as though smeared over with ink: the young bird, which is coated with down for the first month, remains in the nest for a period of about six weeks.

It is a well-known fact that during the breeding season every male lyre-bird is accompanied by two or three females, and it appears to be generally assumed that each of the hens makes a nest of her own, in which the single egg is laid. This belief, however, is questioned by Mr. L. C. Cook, who is of opinion that only one out of each party of hens lays in one year, although the others probably assist in incubation. The evidence in favour of this view is that in several patches of covert inhabited respectively by a single male lyre-bird and his partners only one nest could be discovered in any one year, despite the most thorough search. In one instance two eggs were found in the same nest in Victoria, and the inference in this instance is that two out of the party of hens had laid in the same season.

As to the question whether the male assists in incubation, the same writer observes that he has never seen a cock bird flushed from a nest. Very remarkable is the fact that the hens never desert the nest, however much the egg or young may have been handled; and at least one instance is recorded in which a hen continued to feed and attend her offspring after the nest had been removed a considerable distance from its original situation. A young lyre-bird has also been taken from the nest and kept in a house for a whole night, but on being put back in the morning and made to call out, was forthwith visited and tended by the female parent.

Lyre-birds frequently build on the very outskirts of a covert, within a few yards of a road from which the nest can be distinctly seen, and this when the heart of the covert is a tangle of the densest nature. These birds will also roost at times on trees bordering a frequented road, so that they are plainly visible on their perches to every passer-by, the roosting place being generally in a gum-tree, at a height, it may be, of from 100 feet to 150 feet above the ground. There is reason to fear that the lyre-bird is destined to disappear from the Victorian bush unless it develops the habit of nesting in trees, as is occasionally its practice at the present time. The main persecutor is the European fox, which has been introduced with only too much success into its haunts. In South Gippsland, on the other hand, man is the criminal, and breech-loaders, forest spoliation, and bush-fires will complete the work, and render the lyre-bird unknown in a district where it formerly occurred in thousands.

H. A. MACPHERSON AND R. LYDEKKER

LYRE-BIRD

ORDER II.   PICARIÆ

GENERAL CHARACTERISTICS OF PICARIAN BIRDS

THE assemblage of birds commonly known as picarians —so-called from *picus*, the Latin name of the woodpecker—presents at first sight a marked resemblance to the perching birds just considered, and yet possesses certain common features not found among them. They have, for instance, the hind margin of the breast bone doubly notched ; such a feature being very rarely seen among passerines. Then, again, nearly all the members of the group lay white eggs, which are deposited, often without any attempt at constructing a nest, in some concealed position, such as a hole in a tree or bank.

It is true that the picarians are by no means the only birds which adopt this mode of nesting, since many passerines also lay white eggs and conceal them ; the sand martin, for instance, like the kingfisher, burrowing out a tunnel and depositing its eggs deep in the ground. There are, moreover, instances to the contrary, as in the case of pigeons, which lay two white eggs in an open nest, while humming-birds, which are also picarians, likewise build open nests and lay white or light-coloured eggs. No definite rule can be laid down as to the nesting of the picarians, and there are further exceptions, though of a modified kind and capable of a different explanation.

Although, in addition to the foregoing not very important features, there are certain osteological characters peculiar to picarian birds, such as the form of the upper arm bone, or humerus, which exhibits well-marked differences from the corresponding bone of the perching birds, the definition of the order by means of well-marked and exclusive features is by no means easy. The palate is sometimes of the so-called ægithognathous type, and at others of the bridged, or desmognathous, form ; while the structure of the foot is variable in every degree, some picarians having a foot in which the fourth toe is directed backwards, while in others the foot has the front toes joined together so as to form a very flat, perching surface. Picarians may be divided into two chief sections, called Scansores, or climbing picarians, and Coraciiformes, or roller-like picarians ; the chief differences between these groups occurring in the arrangement of the tendons of the feet.

CLASSIFICATION OF PICARIAN BIRDS MENTIONED IN THIS WORK

ORDER
Picarian Birds—Picariæ
FAMILY 1
Jacamars—Galbulidæ
GENUS 1
Typical Jacamars—Galbula
SPECIES

Green jacamar ....Galbula viridis
Red-tailed jacamar.............G. ruficauda
Black-cheeked jacamar........G. melanogenis
GENUS 2
Urogalba
GENUS 3
Three-toed Jacamars—Brachygalba
GENUS 4
Jacamaralcyon
GENUS 5
Broad-beaked Jacamars—Jacamerops
SPECIES

Broad-beaked jacamar....Jacamerops grandis

FAMILY 2
Puff-Birds—Bucconidæ
GENUS 1
Typical Puff-Birds—Bucco
SPECIES
Dyson's puff-bird ....Bucco dysoni
Red-necked puff-bird .... B. ruficollis
GENUS 2
Malacoptila
SPECIES
Panama puff-bird .... Malacoptila panamensis
GENUS 3
Swallow-winged Puff-Birds—Chelidoptera
FAMILY 3
Woodpeckers—Picidæ
GENUS 1
Ground Woodpeckers—Geocolaptes
SPECIES
Ground woodpecker .... Geocolaptes olivaceus
GENUS 2
Bright-shafted Woodpeckers—Colaptes
SPECIES
Mexican red-winged woodpecker ....Colaptes mexicanus
Golden-winged woodpecker .... C. aureus
Ayres's woodpecker ....C. ayresi
Pampas woodpecker ....C. agricola
GENUS 3
Green Woodpeckers—Gecinus
SPECIES
Green woodpecker .... Gecinus viridis
Sharpe's woodpecker .... G. sharpei
Le Vaillant's woodpecker .... G. vaillanti
Black-naped woodpecker.......G. occipitalis
Grey-headed woodpecker .... G. canus
Japanese green woodpecker ...... G. awokera
Black-napéd woodpecker .... G. occipitalis

GENUS 4
American Green Woodpeckers—Chloronerpes
GENUS 5
African Green Woodpeckers—Campothera
SPECIES
Golden-tailed woodpecker ...... Campothera chrysura
GENUS 6
South American Green Woodpeckers—Chrysoptilus
GENUS 7
Indian Green Woodpeckers—Chrysophlegma
GENUS 8
Asyndesmus
SPECIES
Lewis's woodpecker .. Asyndesmus torquatus
GENUS 9
Red-headed Woodpeckers—Melanerpes
SPECIES
Red-headed woodpecker.. Melanerpes erythrocephalus
White-fronted woodpecker .. M. formicivorus
GENUS 10
Sapsuckers—Sphyropicus
SPECIES
Yellow-bellied sapsucker .. Sphyropicus varius
GENUS 11
Pied Woodpeckers—Dendrocopus
SPECIES
Greater spotted woodpecker .... Dendrocopus major
Lesser spotted woodpecker .... D. minor
Middle spotted woodpecker ...... D. medius
White-backed woodpecker .... D. leuconotus
St. John's woodpecker .... D. sanctijohannis
GENUS 12
Three-toed Woodpeckers—Picoides
SPECIES
Three-toed woodpecker.... Picoides tridactylus
GENUS 13
Dendropicus
GENUS 14
Pigmy Woodpeckers—Iyngipicus
GENUS 15
Bay Woodpeckers—Lepocestes
SPECIES
Crimson-headed bay woodpecker .. Lepocestes pyrrhotus
GENUS 16
Rufous Woodpeckers—Micropternus
SPECIES
Burmese rufous woodpecker .... Micropternus phœoceps
GENUS 17
Ivory-billed Woodpeckers—Campophilus
SPECIES
Ivory-billed woodpecker.. Campophilus principalis

GENUS 18
Hemilophus
SPECIES
Grey Malay woodpecker .. Hemilophus pulverulentus
GENUS 19
Black Woodpecker—Picus
SPECIES
Great black woodpecker ...... Picus martius
GENUS 20
Piculets—Picumnus
SPECIES
Indian piculet .... Picumnus innominatus
GENUS 21
San Domingo Piculet—Nesoctites
GENUS 22
African Piculet—Verreauxia
GENUS 23
Rufous Piculets—Sasia
SPECIES
Himalayan piculet .... Sasia ochracea

FAMILY 4
Wrynecks—Iyngidæ
GENUS
Wrynecks—Iynx
SPECIES
South African wryneck ...... Iynx pectoralis
East African wryneck .... I. pulchricollis
Abyssinian wryneck .... I. æquatorialis
Wryneck .... I. torquilla

FAMILY 5
Honey-Guides—Indicatoridæ
GENUS 1
Honey-Guides—Indicator
SPECIES
Yellow-backed honey-guide.. Indica or xanthonotus
Malay honey-guide .... I. archipelagicus
Lesser African honey-guide .... I. minor
White-eared honey-guide ...... I. sparmanni
GENUS 2
Dwarf Honey-Guide—Prodotiscus
GENUS 3
Dwarf Honey-Guide—Melignomon

FAMILY 6
Barbets—Capitonidæ
GENUS 1
Square-beaked Barbets—Semnornis
SPECIES
Costa Rica barbet .... Semnornis frantzii
Ecuador barbet .... S. rhamphastinus
GENUS 2
Tooth-billed Barbet—Pogonorhynchus
SPECIES
Red barbet .... Pogonorhynchus dubius

GENUS 3
African Barbets—Lybius
SPECIES
Black-collared barbet ...... Lybius torquatus
Pied barbet .... L. leucomelus
GENUS 4
Tinker Barbets—Barbatula
SPECIES
Little tinker barbet ...... Barbatula pusilla
GENUS 5
Brown Barbets—Calorhamphus
SPECIES
Hay's barbet .... Calorhamphus hayi
Sooty barbet .... C. fuliginosus
GENUS 6
Great Barbets—Megalæma
SPECIES
Great barbet ...... Megalæma marshallorum
Green barbet .... M. virens
GENUS 7
Large Green Barbets—Cyanops
SPECIES
Ceylon barbet .... Cyanops flavifrons
GENUS 8
Chotorhea
GENUS 9
Crimson-headed Barbets—Xantholæma
SPECIES
Coppersmith .... Xantholæma hæmatocephala
GENUS 10
Typical Barbets—Capito
SPECIES
Variegated barbet .... Capito versicolor
FAMILY 7
Toucans—Rhamphastidæ
GENUS 1
Toucans—Rhamphastus
SPECIES
Toco toucan .... Rhamphastus toco
GENUS 2
Andigena
GENUS 3
Aracari Toucans—Pteroglossus
SPECIES
Black-throated aracari .. Pteroglossus aracari
Yellow-billed aracari .... P. flavirostris
GENUS 4
Selenidera
GENUS 5
Aulacorhamphus
FAMILY 8
Trogons—Trogonidæ
GENUS 1
Long-tailed Trogons—Pharomacrus
SPECIES
Quezal .... Pharomacrus mocinno
Golden-headed trogon............ P. auriceps
GENUS 2
Typical Trogons—Trogon
SPECIES
Arizona trogon .... Trogon ambiguus
Peruvian trogon .... T. caligatus
Black-tailed trogon .... T. melanurus
Massena trogon................. T. massena
Black-headed trogon .... T. melanocephalus
GENUS 3
Hapaloderma
SPECIES
Narina trogon .... Hapaloderma narina
Ussher's trogon .... H. constantia
Red-bellied trogon .... H. rufiventris
GENUS 4
Heterotrogon
SPECIES
Banded trogon ...... Heterotrogon vittatum
GENUS 5
Asiatic Trogons—Pyrotrogon
SPECIES
Red-headed trogon ...... Pyrotrogon erythro-
cephalus
Kasumba trogon ....P. kasumba
GENUS 6
Hapalarpactes
GENUS 7
Euptilotis
GENUS 8
Tmetotrogon
GENUS 9
Prionotelus
FAMILY 9
Colies—Coliidæ
GENUS
Colies—Colius
SPECIES
White-backed coly .... Colius capensis
South African coly .... C. striatus
White-eared coly .... C. leucotis
FAMILY 10
Humming-Birds—Trochilidæ
GENUS 1
Jamaican Humming-Birds—Æthurus
SPECIES
Long-tailed humming-bird.. Æthurus polytmus

GENUS 2
Microchera
SPECIES
White-crowned humming-bird .... Microchera
albicoronata
Short-beaked white-crown .... M. parvirostris
GENUS 3
Diphlogæna
SPECIES
Rainbow humming-bird ...... Diphlogæna iris
GENUS 4
Comets—Sappho
GENUS 5
Fork-tailed Humming-Birds—Lesbia
SPECIES
Andean fork-tail ....Lesbia gracilis
GENUS 6
Curved-beaked Hermits—Eutoxeres
SPECIES
Peruvian hermit .... Eutoxeres condamini
Salvin's hermit .... E. salvini
GENUS 7
Typical Hermits—Phaëthornis
SPECIES
Grey-throated hermit..Phaëthornis griseigularis
Fly hermit .... P. superciliosus
Pretre's hermit .... P. pretrei
GENUS 8
Sword-billed Humming-Bird—Docimastes
SPECIES
Sword-billed humming-bird ...... Docimastes
ensiferus
GENUS 9
Eugenes
SPECIES
Rivoli humming-bird .... Eugenes fulgens
E. spectabilis
GENUS 10
King Humming-Birds—Topaza
SPECIES
Guiana king humming-bird ...... Topaza pella
Ecuador king humming-bird.......... T. pyra
GENUS 11
Hill-Stars—Oreotrochilus
SPECIES
Pichincha hill-star ....Oreotrochilus pichincha
Chimborazo hill-star .... O. chimborazo
Andean hill-star .... O. adelæ
Chilean hill-star.............. O. leucopleurus
Peruvian hill-star .... O. estellæ
Peruvian black-bellied hill-star. O. melanogaster
GENUS 12
Great Humming-Bird—Patagona
SPECIES
Great humming-bird ....Patagona gigas
GENUS 13
Racket-tailed Humming-Bird—Loddigesia
SPECIES
Racket-tailed humming-bird ...... Loddigesia
mirabilis
GENUS 14
Heliactis
SPECIES
Double-crested humming-bird,Heliactis bilopha
GENUS 15
Coquettes—Lophornis
SPECIES
Tufted coquette ....Lophornis ornatus
Central American coquette .... L. helenæ
FAMILY 11
Swifts—Cypselidæ
GENUS 1
Typical Swifts—Cypselus
SPECIES
Alpine swift ....Cypselus melba
South African swift.............. C. africanus
Swift .... C. apus
Mediterranean pale swift.......... C. murinus
GENUS 2
Pied Swift—Aëronautes
SPECIES
Pied swift ...... Aëronautes melanoleucus
GENUS 3
Feather-toed Swifts—Panyptila
SPECIES
Cayenne feather-toed swift .. Panyptila cayen-
nensis
Salvin's swift ....P. sancti-hieronymi
GENUS 4
Needle-tailed Swifts—Chætura
GENUS 5
Edible Swifts—Collocalia
SPECIES
Edible swift .... Collocalia fuciphaga
GENUS 6
Tree Swifts—Macropteryx
FAMILY 12
Nightjars—Caprimulgidæ
GENUS 1
Typical Nightjars—Caprimulgus
SPECIES
Nightjar..............Caprimulgus europæus
Red-necked nightjar ....C. ruficollis
Virginian nightjar ....C. virginianus

GENUS 2
Pennant-winged Nightjar—Macrodipteryx
SPECIES
Pennant-winged nightjar ......Macrodipteryx
longipennis
GENUS 3
Standard-winged Nightjar—Cosmetornis
SPECIES
Standard-winged nightjar ..Cosmetornis vexil-
larius
GENUS 4
Scotornis
GENUS 5
Macropsalis
GENUS 6
Hydropsalis
SPECIES
Argentine fork-tailed nightjar ....Hydropsalis
furcifera
GENUS 7
Nacunda Nightjar—Podager
SPECIES
Nacunda nightjar ....Podager nacunda
GENUS 8
Wood Nightjars—Nyctibius
SPECIES
Great wood nightjar.........Nyctibius grandis
FAMILY 13
Todies—Todidæ
GENUS
Todies—Todus
SPECIES
Common tody .... Todus pulcherrimus
Jamaican tody ....T. viridis
FAMILY 14
Motmots—Momotidæ
GENUS 1
Typical Motmots—Momotus
SPECIES
Mexican motmot...........Momotus lessoni
Brazilian motmot.............M. brasiliensis
GENUS 2
Urospatha
SPECIES
Costa Rica motmot .... Urospatha martii
Eumomota
SPECIES
Broad-beaked motmot......Eumomota super-
ciliaris
GENUS 4
Hylomanes
FAMILY 15
Bee-eaters—Meropidæ
GENUS 1
Swallow-tailed Bee-eaters—Dichrocercus
SPECIES
West African bee-eater ..Dichrocercus furcatus
South African bee-eater ...... D. hirundineus
GENUS 2
Square-tailed Bee-eaters—Melittophagus
SPECIES
Little square-tailed bee-eater....Melittophagus
pusillus
White-fronted bee-eater .... M. albifrons
Chestnut-headed bee-eater ...... M. swinhoei
GENUS 3
Typical Bee-eaters—Merops
SPECIES
African bee-eater ....Merops persicus
Indian bee-eater ....M. viridis
Arabian bee-eater .... M. cyanophrys
Muscat bee-eater .... M. muscatensis
Bee-eater .... M. apiaster
Malay bee-eater .... M. philippinus
Australian bee-eater .... M. ornatus
Indian bee-eater .... M. bicolor
Sumatran bee-eater .... M. sumatranus
West African bee-eater ....M. breveri
GENUS 4
Meropogon
SPECIES
Celebean bee-eater ....Meropogon forsteni
GENUS 5
Bearded Bee-eaters—Nyctiornis
SPECIES
Blue-bearded bee-eater ..Nyctiornis ashertoni
Scarlet-bearded bee-eater ....N. amicus
FAMILY 16
Hoopoes—Upupidæ
GENUS
Hoopoes—Upupa
SPECIES
Indian hoopoe ....Upupa indica
Hoopoe .... U. epops
FAMILY 17
Wood Hoopoes—Irrisoridæ
GENUS
Wood Hoopoes—Irrisor
SPECIES
Purple-tailed wood hoopoe ......Irrisor viridis
Green-tailed wood hoopoe..I. erythrorhynchus

GREAT BLACK WOODPECKERS

JACAMARS, PUFF-BIRDS, WOODPECKERS, AND WRYNECKS

JACAMARS

BEGINNING with the climbing section of the order, the first for notice are the South American jacamars (family *Galbulidæ*), of which about twenty species are known. All these birds have the so-called zygodactyle type of foot, in which the fourth toe is directed backwards parallel to the first. The beak is particularly long and straight; there is an after-shaft to the body feathers, which does not occur in the allied group of puff-birds, and there are some further differences in the arrangement of the feathers of the under surface, the bare tract on the breast having a branch on the throat. The number of tail feathers varies in a somewhat peculiar manner, the normal number being twelve, although in two genera out of the six (*Brachygalba* and *Jacamar-alcyon*) the outer feather on each side is wanting, thus reducing the number to ten. Although nothing absolutely decisive is known as to the breeding habits of the jacamars, it is stated that in Tobago they build in holes in mudbanks, like motmots, and lay pure white and nearly spherical eggs; while the three-toed Brazilian jacamar has been seen boring holes in banks as if for the purpose of nesting.

Together with four other genera of the family, the typical jacamars constitute a subfamily group, the *Galbulinæ*; among which *Galbula* and the allied genus *Urogalba* have the middle pair of tail feathers elongated, while in the others the tail is short and squared. The three-toed jacamars (*Brachygalba*) are easily distinguished from their relatives by the feature from which they take their name. In these jacamars the prevailing colour of the plumage of the upper parts is in most cases bronzy or metallic green.

GREEN JACAMAR

GREEN JACAMAR

The green jacamar (*Galbula viridis*) is the best-known species of the family, and is found all over Guiana as far as the lower Amazons to the south, and in Venezuela to the west. It is of a coppery green colour, with a bluish sheen on the crown, the under surface being chestnut, the throat white, followed by a band of bright green across the breast, and the outer tail feathers blackish.

RED-TAILED JACAMAR

An allied species is the red-tailed jacamar (*G. ruficauda*), which closely resembles the former, but is distinguished by its rufous outer tail feathers. It is an inhabitant of the same part of South America as the first, but does not extend into Amazonia, being found, however, further to the west, namely, in Colombia. In Trinidad Mr. F. M. Chapman states that it is not uncommon at and near the borders of the forests. "Its appearance, at first sight, would seem to support its reputation for stupidity, but closer observation will, I think, induce one to believe that these birds are by no means so stupid as they have been said to be. They are the most expert flycatchers I have ever seen, and this in spite of the fact that the shape of the bill would seem better to fit them for almost any other mode of existence. Sitting all drawn in on a dead limb, generally near the ground, they may be compared to a set spring.

"Their watchfulness permits no insect to pass in safety. They maintain a constant look-out, turning the head quickly from side to side, above, or even half-way round. The dart into the air is made with wonderful celerity. Sometimes it is straight up, again at various angles, and they go as far as thirty or thirty-five feet from their perch. As a rule, they return to the same perch after each sally, and may occupy this for many minutes. As they rest, they utter a singular call—a loud, clear, piping whistle, not unlike the call of a lost duckling. This is delivered in a variety of ways. Sometimes it is given as a single whole note, but it may be repeated at intervals of a second for minutes at a time. The dart into the air for an insect interrupts this musical reverie only momentarily, and, on returning to their perch, the plaintive calling is continued; at other times their notes are uttered more rapidly, and may rise into a high, prolonged trilling. This may be ground out as revolutions of sound, when the effect is most peculiar."

Mr. Richmond states that on the river Escondido in Nicaragua he met with the black-cheeked jacamar (*G. melanogenis*) on three or four occasions. "It has a piercing cry resembling "kee-u," with the first syllable very shrill, and strongly accentuated. The bird jerks its tail after the manner of a kingfisher."

GREAT JACAMAR

The great jacamar (*Jacamerops grandis*) is the sole representative, not only of its genus, but likewise of the second subfamily of the jacamars; and ranges from British Guiana to Amazonia, and thence to Ecuador, Colombia, and Panama. It is a bird of large size, fully 10½ inches in length, of the usual metallic green above and chestnut below, with a large spot of white on the throat. It has a broader beak than any of the other members of the family, and is further easily recognisable by its large size.

PUFF-BIRDS

Much resembling many perching birds in external appearance, and, like them, having twelve tail feathers, as well as a shrike-like beak, the puff-birds (family *Bucconidæ*) are nevertheless true picarians, having a bridged palate and zygodactyle feet, while the tendons which serve the toes are of the same type as in woodpeckers and honey-guides. There is no after-shaft to any of the contour feathers, the oil gland is naked, and the wing coverts rather resemble those of passerines in their arrangement than those of other picarians. Like the other members of the present order, puff-birds are believed to nest in holes and to lay white eggs, but very little is known about them.

Confined to South America, the puff-birds have no

representatives in the Old World, or even in North America. Seven genera and over forty species are recognised by naturalists ; the range of the family being from Honduras in Central America southwards over the whole of South America, as far as Bolivia and Southern Brazil.

Puff-birds are said to be generally woodland birds, being found singly or in pairs, and are considered to be of a rather sluggish and stupid nature. Dr. P. L. Sclater observes that they are a " purely arboreal and forest-frequenting group of birds, seeming to pass the greater part of their lives sitting upon the topmost or outermost branches of trees, generally selecting twigs that are dry and withered for their perch, and looking out for insects, which are captured flying, and which constitute their only food. The swallow-winged puff-birds (*Chelidoptera*) nest in holes in banks like kingfishers, and lay white eggs.". Mr. Richmond, who met with Dyson's puff-bird (*Bucco dysoni*) in Nicaragua, where it was catching insects and behaving very much like a tyrant flycatcher, states that on making a capture it would seek a new perch, flying in a leisurely way, and showing considerable hesitation about selecting a place on which to settle.

Another of the numerous species of the same genus is the red-necked puff-bird (*B. ruficollis*) of Panama and Colombia. A second genus is represented by the Panama puff-bird (*Malacoptila panamensis*), which is apparently confined to thick forests, where it keeps among the lower branches, at times even descending to the bushes. A female bird killed by the above-mentioned naturalist in May was about to deposit eggs ; it was shot from a twig directly in front of a hole in a bamboo, in which its nest was probably located. The stomach was distended with insects, principally locusts.

WOODPECKERS

Forming a kind of connecting link between the perching birds and the other members of the present

RED-NECKED
PUFF-BIRD

order, the woodpeckers (family *Picidæ*) constitute a group of considerable interest. Like the majority of picarians, they nest in holes, and lay spotless white eggs ; but instead of having either the passerine or the bridged type of palate, they have a somewhat intermediate form, in which the front of the bone termed the vomer is slender, pointed, and slit, instead of being truncated. Moreover, these birds have a distinctly climbing type of foot, thereby showing affinity to the other climbing members of the order, such as barbets or toucans.

The structure of the tongue, however, is almost peculiar to the family ; a similar arrangement of the extensile tongue-bones being elsewhere found only in humming-birds among the picarians, and in sun-birds among the passerines.

The mechanism of the woodpecker's tongue is somewhat as follows. In the majority of these birds the tongue is long, worm-like, pointed, and barbed at the tip. To permit of its being projected or withdrawn, the extremities of the supporting bones are prolonged backwards, sliding in a sheath curving round the top of the skull ; and the glands beneath it are greatly developed and secrete a viscid fluid, which covers the tongue and causes insects to adhere. The peculiar modification of these organs and their application in procuring food are, indeed, closely analogous to those found in the ant-eaters (page 862) and several other mammals, and chamæleons among reptiles.

In some species the extremities of the tongue-bones slide backwards and forwards in the sheath as the tongue is retracted or protruded ; while in others, as in the green woodpecker, the ends are fixed to the sheath, and the protrusion of the tongue is effected by the action of a certain muscle diminishing the curve in which the extremities of the tongue-bones lie when the tongue itself is withdrawn. In only two American genera of the family is this remarkable structure absent. The beak in all woodpeckers is strong and chisel-shaped.

RED-TAILED JACAMAR

and thus admirably adapted for hewing holes and prising off bark to capture insects, the viscid secretion on the tongue being of great use in the latter function ; but in the ground-haunting species the beak is less powerful.

There is very little variation in the habits of the members of this family ; nearly all climbing trees, in the stems of which they bore holes for their nesting place ; the direction of the aperture being at first horizontal and then descending to a depth varying from a few inches to several feet. No nest is formed, the eggs, which are glossy white, or pinkish white, being deposited on the chips accumulated by the birds during the excavation of the hole. They vary from two to seven or eight in number, but the average clutch is four or five.

The young are hatched naked and blind, and in this state they remain for some time, although they soon become vigorous. The clamour with which they greet their parents when the latter bring food to the nest is proverbial. They soon learn to climb to the mouth of the hole, and even sleep in a hanging position. The tenacity with which the claws grasp the bark of a tree is illustrated even in death, for sometimes a woodpecker, when fatally wounded by shot, automatically grips the trunk with such vigour as to remain suspended. The geographical range of the woodpeckers includes the whole of America, Africa, Europe, and northern and tropical continental Asia, although no species are found to the east of Celebes ; the group being unrepresented in Australasia and the Pacific Islands.

The only fossil representative of the group appears to be one from the Tertiary strata of the Uinta Mountains, in the United States, and hence named *Uintornis*, but how close this comes to existing forms does not admit of determination.

Constituting a single family, the woodpeckers may be subdivided into two minor groups, namely, those with stiffened tails and those with soft tails. As with other climbing birds, such as the creepers and wood-hewers among the passerines, the stiffened tail is an accessory in ascending trees. In the present group it is the shaft or stem of the feathers which is stiffened and elastic, the ends of the same being generally narrowed to a point, and the webs often showing signs of wear and tear, as the tail is constantly dragged along the rough bark of a tree, or is used as a support for the bird when it hammers at the bark to procure its insect food.

In some instances the tail feathers assume a more remarkable shape, the hardened webs being turned inwards from their outer edges, so as to make a kind of hollow half-tube ; this being particularly observable in the imperial woodpecker. The tail of some of the larger kinds of woodpeckers must, in fact, work havoc among the insects on the bark of a tree when the bird is climbing ; and the tail of the rufous woodpecker sometimes has the feathers covered with the heads of ants on the under side.

AFRICAN GROUND WOODPECKER

The Cape ground woodpecker (*Geocolaptes olivaceus*), the sole member of its genus, may be taken as the first representative of the typical subfamily of the group,

GREEN WOODPECKER, OR YAFFLE

in all the genera of which the tail is spiny, and has stiffened shafts to the feathers. This is a dull-plumaged bird about 10 inches in length. The colour is olive brown, with yellowish brown shafts to the quills, and orange brown shafts to the tail feathers. There is some crimson on the rump and the under surface of the body. The head is slaty grey, with a slight crimson moustache-mark, and the colour of the eye is orange, although it has been described as whitish pink.

This curious woodpecker is common in certain parts of South Africa, where it enjoys a very limited range, being found in Cape Colony and extending to the Orange River Colony and Natal, but not to the Transvaal. Mr. Layard observes that "this singular bird presents a remarkable instance of the adaptation of creatures to the localities wherein their lot is cast. Though belonging to the woodpecker family, it never pecks wood, but bores its way into the banks of rivers, sides of hills, or the walls of mud buildings in search of its prey, and for a home for its young. It also seeks for food on the ground, in the same manner as the golden-winged woodpecker of North America ; its flight also struck me as very similar. It excavates a hole, sometimes several feet in depth, in which to deposit its eggs, which are pure white, and from three to five in number. Families seem to keep in company, until the arrival of the breeding season separates them. They feed together, and roost together in some deserted hole, while their loud, harsh cries, as they call each other, may be heard for a considerable distance."

In Natal this woodpecker has been observed on the Mooi river creeping with much agility among the crevices and holes in some loose stone walls erected by the Kafirs as enclosures for their cattle. Some of the birds were climbing the face of a perpendicular rock, searching for insects in the same manner as other woodpeckers examine a tree. These birds are fond of perching in twos or threes, sometimes in family parties, on a big rock or ant-hill, with the head and neck only visible to the intruder. One nesting place found in August contained four fresh eggs, and the nest-hole was bored in soft earth on the face of a precipitous rocky bank or cliff overlooking a running stream. The eggs were laid in a depression, with no attempt at a nest, about a foot and a half from the entrance, the passage inclining slightly upwards.

Some naturalists who have seen this woodpecker in a state of nature believe that the bird never perches on trees, but in the Orange River Colony numbers may be seen sitting on the mimosa trees, chattering and making a great noise.

GOLDEN WOODPECKERS

The golden woodpecker (*Colaptes aureus*) and its relatives are distributed over nearly the whole of North and South America, with the exception of some of the forest districts of British Guiana, Venezuela, and parts of Amazonia, and Ecuador, but representatives of the genus occur again in Brazil, as well as in Peru, Chile, and Patagonia. The typical species owes its name of golden-winged to the bright yellow shafts to the quills, the inside of the wing being also bright yellow; but there are certain species to which the name does not strictly apply, such as *C. mexicanus*, the shafts of whose quills and the quill-lining are red instead of yellow.

In certain districts in North America, where the golden woodpecker is chiefly a bird of the Eastern States, and the red-winged species (*C. mexicanus*) a native of the more Western States, there occurs a connecting species (*C. ayresi*), with a habitat between the two. It is not yet satisfactorily determined whether this intermediate form has been produced by the interbreeding of the golden and red-winged species, although it certainly partakes of the characters of both. The beak in these woodpeckers is rather more curved than in ordinary woodpeckers, and also weaker; while the birds themselves are less decidedly frequenters of trees, being more ground-feeders than the rest of the family. They excavate, however, their own nest-holes like the majority of woodpeckers, and also perch horizontally on branches like ordinary passerine birds instead of flying to a tree-trunk and climbing continually, after the manner of the other members of the family.

The typical golden woodpecker, commonly known in the United States as the flicker, is a bird about 11 inches in length, of a drab brown colour above, barred with black, and having the rump white, the head smoky grey, followed by a scarlet nape-band, the sides of the face and throat drab with a black moustache-band, a crescentic patch of black on the chest, the remainder of the under surface white, spotted with black, and all the shafts of the quills and tail feathers golden yellow. A summer visitor to the sub-arctic parts of North America, and breeding even in the high north, in the middle and southern States this woodpecker is a permanent resident. It feeds largely on ants, in search of which it wanders over the open country, being far less of a forest-haunting species than most of its relatives.

An interesting account of the feeding of the young birds by the parents is given by Mr. Brewster, who states that when first he saw them there were five nestlings, about as large as plucked house sparrows, and perfectly naked. Their eyes were tightly closed, and they appeared to be less than a week old. They were writhing and shivering pitifully, the air being cool and damp at the time. He watched the nest for about an hour, but saw nothing of the parent birds, and as a cold rainstorm began soon afterwards, and lasted throughout the following night, he concluded that the young flickers would soon be dead. On July 1, however, he found them all alive and vigorous, and by dint of patience and careful observation discovered the method by which the young were fed. After a little time the male bird became more accustomed to his presence, and visited the nest when he was not more than fifteen feet away.

PAMPAS WOODPECKER

The pampas woodpecker (*C. agricola*) is a species with a weaker beak than usual, while it has also longer legs and a less stiffened tail than is customary with woodpeckers; these modified characters being probably due to the peculiar habits of the bird, which, as its name implies, is an inhabitant of the pampas of Argentina. In size it is a somewhat large species, measuring $12\frac{1}{2}$ inches, and has golden shafts to the wing quills, but black ones to the tail feathers, which are entirely black. The quill-lining is golden buff, the crown of the head black, and the sides of the face and neck as well as the fore neck golden yellow, inclining to orange, the chin and throat b ing white; the male has a red and the female a black moustache-mark. Mr. W. H. Hudson states that these woodpeckers " perch horizontally and crosswise, like ordinary birds, and only occasionally cling vertically to trunks of trees, using the tail as a support. They also seek their food more on the ground than on trees, in some cases not at all on the latter; and they breed oftener in holes in banks or cliffs than in the trunks of trees."

GREY-HEADED AND WHITE-BACKED WOODPECKERS

In Patagonia the species breeds in the cliffs of the Rio Negro, but on the pampas of Buenos Aires, where the conditions are different, there being no cliffs or old mudwalls suitable for breeding places, the bird resorts to a big solitary ombú-tree, which has a very soft wood, and in this excavates a hole seven to nine inches deep, inclining upwards near the end, and

RED-HEADED AMERICAN WOODPECKER

terminating in a round chamber. In the treeless region about the Sierra de la Ventana, in Uruguay, these birds may be observed near holes in the banks of streams, where they doubtless nest.

GREEN WOODPECKERS

Strictly birds of the Old World, the green woodpeckers are distributed over the temperate portions of Europe and Asia, several species occurring in the Himalaya, extending thence through the Burmese countries to the Malay Peninsula, Java, Sumatra, and Borneo. In Europe there are three members of the group, namely, the typical *Gecinus viridis*, *G. sharpei*, and *G. canus*, and in Algeria there is a fourth kind, *G. vaillanti*, allied to the European birds, while the species known by the barbarous name of *G. awokera* occurs in Japan. All the other green woodpeckers are tropical. The principal characteristic of this group of woodpeckers is the green plumage; but the birds are also characterised by the small outer pair of tail feathers.

One of the most interesting of European birds, not only on account of its habits and bright colouring, but from its association with the poetry of Chaucer, who mentions it by the name of yaffle, by which it is known to the present day in many parts of the south of England, the green woodpecker still " laughs loud " in many a woodland district. Its green colour, crimson crown, and yellow rump render it conspicuous, and its unmistakable dipping flight consists of a series of long drops and ascents.

Like many other birds of bright plumage, the green woodpecker is extremely shy, and oftener heard than seen. If undisturbed, it may be seen to settle near the bottom of a tree and work its way to the top, which it does very rapidly, hammering at the bark or prising it off, and gathering insect food with its long suctorial tongue. It feeds largely on ants, and plays great havoc with ant-hills, into which it digs holes with its powerful beak. It is also said to attack wasps' nests for the sake of the grubs, and will catch bees as well as feed on acorns and hazelnuts. These woodpeckers undoubtedly make mistakes on occasions, so that it is not uncommon to find holes driven into trees by the birds and abandoned when the inside of the trunk or branch is sound throughout.

The beautiful symmetry with which the bird cuts the hole has often been noticed, the circular opening appearing as if it had been drilled in the tree. No nest is made, and the glossy white eggs, sometimes seven or eight in number, are deposited on the chips of wood accumulated during the process of excavation. Occurring in suitable localities throughout Europe, this species does not range beyond the Ural Mountains, though it extends to Asia Minor and Western Persia.

In Spain and Portugal its place is taken by Sharpe's woodpecker (*G. sharpei*), and in Algeria by Le Vaillant's woodpecker (*G. vaillanti*). Of one of the Himalayan species, the black-naped woodpecker (*G. occipitalis*), a large regularly-formed nest was found at Darjiling at the bottom of a hollow in a tree; the nest being like that of a babbler, and composed chiefly of coarse moss, roots intermingled with a little moss, and portions of a few broad dry flag-leaves. The finder considered it impossible that the woodpecker had anything to do with making the nest; but as the parent bird was captured on the eggs, there was no mistake about the fact of its having used the nest.

GREY-HEADED WOODPECKER

Another well-known species is the grey-headed woodpecker (*G. canus*), which ranges over the greater part of Europe, but does not visit the British Isles, and also occurs in Siberia, Northern China, and the island of Yezo. Its habits are similar to those of the green woodpecker, which it also greatly resembles in size and colour, being about 12 inches in length. The under surface of the body, however, is perfectly uniform, without any crescentic marking as in most green woodpeckers, and the moustache-streak is black both in the male and female, although in this group the males usually have a red moustache-mark. The nape is always grey, but the male has a red head and the female a grey one.

AFRICAN GREEN WOODPECKERS

Passing over the American green woodpeckers (*Chloronerpes*), of which about seventeen representa-

GREATER SPOTTED WOODPECKER

tives are known, mention may be made of the African green woodpeckers, confined to Africa south of the Sahara. They agree with the American group in their green colouring, but are distinguished by the more rounded wing. Some of the fifteen species are known, but nothing remarkable has been recorded about their habits.

Of the golden-tailed woodpecker (*Campothera chrysura*), Mr. T. Ayres states that these birds "are to be observed throughout Natal, wherever there is bushland, singly or in pairs; their note is loud and harsh; they are very restless in their habits, constantly hunting for food as if they had never obtained a sufficiency. Ants and other insects appear to be their usual food, which they search for and catch on the rough bark of trees. They also hammer away at dead boughs, from which they extract soft grubs, etc.; and their flight is heavy and dipping. This woodpecker makes a hole for the purposes of incubation in the trunk of a decayed tree, just large enough at the opening for the bird to enter, but becoming wider inside and reaching downwards to the depth of a foot or eighteen inches; it lays its eggs on the bare wood, without making any nest."

Several allied genera present no particular features— such as *Chrysoptilus* of South America, and *Chrysophlegma* of India, Burma, and the Malay countries; the species of the last-named genus being characterised by a large yellow or red crest.

LEWIS'S WOODPECKER

Lewis's woodpecker (*Asyndesmus torquatus*) is an inhabitant of western North America, extending into Arizona and Western Texas, and remarkable for the structure of the body plumes of the under surface, which are hairy in appearance, owing to the want of hooks to the webs of the feathers. Its habits are also somewhat peculiar, and it is one of the few species in which the colour of the male and female is exactly alike.

Dr. Elliott Coues observes that this species "is chiefly a bird of the vast forests that clothe most of our mountain ranges with permanent verdure. On seeing it for the first time a person would hardly take it for a woodpecker, unless he happened to observe it clambering over the trunk of a tree or tapping for insects in the manner peculiar to its tribe. When flying, the large, dark bird might rather be mistaken for a crow-blackbird; for although it sometimes swings itself from one tree to another in a long festoon like other woodpeckers, its ordinary flight is more firm and direct, and accomplished with regular wing-beats. It alights on boughs in the attitude of ordinary birds more frequently than any other American woodpecker, except the flicker, and, with the same exception, taps trees less frequently than any."

RED-HEADED WOODPECKER

The well-known North American red-headed woodpecker (*Melanerpes erythrocephalus*) is a representative of a genus exclusively American, and embracing over thirty-three species, with a range extending from the United States to Argentina. In habits these woodpeckers seem to resemble the other members of the family. In the British Museum there may be seen an illustration of the way in which one of these woodpeckers stores up acorns supposed to be for its winter supply of food. A piece of pine-bark has been pierced with a number of holes, drilled for the purpose of receiving the acorns. The species which has acquired this habit is the white-fronted woodpecker (*M. formicivorus*), inhabiting Central America, from Mexico to Panama.

SAPSUCKERS

Certain American woodpeckers, ranging as far south as Central America, with one species in the West Indies, are locally known as sapsuckers. They lack the extensile tongue of other woodpeckers, sharing the want of this essential character with the North American genus *Xenopicus*. Writing of the habits of the West Indian yellow-bellied sapsucker (*Sphyropicus*

varius), Mr. F. Bolles observes: "I found a sapsucker's 'orchard' of about a dozen canoe birches and red maples, most of which were dead, some decayed and fallen. The tree most recently tapped was a red maple about forty feet high, and two feet through at the butt.

MIDDLE AND LESSER SPOTTED WOODPECKERS

The drills made by the woodpeckers began at eighteen feet from the ground, and formed a girdle entirely round the trunk. This girdle contained over eight hundred punctures, and was almost three feet in height. In places the punctures or drills had run together, causing the bark to gape and show dry wood within. The upper holes alone yielded sap, and from this I inferred that what the birds obtained was the elaborated sap descending from the leaves through the fibres of the inner bark. I tasted the sap, and found it unmistakably sweet. The leaves on branches above the drills drooped, but those below were in good condition.

"I watched the drills on this tree from 12.30 until 2 p.m., and from 4 until 6 p.m., while concealed in the bushes to the north-west of the tree. During nearly the whole of this period of three and a half hours, one or more woodpeckers were in the tree engaged at the drills; they were a male, female, and two young birds. Four visits were paid by humming-birds in the time named, but the visitors were driven away by the woodpeckers. At 5.30 I shot one of the young birds in order to determine the number of individuals using the 'orchard.' His absence was unnoticed by the survivors. The next day the male, female, and one young bird were present, the tree being seldom left by all at once. Ten visits were paid by humming-birds; in five cases they reached the drills, and, hovering, drank sap from one or two of them. In the other cases, the woodpeckers being present, the birds were driven away. The work of the woodpeckers seemed to me, furnished as I was with an opera-glass, and sitting not more than thirty feet from the drills, to be perfectly plain in character. During the morning the female drilled four or five new holes; they were above others in perpendicular series, and yielded sap freely. She was closely attended by the young one, who occasionally swallowed pieces of the soft bark, or cambium layer, taken from the bottom of the drills ; the female also ate some of it. When not drilling or resting, the female dipped sap from the holes near by.

"The male drilled no holes, but dipped in those yielding sap. The dipping was done regularly and rather quietly, often two or three times in each hole. The sap glistened on the bill as it was withdrawn, and I could sometimes see the tongue move. The bill was directed towards the lower, inner part of the drill, which, as I found by examination, was cut so as to hold the sap. I looked carefully, again and again, to try to find insects in the sap, but none was there, although numbers crawled upon the bark. Occasionally, with a nervous motion of the head, the birds caught an insect. There was no doubt as to when they did this, either on the bark or in the air, for in swallowing an insect they always occupied an appreciable time in the process."

These birds appear to consume sap in large quantities for its own sake, and not for the insects which it may occasionally contain. The forest trees attacked by sapsuckers generally die, possibly in the second or third year of use, but the damage done by these handsome birds is too insignificant to justify their persecution in well-wooded regions.

PIED WOODPECKERS

The strikingly-coloured birds forming the genus *Dendrocopus* are spread over the greater part of Europe and Asia, as well as North America, but are ab-

THREE-TOED WOODPECKERS

sent from Africa below the Sahara, although represented in Algeria and Morocco, as well as Palestine and Syria.

GREATER SPOTTED WOODPECKER

The greater spotted woodpecker (*D. major*) is a resident species in most parts of the British Islands, a considerable number of immigrants arriving in autumn, when a great many regularly pass over Heligoland. With its conspicuous pied plumage, it is a handsome and striking bird ; but a notable difference exists between the colouring of the two sexes, the males having a red patch at the back of the head, totally wanting in the females, in which the entire head and nape of the neck are black. The young birds, on the other hand, have the crown red, thus possessing a more striking colouring than either of their parents, a feature not often seen in birds. So shy is the great spotted woodpecker that few people are acquainted with the bird in a state of nature, and even where it is known to occur it is by no means easy to get within view. Its single note, resembling the knocking of two stones together—a sort of "chit"—may be often heard, but the bird is not visible, having probably placed the trunk of a big tree between itself and the observer, after the manner of woodpeckers in general. In spring these woodpeckers make a peculiar drumming noise on the smaller branches of trees or on trunks of dead ones ; this noise, which appears to be a sort of signal code between one bird and its mate, being audible for a considerable distance.

The species is found in wooded districts, more especially park lands, where hollow trees occur here and there, in which it can excavate a nesting place. These birds seem to pursue a kind of regular round of trees in search of insects, beginning generally at the bottom and making their way towards the top of one tree, sometimes stopping on the larger branches and betokening their presence by the loud taps they bestow on the bark, or by the fall of fragments prised off with the awl-like beak. Although their chief food consists of insects, secured with great rapidity by means of the long and glutinous tongue, these woodpeckers visit orchards and feed on plums and cherries, while in autumn and winter they consume nuts, acorns, and berries.

LESSER SPOTTED WOODPECKER

The least of the European species of the genus, easily recognised by its small size and the five white bars on the wing, is the lesser spotted woodpecker (*D. minor*), the male of which has the crown red, while in the female the forehead and crown are white, with no red on the head. In general habits this species closely resembles the last, but at certain seasons is found hunting for insects in orchards or on trees in the vicinity of houses, which is not the case with its larger relative. Being, like most of its kin, a shy bird, it is not often seen, and, indeed, its presence is generally revealed by its tapping on the trees, or its flight from one tree to another, when the black and white bars on the extended wings render it rather conspicuous.

It often sits on a branch horizontally, or runs along the under side like a nuthatch ; and has the habit, in the breeding season, of making a drumming noise on the bark of trees, which can be heard for a great distance, and is evidently a call from one bird to the other, since its note is so weak that it could not travel far. This drumming is often performed on the smaller branches of a poplar at a great height from the ground, and the nest-hole is also often drilled in the small branches of the same kind of tree near the top, thus making it a matter of some difficulty and danger to procure the nest. This woodpecker has a range nearly the same as that of the preceding species, and, like the latter, it is represented in North Africa and in Asia by allied species.

Another species found in most parts of Europe, and supposed to have occurred once in England, is the white-backed woodpecker (*D. leuconotus*). As its name implies, it has a white back, with a black mantle, red crown, and broad black streaks on the flanks. In the female, on the other hand, the head is black, as in most species of the genus. The range of this species extends across Northern Asia to Manchuria and Corea. Generally placed in the same genus as the last, the middle spotted woodpecker (*D. medius*) is by some regarded as the representative of a distinct genus (*Dendrocoptes*), on account of its differently-shaped beak and distinct style of plumage. Although unknown in England, this species is distributed over the greater part of Europe, as far east as the Caucasus; but is replaced in Asia Minor and Persia by St. John's woodpecker (*D. sanctijohannis*).

THREE-TOED WOODPECKERS

Agreeing with three Indian genera in the absence of the first toe, the seven species of three-toed woodpeckers (*Picoides*) are distinguished by the somewhat dense character of their plumage, and also by their Arctic or Alpine habitat. They are distributed over the high northern parts of America, Europe, and Asia, and occur elsewhere only on mountainous areas, where a somewhat similar temperature is experienced, as, for instance, in the Rocky Mountains so far south as Mexico, the mountains of Germany and Switzerland, and similar localities in Asia, including the mountains of China, but not the Himalaya. One of the best-known species is the European three-toed woodpecker (*P. tridactylus*), a bird of moderate size, measuring rather more than 8 inches in length, and easily recognised by the yellow head and white breast of the male.

PIGMY WOODPECKERS

With the mention that the African cardinal wood-peckers (*Dendropicus*) are small-sized birds, differing from European forms in the shorter tail and rather longer legs, while most have yellow shafts to the quills of the wings, and the wing markedly rounded, more attention may be directed to the pigmy woodpeckers (*Iyngipicus*).

Of small size and generally of brown plumage, with white bars, most of the species, instead of a red head, have a little ornamental tuft of red feathers on the side of the crown. Pigmy woodpeckers also have more pointed wings than their allies, and their distribution is peculiar, since they occur in Senegambia and North-Eastern Africa, where they are rare, and reappear in India, where they are by no means uncommon, and extend thence through Burma to China, and north to Eastern Siberia and Japan, while southwards they are found throughout the Malay countries, extending eastwards to Lombok and Flores. The habits of these woodpeckers are similar to those of the rest of the family, but they are stated to nest in horizontal boughs like barbets, instead of hollowing out a hole for themselves in the trunk of a tree.

BAY AND RUFOUS WOODPECKERS

Incidental reference may here be made to two allied genera, the first of which is represented by the crimson-headed bay woodpecker (*Lepocestes pyrrops*) and its immediate relatives, which are characterised by their very long and stout beaks, and also by the nostrils being exposed, and not, as in the case of most wood-

peckers, hidden by plumelets. These features, and the remarkable shortness of the tail, are probably adaptations to the habits of these birds, which are so unlike those of other species.

Remarkable for their entirely rufous plumage, and for their nearly obsolete first toe, the claw on which is scarcely to be traced, the rufous woodpeckers (*Micropternus*) also lack the nasal "shelf" on the bill. Several species of

IVORY-BILLED WOODPECKER

the genus are known, ranging from India and China to the Malay countries, among which the Burmese *M. phæoceps* is a silent bird, seldom uttering a note, and creeping about in a quiet, stealthy way. When killed, these birds have a peculiar smell, and look as though they had been smeared with some gummy substance. They nearly always have their tails more or less studded with ants' heads. These ants are the sumput-api, or fire ants of the Malays, which seize hold of the tail feathers of these woodpeckers; their bodies get rubbed off, but the heads remain, sometimes in scores, adhering to the webs of the feathers.

In the Eastern Himalaya the present species builds in ants' nests. In one instance a colony of ants constructed their nest at the end of a large mango-branch; this being a huge, almost globular, structure about thirteen inches long and eleven in diameter, involving, as these nests commonly do, all the leaves and twigs springing from that part of the branch. It was composed of a mass of grey brown half felt-like, half papier-maché-like substance, into which the woodpecker had bored a circular entrance about two inches in diameter, and inside had scooped out a large circular cavity five inches or more across.

IVORY-BILLED WOODPECKERS

The splendid birds known as ivory-billed woodpeckers belong to the second division of the more typical representatives of the family, collectively known as narrow-necked woodpeckers, the narrowing of the neck by which they are distinguished causing the head to appear disproportionately large. The group is common to both hemispheres, and has one genus in Celebes, which is the most easterly representative of the entire family. The group likewise includes the largest members of the assemblage, the great grey Malay woodpecker (*Hemilophus pulverulentus*) being 18 inches in length.

The ivory-billed woodpecker (*Campophilus principalis*), which is the typical representative of its genus, is now met with only in the coast country of Florida and the Gulf States of North America, although about a century ago it had a much more extended range, reaching to parts of the Southern and Central States. It appears always to have been a very shy bird, so shy, indeed, that a nearly completed nest was deserted by the birds when they perceived their breeding home was discovered. The beak of this woodpecker, which resembles a long ivory dagger, must be capable of inflicting a severe wound, and forms a striking contrast to the sable plumage.

GREAT BLACK WOODPECKER

Although the generic term *Picus* was taken by Linnæus to include the whole of the members of the family, it is now restricted to the great black woodpecker (*Picus martius*), the largest of the European woodpeckers. This species is also a member of the narrow-necked group, but the plumage on the neck is denser than in any of its allies, probably on account of the bird inhabiting a more northern area and higher altitudes than any other member of the section. This fine species has the third toe longer than the fourth, and the metatarsus clothed with feathers, indicating a woodpecker of a cold climate. It is a large bird, measuring 17 inches in length, entirely black, with the top of the head and crest crimson in the male, the red in the female being confined to a triangular patch on the occiput (p. 1079).

The species inhabits the pine forests of Europe and Siberia, and also occurs in Northern China and the north island of Japan. It has often been chronicled as a British bird, but no trustworthy evidence of its capture exists, and there is no bird less addicted to migration, while its powerful flight would prevent its being driven from its native pine forests even by the heaviest gales.

PICULETS

While the whole of the preceding members of the family may be included in one subfamily, those remaining for consideration form a second. Diminutive in size, the piculets have the beak and the ways of

GREAT BLACK WOODPECKER

a woodpecker, combined with a soft tail like that of a wryneck, instead of the spiny type characteristic of the majority of the family. Little is known about these birds beyond the fact that there are four genera, with a very remarkable geographical distribution. In two of these genera, *Picumnus* and *Nesoctites*, the face is feathered. Their distribution is chiefly confined to the New World, the second of the two being peculiar to the island of San Domingo. *Verreauxia* and *Sasia*, the other two genera, are, on the contrary, Old World forms, the former being confined to the forest district of Africa and the latter to the Indian region. The largest of the piculets does not exceed 5 inches in length, and many are not more than 3 inches.

For many years the tiny woodpeckers known as green piculets (*Picumnus*) were supposed to be peculiar to South America, which contains over thirty species, but a member of the group inhabits certain parts of the Indian region, while a second species occurs in Southern China. The Oriental species are absolutely of the same type as their South American representatives, the resemblance being carried even to the pattern of the tail, which is peculiar among birds; for not only are the middle feathers half white, but the outer feathers are also for the most part white, and these characteristic markings run through the whole of the species, be they American or Oriental.

INDIAN GREEN PICULET

The American species seem to act the parts of tiny woodpeckers; and very similar habits apparently characterise the Indian species (*P. innominatus*), which ranges from the Himalaya to the Wynad and eastwards to the mountains of Burma, the Malay Peninsula, Sumatra, and Borneo. Like their larger relatives, these piculets nest in holes which they excavate themselves, and in which they apparently lay as many as seven eggs. The species has been found nesting in Sikkim in decaying stumps of small trees, about three feet from the ground, in holes bored by the birds themselves, the entrance being only about an inch in diameter. The hole was three and a half inches deep, and a little more than an inch wide all the way, while, as in the case with other woodpeckers, there were no nesting materials.

HIMALAYAN RUFOUS PICULET

The rufous piculets (*Sasia*) differ from the preceding in having the sides of the face around the eye bare, and only three toes, owing to the absence of the first. In the Himalayan species (*S. ochracea*) the general colour is rufous and olive above, and rufous below; the forehead being golden yellow in the male, and rufous in the female, with a white stripe above the eye. In Tenasserim, Mr. Davison, who found the species frequenting moderately open country, especially where bamboos flourish, observes that "it keeps to the undergrowth and secondary scrub and bamboo jungle, working about the fallen logs. It is wonderful what a loud sound one of these little fellows can produce when tapping a bamboo. I have more than once thought that it must have been some large woodpecker, and was astonished when I could not see it, and when at last I did discover the tiny object I felt quite as much surprised at the sound it was able to produce as it was by my sudden advent. It is very fond of knocking about in low brushwood. I do not know its call, nor do I think that I ever heard one. It is usually alone, but sometimes pairs are met with."

A piece of bamboo selected by this bird for its nesting place was only two and a half inches in diameter, and quite hard and dry. Into this, at a height of about three feet from the ground and six inches above the joint, the bird had drilled a small circular hole; and inside had grooved with its little beak the whole inner aspect of the lower surface of the compartment; the long, fibrous strips thus obtained being collected at the bottom to form a bed for the eggs.

BRAZILIAN PICULET

WRYNECKS

Wrynecks are so closely connected with the more typical woodpeckers, by means of the piculets, that they may well be regarded as forming merely a subfamily (*Iynginæ*) of the *Picidæ*. Since, however, they have long been accorded family rank (*Iyngidæ*), it is unnecessary to upset accepted arrangements.

Of these birds only four species are known, one having a wide range in Europe and Asia, while the other three are confined to Africa south of the Sahara. They include *Iynx pectoralis*, inhabiting the eastern districts of Cape Colony, Natal, and the Eastern Transvaal, and extending to the lower Congo district in West Africa; *I. pulchricollis* from Eastern Equatorial Africa; and *I. æquatorialis* from the southern provinces of Abyssinia and Shoa.

Wrynecks have the tail rather long and not spiny, and the nostrils not concealed by bristles, but partially hidden by a membrane. The colour of their plumage is very remarkable, the whole of the upper surface being mottled, or vermiculated, as it is called, with a crowd of little wavy black lines.

Wrynecks are popularly known as snake-birds on account of the curious way in which they twist and turn their heads and elongate their necks, hissing all the time most vigorously, and spreading out the feathers of the head. These birds are furnished with extensile tongues, like those of woodpeckers, but even longer; and the way in which they dart them rapidly out completes the resemblance of the head to that of a snake.

The European, or typical, wryneck (*I. torquilla*) is a summer visitor to Europe and Northern Asia, and in many parts of Great Britain is known as the cuckoo's mate, since it generally arrives a little before the cuckoo, and is supposed to be a harbinger of that bird's arrival in spring. It is also called in some parts of England the pee-pee, doubtless from its curious note, which resembles the words "pee-pee-pee" uttered in a somewhat shrill voice.

In summer the wryneck ranges over the greater part of Europe and Asia, extending to Japan, its northern limit being about 62°. The Indian and Japanese birds have, indeed, been regarded as distinct species, but are probably only local races of the European, or typical, wryneck.

Those wrynecks which breed in the countries north of the Himalaya, and even in Kashmir, winter in India, while the Japanese birds repair at the same season to China and the Burmese countries. European wrynecks appear to winter in Northern Africa, ranging eastwards to Abyssinia, and on the west coast to Senegambia.

Wrynecks do not climb trees like woodpeckers, though they cling to the trunks of trees in pursuit of insect food. They feed largely on ants, and are often seen on the ground in pursuit of prey. Unlike woodpeckers, they do not bore nest-holes, but select those in trees, generally decayed fruit trees, as they are fond of frequenting orchards.

The eggs, which are sometimes as many as ten in number, although the average is seven or eight, are white, like those of woodpeckers, but not quite so glossy, and are buried among a quantity of rotten wood and other debris which fills up the lower part of the breeding hole.

THE WRYNECK

HONEY-GUIDES

Long classified with the cuckoos, which they resemble in the structure of their feet, and also in the habit of laying their eggs in the nests of other birds, the honey-guides are now recognised as a distinct group (family *Indicatoridæ*). In place of selecting totally different types of birds, honey-guides choose as foster-parents for their eggs and young some of their own nearest kindred, such as barbets and woodpeckers. The little honey-guide, for instance, deposits its white eggs in the nests of the red-vented woodpecker, the little tinker barbet, or the pied barbet, while the large white-backed honey-guide selects the banded barbet as a nurse.

In structure the honey-guides are akin to woodpeckers and barbets, having many characters in common with both groups, especially as regards the zygodactyle foot. The oil-gland is tufted, and there are no blind appendages (cæca) to the intestine. These birds are principally African, but the yellow-backed honey-guide (*Indicator xanthonotus*) is a native of the Himalaya, and in the mountains of the Malay Peninsula and Borneo occurs the most eastern representative of the Malay honey-guide *I. archipelagicus*.

Three genera are known, the true honey-guides (*Indicator*), the dwarf honey-guides (*Prodotiscus*), and *Melignomon*; the last represented only by a single West African species. The second genus contains three African species, distinguished by having only ten tail feathers instead of the twelve characteristic of the typical genus.

Writing of the lesser African honey-guide (*Indicator minor*), Sir John Kirk states that " it is found in forests, and often far from water, even during the dry season. On observing a man, it comes fluttering from branch to branch in the neighbouring trees, as if calling attention. On being followed, it goes farther ; and so it will guide the way to a nest of bees. When this is reached, it flies about, but no longer guides ; and then some knowledge is needed to discover the nest, even when pointed out by the bird to within a few trees. I have known a honey-guide, if a man, after taking the direction for a little while, then turns away, to come back and offer to point out another nest in a different part. But if it does not know of two nests it will remain behind. The difficulty is that it will point to tame bees in a bark hive as readily as to those in the forests. This is natural, as the bee is the same ; the bark hive, musinga, as it is named, being simply fastened up to a tree, and left for the bees to come to. The object the bird has in view is clearly the young bees. It will guide to nests having no honey, and seems equally delighted if the comb containing the grubs be torn out, when it is seen pecking at it."

The lesser honey-guide is only 6 inches in length ; but the white-eared honey-guide (*I. sparmanni*) is one of the larger members of the genus, being about 8 inches in length, of an ashy brown colour above, and whitish below, with a brownish shade on the throat. The three outer tail feathers have their bases white, and there is also some white on the lower part of the back and upper tail coverts, while on the shoulder is a yellow band formed by some of the lesser wing coverts. This species is found over the greater part of Africa, from Cape Colony to the Transvaal, and thence throughout Eastern Africa to Abyssinia, occurring again in Senegambia, so that it is an inhabitant of the open portions of the continent, and quite unknown in the forest regions of the interior and west of the continent. It is a favourite with the natives, who do not like to see one killed. Honey-guides are stated to be in the habit of breaking the eggs of the birds they select as foster-parents for their offspring. In some cases, however, they do not succeed in breaking the rival eggs, in which event it is probable that the strong hooks on the tip of the beak of the young honey-guides come into play for the purpose of aiding in the ejectment of the other occupants of the nest.

WHITE-EARED HONEY-GUIDE

BARBETS

The members of the barbet family (*Capitonidæ*) occupy an intermediate position between the woodpeckers and the toucans ; in many of their ways being like the former, while some bear a remarkable resemblance to toucans. In structure they also have many points in common with these two families, the peculiar zygodactyle foot being exactly like that of the woodpeckers and of the allied families. Barbets have a tufted oil-gland, no blind appendages to the intestine, and ten tail feathers. They have little in common with the puff-birds, also called barbets in many works on natural history. Barbets are found in the tropical portions of both the Old and New Worlds, the American forms being peculiar to Central and South America. From Brazil and Bolivia barbets range to Costa Rica, but no species has been found in Guatemala or Mexico.

In most of the Old World barbets the beak is toothed or ridged, but in the American genus *Capito* it is smooth and toothless, with the ridge rounded. In South America occurs the singular genus *Semnornis*, or *Tetragonops*, in which the beak is four-sided, with the lower half widened at its tip, so as to form a sort of cradle in which the end of the upper half rests. Two species of the genus are known, one from Costa Rica (*S. frantzii*) and the other from Ecuador, the latter being a brightly coloured bird, named *S. rhamphastinus* from the similarity of its colours to those of a toucan. Barbets are found in the tropical portions of Africa and Asia, but do not extend beyond the Malay Islands. Of the numerous genera recorded from the Old World, Africa claims the majority and the Indian region the rest.

GREATER SPOTTED WOODPECKER

"The species is found in wooded districts, more especially park lands, where hollow trees occur here and there, in which it can excavate a nesting place."

GIANT TOUCAN

"In comparison with the size of its owner, the beak of a toucan is of enormous dimensions, giving the bird an almost ludicrous look. If solid, the appendage would be far too heavy to carry; but, in reality, it is extremely light, the outer wall being very thin, and the interior occupied by a fine network of bony fibres, arranged so as to give great strength without weight."

HOOPOES

"The sexes of the hoopoe are alike in colour, and young birds resemble the adults, but have more fluffy plumage. Breeding as a rule in hollow trees, the hoopoe is now rare in those parts of the Continent where the country has been denuded of timber."

GREAT PIED HORNBILL

"The formidable beaks of these birds are useful as weapons of defence, as well as being of the needful shape to serve as trowels for plastering up the nesting holes. The hole is doubtless plastered up as a defence against enemies, of which the hornbills have plenty."

TOOTH-BILLED BARBETS

In the tooth-billed group the distinctive feature is the presence of one or more distinct notches or teeth in the edge of the beak, some of the species also having deep grooves or ridges, similar to those which occur in certain hornbills, the red barbet of West Africa (*Pogonorhynchus dubius*), the only member of its genus, being further characterised by a kind of beard of coarse bristles on the chin. This is, however, absent in the nearly allied genus *Lybius*, or *Melanobucco*, of which there is about a score of species distributed over various districts of Africa. They are described as frequenting the neighbourhood of woods and bush-country, feeding on fruits and berries, seeds, and insects, and nesting in holes of trees, but not making the holes themselves.

The black-collared barbet (*L. torquatus*) is stated to have a particularly loud note, of which the syllables "*kook karoo*," repeated eight or ten times, would give a good idea. Frequently both male and female call at the same time, and, when perched close together, keep up a quick succession of bows to each other, bowing at the repetition of each note.

The pied barbet (*L. leucomelus*) in Damaraland is found singly or in pairs, and is remarkable for its clear-ringing and far-sounding notes, which, heard at all hours of the day, are most frequent in the early morning. Its food consists chiefly of fruits and seeds, but it will, to some extent, accommodate itself as regards food to the produce of the locality in which it happens to be located. It is rather a lively bird, and sometimes suspends itself below the fruit on which it is feeding, and makes its repast while hanging in that position. It has a note of three syllables, "*poo-poo-poop*," not unlike that of its Indian relative the "coppersmith," or crimson-headed barbet.

GREAT BARBET

TINKER-BARBETS

In the tinker group of small barbets (*Barbatula*) the largest is only 6 inches in length, while the majority scarcely exceed 3 inches. They are all inhabitants of Tropical Africa, occurring everywhere from Senegambia and Abyssinia southwards to Cape Colony. The note of the little tinker-barbet (*B. pusilla*) of Natal so much resembles the tapping of a hammer on an anvil (having the same peculiar metallic ring) that this species is called the tinker-bird. It is silent during winter, not beginning its monotonous cry till spring, but continuing it throughout the summer. The colour of the tinker-bird is black, streaked or spotted with yellow, the forehead being red or yellow, but in some of the species there is a white or yellow eyebrow-stripe, and a band of red or yellow across the rump.

HAY'S BARBET

Like the tinker-barbets, a member of the smooth-billed section of the family, Hay's barbet (*Calorhamphus hayi*), which ranges from Southern Tenasserim through the Malay Peninsula to Sumatra, is remarkable for its sombre plumage, being dark brown, washed with olive yellow on the upper parts, and yellowish white below, and having the throat tinted with red. The beak is black in the male, and reddish or ochre-brown in the female. The length of the bird is about 6½ inches. In Borneo a second species occurs with a brighter and more brick-red throat, known as the sooty barbet (*C. fuliginosus*).

GREAT BARBET

The largest members of the whole family are the great barbet of the Himalaya (*Megalæma marshallorum*) and its near relation the green barbet (*M. virens*) of Burma and Southern China, each of which measures about a foot in length. The colour is green, with a brownish mantle, and the hind part of the neck streaked with yellow; the head is blue, as is also the under surface, except on the sides of the body, which are green, and the fore part of the neck, which is dark brown marked with greenish blue, the beak being pale yellow.

The Himalayan species is a well-known bird of the hill country, where its curious wailing cry is often heard, especially in all the warmer and well-wooded valleys. The hillmen have a story that a person who suffered unjustly from law suits was changed into this bird, whose cry is, "*un-ni ow, un-ni ow*," meaning, "injustice, injustice." This species and its Burmese ally both appear to make their own nest-holes, which they drill in trees like woodpeckers; but many of the barbets lay their eggs in natural holes on the under sides of branches, the holes being enlarged by the birds.

CRIMSON-HEADED BARBETS

GREEN BARBETS

All the larger green barbets of the genera *Cyanops* and *Chotorhea* hollow out their own nest-holes, and the Ceylon barbet (*Cyanops flavifrons*) never uses the same hole twice, but, having found a tree with wood suited to its work, perforates it each year for the new nest, as many as eight or ten holes being sometimes visible in a tree by a jungle roadside. It is only when sounding wood before making their nests that these

VARIEGATED BARBET

birds tap with their beaks, the blows being very slowly repeated, with perhaps an interval of ten seconds between each.

There are generally a few bents and grass stalks collected for the eggs to lie on, although they are scarcely worthy of the name of nest. In the nest-hole made by a blue-faced barbet was once discovered a large pad consisting almost exclusively of coarse vegetable fibres, apparently strips of the bark of some herbaceous plant, along with a few pieces of grass, a morsel of red wool, and one or two similar miscellaneous scraps intermingled in the pad.

CRIMSON-HEADED BARBET

Like the African tinker-birds, the Indian crimson-headed barbet (*Xantholæma hæmatocephala*) takes its name of "coppersmith" from its metallic note, which much resembles the clinking of metal when struck by a hammer; this note being heard at all times of the day, and given out with monotonous regularity. On a certain occasion in Ajmir I heard one of these birds, and on creeping up beneath the tree in which it was sitting, found it perched crosswise on a branch, like a passerine, uttering its note at regular intervals, and accompanying each utterance with a jerk of the head, first to the right and then to the left.

The coppersmith is one of the smaller barbets measuring only about half a dozen inches in length. It is green above and pale yellow below, with green streaks on the flanks. The head is variegated in colour, the forehead being scarlet, with a black band across the crown extending to the sides of the face, which are ornamented with a yellow streak above and below each eye. The throat is bright yellow, with a scarlet band across the fore part of the neck. The nesting hole selected by this

species is generally situated in the under side of a hollow bough, the eggs being, in some cases, placed at a distance of four or five feet from the original entrance.

An instance has been narrated where a pair of these little birds had perforated a beam in a vinery, and when they had lengthened the cavity year by year to about five feet they made a second entrance, also from below, about two and a half feet from the nest. This practice of making additional holes for entrance and exit near the nest seems also to be adopted by the birds in a wild state.

VARIEGATED BARBET

As already mentioned, Tropical America is the home of the two species of square-beaked barbets (*Semnornis* or *Tetragonops*), and it may be added that the tropical barbets of the genus *Capito*, of which there is nearly a score of species, are also inhabitants of the same region. The variegated barbet (*Capito versicolor*) of Bolivia and Peru is a good example of the genus, all the members of which differ from other barbets in that the two sexes are not coloured alike; another peculiarity being the presence of bristles at the base of the beak.

TOUCANS

Gaudy in plumage, and ungainly in appearance, the toucans (*Rhamphastidæ*) are denizens of the tropical forests of Central and South America, although they also extend to those of Northern Mexico, almost within sight of the Rio Grande. Resembling woodpeckers and barbets in the internal structure of their zygodactyle feet, they differ in having the front end of the vomer of the skull abruptly truncated in the passerine manner. In comparison with the size of its owner, the beak of a toucan is of enormous dimensions, giving the bird an almost ludicrous look. If solid, the appendage would be far too heavy to carry; but, in reality, it is extremely light, the outer wall being very thin, and the interior occupied by a fine network of bony fibres, arranged so as to give great strength without weight (page 1092).

TOCO TOUCAN

The tongue of these birds is also peculiar, the anterior portion consisting of a narrow, thin, bony plate, flattened horizontally, and supported by a process of the tongue bone, which forms a ridge beneath the tongue. Measuring nearly 6 inches in length in the larger species, at about four inches from its extremity it is obliquely notched on both sides, these notches becoming deeper and deeper towards the apex, thus giving it a bristly appearance.

Toucans resemble barbets in having a tufted oil-gland, and also agree with those birds in the presence of ten feathers in the tail. The beak generally is highly coloured, while frequently the bare face partakes of the same brilliant hues. When asleep, toucans have a curious way of carrying their tails, which are turned up over the back, while the enormous beaks are buried beneath the scapular feathers. Toucans may be divided into the following five generic groups—namely, *Rhamphastus*, *Andigena*, *Pteroglossus*, *Selenidera*, and *Aulacorhamphus*, the number of species exceeding sixty.

According to the account of Prince Maximilian of Wied, " these birds are very common in all parts of the extensive forests of Brazil, and are killed in great numbers in the cooler portion of the year for the purposes of the table. To the stranger, they are of even greater interest than to the natives, from their remarkable form, and from the rich and strongly contrasted style of their colouring, their black and green bodies being adorned with markings of the most brilliant hues—red, orange, blue, and white; the naked parts of the body being dyed with brilliant colours, the legs blue or green, the irides blue, yellow, etc., and the large bill of a different colour in every species, and in many instances very gaily marked. In their habits the toucans offer some resemblance to crows, and especially magpies. Like the latter, they are very troublesome to birds of prey, particularly owls, which they surround and annoy by making a great noise, all the while jerking their tails upwards and downwards. The flight of these birds is

BLACK-THROATED ARACARI TOUCAN

easy and graceful, and they sweep with facility over the loftiest trees of their native forests, their strongly developed beaks, contrary to expectation, being no encumbrance. The voice of the toucan is short and unmelodious and somewhat different in every species."

Toucans are gregarious birds to a greater or less degree, and likewise shy and restless. During the noontide heat they sit motionless on the branches of the trees, but at other times are constantly on the move. They feed chiefly on fruits, although it is stated they will also devour small birds and mammals, while, in the breeding season they eat ants, caterpillars, and the like. The glossy white oval eggs, two in number, are laid in hollow branches of fruit-trees.

TOCO TOUCAN

Among the numerous species, two are selected for notice. Of these, the toco toucan (*Rhamphastus toco*) is black, with a broad white band across the rump, the vent crimson, the throat white, fading into yellow on the neck, and followed by a crimson band on the fore part of the latter. The length is about 2 feet, and the beak is nearly $6\frac{1}{2}$ inches long. This toucan has a wide distribution in South America, being found from Guiana to the Lower Amazon, and extending through Brazil and Bolivia to Argentina. It frequents high forest trees in large flocks.

ARACARIS

Among the smaller-beaked kinds, reference may be made to the black-throated aracari toucan (*Pteroglossus aracari*) of Guiana and Lower Amazonia, the typical representative of a genus containing nearly a score of species. These birds are extremely difficult to detect in their forest surroundings, the traveller Dr. Stolzmann stating that, when procuring a pair of the yellow-billed aracari (*P. flavirostris*), he fired in a high tree at a bird, which uttered some piercing cries as it fell, and in a moment he was surrounded by a mob of ten of the same species, making a fearful din. On a second shot being fired, they all disappeared. Although only one may be visible, these birds associate in small flocks, according to the habit of toucans in Peru.

GREEN-BILLED TOUCAN

TROGONS

THE trogons are birds remarkable for their brilliant colouring and soft plumage, and constitute not only a distinct family (*Trogonidæ*), but are likewise regarded as representing a special suborder, Trogones, mainly distinguished from the families already described by the arrangement of the tendons of the foot. In these birds, the second toe is turned backwards, and the third and fourth toes are moved by the splitting of one tendon, while a second tendon is likewise divided into two branches to supply the first and second toes.

They are further characterised by having the palate of the slit type (schizognathous), and by the feather-tract on the back being continuous in place of forked. Then, again, it may be mentioned that the hind border of the breast bone has four notches, the intestine is provided with a pair of blind appendages (cæca); the oil-gland is naked, and the after-shafts of the feathers of the body are remarkable for their length. Behind the head is a patch of loose skin, and the whole skin is of such a fragile and delicate nature, and the feathers are so loosely attached, that the preservation of these birds tries to the utmost the skill of the taxidermist.

As regards their geographical distribution, trogons are found in the Indo-Malay region, Africa south of the Sahara, and Central and South America, one species alone (*Trogon ambiguus*) being stated to range so far north as Texas and Arizona. Very numerous in Central and South America, in Africa, although widely distributed, these birds are poorly represented in species, but again become more abundant in the Indo-Malay region, although not ranging eastwards of the islands of Java and Borneo. Remains of fossil trogons have been discovered in Tertiary deposits in France belonging to the Oligocene period.

Of the nine genera into which the family is divided, five occur in Central and South America, among them being the typical *Trogon*; and it is noteworthy that two of the genera—namely, *Tmetotrogon* and *Prionotelus* —each with a single species, are exclusively island forms, the one being confined to San Domingo and

the other to Cuba. The four African trogons are comprised in the genera *Hapaloderma* and *Heterotrogon*; and there are two Oriental genera, one of which (*Hapalarpactes*) is peculiar to Java and Sumatra.

QUEZAL

Among the half-dozen representatives of the splendid American long-tailed trogons, special attention may be directed to the well-known quezal (*Pharomacrus mocinno*) of Guatemala. Every naturalist who has had the good fortune to see this bird in its wild state describes it as extremely beautiful, and, even when preserved, its plumage differs from that of its congeners in its retention of the original colour, a skin which has been exposed to the light in the British Museum for fully half a century being still almost as brilliant as when first mounted. In the other species, on the contrary, the bright yellow or crimson of the breast fades rapidly. The range of the quezal extends from Guatemala to Panama, but as considerable numbers of the skins of these birds are sent yearly to Europe as plumes for hats, the species has become very

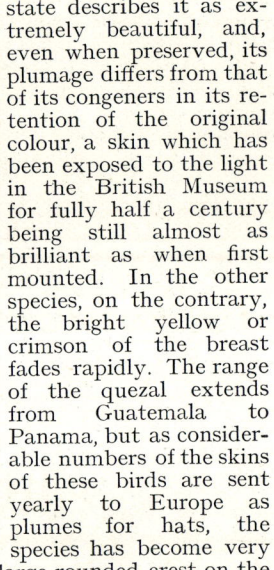

MALE AND FEMALE QUEZALS

scarce. Ornamented with a large rounded crest on the head, the male has the ground colour of the plumage brilliant metallic green, while the throat and chest are also metallic green, as are the wings and upper tail coverts, the two middle plumes of the latter being enormously developed, and fully four times as long as the tail, while the rest of the under parts, from the chest downwards, is deep blood-red. The median wing coverts are metallic green, and so produced as to form elegant drooping plumes, while the outer tail feathers are white, with black bases. The female is much less brightly coloured than her mate, having a brownish breast and the bill black, instead of yellow. The head is golden green, and the outer tail feathers are white barred with black.

Mr. Osbert Salvin states that, when quezal-hunting in Guatemala, after a difficult march through the forest, the way barred by swollen torrents and fallen trees, he at last managed to get within sight of one of the birds, which had been attracted by his guide imitating its notes. This imitation is not difficult, since the whistle is described as a low double note, " whe-oo, whe-oo," uttered softly at first, and then gradually swelling into a loud but not unmelodious cry; this is succeeded by a long note, which begins low, and, after swelling, dies away as it began. The other cries of the bird are harsh, discordant, and not so easily imitated. When detected, the bird was observed sitting almost motionless on its perch, merely moving its head slowly from side to side, with the tail somewhat raised and occasionally jerked open, and again as rapidly closed, thus causing a vibration of its long upper coverts. In spite of the length of the streaming tail feathers, which appear to form no bar to its progress, the flight of this trogon is straight and rapid.

GOLDEN-HEADED TROGON

The golden-headed trogon (*P. auriceps*) of Peru, according to Dr. Stolzmann, is exclusively a bird of the forests, frequenting the lower branches of the highest trees at a considerable distance from the ground. It is generally seen in pairs, but sometimes two or three pairs may be met with together. "I was struck," he writes, "with the vertical position which it assumes on the large horizontal boughs, and I observed by the aid of my field-glasses that, instead of perching on the upper surface of the branch, it remains attached to the side of the latter, just as woodpeckers glue themselves to the trunks and vertical branches of trees. Its flight is rapid but weak.

"It feeds on fruits, especially on nectandras, and in the stomach of one I found a nectandra fruit so large as to fill the whole stomach. I suppose, therefore, that the trogon, like the guacharo, rejects the nut after having digested the flesh, because otherwise some time must elapse before it could swallow another fruit. The species has two cries, both well known to me; one, like a mocking laugh, is seldom heard; the other is a plaintive 'ha-hau,' with the second syllable much prolonged. It has a ventriloquial quality, and often deceives the hearer, who fancies that the bird is ever so far off, whereas it is close at hand all the while.

"At Cuterro I had a good opportunity of observing its singular way of clinging in a vertical position to the trees, spreading its tail out the while and then shutting it suddenly. In this locality it feeds on certain black fruits, which impart to its flesh an odour of marjoram. I never saw it nesting, but the natives said that it nested in holes and laid eggs of a greenish blue. An egg which my companion found on the ground was universally admitted to belong to this trogon."

TYPICAL TROGONS

Before referring to the members of the genus *Trogon*, it may be mentioned that the South American *Euptilotis* is characterised by the presence of tufts of hair-like feathers behind the ear coverts, the sole representative of the genus being an inhabitant of Mexico. Long, hair-like feathers in the same situation are also distinctive of the single species of *Tmetotrogon*, which is confined to the island of San Domingo; while in the Cuban *Prionotelus*, of which there is also but one species, the tail feathers are deeply notched. With the single exception

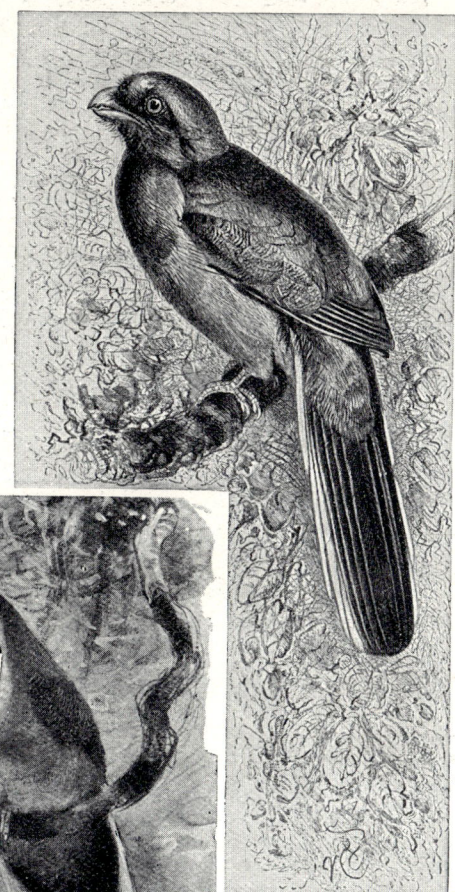

KASUMBA TROGON

NARINA TROGON

of a species (*T. ambiguus*) occurring just within the southern limits of the United States, the members of the typical genus *Trogon* are restricted to Central and South America, where they are represented by some twenty-four species, ranging so far south as Southern Brazil and Paraguay. They are all birds of moderate size, with metallic blue or green colours above, and the breast and under parts bright yellow, scarlet, or blood-red. The females differ from the males in their duller plumage and the colour of the tail, the latter being chestnut, grey, or blackish, whereas in the males it is as brilliant as the rest of the upper parts, being green, blue, or purple.

Their habits seem to be the same everywhere, the birds affecting forest districts and feeding almost entirely on fruits and berries. They are described as rather stupid, and not even startled by the report of a gun, so that a whole flock may be shot out of the same tree. Most of the species go about in pairs, but are occasionally seen in small flocks, sometimes frequenting the lower branches of trees, but more often the middle and higher levels, where they sit motionless, or utter their curious notes at intervals.

In Nicaragua a trogon has been known to fly into a house, but in most parts of South America these birds are inhabitants only of the virgin forests, extending their range to a considerable altitude on some of the mountains. In Peru Dr. Stolzmann shot the only example of *T. caligatus* obtained during his travels at a considerable height on a tree, when he had heard its cry repeated at intervals for the space of a couple of hours; it resembled the words "cou-cou-cou-cou-co-co-co-co," the second half being uttered in a lower tone than the first.

Another kind (*T. melanurus*) was not rare, and allowed of an easy approach, flying off to take up another perch in the neighbourhood of its previous one, always uttering its note "cou-cou-cou-cou-cou." Its flight resembled that of a magpie, and the beating of the wings was distinctly heard; from time to time it called "ke-ke-ke," lowering its tail at the same time, seldom flying more than a distance of fifty paces at a time, and preferring the lower branches of the trees.

MASSENA TROGON

Of the Massena trogon (*T. massena*) of Costa Rica Mr. Nutting writes: "I have never seen the species associating in flocks as the others do. On the contrary, it seems to be rather a solitary bird, preferring the deep recesses of the tropical forests. Its note is a kind of clucking noise, hard to describe; and its native name is aula. In common with all the species of the genus, it seems to be rather a stupid bird, hardly ever taking alarm at the approach of man."

The black-headed trogon (*T. melanocephalus*) is very abundant in Costa Rica, being often seen in flocks of a dozen or more, and commonly found in the dry open woods away from water. It has a sort of chattering note, low and soft. In the same situations is also found *T. caligatus*, which is the only species giving utterance to a clear, distinct whistle.

AFRICAN TROGONS

In Africa trogons are represented by three species belonging to the genus *Hapaloderma*, and one of *Heterotrogon*. The former are characterised by the naked space behind the eye, and the colour of the tail, which is the same in both sexes, the three middle pairs of tail feathers being purplish or greenish, without black bands at the ends of the central ones. The Narina trogon (*H. narina*) ranges from Bogosland in North-Eastern Africa, through East Africa to Natal, extending so far west as the forests of the Knysna district. On the west coast, from Fanti

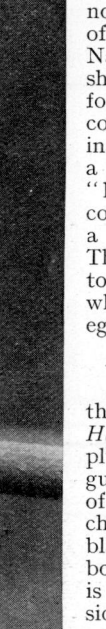

CUBAN TROGON

to the Gabun, occurs Ussher's trogon (*H. constantia*); and Central Africa is the home of the red-bellied trogon (*H. rufiventris*). The allied *Heterotrogon* is represented only by the banded *H. vittatum*, ranging from the Zanzibar forest region to Kikuyu.

Very little has been noted about the habits of these birds, but the Narina trogon is a very shy species only found in forest districts, its food consisting of fruit and insects, and its cry being a loud moaning note, "heot," which has been compared to the bark of a poodle with a cold. This trogon is reported to nest in hollow trees, where it lays four white eggs.

ASIATIC TROGONS

The Asiatic trogons of the genus *Pyrotrogon*, or *Harpactes*, are beautifully plumaged birds, distinguished by the bare sides of the face, and the chestnut tail, barred with black at the tip, of both sexes. The genus is represented by a considerable number of species, some measuring as much as a foot in length, and all characterised by their brilliant coloration.

One of the best known is the red-headed trogon (*P. erythrocephalus*), distinguished by the chestnut breast, deep crimson head, neck, and under parts, and black wings, in which the primaries are edged

LONG-TAILED COLY OR MOUSE-BIRD

with white, the wing coverts and inner secondaries being finely vermiculated with white; the gape and region of the eye bare and purplish blue in colour, the beak bluish with a black tip, the feet pinkish, and the eye dull red. The female is not quite so bright in colour as the male, the lower parts being duller, while the back, neck, and breast are reddish brown, and the vermiculations on the wing coverts buff instead of white.

This trogon differs from its American allies in that its food consists entirely of insects, on which it swoops after the manner of a fly-catcher. It affects thick forests, and, although solitary in its habits, is so common in some of the hill forests that a dozen or more may frequently be seen together. The eggs are three or four in number, of a very pale buff colour, and laid on the bare wood in the hollow of a decayed tree.

Another well-known member of this group is the Kasumba trogon (*P. kasumba*) of the Malay Peninsula, Borneo, and Sumatra, easily recognised by the large, white-bordered throat patch.

COLIES

The colies (family *Coliidæ*), which form a group known as Colii, are the first representatives of a section which includes all the remaining representatives of the picarian order, often conveniently spoken of, for want of a better name, as the fissirostral section. With the exception of the humming-birds, all the members of this section have a similar arrangement of the tendons on the lower surface of the foot, the first toe being supplied by a branch of one tendon, while the fourth is served by a different one. As a rule, the palate is of the bridged, or desmognathous, type, although in some cases it is of the modification characterising the perching birds. The colies themselves are exclusively African, and are remarkable for the structure of their feet, in which all four toes are directed forward, although it is probable that the first can be turned backwards at will. The breast bone is characterised by the presence of four notches, the oil-gland is naked, the intestine is devoid of blind appendages, and there are ten tail feathers.

The whole of the colies are included in the single genus *Colius*, which is represented by more than half a score of species. In South Africa colies are commonly known by the name of mouse-birds. They have a rapid flight, like that of a parrot, with very quick beats of the wings, and are generally found in small flocks, which, when disturbed, fly off together. Their food consists of fruit and berries, occasionally insects being taken when their other sustenance is scanty.

WHITE-BACKED COLY

At the Cape the white-backed coly (*C. capensis*) is not uncommon in gardens during the fruit season, wandering about in small family parties of from six to eight individuals. They fly with a rapid though laboured flight, usually at a lower level than the object at which they aim, and on nearing this they rise upwards with a sudden abrupt curve. They creep about the branches like parrots, and hang, head-downwards, without inconvenience; indeed, it is said that they invariably sleep in this position, many of them congregated in a ball. In Natal the white-backed coly lives entirely on fruits; its flight is short and feeble, seldom extending beyond the nearest bush or tree, on reaching which the bird perches on one of the lower branches, and then gradually glides and creeps upwards through the foliage, using both bill and feet for that purpose. The nest, which is placed in a small bush, is composed externally of grass and twigs, lined internally with soft grass; the eggs are white and three in number.

SOUTH AFRICAN COLY

Another well-known representative of the genus is the South African coly (*C. striatus*), which is brown above with numerous dusky cross-lines on the plumage, the head being crested and a little more ashy, while the forehead and lores are reddish, the sides of the face, throat, and breast ashy brown, the latter with blackish cross-lines, and the rest of the under surface ochry buff.

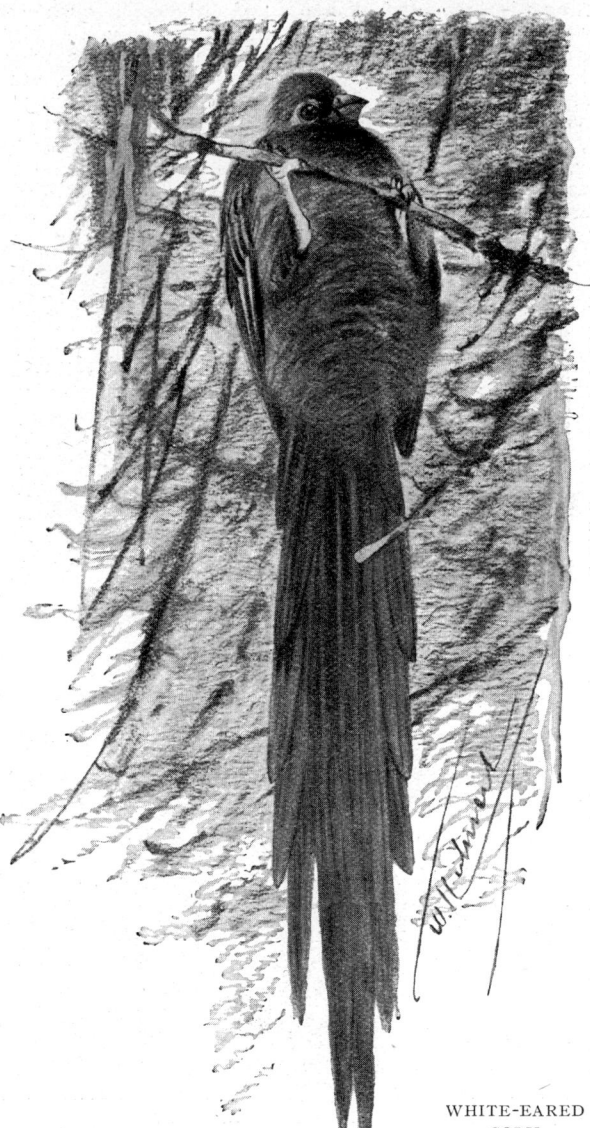

WHITE-EARED
COLY

The total length of the typical form is about 14 inches, but there is considerable local variation in this respect. At the Cape the bird is large, but becomes smaller as it approaches Abyssinia; in Senegambia it is of about the same size, and thence gradually decreases in size in its West Coast habitat. This variation in size is almost an invariable rule with African birds. This coly breeds in Natal, nesting in the fork of a mimosa or other low tree, well sheltered by creepers and foliage above. In Abyssinia and Shoa the group is represented by the white-eared *C. leucotis*.

HUMMING-BIRDS

MAINLY confined to Central and South America, where they range from the tropical forests of Brazil to the barren rocks of Tierra del Fuego, but also extending into Mexico, humming-birds (family *Trochilidæ*), in spite of their difference in form and habits, appear to be near allies of swifts. To a certain extent, indeed, the difference in the two groups is not so strongly marked in the young as in the adult condition, seeing that while in the full-grown humming-bird the beak is always long and slender, in the nestling it is short and wide like that of a swift. In the structure of their palate both groups conform to the passerine type.

Having the keel of the breast bone well developed, in accordance with their marvellous power of sustained fl ght, humming-birds are characterised by the presence of ten feathers in the tail, and the same number of primary quills in the wing, but the secondaries are reduced to six, and are thus very different from those of perching birds. The three forwardly-directed toes are supplied by as many branches of one tendon, while another serves the backwardly-directed first toe. The most remarkable structural peculiarity of humming-birds, however, is to be found in the tongue, which is extensile, with its supporting bones carried backwards over the hind part of the skull.

Although adorned with such brilliant metallic colours, the members of this family do not display their tinselled plumage to any great advantage during flight, many observers having remarked how little of the brilliancy of the bird's body is apparent when it is darting through the trees or hovering in front of a flower. This is due to the extremely rapid motions of a humming-bird's wing, the beats of which are almost invisible from their rapidity.

In describing the appearance of these lovely little birds on the wing, Professor A. Newton wrote : " One is admiring the clustering stars of a scarlet *Cordia*, the snowy cornucopias of a *Portlandia*, or some other brilliant and beautiful flower, when between one's eye and the blossoms suddenly appears a small, dark object, suspended, as it were, between four short black threads, meeting each other in a cross. For an instant it shows in front of the flower ; an instant more it steadies itself, and one fancies the space between each pair of threads occupied by a grey film ; again another instant, and, emitting a momentary flash of emerald and sapphire light, it is vanishing, lessening in the distance, as it shoots away, to a speck that the eye cannot take note of—and all this so rapidly that the word on one's lips is still un-spoken, scarcely the thought in one's mind changed."

Another observer has stated that the flight of a humming-bird was very unlike that of any other bird he had ever seen, and quite different from what he had expected—in fact, exactly the opposite. When poised before any object, the tremulous motion of the wings is so rapid that the eye cannot follow it, and a hazy semicircle of indistinctness on each side of the bird is all that is perceptible. Their actions reminded him of a piece of machinery acted on by a powerful spring, and although frequent intermissions of rest are taken during the day, the bird may be said to live in the air—an element in which it performs every kind of evolution with the utmost ease, frequently rising perpendicularly, flying backwards, pirouetting or dancing off, as it were.

Most humming-birds have more or less the habit of pausing in the air and throwing the body into rapid and odd contortions, this being especially noticeable in the case of the long-tailed humming-bird, on account of the effect which such motions have on the beautiful long feathers of the tail. In these evolutions the birds are engaged in catching insects in the air, and, if close enough, the observer may see the tiny flies, and hear the snapping of the bird's bill as it captures them.

Humming-birds are stated to have the power of flying backwards, and although this power has frequently been doubted, it is confirmed by at least two modern observers, one of whom noticed that the backward motion is greatly assisted by a forward flirt of the expanded tail as the bird shifts from place to place or from one part of a tree to another, sometimes descending, at others ascending. "It often towers up above the trees," writes Mr. R. Ridgway, " and then shoots off, like a little meteor, at a right angle ; at other times it quietly buzzes away among the flowers near the ground ; at one moment it is poised over a diminutive weed, at the next it is seen at a distance of forty yards, whither it has vanished with the quickness of thought. During the heat of the day the shady retreats beneath the trees are very frequently visited ; in the morning and evening the sunny banks, the verandas, and other exposed situations are more frequently resorted to."

Humming-birds, as a rule, do not possess any kind of song, and their few notes are of a twittering character. Mr. F. Stephens, in describing the feeding-note of Costa's humming-bird, states that the female, when feeding, keeps up a pretty constant vocal noise, which somewhat resembles the buzz of the wings, and that the feeding-note of the male is finer and not so frequent. " I

HUMMING-BIRD AND NEST

think that the males are the only ones who sing. The song is sweet and very low, but if it is perfectly quiet around it can be distinctly heard for a distance of ten yards. As might be expected from the size of the bird, it is in a very high key, something like the sound produced by whistling between the teeth, very low, yet at a high pitch. It might be called a warble, and I have heard it kept up for several minutes at a time. On such occasions I have never been able to find a female in the vicinity, and have come to the conclusion that it was sung for the individual's own amusement. There is still another hummer-note —that of the chase. They are very fond of chasing one another, sometimes for sport, often for spite. This note also resembles the feeding-note, but is louder and possesses a chippering character, sometimes almost like the sound produced by lightly and rapidly smacking the lips together.

"I can detect but little difference between the sexes, and it appears much the same whether the chase is in sport or anger. Further-more, it is often made by the pursued as well as by the pursuer. At such times I am always reminded of a lot of schoolboys playing 'tag.' If a hummer is perched and a person passes near, it starts off, uttering a note similar to that made while feeding ; but, should it be a female which you have frightened from her nest, she will go off silently."

Mr. Ridgway mentions only two other records of the song of humming-birds, quoting Mr. P. H. Gosse, to the effect that the tiny *Mellisuga minima* of Jamaica sings, for ten minutes at a time, a sweet but monotonous little song ; while a similar fact has been observed with regard to the wedge-tailed sabre-wing. Mr. Ridgway adds that " although the muffled buzzing or humming noise, which has given this family of birds its distinctive name, is the sound usually accompanying the flight of humming-birds, the males of some species accompany their flight by a most remarkable noise of an entirely different character. While among the mountains of Utah, in 1869, I was for a long time mystified by a shrill screeching noise, something like that produced by a rapidly revolving circular saw when rubbed by a splinter. This noise was evidently in the air, but I could not trace its origin, until I discovered a humming-bird passing through the air overhead in a curious undulating kind of flight. I afterwards heard the same sound produced by males of the same species (the broad-tailed humming-bird) when they were driving other birds away from the vicinity of their nests. At such times they would ascend almost perpendicularly to a considerable height, and then descend with the quickness of a flash at the object of their animosity, which was, perhaps, more frightened or annoyed at the accompanying noise than by the attack itself. Mr. F. Stephens calls this the 'courtship song,' but from the circumstance that, in the broad-tailed humming-bird at least, it is often produced by solitary individuals while wending their way between distant points, I hardly think that it can be so considered."

Mr. Stephens writes of the Costa Rica humming-bird (*Trochilus costæ*) that " the female is sitting on a twig in a low bush, not on an exposed twig, as is often the case when she is merely resting ; but when the male begins she goes farther in, as if she feared that he really intended mischief, while he rises high in the air, and with a headlong swoop comes down, passing her, and, turning with a sharp curve as near her as possible, mounts on high, to repeat the manœuvre again and again. A shrill whistle is heard as he begins to descend, starting low and becoming louder and louder, until, as he passes her, it becomes a shriek, which is plainly audible for a distance of a hundred yards or more. As he mounts again it dies away, only to be repeated at the next descent. This is a common manœuvre with the species, the whistle made during the descent being quite low." The nests are tiny little structures, generally made of moss, and covered externally with lichens, thus resembling the surroundings amid which they are placed. The eggs are two in number, white, and oval at both ends.

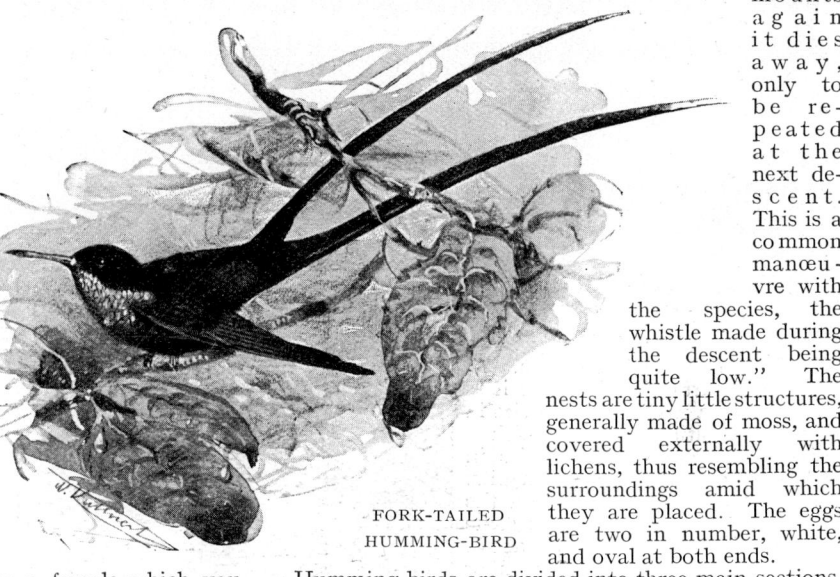

FORK-TAILED
HUMMING-BIRD

Humming-birds are divided into three main sections, the characters of which are not very trenchantly marked ; the fact being that these birds form a very homogeneous group, and thus do not lend themselves to any easily recognisable scheme of classification. The number of species described is about five hundred, divided into considerably more than one hundred genera. In these birds almost every possible variation of form may be observed, from the longest to the tiniest beak, and from the simplest form of tail to the most elaborate of structures, while the metallic plumage, so characteristic of humming-birds in general, is absent in not a few of the genera, and the colour is of the simplest kind.

LONG-TAILED HUMMING-BIRD

As an example of the first section of the family, the members of which are characterised by the serrated cutting edges of the fore part of the upper half of the beak, may be taken the long-tailed Jamaica humming-bird (*Æthurus polytmus*). The group comprises about five-and-twenty genera, the members of which differ infinitely among themselves as regards form and colour. The Jamaican bird, the sole representative of its genus, may be easily recognised by the abnormal conforma-tion of the tail, in which the outermost feather but one on each side is produced to an enormous length.

Its habits have been described by Mr. P. H. Gosse in the following words : " The long-tail is a permanent resident in Jamaica, and is not uncommonly seen at all seasons and in all situations. It loves to frequent the margins of woods and roadsides, where it sucks the blossoms of the trees, occasionally descending, however, to the low shrubs. There is one locality where it is abundant, the summit of the range of mountains known as the Bluefields Ridge. Behind the peaks which are visible from the sea, at an elevation of about half a mile, there runs through the dense woods a narrow path, just passable for a horse, overrun with beautiful ferns of many graceful forms, and always damp and cool. The whirring made by the vibrating wings of the male polytmus is a shriller sound than that produced by the female, and indicates its proximity before the eye has detected it.

"The male almost constantly utters a monotonous, quick 'chirk,' both while resting on a twig and while sucking from flower to flower. They do not invariably probe flowers upon the wing; one may frequently observe them thus engaged when alighted and sitting with closed wings, and often they partially sustain themselves by clinging with the feet to a leaf while sucking, the wings being expanded and vibrating. The humming-birds in Jamaica do not confine themselves to any particular season for nidification. In almost every month of the year I have either found, or have had brought to me, the nests of polytmus in occupation. Still, so far as my experience goes, they are most numerous in June; although another observer considers January as the most normal period.

"It is not improbable that two broods are reared in a season. In the latter part of February a friend showed me a nest of this species in a singular situation, but which I afterwards found to be quite in accordance with its usual habits. It was at Bognie, situated on the Bluefields Mountain, but at some distance from the scene above described. On the 12th of November we took, in Bluefields morass, the nest of a polytmus containing two eggs, one of which had the chick considerably advanced, the other being freshly laid. The nest was placed on a hanging twig of a black mangrove tree, the twig passing perpendicularly through the side, and out at the bottom. It is mainly composed of silk-cotton very closely pressed, mixed with the still more glossy cotton asclepias, particularly round the edge, the seed remaining attached to some of the filaments."

WHITE-CROWNED HUMMING-BIRD

As a second representative of the saw-beaked group, mention may be made of the genus *Microchera*, known by two species, of which one (*M. albicoronata*) is confined to the mountains of Western Panama, while the other (*M. parvirostris*) takes its place in Nicaragua and Costa Rica. Both are remarkable for their snow-white crowns and tiny dimensions, being only about 2½ inches in length. According to its describer, the second is not so persistent in its flight as most humming-birds, and rests more frequently, this habit being probably induced by the shortness of its wings.

The first specimen seen was perched on a twig preening its feathers, and for a few moments the observer was doubtful whether such a tiny creature could really be a bird. Another he noticed bathing, and watched its movements for some time before shooting it. "The little creature," it is stated, "would poise itself about three feet or so above the surface of the water, and then, as quick as thought, would dart downwards, so as to dip its head in the placid pool, then up again to its original position, quite as quickly as it had descended. These movements of darting up and down it would repeat in rapid succession, which produced more than a moderate disturbance on the surface of the water for such a diminutive creature. After a considerable number of dippings it alighted on a twig near at hand, and began pluming its feathers."

RAINBOW AND FORK-TAILED HUMMING-BIRDS

These two beautiful groups may be taken as representatives of the second, or intermediate, section of the family, in which the sheath of the fore part of the upper half of the beak is but feebly serrated at the cutting edge. As with the previous section, all kinds of forms are included within its limits, from the lovely rainbow hummers (*Diplogæna*) to the duller-coloured *Amazilia*. The former, which inhabit the Andes from Ecuador to Bolivia, are remarkable for their brilliant crown-spots, and are among the largest members of the family. They extract the nectar from flowers in a leisurely manner; and they have been seen perched on the branch of a tree, from which they flew out into the air, after the manner of fly-catchers. In this division are likewise included the lovely comets (*Sappho*), with their long coppery or red tails and green throats, whose range extends from the interior of Argentina to Chile, Bolivia, and Central Peru. The typical rainbow humming-bird (*D. iris*) ranges from Peru to Bolivia.

The members of the fork-tailed genus *Lesbia* inhabit the Andes, from Colombia and Venezuela to Bolivia, and are dark green in colour, with short beaks, very nearly straight, but are specially distinguished by their very long, forked tails, in which the feathers are even narrower than in the comets: One of the species (*L. gracilis*) has been seen at a height of between seven and ten thousand feet on the Andes of Peru, and is apparently migratory, as it has been noticed to be common at Tambillo in December and January, whereas in

LONG-TAILED HUMMING-BIRD

June not one was to be seen.

The fork-tailed species displays great antipathy to the racket-tailed *Loddigesia*, which it is always driving away from flowers. Its note is a characteristic " tsi-tsi-tsi," very loudly uttered, and in a descending scale, and on visiting flowers it makes a sort of clapping noise, like that produced by pigeons when striking their wings together over their backs.

CURVED-BEAKED HERMITS

All the remaining members of the family may be included in the smooth-beaked section, characterised by the absence of serrations in the cutting edges of the beak. As our first representatives of the group may be noticed the curved-beaked hermits (*Eutoxeres*), of which there are several species, remarkable for the strong curvature of the beak, which describes fully one-third of a circle. The plumage is dull, and devoid of metallic sheen, and the tail rounded, with the extremities of the feathers pointed.

In Peru one of these humming-birds (*E. condamini*) has been observed feeding from flowers in which the curved form of the corolla exactly corresponds with the curvature of the beak, while at the same time the bald patch on the centre of the crown of the head affords a fair field for the pistils to smear as the bird probes the flower. The plant in question is abundant on the sides of the paths, and always covered with plenty of flowers, but although the bird is often met with, it cannot be called common. It stops but a short time on the flower, and is therefore not easy to procure. In the stomach remains of different species of gnats have been observed.

SALVIN'S HERMIT

In Salvin's hermit (*E. salvini*), ranging from Costa Rica to Panama, the head is wholly feathered; the species also differs from the last in having no buff on the outer tail feathers, which have likewise no white tips, and there is no blue patch on the neck. Mr. Merrill, who met with the species in Panama, writes that "one day, while hunting a short distance from the camp for humming-birds, I was startled by the swift approach of a small object through the close thicket, which darted like a rifle bullet past me, with a loud hum and buzzing of wings. Indeed, it was this great noise which accompanied its flight, being so much greater than I had ever heard before from any of these winged meteors of the southern forests, that especially attracted my attention as something uncommon. The bird continued its flight but a short distance beyond the spot where I stood, when it suddenly stopped in its rapid course directly in front of a flower. There for a moment poising itself in this position, it darted upon the flower in a peculiar manner; in fact, the movements of this little creature, which I now followed, were exceedingly curious to me.

"Instead of inserting its beak into the calyx by advancing in a direct line towards the flower, as customary with this class of birds, according to my limited observations, this one performed a curvilinear movement, at first stooping forward while it introduced its bill into the calyx, and then, when apparently the beak had reached the desired locality in the flower, its body suddenly dropped downwards, so that it seemed as if it was suspended from the flower by its beak. That this was not actually the case the continued rapid movement of its wings demonstrated beyond a doubt. In this position it remained for the ordinary length of time, and then by performing these movements in the reverse order and direction it freed itself from the flower, and afterwards proceeded to the adjoining one, when the same operation was repeated. The flower was that of a species of palm, the blossoms of which are attached alternately on each side to a pendent stalk. Each flower resembles an inverted Roman helmet, and is attached, as it were, by the point of the crest to the stalk. It is a fleshy mass of a deep crimson colour, and the cavity of the calyx extends in a tortuous manner downwards towards the attachment of the flower to the stalk."

TYPICAL HERMITS

The typical hermits constituting the genus *Phaëthornis* are dull-plumaged humming-birds, of a fair size, with wedge-shaped tails, the feathers of which are mostly tipped with white or buff. The beak is long and curved, but not to the same extent as in the last genus. Many species of these hermits are known, ranging from Mexico, through Central America, to Southern Brazil and Bolivia. The nest is an elongated structure, placed at the extremity of one side of a long and pointed leaf, as if for protection from the attacks of monkeys and other animals. The hermits are abundant in Brazil, where they inhabit the gloomy forests, feeding chiefly on insects, instead of courting the sunshine and sucking the honey from flowers.

In Peru, however, the grey-throated hermit (*P. griseigularis*), instead of inhabiting the hot and moist forests, like other species of the genus, frequents dry and arid valleys, where it seeks the densest thickets, and sometimes banana plantations. A naturalist, when passing near some thick bushes, was arrested by the sound of a shrill note, repeated at intervals, which struck him at first as the utterance of a tanager, and he searched in vain to find the bird.

PRETRE'S HERMIT

Baffled, he at last lay down at the bottom of the thicket, and after some minutes discovered a tiny bird perched on a branch quite close to the ground. Here was the meeting-place of the hermits, and the observer at length found four or five of these birds seated at a short distance from each other, at intervals uttering their whistling notes, while sometimes one would take a short flight round, and then hasten back to the same place. Subsequently, the birds were heard on several occasions in the same thicket, uttering their characteristic cry. At another place exactly the same curious habits were observed in an allied species (*P. superciliosus*). These hermits often fly in front of an intruder, and remain suspended in the air, apparently examining him all the time with marked curiosity. Pretre's hermit humming-bird (*P. pretrei*) is a native of Southern Brazil.

SWORD-BILLED HUMMING-BIRD

In the sword-billed humming-bird (*Docimastes ensiferus*), the single representative of its genus, the beak attains a greater development than in any other of the humming-birds, this appendage being equal to the length of the whole bird, and measuring at least as much as 4 inches. The home of this bird is in the Andes, from Venezuela and Colombia to Peru; and the long beak is specially developed to enable its owner to extract insects from elongated tubular flowers. In some parts of Peru the sword-bill is by no means

GUIANA KING HUMMING-BIRD

knocks the one I covet off his perch, and the two go fighting and screaming away at a pace hardly to be followed by the eye. Another time this flying fight is sustained in mid-air, the belligerents mounting higher and higher till the one worsted in battle darts away seeking shelter, followed by the victor, who never relinquishes the pursuit till the vanquished, by doubling and hiding, succeeds in making his escape. These fierce raids are not waged alone between members of the same species. *Eugenes fulgens* attacks with equal ferocity *Amazilia dumerili*, and, animated by no high-souled generosity, scruples not to tilt with the little *Trochilus colubris*.

"I know of hardly any species which shows itself more brilliantly than this on the wing. Yet it is not to the midday sun that it exhibits its splendour. When the southerly winds bring clouds and driving mists between the volcanoes of Agua and Fuego, and all is as in a November fog in England, except that the yellow element is wanting, then it is that *Eugenes fulgens* appears in numbers; *Amazilia dumerili*, instead of a few scattered birds, is to be seen in every tree; and *Trochilus colubris* in great abundance. Such animation awakes in humming-bird life as would hardly be credited by one who had passed the same spot an hour or two before; and the flying to and fro, the humming of wings, momentary and prolonged combats, and the incessant battle-cries seem almost enough to turn the head of a lover of these things." In Arizona this humming-bird has been found building in a pine tree at a height of about fifty feet above the ground. The second species, *E. spectabilis*, is a native of Costa Rica.

KING HUMMING-BIRDS

Two beautiful species alone represent the genus *Topaza*, one being *T. pella* of Guiana, in which the outer tail feathers are cinnamon; while the second is *T. pyra*, from the Rio Negro and Ecuador, distinguished by the purplish black tint of the same feathers. Both species are characterised by the tail feather on each side of the middle pair being elongated, curving outwards, and then crossing its fellow.

HILL-STARS

In the humming-birds commonly designated hill-stars (*Oreotrochilus*) the beak is relatively short and curved, the toes are proportionately large, and the tail is squared, with narrow feathers. These birds are inhabitants of the higher Andes from Ecuador to Chile, each species having a distinct and restricted range. *O. pichincha* and *O. chimborazo* occur, for instance, only in Ecuador, the former being confined to the volcanoes of Pichincha and Cotopaxi, and the latter to that of Chimborazo; *O. adelæ* lives in the Andes of Bolivia, *O. leucopleurus* in those of Chile, while *O. melanogaster* and *O. estellæ* inhabit the Andes of Peru, the latter also occurring in Bolivia.

common, although tubular flowers are met with in abundance, and the bird need fear no rivals, since no others of its kindred could probe these long tubes.

The species frequents a kind of *Jacksonia* with a long red corolla, the bird hovering for a moment before the flower, inserting its beak rapidly, and then withdrawing it two or three inches, when it again drives the beak into the same flower; this manœuvre being repeated many times on the same blossom. The bird is also said sometimes to pierce the side of the flower with its lance-like beak to get at the honey within. In the female the beak is even longer than in the male, reaching a length of 7 inches. The colours of the female are also a little less brilliant than those of her mate.

RIVOLI HUMMING-BIRD

A long, straight beak, a forked tail nearly uniform in colour, without any white in it, and brilliant colouring —namely, a body of bronzy green, a crown of rich metallic violet, a throat of glittering green, and an under surface changing with the light from velvety black to green—are the characters distinguishing the typical species of the genus *Eugenes*, called after the Duc de Rivoli, and first found in the highlands of Guatemala, but extending northwards to Mexico and Southern Arizona.

Mr. Osbert Slavin writes that "it is a most pugnacious bird. Many a time have I thought to secure a fine male, which I had perhaps been following from tree to tree, and had at last seen quietly perched on a leafless twig, when my deadly intention has been frustrated by one less so in fact, but to all appearances equally so in will. Another humming-bird rushes in,

The Chimborazo species is olive green, with the whole of the head, including the crown and the throat, deep glittering violet blue, the rest of the under surface of the body being white, with the middle of the abdomen and flanks blackish brown. Most of these hill-stars have a patch of black or chestnut along the abdomen, and the Chimborazo species differs from its ally only in having the centre of the throat green instead of entirely blue.

PICHINCHA HILL-STAR

Among other species the pichincha hill-star (*O. jamesoni* or *pichincha*) apparently presents many curious features in its habits, as it has been observed clinging to rocks, for which its relatively long feet and claws seem specially adapted. It is also believed that these birds build their nests under overhanging ledges of rock, and breed in companies ; and the size of the nest is certainly very large, equalling that of a man's head. The nest itself is comprised of wool, vicuña's hair, moss, and feathers, while at the top of this great mass is a little cup-shaped depression in which the eggs are deposited. One curious nest was found suspended to a rope hanging from the ceiling of a deserted house. When one side of the nest is lighter than the other, the birds restore the equilibrium by adding a small stone or a piece of earth to the other side, so that the eggs are in no danger of falling out.

GREAT HUMMING-BIRD

The great humming-bird (*Patagona gigas*), the largest member of the whole family, is the sole representative of its genus, and attains a length of 8½ inches, with a wing-length of between 5 and 6 inches. This bird is found among the Andes from Chile northwards to Ecuador, and is easily recognised by its size and somewhat sombre coloration ; while it is further distinguished by its strong feet, and the white band on the rump, which sharply contrasts with the rest of the plumage of the back. The flight is also peculiar, for, although the bird hovers over flowers, it does so with a very slow and deliberate movement, quite unlike the vibratory motion common to most species. When

RACKET-TAILED HUMMING-BIRD

hovering by a flower, its tail is constantly expanded and shut like a fan, the body being kept in a nearly vertical position ; and it has been stated that in no other bird does the force of its wings appear, as in a butterfly, to be so powerful in proportion to the weight of the body. The flight of this humming-bird is as noiseless as that of a butterfly.

In Peru this species is not rare in the ravines, where several may often be met with together. In flight it presents considerable resemblance to a swift, and only differs in its more subdued motions, though it often glides through the air without a movement of the wings. It constantly visits a certain species of *Jacksonia*, so that the head of every specimen is tinged with yellow from the flowers ; and it has also a habit of mounting in the air, beating its wings in a vertical position, and returning to its perch. The only note is a subdued whistle.

RACKET-TAILED HUMMING-BIRD

Unmistakable on account of its relatively long tail and conspicuous crest, the beautiful and curious racket-tailed humming-bird (*Loddigesia mirabilis*) is one of the smallest representatives of the whole family. In the tail, while the two outermost feathers are long and pointed, the second pair is produced in a wire-like form, each crossing the other near the middle of their length, and terminating in a large, racket-like expansion of a beautiful purple hue. First described from a single specimen in 1847, the species was not met with again till 1880, when examples were obtained in Upper

CHIMBORAZO HILL-STARS

Amazonia from the same locality. The bird seems, indeed, to be confined to the valley of the Utcubamba, a little river on the right of the Marañon system, at an elevation of some eight thousand feet.

The country is open, with here and there a little valley more richly clothed with vegetation, while an occasional clump of trees survives as a remnant of the ancient forest which once clothed the region. Dense thickets abound, in which a species of *Alstromeria* (of a red colour) is the favourite flower of the racket-tail; and wherever this occurs the humming-bird may be observed, and as the tree is in flower from August to November and another local humming-bird (*Lesbia gracilis*) does not care for these flowers, the racket-tail thrives.

It is one of the most active of the family, seldom taking rest, the females being especially lively. The adult males are more rarely seen than females and younger males, but they are beautiful objects when viewed in front of a flower, the tail with its two rackets being depressed, while the bird is hovering with the spatules in close proximity to each other. When in flight the humming noise is very loud, on account of the short wings, and more pronounced in the male than in the female.

One of the most curious habits connected with this humming-bird is that of assembling in parties. Eight or ten males, mostly young ones, have been observed to collect in a bare and desolate plateau on which were no flowers at all, the gathering being apparently merely for manœuvres.

Two young males would first stop in the air opposite to one another, with their bodies held vertically, opening their tails and springing first to one side and then to the other, uttering each time the tail was opened a little cry, which the observer likened to the noise of flipping a finger-nail or snapping a watchcase.

As a rule, this aerial dance is shared by two young males only, but sometimes several take part, and the note of the female is almost always to be heard in the vicinity. Sometimes one of the young males hangs below a thin branch while another manœuvres above him, spreading his tail and "snapping." Suddenly in a flash the positions are reversed, and the suspended bird takes the place of the dancer. The old males perform curious antics with the tail, and occasionally bring the two rackets close to the crown of the head.

These humming-birds have been observed drinking water at a little cascade, this being doubtless the only way in which they can appease their thirst. The cry of the young male and of the female is "tsi-tsi-tsi," rapidly repeated when the bird is visiting flowers or executing the manœuvres described above; when perching they are silent.

DOUBLE-CRESTED HUMMING-BIRD

Among a galaxy of beauty it is difficult to decide which species most deserve notice, but mention may be made of the double-crested humming-bird (*Heliactis bilopha*, or *cornuta*) which takes its name from the glittering tufts over the eyes, and is also distinguished by the wedge-shaped tail, with the feathers narrowed at the end into blunt points. The colour is shining grass green, metallic greenish blue on the crown, and inclining to golden on the back, the tufts at the side of the head being metallic purple, shading off into golden, and then to metallic green; while the sides of the head and throat are black, the under surface of the body pure white, the flanks green, and all but the middle feathers white, with their outer webs greyish. The total length is only 4 inches. The female is duller in colour than the male, and has the crown green, the sides of the face dusky, the throat pale buff, and the tail feathers white with a sub-terminal band of black. The home of this species is Brazil, where the bird is said to be not uncommon in some portions of the interior, although little is known of its habits.

MALE AND FEMALE TUFTED COQUETTES

COQUETTES

The so-called coquettes (*Lophornis*) form a very easily recognised group of humming-birds on account of the crested head and the little spangled frills so very conspicuous on each side of the neck. Twelve species are known, and the range of the genus extends from Southern Mexico, throughout the greater part of South America, to Bolivia and Southern Brazil, but does not include Ecuador or Peru. One of the most beautiful species is the tufted coquette (*L. ornatus*), which inhabits the island of Trinidad and the opposite mainland of Venezuela, whence it extends into Guiana. It measures not quite 3 inches in length, with a beak of half an inch, and a wing a fraction more.

The upper surface of the body is glittering golden green, with a buffy white band across the rump, the long crest dark cinnamon, the throat glittering green bordered with cinnamon, and the neck-frill also cinnamon, each of the feathers being tipped with a round spot of glittering green.

The abdomen is grey, the sides of the body and under tail coverts are shining green, the feathers edged with pale cinnamon; the tail is cinnamon, the lateral feathers broadly, the rest narrowly, edged with golden green externally; and the beak is flesh colour, with a black tip.

Scarcely anything has been recorded of the habits of the coquettes; but in the case of the Central American *L. helenæ* the flight is very rapid, and hardly to be followed by the eye as the bird darts from flower to flower; the cry is also peculiarly shrill and unlike that of any other humming-bird.

SWIFTS

ALLIED in some respects to the humming-birds, and in others to the goat-suckers, the swifts (family *Cypselidæ*) are readily distinguished from the former by their short and wide beaks, while from the latter they are differentiated by the palate being constructed after the passerine type. The short beak is curved towards the tip, and very broad at the base, so that the gape is of great extent. As in the humming-birds, the tail feathers are ten in number; whereas in the swallows, which curiously resemble the swifts in external appearance, there are twelve of these feathers.

Of primary quills there are only ten, and the secondaries are also reduced, their number never exceeding nine. The breast bone resembles that of the humming-birds, being free from notches in its hind border; but the upper wing bone, or humerus, is unique on account of its extreme shortness and width. The swifts may be divided into three subfamilies, the first of which (*Cypselinæ*) includes the more typical members of the family.

TYPICAL SWIFTS

In common with two others out of the five genera included in the subfamily, the typical swifts (*Cypselus*) have the metatarsus covered with feathers, and the number of joints in the third and fourth toes reduced to three; while the first toe is capable of being turned forwards like the others. Among the species, the Alpine swift (*C. melba*) is large, and of a general mouse-brown colour, with rather darker wings and tail; the throat and under surface of the body being white, with slight indications of dusky shaft hues to the feathers, while there is a broad band of brown across the fore part of the neck. The length is $8\frac{1}{2}$ inches, and the wing also measures the same in length.

This swift inhabits the countries bordering the Mediterranean as far north as the Alps, extending thence throughout Persia to the Himalaya, but wintering slightly to the south. In Africa it is replaced by the closely allied *C. africanus* extending from Shoa to the Congo. On the Continent, Alpine swifts arrive in spring, towards the end of March or the beginning of April, and depart at the end of October; although there may be a considerable difference in the time of arrival, the backward or forward state of the season appearing to influence the time of their arrival and departure.

In the town of Berne these swifts frequent the tower of the cathedral. A few arrive at the beginning of April, and after a short inspection of their old home disappear. Some, however, return in a few days, and the number is increased day by day until more than two hundred make the cathedral tower their home. When they first come, the swifts are in good condition, and it is well that they are so, as insects are few so early in the year, especially if April happens to be a bad month. At this time they may be seen sitting in rows, hungry and waiting for a more propitious season; and, if they should attempt a flight, they circle round the cathedral without the harsh cries uttered during their gambols.

Every spring some are picked up which have succumbed to the cold, but on the approach of fine weather the cathedral tower becomes the centre of great animation. These swifts are very regular in their habits, at the dawn of day leaving their roosting-places to seek food in mid-air, and continuing their flight until about noon, after which they are not seen. They rest until about five or six o'clock, and then resume the chase until night-time, sometimes, on warm nights, flying till as late as nine o'clock; and even during the night their cries are loud enough to inconvenience persons living in the neighbourhood. Their nests are placed in all kinds of situations in the cathedral, in holes, spouts, or on the arches in the interior; while some of the birds, probably driven away by the inhabitants of the tower, have taken up their abode in a house in one of the most frequented streets of the town.

When once on the ground, these swifts, like their congeners, are unable to rise, their long wings and short feet rendering it difficult or impossible for them to mount in the air again, though they are able to cling to the rough surface of rocks or stones. On account of this disability the swifts place their nests at a higher level than the point of exit, so that they are able to fall at once into mid-air. For the same reason the materials for the nest are collected from any place except the ground. These consist of hair, wool, dead leaves, and the like, and especially fragments of paper, the latter being supplied to the birds by the keeper of the tower, who throws them into the air, when they are seized by the swifts, and carried off to their nests. All the materials are cemented with the birds' saliva to form the nest. The eggs, although usually two, may be three in number.

The typical, or common, swift (*C. apus*), which is among the latest of the summer migrants to reach Europe, is almost entirely black in colour, the only exception being the white throat. In length it measures about 7 inches. Wintering in South Africa and Madagascar, the swift is represented in the Mediterranean regions by the pale swift (*C. murinus*), which accompanies it in winter to the Cape. Much that has been written concerning the Alpine swift will apply to the present species; the nesting habits of both being similar. The flight of the common swift is, however, somewhat less rapid than that of its Alpine cousin, although far swifter than that of any other bird

THE SWIFT

frequenting the British Isles. Indeed, the manner in which a swift twists and turns in the air is often suggestive of the flight of a bat rather than that of a bird.

PIED SWIFT

Differing from the typical swifts of the Old World in its feathered toes, soft plumage, and nearly square tail, the pied swift (*Aëronautes melanoleucus*), which ranges from the South-Western United States to Guatemala, constitutes a genus by itself. Writing of its habits, Dr. Shufeldt observes : " On the Chugwater Creek, Wyoming, we passed some very high and imposing chalk cliffs which constitute the more striking and more prominent features of the landscape, as the country about them is low and unbroken, being quite prairie-like in character. The head of one of these large chalk bluffs, as it stood out against the clear blue sky and far above me, actually looked, with the cloud of white-throated swifts swarming about it, like some great beehive from which the inhabitants had been suddenly aroused. These birds were far above the range of my fowling-piece, though one, now and then, dipped down with the most inconceivable velocity and in a graceful curve over my head, as if to obtain a better view of me. A snap-shot brought down one of these more accommodating individuals, whose cu iosity cost his life, and gave me not only a beautiful specimen, but the opportunity to examine in the flesh, for the first time, one of the then rarest birds in American collections.

" During the past eight years I have only caught glimpses of single specimens of this bird here and there, and sometimes in most unexpected places. Once, far out on the open prairie, in the north-western part of the United States, a magnificent adult swift of this species flew by me with the velocity of a meteor, his white flank-patches contrasting conspicuously with his black-brown body and wings. It was not, however, un il I came to Fort Wingate that the opportunity was really afforded me more intimately to study and observe this swift in its favourite haunts ; for all through North-West-ern New Mexico occur deep, even - walled cañons of rock to which the pied swift resorts to rear its young. Early in the spring of 1885 (April) I found some two dozen pairs of them in just such a cañon about three miles west of Fort Wingate. The walls of this magnificent gorge are of solid rock, being nearly three hundred feet deep in some places, and for the most part roughly perpendicular, though frequently arching over and outwards at their summits. It was

SWIFT AND ALPINE SWIFT

to the deep and crack-like fissures seen in the walls of the eaves of these latter recesses, away high up on either side of this rocky chasm, that the swift resorted to lay its eggs. So wisely had every pair of these birds chosen the cleft wherein their nests were hidden that all my plans and attempts to secure a set of eggs proved futile.

" From the extent of their wings the birds of this family appear formed to live in the air, where, in fact, they pass the most of their time, gliding about in extensive circles without effort, and apparently little motion of the wings. This ease of flight stands them in good need in their migratory movements, allowing them readily to pass into warmer climes. During pleasant weather they find their insect prey in the upper air, but when cloudy or rainy we find them skimming the ground in their pursuit. When on the ground, the shortness and weakness of their legs, added to their length of wing, incapacitate them from again rising in the air ; hence I have several times seen the European species picked up in the streets of Geneva, having fallen there during a quarrel with its fellows. When they wish to take rest during the day, which is rare, they always alight on some elevated point, whence they can throw themselves into the air and take to wing. Though numbers were flying about the rocks near Tucson, I heard them utter no note. Sociable among themselves, gathering in large flocks, they never mingle with the swallows. They generally construct their nests in the crevices of rocks or holes in old buildings ; many species have secretory glands, exuding a glutinous substance with which to fasten them firmly. The eggs, from four to six in number, are pure white, and of an elongated form."

FEATHER-TOED SWIFTS

The two species of feather-toed swifts, although resembling the pied swift in the feathering of the toes, differ in the form of the tail, the outer feathers of which are pointed. The Cayenne species (*Panyptila cayennensis*) ranges through Columbia, Guiana, and Amazonia, while Salvin's swift (*P. sancti-hieronymi*) in-habits Guatemala. The latter is an unusually beautiful bird for such a dull-coloured family, its general hue being silky black, with a narrow white collar round the hinder part of the neck, while the wings and tail also show a good deal of white at the bases of the feathers. Writing of a nest devoid of eggs, which he found in Guatemala, Mr. Osbert Salvin observes that " in this nest we see the saliva of the bird used as an adhesive material in nest-building, as in the genus *Collocalia* of the Old World, but differently applied.

" At first sight the saliva appears to have been used

as far south and east as North Africa, Persia, and the Punjab. In India it is replaced by the nearly allied *A. galgula*, and in North Africa by the thick-billed lark (*A. crassirostris*).

WOODLARK

The woodlark (*Lullula arborea*), which is placed in a genus apart, may be readily distinguished from the skylark by its shorter tail, more distinctly marked breast, and the presence of a distinct light streak over the eye and ear coverts, while its size is considerably smaller. Unlike the skylark, which frequents open country, the woodlark prefers fields that border upon woods. In localities where the soil is sandy and partially covered with second growth, it is generally numerous, but does not frequent dense forest. In habits it is lively and sprightly, fond of the society of its congeners, and not quarrelsome, although more shy than the skylark. Frequenting the ground more commonly than is supposed, it only perches occasionally on branches when singing, and seeks its food almost always on the ground, where it runs with celerity and ease. It roosts on the ground in open places close to woods, under weeds or grass, or in weed-covered furrows, and retires early to rest.

Being more affected by cold than is the skylark, it migrates earlier southwards than the former. The woodlark's song is sweet and flute-like, more melancholy than that of the skylark, and generally uttered from the top of a tree, or on the wing. The bird rises to some height before beginning, then ascends higher and higher, throwing itself from side to side, hovers and floats in the air, and when the song is ended drops with closed wings to the ground again. Woodlarks sing not only in the morning and evening, but at other times, especially at night.

The woodlark constantly builds upon the ground, usually in a tuft of grass, or in a depression of the earth, sheltered by a low bush. Made of stems of grass and moss, and lined with hair and wool or fine bents, the nest is more compact than that of the skylark. The eggs are generally white, finely flecked, and blotched with brown and purplish markings, sometimes arranged in a zone (page 990).

Very local in the British Isles, especially in the breeding season, when it is chiefly found in the southern and western counties, particularly Devonshire, the woodlark is common in Southern Norway and Sweden, and extends eastwards through Central Russia, ranging

south to Spain, Morocco, and Egypt. The plumage of the adult is brown above, each feather being striped with dark brown and edged with rufous; a broad, yellowish white stripe extends from each eye to the nape, forming an irregular collar; the rump and upper tail coverts are greyish brown; and the tail is dark

THE WOODLARK

brown, with the middle pair of feathers much lighter than the others, while the outer pair are dirty white towards the tip, and their outer webs bordered with white.

CRESTED LARKS

The crested lark (*Galerita cristata*) and its relatives are sufficiently distinguished from both the foregoing by the presence on the head of a crest composed of a few long feathers springing from the centre of the crown. The common species is a partial resident in the Continent, and a rare, accidental visitor to the shores of Great Britain. In spring it may be seen in the north of Spain travelling in flocks, which generally frequent the ploughed fields in preference to grass lands. These large flocks are relatively wild; but on other occasions the crested lark is confiding and fearless, and in the neighbourhood of villages and inhabited places one of the most unsuspicious birds.

In Southern Germany and Hungary, where it is common, it may be seen on the high roads and in the streets of small towns and villages pecking about almost as tamely as a sparrow. These larks appear, indeed, partial to inhabited places, and frequent high roads in preference to fields. In different parts of Europe they are resident or migratory according as the locality is suitable or not for winter quarters, but in most districts are partial migrants. In Germany, Dr. Naumann writes that " they leave their northern haunts in the winter, which they spend in smaller or larger companies in milder climates. Many winter on the Maine and Rhine, and in Franconia and Thuringia, arriving in October and November, and disappearing at the beginning of spring. In Northern Germany these larks are resident or partially migratory, these latter rambling in pairs or small companies from place to place, and arriving in winter where they are not observed in summer, but seldom remain there long. The time of migration is in November and December. Old pairs remain year after year at the same breeding place. They migrate from the one inhabited place

DESERT LARK

AFRICAN FINCH LARK

above and beneath a second, passes through the lores ; a black band runs backwards from the eye ; the chin and throat are white, as is the abdomen ; but the fore neck and breast are pale fulvous, spotted with black (page 1039).

FINCH LARKS AND BUSH LARKS

Another genus (*Ammomanes*) belonging to the group with ten primaries to the wings is formed by the finch larks, of which one species is the African finch lark (*A. deserti*), while other species inhabit India. Having the first primary long, as in the preceding genus, these larks are specially distinguished by the thick beak being much shorter than the head, and the nostrils concealed by plumelets. They inhabit open arid plains, from which they rise singing into the air for a short distance, and then suddenly drop.

There are several other genera of the group, such as the Asiatic bush larks (*Mirafra*), which may be distinguished from the finch larks by the open nostrils ; a well-known species being the Madras bush lark (*M. affinis*) of Southern India.

SHORT-TOED LARKS

The short-toed lark (*Calandrella brachydactyla*) and its relatives are inferior in size to most of the family, and have the beak short and stout, with the upper half arched, while there are only nine primaries in the wing, of which the first is long and reaches to the tip. The inner secondaries are lengthened and reach to the end of the primaries, or nearly so ; the tail is rather long and slightly forked, and the slightly curved claws are very short. Several species of short-toed larks inhabit Europe and Northern Asia, and others are found in India. The European short-toed lark is common in Southern Spain and Malta during summer, frequenting the wild parts, where the song of the cock may be often heard while the hen is sitting.

Ranging eastwards to Turkestan, in winter this lark visits India. Its mode of ascending in the air differs from that of the skylark, consisting of a succession of jerks. Their food consists almost exclusively of small seeds, the husks of which they break with their beaks ; but it may be presumed that insects are supplied to the young. On the ground this lark runs quickly, and it is especially fond of grovelling in sand. When at large, it never perches on shrubs or bushes, though in confinement, like the skylark, it will readily take to a perch. The

to the other in the daytime, generally in the forenoon, and fly at a considerable altitude."

The song of the crested lark is sweeter and in some respects more pleasing than that of the skylark. This lark nests upon the ground in any small depression of the soil or behind a clod of earth ; the nest being loosely and simply constructed of stems of dry grass and fine roots, sometimes lined with a little horsehair. The eggs, which are greyish white, marked with dark or light brown and grey, may be found from the middle of April until the middle of July. The crested lark is a favourite cage bird in Germany, and may be seen from time to time exposed in the Paris bird market. The upper parts are brown, the feathers of the neck and back having dark middles fringed with buff ; the crest is conspicuous, and consists of nine or ten narrow feathers, blackish brown in colour, edged with buff ; the lower parts are creamy white, the sides of the throat spotted with blackish brown, and the feathers of the breast and flanks streaked with dark brown.

DESERT LARK

In the desert lark (*Alæmon desertorum*) the beak is very long and slender, gently curved in its terminal half, the nostrils are fully exposed to view, the first of the ten primaries of the wing is short, although longer than the primary coverts. The toes and claws are very short, the latter being stout. The plumage is the same in both sexes.

A native of the deserts of Arabia and Northern Africa, this species extends eastwards into Afghanistan and Western India, where it is sparsely distributed throughout the desolate wastes in which it makes its home, living in pairs, each enjoying the run of its own territory. The song of the male is often uttered in the breeding season, but is short and unpretentious. Breeding in May and June, when it makes a small nest of dried grass on the sand, the desert lark lays greyish white eggs, marked with yellowish brown.

In many birds the plumage serves the purposes of concealment from enemies ; and the desert lark, like other species that haunt deserts, is coloured a pale sandy grey, with ashy tinge on the forehead and upper tail coverts. The first primaries are black, with white bases, the tail feathers black margined with fulvous, the two middle feathers being sandy brown, broadly edged with very bright fulvous ; a black streak, with a white band

CALANDRA LARK

knolls remote from human dwellings. To this there is one remarkable exception. In large cities, where most of the buildings are high, with flat roofs, often covered with gravel, the house-tops are as free from human intrusion as the top of a mountain, and the night-

RED-NECKED NIGHTJAR

hawks take advantage of this artificial desert to lay their eggs and rear their young safe from man, who crawls about in the crevices of streets far below."

PENNANT-WINGED NIGHTJAR

The rare and beautiful African species known as the pennant-winged, or Leona, nightjar (*Macrodipteryx longipennis*), which is the only representative of its genus, is seldom obtained in its full perfection of plumage, since the peculiar, long-shaped primary, which forms the distinguishing character of the genus, is often missing or not developed. The male of this nightjar has the ninth primary quill developed to an extraordinary length, with the shaft bare and ending in a racket-like expansion, so that, as the bird flies, the wing has a long pennant, or streamer, on each side. These pennants are probably only developed in the breeding season, and are not found in the female. The species occurs in Western Abyssinia, and on the West Coast from Senegambia to the Niger. When the bird is sitting in covert on the ground, the pennants are stated to be erected vertically, and thus resemble flowering reeds.

STANDARD - WINGED NIGHTJAR

The standard - winged nightjar (*Cosmetornis vexillarius*), which might perhaps be included in the same genus as the last, is also characterised by an elongation of the primary quills, of which the seventh and eighth are greatly developed, while the ninth is prolonged into a streamer which floats behind the bird

as it flies. The shaft, however, is not bare, as in the Leona nightjar, but feathered throughout its whole extent.

This bird ranges from Equatorial Africa westwards to the Benue River and Fernando Po, and south throughout Eastern Africa to the Zambesi and Damaraland. Sir John Kirk, who met with the species in Nyasaland, writes that it "was first observed about three hundred miles up the Zambesi, a little above Tete, on the Keihrabassa rapids in November, 1858, and was there decidedly common. It was again met with on the western side of Lake Nyasa where, in September and October, it was very plentiful, being seen in flocks of from fifteen to twenty. It was also common at Chibisa on the Shiré, in 16° S. It was only during the months from October to January that the singular prolongation of the wing feathers was observed ; these are peculiar to the males. Like other nightjars, the habits of these birds are crepuscular. When startled during the daytime from the ground, where they always rest, they fly swiftly for a little distance and again settle, but are extremely difficult to follow with the eye. Not so the males in full plumage. In their case there is no difficulty ; their flight is evidently retarded, and they become prominent objects from the long streamers waving behind them.

"A deviation from the usual habits of the bird was observed when cruising on Nyasa Lake. On two occasions, being overtaken in a gale, and riding out a short but dangerous sea, which set in and raised a surf

VIRGINIAN NIGHTJAR

on the shore, through which it was impossible to land, the male birds came off in flocks of about fifteen, and flew over the surface of the water. On no other occasion have I seen them take wing of their own accord."

FORK-TAILED NIGHTJARS

South America is the home of a group of nightjars remarkable for their enormously developed forked tails ; while in Africa there is also a genus (*Scotornis*), the two members of which have tails longer than their bodies, the feathers gradually decreasing in length till the outside ones are the shortest. In South America the genus *Hydropsalis* has the outer tail feathers produced, and the two middle ones also long, while the next pair is the shortest. In *Macropsalis*, however, the outside pair of tail feathers is produced to an enormous length and forms a train, the feathers being gradually reduced in size towards the middle of the tail, where the middle pair is the shortest.

Of the former genus a well-known representative is the Argentine fork-tailed nightjar (*Hydropsalis furcifera*), which is not uncommon near Buenos Aires in spring and autumn, living on the ground in damp situations where the grass is long and thick enough to afford some slight covert. It is generally observed in parties of four or five, and its flight is noiseless, and performed by jerky, erratic movements. In Entre Rios, where it is common in summer, arriving in August and leaving in May, Mr. J. B. Barrows states that "while hunting capivaras and armadillos by moonlight, I had frequently good opportunities for watching its movements. Its flight is nearly as irregular and as noiseless as that of a butterfly, while its beautiful tail is opened and shut in the same manner as with the scissor-tailed flycatcher. Alighting frequently on the ground, or on stones or roots, it keeps up a continual but very soft clucking, which is the only note uttered. It was most often seen in open grassy or sandy spots in the woods, especially along the margins of the streams. By day it sits close on the ground, and, if disturbed, only flies a few yards, though it evidently sees well."

The eggs are a creamy pink, delicately marked with lines and veins of pinkish lilac, something after the manner of bunting's eggs. "On March 17," writes Mr. O. N. Aplin, "I saw a male with the long tail feathers settle on a post of a wire fence which passed through part of the monté (a small wood around a settlement on the pampas); it sat lengthwise to the line of fence. The curious long swallow-tail of the male does not seem to incommode it at all, as the bird can turn and twist about in its rapid gliding flight in a wonderful way, and accomplishes the difficult aerial navigation of the thorny monté with all the ease and grace of a nightjar in an oak wood."

NACUNDA NIGHTJAR

The single representative of its genus, *Podager nacunda*, differs from all the preceding in the slight development of the bristles of the gape, as well as in the shortness of the tail, which only equals about half the length of the wing. The plumage is of the usual mottled hue, but the tail is distinctly barred, and the primary quills are conspicuously white, while the secondaries are lighter brown, with blackish brown bars and vermiculations. The middle tail feathers are coloured like the back, but the outer ones have broad white tips; the abdomen and under tail coverts are white; the lores and upper part of the throat are reddish, with blackish brown bars; the chin is almost uniform rust-colour; and the lower portion of the throat is very dark brown, while the breast is similar to the upper parts. The length is $11\frac{1}{2}$ inches.

Mr. W. H. Hudson writes that "the specific name of this goatsucker is from the Guarané word nacundá, which is the Indian nickname for a person with a very large mouth. In the Argentine country it has several names, being called dormibu ('sleepyhead'), or duerme-duerme ('sleep-sleep'), also gallina riega ('blind hen'). It is a large, handsome bird, and differs from its congeners in being gregarious, and in never perching on trees or entering woods. It is an inhabitant of the open pampas. In Buenos Aires and also in Paraguay it is a summer visitor, arriving at the end of September and leaving at the end of February.

"In the breeding season the male is sometimes heard uttering a song or call, with notes of a hollow, mysterious character; at other times they are absolutely silent, except when disturbed in the daytime, and then each bird, when taking flight, emits the syllable 'kuf' in a hollow voice. When flushed, the bird rushes away with a wild, zigzag flight, close to the ground, then suddenly drops like a stone, disappearing at the same moment from sight as effectually as if the earth had swallowed it up, so perfect is the protective resemblance in the colouring of the upper plumage to the ground. In the evening these nacundas begin to fly about earlier than most nightjars, hawking after insects like swallows, skimming over the surface of the ground and water with a swift, irregular flight ; possibly the habit of sitting in open places, exposed

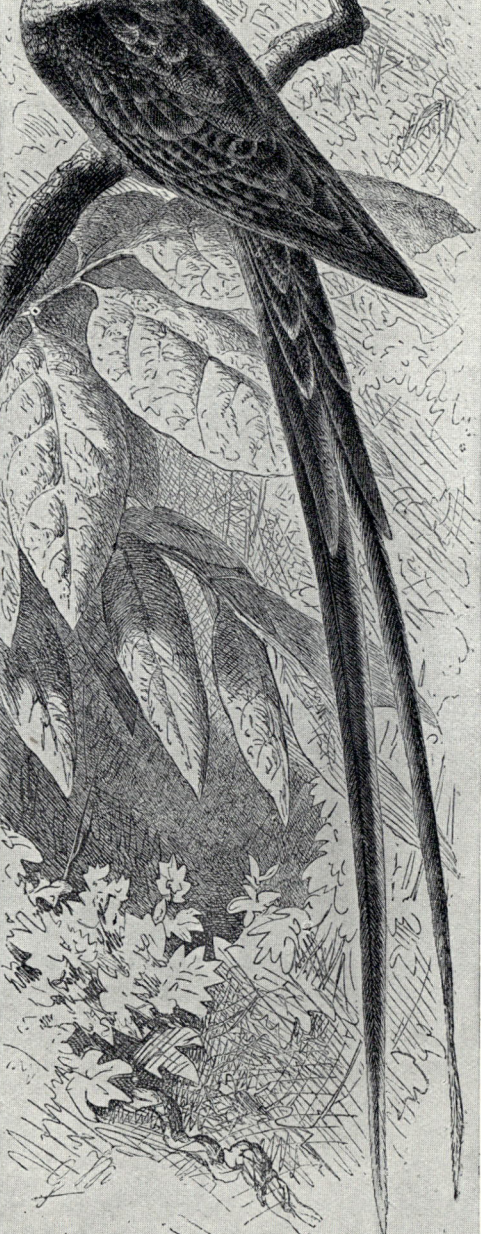

ARGENTINE FORK-TAILED NIGHTJAR

GREAT WOOD NIGHTJAR

belong. There are some half-dozen species, ranging from Mexico to Brazil, and also represented in the island of Jamaica.

The note of these nightjars is described as being more extraordinary than that of any other bird. Mr. Charles Waterton, for instance, writes that "a goat-sucker inhabits Demerara, about the size of an English wood-owl, whose voice is so remarkable that, when once heard, it is not easily to be forgotten. A stranger would never believe it to be the cry of a bird, but would say it was the departing voice of a midnight murdered victim, or the last wailing of poor Niobe for her children before she was turned to stone. Suppose a person in hopeless sorrow, beginning with a high, loud note—'Ha, ha! ha, ha! ha!'—each note lower and lower till the last is scarcely heard, pausing a moment or two between each exclamation, and you will have some idea of the moaning of the great goat-sucker of Demerara."

In Peru the great wood nightjar (*Nyctibius grandis*) has a curious habit of perching upon dead branches, when it looks like a knot or prolongation of the bough, so that it takes an experienced eye to detect the bird. Its cry is extraordinary, and consists of five notes, descending gradually one-fifth in the scale, and producing a weird impression on moonlight nights.

to the full glare of the sun, has made these nightjars somewhat less nocturnal than other species that seek the shelter of thick woods or herbage during the hours of light.

"After the breeding season they are sometimes found in flocks of forty or fifty, and will spend months on the same spot, returning to it in equal numbers every year. One summer a flock of about two hundred frequented a meadow near my house, and one day I observed them rise up very early in the evening and begin soaring about like a troop of swallows preparing to migrate. I watched them for upwards of an hour; but they did not scatter as on previous evenings to seek for food, and after a while they began to rise higher and higher, still keeping close together, until they disappeared from sight. Next morning I found that they had gone.

WOOD NIGHTJARS

The wood nightjars (*Nyctibius*), large and mainly South American birds, are the sole representatives of the second subfamily, and are characterised by the plumage being more mottled than in the typical nightjars, and the extreme shortness of the metatarsus, which is inferior in length to all the toes, as well as by the absence of the comb on the third toe. Moreover, the sides of the body and breast carry large "powder-down" patches, which do not exist in the members of the typical subfamily, to which all the other genera of nightjars

STANDARD-WINGED NIGHTJAR

TODIES

THE curious little green-and-red West Indian birds commonly known as todies constitute the family *Todidæ*, all the members of which are included in the single genus *Todus*. They are represented only by five species, four of which respectively inhabit the islands of Cuba, Jamaica, San Domingo, and Porto Rico, while the fifth (*T. pulcherrimus*) has been stated to come from Jamaica, although its real home is still unknown. In these birds the beak is long and flattened, the palate is of the bridged, or desmognathous, type, the breast bone has four closed perforations on its hind border, the oil-gland is tufted, there are twelve tail feathers, and the first toe is present.

The habits of the todies appear to be very like those of flycatchers, but sometimes these birds hunt insects in trees and bushes after the manner of the American warblers. They seem to be entirely insect-eaters, as no vegetable remains have been met with in the stomachs of those dissected. Todies are becoming rare in Jamaica owing to the introduction of the mongoose, as the burrows on which the eggs are laid are very shallow, and easily robbed by that animal.

JAMAICAN TODY

Of the Jamaican tody (*T. viridis*) Mr. Taylor writes that it " appears to be very generally dispersed throughout the island, and may even be said to be common in most parts. In all localities that I have visited, whether on the mountains at high elevations or among the woods of the plains, it has appeared equally abundant at all seasons. Banks of ravines and gullies, where the fringing forest is of dense and varied but slender growth, hedges with deep banks, woods and thickets bordering many roadways, and especially the steep, narrow bridle-paths that wind up the mountain-sides, where the banks are high, may be mentioned as some favoured haunts. But of all localities there are few, perhaps, where these birds occur constantly in such numbers, or which offer more perfect situations for nesting, than the gullies before-mentioned.

" Many of these dry watercourses, that during prolonged rains become transformed into rushing, impassable torrents, are of considerable extent, and their sandy beds may be traced for miles inland. One gully, in particular, where most of my observations on the habits of the todies have been made, has a wide and tortuous course, and banks that vary in places from low, weed-covered mounds to precipitous cliffs of clay, between ten and twenty feet in height. In their choice of a situation for nesting, the birds are somewhat

JAMAICAN TODY

particular, preference being given to low, overhanging, weed-covered banks, where the soil is light and friable. The tunnels are rarely, if ever, in high situations, but, on the contrary, may frequently be found at the sides of the shallow ditches and hollows that are commonly formed in soft soil during heavy rains. I have often surprised the todies at work. In beginning a tunnel, they cling in an awkward manner to the face of the cliff or bank, fluttering their wings frequently, as if for support.

" So far as I have been able to observe, in digging they appear to employ the beak only, and I once took a tody that had almost the entire half or side of the upper mandible worn away ; this, however, was during a period of drought, when all vegetation was burnt and shrivelled, and the earth hard and unyielding. In most cases the whole work of excavation would seem to be performed by the birds, yet I have noticed, in the gullies at least, that those portions of the banks usually selected for nesting are nearly always riddled with holes and cavities of different depths. Whether the birds ever take possession of one of these, or enlarge others to suit their needs, I have not discovered ; but such a proceeding would seem highly probable, in view of the labour which the work of excavation frequently entails.

" When digging into some of these holes in a search for the true nest of a tody, I often find them in the occupation of strange tenants, such as field-mice, lizards, and spiders. The latter, black, repulsive-looking objects, are of common occurrence, especially in the depressions formed by the falling away of stones, etc., so that some little caution is necessary in prosecuting a search for the eggs of the bird. The burrows run horizontally and to a considerable depth, but invariably, so far as my experience goes, turn at right angles at a few inches from the entrance. The tunnel terminates in a somewhat rounded cell, where, upon a little heap or bed of fine soft earth, without any lining whatever, the eggs are laid. These are usually three or four in number, almost globular, glossy, and of a beautiful pearly white, except that, when fresh, the contents impart a delicate pink tinge to the shell. They are, in fact, miniature kingfisher's eggs.

" The tameness of the tody is well known, but, as Mr. Gosse remarks, this seems rather the tameness of indifference than of confidence. I have accomplished the capture of specimens with a butterfly-net at different times with little difficulty, and frequently a tody has permitted so near an approach that I have been tempted to put out my hand in the hope of taking it.

The todies keep in pairs, if not constantly, for the greater part of a season at least, and during nidification seem to range over a very circumscribed space. Their food appears to consist exclusively of small insects, which they usually pursue and take after a short flight, returning constantly to the same twig, where they will patiently sit and watch, with head drawn in and beak pointing obliquely upwards, the plumage much puffed out, the wings meanwhile being flirted by a continuous, rapid, vibratory movement."

MOTMOTS

Exclusively confined to Central and South America, the motmots (family *Momotidæ*), of which there are seven genera, are closely allied to the kingfishers and bee-eaters of the Old World, being by no means unlike the latter in external appearance, most of them having a long tail, with the middle feathers produced beyond the others. The first toe is always present, the hind margin of the breast bone has four notches, which are converted into perforations, and there are no blind appendages, or cæca, to the intestine. The beak is serrated, its saw-like notches being doubtless for use in nipping off the webs of the tail feathers.

Both in the wild state and in confinement, so soon as the middle feathers for the tail begin to grow beyond the line of the others, the birds commence to nibble the web away, leaving a bare shaft for an inch or an inch and a half, with a large racket-like expansion at the end of the middle pair. In one instance the two middle tail feathers had grown unsymmetrically, one being more developed than the other. The bird was evidently puzzled to find the middle feather, which its instinct warned it to nibble, and began operations on several of the other feathers, until in time the middle one grew out beyond the others, and showed which was the proper one to snip.

There are more than a score of species of motmots, all having long tails, with the exception of the single species of *Hylomanes*, which is a bird of small size, recalling the todies in appearance.

TYPICAL MOTMOTS

As a well-known example of the typical genus may be taken the Mexican motmot (*Momotus lessoni*), a species with the general colour of the plumage green, this tint including the tail feathers, which become blue towards their extremities, where they are tipped with black. On the crown of the head is a patch of black, bordered with silvery blue, which passes into turquoise blue, with an inclination to purple on the nape ; the eyebrow, forehead, and cheeks are likewise black, the latter being ornamented with a band of turquoise blue above and below ; the under surface is olive brown, becoming greener on the abdomen, and inclining to emerald green on the throat ; while on the fore part of the neck

BRAZILIAN MOTMOT

is a tuft of black feathers edged with greenish blue. In length this handsome bird measures about 15½ inches from the beak to the tip of the tail.

Writing of its habits, Mr. A. K. Cherrie observes that " the nests are built in the ground, some bank, such as the side of a stream, being selected. The entrance tunnel extends back horizontally, sometimes for a distance of six feet. At about half its length there is a sharp bend upwards for some six inches, then the course is again horizontal as far as the chamber occupied by the nest. The nest space is twelve or fourteen inches in diameter, being round, and about six inches high, with level floor and ceiling. A few rather coarse dry twigs are strewn over the floor. If one of the nests be opened at about the time the young are ready to leave, it will be found to be one of the dirtiest, most foul-smelling places that can be imagined.

" At the time the young leave the nest, they are able to fly pretty well. They have the same colours as the adults, but the bill is much shorter and more depressed, and the edges are without serration. The tail is shorter than the wings and nearly square. The eye is sepia brown, not chestnut, as in the old bird. With the first utterances of the notes of the adults, the peculiar jerky motions of the tail began. It was most amusing to watch the four birds sitting in a row together, almost motionless, only giving the tail first a jerk to this side, then to that, now up and now down, to see it held for the space of a minute almost at right angles to the body, and then go with a whisk to the other side, the birds all the time uttering their peculiar cooing notes."

The Brazilian motmot (*M. brasiliensis*, or *momota*), ranging from Guiana to Amazonia, has the head cobalt blue, with black on the crown and sides, comparatively little red on the back, which is otherwise green, and the under parts green with a tinge of rufous.

COSTA RICA MOTMOT

Another genus is represented by the Costa Rica motmot (*Urospatha martii*), which ranges southwards to Amazonia, and has the upper parts olive green, with a rufous tinge on the blackish primaries and tips of the tail feathers, of which the middle pair have blue rackets. In contrast with this is the cinnamon of the head and under parts, and the black cheeks and long feathers on the throat.

BROAD-BEAKED MOTMOT

In the broad-beaked motmot (*Eumomota superciliaris*), the single representative of its genus, the beak is very much flattened, and has a grooved ridge on the culmen with hair-like bristles at the gape. The tail is long, exceeding the wing in length, and has a broad racket at the end. The colour of the species is grass green, with the mantle cinnamon, the crown grass green, with a broad white eyebrow, shading off behind into silvery cobalt ; at the base of the cheeks are a few spots of silvery blue ; the under parts are rusty, inclining to grass green on the fore part of the neck and breast, and to oily green on the sides of the face and throat, in the centre of which is a black streak, bordered on each side with silvery blue feathers.

This species, which has a total length of 15 inches, inhabits Central America from Yucatan to Costa Rica, where the bird is locally known by the name of torovoz. " In the breeding season," writes Mr. R. Owen, " these birds are in full song, if their croaking note may be so termed, and are as noisy and busy then as they are mute and torpid during the rest of the year. I do not know of any sound that will convey a better idea of the note than that produced by the laboured respiration occurring after each time the air is exhausted in the lungs by the spasms of whooping-cough. The nest of the torovoz is subterranean, and is usually found in the banks of rivers, or of watercourses which empty into them.

"The excavation is horizontal, and at a distance from the surface varying with the depth of the bank in which it is situated. The size of the orifice is sufficient to allow the bare arm to be introduced, the shape being round and regular for three, or at most nine, feet, where the shaft terminates in a circular chamber about eight inches in diameter and five inches high. In this chamber the eggs, usually four in number, are deposited upon the bare soil.

"The banks of the river which winds through the plain of San Geronimo are full of excavations made by this bird—that is to say, in such places where the soil is light and the bank chops down perpendicularly. It is a simple matter to hit upon those which are inhabited, as the entrance to the abandoned ones will be found perfectly smooth, whereas the mouths of those which contain eggs or young are ploughed up in two parallel furrows made by the old bird when passing in and out. The torovoz is exceedingly tame, and, when startled from its nest, will perch on a bough a few yards distant, watching the demolition of its habitation with a degree of attention and fancied security more easily imagined than described."

BEE-EATERS

The bee-eaters (family *Meropidæ*) constitute a well-marked group confined to the Old World, their place in America being taken by the motmots and jacamars. They have long and curved beaks, with a well-marked ridge along the culmen, and syndactylous feet, like those of kingfishers, with the soles very broad, the third and fourth toes united almost for their entire length, but the second joined to the third for its basal joint only. The tail feathers are ten in number, the palate is bridged (desmognathous), the breast bone has four notches on its hind margin, and there are certain other osteological characters distinguishing the group, into the consideration of which it is unnecessary to enter.

Of the five genera by which the family is represented, two (*Meropogon* and *Nyctiornis*), both of which are Asiatic, are distinguished by tufts of overhanging plumes on the breast, which are wanting in the other three. Of the latter, the swallow-tailed bee-eaters (*Dichrocercus*) and square-tailed bee-eaters (*Melittophagus*) are confined to Africa, while the typical bee-eaters (*Merops*) inhabit the four great continents of the Old World. As a rule, bee-eaters lay glossy white eggs in nests situated at the end of long tunnels excavated by the birds themselves, although the two species of *Nyctiornis* are stated to nest in trees.

SWALLOW-TAILED BEE-EATERS

Distinguished by the absence of a tuft on the breast and the forked swallow-like tail, in which the middle feathers lack the elongation characterising the other members of the family, the African swallow-tailed bee-eaters are represented by two species, one of which (*Dichrocercus furcatus*) comes from the western side of the continent, while the other (*D. hirundineus*) is a southern form.

The latter is distinguished by having the forehead and eyebrow of the same green hue as the rest of the head, instead of being blue ; the general colour of the upper parts is golden green ; the wings are green, and their primary quills light chestnut with black tips, forming a terminal band to the wing feathers ; the upper tail coverts and the middle tail feathers are blue, the remainder golden olive tipped with white, preceded by a shade of black ; a black streak runs along the sides of the head ; the cheeks and throat are orange yellow, followed by a black band ; the breast is green ; the abdomen and under tail coverts are blue, and the eyes crimson. The whole length is 8½ inches, and the sexes are alike in colour.

This bee-eater inhabits Cape Colony and South Africa generally, extending to the east so far north as Zanzibar, and on the west to Damaraland and Benguela. In habits this species is like other bee-eaters, hawking for

MOTMOT WITH UNTRIMMED TAIL
From a specimen in the London Zoological Gardens

CHESTNUT-HEADED BEE-EATER

A well-known member of the genus is the chestnut-headed bee-eater (*M. swinhoei*), in which the lower part of the back and the upper tail coverts are silvery blue ; the primary quills are rufous internally, with a blue bar at the end ; the tail is greenish blue ; the head and mantle are chestnut ; the throat is yellow, with a black band inferiorly ; the under surface of the body is emerald green ; the breast and flanks are marked with yellow, and the abdomen and under tail coverts are blue.

This pretty species is found in the Indian Peninsula and Ceylon, extending through the Burmese countries to Siam and Cochin China, and southwards to the Malay Peninsula. The eggs, like those of the rest of the family, are pure white, and four or six in number, the holes in which they are laid being tunnelled in sandy soil by the birds themselves, either in retired banks of rivers or in the sides of roads, and varying in length from one foot to seven feet, with the chamber at the end larger than the rest of the excavation. The direction of the passages is not always straight, some of them, after a depth of twelve or eighteen inches, turning off almost at right angles, while others take an almost circular direction. There is no nest in the chamber, the eggs being laid on the bare floor, which is about six inches in diameter.

TYPICAL BEE-EATERS

Of somewhat larger size than the last, the typical bee-eaters of the genus *Merops* are represented by about a score of species, all distinguished by having the middle tail feathers elongated beyond the others. Of these, the majority are peculiar to Africa, two (*M. persicus* and *M. viridis*) inhabit both Africa and India, and Arabia owns two species—namely, *M. cyanophrys* from Aden, and *M. muscatensis* from Muscat. In Europe the typical *M. apiaster* is common in summer, *M. philippinus* abounds from the Indian Peninsula to Southern China and even extends over the greater part of Malaya, while *M. ornatus* is Australian. Two (*M. bicolor* and *M. sumatranus*) are confined to the Indian region, and

COSTA RICA MOTMOT

food in the open, and capturing insects in full flight. It seems, however, to fly at a lesser altitude than some of its larger relations, and nests in sandy banks, making tunnels of about three feet in length, with the entrance very small, not more than two inches wide, but opening out into a slightly wider chamber at the end.

SQUARE-TAILED BEE-EATERS

The square-tailed bee-eaters are all of small size, measuring only from 6 to 9 inches in length, and mostly confined to Africa, although two species range into India and the countries east of the Bay of Bengal as far as Java. About fifteen species in number, these bee-eaters are easily recognised by their squared tails ; their general colouring being of the peculiar green hue common to the group, although with considerable contrasts of blue and yellow, some also having a black band on the throat. While the African species frequents watercourses, the little bee-eater (*Melittophagus pusillus*) prefers reedy marshes and swamps, where it perches on low bushes and trees. On the other hand, the white-fronted species (*M. albifrons*) selects higher trees in the neighbourhood of water.

THE BEE-EATER

one of the handsomest species is *M. breveri* from the Gabun and the Congo.

EUROPEAN BEE-EATER

The typical European bee-eater is a rather large species, measuring 10 inches in length. The head and mantle are chestnut, the back and scapulars creamy buff, the lower part of the back is washed with blue like the upper tail coverts, the lesser wing coverts are green, but the rest is chestnut like the secondaries, which are tipped with black, the quills are blue with blackish tips, the tail green with blue edges, and the middle feathers are almost entirely blue; the cheeks

BLUE-BEARDED BEE-EATER

are blue in front and white behind, the crown is chestnut, with a white band on the forehead, followed by a blue line joining a narrow blue eyebrow, the throat is yellow, with a black band across the lower part; the rest of the under surface is greenish blue, and the eyes are yellow.

The sexes are alike in colour, but the young are paler, having a green eyebrow-stripe, with a black bar on the lower part of the throat, and a wash of green over the head, mantle, and back.

This bee-eater visits Southern Europe regularly every summer, and is found so far east as Turkestan, Kashmir, and Sind, breeding in Afghanistan and Kashmir. Its habits are like those of other bee-eaters, the bird taking its food on the wing, and being very destructive to bees in certain parts of Europe, visiting the hives and capturing the insects as they fly in and out. In winter it visits all parts of Africa, and is even said to rear a second brood in its winter home, as stated in a later paragraph.

According to Colonel L. H. Irby, bee-eaters are to be seen everywhere in Spain, and their single note, " teerp," heard continually repeated, magnifies their numbers in imagination. " Occasionally, they venture into the centre of towns when on passage, hovering round the orange trees and flowers in some patio or garden. Crossing the straits for the most part in the early part of the day, flight follows flight for hours in succession.

" When passing at Gibraltar, they sometimes skim low down to settle for a moment on a bush or a tree, but generally go straight on, often almost out of

sight; but their cry always betrays their presence in the air. In some places they nest in large colonies; in others there are, perhaps, only two or three holes. When there are no river banks or barrancos in which to bore holes, they tunnel down into the ground, where the soil is suitable, in a vertical direction, generally on some slight elevated mound.

" The shafts to these nests are not usually so long as those in banks of rivers, which sometimes reach to a distance of eight or nine feet in all; the end is enlarged into a round sort of chamber, on the bare soil of which the usual four or five shining white eggs are placed. After a little they become discoloured from the castings of the old birds, the nest being, as it were, lined with the wings and undigested parts of bees and wasps."

Several species of European birds are reported to nest in the southern countries where they winter, and although most of these records must be received with caution, in the case of the bee-eater the evidence is strong, as Mr. Layard states that not only did he receive information of the breeding of the species in Africa, but himself found it nesting in large numbers on the Berg River in September and October. He observed that " it does not always select a bank into which to bore the hole destined for its nest, for we found one flat piece of sandy ground perforated with numberless holes, into which the birds were diving and scrambling like so many rats."

CELEBES BEE-EATER

The island of Celebes is the home of *Meropogon forsteni*, a species characterised by having the two middle tail feathers elongated, as in *Merops*, but with a bunch of overhanging plumes on the breast. The colour of the bird is green, with the quills dusky at the ends, the middle tail feathers green, but the rest chestnut with green edges, the head, throat, and breast deep ultramarine, the hind part of the neck maroon brown, the abdomen dusky blackish washed with green, and the under tail coverts chestnut with green margins; the total length being 13 inches.

The Celebes bee-eater is only found in dense forests difficult of access, where it inhabits the highest trees, and has the manner and ways of the other bee-eaters.

BEARDED BEE-EATERS

The two kinds of bearded bee-eaters constituting the genus *Nyctiornis* are distinguished not only by the tufts of feathers on the breast, but by the squared tail and densely feathered nostrils. The blue-bearded bee-eater (*N. athertoni*) is an Indian bird, extending east to Siam, but replaced in Tenasserim and the Malay region by the scarlet-bearded bee-eater (*N. amictus*), a beautiful species, with the long feathers of the throat scarlet instead of blue, and the forehead lilac instead of bluish green.

The scarlet-bearded bee-eater is stated to be fairly common in parts of Borneo, frequenting the high forest, where it sits solitary on the lower boughs of trees, making short flights after insects. Although there is a statement as to its eggs having been taken from a tunnel, the scarlet-bearded bee-eater is believed to nest in holes in trees, having been seen to fly out of such cavities in Tenasserim.

HOOPOES AND WOOD-HOOPOES

HOOPOES

THE beautiful birds known from their cry as hoopoes (family *Upupidæ*) form, with the wood-hoopoes, a group having no very close allies, and have been considered as nearly related to the perching birds, from which they are sharply distinguished by the bridged structure of the palate, as well as by the presence of two deep notches in the hind border of the breast bone.

They are further characterised by a perforation in the fore part of the latter bone, which allows the two coracoid bones to meet in the middle line ; a similar condition also obtaining in bee-eaters and hornbills. Indeed, the latter birds, which at first sight appear so different, seem to be the nearest allies to the hoopoes, both groups displaying very remarkable nesting habits, and also having certain structural features in common.

All the members of the present family are included in the single genus *Upupa*, and are desert-loving birds, inhabiting suitable localities in Africa, the greater part of Asia, and temperate Europe, and specially distinguished by the sandy hue of the plumage, which is devoid of any metallic gloss, by the squared form of the tail, and by the open and rounded nostrils. They are represented by six species, three exclusively confined to Africa and Madagascar, while the Indian *U. indica* ranges from the country from which it takes its name to Burma, and on the western limits of its range apparently interbreeds with the European species.

The typical hoopoe (*U. epops*) has the plumage of a general sandy brown colour, with black-and-white bands ; a crest of erectile plumes adorns the head ; the secondary quills are black, with four white bars of equal width ; the primary quills black, with a broad band of white ; the lesser wing coverts are of the same sandy hue as the back, those of the median series are black tipped with buff, and the rump is white. The dark purplish crest feathers are tipped with black, bordered inferiorly by a line of white ; the flanks have blackish streaks ; the under tail coverts are white ; the tail is black, with a broad white band, somewhat bent downwards on the outer feathers ; the beak is black, with a flesh-coloured base, and the feet are black (page 1093). In total length the bird measures about a foot.

The range of this species apparently extends from Southern Sweden and Central and Southern Europe generally to Japan ; its winter home being Senegambia, South-Eastern Africa, and the peninsula of India. In the latter area it probably intergrades with the resident species, which has no white subterminal bar on the crest feathers, although many intermediate specimens are met with showing an indication of a more or less perfect white bar, and may be the result of crossing. The sexes of the hoopoe are alike in colour, and young birds resemble the adults, but have more fluffy plumage. Breeding as a rule in hollow trees, the hoopoe is now rare in those parts of the Continent where the country has been denuded of timber.

The female sits very closely on her eggs, during which period she is fed by her mate. Lord Lilford writes that hoopoes generally " prefer a hole in a hollow ash or willow for nesting in ; but I have seen a nest on the ground under a large stone, others in holes on the sunny side of mud or brick walls, one in a fissure of limestone rock, and one in a small cavern. The eggs, when first laid, are of a beautiful pale greenish blue, but soon become stained and dirty, so that the average hoopoe's egg is of a dirty yellow colour."

Mr. Swinhoe, writing from China, observes that " hoopoes have often bred in the holes of exposed Chinese coffins ; the natives hence have an objection to them, and brand them as the ' coffin-bird.' The young, when hatched, are naked, but soon get covered with small blue quills, which yield the feathers. The little creature has a short bill, and crouches forward, making a hissing noise. It looks a strange compound of the young wryneck and kingfisher. They do not stand upright till nearly fledged. Their crests develop at once, but their bills do not acquire their full length till the following year."

A naturalist in Calcutta, who was one of the first to direct attention to the circumstance of the nesting hen being fed by the cock, states that two pairs of these birds nesting in his veranda became so tame that his presence never disturbed them in the least ; and he twice saw the males with the females just at the bottom of the steps, and within ten yards of where he was sitting. " I was therefore," he continues, " thoroughly familiar with them, and can assert most positively that for a number of days I never saw the female of either pair out. I did not pay any attention at first to the circumstance of there being only two flying about, until I observed both males going up to the nest with gnats in their bills, giving a call, and then

THE HOOPOE

putting their heads inside for the hens to take the food.

"The feeding times were morning and evening, at regular hours—the former about seven or eight o'clock, and again in the afternoon about four o'clock. I have seen the males getting the gnats, etc., close under the very steps I was sitting on, and almost within two yards of my chair, then flying up, giving a call, and coming down again directly the food was taken. The nests were at opposite ends of the veranda, and only one of the broods came out. I saw, some time ago, a notice in 'The Field' mentioning the dirty state of the nest before this could have been caused by the young ; and, if my idea is correct, the explanation is simple. I never saw the males go inside the holes in which the nests were, and I never saw either of the females outside during the time they were hatching, though, of course, it is possible they may have gone out."

In a second communication this naturalist adds : "In continuation of my letter of last year, I may mention that there were again this spring two hoopoes' nests in my veranda, and in the same place. I find that the hens do leave the nest once or twice a day, but I have never seen them stay out longer than to give time to get rid of their droppings, and I have never seen either of them on the ground when out. Generally speaking, they perch on a tree near at hand, and after sitting a few moments for the purpose mentioned, fly back to the nest. Two or three times one of the hens flew out, passed her dropping whilst on the wing, and returned to the nest without having settled anywhere. They are fed most indefatigably by the cocks, and the number of grubs, small worms, and so forth, destroyed by them is very great."

As already mentioned, the name hoopoe is doubtless derived from the note of the bird, rather than from the fact of its possessing a remarkable crest, whence may come the French title, "la huppe." Mr. Swinhoe writes that the notes are produced "by puffing out the sides of its neck, and hammering on the ground at the production of each note, thereby exhausting the air at the end of the series of three notes, which makes up its song. Before it repeats its call it repeats the puffing of the neck, with a slight gurgling noise. When it is able to strike its bill, the sound is the correct 'hoo-hoo-hoo,' but when perched on a rope, and only jerking out the song with nods of the head, the notes most resemble the syllables 'hoh-hoh-hoh.'"

WOOD-HOOPOES

From the members of the preceding family wood-hoopoes (family *Irrisoridæ*) are distinguished by the more or less marked metallic gloss on the plumage, the long, wedge-shaped tail, which exceeds the wing in length, and the elongated nostrils, partly concealed by an overhanging flap. These birds, which are confined to Africa, are represented by three genera, differing from one another merely in the degree of curvature of the beak and the contour of the nostrils. The species taken as the chief example of the family is the purple-tailed wood-hoopoe (*Irrisor viridis*), measuring about 14½ inches in length. The colour of the upper parts is metallic green, inclining to bronze on the back, and with a steely blue tinge on the hind part or the head and neck ; while the feathers of the lower portion of the back, as well as the upper tail coverts, are bluish black edged with dark copper. The wings are steel-blue, their primary coverts being tipped with

RED-BILLED WOOD-HOOPOE

white, the lesser coverts edged with copper, and the primary quills crossed with a band of white consisting of twin spots, the outer smaller than the inner ; the tail is purple, shot with violet, all but the middle feathers showing an oblique subterminal bar of white ; the under surface is glossy steel-blue ; the breast and upper part of the abdomen are shining metallic green ; the lower portion of the abdomen and under tail coverts glossy purplish black ; the beak and feet scarlet, and the eyes dark hazel.

This species is an inhabitant of South Africa, whence it ranges so far north as Angola on the west and Mombasa on the east coast. In North-Eastern Africa and on the west coast, from Senegambia to the Niger, its place is taken by the allied *I. erythrorhynchus*, distinguished by having the tail greenish blue instead of purple. In habits all wood-hoopoes are shy and wary, and very active and erratic in their movements, always frequenting trees, and seldom descending to the ground.

They are said to breed in hollow trees and lay white eggs, and the nests have the same offensive smell as those of hoopoes. The birds have a very disagreeable smell, and may be seen creeping about the trunks of trees, after the manner of woodpeckers, and feeding on cockroaches. They are generally seen in flocks, probably consisting of family parties, and have a loud and harsh cry, which has caused the name of "kachela," or "chatterer," to be given to them by the Boers.

Another species is the red-billed wood-hoopoe (*I. erythrorhynchus*), ranging from Nigeria and Senegambia across the continent to Shoa and Abyssinia, and recognisable by the feature from which it takes its name.

HORNBILLS

Hornbills, which form a well-marked family (*Bucero-tidæ*) by themselves, derive their name from the enormous development of the beak, which is mostly hollow, and furnished with a casque of greater or less prominence, although the latter is sometimes represented merely by a straight and compressed keel. In the case of the solid-casqued hornbill (*Rhinoplax*), the whole of this portion of the beak is solid, and the entire skull consequently very heavy, whereas in the other species it is remarkable for its lightness. The palate is of the bridged type, and the upper part of the breast bone has the same perforation as in the hoopoes and bee-eaters. The spinal feather-tract is not defined on the neck, and the tendons of the foot are split into branches, of which one leads to the first toe and another to the second, while the third and fourth toes are served by one tendon. The tail feathers, as in most of picarian birds, are ten in number. The eggs are white, and the young hatched in a naked and helpless condition.

Confined to the Old World, the hornbills are found in Africa and the Indian region, extending through the Malay countries to Celebes, and thence to New Guinea and the western islands of the Solomon group. They are divisible into three subfamilies, the ground hornbills (*Bucoracinæ*), true hornbills (*Bucerotinæ*), and solid-casqued hornbills (*Rhinoplacinæ*).

ABYSSINIAN GROUND HORNBILL

GROUND HORNBILLS

The curious and vulture-like ground hornbills, constituting the first subfamily, are peculiar to Africa, and have a hollow casque; the back of the neck and middle of the back are feathered, and the metatarsus elongated even to the extent of twice the length of the middle toe and claw. The group is represented only by two species, namely, the Abyssinian hornbill (*Bucorax abyssinicus*) from Western and North-Eastern Africa, and the South African hornbill (*B. cafer*) from South Africa, extending on the west to Angola, and on the east to the Pangani River, and even as far as the Suk country in Equatoria. These two species differ in the form of the casque, that of the Abyssinian bird being very evidently open in front, while in the South African species it is closed, or nearly so.

The Abyssinian species measures upwards of $3\frac{1}{2}$ feet in length, with a wing of 24 inches, and has the entire plumage black, excepting the primary quills, which are white. The beak and casque are black, with a red patch on the lower half of the former, the feet dusky black, and the bare parts of the face red, with the exception of the blue naked skin round the eye and on the middle of the throat. The female has the bare skin of the throat and region of the eye purple.

In North-Eastern Africa these hornbills are stated to be found in the wooded plains and on the mountains up to a height of four thousand feet, though more common between one and two thousand feet. After the breeding season they assemble in small flocks, when as many as ten or a dozen are seen together. Known to the Boers as the "bromvogel," the South African ground-hornbill is regarded as a fetich among many of the native tribes, being a rain-omen with the Kafirs, who believe that if one of these birds is killed there will be rain for a long time, and who, therefore, in times of drought will throw one of the birds into a vley, in order that rain may follow. The bird is so filthy and offensive that, according to native ideas, even throwing its body into the water will "make the river sick," and the only way of getting rid of it is to wash it away to the sea, which can only be done by heavy rains and flooding of the river.

These hornbills seems to be practically omnivorous, and devour great numbers of beetles, worms, mice, small birds, and the like. They associate in small companies of five or six, and when a snake is discovered, come round it, holding one wing stretched out and flapping the reptile with it until it is irritated and seizes hold of the feathers, when all the birds crowd round and peck it, until it looses its hold; this manœuvre being repeated till the snake is dead. If the latter advances, the birds fold both wings in front of them, so as to form a shield, thus covering their head and other vulnerable parts. Their call-note "coo-coo," can be heard at a distance of two miles. The nests are placed in the holes of trees, or in hollows formed by three or four branches striking off from the same spot; and it is believed that several females lay in the same nest.

RHINOCEROS HORNBILLS

The rhinoceros hornbills form the typical representatives of the second subfamily,

Bucerotinæ, all the members of which are more arboreal in their habits than the last group, in correlation with which the metatarsus is proportionately shorter, not exceeding the third toe and its claw in length. The sub-family may be divided into two sections, according to the form of the tail. The first section in which the tail is squared, includes the African trumpeter-hornbills (*Bycanistes*), the members of the present genus, as well as several smaller forms, such as *Penelopides* of the Philippines and Celebes, and *Lophoceros* of Africa, the latter genus containing the smallest member of the family, which measures only 15 inches in length.

MALAY RHINOCEROS HORNBILL

The Malay rhinoceros hornbill (*Buceros rhinoceros*) inhabits the Malay Penisula and the islands of Sumatra and Borneo, and is of large size, measuring nearly 4 feet in length. The colour is black, with a slight gloss of steel-blue or dark green ; the rump and upper tail coverts being white, as is also the tail, which has a broad bar of black just before the tip, while the under surface of the body is black, with the exception of the lower part of the abdomen, thighs, and under tail coverts.

The beak has a large casque, with the fore part turned up into a horn-like protuberance, whence the name of rhinoceros hornbill. The colour of the beak is whitish yellow, black at the base, the casque lake-red, shading off below into orange near the base, which is black, and there is also a black line from the side of the nostrils to the fore part of the casque. The feet are yellowish green, and the eyes deep lake. The female resembles the male in colour, but has no black base and no black median line along the side of the casque. In young birds there is no fully-developed casque, but only a small orange-coloured excrescence on the top of the upper half of the beak.

JAVAN RHINOCEROS HORNBILL

Java is the home of another species (*B. sylvestris*) character-

HEAD OF WEST AFRICAN TRUMPETER-HORNBILL

ised by its nearly straight casque. In many places this great bird is kept in a state of semi-domestication, Mr. Burbidge observing that in Borneo "the rhinoceros hornbill is very often seen in a state of domesticity, enjoying at the same time perfect liberty. When very young they are taken from the nest, and accommodated with a bit of old cloth in a basket as a bed, being fed on rice and soft fruits, until they are strong enough to wander about ; they sit on their haunches, wheezing and shrieking all day long, and continually clamouring for food. Their body is about equal to that of a very fat badly-plucked goose.

"If well fed, however, they soon gain strength and assume their plumage ; and then they flap about the house and steal or beg for food. At one place where I stayed collecting for some time, a native, in whose house I had established myself, had reared a very fine specimen of this bird. It was the most voracious brute I ever saw. It was omnivorous, and nothing came amiss to it or seemed to disagree with it.

"Very often he would descend from a tall camphor-wood tree, which stood a hundred yards or so from the house, in the jungle, to the top of which he was fond of going to sun his wings and clean himself after a meal. When he was very hungry, it was only by tying a string to his leg, and moving him to the side

of the house, that he could be prevented from eating off the same plate as myself, or putting his great horned head into the rice-dish or curry-bowl. Bones of a fowl, curried or not, were gobbled up instantly ; and the wonder was to me how he managed to bolt big bones and tough biscuits without choking himself.

"Whatever was thrown anywhere near his head was sure to fall into his open bill ; indeed, I never saw a dog that could catch food in his mouth better ; everything was caught on the point of his great bill, and then tossed into the air, being again caught and swallowed ; this tossing was always performed. Bones, the entire bodies of small birds from which the skins had been removed for preserving, lumps of bread, biscuits, fruit, fish, or wet rice, shavings, and even nodules of moist earth, all seemed equally welcome ; and after taking in a cargo of provisions which would have formed an ample meal for a pig twenty times his own weight, he would 'saw the air' with his great wings, and, having gained his favourite perch on the tall camphor-tree, would sun himself and plume his wings, and shriek until he became hungry, rather than hoarse."

GREAT PIED HORNBILL

The great pied hornbill (*Dichoceros bicornis*), the largest of the hornbills, and the sole member of its genus, measures nearly 5 feet in length, with a great casque, concave on the top and nearly square, rising into well-marked corners on the fore part. The colour is black, with white bases and tips to the greater wing coverts and quills ; the tail white, with a broad band of black just before the tips of the feathers ; the beak and casque yellow, inclining to orange-red on the top of the latter, with some black marks at the base of the beak and along the margins of the casque, the naked skin round the eyes fleshy pink, and the eyes themselves blood-red (p. 1094).

This hornbill, remarkable for its clumsy-looking beak, inhabits the hills of Southern India and the Himalaya, and its continuation in the Burmese countries to Siam, ranging southwards, through Tenasserim and the Malay Peninsula, to Sumatra. As in the other species of giant hornbills, there is a difference in the sexes, displaying itself in the colour of the beak. In the female there is no black on the casque, the bare skin of the face is reddish, and the eye white, instead of red.

Observers in India discovered the strange nesting habits of hornbills previous to Livingstone, who is generally credited with having been the first to direct attention to the incarceration of the female bird during the period of incubation. Colonel Tickell, for instance, writing in 1855 of the nesting of the great pied hornbill in Tenasserim, observes that : "On my way back to Moulmein from Mooleyit, when halting at Kyik, I heard by the merest chance from the Karen villagers that a large hornbill was sitting on its nest in a tree close to the village, and that for several years past the same pair of birds had resorted to that spot for breeding.

"I accordingly lost no time in going to the place the next morning, and was shown a hole high up in the trunk of a moderately large straight tree, branch-less for about fifty feet from the ground, in which I was told the female lay concealed. The hole was covered

TYPES OF HORNBILLS

SOUTH AFRICAN GROUND HORNBILL

ABYSSINIAN GROUND HORNBILL

BARE-BEAKED HORNBILL

BLACK HORNBILLS

BARE-BEAKED HORNBILL

BLACK HORNBILL

TWO-HORNED HORNBILL

with her own droppings and various decaying vegetable substances, so that the nests are often filthy, and give forth an intolerable stench. In all probability, one chief reason for the retirement of the female into the recess of a tree is that she is about to moult, and that she may undergo safely the whole of this while concealed. In this manner, the emaciated condition of some of the birds when liberated can be accounted for, while their subsequent fat condition and good plumage would be the result of the completed moult. The hole is doubtless plastered up as a defence against enemies, of which hornbills have plenty. The formidable beaks of these birds are useful as weapons of defence, as well as being of the needful shape to serve as trowels for plastering up the nesting-holes.

CRESTED HORNBILLS

The wedge-tailed hornbills, as the members of the second section of the typical subfamily are collectively termed, comprise several genera distinguished from the first section by the elongation of the middle pair of feathers in the tail. In the case of the genus *Berenicornis* of Malaya, as well as in the West African *Ortholophus*, the tail is much elongated, and forms a graceful appendage of graduated feathers, with conspicuous white tips. To this section belong the members of the genus *Lophoceros*, which are peculiar to Africa, and comprise nearly a score of species. They are all small birds, compared with the general run of the species of *Bucerotidæ*, and their mode of life seems to be somewhat different from those of the big hornbills of the east, though they have the same habit of plastering up the female in a tree at the season of incubation. They are often found on the ground, and feed on berries, seeds, and insects, but considerable quantities of sand have been found in the stomach, picked up by the birds when on the ground.

YELLOW-BEAKED HORNBILL

Of the yellow-beaked hornbill (*L. melanoleucus*) Mr. C. J. Andersson remarks that it "is the most common of the hornbills in the middle of the southern parts of Damaraland. It is found singly or in pairs, and, being a comparatively fearless bird, is easily killed, especially during the heat of the day, when it invariably perches on or near the top of a lofty tree (where such are to be found), and will remain for hours in this situation, keeping up, with short intermissions, a kind of subdued chattering note of 'tŏe tŏc tŏe tŏckĕ tŏckĕ tŏcke tŏc,' in a tone not unlike the quick yelping of young puppies, and accompanied at intervals by a flapping and raising of the wings, and an alternate lowering and erecting of the head."

This species is about 21 inches in length, with a tail about 9 inches long, and is distinguished by its yellow beak and by the white feathers on the chest being edged with black. It is found all over South Africa.

SOUTH AFRICAN GREY HORNBILL

Another species, namely, the South African grey hornbill (*L. epirhinus*), is recognised by the pale buff

with a thick layer of mud, all but a small space, through which she could thrust the end of her bill, and so receive food from the male. One of the villagers at length ascended with great labour by means of bamboo-pegs driven into the trunk, and began digging out the clay from the hole. While so employed, the female kept uttering her rattling sonorous cries, and the male remained perched on a neighbouring tree, sometimes flying to and fro, and coming close to us. Of him the natives appeared to entertain great dread, saying that he was sure to assault them, and it was with some difficulty that I prevented them from shooting him before they continued their attack on the nest.

"When the hole was sufficiently enlarged, the man who had ascended thrust in his arm, but was so soundly bitten by the female, whose cries had become perfectly desperate, that he quickly withdrew it, narrowly escaping a tumble from his frail footing. After wrapping his hands in some folds of cloth, he succeeded with some trouble in extracting the bird, a miserable-looking object enough, wasted and dirty. She was handed down and let loose on the ground, where she hopped about, unable to fly, and menacing the bystanders with her bill, and at length ascended a small tree, where she remained, being too stiff to use her wings. At the bottom of the hole, nearly three feet from the orifice, was a solitary egg, resting upon mud, fragments of bark, and feathers."

The number of eggs laid by hornbills seems to vary, sometimes only one being deposited, while at other times four or even five are found in the nest; the present species, apparently, never laying more than four. The female seems to assist in the matting-in of the nest-hole, using leaf-mould and earth, mixed

line down the middle of the back, and the white shafts to the middle pair of tail feathers ; the head and neck being grey, with a broad white eyebrow streak, the beak brown, the quills tipped with white, and the under surface of the body white, with the chest brownish grey.

The length is about 20 inches, and that of the wing 9 inches. This species is a great fruit-eater, and lives in small companies. Mr. Ayres states that he was once much surprised to hear one of these birds perched on the top of a small tree, singing with the voice of a thrush. " I could scarcely believe my ears," he observes, " until I had watched the bird for a considerable time ; at last he flew away, and the woods were silent."

In Damaraland and the lake regions of South-Western Africa these hornbills may be seen in small families, rarely exceeding six in number. In common with the rest of their kind, they appear to suffer much from the heat during the most trying season of the year, when they may be found perched at noon in the shadiest part of the forest, gasping as if for breath. When on the wing they occasionally utter short, piercing cries.

BARE-BEAKED HORNBILLS

The bare-beaked hornbill (*Ceratogymna elata*) and the black hornbill (*C. atrata*) represent a West African genus, which is allied to *Lophoceros*.

MALAY WEDGE-TAILED HORNBILL

In connection with the Malay wedge-tailed hornbill (*Anorhinus galeritus*) reference may be made to an experience by Mr. J. Whitehead, who found a nest of the species in Northern Borneo. He shot three of the birds before he became aware that there was a nest-hole in the tree, but, on being assured of the fact, sent one of the natives to climb up and let the old female out. When the native went to do this, he found two or three birds engaged in feeding her and her young one.

The hole is fastened up with guttapercha, dirt, and various gums ; the same hole, judging by the heaps of excrement at the foot of the tree, being often used for many years. The plastering of the hole is necessary to protect the helpless birds against the attacks of monkeys, and the huge tree-climbing monitor lizards, which cause immense destruction among the feathered population of the forests.

SOLID-CASQUED HORNBILL

In marked contrast to the light and cell-filled casques of the other members of the family, the beak of the solid-casqued hornbill (*Rhinoplax*) has a perfectly solid upper appendage, on which account this bird is referred to a separate subfamily. In this species the beak has the consistence and appearance of ivory, and is, in consequence, much in demand by the Chinese and Malay artists, who carve figures on its surface and make charms and brooches by cutting it into thin plates, which can easily be recognised from their bright yellow colouring with scarlet rims. The species is an inhabitant of Southern Tenasserim, the Malay Peninsula, and the islands of Sumatra and Borneo. In addition to its solid beak, it is remarkable for having the whole of the throat and back of the neck bare.

The length of this bird is nearly $5\frac{1}{2}$ feet, the tail alone being almost 3 feet long. The general colour is brown, the quills are black with white tips, and the tail is brown tipped with white, the tips being preceded by a black band. The two middle feathers are more than double the length of the next pair, and the outer pair are entirely white. The under surface of the body is white, the breast brown, the beak yellow, with the posterior portion red, like the bare throat and neck, and the feet and eyes also red. Mr. Davison, who found this species in Tennasserim, where he procured a single specimen in the evergreen forests, states that it is very shy, which is not to be wondered at, since, whenever one appears near a village, everyone who can shoot or get hold of a gun is sure to try and kill it ; as the heads are in great demand for carving into love-charms, and bring as much as fifty rupees apiece to the fortunate securer.

" The birds," he writes, " confine themselves almost exclusively to the evergreen forests, where they frequent the very highest trees. The cry begins with a series of whoops, uttered at intervals of about half a minute for five or ten minutes ; then the interval between each whoop grows shorter and shorter, till the ' whoop, whoop, whoop,' is repeated very quickly ten or a dozen times, the bird ending up by going into a harsh, quacking laugh. Then there is a pause of ten minutes, or a quarter of an hour or more, and then it begins again. The bird utters this call in the morning and evening, but occasionally also during the day. It never seems to descend to the ground, and feeds on fruit."

YELLOW-BILLED HORNBILL

KINGFISHERS—ROLLERS—KIRUMBOS

KINGFISHERS

IT is scarcely possible to name a country in the world where kingfishers (family *Alcedinidæ*) of some sort or another are not found ; and although the great majority of these well-known and handsome birds may be recognised by the long and dagger-like beak, the shape of this formidable weapon is subject to variation according as to whether its owner is a fish-catcher or a devourer of reptiles and other food than fish. The structure of the foot, however, scarcely changes throughout the group, for every kingfisher is flat-soled and has an anisodactyle foot, with the toes for the most part united, so that the whole foot is by no means unlike that of a hornbill, to which group some of the larger kingfishers make an approach in appearance.

Unlike so many of the picarian birds, most kingfishers have twelve tail feathers instead of ten, though a few possess the ordinary picarian number. As in hornbills and rollers, the deep tendons of the foot are peculiar; the one which usually supplies the first toe not serving that function in these three families, that toe being connected with the tendon which usually works the three front ones.

The eggs of kingfishers are always laid in holes of banks of some kind, or in trees, and are glossy white ; while the young birds, when hatched, are naked and helpless, although in a little time they become covered with feathers, each enclosed in a sheath, thus giving the nestling a peculiar bristly appearance. This sheath encloses the feather till it is almost fully grown, and then falls off rapidly, leaving the feather exposed. In none of the kingfishers and their allies is the plumage very dense. Indeed, in birds which have to plunge into the water a fluffy plumage would be greatly in the way, and kingfishers are therefore provided with a closely-fitting body-plumage, which does not get draggled or wet by the immersion it has to undergo.

Kingfishers have been divided into two subfamilies, namely, the fish-eating *Alcedininæ*, and the insect or reptile-eating *Daceloninæ*, and seem to afford an illustration of the importance of habits as a guide to affinity. In this instance structural characters are found to be correlated with difference in the mode of life. Thus the fish-eating kingfishers are equipped for their manner of living by the development of a long and narrow beak, and a tail just long enough to act as a rudder, but not of sufficient length to be in the way.

On the other hand, bush-kingfishers, which feed less on fishes and more on insects and reptiles, have the beak less narrow and compressed, but more flattened, and in some instances even hooked. Then, again, whereas in the typical subfamily there is almost always a perceptible groove along the beak, leaving the upper part in the form of a ridge, in the second group the ridge of the beak is either rounded or flattened, and in one or two instances there is even a groove along the middle of its upper surface.

A WOOD KINGFISHER

STORK-BEAKED KINGFISHERS

The first, or typical subfamily, *Alcedininæ*, comprises five genera, the members of all of which are essentially fish-catchers, although on occasion they eat small insects and crustaceans as well as other kinds of food. Two of the genera, *Pelargopsis* and *Ceryle*, although their representatives are thorough fish-eaters, have long tails, exceeding the length of the wings ; but in the other three, *Alcedo*, *Corythornis*, and *Alcyone*, the tail is conspicuously shorter than the wings.

Stork-beaked kingfishers inhabit the Indo-Malay region, and differ from the species of *Ceryle*, the only other fish-eating group with long tails, in having the sexes alike in colour, the beak very sharp and pointed, and the base of the upper edge or culmen flattened and somewhat ridged, instead of rounded and smooth. The species of this genus are further characterised by their bright blue backs, thus resembling those of the undermentioned *Halcyon*, whereas in *Ceryle* there is no bright blue.

Of the stork-beaked kingfishers over a dozen species are known, ranging from the Indian Peninsula and Ceylon through the Burmese and Malay countries to Java, Sumatra, the Philippines, Borneo, and Celebes. The species (*Pelargopsis melanorhynchus*) inhabiting the last-named island differs from all the others in having a black beak, whereas in all the rest it is coral-red.

One of the best known species is the Indian stork-beaked kingfisher (*P. gurial*), which is a large bird, measuring 14 inches in length, with a wing of nearly 6½ inches. The general colour of the plumage is dull green, with a slight shade of blue on the wing coverts; the outer aspect of the quills and the tail are greenish blue ; the head and nape are dark chocolate brown ; round the hind part of the neck is a collar of pale ochre ; the under surface of the body is of the latter colour ; and the beak and feet are dull red. This species is an inhabitant of Ceylon and the greater part of the Indian Peninsula, but does not reach the United Provinces, though extending along the lower Himalaya and Terai as far as Masuri and Dehra Dun. Eastwards it ranges to Assam, but is replaced to the south by the Burmese stork-beaked kingfisher (*P. birmanica*).

Generally found along rivers, streams, and backwaters, but only where well shaded by trees, it sits on a branch overhanging the water, and pounces on fishes, crabs, and occasionally frogs. Mr. Stuart Baker writes that " this kingfisher is by no means common in the Kachar district, so that I have been able to make but few observations on its breeding and other habits. Personally I have only taken two nests. One of these was placed in a hole about 2½ feet deep, and so large that without much difficulty I was able to put my arm into it and search for the contents. The other burrow was fully 4 feet deep, and the diameter at the entrance about 3¾ inches. Both nests were placed in high sandy banks of the Diyung River, upon which and the Jatinga the species is most often met with. The first hole contained four young birds, and the second a single egg. The latter seemed to be rather abnormal in shape, and was smaller at one end than the other. I have never seen the bird fishing on small streams, but it is by no means unusual to find it perched on trees at some distance from water, and it occasionally haunts ravines and other insect-producing places, where there is no water at all. Fish, I believe, form the staple article of its diet, but it varies this with any living thing which is small enough. It is on record that it devours lizards and similar small reptiles, and it is not averse from taking young birds from their nests.

"In Rungpore, in the collector's compound, there stands, or stood some years ago, a large tree full of crevices and holes, and much used as a nesting place by many mynas and other birds. One morning I was passing under this tree when I was attracted by the loud shrieking of a pelargopsis, accompanied by the cries of many other birds. The most vehement and excited amongst these last were a pair of mynas, whose newly-hatched brood were in a large hollow in a big limb some forty feet from the ground, and this had evidently attracted the attention of the blood-thirsty kingfisher. For some time he sat on a branch close to the nest-hole, giving vent every now and then to his loud cries, but taking no notice of the small birds which came half-heartedly close to him, with the evident wish, but not the pluck, to attack him.

"Finally, in spite of the frantic shrieks of the parent birds, who ultimately approached quite close to the kingfisher, the latter made a dive into the hollow, and when he came out of it in his powerful beak there struggled a callow young myna. Seating himself comfortably on a branch, he proceeded to swallow it in just the same manner as he would have done a fish; and it may have been the necessity of getting into position before he swallowed his prey which prevented him from completing his meal inside the cramped hollow of the tree. At all events, his action was the saving of the other young birds, for the mynas, rendered furious by the disappearance of one of the youngsters down the throat of the kingfisher, summoned up courage to attack him in earnest, whereupon he quickly decamped."

PIED KINGFISHERS

To the members of the genus *Ceryle* it is almost impossible to assign a collective English name, for whereas in the Old World they are pied, their Transatlantic cousins are either grey or green. The genus comprises a small assemblage of long-beaked and long-tailed kingfishers of fish-catching habits, few of which are such strongly built birds as their short-beaked allies, although some of the Indo-Malay species are nearly their equals in size. Their great distinctive feature is that the sexes differ in colour or markings, this difference generally displaying itself by the presence in either the male or the female of an additional band on the breast.

Sixteen species of these kingfishers are known, eleven of which are American. In colour, most of the latter are glossy green, but four are grey, the best-known species being the belted kingfisher (*C. alcyon*) of North America. In the Old World all the species of the genus are either black and white or grey and white, one of the largest being the great pied kingfisher (*C. lugubris*), from the Himalaya and the mountains to the east of that chain throughout China to Japan. The head is crested, the crest feathers being black with white spots; there is a tuft of white feathers in the centre of the crown, while the rest of the upper surface is banded with grey and white; round the hind portion of the neck runs a broad white collar; the under surface of the body is white, with a chest band of black and white feathers; and the sides of the body are also barred with black. The female is generally like the male in colour, but does not show the tinge of rufous on the cheeks and breast band characteristic of the latter; the under wing coverts and axillaries are also pale rufous.

Writing of a nest with young found in the North-Western Himalaya, Mr. A. O. Hume states that "the entrance was a large hole, fully four inches in diameter, and at the end was a chamber fully ten inches across, in which were four young birds; in the chamber was a quantity of fish-bones and some grass. The eggs are three or four in number, and the birds are in the habit of carrying to their young fishes from six to seven inches in length, and these are always swallowed whole."

Mr. Stuart Baker writes that "I have seen but three nests of this bird, the first nest taken was found in July, and was placed at the end of a short tunnel in a bank of one of the biggest rivers in North Kachar,

THE KINGFISHER

tne Diyung. The burrow itself was about two feet long, and the egg chamber was over seventeen inches long by nearly ten broad, the height being almost as much. The eggs, of which there were four, reposed on a quantity of malodorous fish-bones, these extending nearly a couple of inches up the sides of the walls and partially burying the eggs, so this unpleasant material must have been added after the eggs were laid. The soil in which these were found was loose and sandy.

"The second nest was found by a Naga in a small stream called the Mahor, running between thickly-wooded banks, nowhere much over fifty yards from bank to bank, and, where the nest was taken, under thirty yards across. This nest was in dimensions much the same as that already described, the entrance tunnel being a few inches shorter. The fish-bones also were not so abundant in this nest, doubtless owing to its being newer, as the eggs when found were quite fresh, whereas in the last they were very hard set, indeed almost on the point of hatching. This hole was made in a rather harder soil than the other, but still not in a clay or really stiff material.

"The only other nest I have seen was found on April 10, 1893, the day before this was written. The female bird I shot as it left the nest, and the male as it came up calling loudly to its mate. The burrow, chamber and all, was complete when found, but was quite empty, containing neither eggs nor nest. The tunnel in this case was not six inches long, and the chamber was about fifteen inches long by about seven broad and six high. The soil in which this nest-hole was excavated was composed of clay and sand mixed, and was decidedly stiff. Judging from the three nests above described, it seems probable that the bird only makes very short burrows. *Halcyon smyrnensis*, *Alcedo ispida*, and many other kinds of kingfishers would have dug out a hole some four to six feet deep in the ground in which the first nest was taken, and would certainly have made them of over three feet in the other places.

"In texture and shape the eggs do not differ from the majority of other kingfishers' eggs, although they are unusually small in size. Amongst the bed of bones found in the first and second burrows, there were a good many which must have belonged to fish fully six inches long, but the greater number of them were those of very small fish. The Kacharis tell me that, as a rule, this bird only lays two or three eggs, and that my finding four was exceptional, but a Kachari's word is not particularly reliable. They are also said to breed principally in May, after the first heavy floods, not, as nearly all other birds which make similar excavations for their eggs do, before the floods.

"This kingfisher is very common on nearly all the hill streams of any size, up to about two thousand feet; above this it is much less common; but I have seen

it now and then on the Laisung, a little stream at an elevation of about three thousand feet. During the breeding season it ascends higher up than in the cold weather, during which latter season it is often found well in to the plains, but after April I have not heard of any being met with below about five or six hundred feet.

"On the Dryring, Kopili, and Zelinga rivers this bird and *C. rudis* meet one another, and for a few miles at their junction both may be met with, but their limits seem to be very distinctly defined, and a straggler of either kind is but seldom met with far beyond them. I believe they are entirely fish-eaters. I have never seen them except on fair-sized streams, and the stomachs of those I have examined contained nothing but fish. Whilst waiting for fishes, they perch very low down among the scrubby bushes bordering the streams, or else on some overhanging bamboo; but whatever the position selected, it seems nearly always to be one well in shadow, and, instead of sitting on some outside twig or bough, they choose one well inside or under the bush or bamboo clump. In the same manner their love of shade and darkness leads them always to select the shady side of the stream, whenever practicable.

LAUGHING KINGFISHERS

"As a rule, they are to be found in pairs, seldom singly, for, though the male and female may be some distance apart, they keep within hailing distance of one another. They do not fly at all fast or far at a time, unless frightened, but on such occasions are capable of flying extremely fast and powerfully, rising high in the air, well out of gunshot, to avoid any danger, and then dropping again when past it, continuing their flight low down close to the water. Their manner of taking prey from the water is by swooping down obliquely towards it, after which they move farther on, seldom returning to their original perch.

"Occasionally, as they fly along and are attracted by something in the water below them, they will hover momentarily, after the manner of *C. rudis*, and then drop perpendicularly down into it; in these cases, however, they seldom dive to any depth, and do not immerse more than their head and shoulders. The usual cry is much like the typical cry of the family, but it is very loud, and generally uttered in a very quick succession of notes. Besides this cry, it gives a low hoarse croak from time to time when seated in the shadow, which same note is, I think, merely a call to its mate."

Of the American belted kingfisher the following account is given by Mr. W. Dutcher: "The belted kingfisher is found throughout North America, but is nowhere very common, owing to its solitary and unsociable disposition. During the breeding season its range extends from the Gulf of Mexico to the Arctic Sea, and from the Atlantic to the Pacific Ocean. When the ice closes the waters of the north, the kingfishers move southwards, and their winter range is from the

West Indies and Northern South America to the Canadian border of the United States. Open water and a food supply are the factors that determine their winter quarters.

"One of the singular habits of this peculiar bird is connected with its breeding. It does not build a nest in a tree or on the ground, but excavates a hole in the side of a bank, usually near water, but not always, as railway cuttings are sometimes selected. The situation of the burrow is probably determined largely by the character of the soil, the favourite kind being clay, compact sand, or mixed gravel and loam. Both the male and female bird join in the labour of excavation, which is done with their large and powerful bills, the feet being used to push out the loosened soil.

"The passage is round and about four inches in diameter and extends inward, straight or with bends, to a varying depth from four to twenty feet, and terminates in a round domed living-room. Here the clutch of five to eight pure white eggs is laid and the young are hatched. As the nestlings are protected from cold, heat, and storms, there is little or no nesting material used, although in old excavations a considerable amount of fish-bones and scales may be found. If the birds are not disturbed, a burrow will be used for a number of successive seasons."

TYPICAL KINGFISHERS

The European kingfisher (*Alcedo ispida*) is the best-known representative of the short-tailed fish-eating section of the family, containing the genera *Alcedo*, *Corythornis*, and *Alcyone*. Of these, the last is exclusively Australian, and characterised by having only three toes; while the second is confined to Africa and Madagascar, and distinguished by its well-developed crest. The members of the genus *Alcedo* are likewise crested, although to a smaller degree, the feathers giving a pointed form to the structure. Confined to the Old World, these kingfishers are represented by several species, three of which are African, eight Indo-Malay, one Papuan, while the last is the typical kingfisher, which extends all over Europe and North-Western Asia, and is represented in Siberia and the Indo-Malay region by a smaller and brighter form sometimes separated as *A. bengalensis*.

The European kingfisher is a beautiful bird, of a greenish blue colour, with the back brilliant cobalt blue, and the crown greenish blue banded with dusky black. Above the lores is a rufous sheath; the ear coverts are orange rufous, succeeded by a band of white feathers on the sides of the neck; the cheeks light blue, with dusky blackish bars; the throat buffy white; the remainder of the under surface rich orange rufous, with a patch of greenish blue on the sides of the upper part of the breast; the beak black; the feet coral red; and the eyes brown (p. 1144). The total length is 7½ inches. The female, which is a trifle smaller, may be distinguished by having a red base to the lower half of the beak.

LEACH'S LAUGHING KINGFISHER

In England, owing to the protection which has been afforded to birds on the Thames and other rivers, the kingfisher is now more common than was the case some years ago, when it was much sought after for decorating ladies' hats. Especially in the autumn, when a considerable migration takes place, kingfishers may be noticed on the rivers in the south of England, and there are few more beautiful sights than one of these birds skimming over the water. Seated under overhanging willows or on an exposed bough or stump, the kingfisher watches patiently for the approach of its prey, when it dives like a flash under the water. It is, however, by no means always successful in capturing the fish, not infrequently missing its stroke. Sometimes it may be seen hovering over the water like a kestrel, and dropping like a stone on a fish; while at other times it will perch on an overhanging reed, in order to dive after its prey. The latter comprises insects as well as fishes; and on the sea coast, where they remain for some time before beginning their migration across the Channel, kingfishers feed on small crabs.

Although so exclusively a water bird, at most times of the year the kingfisher often makes its nest at some distance from a river. Some years ago, for instance, a nest with seven eggs was found in the middle of a wood bordering the Thames, fully a quarter of a mile from the water. This distance had to be traversed by the parent birds every time they brought a fish to their young. The nest had been tunnelled under the roots of a fallen tree, which had excavated a deep hole in a sandy bank as it fell, and in this instance the tunnel was by no means straight, but was carried over and under the roots which barred the progress of the bird in a direct line. It has been maintained that the kingfisher not only bores its own hole in the banks, but that the fish-bones found in the chamber at the end of the tunnel are placed there by the birds with the idea of forming a nest. There is, however, quite as often no nest whatever, the eggs being laid on the floor of the chamber.

In Africa and Madagascar the crested kingfishers (*Corythornis*) take the place of the typical species. Like the latter, these birds feed on fish and small crustaceans; boring holes into some sandy banks, they lay their eggs, which are four or six in number, on small platforms of fish-bones. The three-toed Australian kingfishers (*Alcyone*) seem to have similar habits.

INSECTIVOROUS KINGFISHERS

The insectivorous three-toed kingfishers of the genus *Ceyx* and their immediate relatives represent the second subfamily (*Daceloninæ*), all the members of which, although not disdaining a fish diet and thus frequenting rivers, are more exclusively inhabitants of forest and bush-clad country, where they subsist mainly on small reptiles, insects, crabs, and such-like creatures. The subfamily is characterised by the generally great development of the tail; the beak being either rounded or flattened, according as the fish-eating habit is more or less predominant.

Although forest-haunting, the members of the four genera *Ceyx*, *Ceycopsis*, *Ispidina*, and *Myioceyx* are characterised by having their tails as short as the typical kingfishers. The first of these genera comprises a number of brilliantly coloured kingfishers of small size inhabiting India and the countries to the east of the Bay of Bengal, and the whole of the Malay Archipelago as far as Northern Australia. While many have the plumage of a brilliant red, shot with a lilac gloss, and with blue on the wings and scapulars, some of the Malay and Papuan forms are mostly blue or black, with brilliant cobalt or silvery lower shades.

INDIAN THREE-TOED KINGFISHER

One of the most striking of the red group is the Indian three-toed kingfisher (*Ceyx tridactyla*), in which the back is black with a deep blue or purple mark, the lower part of the back glossed with lilac, the wing coverts black edged with blue, the tail cinnamon rufous, the head rufous marked with lilac, the ear coverts, cheeks, and under parts orange yellow, the beak and feet deep vermilion, and the eyes brown. The total length is 5½ inches. This pretty little bird inhabits the forest districts of Southern India and Ceylon, and is found from Nepal eastwards through the Burmese countries down the Malay Peninsula. It is fairly common in Kachar, and more of a fish-eater than the exclusively Malay species, which are forest birds, living chiefly on insects. This kingfisher, indeed, feeds chiefly on fishes and water insects, with an occasional shrimp or fresh-water prawn.

Its cry is a shrill, piping note, not unlike that of the typical kingfisher, but shriller and less powerful, and apparently uttered only when on the wing. It has a very powerful flight, and is capable of great speed, darting along the stream like a ruby meteor. Even when the bird is not disturbed, but merely moving

AFRICAN WHITE-BREASTED KINGFISHER

from place to place, its flight is very swift. When it feeds, it returns again and again to the same perch, and keeps to a confined area, being found day after day about the same spot, from which it seldom flies more than a mile. These birds make their tunnels in sandy banks, and apparently dig out the earth with their beaks, and eject it by a backward motion of the feet.

LAUGHING KINGFISHERS

The laughing kingfisher, or laughing jackass (*Dacelo gigas*), as it is commonly called in Australia, is the typical representative of a genus containing two other Australian and a single Papuan species. The typical species is a large bird, measuring 17 inches in length, with a wing of 8½, and a tail of 6½ inches. The general colour is brown, with the lower part of the back greenish blue, the median wing coverts washed with greenish blue, the head strongly crested, and brown in colour with rufous frecklings on the fore part, and the long crest-feathers edged with white. A broad white eyebrow stripe extends backwards to join a collar on the neck, the tail is rufous with irregular black bars, and the under surface of the body white with a few margins of brown on the chest feathers, more distinct on the flanks. The female is like the male, but rather more rufous on the head.

Mr. J. Gould states that this kingfisher "frequents every variety of situation—the luxuriant bushes stretching along the coast, the more thinly-timbered forest, the belts of trees studding the parched plains, and the brushes of the higher ranges being alike favoured with its presence; over all these localities it is rather thinly distributed, being nowhere very numerous. Its food, which is of a mixed character, consists exclusively of animal substances. Reptiles, insects, and crabs, however, appear to be its favourite diet; it devours lizards with avidity, and it is not an infrequent sight to see it bearing off a snake in its bill, to be eaten at leisure; it also preys on small mammals. I recollect shooting one of these birds in South Australia, in order to secure a fine rat which I saw hanging from its bill, and which proved to be a rare species."

THE LAUGHING KINGFISHER

The laughing kingfisher breeds during August and September, and generally selects a hole in a large gum-tree for the purpose, where it deposits its beautiful pearl-white eggs on the decomposed wood at the bottom. When the young are hatched, it defends its breeding place with great courage and daring, darting down upon any intruder who may attempt to ascend the tree. The other species, including *D. leachi*, show a sexual difference in the colour of the tail, which is blue in the male and rufous in the female.

Closely allied to the "jackasses" are the two species of hook-beaked kingfishers, one (*Melidora macrorhina*) from New Guinea and Waigiou, and the other (*M. jobiensis*) from Jobi Island. They take their name from the presence of a distinct notch near the tip of the upper half of the beak, which terminates in a hook.

WOOD KINGFISHERS

The wood kingfishers (*Halcyon*), many of which do not fish, constitute the largest group in the whole sub-family, the genus containing fully seventy species, all distinguished from the laughing kingfishers by their more rounded wings and more compressed beak, which has a groove along the side of the upper half. The best-known species is, perhaps, the white-breasted kingfisher (*H. smyrnensis*), a bird of large size, measuring nearly a foot in length, with a wing of 4½ inches or more. It is found all over India and Burma, extending eastwards as far as China, while it also occurs in Palestine and Asia Minor in the west. The beak is red, the general colour chestnut red, with the lower part of the back and scapulars bright greenish blue, and the throat and breast pure white.

This species generally makes its nest by burrowing in sandy banks, the length of the tunnel varying from one to over three feet. In Rajputana a nest-hole has been found in a well at least a hundred feet below the surface. In India this bird frequents all kinds of situations, often far away from water.

The nest is sometimes composed of a few layers of loose moss crammed into crevices in rocks ; but in most cases there is no attempt at a nest, the eggs being deposited on the floor of the chamber at the end of the tunnel. Fishes form a very minor part of the diet, the principal constituent of which consists of locusts and crickets, the bird taking these by swooping down from some perch, as if diving after fishes, and seizing them from the bushes and grass without halting in its flight. It also captures prawns, small crabs, and water insects from stagnant pools, and occasionally takes cicalas from the trunks of trees.

These kingfishers are very abundant in Africa, one of the most beautiful species being the African white-breasted kingfisher (*H. semicœrulea*), which has an entirely red beak, and is distinguished by its ashy white head and chestnut breast and under wing coverts; the back being black, with the lower part bright blue, while the outer surfaces of the wings and tail are blue, and the throat and chest ashy white like the head. The length of the bird is about 8 inches, and the wing 4 inches. This species is found over the greater part of Africa, as far as Zanzibar on the east and Angola on the west, being replaced in South Africa by the allied *H. pallidiventris*, and by *H. erythrogaster* in the Cape Verde Islands. In North-Eastern Africa the species may be found both near water and in wooded districts; it feeds on beetles and other insects, but also catches fish, which it seems to prefer.

RACKET-TAILED KINGFISHERS

Perhaps the most beautiful members of a beautiful family are the Australasian racket-tailed, or long-tailed, kingfishers (*Tanysiptera*), characterised by the number of tail feathers being reduced to ten, of which the middle pair is greatly elongated and exceeds the body in length, generally ending in a racket-like expansion. Over twenty species are known, all of which are inhabitants only of the Moluccas, the Papuan islands, and the Cape York Peninsula of Northern Australia.

These birds frequent forests and also rocks by the side of streams; the beautiful *Tanysiptera sylvia* of North-Eastern Australia being found amid dense bushes and sunny glades in woods. The bird shoots away among the dense foliage like an arrow; and is very wary, keeping a good look-out from the bare branch of a tree, and darting on to some passing insect, and then returning to the same perch. Its cry resembles the words "wheet, wheet, wheet," and the bird is said to tunnel into the red clay ant-hills common in that part of Australia.

ROLLERS

Birds of brilliant colour, inhabiting most parts of the Old World, rollers (family *Coraciidæ*), in shape

PITTA-LIKE GROUND ROLLER

of body and conformation of beak, strikingly resemble crows. The palate, however, is of the bridged type, and the feet are like those of kingfishers in respect both of the flat sole and the union of the toes, while there are twelve tail feathers. Possibly the blue and green colouring may be indicative of affinity with the kingfishers.

GROUND ROLLERS

The six genera are arranged under two subfamilies. The first of these (*Brachypteraciinæ*) is represented by four genera confined to Madagascar, and characterised by the relatively great length of the metatarsus, and their terrestrial habits. Of the typical *Brachypteracias*, as well as of *Geobiastes*, little has been related, but *Atelornis squamigerus* lives alone on the ground in the forests, the flight being straight, and the birds only perching on the lower branches. These birds, which may be observed in the dusk of the evening near the ground, have a curious way of jerking the tail when alighting on a branch. The pitta-like ground roller (*Coracopitta pittoides*) is one of two members of a closely allied genus.

TYPICAL ROLLERS

The European blue roller (*Coracias garrula*) is the typical representative of the second subfamily (*Coraciinæ*), all the members of which are arboreal in their habits, and characterised by the relative sharpness of the shank, or metatarsus. In addition to the rollers, the subfamily also includes the broad-beaked rollers (*Eurystomus*). In the European roller and its allies the beak is relatively elongated and compressed, being much longer than it is broad at the base; all the members of the genus being of brilliant plumage, and ranging over Africa, Southern Asia, and Malaya as far as the island of Celebes.

The European species is drab brown above, the rump greenish blue washed with purple, the wing coverts blue, the lesser ones purple, the head green with a bluish eyebrow stripe, the base of the forehead sandy buff, the under surface of the body blue, the breast lilac brown, the sides and hind part of the neck purplish lilac, and the wings and tail purplish blue with a band of silvery cobalt; the total length being 12 inches.

Writing of the habits of this bird, Dr. Naumann observes that it " is always restless and uneasy, moving from tree to tree, where it always settles on the summit, or on a dead branch. When undisturbed, it is fond of sitting in the sunshine, but during rainy weather is dull and moping. It never hops about among the branches, but flies from branch to branch, now and then descending to the ground, where it hops heavily, and with an awkward demeanour. Its flight is quick, very easy, and much resembles that of a pigeon; in flying straight it flaps the wings quickly; turns and overbalances itself often, and glides or shoots through the air for some distance before dropping on to a dead branch.

" The ordinary voice may be best compared to that of the magpie. Rollers continually give a deep, harsh ' racker-racker-racker-racker,' which is very quickly uttered when they are squabbling ; and with this they mingle a harsh 'rräk.' When sitting peaceably, the note is a high ' rack' and 'rack-rack,' and also a plaintive high ' kräk,' not unlike that which a young jackdaw sometimes utters ; this last is their call-note. These notes very often vary, and the bird is generally heard before he is seen. In fine weather the male rises in the air near where the female is incubating, uttering a single 'rack-rack-rack,' etc., until he attains a considerable height, from which he suddenly falls, always turning a somersault, and throwing himself here and there in the air, uttering quickly the following ' räh-räräh-rräh-rrä,' etc., which he always changes to the 'rack' as soon as ever he begins to turn his somersault, and then returns to his seat on a dead branch. This appears to represent his song. The bird chooses a sandy country as its breeding home, and affects thin woods, where old oaks are scattered through, and which are adjacent to open fields and near large forests, particularly of pines, making its nest in hollow oak,

MALAGASY KIRUMBO

ash, or other trees, and lining the interior with roots, straw, feathers, and hair. The male and female incubate in turn for the space of not quite three weeks, and when breeding they sit so close that, though at other times very shy, they may be caught on the nest." In Eastern Europe these birds are known as Polish parrots.

BROAD-BEAKED ROLLERS

The broad-beaked rollers (*Eurystomus*), which inhabit Africa, Madagascar, India, and China, ranging north to Eastern Siberia and south to the Malay Archipelago and Australia, are specially characterised by the width of the beak, which at the gape is equal to its length.

ORIENTAL ROLLER

Among them, the Oriental roller (*E. orientalis*) has the tail black with a bluish base ; the head and mantle blackish, the back green, the under surface blue, and the throat streaked with bright purplish blue, forming a gular patch; the total length being 11 inches. It inhabits the Burmese countries, extending down to the Malay Peninsula and to the islands of Borneo, Java, and the Philippines.

Mr. Bourdillon, after stating that he was attracted by the chattering of a pair of these rollers, says that " on going to the spot I found them engaged in ejecting from a hole in a stump, about forty feet from the ground, a pair of our hill-mynas. One of the rollers was in the mouth of the hole, and enlarging it by tearing away with its beak the soft rotten wood ; the other roller, seated on a tree close by, was doing most of the chattering, making an occasional swoop at the mynas whenever they ventured too close. I watched the birds for some time until the mynas went off, and there and then began building in a pinney-tree within the distance of one hundred yards.

"Ten days after I sent for some hillmen, who managed to ascend by tying up sticks with strips of cane, in the way they erect ladders to obtain the wild honey from the tallest trees in the forest. It was past six o'clock in the evening before a man reached the hole in which the birds had bred. He found not the slightest vestige of a nest, but a few chips of rotten wood, upon which were laid the three eggs. These I found to be slightly set. While the man was climbing the tree, the birds behaved in a very ridiculous and excited manner. Seated side by side on a bough, they alternately jerked head and tail, keeping up an incessant harsh chatter, and as the crisis approached, and the man drew nearer their property, they dashed repeatedly at his head."

KIRUMBOS

The remarkable birds known by their native name of kirumbos (family *Leptosomatidæ*) are confined to Madagascar and some of the neighbouring islands, and may be regarded as aberrant rollers, although they also exhibit affinities to the frogmouths in the possession of "powder-down" patches on the sides of the lower part of the back. Only two members of the family are known, both of which are included in the genus *Leptosoma*. The beak is roller-like, but the nostrils are peculiar in situation, being placed in the middle of the upper half of the beak, and shut in by a horny plate; while the plumes on the lores are curved forward so as entirely to hide the base of the beak. The feet are semi-scansorial, that is, the fourth toe is cleft to the base and partly reversible, and the tail feathers are ten in number.

The sexes are different in colour, the male showing considerable sheen above, and the upper surface being green, glossed with a distinct coppery shade, while the tail is greyish black, glossed with metallic

ORIENTAL ROLLER

green and, more slightly, with coppery red. The entire under surface is dark ashy grey, becoming white on the abdomen and under tail coverts; and the head is crested and of a leaden grey colour, glossed with metallic green and copper; the total length being 16 inches. The female is quite different, being rufous brown above, with the upper surface of the head black, and the sides of the head and back of the neck barred with black, the back spotted with buff and glossed with dull green and copper, the tail brown, but blackish towards the tip, which is edged with rufous; and the under surface of the body pale fawn spotted with greenish black.

The Malagasy *L. discolor* inhabits the island from which it takes its name, as well as Mayotte and Anjouan Islands, but in the great Comoro Island is replaced by the smaller *L. gracile*. These birds are stated to live in parties of ten or twelve on the edges of woods. As soon as one of the birds is shot, all the others come near the gunner or hover over their dead companion, so that ten or more can be obtained in a quarter of an hour.

That the kirumbo has a certain element of a roller in its composition, is shown by its habit of playing in the air, which Sir Edward Newton describes as follows: "It plays for some time over the same place, ascending almost perpendicularly, as it were by a jump, to a great height, and descending again in a curve nearly to the top of the trees by almost closing its wings, at the same time uttering a whistle so like that of an eagle that it was doubted for a long time by us whether the bird that performed this wonderful freak was not a raptorial. However, after having watched it several times with our glasses, we satisfied ourselves that it was this species."

BLUE ROLLER

FROGMOUTHS

THE frogmouths (family *Podargidæ*) have been associated with the nightjars, to which they approximate in their wide mouths and mottled plumage, although they differ in the more important feature of the palate being constructed on the bridged, or desmognathous, instead of on the slit, or schizognathous, type. Accordingly, it seems most probable that their true position is between the kirumbos and the oil-bird. From the former they are distinguished by the absence of an oil-gland, and the presence of only ten feathers in the tail ; while from the latter they differ in the absence of the articular surfaces on the cylindrical rod, or rostrum, of the hind part of the palate known as basipterygoid processes. Unlike nightjars, these birds have no comb-like appendage to the third toe, while they further differ in building nests, or laying their eggs in hollow trees. Two notches occur in the hind border of the breast bone.

TYPICAL FROGMOUTHS

The typical frogmouths (*Podargus*) represent the first (*Podarginæ*) of the two subfamilies into which the group is divided ; the members of this subfamily being distinguished by the narrow, slit-like nostrils, protected by an overhanging membrane, and hidden by plumes and feathers. Powder-down patches occupy each side of the rump, and the metatarsus is shorter than the third toe. The genus, which is characterised by the pointed tail feathers, includes seven species, all inhabitants of Australia and the adjacent Papuan Islands. The Australian species are dull and sluggish birds, depending for food less on their power of flight than on their habit of traversing the branches of trees on which their favourite insects reside. At intervals during the night they sit in open places, on rails, stumps of trees, or the roofs of houses.

Frogmouths are nocturnal in habit, sleeping during the day, and are mostly found in pairs, perched near each other on the branches of gum trees, in situations unsheltered from the midday sun. "So lethargic are its slumbers," writes Mr. J. Gould of the typical species, "that it is almost impossible to arouse it, and I have frequently shot one without disturbing its mate sitting close by ; it may also be knocked off with sticks or stones, and is sometimes even taken with the hand. When aroused, it flies lazily off with heavy flapping wings to a neighbouring tree, and again resumes its slumbers till the approach of evening, when it becomes as animated and active as it had been previously dull and stupid."

In New South Wales the tawny-shouldered frogmouth (*P. phalænoides*) begins to breed in September ; the breeding season being at its height in October, and continuing for the two following months. It builds a flat nest of sticks, loosely placed together on the horizontal branch of any suitable tree ; the eggs, three in number, being perfectly white, elongated in form, with the shell finely granulated.

EARED FROGMOUTHS

Their smaller size and rounded tail feathers distinguish these birds from the preceding, the side of the head in some of the species being adorned with ear-tufts, ending in bristly plumes, which give the name to the group. The sexes also are mostly different in colour, the female being rufous and the male greyer.

One of the largest species is the great eared frogmouth (*Batrachostomus aurilus*), inhabiting the Malay Peninsula, Sumatra, and Borneo, which measures about 16 inches in length, and is chestnut brown, marked with very fine blackish lines, and whitish bars. On the hind part of the neck is a collar of buffy white feathers, with a black border, forming bands ; the median and greater wing coverts show large spots of white edged with black, the throat and breast are brown, with spots and bars of white, and the under parts pale buff.

Of the nest of the South Indian frogmouth (*B. moniliger*) Mr. A. O. Hume writes that "instead of moss, a few fragments of dead leaves are incorporated, but the material is chiefly a soft, felt-like mass, precisely similar to that used by *B. hodgsoni*, but greyish white instead of brown. It is a mere pad with a shallow depression on the outer surface, a broad groove on the base of the nest showing where it had rested on the upper surface of an almost horizontal bough."

The egg is white, and the pad in the nest is formed by the down taken from the "powder-downs" of the bird itself, and then completed by having the outside interwoven and covered with bits of bark and lichen, so that the nest entirely resembles the branch to which it is attached. The nest of the Himalayan *B. hodgsoni* is about three and a half inches in diameter, and three-

GREAT EARED FROGMOUTH

quarters of an inch in thickness ; the lower surface of the pad, where it comes in contact with the branch, having a thin coating of moss. The whole of the nest is a compact, brown, felt-like mass, very soft and downy, and composed of what looks like excessively fine moss rootlets, but as soft as the fur of a chinchilla, this soft substance being doubtless the powder-down of the bird itself.

OWLET FROGMOUTHS

The owlet frogmouths (*Ægotheles*) differ from the other groups in having the nostrils situated near the tip of the beak, and open and prominent. There are no distinct powder-down patches, and the metatarsus is longer than the middle toe. The bristles on the lores are greatly elongated, so as to give the face a peculiar appearance. More than a dozen species are known,

AUSTRALIAN OWLET FROGMOUTHS

ranging from Australia and the Moluccan and Papuan Islands to New Caledonia. The Australian owlet frogmouth (*Æ. novæ-hollandiæ*), which is about 8½ inches in length has the general colour dusky with whitish markings; the head being darker, with two longitudinal stripes and two crescentic marks of white on the hind part and nape, while the under surface of the body is white with dusky limbs, and the abdomen and under tail coverts are more or less uniform.

This species ranges all over Australia and Tasmania, the eggs, which are four or five in number, being white, and laid in holes of trees without any attempt at a nest. "During the day," writes Mr. J. Gould, "the bird resorts to the hollow branches, or spouts, as they are called, and the holes of the gum trees, sallying forth as night approaches in quest of insects, particularly small beetles. Its flight is straight, and not characterised by the sudden turns and descents of the goatsuckers. On driving it from its haunts, I have sometimes observed it to fly direct to a hole in another tree, but more frequently to alight on a neighbouring branch, perching across and never parallel to it. When assailed in its retreat, it emits a loud, hissing noise, and has the same stooping motion of the head observable in the owls; it also resembles these birds in its erect carriage, the manner in which it sets out the feathers round the ears and neck, and in the power it possesses of turning the head in every direction even over the back, a habit it is constantly practising."

OIL-BIRD OR GUACHARO

Forming a family group by itself (*Steatornithidæ*), the South American oil-bird (*Steatornis caripensis*) in external appearance is not very unlike a nightjar, to which group it also approximates in habits, only coming out to feed in the dusk. It is, however, more nearly allied to the frogmouths, having a similar bridged palate, although differing in certain features of the skeleton. The plumage is less soft than in either nightjars or frogmouths, and the beak and the form of the wing are not unlike those of the rollers. The tail carries ten feathers, and in the wing the third and fourth primary quills are the longest; while the naked metatarsus does not exceed the third toe in length. In the skull the basal rostrum carries articular basipterygoid processes.

Measuring from 17 to 20 inches in length, the oil-bird is chestnut brown in general colour. On the upper parts the plumage is marked by numerous dark cross-bars, the median wing coverts are ornamented with large white spots, similar spots also occurring on the lateral upper tail coverts; and the under surface is pale chestnut, with a greyish tinge, each feather being marked with three rhomboidal spots of white bordered with black. The beak is chocolate brown; the feet are flesh coloured, with a violet tinge; the claws are grey; and the eyes black, with a narrow, dark brown ring.

The gaucharo has long been known as an inhabitant of Trinidad, where it frequents caves, in which it builds huge nests, having the appearance of large cheeses. The popular name of oil-bird is derived from the peculiar covering of the nestlings, which are simply masses of yellow fat. Elsewhere local, the oil-bird is found not only in Trinidad, but also in Guiana, Venezuela, Ecuador, and Peru, occurring in the latter countries in valleys at an elevation of seven thousand feet. In the Tatora district of Peru there are several caverns, situated in a very wild country, clad from the base to the summit of the hills with dense virgin forest, frequented by these birds. If a gun be fired, or any loud noise be made, the birds quit their retreats in the nooks and crannies, flying to the roof with piercing cries, and the only way to obtain specimens is to fire at random in the darkness. This, however, is haphazard work, and once in the Ninabamba cavern only eleven birds were killed after sixty shots.

When the birds are tired, they gradually retire to their hiding places, from which no amount of firing or shouting will induce them to emerge again. When undisturbed, the guacharos quit their retreats about sunset to fly in the forest, some of them rising to a considerable elevation, apparently in pursuit of moths. Their noiseless flight much resembles that of goatsuckers; but in descending rapidly the wings are frequently raised and held together in a point.

Their principal food consists of the fruit of the nectandra-tree, these fruits being seized by the birds, while in full flight, from the tips of the slender boughs, otherwise too frail to bear the weight of the gaucharo. For seizing such fruits the hooked and powerful bill is most admirably adapted. The rapidity with which the guacharos feed is remarkable, two specimens killed early in a summer evening having their crops empty, whereas one shot a quarter of an hour later had swallowed seven fruits, and a second killed after another quarter of an hour, no less than eleven.

The note is harsh and disagreeable, and has been compared to the syllables "cri-cri-cirri," although there is another cry which cannot be rendered in words. From observations on a young bird in the grey nestling plumage, it has been ascertained that the large nect-andra stones are regurgitated after the fleshy covering has been digested. This rejecting process is accomplished without any apparent effort on the part of the bird; a slight movement of the feathers of the throat takes place, the beak opens gently, and the stone appears; while if any of the fleshy covering adheres to it, the bird picks it off.

The old birds apparently cast up the stones during flight. Humboldt and Bonpland visited the cavern of Caripe, from which these birds take their specific name, and the following account of their visit is taken from a biographical work: "The Indians," it is written, "showed the travellers the nests of the guacharos by fixing a torch to a long pole. These nests were fifty or sixty feet high above their heads, in holes in the shape of funnels, with which the roof of the grotto was pierced like a sieve. The noise increased as the travellers advanced, and the birds were scared by the light of the torches. When this noise ceased for a few minutes, around them they heard, at a distance, the plaintive cry of the birds roosting in other ramifications of the cavern; and it seemed as if different groups answered each other alternately.

"The Indians were in the habit of entering this cavern once a year, near midsummer, when they went armed with poles, with which they destroyed the greater part of the nests. At that season several thousand birds were killed, and the old ones, as if to defend their brood, hovered over the heads of the Indians, uttering terrible cries. The young, which fell to the ground, were opened on the spot for their fat. At the period commonly called at Caripe the oil harvest the Indians built huts with palm leaves near the entrance, and even in the porch of the cavern, where, with a fire of brushwood, they melted in pots of clay the fat of the young birds just killed, this fat being known by the name of guacharo butter." The eggs have thick shells, which are at first chalky white, but by contact with the nest become yellowish green.

Mr. Cherrie, who collected on behalf of the museum of the Brooklyn Institute of Arts and Sciences, has recorded certain particulars which appear to have escaped the notice of earlier observers. He first endeavoured to enter the guacharo caves on Mono Island, a small islet off Trinidad, but his boatmen thought the attempt too dangerous at the time of his visit, and he accordingly changed his plans and resolved to visit the caves high up in the mountains of Aripo, on the mainland. The interiors of the caves were heaped with blocks of stones, rendered slippery by the constant drip from stalactites depending from the roof, and by the excrement of the birds. The season was the latter part of March, when the earlier broods were beginning to acquire their plumage. At this stage, strange to say, the young guacharos are double the weight of their parents, weighing on an average about 1 pound 12 ounces, against a little less than 13 ounces, which is the average weight of the former.

THE OIL-BIRD

Owing to constant persecution the birds place their nests in the most inaccessible positions, every projection on the roof and every crevice and chink in the walls of the cave being utilised as a nursery. Previous observers have stated that the nests are made of clay, but Mr. Cherrie found them to be entirely composed of the birds' excrement. Where space permitted, some of them reached a height of between two feet and three feet, and must have been many years old. It seems doubtful if there is any nest-building in the proper sense of that term, the nest being merely the roosting place of the parent birds. The cavity, although shallow, is very large, averaging from twelve inches to fourteen inches across.

Both parents apparently assist in incubation, and, what is most remarkable, sit side by side on the same nest. An ordinary clutch consists of two or three eggs, although five may occasionally be found. Mr. Cherrie gives no credit to the theory that a part of the food of the oil-bird consists of insects; in his opinion the diet is entirely of fruit. So strictly nocturnal are the guacharos, that all attempts to drive them out of the caves during the daytime proved ineffectual.

The young guacharos are taken by means of bamboo poles, furnished at the tips with a torch on one side and an iron hook—like a fish-hook—on the other. They are fried till the fat becomes crisp and dry, when they are eaten, bones and all.

ORDER III. CUCULI
CLASSIFICATION OF CUCKOOS AND PLANTAIN-EATERS

Although cuckoos and their relatives the plantain-eaters are often classified with the picarian birds, they are here regarded as representing an ordinal group by themselves, whose nearest affinities are apparently with the parrots. In the present group the palate of the skull is of the bridged, or desmognathous type; while the arrangement of the tendons of the muscles of the foot is different from that obtaining in the scansorial picarians.

ORDER
Cuckoos and Plantain-Eaters—Cuculi
FAMILY 1
Cuckoos—Cuculidæ
GENUS 1
Crested Cuckoos—Coccystes
SPECIES
Indian pied cuckoo ..... Coccystes jacobinus
Indian cuckoo .... C. coromandus
Great spotted cuckoo .... C. glandarius
GENUS 2
Hawk Cuckoos—Hierococcyx
SPECIES
Hierococcyx sparveroides
GENUS 3
Typical Cuckoos—Cuculus
SPECIES
Sonnerat's cuckoo .... Cuculus sonnerati
South African cuckoo .... C. gularis
Red-chested cuckoo .... C. solitarius
Black cuckoo .... C. clamosus
Indian cuckoo .... C. micropterus
Asiatic cuckoo .... C. intermedius
The cuckoo .... C. canorus
GENUS 4
Bronze Cuckoos—Chalcococcyx
GENUS 5
Golden Cuckoos—Chrysococcyx
SPECIES
Emerald cuckoo ..Chrysococcyx smaragdineus
Golden cuckoo .... C. cupreus
GENUS 6
American Cuckoos—Coccyzus
SPECIES
Yellow-beaked cuckoo ..Coccyzus americanus
Black-beaked cuckoo ....C. erythrophthalmus

GENUS 7
Koels—Eudynamis
SPECIES
Philippine koel ...... Eudynamis mindanensis
Indian koel, or rain-bird .... E. honorata
GENUS 8
Coucals—Centropus
SPECIES
Australian pheasant-cuckoo ..... Centropus phasianellus
Indian coucal .... C. sinensis
GENUS 9
Bush-Cuckoos—Phœnicophäes
SPECIES
Ceylon bush-cuckoo .... Phœnicophäes pyrrhacephalus
GENUS 10
Ceuthmochares
GENUS 11
Saurothera
GENUS 12
Hyetornis
SPECIES
Jamaican rain cuckoo .... Hyetornis pluvialis
GENUS 13
Malagasy Cuckoo—Coua
GENUS 14
Malkohas—Rhopodytes
SPECIES
Green-beaked malkoha .... Rhopodytes viridirostris
GENUS 15
Pheasant-Cuckoo—Carpococcyx
SPECIES
Bornean pheasant-cuckoo ..... Carpococcyx radiatus

GENUS 16
South American Ground Cuckoo—Neomorphus
GENUS 17
American Ground Cuckoos—Geococcyx
SPECIES
Road-runner .... Geococcyx mexicanus
GENUS 18
Morococcyx
GENUS 19
Guira Cuckoo—Guira
SPECIES
Guira cuckoo................. Guira pirigna
GENUS 20
Savanna Cuckoos—Crotophaga
SPECIES
Brazilian cuckoo .... Crotophaga major
Anis .... C. anis
Furrow-beaked cuckoo .... C. sulcirostris

FAMILY 2
Plantain-Eaters, or Turacos — Musophagidæ
GENUS 1
Crimson-winged Plantain-eaters—Turacus
SPECIES
Fraser's uraco ...... Turacus macrorhynchus
Buffon's turaco .... T. buffoni
GENUS 2
Great Plantain-eater—Corythœola
SPECIES
Great plantain-eater ....Corythœola cristata
GENUS 3
Typical Plantain-eaters—Musophaga
SPECIES
Violet plantain-eater ....Musophaga violacea
Rosy plantain-eater .... M. rossea

CUCKOOS—PLANTAIN-EATERS

As a family, cuckoos (*Cuculidæ*) are especially distinguished by having a zygodactyle foot, and a naked oil-gland; the after-shafts of the body feathers are wanting, and the arrangement of the feathers shows the track on the back forked between the shoulders. They are birds of universal distribution, very varied in form and habits, some being nearly parasitic as regards breeding habits on other birds, while others build nests of their own, and hatch their young after the ordinary fashion. The usual number of tail feathers is ten, but in one group (*Crotophaginæ*) only eight feathers are present.

In regard to the general affinities of the cuckoos, Dr. R. W. Shufeldt, although not committing himself definitely to any opinion, and dwelling upon the imperfect state of our knowledge of the bony structure of this large group of birds, is inclined to confirm the view of their relationship to plantain-eaters and also to bee-eaters. He believes, however, that several families of picarian birds have a cuckoo-vein running all through them, strongly impressed in some cases, barely discernible in others. Indeed, these groups of birds seem to have arisen from some very ancient and common stock, but by the extinction of numerous types it has left in recent times the most puzzling collection with which the systematist has to deal.

CRESTED CUCKOOS

The family is split up into a number of subfamily groups, of which the typical *Cuculinæ* may be taken first; among the members of the group are the crested cuckoos (*Coccystes*), which have pointed wings and are strong fliers. They take their name from the presence of a crest on the head. Of the nine species six are African, while one (*C. jacobinus*) is common to Africa and India, another (*C. coromanaus*) is peculiar to the Indian region, and the last (*C. glandarius*) is European.

GREAT SPOTTED CUCKOO

GREAT SPOTTED CUCKOO

Although the last, commonly known as the great spotted cuckoo has occurred in England, its home is in South-Western Europe and the Mediterranean countries, extending thence through Syria and Asia Minor to Persia, while in winter it ranges into Africa so far south as Cape Colony. This fine bird is ashy brown above and white below, with a buff-coloured throat, and is distinguished by its crested grey head, and the long graduated tail, broadly tipped with white. The total length is about 16 inches. Its ordinary note has been described as "kee-ow, kee-ou," but it has also an alarm note resembling the word "cark," as well as a third note, like "wurree, wurree."

Although parasitic, like the members of the genus *Cuculus*, this species does not victimise small birds, after the fashion of the latter, but selects the nests of crows and magpies, whose eggs bear a considerable resemblance to its own. Moreover, instead of depositing only one, the female of this species frequently places two, or even four, of its eggs in a nest, where the young cuckoos often live in peace with the offspring of the foster - parents, and, so far as is known, do not attempt to eject the rightful owners.

INDIAN PIED CRESTED CUCKOO

The Indian pied crested cuckoo (*C. jacobinus*), on the other hand, lays blue eggs, resembling in colour those of babblers (*Crateropus* and *Argya*), in whose nests they are deposited. In this case it appears that the young cuckoo ejects the young when hatched, as the babblers are often seen in attendance on their parasitic dependents without any of their own young being of the party. Sometimes the cuckoo puts two of its own eggs into a babbler's nest, and it is said to break some of the foster-parents' eggs to make room for its own. When they discover the nest of a babbler which does not suit them to lay in, the cuckoos invariably destroy the eggs already laid by driving a hole into them with their beaks and sucking the contents.

HAWK CUCKOOS

The seven representatives of the Asiatic hawk cuckoos (*Hierococcyx*) are remarkable for their exact resemblance in colour and flight to sparrow-hawks, being grey birds with a good deal of rufous below, large yellow eyes, and very broadly banded tails. They lay white or greenish blue eggs, and one species (*H. sparveroides*) is reported to build its own nest and sit on the eggs in the Nilgiri Hills of Southern India, although in the Himalaya it is stated to be parasitic on the babblers. The range of the group extends from India to Celebes, Japan, and Eastern Siberia.

TYPICAL CUCKOOS

While hawk cuckoos may be distinguished from crested cuckoos by the absence of a crest, the typical cuckoos differ from the former in the shape of the tail, in which the outer feathers are nearly of the same length as the others, instead of decidedly shorter; the tail feathers also lacking the transverse dark bars of the hawk cuckoos. The genus is represented by eleven species, all very similar to one another, and hawk-like in coloration and appearance; old birds being grey while the young ones are more or less rufous, although in the Oriental Sonnerat's cuckoo (*Cuculus sonnerati*) the plumage is for the most part rufous barred with black.

Of the eleven species, six are African, one Australian, and the rest Asiatic. Their notes vary greatly, only one other species besides the European having the "cuckoo" note from which the bird takes its name, this being the South African cuckoo (*C. gularis*), which has a note similar to that of the common species, but more slowly uttered, and the first syllable not in such a high key. The red-chested cuckoo of Africa (*C. solitarius*) has a whistling note, on account of which it is known to the Colonists at the Cape by the name of "piet-mijn-vrouw," but the black cuckoo (*C. clamosus*) is, as its Latin name implies, a noisy bird, uttering a very loud, harsh note. The Indian cuckoo (*C. micropterus*) has a note which has been rendered as "bho - kusha - kho," while the Asiatic cuckoo (*C. intermedius*), on the other hand, possesses only a single note, a guttural and hollow-sounding "hoo," resembling the cry of the hoopoe.

YOUNG CUCKOO
IN FLIGHT

EUROPEAN CUCKOO

One of the most interesting of all birds is the European cuckoo (*C. canorus*); not the least remarkable feature in its conformation being its great similarity to a hawk, the likeness being displayed not only in the matter of colour and form, but extending to the mode of flight, which is so hawk-like that cuckoos are always mobbed by smaller birds, as if they really were birds of prey. According to an old belief, cuckoos were supposed to turn into kestrels, which are seldom seen in England during winter, when cuckoos are unknown.

As regards colour, the adult cuckoo is grey above and white below, regularly barred with black like a hawk, while the throat is buff. It has also long thigh feathers, like those of a bird of prey, so that with its yellow eye the resemblance is complete, and when seen flying it is by no means easy to tell at the first glance whether it is a cuckoo or a hawk in the air. An accustomed eye may, however, detect the more elongated look of the head, owing to the long beak of the cuckoo, whereas a hawk in flight often looks as if it had no beak at all, so blunt is the aspect of its head when seen at a short distance. Young cuckoos have the tail barred.

The interest in the history of the cuckoo is concentrated on its nesting habits, and the success with which it imposes on other birds in getting them to rear its young. There can scarcely be any doubt that the number of males considerably exceeds that of the females, and some naturalists not only speak of the species as polyandrous, but declare that the female bird does all the courting. Certain it is that the presence of the female cuckoo excites the interest of more than one male, as may be seen in spring-time by those who know how to detect what has been well described as the "water-bubbling" note of the female cuckoo, which has been rendered as "kwik-wik-wik" and "kwow-ow-ow-ow." The female, on giving utterance to this note, is answered at once by every male in the neighbourhood, and the latter lose no time in flying towards the tree where she is seated, so that there are often quarrels and fierce fights among them. It is during the breeding season that the double call "cuk-cuc-koo" is heard, as if the male were trembling with passion.

Although the general belief is that cuckoos do not lay many eggs, it has been concluded that each hen deposits about twenty in the season. The variability in the colour of the eggs is well known, and in each individual the colour of the eggs is hereditary. That is to say, cuckoos brought up by meadow pipits always select that species to be the foster-parents of their young, this being the case with regard to hedge-sparrows, wagtails, and other ordinary victims of the cuckoo.

The small size of the egg, and the extraordinary similarity which it often shows to the egg of the foster-parent renders it difficult to distinguish the cuckoo's egg from those of the rightful owner of the nest; and sometimes a cuckoo will lay a blue egg exactly like that of the redstart or pied flycatcher, the nest of which it is about to utilise. This is perhaps the most curious instance known of strict similarity in colour, the true cuckoo's egg looking merely like a somewhat larger egg of the redstart. That such eggs are really those of cuckoos was, however, proved by Seebohm and Elwes, who were in Holland together when a redstart's nest was brought to them, the eggs of which were hard-set. On blowing them, the young birds had to be picked out, and the little cuckoo exhibited the characteristic zygodactyle foot perfectly formed.

MALE CUCKOO SINGING

In the case of eggs laid by the cuckoo in the nests of wagtails and other birds, the resemblance is exact; and when a cuckoo's egg is found in a nest where the eggs of the foster-parent are different, it is probable that the cuckoo has not been able to find a nest at the moment in which the eggs belonged to its own hereditary type. The nest of a sedge warbler has, indeed, been found containing a cuckoo's egg which was the exact counterpart of those of the foster-parent, and a few days afterwards the finder, having noticed the female cuckoo to be hovering about the neighbourhood all the time, saw a cuckoo's egg of the same sedge warbler type in a reed bunting's nest, where, of course, it looked thoroughly out of place. From these facts it would appear that a cuckoo, laying a "sedge warbler" egg, had been unable to find a second sedge warbler, and had been constrained to put it into a reed bunting's nest.

A series of nests of the meadow pipit, each with a cuckoo's egg, was presented some years ago to the British Museum, all of which were taken near Portsmouth in 1893. There would seem to have been three cuckoos which visited these nests, since three of the nests contained a greyish type of egg, three an egg of lighter character, and three an egg of purplish grey type.

The method of eviction has been frequently studied by observers. The young cuckoos, probably not more than thirty hours old at the time, getting well below the nestling lawfully entitled to the home, gradually "works" it to the edge of the nest, and then, with a final effort, pushes it over. The cuckoo feeds entirely on insects, and is believed to be the only bird which eats hairy caterpillars. It has also been accused of devouring eggs, but this idea may have arisen from their own eggs being found in the mouths of cuckoos, which were no doubt being conveyed to the nests of other birds.

Mr. A. H. Meiklejohn has contributed important evidence as to the manner in which the cuckoo carries her egg when about to deposit it in the nest of the bird selected to act as foster-mother. It is commonly supposed that the egg is carried in the beak, and several instances are quoted where observers state they have actually seen the *modus operandi*. Mr. Meiklejohn, who was fortunate enough to observe a cuckoo in the act of depositing its egg in a robin's nest, is, however, of opinion that the throat of the bird serves as the receptacle for the egg. He states (1) that the cuckoo was constantly opening her mouth during

YOUNG CUCKOO ON A WHITETHROAT'S NEST

a preliminary encounter with the robins ; (2) that the egg was certainly not laid in the ordinary way in the nest ; (3) that the egg itself was slightly moist and sticky ; and (4) that the throat of the bird presented a slightly distended appearance, which might well be due to the presence of the egg.

In winter cuckoos migrate to South Africa, but it appears that their characteristic note is uttered only in Europe and North Africa.

GOLDEN CUCKOOS

Represented in India and Australia by the nearly allied group of bronze cuckoos (*Chalcococcyx*), the golden cuckoos (*Chrysococcyx*) form a genus confined to Africa, and represented by three species. The birds differ from the typical cuckoos by their metallic colouring, of which the latter show no trace. Among them, the emerald cuckoo (*Chrysococcyx smaragdineus*) is one of the most beautiful of birds, being a brilliant metallic emerald green on the upper parts, and also on the throat and chest ; while the breast and under parts are bright yellow. Found all over tropical Africa, it inhabits the wooded country, and is conspicuous, not only from its brilliant colouring, but also from its habit of sitting on the top of a tree, sometimes for hours together, uttering its loud call of love or defiance.

The typical golden cuckoo (*C. cupreus*) is a somewhat smaller species, with the plumage metallic golden green, and the throat white. Mr. Layard states that "this beautiful little cuckoo is known by the name of didric, from its oft-repeated mournful cry of 'di-di-di-didric.' We have frequently seen a dozen or more in a morning, while their loud notes were incessantly ringing in our ears ; they are, however, so shy that we only procured three specimens in as many months. When calling, they perch on the summit of some dead branch, ready to do battle with any male, or engage in an amorous chase after any female that comes within their ken. They pursue each other with great ardour, turning, twisting, and dashing about with great rapidity. The stomachs of those examined contained nothing but small insects, chiefly swallowed whole."

As the remains of an egg of the Cape sparrow have been found in the stomach of one of these cuckoos, and as the latter are parasitic on the former, it looks as though the intruders sometimes devour the eggs of the foster-parent to make room for their own.

AMERICAN CUCKOOS

The American cuckoos (*Coccyzus*), although of sober grey and brown shades of colouring, in which respect they resemble the true cuckoos, may always be distinguished by their oval and not rounded nostrils. They are grey or brown, generally with an olive gloss, although two species have rufous backs. Except as regards their nesting habits, they are nearly allied to the cuckoos of the Old World. One of the best-known species is the yellow-beaked cuckoo (*C. americanus*), which is olive brown in colour, with white tips to the tail feathers ; the under parts being white, and the inner side of the quills rufous. This cuckoo, together with its ally the black-beaked cuckoo (*C. erythrophthalmus*), is migratory to the United States in summer, the latter extending its breeding range so far north as Manitoba and Labrador.

In habits these cuckoos are shy and retiring. They are more often heard than seen ; they pass from one tree to another stealthily, with a rapid, gliding, noiseless flight, and often rest motionless for a long time, especially when crying out, or when they detect suspicious objects. Their notes, sounding like the syllables, " koo-koo-koo," indefinitely repeated, are uttered more frequently before bad weather, and have given rise to the name " rain-crow," by which both are known. They plunder the eggs of small birds and devour nestlings. The nest is like that of a crow, but poorly constructed. In connection with the supposition that the European cuckoo lays its eggs at intervals, it is interesting to find that the yellow-beaked cuckoo does so, since in its nests have been found fresh eggs and young in all stages, showing that there must be a considerable interval between the laying of each egg. One instance is given in which eleven young birds were hatched in a season. The eggs are pale greenish.

GOLDEN CUCKOO

YELLOW-BILLED CUCKOO

BLACK HORNBILLS

"The black hornbill of West Africa belongs to the subfamily Bucerotinæ, which frequent dense forest and tall jungle, but at times descend to the ground and dig up the loose soil with their bills. Their food consists chiefly of fruit and berries."

EUROPEAN KINGFISHERS

"Especially in the autumn, when a considerable migration takes place, kingfishers may be noticed on the rivers in the south of England, and there are few more beautiful sights than one of these birds skimming over the water."

KAKA PARROTS

"The kaka is an eminently social bird, and by far the noisiest of the denizens of the woods of its native islands. Being semi-nocturnal in its habits, it generally remains quiet and concealed during the day."

LEADBEATER'S COCKATOOS

"Far more gorgeous than all the others is the beautiful Leadbeater's cockatoo of South Australia. . . . Their elegant plumage, graceful movements, and the readiness with which they are tamed, render cockatoos great favourites as domestic pets."

Mr. W. Dutcher remarks that, compared with the European species, the American " cuckoo has better habits, inasmuch as it tries to care for its own young ; indeed, the parents are very courageous in their defence, but the architecture of the cuckoo is so very inferior that it is really remarkable that many young reach maturity. The nests are often so frail that the eggs can be seen through the bottom, and are so small that they are strikingly out of proportion to the size of the incubating bird."

KOELS

Inhabiting the Indo-Malay and Australian regions, the koels show a remarkable sexual difference in colour, the males being black, and the females rufous with black bands. In most birds, when the parents differ in plumage, the young at first resemble the hens, but in the instance of the koels the young of both sexes are black like the cocks. Koels may also be distinguished from the members of the preceding genus by the much rounder and stouter beak. The tail is long and wedge-shaped.

Regarding the colouring of the young, Mr. J. Whitehead, writing of the Philippine koel, or phou, (*Eudynamis mindanensis*), asks, " Why should the young birds not follow the general rule, and take the plumage of the female, or have a plumage distinct from that of both parents ?

GREEN-BILLED MALKOHA

The answer appears to be that the phou lays its eggs in the nest of the yellow-wattled myna. The young cuckoo, being black, does not differ from the young myna, and so the deception is carried on until the young bird can take care of itself.

" If the young followed the general rule, and resembled their mother in being of a brown colour, the mynas might not recognise them. The myna breeds in holes of old rotten trees, sometimes using woodpeckers' holes, making it more difficult to see the intruder in the dark ; when the young bird emerges into daylight, it would startle the old birds to see the young cuckoos of any other colour. One of the young cuckoos was shot whilst being fed by the foster-parents, and no doubt the young cuckoo gets rid of the nestling myna at an early period."

The Indian koel (*E. honorata*), the " rain-bird " of the natives, is parasitic on crows ; but they appear to look after their offspring to a certain extent, as they have been seen feeding them after they have left the nest.

COUCALS

Distributed over the greater part of Africa, India, China, and southwards through Malaya to Australia, coucals (*Centropus*) form not only a genus, but a separate subfamily (*Centropodinæ*). They are ground-birds, of medium or large size, remarkable for the long spur on the first toe, from the presence of which the English name is derived. They build nests, and lay several white eggs, the shell of which is chalky, showing an approach to the remarkable eggs of the anis. The general colour of the coucals is red and black, but some are entirely black, while the Australian pheasant-cuckoo (*C. phasianellus*) is banded with brown and buff.

The young of all the other species have a similar kind of plumage, and some are said to possess a winter garb, or " seasonal plumage," but if this be the case it lasts for a very short period.

The Indian coucal (*C. sinensis*) is a large species, measuring nearly two feet in length, and is black in colour, with the mantle and wings chestnut, and a blue gloss on the head and a green sheen on the under parts. It is found all over India and Ceylon, and, like other members of the genus, has a curious howling note, " whoot, whoot, whoot, whoot," followed after a pause of four or five seconds by " kurook, kurook, kurook, kurook."

The nest, which is generally domed, is a rough structure, described by Mr. A. O. Hume as a " hollow, oblate spheroid, some eighteen inches in external diameter, and from six to eight inches in height, with a large hole on one side, from the entrance of which to the back of the nest inside may be twelve inches. This, of course, is not large enough to admit the whole bird, so that, when sitting, its tail is commonly seen projecting outside the nest. The latter is placed at varying heights above the ground, in the centre of thick, thorny bushes or trees. It is usually made of dry twigs, lined with a few green leaves, but all kinds of odds and ends are at times incorporated into the fabric. Occasionally quite different materials are made use of, the nest consisting almost wholly of leaves, rushes, or coarse grass."

RAIN-CUCKOOS

The so-called rain-cuckoos of the West Indies are some of the best-known representatives of a third sub-family, the *Phœnicophäinæ*, which includes some sixteen genera, and is typified by the Ceylon bush-cuckoo (*Phœnicophäes pyrrhocephalus*.) Their bright metallic plumage and short, rounded wings show that they are resident in the countries where they live, and are not migratory, like long-winged cuckoos. They are mostly Indian and Malayan, but one genus (*Ceuthmochares*)

YOUNG MALE INDIAN KOEL

Ceylon, easily recognised by the feature to which it owes its name.

GROUND-CUCKOOS

Another subfamily, the *Neomorphinæ*, is represented by the four genera of ground-cuckoos, all of which are terrestrial birds with powerful feet for running, and weak wings in which the secondary quills are as long as the primaries. In Borneo and Sumatra the pheasant-cuckoos (*Carpococcyx*) represent the group; the species from the former island (*C. radiatus*) measuring two feet in length, and having the aspect and ways of a game bird. In South America the subfamily is represented by the genus *Neomorphus*, which extends from Northern Brazil to Guiana, Amazonia, Ecuador, Colombia, and Nicaragua. All the five species of this genus are extremely rare, and nothing is known of their habits. In all the genera above mentioned the beak is very stout, but there remain the two American genera *Geococcyx* and *Morococcyx*, in which it is longer.

THE ROAD-RUNNER

A familiar example of the former of these is the so-called road-runner (*Geococcyx mexicanus*), whose plumage is brown above, with rufous or white streaks, the under surface whitish, and the throat buff-coloured streaked with black. There is, however, some bright colour on the face, as in the preceding genera, the eyes being red, and a bare space round the eye blue, fading into white behind, and followed by a patch of orange red. The length of the bird is about two feet.

The road-runner, which is an inhabitant of the southern United States, from Texas to New Mexico, Southern Colorado, and California, has obtained its name from the speed with which it flies over the ground; some idea of this being gained from a statement to the effect that in Southern California a ranchman has been seen to chase one of these birds on horseback for a distance of a mile or more at full speed,

is African; while the two genera *Saurothera* and *Hyetornis*, or typical rain-cuckoos, belong to the New World. With the exception of *Coua*, which is a Malagasy type, all have some bright colours on the face or beak, the latter being in many of the genera parti-coloured and brilliant. The rain-cuckoos in the West Indies inhabit only the Greater Antilles and Bahamas. They attain to a size of 18 or 20 inches, and are mostly of an ashy brown colour, with rufous wings and white-tipped tail feathers, which show a black bar before the tips.

The Jamaican species (*Hyetornis pluvialis*) is a bird of retiring habits, generally sitting immovable in a dull and sluggish manner, but on alighting on a tree it traverses the branches with facility by a succession of vigorous jumps, and then appears active enough. The nest is placed high on a tree, and is a loose, flat structure of twigs; the egg being chalky white.

MALKOHAS

In India and the Malay countries occurs an assemblage of genera of bush-dwelling cuckoos, of which the best known are the malkohas (*Rhopodytes*). These birds frequent gardens, thin tree-jungle, and secondary scrub, and display marvelous capacity for making their way through dense covert. The notes of the malkohas seem to vary considerably, being described as a "cat-like chuckle" in one species, in another as a "hoarse chatter, much like that of a magpie," and in a third as a "cat-like mew." These cuckoos build their own nests, and lay white eggs.

The green-beaked species (*R. viridirostris*) is a well-known bird in India and

EGYPTIAN COUCAL

when the cuckoo, though still in advance, suddenly stopped and flew up among the limbs of a stunted tree near the roadside, and the rider, having kept it in view all the way, dismounted and took the exhausted bird from its perch.

SAVANNA AND GUIRA CUCKOOS

The last subfamily (*Crotophaginæ*) is represented by the so-called savanna and guira cuckoos, three of which belong to one genus, while the fourth constitutes a genus apart. Distinguished from other cuckoos by having only eight tail feathers, these birds are further remarkable for their eggs. Externally the eggs are blue, covered with chalky white scratches, produced by contact with the lining of the nest; but this blue colour belongs only to the outer covering, so that, when removed, the true egg-shell, which is white, is revealed.

The guira cuckoo (*Guira pirigua*) has a very slender beak and crest; the plumage brown streaked with black, the under surface buff, and the back white; the length being about 18 inches. It inhabits Brazil and Paraguay. The members of the other genus are black, and have extraordinary beaks, with a kind of high and narrow keel on the upper half. Of the three species, the largest is *Crotophaga major*, which is 18 inches in length, and ranges from Brazil and Amazonia to Guiana and

GREAT PLANTAIN-EATERS

Colombia. The other species, *C. anis* and *C. sulcirostris*, are smaller, not exceeding 13 inches in length; the anis inhabiting much the same areas as its larger relative, but occurring also in the West Indian Islands and the southern United States. The former has the beak smooth, while in the latter there are several grooves on the sides. The species last referred to occurs in the southern United States, and extends throughout Central America to Colombia and Peru, but does not seem to reach Brazil.

The savanna cuckoos are gregarious and nest in company. Mr. Alfaro states that in Costa Rica he found the "zopilotillo," as it is called, very abundant in the fields near Tambor, north-west of San José, where they seek their insect food along hedgerows and in scrubby timber, as well as on the hides of cattle; the woodticks infesting the legs, heads, and necks of the cattle being favourite morsels. The bird is also called "tijo-tijo," in imitation of its peculiar notes, which seem to repeat the word "ti-ho" over and over again. The same observer records the finding of three nests, one of which was situated in the branches of a mango tree, and contained fourteen eggs. Noticing on a certain occasion one of these birds building its nest, he returned in a week's time, and

THE ROAD-RUNNER

found the nest completed, and containing six eggs, while in the thorns and leaves in the immediate neighbourhood were scattered seven more.

"In the finding of some of the eggs scattered in the leaves was revealed one of the architect's peculiarities. A hole had been left in the centre of the nest, and only recently filled with leaves, whose fresh green colour testified that they had been cut and placed there later than the others, forming the carpeting to the bottom of this common incubator. The eggs were all fresh, the six occupying the nest having the characteristic white calcareous surface perfectly clean, and without the slightest variation in colour. Not so with the eggs found about the outside of the nest: those found in contact with the leaves had taken on a dirty yellowish tinge, while those suspended among the leaves and thorns showed various spots and lines of the lustrous blue colour forming the base for the chalky external coat."

PLANTAIN - EATERS OR TURACOS

Having many characters in common with cuckoos, the plantain-eaters, or turacos, (family *Musophagidæ*), of Africa, are regarded as indicating a separate group, distinguished by having the oil-gland tufted, after-shafts to the body feathers, and the feet not wholly zygodactyle, the fourth toe being capable of being turned either backwards or forwards. The tail feathers are ten in number. More than twenty species are known, and may be divided into two sections, one including such as have crimson quills, and the other those in which there is no red in the wings.

CRIMSON-WINGED PLANTAIN-EATERS

The crimson-winged plantain-eaters, often called "lories" in South Africa, frequent forest districts, building open nests of sticks in bushes, and laying white eggs, in both of which respects they resemble pigeons. Of the habits of Fraser's turaco (*Turacus macrorhynchus*), as observed in Liberia, Mr. Büttikofer gives some account, stating that it is a splendid and lively bird in a wild state, always keeping to the densest crowns of the trees in the virgin forest, where it lives in pairs or in families after the breeding season. It is so shy that it would not be easily found if it were not for its crow-like voice, interrupted now and then by a mewing, exactly like that of a cat.

When not disturbed, these birds can be very noisy, flapping their beautiful red wings, and running after each other like squirrels among the branches. As their bright wings would render them too obvious

to their enemies, they seldom fly very far at once, but advance by running through the foliage of the trees, hidden by the resemblance of their colour to that of the surrounding leaves.

Their food consists of different kinds of wild fruits; and insects were never found in dissected specimens. The colouring matter in the wing of the turacos consists of a soluble substance containing copper, and known as turacin. It was at one time supposed that this colouring matter of the wing could be accounted for by the bird picking up grains of malachite, but the turacos are birds which live in trees, and do not apparently descend to the ground, while the red feathers have been assumed by specimens in captivity, some of which moulted more than once. Another well-known African specimen is Buffon's turaco (*T. buffoni*), ranging from the Congo to Senegal.

GREAT PLANTAIN EATER

The sole representative of its genus, the great plantain-eater (*Corythæola cristata*) is the largest of the family, measuring nearly three feet in length, and remarkable for its fine crest and varied colouring. The upper surface is blue, the head and crest bluer, the tail feathers yellow with blue bases and a broad bar of black near the end, the neck is blue, with the chin and cheeks white, the rest of the under surface of the body is rufous brown, and the beak yellow with the tip scarlet, and the eye red.

This handsome bird is found all over the forest districts of West Africa from Senegambia to Angola, and extends throughout the Congo region to Equatorial Africa. It seems to be confined exclusively to the virgin forest, where it lives in companies of five or six together in the crowns of the tallest trees, generally out of reach of gunshot. Its food includes a kind of bush plum and other wild fruits, of which an enormous quantity is sometimes found in its crop.

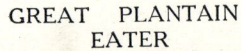

BUFFON'S TURACO

TYPICAL PLANTAIN-EATERS

Of the typical genus *Musophaga*, two species only are known. The violet plantain-eater (*M. violacea*), which is about the size of a crow, may be recognised by the yellow base of the beak extending backwards so as to form a kind of shield on the forehead, and the presence of a white streak behind the eye.

The second species (*M. rossea*), which is very rare, has the same frontal shield, but lacks the eye-stripe. The crown of the head and the primary quills are crimson in both kinds, which are restricted to the forest region of Western Africa.

ORDER IV. PSITTACI
GENERAL CHARACTERISTICS OF THE PARROT TRIBE

One of the most interesting groups of birds is that of the parrots, Psittaci, under which term may be included not only the birds properly so called, but likewise macaws, lories, love-birds, cockatoos, and so on. This general interest is due not only to the beauty of form and gorgeousness of plumage characterising so many members of the group, but likewise to the ease with which they are domesticated, their pleasing manners when in this state, and, above all, to the extraordinary facility with which they recollect and repeat sentences of human speech. That the memory of parrots is very strongly developed there can be no sort of doubt; but whether their intellectual powers rank really higher than those of some of the passerine birds is problematical. The appropriateness to the occasion with which sentences learned by these birds are sometimes uttered is probably mainly or entirely due to association, and in no sense implies any knowledge of the meaning of the phrases. It may be added that the occasions when such phrases are introduced inappropriately are, perhaps, not much less infrequent than when they are apposite.

Parrots form a large group, including considerably more than five hundred species, and presenting well-marked characters by which its members can be readily distinguished from all other assemblages of birds. Their most obvious external characters are displayed by their feet and bills. In the feet the fourth toe (as in some of the picarians) is permanently turned backwards, and as the first toe has likewise a similar direction, the whole foot is divided into a front and back portion, each comprising two digits; this type of foot-structure being termed zygodactyle.

The covering of the feet takes the form of rough, granular scales. As regards the beak, its base is invested with the wax-like protuberance termed the cere, which is frequently feathered; while in form it is short, stout, and strongly hooked at the extremity. In addition to the above, it may be noted that, owing to the presence of a transverse hinge in the skull, the upper half of the beak is movable, while the palate is of the bridged (desmognathous) type.

The skull is also very generally distinguished by the presence of a complete bony ring surrounding the socket of the eye; and the symphysis, or union, in front of the two branches of the lower half of the beak is short, obtuse, and deeply channelled. The tongue is also thick and fleshy, and may be fringed or brush-like at the extremity. Extreme shortness characterises the legs of most of the species, this shortness being most marked in the shank, or metatarsus, of which the bone is greatly expanded. The leg bone, or tibia, generally has no bony bridge at the lower end. The furcula is always weak, and may be incomplete or even wanting. The feathers are provided with after-shafts; and the number of quills in the tail is, except in one genus, ten. If an oil-gland be present, it is furnished with a tuft of feathers. Finally, the young are born in a nearly naked and completely helpless condition; and the eggs are usually, if not invariably, white.

TWO ROSE HILL BROADTAILS IN A GUM TREE
Photo, C. Grant Lane

For the most part, parrots are thoroughly arboreal and climbing birds, essentially characteristic of the tropical and subtropical regions of the globe. At the present day none inhabits Europe, though the remains of an extinct parrot, apparently allied to a living West African species, have been obtained from the Miocene rocks of France. In America one species extends so far south as the Straits of Magellan, while another ranges far into the United States; and in the Macquarie Islands of the Australian region the group extends so far south as the 55th parallel. Although ranging over all the warmer regions of the globe, these birds are very unequally distributed, being poorly represented in India, and still more so in Africa, while in Malaya and Australasia they attain their maximum diversity of type, and in South America their greatest numerical development.

All parrots make their nests in the hollows of trees, where they usually lay from two to three white eggs, although in the case of some of the smaller species the number is often considerably more. Frequently the males take their share in the work of incubation, which generally lasts for about twenty-one days. Nestling parrots are fed by the parents disgorging half-digested food from their own crops into the open mouths of the young, after the manner of pigeons. The food of the adult consists in most cases of various fruits and nuts.

Regarding their general habits, and the important part these birds play in tropical scenery, Dr. A. R. Wallace writes as follows: "They usually feed in flocks; they are noisy, and so attract attention; they love gardens, orchards, and open, sunny places; they wander about far in search of food, and towards sunset return homewards in noisy flocks or in constant pairs. Their forms and motions are often beautiful and attractive. The immensely long tails of the macaws, and the more slender tails of the Indian parraquets; the fine crests of the cockatoos, the swift flight of many of the smaller species, and the graceful motions of the little love-birds and allied forms; together with their affectionate natures, aptitude for domestication, and powers of mimicry, combine to render them at once the most conspicuous and the most attractive of all the specially tropical forms of bird life."

As is so generally the case with arboreal fruit-eating birds, the prevalent colour among parrots is green. This is, however, frequently relieved by patches, bands, or spots of other hues; while in certain groups or species it is replaced by blue, yellow, cinnamon, crimson, white, and occasionally black. Judging from the characters of the skeleton, there seems some reason to believe that the nearest allies of parrots are owls. The more general opinion is, however, to the effect that their nearest relatives are the cuckoos, with which they are brigaded by some naturalists in a single group. The order may be divided into six families.

CLASSIFICATION OF THE PSITTACI MENTIONED IN THIS WORK

ORDER
Parrot Tribe—Psittaci

FAMILY 1
Nestor Parrots—Nestoridæ
GENUS 1
Nestors—Nestor
SPECIES
Kea .... Nestor notabilis
Kaka .... N. meridionalis
Phillip Island parrot (extinct).... N. productus
Norfolk Island parrot .... N. norfolcensis

FAMILY 2
Lories and Loriquets—Loriidæ
GENUS 1
Typical Lories—Lorius
SPECIES
Purple-capped lory .... Lorius domicella
Black-capped, or tricoloured, lory ...... L. lory
GENUS 2
Black Lory—Chalcopsittacus
GENUS 3
Red-winged Lory—Eos
GENUS 4
Loriquets—Trichoglossus
SPECIES
Swainson's loriquet ...... Trichoglossus novæ-
hollandiæ
GENUS 5
Psitteuteles
GENUS 6
Arfak Parrot—Oreopsittacus
SPECIES
Arfak parrot .... Oreopsittacus arfaki

FAMILY 3
Cyclopsittacidæ
GENUS 1
Neopsittacus
SPECIES
Iris parrot .... Neopsittacus iris
New Guinea parrot ...... N. musschenbroeki
GENUS 2
Cyclopsittacus

FAMILY 4
Cockatoos—Cacatuidæ
GENUS 1
Microglossus
SPECIES
Great black cockatoo .. Microglossus aterrimus
GENUS 2
Raven-Cockatoos—Calyptorhynchus
SPECIES
Banksian cockatoo ...... Calyptorhynchus banksi
Funereal cockatoo .... C. funereus
South Australian raven-cockatoo .. C. xantho-
notus
GENUS 3
Callocephalum
SPECIES
Ganga cockatoo ...... Callocephalum galeatum
GENUS 4
Typical Cockatoos—Cacatua
SPECIES
Greater sulphur-crested cockatoo .... Cacatua
galerita
Lesser sulphur-crested cockatoo .. C. sulphurea
Citron-crested cockatoo .... C. citrino-cristatus
Leadbeater's cockatoo .... C. leadbeateri
Ducorp's cockatoo .... C. ducorpsi
White-crested cockatoo .... C. alba
Rose-crested cockatoo .... C. moluccensis
Red-breasted cockatoo .... C. roseicapilla
Blood-stained cockatoo ,,,,,,, C. sanguinea

GENUS 5
Slender-billed Cockatoos—Licmetis
SPECIES
Slender-billed cockatoo ...... Licmetis nasica
L. pastinator
GENUS 6
Cockatiel—Callopsittacus
SPECIES
Cockatiel ...... Callopsittacus novæ-hollandiæ

FAMILY 5
Parrots, Macaws, etc.—Psittacidæ
GENUS 1
Pigmy Parrots—Nasiterna
SPECIES
Pigmy parrot .... Nasiterna pygmæa
Red-capped pigmy parrot .... N. bruijni
GENUS 2
Blue Macaws—Anodorhynchus
SPECIES
Blue macaw .... Anodorhynchus hyacinthinus
GENUS 3
Cyanopsittacus
SPECIES
Spix's macaw .... Cyanopsittacus spixi
GENUS 4
Typical Macaws—Ara
SPECIES
Red-and-blue macaw .... Ara macao
Blue-and-yellow macaw .... A. ararauna
Military macaw .... A. militaris
GENUS 5
American Parraquets—Conurus
SPECIES
Golden parraquet .... Conurus solstitialis
GENUS 6
Conuropsis
SPECIES
Carolina parraquet ...... Conuropsis carolinensis
GENUS 7
Henicognathus
SPECIES
Slender-billed parraquet ...... Henicognathus
leptorhynchus
GENUS 8
Myopsittacus
SPECIES
Grey-breasted parraquet .... Myopsittacus
monachus
GENUS 9
Bolborhynchus
SPECIES
Aymara parraquet .... Bolborhynchus aymara
GENUS 10
Parrotlets—Psittacula
SPECIES
Blue-winged parrotlet .... Psittacula passerina
Turquoise-rumped parrotlet...... P. spengeli
Green-rumped parrotlet........ P. guianensis
GENUS 11
Brotogerys
SPECIES
All-green parraquet........ Brotogerys tirica
GENUS 12
Amazon Parrots—Chrysotis
SPECIES
Red-fronted Amazon........ Chrysotis festiva
GENUS 13
Deroptyus
SPECIES
Hawk-billed parrot .... Deroptyus accipitrinus
GENUS 14
African Green Parrots—Pœocephalus
SPECIES
Le Vaillant's parrot .. Pœocephalus robustus
Jardine's parrot .... P. guliemi
Brown-headed parrot ...... P. fuscicapillus

GENUS 15
Typical Parrots—Psittacus
SPECIES
Grey parrot.............. Psittacus erithacus
Liberian parrot .... P. timneh
GENUS 16
Vasa Parrots—Coracopsis
SPECIES
Vasa parrot .... Coracopsis vasa
GENUS 17
Dasypterus
SPECIES
Papuan black parrot ..... Dasypterus perqueti
GENUS 18
Eclectus
SPECIES
Red-flanked parrot ...... Eclectus pectoralis
GENUS 19
Ring-necked Parraquets—Palæornis
SPECIES
Ring-necked parraquet .. Palæornis torquatus
Blossom-headed parraquet ..P. cyanocephalus
GENUS 20
Love-Birds—Agapornis
SPECIES
Rosy-faced love-bird ....Agapornis roseicollis
Grey-headed love-bird ....A. canus
GENUS 21
Hanging Parrots—Loriculus
SPECIES
Bonaparte's hanging parrot ..Loriculus bona-
partei
Blue-crowned hanging parrot .....L. galgulus
Indian hanging parrot .... L. vernalis
GENUS 22
Broadtails—Platycercus
SPECIES
Rose Hill broadtail .....Platycercus eximius
GENUS 23
Grass-Parraquets—Neophema
SPECIES
Turquoisine grass-parraquet ...... Neophema
pulchella
GENUS 24
Cyanorhamphus
SPECIES
Red-fronted parraquet ...... Cyanorhamphus
novæ-zealandiæ
GENUS 25
Crested Parraquets—Nymphicus
SPECIES
New Caledonian parraquet .....Nymphicus
cornutus
Uvæan parraquet.............. N. uvæensis
GENUS 26
Melopsittacus
SPECIES
Budgerigar .... Melopsittacus undulatus
GENUS 27
Nanodes
GENUS 28
Ground-Parraquets—Pezoporus
SPECIES
Long-tailed swamp-parraquet ....Pezoporus
formosus
GENUS 29
Geopsittacus
SPECIES
Short-tailed ground-parraquet ...Geopsittacus
occidentalis

FAMILY 6
Owl-Parrot—Stringopidæ
GENUS
Stringops
SPECIES
Kakapo ,,,,,,,,,,,,Stringops habroptilus

NESTOR PARROTS

Under the common title of nestors (family *Nestoridæ*) may be included a small group of peculiar parrots confined to New Zealand and certain neighbouring islands, all belonging to the single genus *Nestor*, and one of which is known to the Maori as the kea and the other as the kaka. The nestors belong to an assemblage of three families of the order characterised by the under surface of the hook of the beak being either smooth or merely marked by some fine longitudinal lines.

As a family, nestors are distinguished by the more or less elongated beak being much compressed, and longer than deep, with the middle line (culmen) of its upper moiety marked by a longitudinal groove, while the profile of the symphysis of the lower half slopes upwards to the tip with scarcely any curvature. The tip of the tongue is provided with a fringe of fine hairs, and the cere of the beak is partially feathered. All the feathers are soft, those situated at the base of the lower half of the beak being hairy, and projecting forwards; and the quills of the tail have pointed shafts projecting beyond the vanes. The metatarsus is longer than usual, and the bony ring round the socket of the eye incomplete.

The nestors are represented by four well-defined species, two of which are now extinct. Of these the kea (*Nestor notabilis*), which is restricted to the South Island of New Zealand, has the general hue of the plumage dull olive-green, with black edges to the feathers. There is no yellow band across the breast, and the under parts are olive-brown without any tinge of red; orange-red is, however, present on the under wing coverts and axillaries. The wing feathers are dusky brown, the primaries having the outer web bluish, and the inner one toothed with lemon yellow. The tail is bluish orange, with a broad, transverse band of blackish brown near the end; the inner webs of the feathers being toothed with yellow.

In size the kea may be compared to a raven, its total length being 19 inches, of which 1¾ inches is taken up by the beak.

The kaka (*N. meridionalis*), which inhabits both islands, is a rather smaller bird, readily distinguished by the presence of a red tinge on the abdomen and under wing coverts, as well as by a wash of golden yellow on the ear coverts (page 1145). It is subject to a considerable amount of local variation. Still smaller, although with a longer beak, was the extinct Phillip Island parrot (*N. productus*). This bird attained a length of about fifteen inches, and was distinguished by the broad yellowish white band across the chest. Also extinct, the Norfolk Island parrot (*N. norfolcensis*), the smallest of the group, was distinguished from the Phillip Island species by the high curvature and length of the beak, which measured 3½ inches, and the absence of a dark bar on the tail.

Confining attention to the New Zealand representatives of the genus, it may be observed in the first place that the brush-like extremity of the tongue of these birds indicates flower-sucking habits. They are generally found in mountain regions, the kea ascending to elevations of some six thousand feet. The kaka is an eminently social bird, and by far the noisiest of the denizens of the woods of its native islands. "Being semi-nocturnal in its habits," writes Sir W. Buller, "it generally remains quiet and concealed during the heat of the day. If, however, the sportsman should happen to find a stray one, and to wound instead of killing it, its cries of distress will immediately raise the whole fraternity from their slumbers, and all the kakas within hearing will come to the rescue, and make the forest echo with their discordant cries.

PHILLIP ISLAND PARROT

"Unless, however, disturbed by some exciting cause of this sort, they remain in close covert till the approach of the cooler hours. Then they come forth with noisy clamour, and may be seen, far above the tree-tops, winging their way to some feeding place; or they may be observed climbing up the rough vine-clad boles of the trees, freely using their powerful mandibles, and assuming every variety of attitude, or diligently tearing open the dead roots of the close, epiphytic vegetation in their eager search for insects and their larvæ.

"In the spring and summer, when the woods are full of wild blossom and berry, these birds have a prodigality of food, and may be seen alternately filling their crops with a variety of juicy berries or sucking nectar from the crimson flowers of the rata (*Metrosiderus*) by means of their brush-fringed tongues. With the earliest streaks of dawn, and while the underwoods are still wrapped in darkness, the wild cry of this bird breaks upon the ear with strange effect."

It is from the oft-repeated cry of "kaka-kaka" that the bird derives its name. In dull weather kakas may often be seen abroad in the daytime, while occasionally flocks may be observed sweeping across a forest glade in the full sunlight. In spite of their slow and measured flight, these birds periodically migrate from one part of the country to another, generally travelling in parties of three or more, and frequently stopping to rest on the bare boughs of some dead forest tree.

During the pairing season the male and female are constantly in each other's company, flying side by side, and calling as they go. The breeding begins in November, the nest being a poor affair, made in the hollow of the trunk of a decayed tree. Here four eggs are usually laid, although it is said that there may sometimes be as many as six; and the young are able to fly early in January. Being an excellent mimic, the kaka is highly esteemed by the Maori as a pet, and, like most parrots, will live many years in captivity.

The habitat of the kea is very different from that of its cousin. In place of being confined to wooded districts, this bird frequents the almost inaccessible rocks of the mountains of the South Island at elevations where only dwarf vegetation is to be found. Here the keas may be seen among the crevices of the rocks when the mountains are shrouded in mist or sleet, or covered with a mantle of snow; while at other

KEA PARROT

times they may be observed soaring with motionless wings from peak to peak. During the depth of winter these birds are, however, driven to seek their food at lower elevations. The usual cry of the kea has been compared to the mewing of a cat, but a scream not unlike that of the kaka is also uttered at times.

The most remarkable feature in connection with the habits of the kea is its carnivorous propensities, which have been developed since the introduction of sheep into the colony, and have led to a great increase in the number of these birds (page 920). Sir W. Buller

writes that those keas which "frequent the sheep stations appear to live almost exclusively on flesh. They claim the sheeps' heads that are thrown out from the slaughter-shed, and pick them perfectly clean, leaving nothing but the bones. The plan usually adopted on the stations for alluring this bird is to expose a fresh sheepskin on the roof of a hut; and whilst engaged in tearing up the bait, it is easily approached and snared. Of recent years the keas have gone even farther than this, and now actually kill sheep for themselves, alighting upon the backs of the unfortunate ruminants, and tearing down through the skin and flesh until they reach the kidneys, the fat of which is greedily devoured. In disposition keas display extreme curiosity, and in the mountains they display so little fear of man that they may easily be knocked over with a stone."

Although some doubt has been thrown on the sheep-killing habits of the kea, in the main the accusation is perfectly true, although the story of their digging down to the kidneys seems to be incorrect.

Two or three keas in a party are said often to do the whole of the slaughter. As an instance of the extent of the damage done by these birds, it may be mentioned that on one occasion a farmer shut up 400 sheep in an enclosed and sheltered paddock, where he thought they would be safe for the winter, but on going to inspect them in the spring found that 200 had been killed by the keas. The most remarkable fact about these birds is that they nest and rear their young in midwinter high up among the glaciers and snowfields of the New Zealand mountains.

LORIES AND LORIQUETS

ALTHOUGH agreeing with the nestors in the general structure of their beaks, the beautiful birds known as lories and loriquets (family *Loriidæ*)), of which there are several genera, differ by the tongue being furnished with a kind of brush instead of a fringe, and also by the middle of the upper half of the beak being devoid of a groove. The beak, which is much compressed and generally longer than deep, has no notch; and the cere decreases in width from the middle line of the head to the sides of the beak. There is great variation in the length of the tail, but it is generally shorter, although occasionally longer, than the wing; while in form it may be either graduated or rounded. The wings are sharply pointed (acute), and generally have the first three feathers the longest.

Although unrepresented in New Zealand, the members of the family are confined to the Australasian region, inclusive of Polynesia. They comprise upwards of fourteen genera, of which only a few can be noticed in this work; the dimensions of the species varying from those of a turtle-dove to little more than those of a sparrow. There is one genus (*Oreopsittacus*),

confined to New Guinea, in which the tail has fourteen feathers, and thereby differs from that of all the other parrots.

TYPICAL LORIES

As the first example of the family, reference may be made to the well-known purple-capped lory (*Lorius domicella*) from Ceram and Amboyna, which is the typical representative of the genus to which it belongs. All the members of this genus—about ten in number—are characterised by the tail being of moderate length and rounded, with the two middle feathers longer than the others. The bill is orange-red, thus distinguishing the group from the black lory and its allies (*Chalcopsittacus*), where it is black; while the green wings serve to differentiate these parrots from the blue-necked lory and the other members of the genus *Eos*, in which there is a considerable amount of red on the wings.

The purple-capped lory measures about a foot in total length, a third of which is taken up by the tail. It is a gorgeously-hued bird, the general ground colour of the plumage being scarlet, while the breast is adorned with a gorget of gold; the wings are green, with blue at the bend and on the under coverts; and the tail is red, with a band at the tip, which is dark purple-red above and golden-red below. The feature from which the species takes its popular name is the deep purple cap on the head, which is often of so dark a tint as in some lights to appear almost black.

Like other lories, this species is a honey-sucker, but as the brush on its tongue is less developed than in some of the other members of the family, it is capable of living on other substances than honey, and is thus more easily kept in captivity. Lories are generally found in small parties of half a dozen or so, and in the Moluccas may frequently be seen devouring the soft fruits of various kinds of figs. They generally lay from three to four eggs on the bare wood in some hollow bough; and the young leave their domicile in about six weeks after the beginning of incubation.

The purple-capped species is remarkable for its gentle and affectionate disposition, as well as for its talking powers; for which reasons, together with the gorgeousness of its plumage, it is in much request as a pet.

The black-capped, or tricoloured, lory (L. lory), from New Guinea and the neighbouring islands, belongs to a group in which there is no yellow gorget, and has the whole of the abdomen blue, a red throat, green wings, and a black cap.

LORIQUETS

The loriquets are smaller birds than lories, with the tail feathers elongated and gradually tapering to a more or less acute point. Of this group Swainson's loriquet (Trichoglossus novæ-hollandiæ) is a well-known example, in which the prevailing colour of the plumage, both above and below, is green; the tail feathers being entirely of this hue, and moderate in length. The two middle feathers of the tail are not greatly elongated; while the four or five first primaries of the wings are not markedly narrowed at their tips. On the forehead the streaks on the shafts of the feathers are more or less blue, while the breast is somewhat tinged with red; these two characters serving to distinguish these birds from the members of the allied genus Psitteuteles. The range of these loriquets extends from New Guinea to Celebes.

Swainson's loriquet attains a total length of 12 inches, of which $5\frac{1}{2}$ are taken up by the tail, and is thus one of the largest representatives of the genus. In colouring it is, perhaps, the handsomest of all the Australian parrots; the head and throat being of a brilliant purplish blue, the nape of the neck greenish yellow, the abdomen blue, and the remainder of the body, together with the upper surface of the wings and tail, green. The under tail coverts are yellow at the base and green at the tip, while the under wing coverts are red. A yellow tip characterises the red

SWAINSON'S LORIQUET

bill, and the feet are slaty grey. This handsome bird is an inhabitant of Eastern Australia, ranging from Cape York to Victoria, and is likewise found in Tasmania. By the colonists it is commonly termed either the blue mountain lory or the blue mountaineer. Like its allies, it is almost exclusively a honey-sucker; and so much honey do these birds gather, that when shot it is quite common to see this fluid streaming out of their beaks.

These lories generally associate in small flocks, and during their flight utter loud, screaming cries. During their migrations they may, however, congregate in immense numbers, and may then be seen flying at great heights. With regard to these periodical movements, an anonymous writer observes that these birds are " migrants to and from different districts, and their migrations are regulated by the state of the blossoms of the gums and honeysuckles upon which they feed; not that they ever entirely left our forests, for I rarely at any time went out without seeing a pair or so. But the large flocks of them only come at such times as the trees are full of honey, and depart as suddenly as they come. They are always in larger or smaller flocks, do not associate with the other parrots, and are never seen feeding on the ground."

The female lays from three to four eggs; and in their first plumage the young have the breast yellow, with scarcely any tinge of red, and the band on the nape of the neck barely visible.

ARFAK PARROT

The Arfak parrot (Oreopsittacus arfaki), already referred to as having fourteen tail feathers, is a native of the Arfak Mountains in New Guinea, and measures only 6 inches in length. The general colour is dark green, with the cheeks and ear coverts blue, a tinge of red on the abdomen, the tail feathers black, with red tips, and the beak black.

OTHER GROUPS

Two genera of parrots from Australia, New Guinea, and the Eastern Malay Islands, known as Neopsittacus and Cyclopsittacus are regarded as indicating a distinct family (Cyclopsittacidæ) of the order, allied to the lories. While agreeing with the two preceding families in having the under surface of the hook of the beak nearly smooth, they differ in that the whole beak is deeper than long, and much swollen on the sides, the profile of the symphysis of the lower half being highly convex. In these respects these parrots serve to connect the lories with the succeeding families.

Perhaps the best-known representative of the group is the iris parrot (N. iris), from the island of Timor—a small, green parrot, measuring $7\frac{3}{4}$ inches in length, with an orange yellow bill.

There is but one other species of this genus (N. musschenbroëki), from New Guinea. All the species of the allied genus Cyclopsittacus are distinguished by the dark colour of their beaks.

transverse notch by a lateral sawing motion of the sharp-edged lower mandible. This done, it takes hold of the nut with its foot, and, biting off a piece of leaf, retains it in the deep notch of the upper mandible, and, again seizing the nut, which is prevented from slipping by the elastic tissue of the leaf, fixes the edge of the lower mandible in the notch, and by a powerful nip breaks off a piece of the shell. Again taking the nut in its claws, it inserts the very large and sharp point of the bill and picks out the kernel, which is seized hold of, morsel by morsel, by the extensile tongue. Thus every detail of form and structure in the extraordinary bill of this bird seems to have its use, and we may easily conceive that the black cockatoos have maintained themselves in competition with their more active and more numerous white allies by their power of existing on a kind of food which no other bird is able to extract from its stony shell."

In New Guinea it is extremely difficult to obtain these birds alive, and when in captivity their movements are slow and clumsy in the extreme. As the muscles of the breast are small and meagre, when compared to the enormous head and beak, it is probable that these cockatoos resort to flight as seldom as possible. The colour of the eye in young male birds is quite different from that of the adult.

RAVEN-COCKATOOS

Under the general name of raven-cockatoos may be included a group of several species, which, while agreeing with the last in their black or brown coloration, are distinguished by their completely feathered cheeks, the more ordinary form of the beak, and the shorter and broader feathers of the chest. Of this group the Banksian cockatoo (*Calyptorhynchus banksi*) may be taken as a well-known example. In all these birds the tail feathers are rather long, with the middle ones shorter than those on the sides, and are crossed by a light-coloured transverse band. The beak is characterised by its shortness and depth,

and its highly curved profile. The seven species are confined to Australia.

The Banksian cockatoo belongs to a group of four species in which, there is no light-coloured patch on the ear coverts; while in the adult males the band on the tail is red, although more or less tinged with yellow in the young and perhaps in females of all ages. On the other hand, in the second group, of which the funereal cockatoo (*C. funereus*) is a well-known representative, the ear coverts are marked by a yellow or white patch, the tail-band being of one of these two tints at all ages. The Banksian cockatoo, which measures 24 inches in total length, has the general colour of a greenish black, with a vermilion tail band. It is confined to Eastern Australia.

Of a South Australian species (*C. xanthonotus*) belonging to the group with a yellow tail-band, a writer who disguises his identity under the *nom de plume* of the "Old Bushman" observes that it "was common in our forests from about December, when the old and young birds came down from their breeding places, and remained with us during the winter. They did not breed in our neighbourhood (near Port Phillip); but I think they went to nest very early, for I once shot a female in May with a large egg in her. They principally frequent the honeysuckles, but are often in the large gums. The old birds are very shy, and have a loud, hoarse call-note, or cackle. When they first come, they are in large flocks, and they then always frequented the large honeysuckles, over the tops of which they would fly, or rather float through the air, with a wavering kind of flight, toying and playing with each other, after the manner of the rook at home. As the winter advanced, they appeared to separate, and, although you hardly ever see a single bird, they disperse themselves much more generally over the forests. Their principal food appeared to be large seeds and grubs, and they score the young honeysuckles round with their powerful beaks in search for these latter as if cut with a knife. The young birds are excellent eating."

GANGA COCKATOO

The curiously coloured ganga, or helmeted, cockatoo (*Callocephalum galeatum*), of South-Eastern Australia and Tasmania, differs so decidedly from all its allies as to constitute a genus by itself. The tail, as in the two following genera, is of moderate length and nearly even; while the head and crest of the male are flaming red, and the general colour of the upper and under parts is grey. The cere is peculiar in being feathered, and, while the beak is horn-coloured, the feet are nearly black. There is a tinge of green on the primaries of the wings. The length of this cockatoo is 13½ inches. It is a shy and forest-loving species, generally leading a solitary life among the topmost boughs of the tallest gum trees, on the seeds of which it subsists.

TYPICAL COCKATOOS

With the exception of the rose-breasted species, the typical cockatoos (*Cacatua*), which are those generally kept as pets, have the predominant colour of the plumage either white or rosy white, and the upper half of the beak is furnished with a short hook curving downwards nearly at a right angle to its

GREAT BLACK COCKATOO WITH CREST RAISED

of the plumage being scarlet, while the breast is adorned with a gorget of gold ; the wings are green, with blue at the bend and on the under coverts ; and the tail is red, with a band at the tip, which is dark purple-red above and golden-red below. The feature from which the species takes its popular name is the deep purple cap on the head, which is often of so dark a tint as in some lights to appear almost black.

Like other lories, this species is a honey-sucker, but as the brush on its tongue is less developed than in some of the other members of the family, it is capable of living on other substances than honey, and is thus more easily kept in captivity. Lories are generally found in small parties of half a dozen or so, and in the Moluccas may frequently be seen devouring the soft fruits of various kinds of figs. They generally lay from three to four eggs on the bare wood in some hollow bough ; and the young leave their domicile in about six weeks after the beginning of incubation.

The purple-capped species is remarkable for its gentle and affectionate disposition, as well as for its talking powers ; for which reasons, together with the gorgeousness of its plumage, it is in much request as a pet.

The black-capped, or tricoloured, lory (*L. lory*), from New Guinea and the neighbouring islands, belongs to a group in which there is no yellow gorget, and has the whole of the abdomen blue, a red throat, green wings, and a black cap.

LORIQUETS

The loriquets are smaller birds than lories, with the tail feathers elongated and gradually tapering to a more or less acute point. Of this group Swainson's loriquet (*Trichoglossus novæ-hollandiæ*) is a well-known example, in which the prevailing colour of the plumage, both above and below, is green ; the tail feathers being entirely of this hue, and moderate in length. The two middle feathers of the tail are not greatly elongated ; while the four or five first primaries of the wings are not markedly narrowed at their tips. On the forehead the streaks on the shafts of the feathers are more or less blue, while the breast is somewhat tinged with red ; these two characters serving to distinguish these birds from the members of the allied genus *Psitteuteles*. The range of these loriquets extends from New Guinea to Celebes.

Swainson's loriquet attains a total length of 12 inches, of which 5½ are taken up by the tail, and is thus one of the largest representatives of the genus. In colouring it is, perhaps, the handsomest of all the Australian parrots ; the head and throat being of a brilliant purplish blue, the nape of the neck greenish yellow, the abdomen blue, and the remainder of the body, together with the upper surface of the wings and tail, green. The under tail coverts are yellow at the base and green at the tip, while the under wing coverts are red. A yellow tip characterises the red

SWAINSON'S LORIQUET

bill, and the feet are slaty grey. This handsome bird is an inhabitant of Eastern Australia, ranging from Cape York to Victoria, and is likewise found in Tasmania. By the colonists it is commonly termed either the blue mountain lory or the blue mountaineer. Like its allies, it is almost exclusively a honey-sucker ; and so much honey do these birds gather, that when shot it is quite common to see this fluid streaming out of their beaks.

These lories generally associate in small flocks, and during their flight utter loud, screaming cries. During their migrations they may, however, congregate in immense numbers, and may then be seen flying at great heights. With regard to these periodical movements, an anonymous writer observes that these birds are " migrants to and from different districts, and their migrations are regulated by the state of the blossoms of the gums and honeysuckles upon which they feed ; not that they ever entirely left our forests, for I rarely at any time went out without seeing a pair or so. But the large flocks of them only come at such times as the trees are full of honey, and depart as suddenly as they come. They are always in larger or smaller flocks, do not associate with the other parrots, and are never seen feeding on the ground."

The female lays from three to four eggs ; and in their first plumage the young have the breast yellow, with scarcely any tinge of red, and the band on the nape of the neck barely visible.

ARFAK PARROT

The Arfak parrot (*Oreopsittacus arfaki*), already referred to as having fourteen tail feathers, is a native of the Arfak Mountains in New Guinea, and measures only 6 inches in length. The general colour is dark green, with the cheeks and ear coverts blue, a tinge of red on the abdomen, the tail feathers black, with red tips, and the beak black.

OTHER GROUPS

Two genera of parrots from Australia, New Guinea, and the Eastern Malay Islands, known as *Neopsittacus* and *Cyclopsittacus* are regarded as indicating a distinct family (*Cyclopsittacidæ*) of the order, allied to the lories. While agreeing with the two preceding families in having the under surface of the hook of the beak nearly smooth, they differ in that the whole beak is deeper than long, and much swollen on the sides, the profile of the symphysis of the lower half being highly convex. In these respects these parrots serve to connect the lories with the succeeding families.

Perhaps the best-known representative of the group is the iris parrot (*N. iris*), from the island of Timor—a small, green parrot, measuring 7¼ inches in length, with an orange yellow bill.

There is but one other species of this genus (*N. musschenbroëki*), from New Guinea. All the species of the allied genus *Cyclopsittacus* are distinguished by the dark colour of their beaks.

SOME STRIKING MEMBERS OF THE COCKATOO FAMILY

BARE-EYED COCKATOO

TRITON COCKATOO

ROSE-CRESTED COCKATOO

RED-VENTED COCKATOO

SULPHUR-CRESTED COCKATOO

SULPHUR-CRESTED COCKATOO

LEADBEATER'S COCKATOO

LEADBEATER'S COCKATOO

COCKATOOS

The remaining groups of the order are distinguished from those already noticed by the nature of the under surface of the hook of the beak. This, in place of being smooth, or with fine longitudinal striæ, is marked by a series of bold transverse ridges, running from each side of the middle line in a more or less oblique direction, so as to produce a file-like surface. In all of them the tongue is quite simple, being unprovided with any kind of brush or fringe.

The cockatoos (family *Cacatuidæ*) are readily distinguished by the presence of a crest of feathers on the head, which is wanting in all the members of the next family, with the exception of the peculiar horned and Uvæan parraquets (*Nymphicus*), respectively from New Caledonia and the island of Uvæa in the Loyalty group. An absolutely distinctive feature between the two families is, however, to be found in the skull. Thus, in all the cockatoos the socket of the eye is surrounded by a complete ring of bone, from the lower border of which is given off a process extending backwards to the hind part of the skull; whereas in the true parrots (*Psittacidæ*) this ring is generally incomplete, while in such instances as it is entire it lacks the posterior bony process.

As minor characters, it may be mentioned that the nostrils open in a cere which is not much swollen and generally naked, although occasionally feathered. The beak is of great depth, and usually very short, the upper half being generally much compressed, with its hook at right angles to the axis of the base. In all cases the metatarsus is extremely short.

Cockatoos are characteristic of the whole Australasian region, and range also as far west as the islands of Celebes and Lombok, and are represented in the Philippines; eastwards, however, their range is limited by the Solomon Islands, and they are consequently unknown in New Zealand. With the exception of the aberrant cockatiel (*Callopsittacus*) of Australia, which constitutes a separate subfamily, the whole of the members of the family are characterised by their short and broad tails.

Their colouring differs markedly from that of the other groups of the order. In the majority of the species white is predominant, but this may be more or less tinged with red or yellow, more especially in the crest and on the under surface of the tail. In the rose-breasted cockatoo the whole breast is, however, red, while the upper surface of the body, together with the wings and tail, is of various shades of grey, and the ganga is wholly grey, with the exception of the red head. In other species the prevalent tint is black or dark blackish brown. All lack the green so characteristic of parrots in general, although a tinge of this colour exists on the wings of the ganga.

GREAT BLACK COCKATOO

The largest of all the cockatoos, and, indeed, one of the biggest of the whole parrot tribe, is the great black cockatoo (*Microglossus aterrimus*) of the Papuan Islands and North Australia, which is the sole representative of its genus, and may be compared in size to a raven. It differs from all the other members of the family in that the flesh-coloured cheeks are entirely naked, and takes its generic name from the small size of its tongue, which is slender and worm-like, and thus quite unlike that organ in other parrots. It is further characterised by the upper half of the huge beak being much compressed, and narrower than the lower one; while the great elongation and narrowness of the feathers of the crest are also distinctive.

In the living state the plumage is slaty black, powdered with grey; the forehead and lores being deep velvety black, and the feathers of the wings and tail exhibiting green reflections. The naked cheeks are pale red, bordered with equally pale yellow, and the beak and feet black. In length this magnificent but funereal-looking bird measures from 29 to 31 inches, some ten of which are taken up by the tail. The largest specimens come from the mainland of New Guinea, those inhabiting the Aru Islands being considerably smaller. The tongue, which occupies only a small space in the enormous mouth, has been compared to a round pink worm with a black head, and is partially extensile. The colour of the naked skin of the face is subject to considerable variation in the living bird, and at times of excitement, owing to a kind of blushing process, becomes of a deep blood-red.

HEAD OF GREAT BLACK COCKATOO

That the enormously powerful beak of this bird must have some special use is quite evident, and its particular office has been described by Dr. A. R. Wallace in the following interesting account of the bird's habits: "The great black cockatoo," writes this observer, "frequents the lower parts of the forest, and is seen singly, or at most two or three together. It flies slowly and noiselessly, and may be killed by a comparatively slight wound. It eats various fruits and seeds, but seems more particularly attached to the kernel of the kanary-nut, which grows on a lofty forest-tree (*Canarium commune*), abundant in the islands where this bird is found; and the manner in which it gets at these seeds shows a correlation of structure and habits which would point out the kanary as its special food. The shell of this nut is so excessively hard that only a heavy hammer will crack it; it is somewhat triangular, and the outside is quite smooth.

"The manner in which the bird opens these nuts is very curious. Taking one endways in its bill, and keeping it firm by a pressure of the tongue, it cuts a transverse notch by a lateral sawing motion of the sharp-edged lower mandible. This done, it takes hold of the nut with its foot, and, biting off a piece of leaf, retains it in the deep notch of the upper mandible, and, again seizing the nut, which is prevented from slipping by the elastic tissue of the leaf, fixes the edge of the lower mandible in the notch, and by a powerful nip breaks off a piece of the shell. Again taking the nut in its claws, it inserts the very large and sharp point of the bill and picks out the kernel, which is seized hold of, morsel by morsel, by the extensile tongue. Thus every detail of form and structure in the extraordinary bill of this bird seems to have its use, and we may easily conceive that the black cockatoos have maintained themselves in competition with their more active and more numerous white allies by their power of existing on a kind of food which no other bird is able to extract from its stony shell."

In New Guinea it is extremely difficult to obtain these birds alive, and when in captivity their movements are slow and clumsy in the extreme. As the muscles of the breast are small and meagre, when compared to the enormous head and beak, it is probable that these cockatoos resort to flight as seldom as possible. The colour of the eye in young male birds is quite different from that of the adult.

RAVEN-COCKATOOS

Under the general name of raven-cockatoos may be included a group of several species, which, while agreeing with the last in their black or brown coloration, are distinguished by their completely feathered cheeks, the more ordinary form of the beak, and the shorter and broader feathers of the chest. Of this group the Banksian cockatoo (*Calyptorhynchus banksi*) may be taken as a well-known example. In all these birds the tail feathers are rather long, with the middle ones shorter than those on the sides, and are crossed by a light-coloured transverse band. The beak is characterised by its shortness and depth,

and its highly curved profile. The seven species are confined to Australia.

The Banksian cockatoo belongs to a group of four species in which, there is no light-coloured patch on the ear coverts; while in the adult males the band on the tail is red, although more or less tinged with yellow in the young and perhaps in females of all ages. On the other hand, in the second group, of which the funereal cockatoo (*C. funereus*) is a well-known representative, the ear coverts are marked by a yellow or white patch, the tail-band being of one of these two tints at all ages. The Banksian cockatoo, which measures 24 inches in total length, has the general colour of a greenish black, with a vermilion tail band. It is confined to Eastern Australia.

Of a South Australian species (*C. xanthonotus*) belonging to the group with a yellow tail-band, a writer who disguises his identity under the *nom de plume* of the "Old Bushman" observes that it "was common in our forests from about December, when the old and young birds came down from their breeding places, and remained with us during the winter. They did not breed in our neighbourhood (near Port Phillip); but I think they went to nest very early, for I once shot a female in May with a large egg in her. They principally frequent the honeysuckles, but are often in the large gums. The old birds are very shy, and have a loud, hoarse call-note, or cackle. When they first come, they are in large flocks, and they then always frequented the large honeysuckles, over the tops of which they would fly, or rather float through the air, with a wavering kind of flight, toying and playing with each other, after the manner of the rook at home. As the winter advanced, they appeared to separate, and, although you hardly ever see a single bird, they disperse themselves much more generally over the forests. Their principal food appeared to be large seeds and grubs, and they score the young honeysuckles round with their powerful beaks in search for these latter as if cut with a knife. The young birds are excellent eating."

GANGA COCKATOO

The curiously-coloured ganga, or helmeted, cockatoo (*Callocephalum galeatum*), of South-Eastern Australia and Tasmania, differs so decidedly from all its allies as to constitute a genus by itself. The tail, as in the two following genera, is of moderate length and nearly even; while the head and crest of the male are flaming red, and the general colour of the upper and under parts is grey. The cere is peculiar in being feathered, and, while the beak is horn-coloured, the feet are nearly black. There is a tinge of green on the primaries of the wings. The length of this cockatoo is 13½ inches. It is a shy and forest-loving species, generally leading a solitary life among the topmost boughs of the tallest gum trees, on the seeds of which it subsists.

TYPICAL COCKATOOS

With the exception of the rose-breasted species, the typical cockatoos (*Cacatua*), which are those generally kept as pets, have the predominant colour of the plumage either white or rosy white, and the upper half of the beak is furnished with a short hook curving downwards nearly at a right angle to its

GREAT BLACK COCKATOO WITH CREST RAISED

base. The species, about fifteen in number, range over Australia and the islands to the north as far as the Philippines, and include the most gorgeously coloured representatives of the family. The crest is subject to considerable variation in form and colour, such variations being of the highest importance in the determination of the various species. In the first place, the genus may be divided into two groups, according to the form of the crest. In one of these two main groups the crest feathers are slender and terminate in sharp points which curve forwards.

One of the best-known representatives of this group is the greater sulphur-crested cockatoo (*C. galerita*) of Australia, in which the feathers of the body are pure white, the cere naked, the crest sulphur-yellow, and the naked skin round the eyes white. This is one of the largest species, measuring from 18 to 20 inches in total length.

In the much smaller lesser sulphur-crested cockatoo (*C. sulphurea*), in which the length does not exceed 13 inches, the body feathers are slightly tinged with yellow, and there is also a patch of yellow on the ear coverts, in addition to that on the crest; this species inhabiting Celebes and some of the neighbouring islands. From both of these the citron-crested cockatoo (*C. citrino-cristatus*), from the island of Timor Laut, is readily distinguished by the orange yellow of the crest.

Far more gorgeous than all the others is, however, the beautiful Leadbeater's cockatoo (*C. leadbeateri*) of South Australia, in which the crest is vermilion at the base, with a yellow band traversing this coloured area, while the tips of the feathers are white (p. 1146). The cere is also feathered. The plumage of most of the upper parts is white, but the sides of the head, the neck, breast, under parts, and tail coverts are tinged with pale rose-colour, which is specially bright under the wings. In size this species comes next to the greater sulphur-crest, its total length being about 16 inches.

In the second great group the feathers of the crest, as well exemplified in Ducorps' cockatoo (*C. ducorpsi*) of the Solomon Islands, are broad with rounded tips, which do not curve forwards. In the larger forms, which correspond in size to the greater sulphur-crested species, the feathers of the crest are very long, and the cere is naked. One of the best-known species is the great white-crested cockatoo (*C. alba*), from the Halmahera Group of the Moluccas, in which the whole plumage is white. Readily distinguished by its vermillion crest is the rose-crested cockatoo (*C. moluccensis*), which appears to be confined to the islands of Ceram and Amboyna.

The remaining species are smaller, and have the cere feathered. Most of them have the under surface of the body white; but the red-breasted cockatoo (*C. roseicapilla*) differs from all the other members of the

BANKSIAN AND SLENDER-BILLED COCKATOOS

genus in having the whole of the under surface of the body of a brilliant full rose-colour, the upper parts grey, and the crown of the head pale rosy white. It is widely distributed in Australia, and measures 14 inches in total length. The blood-stained cockatoo (*C. sanguinea*) is from North Australia.

All the cockatoos of this group are gregarious, some of the species, like the greater sulphur-crest, associating in immense flocks; and those who have seen these birds soaring over the trees of an Australian forest bear testimony to the beauty of the spectacle. At times they will ascend in the sky, during the full blaze of a tropical noon, far above the range of the unaided human vision, while at others they may be seen scattered so thickly over a field as to give almost the appearance of a coating of snow.

Some years ago it was attempted to naturalise these

birds in the woods of Norfolk, but the attempt was, to a great extent, rendered abortive through their wandering habits, whereby many fell victims to the guns of the idlers of the neighbourhood. When flying at such a height in the air as to be invisible to the naked eye, the whereabouts of a flock of great white cockatoos is often revealed on a calm day by the sound of the characteristic cry from which these birds derive their name. This repetition of the syllables "cockatoo-cockato" is the ordinary cry of that species, but the harsh, screaming yell, denoting anger or surprise, is only too well known to all who have kept these birds.

Their food consists mainly of seeds, but it is probable that in the wild state larvæ of insects form a considerable portion of the diet of many of the species, as in captivity they will readily eat both gnats and flesh. Like most of the parrot tribe, cockatoos do little or nothing in the way of nest-making, generally laying their eggs on the bare wood in hollow trees. The eggs vary from three to four in number, and usually two broods are reared in a year. Their elegant plumage, graceful movements, and the readiness with which they are tamed, render cockatoos great favourites as domestic pets, although their discordant cries—worse in some species than others—are a serious drawback.

Writing of the great white cockatoo, Mr. W. T. Greene observes that "occasionally one of these birds will learn to pronounce a few words with tolerable distinctness, but their *forte* lies in the imitation of the barking of dogs, the crowing of cocks, the gabbling of turkeys, and the cackling of ducks, hens, and geese; and more particularly in the rendering, with much fidelity but in an exaggerated key, the outcries of a domestic fowl that has just produced an egg. They may be readily taught to throw up their wings, dance on their perch, hold out their foot to shake hands, and bow their heads in salutation of a visitor."

Not infrequently these birds can be tamed sufficiently to permit their being allowed to wander at large. The rose-breasted species assembles in smaller flocks than most of the other kinds, from which it also differs in its fondness for shade, resting quietly in the tree-tops while its white cousins are soaring in the empyrean above during the midday heat. From its splendid colours and engaging ways it would make an attractive pet, were it not that its discordant screams are more piercing and more frequently uttered than are those of its allies.

SLENDER-BILLED COCKATOOS

The slender-billed cockatoos, of which there are two species, one (*Licmetis nasica*) having a wide range in

Australia, while the other (*L. pastinator*) is confined to Western Australia, take their name from the great length and slenderness of the upper half of the beak, which projects obliquely forwards. In the former species, which measures 15 inches in length, the general colour of the plumage is white, but the lores and a narrow band on the forehead are red, while the feathers covering the head, neck, and breast are scarlet at the base, and the under surface of the wings and tail are washed with yellow. The crest of the slender-billed cockatoo is small, and confined to the front of the head.

THE COCKATIEL

The small long-tailed Australian species known as the cockatiel (*Callopsittacus novæ-hollandiæ*) differs so remarkably in appearance from the other members of the family that it has been considered to be an ally of the grass-parraquets. Nevertheless, as it has the crest and skull of the cockatoos, it may be included in the present family. It differs from all the other members of the family in its narrow and pointed tail feathers, of which the middle pair is much longer than the others. The male has a length of about 12½ inches, rather more than half of which is taken up by the tail.

The cockatiel's colouring, without being very striking, is pleasing. The prevailing hue is dark grey, becoming much paler on the upper coverts; the forehead and cheeks are lemon yellow, and the feathers of the crest, which cannot be depressed, are yellow at the base and grey above. A bright patch of reddish orange on the ear coverts occupies the middle of the yellow area, and the median and greater coverts, as well as a portion of the secondaries of the wings, are ornamented with a broad band of white. The female

COCKATIEL

lacks the brilliant head colours of her consort.

The cockatiel is found all over Australia, with the exception of North-Eastern Queensland, and associates in flocks of considerable size. The female lays from five to seven, or even nine eggs, in the incubation of which the male takes a full share.

These birds will breed freely in confinement, and have the advantage of an equable and contented disposition, which enables them to live peaceably with the other inhabitants of an aviary, whether great or small. Indeed, so easy-going in disposition is the cockatiel, that it will frequently allow itself to be hustled about and bullied by its smaller cousin the budgerigar, the description of which comes later on in this work.

Strong in its flight, the cockatiel is a somewhat restless, and at the same time a noisy bird.

TYPICAL PARROTS

With the exception of the peculiar kakapo, or owl-parrot, of New Zealand, the whole of the remaining members of the order are included in a single family (*Psittacidæ*), which comprises a far larger number of genera and species than either of the others. The group is one very difficult to define ; but, with the exception of the Uvæan parrot and a kindred species, all its members are distinguished from the cockatoos by the absence of a crest ; while in the skull the ring of bone is generally imperfect, and if complete always lacks the posterior process characterising that part in the cockatoos.

The members of this family have a very wide geographical distribution, ranging over the whole of the tropical regions, and being the only representatives of the order met with in Africa and America. In the Australasian region they are found in association with all the other five families. The family is divided into six subfamilies.

RED-CAPPED PIGMY PARROT

PIGMY PARROTS

New Guinea is a country of strange creatures, but none of its living products is more remarkable than the pigmy parrots (*Nasiterna*) some of which are actually smaller than an English sparrow. These birds, which constitute a separate subfamily, the *Nasiterninæ*, have the beak shaped as in the cockatoos, with a broad band-like cere, becoming narrower in the middle line. They are, however, specially distinguished by the short and squared tail, in which the pointed extremities of the shafts of the feathers project beyond the vanes. When folded, the long wings reach beyond the end of the tail, and the claws are remarkably elongated. The males of these pigmies are most gorgeous in colour, but their consorts show much more sober tints. Altogether nine species of these parrots are recognised. In the typical species (*N. pygmæa*) the total length is just over 3 inches, but it is rather more in the red-capped species (*N. bruijni*).

BLUE MACAWS

Leaving the pigmy parrots, attention may be directed to another, and very large, subfamily, the *Conurinæ*, exclusively confined to the New World, and ranging from Carolina to Patagonia. These parrots, which include the well-known macaws and the smaller American parraquets, are characterised by their graduated and generally long tails, in which each of the feathers tapers to a point, and the middle pair is longer than any of the others. The beak is strong, almost always deeper than long, and generally devoid of any notch, while its usual colour is whitish or pale brown.

Except in one genus, the two sexes are alike, and the predominant colour of the plumage is usually

PIGMY PARROT

green, although in some species blue or yellow. The cere, which may be either naked or feathered, surrounds the whole base of the beak like a band, and the nostrils may be either exposed or concealed among the feathers. In the skull the ring round the socket of the eye is generally complete. As there are no less than fifteen genera in the group, only some of the more interesting can be noticed.

From their large size, the length of their tails, and the gorgeous tints of blue, red, and yellow adorning their plumage, the macaws are the most showy and conspicuous of all parrots ; but they have the disadvantage of being the most noisy of the whole confraternity, and are therefore far from desirable in the house. By many naturalists the whole of them are included in a single genus, but others consider that they may be divided into three generic groups.

The blue macaw (*Anodorhynchus hyacinthinus*), from Central Brazil, is the best-known representative of a small genus characterised by the general colour of the plumage being blue both above and below, while the lores are feathered (page 1195). In the present species the whole plumage is of a nearly uniform cobalt-blue, becoming a little lighter on the head and neck, and somewhat duller below, and the under surface of the wings and tail is black. In marked contrast to the prevailing azure, stands out the yellow of the naked skin surrounding the eye and also present at the base of the lower half of the beak. The black beak is of unusually large size even for a macaw, and the feet are blackish. The total length of this fine bird is about 34 inches, of which $20\frac{1}{2}$ inches are taken up by the tail.

The blue macaw is a somewhat rare species, and although inhabiting the dense tropical forests affected by the other macaws, is said to differ markedly in regard to its breeding habits. In place of building in some hollow tree, it is stated to scoop out a burrow on the bank of a river, where it lays a pair of eggs, two broods being reared in a season. These birds—the ararauna of the natives—fly in pairs, and feed on palm-nuts, which, although so hard as to be difficult to break with a heavy hammer, are crushed to pulp by their beaks. The skulls of the blue macaw and its congeners differ from those of ordinary macaws in the incompleteness of the bony ring round the eye.

The same feature in respect of the skull is probably also characteristic of Spix's macaw (*Cyanopsittacus spixi*), which, although agreeing with the ararauna in its blue colour, differs by the naked lores, on which account it is regarded as representing a distinct genus.

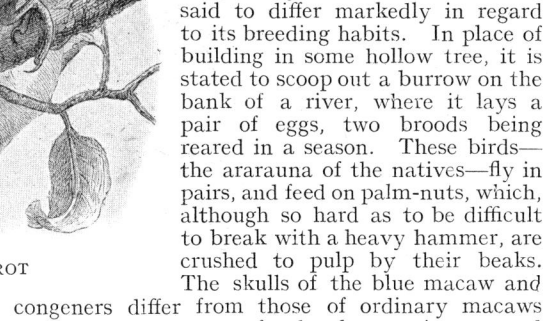

TYPICAL MACAWS

The macaws of the genus *Ara* differ from the preceding groups in the absence of blue on the under parts of the body, and also by the completeness of the bony ring in the skull round the eye. In all of them the lores, as well as a larger or smaller area of the cheeks, are devoid of feathers. The range of these splendid birds, which are locally known as araras, extends from Mexico to Bolivia and Paraguay, certain species ranging in the Andes to elevations of some ten thousand feet above the sea.

Of the fourteen recognised species, a few of the better known will alone be mentioned. Among these, the red-and-blue macaw (*A. macao*) is one of the handsomest, the general colour of both the upper and under parts being vermilion red, while the upper wing coverts are chrome yellow, and the lower parts of the back, the rump, upper and lower tail coverts, together with the quills of the wings, blue. The tail feathers are scarlet, with more or less blue at their tips (except in the middle pair) and on their outer edges, the outermost being almost wholly blue. Beneath, both the tail and wing feathers are golden red, while the greater and upper median wing coverts, as well as the scapulars, are yellow tipped with green (page 1195). In size this splendid bird attains a total length of 3 feet, nearly 2 of which are taken up by the tail. Its range is large, extending from Mexico to Guiana and the Amazon valley.

In marked contrast to the above is the colouring of the blue-and-yellow macaw (*A. ararauna*), in which the upper surface of the body, wings, and tail is blue, while almost the whole of the under parts is yellow, and the throat is marked by a broad black gorget. The crown of the head is grass-green, and the contrast of the light blue of the feathers of the back with the dark blue of the quills of the wings is very pleasing (page 1195). This species, which is smaller than the last, is also widely distributed in tropical America, ranging from Panama to the Amazon valley.

A third type of colouring is presented by the still smaller military macaw (*A. militaris*), in which, as in the majority of the species, the prevalent tint is green. The forehead is, however, scarlet, but the lower part of the back, the rump, and the upper tail coverts are light blue. Blue also appears on the quills of the wings, as well as on the primary and outermost wing coverts; while in the tail the four middle feathers are brownish red tipped with blue above, and the outer ones largely blue. The length of this species is only 27 inches, and its range extends from Mexico to Peru and Bolivia.

All the macaws of this genus are denizens of the dense forests of tropical America, associating in flocks, and feeding on fruits, seeds, and nuts. A flock of the red-and-blue species, feeding on the fruits of a palm tree, has been compared to a cluster of flaunting banners suspended beneath its crown. When on the wing, such flocks make the air resound with their loud, harsh screams. In the fruit season the palms in parts of Guiana are sometimes absolutely covered with these birds, so that any number may be killed with the blowpipe and arrows of the Macusi Indians.

HEAD OF RED-AND-BLUE MACAW

They all nest in the hollows of trees, which they enlarge according to their requirements. The eggs, usually two, but occasionally three in number, are about the size of those of a hen, although less pointed. Both males and females take their share in incubation, and there are usually two broods in the year. Not infrequently the whereabouts of a macaw's nest is betrayed by the protruding tail of the sitting bird.

Macaws awake from slumber with the first streaks of dawn, and at once begin their deafening clamour; the whole flock generally repairing to some common meeting place, where its members open their wings and warm themselves in the sun's rays. Soon the flock departs to its feeding ground, which may be either in the forest or among the cultivated lands. Feeding is continued till about ten o'clock, after which the host repairs to a neighbouring stream to drink and bathe. Towards noon the macaws seek the deepest shade of the forest, where they spend the hottest hours of the day, till the declining sun once again calls them forth. Before settling down to roost for the night, the flock, after the manner of rooks, assembles at the meeting place—usually some large bare tree. Most of the macaws can be readily tamed, and will live in captivity for long periods. They are, however, but poor talkers, and never give up their pernicious habit of screaming. Moreover, although properly tamed birds seldom attempt to bite adults, many of them cannot safely be trusted where there are children.

CAROLINA PARRAQUETS

AMERICAN PARRAQUETS

Next to the macaws, the best known representatives of this sub-family are the smaller American parraquets, mostly included in the genus *Conurus*, although the Carolina species (*Conuropsis carolinensis*) is the sole representative of a distinct genus. These long-tailed parrots differ from the true macaws by the lores being feathered, and are further characterised by the rather swollen form of the beak, which is not in the least degree compressed, while the lower half of the beak is broad and not grooved. In the typical kinds, or those included in the genus *Conurus*, the fourth primary

YELLOW-AND-BLUE MACAW

HYACINTHINE MACAW

feather of the wing is attenuated, and the nostrils are exposed; whereas in the Carolina parraquet (*Conuropsis*) the corresponding feather is not narrowed, and the nostrils are concealed among the feathers covering the cere.

Various shades of green, yellow, and orange may be regarded as the prevalent colours of these parraquets, although there is frequently more or less blue on the quills of the wings, while there may be red on the head and breast; the under parts are, however, never blue. In the Carolina species, which measures $12\frac{1}{2}$ inches in length, the general colour is green, becoming yellowish on the under parts, but the forehead and cheeks are orange red, and the rest of the head and neck bright yellow. Spots of orange red with patches of yellow adorn the shoulders, and the outer webs of the quills are bluish green, becoming yellow at the base.

The typical members of the group, about thirty in number, range from Mexico through Central America and the West Indies to Bolivia and Paraguay. Formerly the Carolina parraquet had a more northern range than any other parrot, extending to Iowa, the great lakes, and New York, but it is now confined to the States bordering the Gulf of Mexico and the Mississippi valley, where it is very local. At one time these birds were found in enormous flocks, which used to do great damage to the crops, but of late years their numbers have been greatly reduced.

Mr. Wilson writes that the Carolina parrots " are particularly attached to the large sycamores in the hollows of the trunks and branches of which they generally roost; thirty or forty, and sometimes more, entering at the same hole. Here they cling close to the sides of the tree, holding just by the claws, and also by the bill. They appear to be fond of sleep, and often retire to their holes during the day, probably to take a regular siesta. They are extremely sociable and fond of each other, often scratching each other's heads and necks, and always at night nestling as close as possible to each other, preferring at that time a perpendicular position, supported by their beaks and claws." They lay from three to five eggs; and, if taken young, are readily tamed. The golden parraquet (*C. solstitialis*), of Guiana, is golden yellow, with the exception of parts of the wings which are green and blue.

SLENDER-BILLED PARRAQUET

The great length and comparative straightness of the upper half of the beak of the slender-billed parraquet (*Henicognathus leptorhynchus*) serves to distinguish it from its kindred. It is the sole representative of its genus, and restricted to Chile, where it appears to be abundant. It is about 15 inches in total length; and the general colour of the plumage is dull green, becoming somewhat brighter on the top of the head, in which region each feather has a dusky edge. This colour is relieved by dull crimson on the forehead, lores, and round the eyes, and there is a faint patch of dull red on the abdomen, and some amount of bluish tints on the wings. The eyes are orange, and the beak and feet lead colour.

These parrots are met with in large flocks, which may number hundreds or thousands of individuals, and keep up an incessant screaming. For a part of the year they inhabit the forests, but from October to April they make their appearance in the cultivated districts of Valdivia, for the purpose of feeding on the crops. At this season they appear every morning in large flocks flying from the northward, and returning in the evening. With their long beaks they extract the grains of maize and wheat from the growing crops, and also dig up roots of grass, which form their staple food. Indeed, they are more terrestrial than arboreal in their general habits, although they nest in hollow trees. It is seldom that these parrots are brought alive to Europe.

GREY-BREASTED PARRAQUET

The grey-breasted parraquet (*Myopsittacus monachus*) belongs to a group of genera distinguished from the three preceding ones by the bony ring round the eye being incomplete; this particular genus being characterised by the beak being rather swollen at the sides and rounded above, as well as by the tufted oil-gland, and the concealment of the nostrils by the forward projection of the feathers at the base of the beak. The general colour of this parrot is green, with the upper part of the head, lores, cheeks, throat, and breast grey, the under parts yellowish green, and the primary feathers and wing coverts blue, edged with green on their outer webs. The beak is reddish white, the eye brown, and the foot grey. The total length of the bird is 11½ inches. It is a native of Bolivia, Paraguay, Argentina, and Uruguay.

The most interesting point in connection with this parrot is its habit of building nests in trees, whereby it differs from all other members of the order; the

GREY-BREASTED PARRAQUETS

illustration representing one of these nests built by a pair in captivity in one corner of their cage. In Parana these birds select tall trees in which to build, a number of nests being placed so close together as to form one great mass of sticks. They always associate in immense flocks, and commit great ravages on the corn-crops. On this account they are much persecuted by the inhabitants, Darwin relating that so many as two thousand five hundred of these birds were killed near Colonia in the course of a year. In some districts the nests are constructed in trees growing in swamps, and attain a huge size; each nest generally having several entrances, and being frequented by two or three pairs of birds. On this account the name of the swamp-parrot is frequently applied to the species. From observations made on captive specimens, it appears that, although the cock aids in building the nest, the work of incubation is performed by the hen alone; the usual number of eggs being two.

Nearly allied to this species are several South American parrots, constituting the genus *Bolborhynchus*, distinguished by the nostrils being exposed and opening in a much swollen cere, from which the name of the genus is derived. These parrots range from Mexico to Northern Chile and the Argentine, a well-known species being the Aymara parraquet (*B. aymara*).

PARROTLETS

The smallest representatives of this subfamily are the pretty green and blue birds which may be termed, from their Latin name, parrotlets (*Psitacula*), and occupy a position in this section analogous to that held by the love-birds in the parraquet group. The largest of these, parrotlets is only 5½ inches in length, while none of the others exceeds 5 inches. They differ from all the other members of the subfamily in the relative shortness of their tails, and also in that the two sexes are unlike, while their skeletons are distinguished by the absence of the furcula. They range from Mexico to Bolivia and Brazil, and are divided into three groups, according to the colour of the rump in the male. In the first group, as represented by the blue-winged parrotlet (*P. passerina*) the rump is ultramarine blue, in the second (*P. spengeli*) turquoise, and in the third (*P. guianensis*) green.

In this place attention may be directed to the fact that a very large number of members of the parrot tribe are restricted to the Southern Hemisphere, where they are especially numerous in South America, Australia, and the Papuan Islands. This has been taken to indicate that these birds constitute an originally southern group, although there is an almost equal probability that they may have been primarily developed in the Northern Hemisphere.

ALL-GREEN PARRAQUET

The last example of the subfamily to be mentioned is the all-green, or tirika, parraquet (*Brotogerys tirica*), representing a genus with several species distinguished by the long tail, the somewhat compressed form of the beak, in which the nostrils open in a completely naked cere, and the absence of a tufted oil-gland. The typical species, which is the largest of the genus, measuring 10 inches in total length—whereas some of the others are less than 7 inches—takes its name from the all-pervading green of the plumage, the only exceptions being the blue primaries and primary coverts, a

SLENDER-BILLED PARRAQUET

slight tinge of olive brown on the lesser upper wing coverts, and of blue on the middle tail feathers.

This species is an inhabitant of Eastern Brazil, but the range of the genus extends from that country to Peru, Bolivia, and Central America. In Eastern Brazil the tirika is one of the commonest of the parrot tribe, associating in countless flocks, which may be seen flying from grove to grove, or descending to ravage the rice and maize fields. The cry is a short, sharp, clear scream. In captivity these parraquets thrive well.

AMAZON PARROTS

The familiar Amazon parrots (*Chrysotis*) are among the best-known representatives of a large subfamily (*Pioninæ*) containing several American genera and a single African one. All these parrots are distinguished from the members of the preceding subfamily by their broad and short or moderate tails, which are never of the acuminate and pointed forms characteristic of the American parraquets, and have the tips of the feathers rounded. In the whole of them the cere is entirely naked, and the predominant colour of the plumage green. Usually the tail is about half the length of the wing, and may be either squared or rounded at the end, and the beak is of moderate strength, sometimes rather longer than deep. The New World species are all tropical.

Most Amazon parrots, of which there are over forty species, are comparatively large birds, sometimes exceeding 17 inches in length, and range from Mexico to Argentina, although especially characteristic of the great river-valley from which they take their name. They are characterised by the tail being of moderate length and rounded, with the under coverts always green ; and also by the absence of a tufted oil-gland,

as well as by the completeness of the bony ring round the eye.

One of the best-known species is the red-fronted Amazon (*C. festiva*), from the Amazon valley, which is a green bird with a red frontlet, a line of blue above and behind the eye, the back and rump red, and the bastard wing, together with the primary wing coverts and outer webs of the primaries, deep blue. Most of the species are distinguished from one another by the markings of the head and face, while a few differ by their smaller size. They are all essentially forest-dwelling birds, associating in flocks, and feeding on the fruits of palms and other trees.

They usually lay from three to four eggs, and produce but one brood in the year. If taken sufficiently early, the young are extraordinarily tame ; and as these birds are very hardy, they are favourites in captivity, more especially as many of them rival the grey parrot in talking and mimicry. Indeed, the amazon frequently becomes sufficiently domesticated to be allowed to wander in gardens at large.

HAWK-BILLED PARROT

One of the most remarkable members of this subfamily is the hawk-billed parrot (*Deroptyus accipitrinus*) of Guiana, the Amazon valley, and North-East Brazil, which is the sole representative of its genus. It differs from the Amazons by the presence of a tufted oil-gland, and the relatively longer tail, and is specially characterised by the beak being rather short, and deeper than long, but above all by the elongation and breadth of the feathers on the hind part of the neck, which form an erectile collar or ruff.

The colouring of this extraordinary bird is very striking. While the back and upper surface of the wings are green, the head is brown, with hoary streaks on the sides, the elongated feathers of the nape, together with those on the abdomen and breast, are dark red, with blue edges, and the bastard wing, primaries, and

ALL-GREEN PARRAQUET

HAWK-BILLED PARROTS

the bend of the wings, and legs. The whole length of the bird is about 11 inches. All are readily tamed, and may be trained to talk fairly well.

GREY PARROTS

The second group of short-tailed parrots, which forms the subfamily *Psittacinæ*, and is mainly confined to Africa and Madagascar, although represented by one genus in New Guinea, is readily distinguished from the members of the preceding subfamily by the prevalent colour being either grey or black, with or without a mixture of red. The sides of the head are more or less naked, the beak is never red, and in the skull the bony ring round the eye is always incomplete. The cere is broad, but narrows towards the nostrils, which it does not enclose in a swelling ; while the beak is without a notch, and has its lower half longer than deep. The tail may be either squared or rounded, and is sometimes rather more and at others rather less than half the length of the wing.

Such a universal favourite as the grey parrot (*Psittacus erithacus*), the parrot *par excellence* and the type of the whole order, scarcely requires description, as its appearance is familiar to all. It may be mentioned, however, that it is characterised by the squared tail being less than half the length of the wing, by the rather compressed and lengthened beak, and by the papillæ covering the naked portions of the face. The general colour of the plumage is ashy, with a bright red tail. The range of this species extends from the Congo and Guinea coast across Equatorial Africa to the east of Lake Nyasa. In Liberia and Sierra Leone it is replaced by *P. timneh*, distinguished by its dark grey plumage, and the dark red of the tail.

One of the best accounts of the habits of the grey parrot in its wild state is by Mr. J. G. Keulemans, who had an opportunity of studying these birds during a long residence on Prince's Island, where they especially frequent a hill, known as the Pico do Papagaio, and states that " these parrots are always found in flocks, which go about the island during the day, returning to their own appointed place on the mountain in the evening to roost. Their food consists of fruits, such as the palm nut, the avocat, the banana, goyave, mango, and many other fruits of a smaller kind, but they always give the preference to the palm nuts.

"They drink but little, and as no water is found on the Pico, they must obtain what they require during the day on the lowland. They make no nest, but deposit their eggs (which are from two to four in number) on the bottom of the hole. The eggs are in size, shape, and colour similar to those of the wood pigeon ; when unblown they are of a pinkish hue, which may be owing to the thinness of the shell. Both birds take it by turns to sit, and while one is sitting the other often comes and feeds it out of its crop. The young ones are fed in the same way. In time of danger the old birds defend their progeny vigorously, and should the enemy prove too strong to be successfully resisted by one pair, other parrots come up to their assistance, and, joining forces, either kill or put the aggressor to flight.

primary coverts black. The tail feathers are green, tinged with blue near the tips, and below both the tail and wings are black The beak is dusky horn in colour, the eye brown, and the foot black. In length this bird measures about 14 inches. In repose the elongated feathers of the nape are depressed, and it is only when the bird is excited or angry that the ruff is raised in the manner depicted in the illustration.

Little is known of this parrot in its native state, beyond the fact that it is an inhabitant of dense forests, and far less common than most other species. It is frequently found on the sawari palms, and its cry is described as of piercing shrillness. The usual number of eggs laid is stated to be four. Although rarely imported into Europe, the hawk-billed parrot forms an admirable bird as a pet, being very hardy, agile, and graceful in its movements, readily tamed, and almost as good a talker as the grey parrot.

AFRICAN GREEN PARROTS

Passing by the other American representatives of th present subfamily, brief mention may be made of the African genus *Pæocephalus*, which contains several medium-sized parrots, with rather short tails, and very short and deep beaks, especially as regards the lower half, in which the depth exceeds the length. These parrots are found throughout Africa south of the Sahara, and agree with their American cousins in the general green hue of their plumage ; well-known examples being Le Vaillant's parrot (*P. robustus*) of South Africa, Jardine's parrot (*P. guliemi*) from the west coast, and the brown-headed parrot (*P. fuscicapillus*) from Zanzibar.

In the second of these, while the general hue is green, the feathers of the back are black edged with green, the tail feathers and primaries black, and the other wing feathers like those of the back. These colours are relieved by red on the front of the head,

"The grey parrot delights to dwell in companies; many nests are found within a few feet of each other, and often in one tree two or more holes may be seen occupied by hatching pairs. The young birds are covered with a long and fluffy down, which afterwards, when moulting, falls off. Their first plumage is darker, and the iris dark grey, instead of pale yellow. They leave the nest when about four weeks old, but may be seen looking outside the hole some time before they are able to fly."

In captivity this parrot is the best of talkers, and, did space permit, many interesting anecdotes might be quoted relative to this accomplishment. Contrary to what usually prevails among higher bipeds, the male is commonly the more voluble and fluent speaker of the two, although the female pronounces her words more distinctly. Like most parrots, this species attains a great age, and there seems no doubt that examples have been kept in captivity for periods of between sixty and eighty years. Whether, however, they have lived in this state for upwards of a century, as reported, seems doubtful. The anecdote of the old lady of eighty, who purchased a parrot with the view of testing by experiment the truth of such report, is probably known to most readers.

It is stated that a third species of grey parrot inhabiting Prince's Island, West Africa, is similar to the common grey parrot, but larger and darker. The entire upper and under parts are very dark grey, almost blackish; the feathers, especially of the under parts, being edged with dark blue, giving the bird when viewed in certain lights the appearance of being strongly washed with inky blue.

GREY PARROTS

VASA PARROTS

The peculiar vasa parrot (*Coracopsis vasa*), together with four other nearly-allied species inhabiting Mada-

PAPUAN BLACK PARROT

gascar and certain neighbouring islands, constitutes a genus easily recognised by the black or blackish brown plumage, which gives the birds at a distance somewhat the appearance of crows. The region round the eye is naked, the lore also partially bare, and the whitish

beak somewhat thickened and swollen. The typical or greater vasa attains a length of about 20 inches. Although common in their native islands, very little is known of the habits of these parrots in the wild state; but the few brought to Europe are readily tamed, and soon learn to talk.

PAPUAN BLACK PARROT

Another mainly sable species, the Papuan black parrot (*Dasypterus perqueti*), is distinguished from its Malagasy allies by its longer and shallower beak, and the larger amount of bare skin on the sides of the face. The general sable hue is relieved by a red band on each side of the back of the head, and the under wing coverts are likewise red. Little or nothing appears to have been ascertained with regard to the habits of this striking bird.

RED-FLANKED PARROT

The typical parraquets, together with the love-birds and certain other allied forms, constitute a fifth subfamily (*Palæornithinæ*), confined to the Eastern Hemisphere, but exceedingly difficult to define from external characters. All of them differ, however, from the members of the foregoing groups, except the pigmy parrots, by certain peculiarities connected with the course of the carotid arteries of the neck. As a rule, the females are markedly distinct from the males, which, with the exception of the parrotlets, is not the case in the preceding groups; the tail feathers are frequently pointed; and the sides of the head are either completely feathered, or only naked just round the eyes.

The beak is often very strong, and frequently, especially its upper moiety, red in colour. In the skull the ring round the eye is incomplete. The cere is always narrow, surrounding the whole base of the beak with a band of equal width, and is generally partially feathered, while the nostrils may be either exposed or concealed. The group ranges over the Indo-Malay, Ethiopian, and Australasian regions. The Moluccas and Papuan Islands are the home of a genus of parrots of this group, of which the typical red-flanked parrot (*Eclectus pectoralis*) exceeds the grey parrot in size; its total length being from 16 to 18½ inches. In this genus the beak is thick, notched, and very deep, with its lower half marked by a keel along the middle line of the symphysis. The tail is of

RED-FLANKED PARROTS

moderate length and nearly squared, with its middle feathers of normal form, and the nostrils are hidden. In the females the general hue of the plumage is red, while in the males it is green.

So different are the two sexes of the red-flanked species that it is at first sight difficult to believe they belong to the same species. In the female the beak is black and the eye yellow; the plumage of the head and upper parts of the neck and breast is rich crimson red; a band across the upper part of the back, the lower part of the breast and abdomen, as well as the edge of the wing and under coverts, are blue; the back, rump, upper tail, and wing coverts, and the secondaries blood-red; the primaries and their coverts blue edged with green on their outer webs; and the tail feathers blood-red above, and somewhat dusky beneath.

In the more soberly clad male the general green hue is relieved by red on the axillaries and under wing coverts, there is blue on the angle of the wing and the primaries and their coverts, and the under surface of both the wings and tail feathers is black. In the beak the upper half is vermilion, and the lower one black. No adequate conception of the gorgeous colouring of these birds can, however, be conveyed without the aid of coloured illustrations.

This splendid parrot ranges from the Aru Islands through New Guinea to the Solomon Islands, but, as with its allies, scarcely anything is known concerning its habits in the wild state. In captivity it is readily tamed, but its chief attraction lies in its brilliant plumage, as its movements are listless and devoid of interest, and it is at times subject to fits of deafening screaming.

RING-NECKED PARRAQUETS

All who have travelled or resided in India are familiar with the flights of long-tailed parraquets which swarm in every jungle, and form one of the most characteristic features of an oriental landscape. These parraquets, of which there are many species, belong to a genus ranging from Africa north of the Equator, through Mauritius and the Seychelles, to India, Burma, the south of China, and Malaya, and taking its name of *Palæornis* (ancient bird) from the circumstance that one of the species was brought to Europe by Alexander the Great from the Punjab. They are characterised by the long and graduated tail, in which all the feathers, but especially the middle pair, are narrow, and the presence of a notch in the upper half of the beak; while very frequently there is a rose-coloured collar round the neck, at least in the males. The general hue of the plumage is green; but while in one large group the head is of this colour, in a second it is only partially green, or not green at all.

The best-known species is the ring-necked parraquet (*Palæornis torquatus*), belonging to the former group, and ranging from India to Cochin-China. In length, this bird varies from 16 to 17 inches, of which from 9½ to 10 are taken up by the tail; and while its general colour is green, the neck of the male is ornamented with a rose-red collar, incomplete in front, above which is a black ring imperfect behind. Far handsomer, however, is the Indian blossom-headed parraquet (*P. cyanocephalus*), in which the head of the male is red, tinged with plum-colour on the sides and back and defined by a narrow black collar, while the middle feathers of the tail are blue.

The following account of the habits of the Indian ring-necked species is given by Dr. Jerdon, who writes that it frequents " cultivated grounds and gardens, even in the barest and least wooded parts of the country, and it is habitually found about towns and villages, constantly perching on the housetops. It is very destructive to most kinds of grain, as well as to fruit gardens. When the grains are cut and housed, it feeds on the ground, on the stubble cornfields, also on meadows, picking up what grains it can; and now and then takes long flights, hunting for any tree that may be in fruit; and when it has made a discovery of one in fruit, circling round, and swirling with outspread and down-pointing wings till it alights on the tree.

" It associates in flocks of various size, sometimes in vast numbers, and generally many hundreds roost together in some garden or grove. It breeds both in holes in trees, very commonly, in the south of India, in old buildings, pagodas, tombs, etc.; and lays four white eggs. Its breeding season is from January to March. The ordinary flight is rapid, with repeated strokes of the wings, somewhat wavy laterally or arrowy. It has a harsh cry, which it always repeats when in flight, as well as at other times."

These parraquets are readily tamed, and in India will breed in that state. If well trained, they are fairly quiet, but if their tempers have been unduly tried they are wont to exercise their powers of screaming.

LOVE-BIRDS

The pretty little parrots commonly known as love-birds (*Agapornis*) derive both their popular and scientific titles from the attachment the members of a pair appear to entertain for one another. In spite of this, however, a single bird will live in captivity for years without any apparent signs of pining, and will actually become more attached to its owner than if it formed one of a pair; and the reason why, if one of a pair dies the other generally soon follows its companion, is that the constitutions of the two have been undermined by the hardships of the voyage to Europe. This demolishes the pretty fable that the death of the survivor of a pair is due to inconsolable grief at the loss of its mate.

Love-birds, of which the largest does not exceed 6½ inches in length, differ from all the other members of the subfamily in that the thick and deep beak has no ridge along the inferior surface of the symphysis of its lower half; and are further distinguished by the shortness of the tail, which is marked with a black band near the extremity. The skeleton is peculiar in that the furcula is absent. In the latter respect, as well as in their small size, and the occasional difference in colouring of the two sexes, love-birds resemble the American parrotlets, with which they have frequently been classed. They may, however, be at once distinguished from the latter by their rounded instead of pointed tail feathers.

The love-birds, of which there are about nine species, are confined to Africa south of the Sahara and Madagascar, although they have been introduced into the Mascarene Islands. Among them the rosy-faced species (A. roseicollis) belongs to a group in which the rump and upper tail coverts are blue, and the under wing coverts green. In both sexes the general colour is green, becoming yellowish beneath; the rump and upper tail coverts being light blue, the forehead bright red, and the sides of the face and throat rose-colour. This species inhabits South-Western Africa from Angola to Namaqualand, and is also reported from the opposite side of the continent, in the neighbourhood of the Limpopo. The two sexes are almost indistinguishable.

These love-birds are common in Namaqualand, where they are met with in small flocks, never far removed from the vicinity of water. Their flight is rapid, and while on the wing they utter their sharp cry. Their food consists of berries and large berry-like seeds. Instead of making nests for themselves, they take possession of those of other birds; but it does not appear to be ascertained whether they accomplish this by dispossessing the rightful owners, or whether they are content with deserted domiciles. The number of eggs is not mentioned. The grey-headed species (A. canus) is a Malagasy bird.

From their small size and engaging manners, love-birds are great favourites in captivity, although they are more or less delicate. The rosy-faced species is, however, the most hardy, and will readily breed in confinement, often producing two broods in the year. That love-birds have not always the angelic disposition commonly attributed to them is indicated by the following extract from a correspondent of Mr. W. T. Greene, who writes, that "I have a red-faced love-bird, to which it would puzzle you to apply the epithet 'amiable,' for a more surly, ill-tempered little glutton never existed. She quarrels with her husband, whom she drives out, compels to feed her with partly digested food from his craw, and then thrashes if he does not sit closely enough to her, or if he dares to move before she is ready. In fact, a more hen-pecked wretch never

lived, and yet he seems to like it, and to be specially proud of his beautiful but utterly unamiable wife."

HANGING PARROTS

The last group of this great subfamily is formed by the curious hanging parrots—so called from their habit of sleeping head-downwards, suspended by their feet from boughs. These parrots, which are about the same size as love-birds, comprise some twenty species, ranging from India and the Philippine Islands through the Malay region as far east as Duke of York Island. They differ from all the other members of the subfamily in the thinness of the beak, in which the length exceeds the depth; the upper half being long and little curved, while the profile of the lower portion slopes upwards with very little convexity.

In all of them the under surface of the quills and tail feathers is bright verditer-blue. They are brilliantly coloured, with green as the predominant tint; and a species from the Sulu Islands (Loriculus bonapartei) has been described as looking like a little glowing ball of vivid crimson, yellow, and green. The blue-crowned species (L. galgulus) is an inhabitant of the Malay Peninsula and Islands, and measures just over 5 inches in total length. In the male the general colour is green, with a deep blue spot on the top of the head, another of yellow on the interscapular region, a broad band of yellow across the lower part of the back, the rump and upper tail coverts scarlet, and a patch of the same colour on the throat. The female is duller.

ROSY-FACED LOVE-BIRDS

As might be inferred from the conformation of their beaks, all the hanging parrots are flower-suckers, subsisting largely on honey, although they also eat flower-buds and young shoots. The Indian species (L. vernalis) is usually found in open spaces in the forests, where it associates in small flocks. When feeding, it keeps up a continual chirping cry; and is said, like flying-foxes, to be at times taken in a stupefied condition lying beneath the pots suspended to catch palm-juice. These birds appear to pass a large portion of their time in sleep, but when awake exhibit marvellous activity in climbing. From the nature of their food, these little parrots are not well adapted for captivity, although they can be kept on a diet of rice boiled in milk and well sweetened, with the addition of fruit and ants' eggs; and if several are kept in a cage, they will hang suspended side by side from the roof for hours at a time, in which position they will caress and feed one another.

BROADTAILS

The last subfamily (*Platycercinæ*) of the parrot tribe is represented by the broadtails, grass-parraquets, and their allies, and is entirely confined to Australia, New Zealand, New Caledonia, and the Society Islands. The subfamily is distinguished from all the preceding groups, with the exception of the parrotlets and lovebirds, by the absence of the furcula—the single species of *Nanodes* is an exception in this respect, and it also differs from all other *Psittacidæ* in its brushlike tongue—while in the skull the ring round the eye is incomplete. The tail is rather long, graduated, and often pointed, and the beak of moderate size, and never red in colour. The cere is small, merely surrounding the nostrils; the beak short and thick, with its lower half generally concealed by the feathers of the cheeks, and the plumage much variegated.

The broadtails, of which the best known example is the Rose Hill broadtail, or Rosella parraquet (*Platycercus eximius*), take their name from the breadth of the tail feathers, which are not acuminate. The beak is distinctly notched; and the feathers of the back are black, with broad, light edgings, and presenting a general scale-like appearance. The genus, of which there are some sixteen species, is restricted to Australia, Tasmania, and Norfolk Island.

The Rose Hill broadtail is one of the handsomest of the Australian parrots, and belongs to a group of three species in which the cheeks are white and the head red. The nature of its colouring may be briefly indicated by saying that the head, neck, and breast are red; the cheeks white, the nape yellow; the feathers of the back black, with greenish yellow borders; the rump, upper tail coverts, and lower part of the abdomen yellowish green; and the lower portion of the breast yellow, with a scarlet band in the middle. A large portion of the wings is blue; and while the two middle tail feathers are green, tipped with blue, the outer ones are darker. The total length is 13½ inches.

This species, which inhabits South-Eastern Australia and Tasmania, generally assembles in small flocks, and, although strong on the wing, is not migratory. Its favourite haunts are open districts, and it specially frequents cultivated lands, where it inflicts much damage on crops. In addition to seeds of various kinds, this parraquet is believed to consume insects and their larvæ. It may be distinguished from most other parrots by its cry, which is described as a kind of chattering or warbling, with some approach to a whistle. Frequently the flocks may be observed feeding on the ground, and exhibiting little fear of man, except when they have been much fired at.

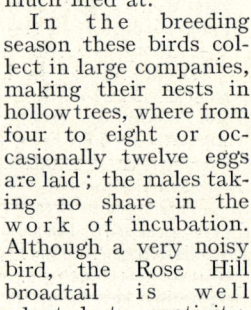

BLUE-CROWNED HANGING PARROTS

In the breeding season these birds collect in large companies, making their nests in hollow trees, where from four to eight or occasionally twelve eggs are laid; the males taking no share in the work of incubation. Although a very noisy bird, the Rose Hill broadtail is well adapted to captivity, being active and lively in its habits, and during the breeding season dancing and singing in an amusing manner. It has frequently bred in Europe.

GRASS-PARRAQUETS

The grass-parraquets, of which the lovely turquoisine (*Neophema pulchella*) is the most familiar example, form a small genus restricted to the south of Australia and Tasmania. They belong to a group of genera readily distinguished from the broadtails by the uniform colour of the feathers of the back, and are specially characterised by the beak being deeper than long, without any notch in the upper half, the absence of a yellow collar on the neck, and the nearly uniform length of the four middle feathers of the tail.

The turquoisine, which is about the size of a lark, its total length being 8½ inches, of which rather more than half is occupied by the tail, derives its name from the turquoise blue on the front of the head and wing coverts. The general colour of the upper parts is green, with the forehead, a streak over the eye, the cheeks, and wing coverts turquoise blue, the breast, abdomen, and under tail coverts rich yellow, the sides green, and the inner wing coverts marked by a chestnut red patch. The outer upper wing coverts, together with the under coverts, are bright blue, and the primaries and primary coverts deep blue. In the tail the four middle feathers are green with black tips, and the remainder bluish green at the base, with the inner webs black and the tips yellow. The female is somewhat paler.

Turquoisines inhabit the south-east of Australia, not ranging far inland, and being generally found in family parties of from six to eight, although when the grass is in seed they assemble, with others of their kindred, in large flocks, to feast on their favourite food. These parrots are largely terrestrial in their habits; and although the turquoisine nests in hollows of trees, other species select clefts of rocks in which to lay their eggs. The number of the latter is generally eight, and the male renders no assistance in incubation. In New Zealand and some of the neighbouring islands this group of parrots is represented by the genus *Cyanorhamphus*, characterised by the upper half of the beak being black at the tip and pearly grey at the base, the red-fronted parraquet (*C. novæ-zealandiæ*) being a well-known species.

CRESTED PARRAQUETS

Agreeing with the above-mentioned New Zealand parraquets in their parti-coloured beaks, the crested parraquets of New Caledonia and the Loyalty Islands differ from other members of the family in the presence of a small crest of feathers on the head. In the New Caledonian crested parraquet (*Nymphicus cornutus*), of which the general colour is green, and the total length about 14 inches, the crest consists of two black feathers tipped with red, the nape has a yellow collar connecting the ear coverts, the top of the front of the head is red, and the face black. In the smaller Uvæan species (*N. uvæensis*), confined to Uvæa, and perhaps Lifu, in the Loyalty group, the crest consists of six dark green feathers, curving forwards at the tips ; there is no yellow collar on the neck, the middle of the forehead is red, and the face dark green.

THE BUDGERIGAR

One of the prettiest, and at the same time the best known, of the smaller parraquets is the Australian budgerigar (*Melopsittacus undulatus*), also called the Australian love-bird, undulated grass-parraquet, or shell-parraquet, which is the sole representative of its genus. It differs from all the members of the subfamily

ROSE HILL BROADTAIL

yet noticed by the long tail feathers being narrow and acuminate ; and is distinguished from the allied genus *Nanodes* by the absence of a notch in the beak. Widely distributed in Australia, it attains a total length of 7½ inches, 4 of which are taken up by the tail.

Such a well-known species as the budgerigar (a term meaning " pretty bird ") requires but little description ; and this is the more fortunate, as the complex colouring renders any exact description somewhat difficult. Its general colour is grass green, with the front of the

head primrose yellow, the tail blue, and the remainder of the head, neck, back, and wings mottled with undulating and alternating bands of greyish black and yellow. Each cheek has an oblique patch of blue, below which are three round black spots. The male is distinguished by the cere being black, instead of brown or cream-coloured, as it is in the female.

The budgerigar is a very common bird in the neighbourhood of Adelaide, where it may be seen in large flocks, either perching on the gum trees or feeding on the ground. Its food consists mainly of seeds, and the female lays from four to nine eggs at a time, and produces two broods in the year. Its voice is a kind of warble, not devoid of melody, and in constant use. In the domestic state these little parraquets breed very freely, the great majority of those imported into England being bred on the Continent. Although readily tamed, the budgerigar is always apt to bite severely ; while it is an undesirable inhabitant of an aviary, on account of its propensity to attack and disable smaller birds.

GROUND-PARRAQUETS

The long-tailed ground-parraquet, or swamp-parraquet (*Pezoporus formosus*) and the short-tailed ground-parraquet (*Geopsittacus occidentalis*) are two peculiar Australian species of terrestrial habits, easily distinguished from all others by the alternate dark and light bars with which the feathers of the tail are marked. Hence comes the name of " pheasant-cuckoo " which is sometimes applied to the former.

The swamp-parraquet may be compared in size to a thrush, its total length being 12½ inches, of which the tail takes up 7½ inches. It is characterised by the length of the tail, which exceeds that of the wings, and also by its long and straight nails ; while the legs are likewise of considerable relative length. The general colour is green, with a band of dark orange on the forehead, and the feathers of the crown and nape marked with a broad median streak of black. The remainder of the body plumage is mottled with irregular bands of black and yellow ; the quills are brown, greenish outwardly, and marked with a yellow spot, and the bars on the tail feathers alternately green and yellow.

The " Old Bushman " writes that the swamp-parraquet " lives on the ground (but I have seen them perch on the tea tree scrub), runs much and quickly, is hard to rise, flies in jerks, goes away very sharp before a wind, and is very pretty shooting, rising from the grass and heather. We used to find them during the whole year, frequenting different localities at different times ; and although they could scarcely be said to flock, I generally rose three or four on the same spot. Dogs will set them like quail." They generally frequent sandy tracts covered with sparse grass and other herbage, and are but rarely seen in the neighbourhood of trees. The eggs are laid on the bare ground, and brooded by both sexes in turn.

The short-tailed ground-parraquet of the south and south-west of Australia differs by the tail being shorter than the wings, and the short and curved claws, as well as in colour. It is essentially a nocturnal bird, spending the day in holes in the ground, and only issuing forth at sunset to wander abroad in search of food. A specimen in the London Zoological Gardens, which remained quiet and drowsy during the daytime, only became lively and inclined to feed towards evening.

It never attempted to perch, always remaining on the floor of its cage. Its cry was a sharp monotonous whistle; and its food consisted of corn and young shoots of grass. The flesh of both species of ground-parraquets is said to be delicate and well flavoured.

THE KAKAPO OR OWL-PARROT

From the practical absence in those islands of indigenous mammalian life, many of the birds of New Zealand have more or less completely lost the power of flight, owing to the disuse of their wings; and among these flightless species is a remarkable member of the present order—the kakapo, or owl-parrot (*Stringops habroptilus*), which is not only the representative of a distinct genus but likewise of a separate family (*Stringopidæ*).

This bird is distinguished from other members of the order by the rudimentary condition of the keel of the breast bone, or sternum; and likewise by the radiating disc of feathers around the eye, which communicates the characteristic owl-like appearance to the head. The beak is thick and swollen on the sides, with no notch; and the nostrils open in a much inflated cere.

The wings are short and rounded, with the fourth, fifth, and sometimes the sixth primaries the longest; and the tail is also comparatively short, with its extremity rounded, but the individual feathers pointed. The metatarsus is somewhat elongated, the toes are moderately long, and the whole plumage is rather soft.

The owl-parrot is a somewhat large bird, attaining a total length of about 24 inches, 9 of which are occupied by the tail. The general colour of the plumage of the upper parts is sap-green, each feather having a median yellow line margined with black, from which spring irregular black rays. The feathers of the front and

its semi-fossilised remains being found in association with those of the extinct moas. From many parts of the country it has been recently exterminated; it is rare in most regions, and mainly restricted to mountainous regions, and is probably doomed to extinction at no very distant date.

With regard to its habits, Sir George Grey states that during the day the kakapo "remains hid in holes under the roots of trees or rocks, or very rarely perched on the boughs of trees with a very dense thick foliage. At these times it appears stupid from its profound sleep, and if disturbed or taken from its hole, immediately runs and tries to hide itself again, delighting, if practicable, to cover itself in a heap of soft dry grass; about sunset it becomes lively, animated, and playful, issues forth from its retreat, and feeds on grass, weeds, vegetables, fruits, seeds, and roots. When eating grass, it grazes rather than feeds, nibbling the grass in the manner of a rabbit or wombat.

"It sometimes climbs trees, but generally remains upon the ground, and only uses its short wings for the purpose of aiding its progress when running, balancing itself when on a tree, or in making a short descent—half jump, half flight—from an upper to a lower bough. When feeding, if pleased with its food, it makes a continued grunting noise. It eats greedily, and is choice in its food, showing an evident relish for anything of which it is fond. It cries repeatedly during the night, with a noise not very unlike that of the kaka, but not so loud. The kakapo is a very clever and intelligent bird—in fact, singularly so; contracts a strong affection for those who are kind to it; shows its attachment by climbing about and rubbing itself against its friend; and is eminently a social and playful bird. It builds in holes under trees and rocks, and lays two or three white eggs about the size of a pullet's in the month of February; and the young birds are found in March. The natives assert that, when the breeding season is over, the kakapo lives in societies of five or six in the same hole; and they say that it is a provident bird, and lays up in the fine season a store of fern-root for use in the bad weather."

KAKAPO OR OWL-PARROT

sides of the head are, however, pale umber-colour, with median lines of yellowish white, and those of the wings and tail mainly brownish buff, variously mottled with black and lemon-yellow. Beneath, the prevailing tint is greenish yellow, tinged with lemon-yellow, and with somewhat similar dark markings.

Although formerly distributed over the whole of New Zealand, the kakapo is now confined to the North Island and the northern half of the South Island;

The extermination or reduction in the numbers of the kakapo in certain districts is attributed to the ravages of dogs, cats, or rats, which have run wild in many parts of the island; and it is not improbable that in some parts, at least, pigs have likewise had a share in the work of destruction. These birds are generally found in the open mossy glades of the beech forests; although they also frequent open hillsides, where they hide among blocks of stone. On a few occasions a single kakapo has been met with during broad daylight, from which it may be inferred that these parrots are not so strictly nocturnal as has been supposed.

R. Lydekker

ORDER IV. STRIGES
GENERAL CHARACTERISTICS OF OWLS

THE well-known and peculiar physiognomy characterising most kinds of owls renders the group as readily distinguishable as that of the parrots. This characteristic "owl-face" is due, firstly, to the forward direction of the eyes ; and, secondly, to a circular disc of radiating feathers, more or less distinctly developed round each eye, which may be bounded by a ruff of closely-set feathers.

In common with many diurnal birds of prey, owls have a short, stout beak, of which the upper ridge is strongly curved, and the tip deflected in a perpendicular direction ; at its base is a cere, usually covered with stiff bristles concealing the nostrils. The feet are furnished with strong, curved, and sharp claws, and have the fourth toe reversible. The metatarsus, or shank bone, although longer than in parrots, is comparatively short and wide, with the upper part of its front surface deeply excavated, and usually furnished with a bony ridge over the outer part of the hollow ; at its lower end the three pulley-like trochleæ, when viewed from below, are arranged in an arch.

In the tibia there is no bony bridge at the lower end, as in most parrots. The short skull has no well-marked hinge at the root of the beak ; the palate is of the bridged, or desmognathous, type ; and the two branches of the lower half of the beak are united in front by a short and shallow symphysis, and the posterior angle is not produced behind the surface for articulation with the quadrate bone. The oil-gland is present, but naked.

The foregoing characters, especially those of the toes and leg bones, serve to distinguish owls from parrots on the one hand, and the more typical diurnal birds of prey on the other, but the two are in some degree connected in these respects by the osprey. In addition to the features noticed, owls, as a rule, are characterised by the large size and dense feathering of their heads, the softness and fluffiness of the whole plumage, and their big, round eyes ; the feet being usually feathered down to the toes. The ears are usually of large size, and are often protected by an operculum or lid ; from which it may be inferred that the sense of hearing in these birds is highly developed. Many owls are furnished with tufts or crests of feathers above the eyes, popularly known as horns or ears, but more properly termed ear tufts.

The colouring of the plumage is usually a mottled blending of various sombre tints ; bright colours being, as might be expected in nocturnal birds, invariably absent. The young are born in a helpless condition, and covered with down ; and the eggs are invariably white and rounded. In size these birds are subject to great variation ; the eagle-owls reaching to 28 inches in length, while the owlets are not larger than a thrush.

Considerable diversity of view has obtained as to the affinities of the owls, some naturalists considering that their nearest relationships are with the diurnal birds of prey, while others regard them as more nearly related to the nightjars and other picarians. Indeed, it has been proposed to include owls and picarians in a single ordinal group, the Coraciiformes.

Unlike parrots, owls (of which there are probably about two hundred species) enjoy a cosmopolitan

EAGLE-OWL SEIZING ITS PREY

distribution, ranging from the Arctic regions to the most distant islands of Oceania. The great majority are birds of the evening and the night, and are more or less completely dazed if disturbed and driven from their haunts during the daytime. Others, however, are but little incommoded by daylight, while the hawk-owls actually seek their prey in the full glare of the sun.

As owls subsist entirely on living prey, which at night must be closely approached before it can be detected, an absolutely silent flight is essential, and this is effected by the soft and fluffy nature of their plumage. It is doubtless from this ghost-like, stealthy flight, coupled with their nocturnal habits, their large glaring eyes, and their weird hootings and screechings, that these birds have in all ages and in all countries been regarded as creatures of ill-omen. Indeed, in this respect, owls hold a position among birds precisely similar to that occupied by lemurs among mammals; with the difference that, owing to the wider distribution of owls as compared to lemurs, the superstition in the one case is universally diffused, while in the other it is confined to certain races inhabiting the warmer regions of the Old World.

While the majority of owls are arboreal, some of the species roost in holes or clefts of rocks or in buildings. It is common to see owls in museums mounted with three toes in front of and one behind the perch on which they are seated; but this is totally incorrect, and no living owl ever places three toes in front of its perch, although it could do this for a moment if it felt so minded. It may be added that no owl seizes its prey or holds it with both feet, though both feet may be used to carry it when the victim is a large one, such as a full-grown rat. With one foot the owl grasps its prey, and with the other foot grips a tuft or some other inequality of the ground; then the bird goes to work.

Owls feed chiefly on small mammals, such as rats, mice, field mice, and shrewmice—more especially the two latter—as well as on birds, reptiles, fishes, and insects. The large eagle-owls will readily attack and kill hares, rabbits, and the largest game birds, and it is undoubtedly the case that such species inflict much harm on game preserves. The smaller kinds do, however, far more good than harm to the agriculturist; and although they were formerly shot down ruthlessly, both by the gamekeeper and the farmer, there is some reason to believe that the latter, at least, is beginning to see the error of his ways.

If proof were needful of the usefulness of these birds in keeping in check the pestilential field mouse, it is afforded by the flocks of owls that collect from all sides to prey on the hosts of these rodents which from time to time make their appearance in various parts of the world. In all owls the indigestible remnants of their food, such as bones, feathers, hair, scales, and the like, are formed into pellets in the stomach, and disgorged; such castings affording incontestible evidence of the nature of the food of these birds.

All owls are furnished with a syrinx, or organ of voice, which most of them know only too well how to use; their cries taking the form of hooting, howling, screeching, or a weird kind of laughter. It is from these cries that the names of these birds are derived in many languages, as witness the English *owl*, the German *eule*, the Latin *ulula*, and the Hindustani *ulu*.

The members of the group are commonly divided into the two families *Strigidæ* and *Bubonidæ*; although these groups might be preferably regarded as subfamilies of the single family *Strigidæ*.

CLASSIFICATION OF THE OWLS MENTIONED IN THIS WORK

ORDER
Owls—Striges

FAMILY 1
Barn-Owls—Strigidæ
GENUS 1
Barn-Owls—Strix
SPECIES

Barn-owl .... Strix flammea
Grass-owl .... S. candida
Cape barn-owl .... S. capensis

FAMILY 2
Other Owls—Bubonidæ
GENUS 1
Nyctala
SPECIES

Tengmalm's owl .... Nyctala tengmalmi
Acadian owl .... N. acadica
GENUS 2
Wood-Owls—Syrnium
SPECIES

Tawny owl .... Syrnium aluco
Great grey owl .... S. cinereum
Lapp owl .... S. lapponicum
Ural owl .... S. uralense
Dusky owl .... S. fuscescens
Barred owl..................... S. nebulosum
Mottled wood-owl .... S. ocellatum
Bornean owl .... S. leptogrammicum
Indian brown wood-owl .... S. indiani
Nepalese brown wood-owl ...... S. newarense

GENUS 3
Eared Owls—Asio
SPECIES

Short-eared owl .... Asio accipitrinus
Cape eared owl .... A. capensis
Long-eared owl .... A. otus
American long-eared owl ...... A. americanus
Jamaican long-eared owl .... A. grammicus
Stygian owl .... A. stygius
GENUS 4
Pigmy Owls—Glaucidium
SPECIES

European pigmy owl .. Glaucidium passerinum
Jungle owlet .... G. radiatum
Large barred Indian owlet ...... G. cuculoides
GENUS 5
Oriental Hawk-Owls—Ninox
SPECIES

Australian hawk-owl .... Ninox strenua
Indian hawk-owl .... N. lugubris
GENUS 6
Burrowing Owls—Speotito
SPECIES

American burrowing owl .. Speotito cunicularia
West Indian burrowing owl .. S. guadelopensis
GENUS 7
Little Owls—Carine
SPECIES

The little owl.................... Carine noctua
Desert-owl .... C. glaux
Indian spotted owlet .... C. brama

GENUS 8
Heteroglaux
GENUS 9
Hawk-Owls—Surnia
SPECIES

Hawk-owl .... Surnia ulula
GENUS 10
Snowy Owl—Nyctea
SPECIES

Snowy owl................ Nyctea scandiaca
GENUS 11
Screech-Owls or Scops-Owls—Scops
SPECIES

Scops-owl.................... Scops gihu
Flammulated screech-owl ...... S. flammeolus
North American screech-owl .... S. asio
Amazonian screech-owl .... S. cristatus
GENUS 12
Eagle-Owls—Bubo
SPECIES

Great eagle-owl................ Bubo ignavus
Central Asian eagle-owl....... B. turcomanus
Virginian eagle-owl .... B. virginianus
Indian eagle-owl .... B. bengalensis
GENUS 13
Asiatic Fish-Owls—Cetupa
SPECIES

Indian fish-owl........... Cetupa ceylonensis
GENUS 14
African Fish-Owl—Scotopelia
SPECIES

Pel's fish-owl .... Scotopelia peli

BARN-OWLS

ALTHOUGH one of the commonest and most familiar of all the group, the barn-owl (*Strix flammea*) is of special interest as constituting, together with a few nearly-allied forms, a family apart from the one which includes all the other representatives of the order. This family (*Strigidæ*) is characterised by the breast bone, or sternum, having its lower margin entire, and also by its keel being firmly united with the furcula. Then, again, the third claw has its inner margin serrated, while the second and third toes are of equal length.

An additional peculiarity is to be found in the presence of a small patch of stiff feathers between the adjacent portions of the face discs. In the shank bone the bridge over the hollow at the upper end is absent. As a genus, barn-owls are characterised by the completeness of the discs round the eyes, which are large, and narrow rapidly as they approach the beak. The wings are long, and extend considerably beyond the tail, the beak is straight at the base, and decurved only at the tip, and the aperture of the ear large, and furnished with a distinct lid. The head is devoid of tufts, and the rather long legs are feathered down to the origin of the toes.

The typical barn-owl has a wider distribution than any other member of the order, being in fact almost cosmopolitan, although comparatively rare in the extreme north, and unknown in New Zealand, parts of Oceania, Persia, Japan, and China. With this extensive distribution, it would be only natural to expect great variation in the colour of the plumage; and, as a matter of fact, the representatives of this owl from widely distant regions are so unlike one another that it is at first sight difficult to believe that they belong to the same species, more especially as there are also differences in point of size.

In the ordinary British form, of which the length averages 14 inches, the face discs are white, with their margins defined by the feathers being tipped with brown; the top of the head and the neck are pale buff, dotted with specks of black and white; on the back and wings a darker buff, speckled with grey and irregularly mottled with black-and-white, obtains; the tail feathers are pale buff above, marked with five transverse grey bands; and the whole of the under parts is white. From this normal type of colouring there is every intermediate stage to one where the eye discs are rusty red, the under parts tawny, and the back darker than usual; while in other cases the discs may be grey, and the whole plumage tending more or less to this tinge. In other instances, however, grey may exist only on the discs, while both the upper and under parts are of various shades of tawny and yellowish brown. The North American barn-owl (*S. fl. pratincola*) is slightly larger and darker than the European bird, while the Indian race is both darker and of a clearer grey above than the ordinary type.

In Britain the barn-owl is generally distributed, and resident throughout the year, although it becomes less numerous in Scotland, where it ranges so far north as Ross and Caithness, but seldom nests there. Strictly nocturnal in its habits, this owl spends the day in the recesses of buildings, or in hollow trees, generally standing with closed eyes. Like other owls, it associates in pairs, and such pairs, if undisturbed, will return year after year to the same nesting place. In hunting, the barn-owl quarters its ground with the regularity of a spaniel, and its food consists chiefly of field-mice. Its usual cry is a kind of scream, but the young utter a snorting sound.

In Europe this owl is a late breeder, usually beginning to lay from the middle to the end of April, but sometimes not till May. The number of eggs in a nest generally ranges from three to six, although seven have been taken. In California the

BARN-OWL WITH ITS NEST AND EGGS
Photo, Underwood & Underwood, London

nesting may be as early as January, and there, as in other parts of America, the nest may be made in a hole in a bank, enlarged to suit the requirement of its tenants.

Writing of the habits of the American barn-owl,

Major Bendire observes that, strictly speaking, this owl " makes no nest. If occupying a natural cavity of a tree, the eggs are placed on the rubbish that may have accumulated at the bottom; if in a bank, they

MEXICAN BARN-OWL

are laid on the bare ground and among the pellets of small bones and fur ejected by the parents. Frequently quite a lot of such material is found in their burrows, the eggs lying on and among the refuse. Incubation usually begins with the first egg laid, and lasts about three weeks. The eggs are almost invariably found in different stages of development, and young may be found in the same nest with fresh eggs. Both sexes assist in incubation, and the pair may be sometimes found sitting side by side, each with a portion of the eggs under them."

When the eggs are hatched at distant intervals, it is probable that the warmth of the young birds aids in their incubation during the absence of the parents. It is on record that the eggs of a barn-owl have been removed and replaced by those of a hen, which were successfully hatched.

Major Bendire adds that, "looked at from an economic standpoint, it would be difficult to point out a more useful bird than this owl, and it deserves the fullest protection; but, as is too often the case, man, who should be its best friend, is generally the worst enemy it has to contend with, and it is ruthlessly destroyed by him, partly on account of its odd appearance and finely coloured plumage, but oftener from the erroneous belief that it destroys the farmer's poultry."

Barn-owls, in England, at any rate, are sometimes more or less distinctly luminous, owing probably to the presence in their plumage of phosphorescent bacteria derived from the rotten wood of the trees forming their dwelling-places.

The grass-owl (*S. candida*) is an allied species, ranging from India to Japan and Formosa, and found almost exclusively in long grass; while in South Africa the common species is replaced by the Cape barn-owl (*S. capensis*). Both these species differ from *S. flammea* in having the upper surface of a uniform brown colour, with spots of white, and lacking the mottlings of grey and black characterising the former.

OWLS

The members of the second family, *Bubonidæ*, which includes all the other species, differ from barn-owls by the breast bone having two or more distinct notches in its lower border, and also by its keel being firmly attached to the furcula ; in addition to which the third toe is not serrated and is always longer than the second. The shank bone, or metatarsus, has a bridge over the hollow at the upper end.

TENGMALM'S OWL

The comparatively small Tengmalm's owl (*Nyctala tengmalmi*), belongs to a group of three genera of the *Bubonidæ* collectively characterised by having the tube of the ear large and furnished with a well-developed lid, and also by the face disc being distinct and extending as much above as below the eye.

As a genus, Tengmalm's owl and the nearly related Acadian owl (*N. acadica*) of North America are distinguished by the absence of tufts on the head, the extreme shortness of the cere, and the curious circumstance that the bony tube of the ear is quite unsymmetrical on the two sides of the skull. The toes are thickly feathered, the head is relatively large, the lower half of the beak notched, the wings long and rounded, and the tail short. This owl measures only from 8½ to 10 inches in length, and may be easily recognised by its thick and fluffy plumage, which stands out widely on each side of the head, and by its prettily-mottled colouring.

The general colour of the upper parts is pale brown, mottled with white bars, and the forehead spotted with white. The tail feathers are marked with five interrupted whitish bars, and the under parts greyish white, mottled with clove-brown. This species, which is rarely met with as a straggler in the British Isles, is an inhabitant of the forest regions of Northern Europe and Siberia, ranging in Russia as far as the Urals, and also occurring as a straggler in Nepal, Southern Europe, and North America. Across the Atlantic it reappears in Eastern North America. In habits it is strictly nocturnal, rarely being seen abroad in the daytime, and always dazed and stupid in a strong light. It frequents the densest recesses of forests, and nests early in hollow trees, laying its eggs, from four to six in number, on the bare wood at the bottom of the hole.

TENGMALM'S OWL AND PIGMY OWL

The second member of the genus, the so-called Acadian owl (*N. acadica*), in addition to its smaller size, differs by the nearly uniform colour of its upper surface, the replacement of the spots on the forehead by stripes, and the presence of only three white bars on the tail. In length it only measures 6½ inches, so that it is smaller than a thrush. Both species feed chiefly on insects. Writing of the Acadian owl, a correspondent observes that, " in the hollow of an oak tree, not far from Germantown, lives an individual of the common chickari squirrel with a specimen of this owl as his sole companion. They occupy the same hole together in perfect harmony and mutual goodwill. It is not an accidental temporary association, for the bird and the squirrel have repeatedly been observed to enter the same hole together, as if they had always shared the apartment. But what benefit can either derive from the other ? "

WOOD-OWLS

The clear, hooting cry or laughter-like scream of the common English tawny or wood-owl is probably familiar to most residents in wooded districts. The genus (*Syrnium*) of which this owl is the best known representative includes comparatively large species, distinguished from *Nyctala* by the ears and their tubes being symmetrical, while the toes may be either feathered or bare. All the species frequent woods and groves, where hollow trees are abundant, and are strictly nocturnal in habits. Their flight is soft and noiseless, and their food, in addition to small birds and mammals, may include frogs and fish. They breed early, and while some of the species select woods as their nesting places, others prefer old buildings. Nearly thirty members of the genus are recognised, whose range embraces the whole world, with the exception of Madagascar, certain of the Malay I lands, Australia, and Oceania.

TAWNY OWL

TAWNY OWL

The tawny brown, or wood-owl, as it is indifferently called (*S. aluco*), belongs to an extensive group of the genus, characterised by the crown of the head being either barred or mottled, and the completely feathered toes. It is by no means one of the largest representatives of the genus, its total length being about 15 inches. The colour of the face disc is greyish white, margined with brown ; the crown of the head, neck, back, and wings are a mixture of ashy grey mottled with shades of brown ; the primary quills are barred with dull white and brown ; and the tail feathers, with the exception of the middle pair, are also barred with the latter colour. On the under parts the ground colour is greyish white, upon which are longitudinal streaks and mottlings of brown, without any trace of transverse bars.

The tawny owl is still common in England, although rare in Scotland, most English woods having a pair of these birds. From Britain their range extends over Europe as far as 67° north latitude, and eastwards to the Urals ; while it also embraces Northern Africa, Syria, and Turkestan. This owl is essentially nocturnal, seldom stirring from its sylvan resting place during the daytime, and if driven forth being more completely dazed than any other British species. It is this species which is generally mobbed by a crowd of small birds, such as titmice, finches, and warblers, when seen abroad by day. Oak and beech woods, where hollow trunks are numerous, are the favourite haunts of the tawny owl, although occasionally the choice falls on ruins or towers. In addition to field-mice, shrew-mice, rats, and mice, its food includes an occasional young hare or rabbit, and sometimes frogs, fish, and beetles.

This species is an early breeder, laying its three or four eggs in March, or even earlier. These are usually deposited in a hollow tree, but sometimes in ruins or old chimneys, or even in a deserted rabbit-hole, or on the bare ground, and occasionally an old rook's nest is selected. The clear hooting cry, like the words "tu-whit, to-who," is uttered at morning and evening, but the laughter-like cry appears to be peculiar to the breeding season.

TAWNY OWL

The young owls are fed by the parents for a considerable time after leaving the nest, and are reported to be more easily reared in captivity than are those of any other species.

GREAT GREY AND LAPP OWLS

The great grey owl (*S. cinereum*) of Arctic America, and the closely allied Lapp owl (*S. lapponicum*) of Northern Europe and Asia, are much larger birds than the tawny owl, and easily recognised by the grey face disc being marked by a number of fine concentric brown lines. The grey owl has the plumage darker, with less distinct streaks on the breast, than its European cousin ; but Major Bendire regards the two as merely varieties of a single species. The great grey owl ranges from the shores of Hudson Bay to the limits of forest in about latitude 68°, but in winter migrates southwards even beyond the Canadian border into the Northern United States.

The Lapp owl, which is one of the rarest of the European species, is confined to the boreal districts, in the upper part of the forest-belt, occasionally straying to North Central Europe. It is distributed over Northern Scandinavia, Finland, and North Russia. The total length of the grey owl may be as much as 30 inches. The Lapp owl nests on the summits or forked branches of broken firs, in the former case making little or no nest, but in the latter erecting a large structure of twigs. The number of eggs in a clutch is probably from two to four.

Writing of the great grey owl, Major Bendire observes that "from the limited information we possess about the nesting habits of this species it appears that in Alaska these birds nest sometimes as early as April, and in the interior as late as June. From two to four eggs seem to be laid to a set, and these are small for the size of the birds. The body of the great grey owl is, however, much smaller than that of the great horned owl, in fact but little larger than that of the barred owl. The long tail and the loose fluffy plumage of the bird make it look much larger than it really is."

URAL OWL

The Ural owl (*S. uralense*) belongs to a subgroup distinguished from the preceding forms by each of the feathers of the head and neck having a simple median dark streak, without any lateral bars. In this species the facial disc is dusky white, and the ruff pure white with dark, median streaks to the feathers ; on the upper parts the general colour is dull white streaked with dark brown, each feather being brown in the middle and white on the sides ; on the under parts below the head the hue is whitish, some of the feathers being tinged with yellow, and each of them with a dark, median streak. The quills of the wings are brown, with whitish tips, marked with bands of paler brown, tending to ashy on their outer webs ; and the tail feathers are very similarly coloured. The total length of this fine bird is 27½ inches.

The Ural owl is distributed over Northern and Eastern Europe, and North and Central Siberia, where it is locally not uncommon, especially in Scandinavia, Russia, South-East Germany, and Transylvania.

DUSKY OWL

In Mongolia, China, and Japan, the Ural owl is replaced by the dusky owl (*S. fuscescens*), which is smaller in size and darker and redder in colour. Its habits are still imperfectly known, but in the breeding season it frequents forests and hills, and in the winter seeks the open country. It nests early in April ; and its pairing call has been compared to the bleating of a goat. Occasionally it may be seen hunting during the daytime.

BARRED OWL

Another well-known representative of the genus is the barred owl (*S. nebulosum*) of Eastern North America, distinguished from all the preceding species by the chest having a regular series of dark cross-bands, in addition to the longitudinal streaks. The general colour of the upper surface is light brown, with white cross-bands; the dark tail being marked with six light brown bars; and the beak greenish yellow.

Major Bendire writes that the barred owl "is nocturnal

URAL OWLS

in its habits, but nevertheless sees well enough, and even occasionally hunts, in the daytime, especially during cloudy weather. The flight is easy, and, though quite swift at times, it is perfectly noiseless. A rapidly passing shadow distinctly cast on the snow-covered ground is often the sole cause of its presence being betrayed as it glides silently by the hunter's camp-fire in the still hours of a moonlight night. Far oftener, however, it announces itself by the unearthly weird call notes peculiar to this species, which surpass in startling effect those of all other owls with which I am familiar. It is necessary to listen to such a vocal concert to fully appreciate its many beauties (?), as it is impossible to give an accurate description of the sounds produced when a pair or more of these birds try to outdo one another."

The barred owl generally nests in hollow trees among damp forests, the time of laying ranging from February to April, according to the latitude. Occasionally eggs have been taken resting on a solid cake of ice. No matter how frequently the nest be despoiled, a pair of birds will return to the same site year after year; and if one clutch of eggs be taken, they will soon be replaced by a second.

MOTTLED WOOD-OWL

The mottled wood-owl (*S. ocellatum*) of India, which attains a length of 12 inches, may be selected as an example of another section of the group with feathered toes, characterised by the under surface of the body being marked with regular cross-bars without any dark longitudinal streaks. This particular species has a blackish beak, the dark bars on the breast very narrow,

and the upper surface uniform brown with spots or bars of white. This owl is most commonly met with in moderately dry country, well furnished with large groves. It usually lays two eggs in a cavity or fork of some large tree, at a height of from eight to twenty-five feet from the ground, without any attempt to form a nest.

BORNEAN AND OTHER WOOD-OWLS

Certain other species of the genus, such as *S. leptogrammicum* of Borneo and several South American forms, while agreeing with all the preceding in having the plumage of the crown of the head either mottled or barred, differ in their more or less completely naked toes. In the second main group of the genus, comprising five species, of which the Indian brown wood-owl (*S. indiani*) will serve as an example, the crown of the head is, on the contrary, always of a uniform brown; the toes being either feathered or bare. The Indian brown wood-owl, which is uniform chocolate brown above, becoming darker on the head, attains a length of 28 inches; it is replaced in the Himalaya by the rather smaller Nepal brown wood-owl (*S. newarense*).

EARED OWLS

Although several groups of owls are furnished with the tufts of feathers commonly denominated ears, it will be convenient to restrict the title of eared owls to the members of the genus *Asio*, among which are the common long- and short-eared owls of Britain. While agreeing with those of the two preceding genera in the structure of their ears and the form of the facial disc, the owls of this genus are readily distinguished by the presence of longer or shorter ear tufts, and also by the cere being of much greater length. In all of them the lower half of the beak is notched, the tube of the ear very large, the wings long, usually with the second quill the longest, and the legs and toes generally more or less feathered to the claws. They are all purely nocturnal birds, seldom or never hunting by day, and not leaving their roosts till evening. They may frequent either woods or open country, and nest either in trees or on the ground. Their flight is very silent, and their cry a loud hoot. The species of the genus *Asio* are few.

SHORT-EARED OWL

The short-eared owl (*A. accipitrinus*) is a common and well-known British species, having an almost world-wide distribution, and ranging from the Arctic regions to South America and Africa, although unknown in Australia and Oceania. The distinctive character of the species is the shortness of the ear-tufts, which are less than the length of the third toe and claw. The general colour of the upper parts is fulvous or tawny, with each feather streaked with brown down the middle; whereas in the allied Cape eared owl (*A. capensis*), the same surface is uniform brown.

In the European species the under parts are pale buff, with streaks of blackish brown, the wings and tail barred with brown (five stripes on the latter), the facial disc dusky with a whitish border, the beak horn colour, and the eye golden-yellow. The whole length of the bird varies from 14 to 15 inches, and, when closed, the wings reach beyond the end of the tail.

Widely distributed in Great Britain, the short-eared owl breeds but sparingly, many of the specimens seen being merely winter visitors. In place of frequenting woods and groves, this owl haunts open moors, fields—either stubble, grass, or turnips—and generally nests on the ground rather than in trees or bushes. Although mainly nocturnal, if flushed during the day—as not unfrequently happens in partridge-shooting—it flies strongly and well, and is even said to hunt its prey at times in cloudy weather during daylight. Its cry is said to resemble the words " keaw-keaw."

In most parts of Europe the chief food of the short-eared owl consists of field-mice, but in Scandinavia it preys almost exclusively on lemmings. It also kills small birds and beetles. At such times as swarms of short-tailed field-mice have made their appearance in the British Isles it has been this owl which has made its appearance in the greatest numbers to prey upon the obnoxious rodents; and it also collects in similar flocks during the periodical migrations of the lemming in Norway.

It is a curious circumstance that although the number of eggs laid by this bird is generally four, yet when food is unusually abundant, as during a lemming migration, the number in a clutch will rise to seven or eight; and during a field-mouse invasion in Scotland even larger numbers were recorded, reaching to as many as thirteen. The eggs are usually laid in a hollow of the ground, with only a very slight nest.

In India Dr. Jerdon states that this owl " is almost exclusively found in the long grass, and in beating for florikan many are always flushed; one now and then paying the penalty of keeping company with such a game bird by falling to the gun of some tyro. It is migratory in India, coming in at the beginning of the cold weather, and leaving about March."

In North America the breeding range of this owl extends from the middle of the United States to the Arctic regions. " Its home," writes Major Bendire, " is amidst the rank grasses or weeds usually found along the borders of lakes and sloughs in the open prairie country, where it hides during bright sunshiny days. If the sky is clouded, this owl may be frequently seen hunting in the early morning or evening, and sometimes in the middle of the day, and at such times it flies very low, not more than a few feet from the ground, which it carefully scans for its humble prey. Its flight is remarkably easy, graceful, and perfectly noiseless. From the fact that these owls are generally seen in pairs at all seasons of the year, it is very probable that they remain mated through life."

While in the Arctic region the nesting of this owl is often deferred till June, in the more southern portions of its range it takes place in March or April. In defence of their eggs or young, both sexes of the short-eared owl display but little boldness, usually circling round and round the intruder, uttering a shrill cry, accompanied by a snapping of the beak, but not making any attempt at a direct attack.

Mr. W. Dutcher states that he once " kept a short-eared owl in captivity for about a month, in order to study its habits. It was confined in a large box with wire front, at first in the open air, and subsequently in a light cellar. Every effort was made to tame its wildness, by handling it with the greatest gentleness and never approaching it abruptly. No measure of success attended the effort; on the contrary, the owl seemed to grow wilder and more excitable when approached. A visitor was always saluted with a series of violent hisses, accompanied by a ruffling of the feathers over the whole body. The hisses were often accompanied by a violent snapping of the mandibles, which was continued for some time, especially if food were not given.

" If the visit were in the daytime, the exhibitions of fear and temper were much more violent than at night. This may be accounted for from the fact that at night the owl was dazzled by a bright light being held within a few inches of the cage. If the light were moved from end to end of the cage the eyes of the owl always followed it, thus showing that the light was a much stronger attraction than the visitor; however, the light was by no means so absorbing that it prevented the owl from seizing food when presented, if hungry; if not hungry, no attention would be paid to anything but the flame. If food were seized, it was merely held by the claws until the light was removed. It was also one of the owl's habits to hold surplus food with one foot when its hunger was satisfied. On a number of occasions a surfeit of house-mice was offered, but the owl would not eat to exceed more than three mice at one time.

" Once the process of disgorging a pellet was observed. The owl was about to be fed, when it began a series of contortions which seemed to involve the whole body. Three of these movements or contortions took place, then a pellet was thrown from the owl's mouth. It was nearly two inches long and about three-quarters of an inch at its greatest diameter. It was covered with a slimy substance which made it very slippery. The pellet dried quickly, when no trace of any greasy

SHORT-EARED OWLS

substance was found, and it is therefore probable that the lubricating matter must be lodged in the throat and stomach of the owl, and is only used in small quantities on the surface of the pellet, not being mixed with the whole mass."

LONG-EARED OWL

As its name implies, the long-eared owl (*A. otus*) belongs to a group of which there are three or four representatives, characterised by the great length of the ear tufts, which are about as long as the third toe and claw. From its beautifully mottled plumage, of which the general colour above is blackish brown variegated with orange buff, and beneath orange brown streaked and barred with black, this owl is one of the handsomest of the British species. The facial disc is dusky white, with hair-like lines of brown, while immediately round the eyes the feathers are blackish. The head is finely mottled dusky and tawny, and both the quills and tail feathers are barred with dark brown, the number of such bands on the tail being seven. The beak is dusky horn-colour, and the iris of the eye orange yellow.

In size this owl is rather inferior to the short-eared species, its total length being 13½ inches. The typical form of the long-eared owl is distributed all over Europe so far north as the 64th parallel, while southwards it ranges from North Africa in winter, and eastwards it extends to China, Japan, and North-Western India.

In North America, as far south as Mexico, it is replaced by the American long-eared owl, regarded by some naturalists as a local race of the European bird, but by others considered to represent a distinct species (*A. americanus*). It is distinguished from the European bird by the darker tone of the entire plumage, and by the white feathers of the breast being striped down the middle with brown, and barred on both sides with the same tint.

The European long-eared owl is a forest-dwelling bird in Britain resident through the year, but on the Continent and eastwards more or less migratory. On the Continent it is much more numerous in winter than summer, and it is not infrequent in the former season to see parties of from ten to sixteen, or even more, together, such parties assembling in the open fields. In England a pair of these birds always keeps to one particular wood. Unlike the majority of its kindred, this owl is a silent bird, making little or no noise, except when young ; on which account its presence is often unsuspected in districts where it may be comparatively common. It nearly always nests in woods, frequently selecting a deserted squirrel's drey or crow's nest in which to deposit its four or five eggs ; the usual laying time being March.

Although mainly nocturnal, this species is not exclusively so, as in Yorkshire it has been observed in the woods sailing quietly along, as if hawking, on a bright sunny day. In its nest have been detected remains of numerous small birds, as well as the foot of a young hare or rabbit. Both in Europe and America its chief food consists, however, of the various kinds of smaller rodents, although, where frogs are numerous, these also contribute to the menu. In America few of the nests are built by the birds themselves, but one which had been thus constructed was formed of twigs of willows and aspens, and remarkable for the depth of the cup, which was lined with hair. In mountainous regions it is stated that nests are occasionally made on cliffs.

Writing of the American bird, Major Bendire states that " in the daytime, particularly on a bright, sunny day, the long-eared owl will allow itself to be closely approached, and on discovering the intruder will try to make itself look slender and long by pressing the feathers, which are usually somewhat puffed out, close to the body, and sitting very erect and still. It might in such a position very readily be mistaken for a part of the limb on which it may be sitting. Occasionally, while on the ground, for instance, and being suddenly disturbed at a meal, they throw themselves into quite a different attitude— one of defiance, making themselves look much larger than they really are, and presenting a fierce and formidable front."

A TRIO OF LONG-EARED OWLS

The Jamaican long-eared owl (*A. grammicus*) differs from the other representatives of the genus in that the number of light bands on the quills is ten, there being also about the same number on the tail feathers. It is further distinguished by the toes being completely bare, although it is approached in this respect by the Stygian owl (*A. stygius*) of Brazil.

PIGMY OWLS

The pigmy owls, few of which exceed 8 inches in length, while several are less than 6, form the first representatives of the second section of the *Bubonidæ*, which includes all the remaining members of the order. The group is characterised by the ear tube being not larger than the eye, and unprovided with an operculum, and also by the facial disc being unequal, and in some cases very imperfectly developed, the portion below the eye being always much larger than that above the same.

The pigmy owls, of which the European *Glaucidium passerinum* is the typical representative, in addition to their small size, may be distinguished by the absence of ear tufts, the inflated and swollen cere, in which are pierced the nostrils, by the first primary of the wing being short, the whole wing short and rounded, the tail also rounded and more than half the length of the wing, and the metatarsus of moderate length and densely feathered.

There is not infrequently some confusion between the members of this genus and the little owls of the genus *Carine*, but if it be remembered that while in the former the first primary is short, and in the latter it is

EUROPEAN PIGMY OWL

long, the difficulty will vanish. There are some twenty species of pigmy owls, ranging over the greater part of the Old World, but not found eastwards of the Malay Islands, and also occurring in southern North America and the whole of South America. For their size, these little owls are bold and rapacious, many of them flying at birds of larger bulk than themselves. Usually nocturnal, and hunting in the morning and evenings, they may at times be seen abroad in daylight. Field mice, lemmings, small birds, and large insects form their chief food ; and their cry is a kind of whistling note, which may be imitated by blowing into a key. They build in hollow trees, without forming a nest.

EUROPEAN PIGMY OWL

The typical pigmy owl, which is unknown in Britain, is the smallest European representative of the order, and ranges over Europe and Northern Asia from Norway to Eastern Siberia. It belongs to a group of the genus in which the head is usually spotted or streaked, although occasionally nearly uniform ; the second great group of the genus being distinguished by the regular barring of the top of the head. In size this species attains a length of $8\frac{1}{2}$ inches ; and its general colour above is umber brown, becoming ashy on the head and back, and variegated with yellowish white spots, tending to bars, on the back. The head is thickly dotted with these round spots, the sides of the face are white, barred with dark brown, and the white breast is marked with longitudinal splashes of dark brown. The toes are thickly feathered.

This owl is generally distributed in Norway, where it is commonly found during the summer in forests, either evergreen or deciduous, but in winter approaches human habitations. A certain number of individuals migrate in winter. It may frequently be seen at midday, sitting silently on some bare tree, and when made bold by hunger, it will fly at and seize sparrows and tits while on the wing. It generally nests in hollow aspen trees, and lays four eggs at a time.

JUNGLE AND OTHER PIGMY OWLS

Among the second group of the genus, or those in which the head is regularly barred across, mention may be made of the jungle pigmy owl (*G. radiatum*), of the plains of India, and the barred pigmy owl (*G. cuculoides*), ranging from the Himalaya to Burma, and attaining a length of 11 inches. The former does not exceed 8 inches in length, and has nine bars of white, including the one at the tip, whereas in the second species there are seven such bands. The barred pigmy owl has the whole plumage brown, banded with five transverse white bars, giving it a very unmistakable appearance, but in the jungle pigmy owl there is a large white patch at the base of the neck in front. The latter species is dispersed in forest regions all over India, and breeds in April and May, laying three or four eggs in the hollows of trees.

These pigmy owls are strong fliers, and will kill small birds on the wing in the daytime. They can easily be tamed, and will eat cooked meat, frogs, insects, or almost anything that may be offered them. A pair kept by Mr. A. O. Hume were excessively noisy birds, both by night, and even at intervals by day, in fact at times a perfect nuisance.

In the Eastern Himalaya the barred pigmy owl may frequently be seen sitting on trees or stumps in the full glare of the midday sun ; its presence being very easily recognised by its chuckling, vibrating call. It generally nests in hollow oaks, at a height of twenty or thirty feet from the ground, laying four eggs in a clutch.

ORIENTAL HAWK-OWLS

As the name hawk-owl is commonly applied both to the members of the present genus (*Ninox*), and also to the true hawk-owl (*Surnia*), it is necessary to distinguish the former by the affix Oriental. These owls agree with those of the preceding genus in the shortness of the first primary quill of the wing ; the interval between its tip and that of the third primary being in all the group

LONG-EARED OWL

either equal to or greater than the length of the metatarsus. Whereas, however, in the pigmy owls the wing is short and rounded, in the present genus it is long and pointed, the interval between its points and the end of the tail being not more than equal to the length of the metatarsus.

From their nearest allies the Oriental hawk-owls are distinguished by the short metatarsus, of which only a very small portion is bare. Most of them have relatively small heads, in which the face disc may be very imperfectly developed, and short beaks, the tail long and firm, and the plumage of the wings likewise hard. The genus comprises a large number of species, ranging from India through China, Japan, and the Malay region to Australia and New Zealand, and likewise represented in Madagascar. The species vary greatly in size, the great Australian hawk-owl (*N. strenua*) attaining a length of 24 inches. In the small size of the head, the slight development of the disc, the firm plumage, and the length of the tail, these owls approach the diurnal birds of prey in appearance.

The Indian brown hawk-owl (*N. lugubris*), which measures 12 inches in length, and is uniform glossy brown above, with a greyish tinge on the head, is common in the wooded parts of India. Although generally nocturnal, it occasionally issues forth before dark; its food being mainly insects, although also including small mammals and reptiles.

BURROWING OWLS

The curious little burrowing owl (*Speotito cunicularia*) of America has a special interest on account of its habits, and accordingly demands a somewhat full notice. This bird is only some 9 inches in length, and may be easily recognised by the length of its legs, of which a considerable portion is bare, and its spotted plumage. It differs from the preceding group by the length of the first primary quill; the interval between its tip and that of the third feather of the same series being less than that of the metatarsus. The wings are comparatively short, and have little power of sustained flight.

The general colour of the plumage is sandy brown, the head being marked with oval splashes of buffish white, while all the back, wings, and tail are mottled and barred with white or buff. The throat and the front of the neck are white, but most of the remainder of the under surface is creamy white, with transverse bars of sandy brown, gradually becoming more and more indistinct towards the under tail coverts, where they disappear.

Although it has been considered that there are several distinct species of burrowing owls, it is probable that only two can be distinguished, one of which ranges throughout the southern and western portions of the United States and the whole of Central and South America; while the second (*S. guadelopensis*) is confined to the West Indies. There are two great peculiarities in the habits of burrowing owls, firstly, that they are largely diurnal, and secondly, that they always take up their residence in underground burrows.

Regarding the diurnal habits of the typical species in South America, Mr. W. H. Hudson writes that, " all

EUROPEAN LITTLE OWL

day long, in cold and in heat, it stands exposed at the mouth of its kennel, or on the viscacha's mound, staring at the passer-by with an expression of grave surprise and reprehension in its round yellow eyes; male and female invariably together, standing stiff and erect, almost touching—of all birds that pair for life the most Darby-and-Joan-like."

In North America, where these owls are mainly confined to the prairie regions, Major Bendire writes that they " may be seen sitting in front of their burrows at any hour of the day. When not unduly molested, they are not at all shy, and usually allow one to approach them near enough to note their curious antics. Their long slender legs give them rather a comical look, a sort of top-heavy appearance, and they are proverbially polite, being sure to bow to you as you pass by. Should you circle around them they will keep you constantly in view, and if this is kept up, it sometimes seems as if they were in danger of twisting their heads off in attempting to keep you in sight. If you venture too close, they will rise and fly a short distance, and generally settle down near the mouth of another burrow close by, uttering at the same time a chattering sort of note, and repeat the bowing performance. Occasionally, when disturbed, they alight on a small sage bush, probably to get a better view of the surroundings."

In many parts of North America, the burrowing owl takes up its quarters in the warrens of the prairie marmot (*Cynomys ludovicianus*), one pair of birds to a burrow; and it was at one time thought that both owls and marmots, together with the rattlesnakes which likewise frequent the colonies, lived together as a kind of happy family. Modern research has, however, shown that this is one of many zoological fables, Major Bendire is, indeed, of opinion that, in spite of its diminutive stature, the owl is a match both for the marmot and the snake, and that it subsists to some extent on the young marmots, if not also on the old ones. In parts where there are no marmots, such as California and Oregon, the owls generally frequent the burrows of the susliks (*Spermophilus*), which they enlarge to suit their own requirements; and they sometimes occupy the earths of wolves, foxes, or badgers.

From having been found living alone, it has been suggested that the owls may sometimes excavate their own burrows, but this is now considered improbable. On the pampas of Argentina, the burrowing owls take up their residence with the viscacha (*Lagostomus*). Mr. Hudson observes that the " birds generally make their own burrows to breed in, or sometimes take possession of one of the lesser outside burrows of the village; but their favourite residence, when not engaged in tending their eggs or young, is on the viscacheria."

During the daytime they are exceedingly bold, flying and screaming round the head of the intruder on their domains (as I have often witnessed); while at night their weird cry resounds across the silent pampas. In North America the food of these owls consists of young prairie marmots, susliks, chipmunks, gophers, and other small mammals, as well as lizards, frogs, fishes, large insects, and perhaps small birds. The owls hunt their prey mainly in the early evening and during the night, and but rarely in the daytime; they are exceedingly voracious, each bird being said to eat fully its own weight in the twenty-four hours, if it can obtain a sufficient supply.

In North America the breeding season begins in the latter part of March; the same burrow being generally used year after year, and cleaned out and repaired when necessary. The burrows vary from 5 to 10 feet in depth, and are usually about 5 inches in diameter; the nesting chamber being, however, from 12 to 15 inches across. Frequently the burrow is much curved, so that the nest may lie within a couple of feet off the surface; at times the nest is lined with grass or feathers, but more generally with cow-dung. Seven to nine is the usual number of eggs, but there may be as few as six or as many as eleven. Both sexes assist in incubation; and, unless the eggs be taken, only a single clutch is laid in a season. In defence of their eggs and young, these little owls exhibit determined ferocity; retreating to the ends of their burrows, and striking out at the intruder with beak and claws.

The following remarkable anecdote concerning these owls has been published by Mr. F. B. Loomis. "In the summer of 1904 a party of fossil hunters was travelling up Bridger Creek, a tributary of the Bad Water River in Wyoming, when the horses, in passing a spot full of prairie dog burrows, shied suddenly off the track, owing to a loud 'rattle.' Search was made without result for the presumed rattlesnake, when a second rattle was heard, and at the same time a burrowing owl rose and settled upon a neighbouring post, where it commenced a third rattle. The members of the party saw the stretched neck, bulging eyes, and vibrating tongue of the bird, the whole appearance of which indicated assurance that it had the power of frightening away an enemy. It certainly succeeded in scaring four plain-bred horses, as well as the men of the party, all of whom had been familiar with rattlesnakes for weeks, and two for years."

Mr. Loomis adds that he himself has been startled by the sound of the dry lupin-pods, known as "rattle-weeds," but that on such occasions the horses took no notice, although those of the Bridger Creek party were clearly frightened by the owl. As a rule, the burrowing

EUROPEAN LITTLE OWLS

owl is a silent species, although it has a note usually described as a squawk, and not unlike the syllables "qua-qua-qua-qua," with variations in the last part. The unusual sound made by the Bridger Creek bird was heard repeatedly by the party of which Mr. Loomis was a member, as the camp was only about a mile from the prairie-dog burrows, and on every day for over a week at least one of them—and sometimes all—passed the spot. The owl, it is added, never failed to warn with its rattle, and the horse or horses—no matter how tired—as regularly shied off the track, not having learnt to associate the sound with the bird. If the latter should succeed in teaching the trick to its young, a protective habit of great value would be formed.

LITTLE OWLS

Although the name little owl, or owlet, is, of course equivalent to pigmy owl, yet it is convenient to restrict the latter term to the members of the genus *Glaucidium*, and the former to those of the genus *Carine*, or *Athene*. As already mentioned, little owls are frequently confounded with pigmy owls, but the two differ essentially, in that the former have a long and the latter a short first primary quill. The little owls differ from burrowing owls in that both the fourth and fifth primaries have their outer webs deeply scalloped, and also in having the upper part of the metatarsus hidden by feathers, and the bases of the toes enveloped in the plumage of the metatarsus, their legs thus appearing very short.

In having the nostrils pierced near the front of the cere, the little owls are distinguished from an allied Indian owl known as *Heteroglaux*, in which the nostrils occupy the middle of the cere. The wings are large, with the third and fourth quills of nearly equal length; and the head is large and round. The five species of this genus range from Europe and North Africa across Central Asia to China, and also from the Mediterranean countries across Persia to India and Burma.

EUROPEAN LITTLE OWL

The European little owl (*C. noctua*) is about the same size as Teng-

BURROWING OWL

malm's owl—from which it may be at once distinguished by its compact plumage—and is an occasional straggler to the British Isles. The general colour of the upper parts is brown, mottled with oval white spots; the facial disc being greyish white, passing into brown externally, while the greater portion of the under surface is whitish, streaked with brown, each feather on this aspect having a dark median line and light edges. This bird is found all over continental Europe, except the extreme north, but its extreme eastern limits are not fully known.

A desert-hunting variety or species (*C. glaux*) differs by its paler colouring, the ground colour of the upper parts being rufous fawn, and the under surface pure white streaked with rufous. Moreover, while in one kind the toes are scantily covered with hair-like feathers, in another they are thickly plumed. The pale desert form of the little owl inhabits the countries to the south of the Mediterranean, except near Tangiers (where the ordinary form occurs) and it also ranges into North-Eastern Africa, and extends eastwards into Persia, India, and Afghanistan. The ordinary form is the commonest owl in Italy, and is also abundant in Sicily, although there it is migratory. It breeds in Italy, Gibraltar, Spain, Greece, and Holland.

Professor A. Newton observes that " the little owl is not strictly nocturnal in its habits, for one observer has seen it at midday, when the sun was shining brightly, carry off a sparrow from a flock ; but, as a rule, towards the evening it becomes more active and vigilant. It seldom haunts forests, but frequents old buildings, towers, and church walls, where, as well as in hollow trees and even in a rabbit-hole, its nest is found."

The number of eggs varies from three to five, and both sexes take their share in incubation. No nest is formed. In Italy the flesh of this owl is commonly eaten ; and this species has a peculiar interest as being the owl associated with the goddess Pallas in classical literature. In Persia five or six individuals of the pale-coloured desert race may often be seen in company; and almost every garden in that country has a pair, whose melancholy cries are regularly heard at night.

INDIAN SPOTTED OWLET

In India the genus is represented by the spotted owlet (*C. brama*), in which the under parts are barred, instead of streaked, and the general colour above, greyish brown, with large and distinct white spots, and five bars on the tail. To the eastward of the Bay of Bengal there is a variety of this species, in which the ground colour of the upper parts is slaty brown, and the white spots very small, while the tail has six bars.

Dr. Jerdon states that the spotted owlet is to be found everywhere in India except dense forests. " Every clump of trees, and often a large single tree, especially near a village, is sure to be tenanted by a pair or a small colony of these noisy birds. It often takes up its abode and roosts during the day in the eaves of houses, or under the roof, and if anything disturbs its rest, comes forth with its noisy, chattering, and disagreeable chorus. About sunset it is always on the alert, and soon after it sallies forth to feed. It takes short flights, frequently seating itself on the ground, or a paling, or low branch, or outhouse ; and thence captures beetles and other insects on the wing, or snatches one off the branch of a tree ; now and then making a low, undulating flight over the plain or garden, and dropping on any small mouse, shrew, lizard, or insect it may spy on the ground."

I have often put my hand into a hole in a tree and had my fingers seized by one of these owlets, and have frequently noticed the calm nonchalance with which the birds have sat and regarded me when they have been dragged forth. The spotted owlet lays from two to four eggs, generally deposited in March.

HAWK-OWLS

As already mentioned, the term hawk-owl, although commonly applied to the members of the genus *Ninox*, properly belongs to the species here represented, and it may be well to add that the reader must avoid confusing the scientific title of this genus (*Surnia*), with the name *Syrnium*. The hawk-owl belongs to a group of genera differing from those already described by the cere not being inflated, with the oval nostrils always pierced in its front margin ; the present species, which has no distinct ear tufts, being characterised by the long and graduated tail approaching the wing in length. The head is unusually flat, with the facial disc nearly obsolete, a strongly curved and powerful beak, and a small orifice to the ear. The wings are short, the whole plumage is hard and compact, the legs are rather short, and the toes thickly feathered.

The hawk-owl (*S. ulula*) is the most hawk-like member of the order, both as regards appearance and habits. The typical form is distributed over Northern Europe and Asia, ranging through Siberia to Kamchatka and Amurland ; a few stragglers ranging into Central Europe in the winter. It is represented in North America, to the northward of latitude 40°, by a darker race (*S. u. funerea*) ; and, according to Dr. E. Coues, it is to this variety that some of the specimens taken in Britain belong. In length this owl reaches 15 or 16 inches.

The general colour of the upper parts is brown mottled with white—the white being most abundant on the head and neck, and least so on the umber wings. The face disc is dirty grey, bounded on the sides by a crescentic purplish brown patch, extending down from the ears. The chin is dusky, the throat and upper part of the breast are dull white, and the remainder of the under parts dull, with numerous dusky bars, the under surface of the tail being barred with greyish brown and dull white. In addition to the darker colour of the upper surface, the American race is distinguished by the broader and redder bars on the breast, and the smaller size of the white gorget.

THE HAWK-OWL

SNOWY OWL

In habits the hawk-owl is strictly diurnal, pursuing its prey in the bright sunshine. It is an inhabitant of the subalpine districts of Norway, sometimes reaching so high as the zone of birch trees, although its true home is the fir woods. Frequently it may be seen sitting in the full sunlight on some bare tree, surrounded by a mob of small birds, which the owl generally disregards, although sometimes it makes a sudden swoop on one of its tormentors. At times when lemmings are migrating, hawk-owls make their appearance in great numbers to prey upon the hosts.

The nesting place is usually upon the broken top of some dead tree ; the eggs (five to eight in number) being laid either on the bare rotten wood or a thin layer of dried grass. The female begins to sit from the laying of the first egg. Never shy, in the breeding season this owl is bold in the extreme. When the nest is approached, the bird rapidly raises its head and tail in a series of jerks, after the manner of a cuckoo, and then suddenly dashes at the intruder.

Writing of the habits of this species in Lapland, Mr. J. Wolley observes that the " hawk-owl flies much in the daytime ; and, with its long tail, short, sharp wings, and quick flight has a very hawk-like appearance in the air, when its large, square head is not seen. It carries itself much after the fashion of the more regular owls ; but whilst all the feathers at the back give a great breadth to its full face, there is quite a table at the top of its head. It casts its bright yellow eyes downwards with the true air of half-puzzled wisdom, or turns its head round for a leisurely gaze in another direction ; to glance backwards is out of the question, and to look at anyone with a single eye is much beneath its dignity."

The chief food of this owl consist of lemmings, field mice, and birds. The breeding season apparently begins in the middle of April and continues till the end of June ; and, as the eggs are laid at intervals, some may frequently be found far on in the latter month. In America the hawk-owl probably breeds only in the fur country and the wooded districts of Alaska. It is there very destructive to ptarmigan, as it is in the Old World to willow-grouse. In America the number of eggs laid varies from three to seven. Mr. R. MacFarlane states that on the Anderson river

" four nests of this species were discovered, and the eggs taken therefrom. All of them were built in pine trees at a considerable height from the ground. One was actually placed on the topmost boughs, and, like the others, constructed of small twigs and sticks, and lined with hay and moss."

SNOWY OWL

Conspicuous for its snowy plumes—generally more or less mottled with black or brown—the great snowy owl, or snow-owl (*Nyctea scandiaca*), cannot be confounded with any other member of the order, being the only representative of its genus. As a genus it is distinguished from the preceding by the shortness of the tail, which is only about the length of the wing, and also by the under tail coverts being produced nearly to the tip of the tail, and there are slight rudiments of ear tufts. The plumage of the adult may vary from pure white to white largely spotted with black ; when present, the dark markings are placed near the tips of the feathers, and while those on the under parts are crescentic, those above approach a linear form.

Although the nestling is covered with sooty black down, the first feathers are similar to those of the adult, from which it may be concluded that the evolution of the white plumage dates from an extremely remote period. While some naturalists are disposed to regard the amount of black in the plumage as an individual peculiarity, others believe that the pure white plumage occurs in the oldest birds, and then only in the male sex. In length the snowy owl measures 26 inches.

The snowy owl has a circumpolar distribution, inhabiting the northern regions of both hemispheres, and straggling southwards in winter. Common in Lewis, and blown over to the east coasts of Scotland in considerable numbers, and likewise visiting Ireland

SNOWY OWL

in winter, the snowy owl does not breed in any portion of the British Islands. Found in Iceland during the winter, it is a permanent resident in Scandinavia, Greenland, and Northern Russia ; while in winter it ranges all through Siberia to Amurland, and has been taken in Poland and Lithuania, as also at Peshawur. Although rare in Spitsbergen, it is common in Novaia Zemlia and on the northern coast of Asia.

At the present day this owl is very rarely seen in the south of England, but during the Pleistocene period it appears to have been not uncommon, a shank bone having been obtained from a cave in Devonshire. It is noteworthy that during the period in question lemmings, which now form such a large portion of the prey of this species, were also common in England. In America this owl ranges as far south as Texas. The open and desolate moss-covered tundras of Northern Siberia and Lapland, as well as the corresponding regions of North America, are the favourite haunts of the snowy owl.

A shy bird, hunting both by day and night, and endowed with noiseless though powerful flight, it falls suddenly on its prey, which is always immediately devoured on the spot. In the Old World its food consists of lemmings, young seabirds, ptarmigan, grouse, ducks, and, it is said, the Arctic fox and hare ; while in the Transbaikal districts susliks are largely consumed. Wherever lemmings are on the move, numbers of snowy owls are sure to collect. In America these birds often take the musquash from the trap, and in both hemispheres have been known to fish.

The nest is usually placed on the bare ground, in a spot

GREAT EAGLE-OWL

raised somewhat above the general level of the plain, but may be situated on a ledge of rock. It is a poor affair in the way of structure, the eggs resting merely on few feathers. The usual number of eggs is from four to seven, but in seasons when lemmings are numerous as many as ten may be laid at considerable intervals of time. Incubation begins with the first egg, so that eggs and young are frequently found in the nest together. While the female is sitting, the male remains on the watch near by, and gives the alarm in case of danger. Old birds, and more especially females, exhibit great boldness in defence of their nests, flying close to the head of an intruder with outstretched talons and snapping beaks.

In such cases the natives are reported to seize a young bird, whereupon one of the parents charges the despoiler, who holds up his gun-stock, against which the bird dashes headlong till it is either killed or beaten off.

SCREECH-OWLS OR SCOPS-OWLS

The screech-owls, or scops-owls, represent a genus, *Scops*, of mostly small species distinguished from the preceding representatives of the group with uninflated ceres by the presence of distinct ear tufts. In this character these owls agree with the large eagle-owls to be mentioned next, from which they are distinguished, in addition to their generally smaller size, by the wings being very long, and reaching nearly or quite to the tip of the tail. As a rule, the toes are feathered, although in certain species the metatarsus is completely bare.

There are between twenty and thirty species of these small horned owls, which range over the greater part of both the Old and New Worlds, although only one of them occurs in Europe. In habits largely nocturnal, they may at times be seen abroad in the daytime. Groves, gardens, and wooded districts are their favourite resorts ; their nests are made in trees, and the food of some of them is to a great extent composed of the larger insects. The various species of screech-owls are more difficult to distinguish than those of any other genus, although the Old World forms are very distinct from those of America.

EUROPEAN SCREECH-OWL

The typical screech-owl, or scops-owl (*S. gihu*), is one of the smallest European members of the family, and is occasionally met with in England. It ranges over southern continental Europe in summer, and in winter reaches Northern Africa, while eastwards it extends to Persia and Turkestan, being replaced by allied races, or species, in Japan, India, Malaya, and South Africa.

In length not exceeding 8 inches, this little owl belongs to a group characterised by the dusky hue of the beak, the greyish brown colour of the face disc, the slender and feathered metatarsus, and the general grey or brown hue of the plumage, of which the upper surface is marked with closely approximated fine dark lines, while on both aspects the middle lines of the feathers are distinctly streaked with black.

Although generally nocturnal, the scops-owl has been observed in Spain in the full summer sun. Its flight is very like that of the little owl, and its food consists almost wholly of insects. In May the female lays from five to six eggs in the hollow of some tree, and the bird sits so close that it may often be taken by the hand.

"This owl," as Professor A. Newton observes, "is remarkable for the constancy and regularity with which it utters its plaintive and monotonous cry, sounding like ' kew-kew,' and pronounced at intervals of about two seconds throughout the livelong night."

AMERICAN SCREECH-OWLS

Among American species mention may be made of the southern screech-owl (*S. flammeolus*), ranging from the southern United States to Guatemala, which is of small size, with the metatarsus feathered for more than half its length, and the toes bare ; and also of the North American screech-owl (*S. asio*), which has a very extensive range and numerous varieties, and is distinguished by its feathered toes. A third species is the crested screech-owl (*S. cristatus*) of Amazonia, which attains a length of fully 16 inches. The common screech-owl is an abundant bird, exhibiting a grey and a red phase of plumage, and not migratory. Although living for the greater part of the year in forests, when the ground is mantled in snow, this owl seeks the protection afforded by buildings, and is then more frequently seen. It is considered a true friend to the farmer, as it lives almost exclusively on field mice and other small rodents and the larger insects. Hollow apple and oak trees are its favourite nesting resorts ; the eggs, usually five or six in number, being laid on the bare wood.

Writing of the American species, Mr. W. Dutcher observes that in the eastern United States "screech-owls are very fond of living in apple orchards, especially if the trees have been neglected and are decaying, thus furnishing holes in which the owls may breed or hide. The farmer who is so fortunate as to have a pair or more of screech-owls attach themselves to his orchard should consider himself specially favoured, for the good they will do him by keeping in subjection the mice-pest is beyond calculation. A farmer living in Seneca County, New York, informed me that mice and rabbits, principally the former, had in one winter (1899–1900) killed every tree in a five-acre peach orchard. The trees were girdled a few inches from the ground by these rodents.

" In this case would it not have been more economical for the owner to have encouraged owls and other so-called birds of prey that live largely on mice and rabbits to remain on his premises, even though a chicken might have to be sacrificed occasionally ? It is probably a fact that screech-owls remain mated during life ; and, as they are non-migratory, if once they become attached to a locality, they are apt to remain there, unless harassed and driven away, or their home-tree destroyed and they are compelled to seek another, in which case they do not move any great distance. For this reason they are doubly of value to the agriculturist, as they are his helpers during the entire year. Their prey, the mice, are yearly tenants and the farmer

INDIAN FISH-OWLS

who is wise will give the screech-owl on his acres a perpetual free lease."

EAGLE-OWLS

The great horned owls, or eagle-owls (*Bubo*), include the largest and most powerful representatives of the entire order, few of the species falling short of 20 inches in length. Allied to the screech-owls, they may be distinguished by their relatively shorter wings, which never reach within a considerable distance of the end of the tail ; while the great size of the ear tufts and the beautifully barred plumage aid in identifying these magnificent birds (page 1196). Although the toes may be sometimes bare or sparsely feathered, the metatarsus is always plumed throughout. The beak is short and strong, with a compressed tip, and the large nostrils are either oval or rounded.

Of eagle-owls there are nearly a score of species, ranging over the greater part of the Old and New Worlds although unrepresented in Australasia.

GREAT EAGLE-OWL

As being the only species found in Western Europe, the best known of all is the great eagle-owl (*B. ignavus*), of which specimens are occasionally taken in Britain. This splendid bird, of which the total length may reach 28 inches, belongs to a group of two or three species characterised by the toes being so thickly feathered that even their last joints are concealed. It has a black beak and bright orange eye ; the plumage being a beautiful blending of various shades of brown ; the ear tufts include a few dark feathers with light bars on the inner webs ; the hind part of the neck and the back are mottled dark and reddish brown, with the dark tint occupying the middle of the feathers ; and the same colours, but arranged in transverse bars, are repeated on the primary quills and tail feathers. On the face disc the feathers are light brown with greyish black speckles, the breast is pale brown, with longitudinal streaks of darker brown, and the remainder of the under parts displays shades of brown banded with darker bars.

The great eagle-owl inhabits the larger part of Europe and Northern Asia, the Central Asian form (*B. turcomanus*) being paler than ordinary. In Asia it extends as far south as the Pangong Lake and the Himalaya ; and it has also been obtained from North-Eastern Africa.

Common in Scandinavia and South Germany, this owl is rare in Denmark, and although not infrequent in Italy, is unknown in Sardinia. Many at least of the specimens taken in England have been birds escaped from captivity. The eagle-owl is one of the boldest and most rapacious of the European birds of prey, attacking and devouring young fawns, hares, rabbits, other small rodents, capercaillie, grouse, pheasants, and many smaller birds, as well as reptiles and frogs. Mainly nocturnal, it appears early in the evening, and can fly well and strongly in the daylight. Its cry has been compared to the syllables "boo boo."

When reposing during the day, the eagle-owl usually sits with its feathers ruffled up, and thus appears much larger than is really the case. When irritated, it spreads and drops its wings in the manner represented in the illustration, at the same time snapping its beak and hissing, and thus rushes with flaming eyes at its aggressor in the most menacing manner.

The breeding season begins in the latter half of March or the early days of April; and the two or three eggs are usually laid on a ledge or shelf of rock with little if any attempt at a nest. Occasionally, however, a large nest of twigs is formed, which, in the absence of suitable rocks, may be placed in a tree, and sometimes the eggs are deposited in a hole in the ground. The young, which are hatched in about three weeks, are able to fly in eight weeks after birth, although they frequently remain in the nest for some time longer. These owls breed freely in captivity, and in this state sometimes attain very great ages.

VIRGINIAN EAGLE-OWL

The Virginian eagle-owl (*B. virginianus*) is a somewhat smaller bird, distinguished by the head and neck being of the same hue as the blackish back instead of yellowish and lighter. It ranges over the whole of North America, whence it extends into Central America, and is liable to a great local variation in colour. Where the primitive forests have been destroyed, the owls breed in the deserted nests of eagles, hawks, or crows, but elsewhere nest in hollow trees. Usually there are but two or three eggs, although occasionally four or five; and so early in the year are these laid that in Nova Scotia and Newfoundland they are not infrequently found frozen in the nests.

INDIAN EAGLE-OWL

The Indian eagle-owl, or rock horned owl (*B. bengalensis*), may be taken as an example of the second group of the genus, in which the covering of the feathers on the toes is more or less scanty, the last joint and sometimes the whole toe being bare. This species, which attains a length of 20 inches, is confined to India; and its habits appear to be very similar to those of other species, the nesting season lasting from February to April, and the eggs being usually laid on a shelf of rock near water, although occasionally in a hole in the ground.

That eagle-owls are an old group is proved by the occurrence of remains of extinct species in the lower Miocene Tertiary formations of France; those of the existing European species occurring in the Pleistocene deposits of Norfolk. The metatarsus may be distinguished from that of the snowy owl by its longer and more slender form.

INDIAN AND AFRICAN FISH-OWLS

The fish-owls of the Indo-Malay region and Africa form a group distinguished from all other members of the order by the under surface of the toes being covered with a number of small spicules, thus presenting an admirable holding surface. In most cases the metatarsus is naked. These owls are divided into two genera, one of which (*Cetupa*) is confined to Palestine, India, Malay, and China, and characterised by the possession of large ear tufts, while the second (*Scotopelia*) is African, and lacks those appendages.

Of the Oriental genus one of the best-known species is the Indian fish-owl (*C. ceylonensis*), which inhabits Palestine, India, Ceylon, the countries on the east of the Bay of Bengal, and part of China. A large bird, measuring 25 inches in length, it is of a general tawny colour above, with the individual feathers broadly streaked with black down the middle. The quills are brown with pale bands; the tail is also brown with pale fulvous bars, and the greater part of the under surface golden tawny, with black streaks down the middle of the breast feathers. The feet are dark, and, as in all the other members of the genus, the eyes bright yellow.

PEL'S FISH-OWL

This fish-owl inhabits wooded districts near water, and is mainly nocturnal, although it has been seen flying in the daytime. Dr. Jerdon states that it feeds much on fish, and more particularly on crabs. Mr. A. O. Hume states, however, that he has invariably found remains of birds or small mammals round their breeding places, and observes that these owls breed from December to March, but appear, as a rule, to lay in February. "They always nest in the vicinity of water, sometimes choosing a cleft in rocks overhanging a mountain stream, sometimes a broad shelf in the clay cliffs of some river, sometimes a huge cavity in some old banyan tree, and at times appropriating an old nest of *Haliaëtus*. Where they make their own nest on a ledge or a recess of a cliff, it consists of little but a few sticks, mingled with a few feathers, or, when in holes in trees, of a few feathers and dead leaves; but when they annex an old nest of the fishing-eagle's they seem to line it more carefully with finer twigs, grass, and feathers." The usual number of eggs is two.

Of the species of African fish-owls, two are restricted to the west side of the continent, from the Gabun to Senegambia, while the third (*Scotopelia peli*) is common to those districts and the neighbourhood of the Zambesi mouth. Pel's fish-owl is the largest, measuring 23 inches in length. In habits these owls appear to be very similar to their Indian cousins, frequenting the borders of lakes and rivers, but are all comparatively rare. A captive specimen fed eagerly on fish, which is probably the food of these birds in the wild state. The general hue of the plumage in Pel's fish-owl is deep rufous-bay above, marked with transverse black bars and beneath pale bay, with heart-shaped black markings. The eye is dark brown, instead of showing the yellow tint of Indian fish-owls. R. LYDEKKER

FOUR TYPES OF EAGLE-OWLS

VIRGINIAN EAGLE-OWL

SPOTTED EAGLE-OWL

FRASER'S EAGLE-OWL

MILKY EAGLE-OWL

From photographs taken at the London Zoological Gardens

ORDER VI. ACCIPITRES
CHARACTERISTICS OF DIURNAL BIRDS OF PREY

THE diurnal birds of prey were long classed in a single group with the owls, but are now regarded as a totally distinct group, whose affinities, according to some naturalists, appear to be with the duck tribe. The falcons, hawks, kites, eagles, buzzards, harriers, vultures, and the secretary-bird of Africa form the typical section of the order; while the condors of America constitute a second suborder, the Cathartæ.

By the older naturalists the accipitrines were placed at the head of the birds, but by common consent they have now to yield this position to the passerines, which are, on the whole, the most highly organised members of the entire class. It must, however, be remembered that, for their own particular mode of life, the organisation of these birds is as perfect as it is possible to conceive; and, from the mechanical point of view, the spectacle of a falcon swooping on its quarry presents one of the very highest developments of bird life.

While agreeing with the owls in the desmognathous palate, their hooked beak and curved talons, and the presence of a cere, the eagles and falcons (with the exception of the osprey) differ in that the fourth toe is not reversible, and by the laterally-directed eyes, which are never surrounded by complete discs, and the firm plumage. In the bones of the leg the tibia differs from that of owls in possessing a complete bony bridge at the lower end, while in the more typical forms this lower end is remarkably flattened from back to front.

I., Right metatarsus of snowy owl; II., the left metatarsus of buzzard; from the upper (*A*), front (*B*), lower (*C*), and hind (*D*) aspects. *cd*, hind processes of upper end; *ab*, points of muscular attachment; *f*, foramen; *h*, facet for first toe.

The shank bone, or metatarsus, except in the case of the osprey, is longer than in the owls, and lacks the bridge at the upper end found almost universally in that group; while at its lower end the three trochleæ, instead of forming a very high arch when seen from below, are situated nearly in the same transverse plane. Hence, with the aforesaid exception, the metatarsus serves to distinguish an owl from an accipitrine. In addition to its bridged palate, the skull of an accipitrine bird agrees with that of an owl in the absence of any production of the hind portions of its lower half beyond the point of articulation with the quadrate bones, but differs by its more elongated form.

Like those of owls, the young have a downy covering, but the eggs, although occasionally white, are very generally more or less coloured, usually with reddish blotches on a pale ground. The whole group is carnivorous, like the owls, but, while some of its members kill their own prey, others live on carrion.

Accipitrines may be divided into five families, namely, the *Pandionidæ*, represented only by the osprey; the *Falconidæ*, including falcons, hawks, buzzards, eagles, etc.; the *Vulturidæ*, or Old World vultures; the *Serpentariidæ*, represented by the African secretary-bird; and the *Cathartidæ*, including the condors, or American vultures. Of these, the first four, constituting the typical Accipitres, are collectively characterised by the presence of a median partition between the two nostrils.

CLASSIFICATION OF ACCIPITRES MENTIONED IN THIS WORK

ORDER
Accipitres
FAMILY 1
Osprey—Pandionidæ
GENUS 1
Osprey—Pandion
SPECIES
Osprey .... Pandion haliaëtus
FAMILY 2
Hawk Tribe—Falconidæ
GENUS 1
True Falcons—Falco
SPECIES
Greenland falcon .... Falco candicans
Iceland falcon .... F. islandicus
Norway gerfalcon .... F. gyrfalco
Saker falcon .... F. sacer
Central Asian falcon .... F. milvipes
Lanner falcon .... F. feldeggi
Lagger falcon .... F. jugger
Barbary falcon .... F. barbarus
Red-capped falcon .... F. babylonicus
Peregrine falcon .... F. peregrinus
Lesser peregrine falcon .... F. minor
Shahin falcon .... F. peregrinator
Black-cheeked falcon ..... F. melanogenys
Chilian black-cheeked falcon ..... F. nigriceps
Turumti falcon .... F. chiquera
Tawny-headed falcon .... F. ruficollis
Hobby .... F. subbuteo
Merlin .... F. æsalon
Pigeon-hawk .... F. columbarius
Kestrel .... F. tinnunculus
American sparrow-hawk .... F. sparverius
Lesser kestrel .... F. cenchris
GENUS 2
Pigmy Falcons, or Falconets—Microhierax

SPECIES
Black-legged falconet .. Microhierax fringillarius
White-legged falconet .... M. melanoleucus
Philippine falconet .... M. erythrogenys
Red-legged falconet .... M. cœrulescens
GENUS 3
Ictinia
SPECIES
Mississippi falcon .... Ictinia mississippiensis
Lead-coloured falcon .... I. plumbea
GENUS 4
Crested Falcons—Baza
SPECIES
Black crested falcon .... Baza lophotes
Philippine crested falcon .... B. magnirostris
West African cuckoo-falcon ..... B. cuculoides
GENUS 5
Harpagus
GENUS 6
Honey-Buzzards—Pernis
SPECIES
Honey-buzzard .... Pernis mellivora
Crested honey-buzzard .... P. ptilorhynchus
Celebean crested honey-buzzard .. P. celebensis
GENUS 7
Elanus
SPECIES
Black-winged kite .... Elanus cœruleus
White-tailed kite .... E. leucurus
GENUS 8
Kites—Milvus
SPECIES
Typical, or red, kite........... Milvus ictinus
Black, or migratory, kite........ M. migrans
Egyptian kite .... M. ægyptius
Pariah kite .... M. govinda
Indian pariah kite .... M. melanotis
GENUS 9
American Swallow-tailed Kite—Elanoides

SPECIES
Swallow-tailed kite .... Elanoides furcatus
GENUS 10
African Swallow-tailed Kite—Nauclerus
SPECIES
African swallow-tailed kite.. Nauclerus riocouri
GENUS 11
Vulturine Sea Eagle—Gypohierax
SPECIES
Vulturine sea eagle .... Gypohierax angolensis
GENUS 12
Haliastur
SPECIES
Bramini kite .... Haliastur indus
GENUS 13
Sea-Eagles—Haliaëtus
SPECIES
White-tailed sea-eagle ..... Haliaëtus albicilla
Steller's sea-eagle .... H. pelagicus
Corean sea-eagle .... H. branicki
White-headed sea-eagle .... H. leucocephalus
Pallas's sea-eagle .... H. leucophæus
White-bellied sea-eagle .... H. leucogaster
African sea-eagle .... H. vocifer
Madagascar sea-eagle........... H. vociferoides
GENUS 14
Oriental Fish-Eagles—Polioaëtus
SPECIES
Oriental fish-eagle...... Polioaëtus ichthyaëtus
Lesser Oriental fish-eagle .... P. plumbeus
GENUS 15
Bateleur Eagle—Helotarsus
SPECIES
Bateleur eagle .... Helotarsus ecaudatus
GENUS 16
Buzzard-Eagles—Butastur
GENUS 17
Harrier-Eagles—Circaëtus

CLASSIFICATION OF ACCIPITRES

SPECIES
European harrier-eagle......Circaëtus gallicus
GENUS 18
Serpent-Eagles—Spilornis
SPECIES
Indian serpent-eagle ....Spilornis chila
Banded serpent-eagle ....S. suluënsis
Philippine serpent-eagle ....S. holospilus
GENUS 19
Crested Eagle—Lophoaëtus
SPECIES
African crested eagle ...Lophoaëtus occipitalis
GENUS 20
Spizaëtus
SPECIES
South African crested eagle..Spizaëtus bellicosus
Marsh crested eagle ....S. limnaëtus
Indian crested eagle .... S. caligatus
GENUS 21
Hawk-Eagles—Nisaëtus
SPECIES
Bonelli's hawk-eagle ...... Nisaëtus fasciatus
Booted hawk-eagle ....N. pennatus
Australian hawk-eagle ....N. morphnoides
GENUS 22
True Eagles—Aquila
SPECIES
Golden eagle ....Aquila chrysaëtus
Imperial eagle ....A. heliaca
Adalbert's eagle ....A. adalberti
Spotted eagle..................A. maculata
Larger spotted eagle ....A. clanga
African tawny eagle ....A. rapax
Indian tawny eagle ....A. vindhiana
Wahlberg's eagle ....A. wahlbergi
Vulturine eagle................A. verreauxi
GENUS 23
Wedge-tailed Eagle—Uroaëtus
SPECIES
Australian wedge-tailed eagle..Uroaëtus audax
GENUS 24
Monkey-Eating Eagle—Pithecophaga
SPECIES
Monkey-eating eagle ....Pithecophaga jefferyi
GENUS 25
Harpy-Eagles—Morphnus
SPECIES
Guiana harpy-eagle......Morphnus guianensis
GENUS 26
Harpyhaliaëtus
SPECIES
Crowned harpy .....Harpyhaliaëtus coronatus
GENUS 27
Thrasaëtus
SPECIES
Harpy-eagle ....Thrasaëtus harpyia
GENUS 28
Buzzard-like Eagles—Urubitinga
GENUS 29
Buteogallus
GENUS 30
Busarellus
GENUS 31
Buzzards—Buteo
SPECIES
Buzzard .... Buteo vulgaris
Desert buzzard ....B. desertorum
Chinese buzzard ....B. plumipes
Swainson's buzzard ....B. swainsoni
Red-shouldered hawk...........B. lineatus

GENUS 32
Rough-legged Buzzards—Archibuteo
SPECIES
Rough-legged buzzard ....Archibuteo lagopus
St. John's buzzard ....A. sancti-johannis
Ferruginous buzzard ....A. ferrugineus
Brown buzzard ....A. strophiatus
GENUS 33
American Buzzard-like Hawks—Asturina
GENUS 34
Australian Buzzard-like Hawks—Urospizias
GENUS 35
Sparrow-hawks—Accipiter
SPECIES
Sparrow-hawk ....Accipiter nisus
Besra hawk ....A. virgatus
Sharp-shinned hawk ....A. fuscus
Cooper's hawk ....A. cooperi
GENUS 36
Goshawks—Astur
SPECIES
Goshawk...............Astur palumbarius
American goshawk ....A. atricapillus
GENUS 37
Whistling Hawks—Melierax
SPECIES
Many-zoned hawk ....Melierax polyzonus
South African whistling hawk .....M. canorus
Black whistling hawk .:........M. niger
GENUS 38
Parabuteo
GENUS 39
Geranospizias
GENUS 40
Urotriorchis
GENUS 41
Micrastur
GENUS 42
Harriers—Circus
SPECIES
Hen-harrier ....Circus cyaneus
American harrier .... C. hudsonianus
Pale-chested harrier ....C. macrurus
Montagu's harrier ....C. pygargus
Marsh-harrier ....C. æruginosus
GENUS 43
Bare-cheeked Hawks—Polyboroides
SPECIES
African bare-cheeked hawk......Polyboroides
typicus
Madagascan bare-cheeked hawk....P. radiatus
GENUS 44
Caracaras—Polyborus
SPECIES
Brazilian caracara ....Polyborus tharus
Audubon's caracara ....P. cheriway
Guadeloupe caracara ....P. lutosus
GENUS 45
Ibycter
SPECIES
Falkland Island caracara ...Ibycter australis
Black caracara ....I. ater
Chimachima ....I. chimachima
Chimango......................I. chimango

FAMILY 2
Vultures—Vulturidæ
GENUS 1
Lammergeiers—Gypaëtus

SPECIES
Lammergeier .... Gypaëtus barbatus
Bare-legged lammergeier ....G. ossifragus
G. atalantis
GENUS 2
Typical Vulture—Vultur
SPECIES
Cinereous vulture ....Vultur monachus
GENUS 3
Griffon-Vultures—Gyps
SPECIES
European griffon ....Gyps fulvus
Himalayan griffon ....G. himalayensis
Ruppell's vulture ....G. rueppelli
Long-beaked griffon.............G. indicus
GENUS 4
White-backed Vultures—Pseudogyps
SPECIES
Indian white-backed vulture....P. bengalensis
African white-backed vulture.....P. africanus
GENUS 5
Eared Vultures—Otogyps
SPECIES
African eared vulture ....Otogyps auricularis
Pondicherry eared vulture.........O. calvus
GENUS 6
Lophogyps
SPECIES
Abyssinian vulture......Lophogyps occipitalis
GENUS 7
Scavenger-Vultures—Neophron
SPECIES
White scavenger-vulture....Neophron percno-
pterus
Brown scavenger-vulture ....N. pileatus

FAMILY 3
Secretary-Birds—Serpentariidæ
GENUS 1
Secretary-Birds—Serpentarius
SPECIES
Secretary-bird.......Serpentarius secretarius

FAMILY 4
Condor Tribe—Cathartidæ
GENUS 1
Typical Condors—Sarcorhamphus
SPECIES
Andean condor ......Sarcorhamphus gryphus
Lesser condor ....S. æquatorialis
GENUS 2
King Condor—Gypagus
SPECIES
King condor ....Gypagus papa
GENUS 3
Black Condor—Catharistes
SPECIES
Black condor..............Catharistes uruba
GENUS 4
Turkey-Vultures—Cathartes
SPECIES
Turkey-vulture ....Cathartes aura
Black turkey-vulture ....C. perniger
Grey-winged turkey-vulture ...C. falclandicus
Orange-headed turkey-vulture ..R. urubitinga
GENUS 5
Pseudogryphus
SPECIES
Californian condor....Pseudogryphus califor-
nianus

OSPREY IN FLIGHT

THE OSPREY

THE osprey (*Pandion haliaëtus*) constitutes a family (*Pandionidæ*) characterised by the fourth toe being reversible, and by the form of the metatarsus, which has a bony bridge over the hollow at the upper end, and likewise by the general shape of the lower end of the tibia, although the latter retains the bony bridge which has been lost in the owls. The osprey also agrees with owls, and thereby differs from the more typical diurnal birds of prey, by the absence of distinct after-shafts to the feathers. The nostrils are not concealed by bristles, and the toes are naked, and furnished beneath with spicules like those of fish-owls.

According to modern views of relationship, such structural resemblances as are presented by the osprey to owls is due to what is termed convergence, rather than to blood-affinity.

The osprey, or fishing-hawk, which is the sole representative of its genus and family, is characterised by the length of its wings, and the naked and rather short metatarsus, entirely covered with reticulate scales. In length it varies from 22 to 24 inches.

In colour the beak is black, the cere blue, and the eye yellow. The elongated feathers at the tip of the head and nape of the neck are whitish, streaked with brown ; the upper surface of the body and wings is dark brown, with the ends of the primaries black, and that of the tail two shades of brown.

Beneath, the chin and throat are white, the upper part of the latter being marked with a pale brown band ; and the abdomen, thighs, and under tail coverts are also white. The wing is partly white and partly brown beneath, and the lower surface of the tail white, barred with greyish brown. The legs and toes are blue.

The osprey has an almost cosmopolitan distribution, although unknown in the extreme south of South America, as well as in parts of Oceania. In England it is now a rare summer visitor, but it used formerly to breed in many parts of Scotland, where it is well-nigh exterminated. For nearly a century a pair bred at Loch-an-Eilan Castle. In 1890 three birds appeared at the nesting place, one of which, after a fierce encounter, was killed, whereupon the others disappeared. In 1891 a pair again visited the district, but, instead of taking up their old quarters, selected Loch Merlich —some miles distant—as their abiding place. Here they were unfortunately disturbed, but in 1892 they once more reappeared at Loch-an-Eilan, where effective measures have been taken to secure them from molestation.

The osprey feeds almost exclusively on fish, which it captures both at sea and in fresh water ; and it is doubtless for the purpose of holding its slippery prey that the fourth toe is reversible, and the soles of the feet covered with spicules. Sir J. Richardson writes that " when looking out for its prey, it sails with great ease and elegance, in undulating and curved lines, at a considerable altitude above the water, whence it precipitates itself upon its quarry, and bears it off in its claws ; or it not infrequently, on the fish moving to too great a depth, stops suddenly in its descent, and hovers for a few seconds in the air, like a kite or kestrel, suspending itself in the same spot by a quick flapping of its wings ; it then makes a second, and, in general, unerring dart upon its prey, or regains the former altitude by an elegant spiral flight.

" It seizes the fish with its claws, sometimes scarcely appearing to dip its feet in the water, and at other times plunging entirely under the surface, with force sufficient to throw up a considerable spray. It emerges again, however, so speedily as to render it evident that it does not attack fish swimming at any great depth."

On the Continent the osprey generally builds in the later part of April, laying three, or rarely four, eggs, which resemble those of other accipitrine birds in being blotched with shades of reddish brown. The nest is large, and composed of sticks, and may be placed either on a tree, a ledge of rock, or in a ruined building.

In North America, where ospreys are numerous, the nest is usually built in a tall tree —frequently on the top of the broken stem of a pine ; but in places where trees are scarce, as in some parts of California, it may

OSPREY AND YOUNG

be situated either on the ground or on a cliff.

Mr. W. W. Worthington writes that on Plum Island many pairs of ospreys " nest on the ground, on the tops of sand-dunes, in such cases depositing the eggs on the sand ; the nest consisting of a few sticks, bunches of seaweed, and pieces of various kind of rubbish arranged in a circle. In other cases the nests are built up several feet, the height in all probability being regulated by the number of years the nest has been occupied, and the amount added to it from year to year."

Only a single brood is produced during the year, and, while the period of incubation has been commonly considered to be twenty-one days, Major Bendire believes it to be a week longer.

THE HAWK TRIBE

THE family *Falconidæ*, which includes falcons, hawks, kites, buzzards, eagles, and so on, constitutes together with that of the vultures the typical Accipitres. There are no basipterygoid processes on the rod at the base of the skull, the feathers have well-developed after-shafts, and the oil-gland is crowned with a circle of feathers. Inferiorly the windpipe is provided with an organ of voice.

Although very closely connected by the lammergeier, falcons and their allies differ from vultures (except the lammergeier) by the head being clothed with true feathers, and by the size of the females exceeding that of the males.

The group includes the smallest members of the order, while its largest representatives are second only in size to the vultures. As a rule, these birds subsist mainly or exclusively on prey killed by themselves, although some eat carrion, and a few feed on honeycomb. Like other accipitrines, the two sexes associate in pairs, which mate for life, and the number of young produced in a brood seldom exceeds four, and is frequently less. They have a cosmopolitan distribution, and may be divided into five subfamilies.

TRUE FALCONS

The true falcons, as represented by the gerfalcons, the peregrine, and the kestrel, are the typical members of a subfamily (*Falconinæ*) characterised by the length of the tibia being considerably greater than that of the metatarsus, by the scutes on the hind aspect of the metatarsus being arranged in a reticulate, or net-like, manner, and by the sides of the upper half of the beak being notched. In all the cere is large, and often brightly coloured.

With regard to the extent of the genus *Falco*, there is a certain amount of difference of opinion among naturalists, some including in it the whole of the European falcons, while others separate the gerfalcons (as *Hierofalco*) and the kestrels (as *Tinnunculus*, or *Cerchneis*).

Used in the wider sense, the genus will include (with the exception of one peculiar species from the Argentine and another from New Zealand) all the falcons in which the nostrils are circular and furnished with a distinct tubercle in the middle. The beak in all is short and curved, with one notch in the upper half; the wings are long and pointed, with the first and third quills of equal length, and the second the longest, and the toes elongated. Many of the larger species have a distinct dark stripe on the cheek, which in the peregrine

GREENLAND FALCON

expands into a large patch. All are subject to great variation of plumage, according to age, which renders the discrimination of many of the species a matter of exceeding difficulty

Under the common title of gerfalcons are included several closely allied falcons of large size from the northern regions of the Northern Hemisphere distinguished by the comparative shortness of the toes, more especially the fourth, which (exclusive of the claw) is about equal in length to the second. The wings are rather short, and the length of the interval between the tips of the primary and secondary quills does not exceed half the length of the tail. The beak is somewhat elongated; and the colour of the plumage tends to slaty grey or white, these being the only falcons in which there is such a type of coloration.

GREENLAND FALCON

One of the best known of these species is the Greenland falcon (*F. candicans*), of Greenland and North America, of which young birds occasionally straggle to the British Islands. This is the lightest-coloured member of the group, and hence sometimes termed the white gerfalcon. Its distinctive characters are to be found in the yellow tint of the cere, beak, and claws, and by the ground colour of the plumage being white at all ages.

In old birds the head, under parts, and tail become almost or completely white, although the upper parts retain small black spots. In the young the breast and flanks are longitudinally streaked with brown. The length of the female reaches 23 inches.

ICELAND FALCON

In the Iceland falcon (*F. islandicus*) the beak and claws are dusky horn colour, and the plumage is darker than the last, with the ground colour brown in the young and grey in the adult. In the case of adult birds the flanks show transverse arrow-head dark bars, and the tail is likewise barred; the crown of the head being lighter-coloured than the back. In young birds, on the other hand, the dark markings on the under parts are longitudinal; this change from longitudinal to transverse bars being common in the group. The home of this bird is Iceland, from which a certain number of individuals migrate to the south-east, a few from time to time reaching Britain.

NORWAY GERFALCON

The Norway, or true, gerfalcon (*F. gyrfalco*) is a somewhat larger bird, with the crown of the head as dark as or even darker than the back, and the whole tone of the plumage tending more to brown. It has also frequently a distinct cheek stripe, while the wings are relatively longer, and the tail shorter. This falcon inhabits all Northern Europe and Asia, as well as North America, and migrates southwards in winter, although not reaching Britain. It is replaced on the Labrador coast by the still darker Labrador falcon (*F. obsoletus*).

The habits of all the gerfalcons are probably very similar ; although, from the general absence of trees in its native country, the Greenland species is compelled to breed exclusively on cliffs, while the others often resort to trees. The eggs, usually three or four in number, are of a creamy white ground colour, blotched with cinnamon or reddish brown. All the species are extremely shy, but display great boldness in defence of their nests, circling round the head of the aggressor with loud screams.

When sitting on its nest in the snow, with its white breast towards the hunter, the Greenland falcon will often escape detection. Its prey consists chiefly of water-fowl and ptarmigan. Gerfalcons, and especially the white kind, were formerly much esteemed in falconry, and commanded high prices ; the white Greenland falcons imported to the Continent being captured in Iceland. Although larger and more powerful birds, all the gerfalcons lack the supreme dash and " go " of the peregrine ; and their former estimation was probably mainly owing to their size and beauty.

SAKER FALCON

The large and handsome falcon known as the saker (*F. sacer*), a term apparently derived from the Arabic, is a southern species, agreeing with the gerfalcons in the proportionate length of its toes and wings, but differing markedly in plumage.

In length the male saker measures upwards of 18½ inches, while the female falls but little short of 25 inches. By this large size and the relative length of the claws, the saker may be readily distinguished from all the other falcons of Europe and Asia.

YOUNG ICELAND FALCON

In its ordinary dress it is further characterised by the upper surface of the tail feathers, instead of being completely barred, showing whitish bars on the inner webs, and spots on the outer ones ; these spots being especially marked in the middle pair. The cheek stripe, if present at all, is always very narrow. The head is pale rufous, sometimes turning nearly white, with narrow black stripes along the middle of the feathers.

The general colour of the under parts is pale brown, each of the feathers being margined with rufous ; but the quills are darker brown, with white or rufous markings, and the paler tail is ornamented in the manner already noticed. The sides of the face and throat are white, and the rest of the under parts whitish, with longitudinal streaks of brown, largest on the flanks and abdomen. The cere and feet of the adult are yellow, and the beak is greenish horn colour ; but in young birds the feet are bluish green.

When in its full adult dress, which is not assumed till late, and seldom seen, the saker becomes completely barred on the whole of the upper surface with rufous, and may then be compared to a gigantic kestrel ; the under parts being creamy white, with a few blackish spots on the abdomen passing into bars on the flanks.

The range of the saker extends from South-Eastern Europe and North-Eastern Africa through Central Asia to the north of China. Although not definitely known to breed in the plains of India, this bird extends from Afghanistan and Gilgit to Peshawur, and thence straggles as far south as Delhi and Amballa.

F. milvipes, of Central Asia, is now regarded as a distinct species. This noble falcon is common in the Danubian principalities, and generally frequents open country, although nesting in trees —usually in the neighbourhood of water. The nest is not large, and the eggs, which are generally four in number, are more pointed than those of most accipitrines. In the Harriana Desert of India these falcons feed largely on the spiny-tailed lizards of the genus *Uromastix*.

In Palestine the saker is trained for the chase of gazelles ; while in India, where it is termed the cherug, it is flown not only at cranes, bustards, hares, and similar prey, but likewise at kites. The chase of the latter is described as being exciting in the extreme, the two birds doing all they know to obtain the higher position, and often flying far from the hawking party.

On one such occasion, Mr. R. Thompson states that " after going a considerable distance from his quarry, and thereby acquiring what he wanted—superior height—the saker resumed the chase, returning downwards like a thunderbolt on the kite. Blow after blow was struck, and the helpless kite, with his merciless enemy, descended, clutched fast together, their wings expanded, in wheeling circles to the earth, where the kite, already half dead, was soon despatched." Apparently all kites seem to recognise the saker as their enemy, as, immediately one is unhooded, all the kites in the vicinity will disperse, although they take not the least notice of other falcons.

HYACINTHINE, BLUE-AND-YELLOW, AND RED-AND-BLUE MACAWS

"From their large size, the length of their tails, and the gorgeous tints of blue, red, and yellow adorning their plumage, the macaws are the most showy and conspicuous of all parrots; but they have the disadvantage of being the most noisy of the whole confraternity."

I S.

HORNED OWL

"The great horned owls, or eagle-owls, include the largest and most powerful representatives of the entire order, few of the species falling short of 20 inches in length"

THE GOLDEN EAGLE

"In the United Kingdom the golden eagle still holds its own to a limited extent in the Scottish Highlands, and probably also breeds in some of the wilder mountainous districts of Ireland."

THE KING-CONDOR

"Reaching in the mountains to an elevation of about five thousand feet, this splendid bird has its true home in primeval forest or well-wooded plains, and is utterly unknown in dry, open districts or on barren mountains."

THE LANNER

The falcon known as the lanner (*F. feldeggii*), although much smaller, has been frequently confounded with the saker, but, together with the nearly allied laggar, belongs to a group agreeing with the peregrine in the relative length of the toes and wings, although resembling the saker in the absence of the distinct dark barring on the thighs in the ordinary dress. The lanner, which is chiefly characteristic of the countries bordering the Mediterranean, and attains a length of 17 inches in the male, has the back barred, the forehead blackish, and the hind part of the head and nape rufous, with a narrow line of black on the forehead, and a thin black cheek-stripe; the general colour of the upper parts being ashy brown and the tail feathers distinctly barred with pale rufous.

THE LAGGAR

The laggar (*F. jugger*), which is confined to peninsular India, is a still smaller species, measuring only 15½ inches in the male, and having the thighs with scarcely any or no dark markings, and the middle tail feathers not barred; the crown of the head being dull rufous, and the back with lines of ashy black. Other well-known species of this group are the Barbary falcon (*F. barbarus*), ranging from West and North-East Africa to North-Western India and the Himalaya, and the red-capped falcon (*F. babylonicus*), with a nearly similar range, but extending into Turkestan, and unknown in West Africa. The former, which is next in size to the saker, the female reaching a length of 22½ inches, may be distinguished from the lanner by the rufous forehead and nape, and the bluish grey of the hind part of the crown. The latter is much smaller and has the under parts uniform sandy rufous, instead of with wavy dark bars.

PEREGRINE FALCON

In common with the group last noticed, the peregrine falcon (*F. peregrinus*)—so named from the migratory habits of the younger birds—differs from the gerfalcons and saker by its longer toes, especially the fourth, which, exclusive of the claw, exceeds the second in length; and also by the elongation of the wings, in which the interval between the primary and secondary quills is greater than half the length of the tail. The peregrine, which attains a length of 15 inches in the male, and 17 in the female, is easily recognised by the distinct narrow black transverse bars on the thighs, the blackish colour of the crown of the head, and the expansion of the cheek-stripe into a large black patch.

In the adult the whole of the crown of the head, the nape, and the space below the eyes are nearly black; the back, wing coverts, and tail some shade of bluish grey, with darker bars; the primary quills brownish black, with the inner webs barred and spotted with reddish white; the throat is nearly white, and the breast reddish white, with short dark brown transverse bars; the remainder of the under parts, as well as the lower surface of the tail, being marked with more continuous bars of brown or grey. The beak is blue, tending to black at the tip; and the cere, legs, and toes are yellow. Such is the general coloration of the typical northern peregrine, which ranges all over Europe, except Iceland and Spitzbergen; while eastwards it extends across Siberia to China and Japan, and thence to the Malay Islands. It also occurs in North-Eastern Africa as far as Kordofan, and occasionally straggles so far as the Cape, where, however, its place is normally occupied by the very distinct lesser peregrine (*F. minor*). Entering India on the extreme north-west, it is replaced in the peninsula by the shahin falcon (*F. peregrinator*).

In Java occurs another southern form, known as the black-cheeked falcon (*F. melanogenys*), ranging to Australia, and distinguished by its redder and more finely barred plumage. Naturalists are now pretty well agreed that the peregrine of North America—where it is commonly known as the duck-hawk—is merely a variety of the European species; but in Chile, and the adjacent parts of South America, there occurs another form, apparently allied to the black-cheeked falcon, and known as *F. nigriceps*, or *F. cassine*.

PEREGRINE FALCON

Breeding on the cliffs of the sea-coast in the south, and in the more mountainous districts in the interior of the country, the peregrine is best known in England as a migrant. These migratory individuals are chiefly birds of the first year, and most commonly met with in the autumn; but there is also a certain number of old birds which make their appearance in spring on their northward journey. Although nearly always nesting on some lofty cliff, there are instances of peregrines having bred in an open marsh, and also in a tree. The nest is usually of large size, and generally contains four eggs, remarkable for the depth of the colour of their red blotchings.

Feeding chiefly on birds of different kinds, the peregrine undoubtedly kills a considerable quantity of game; although the harm it inflicts is probably not so great as might first appear to be the case, since all falcons invariably seize the weakest birds, and the

A PAIR OF PEREGRINES—RED FALCON AND BLUE TIERCEL

claws, and not, as often represented, with its beak. In India the peregrine, locally known as the bhyri, used to be employed by the native chiefs in hawking egrets, stalks, herons, cranes, and similar birds, only a single bird being flown at each quarry. The smaller shahin, or royal falcon (*F. peregrinator*), was, however, held in still higher estimation for this sport. It may be added that the shahin differs from the peregrine by the more rufous tinge of its under parts, and its dark head and nape.

TURUMTI FALCON

The Indian turumti falcon (*F. chicquera*), which scarcely exceeds the European kestrel in size, is the first of several much smaller representatives of the present section of the genus. This species resembles the peregrines in having the feathers of the thighs distinctly barred, but is at once distinguished from that group by the chestnut-coloured head, nape, and cheek-stripe. The rest of the upper parts is pale grey, with dark markings, the quills being dark slaty, and the tail light grey, with a broad black terminal band tipped with white. The lower surface is white to the breast, behind which are narrow cross-bars of dusky grey. The beak is greenish yellow at the base, and the cere and legs are bright yellow.

This species is confined to India, but is replaced in Africa by the rather paler tawny-headed falcon (*F. ruficollis*), which is perhaps only a local race. The female attains a length of 13, and the male of 11½ inches. The turumti is spread all over India, generally haunting

elimination of such weaklings is probably to the general advantage of the breed. In North America, although by no means common, the peregrine is the most numerously represented of all the larger falcons. Major Bendire writes that in the northern portion of its range it is only a summer resident, following the immense flocks of water-fowl during their migrations.

"Hares, ptarmigan, grouse, bob-whites, pigeons, as well as smaller birds, enter largely into its bill of fare, and the poultry yard as well occasionally suffers. Next to the goshawk, the peregrine falcon is our most audacious bird of prey. Its flight, when once fairly started in pursuit of its quarry, is amazingly swift; it is seemingly an easy matter for it to overtake the fleetest of birds, and when once in its grip resistance is useless. I have seen this falcon strike a teal almost within gunshot of me, kill it apparently instantaneously from the force of the shock, and fly away with it without visible struggle, and as easily as if it had been a sparrow instead of a bird of its own weight."

From its docile disposition, powerful flight, and the ease with which it can be procured, the peregrine has always been a favourite bird in falconry, and is the one most commonly employed in the modern revival of that sport. In falconry it is the female only that is termed the "falcon"; the male being designated the "tiercel," corrupted into "tassel." While the tiercel was commonly flown at partridges and occasionally at magpies; herons, and, next to them, rooks, were the favourite quarry for the falcon. In heron-hawking the birds were intercepted on their way home, and, if possible, when flying against the wind. When a heron was viewed, a cast, or pair, of falcons was loosed, and thereupon pursuers and pursued immediately began to try to soar above the other, the heron lightening himself by disgorging his food.

The falcons fly in a spiral, and so soon as one has gained a position of advantage and made its swoop, it should be succeeded by its fellow, the manœuvre being repeated until the heron is brought to the ground. In striking, the falcon attacks only with its

THE HOBBY

open country in the neighbourhood of cultivation. Dr. Jerdon writes that "it frequents gardens, groves of trees, and even single trees in the open country, whence it sallies forth, sometimes circling aloft, but more generally, especially in the heat of the day, gliding with inconceivable rapidity along some hedgerow, dam of a tank, or across fields, and pouncing suddenly on some lark, sparrow, or wagtail. It very often hunts in pairs, and I have now and then seen it hover like a kestrel for a few seconds."

In addition to the smaller birds, the turumti will attack starlings, quails, and doves, while it will sometimes prey on bats. It nests from February to May— apparently always in trees — laying usually four eggs, of which the colour varies from yellowish brown, with a few reddish specks, to nearly uniform brownish red. Mr. R. Thompson observes, "I have trained this species to be thrown from the hand at quails and partridges. The bird readily learns the lesson, and makes a good bag. The quail or partridge is allowed a good start, the turumti being held up so as to eye the receding bird, and then thrown in the direction of the latter with some force, shooting off at once, more like a dart than anything else, at the quarry."

THE HOBBY

The hobby (*F. subbuteo*), which is one of the most elegant of the British falcons, belongs to a group in which the thighs are perfectly uniform ; their colour in this species being rufous, while the throat and breast are white, and the latter marked with black stripes.

A PAIR OF MERLINS

TURUMTI FALCON

Above, the general colour is dark slaty grey, tending to black on the head. The length is $11\frac{1}{2}$ inches in the male, and $13\frac{1}{2}$ in the female.

The hobby is a migratory species, ranging over Europe and Northern Asia, and extending into India and North China ; while in winter it journeys to South Africa. By no means numerous in Britain, it is still not uncommon in the inland wooded and cultivated districts of the South of England. In addition to preying on small birds, it also feeds on dragon-flies and beetles, and is thus a benefactor to the farmer.

THE MERLIN

The merlin (*F. æsalon*), together with the smaller pigeon-hawk (*F. columbarius*) of North America, may be distinguished from other members of the genus by the longitudinally streaked thighs and the nearly uniformly coloured back, in which each feather has only a median dark streak. Above, the colour of the merlin is uniform clear bluish grey, with the tail marked by one broad band near the end. The head is dark slaty, with broad median stripes to the feathers ; the forehead and sides of the face are whitish, with narrow median lines, the ear coverts greyish, the throat white, and the remainder of the under parts white tinged with rufous, with broad median black streaks, becoming narrower on the thighs.

In the young bird the general colour of the upper parts is brown with a faint tinge of grey, and the feathers margined with sandy rufous ; while on the under parts, except the throat, the whitish feathers have very broad reddish brown streaks and black median stripes, the thighs showing smaller brown spots, and the lower part of the abdomen and under tail coverts being only sparsely marked. It is probable that very old female merlins assume a blue plumage like the males. The adult male measures 10 inches, and the female about two inches more.

The merlin is an inhabitant of Europe and Northern Asia, but extends southwards into India and China. An anonymous writer observes that "on the bleak hills of Wales, round the Peak, and in the wildest

Midland heights, further north on the barren moors and bold bluffs of Yorkshire, over the rugged and romantic ranges of Scotland, on the short turf of the downs, in the mountain heather, by the slaty and granitic boulders of upheaved rocks, the merlin has its home. Even in the desolate regions it affects, no member of the pariah family is free from attack ; yet, like the other small falcons, it holds its own against the destroying band, and manages to live on and do its appointed work against all odds."

In Britain the merlin usually nests on the ground, generally on the open moors ; but in Lapland and other parts of the continent it commonly takes possession of the deserted nest of some other member of the family, while in other cases it lays on a shelf of rock. When on the ground, scarcely any nest is made. The eggs, which vary from four to six in number, are frequently of a uniform brick-red colour, but may be mottled with a darker shade.

The merlin commonly preys upon small birds, and has been trained to fly at snipe, larks, thrushes, etc. According to Messrs. Salvin and Brodrick, "the strongest female merlins may be trained to fly at pigeons admirably, and from their small size, and the way in which they follow every turn and shift of the quarry, are better adapted for this chase than the peregrine ; unlike it, they do not stop when the pigeon takes refuge in a hedge or tree, but dash in and generally secure it."

PIGEON-HAWK

In addition to its smaller size and much darker general colour, the American pigeon-hawk (*F. columbarius*) is distinguished by having four black bars on the tail, of which the last is much the widest. This

LESSER KESTRELS

falcon is a migratory species, with a swift and powerful flight, breeding in open nests or hollows of trees, as well as on cliffs, and in cavities in the banks of rivers.

The following interesting anecdote is given by Mr. R. Macfarlane regarding this species. On May 25, 1864, an Indian in his employ "found a nest placed in the midst of a thick branch of a pine-tree at a height of about six feet from the ground. It was rather loosely constructed of a few dry sticks and a small quantity of coarse hay ; it then contained two eggs ; both parents were seen, fired at, and missed. On May 31 he revisited the nest, which still held but two eggs, and again missed the birds. Several days later he made another visit thereto, and, to his surprise, the eggs and parents had disappeared. His first impression was that some other person had taken them ; after looking carefully around he perceived both birds at a short distance, and this led him to institute a search, which soon resulted in finding that the eggs must have been removed by the parent birds to the face of a muddy bank at least forty yards distant from the original nest. A few decayed leaves had been placed under them, but nothing else in the way of lining. A third egg had been added in the interim."

THE KESTREL

A large group of small falcons, of which the European kestrel or windhover is the most familiar representative, constitutes an extensive and easily recognised subgenus (*Cerchneis*), distributed all over the globe with the exception of Oceania. They are all short-toed birds, agreeing with gerfalcons in the proportionate lengths of the second and fourth digits, but resembling peregrines in the length of their wings, as shown by the interval between the tips of the primary and secondary quills exceeding half the length of the tail. They have a peculiar and characteristic type of colouring, easy of recognition but difficult of description ; and in the majority of the species the plumage is very differently coloured in the two sexes, the hens being barred, but the cocks more uniform. Although the kestrel feeds chiefly on field-mice, many of the other species subsist to a great extent on insects.

The typical kestrel (*F. tinnunculus*) derives its name of windhover from its habit of hanging suspended in mid-air, with its wings in rapid motion, its fan-like tail spread out, and its head directed to windward. When in this position it spies a field-mouse or small bird below, it drops upon it suddenly and noiselessly with unerring aim. The male kestrel, which attains a length of 12½ inches, has a yellow cere and limbs, bluish beak, and black claws. The crown of the head, nape, and cheeks are ashy grey with dark streaks ; the upper parts reddish fawn, with a small black spot on each feather ; the quills blackish grey with lighter margins ; and the tail feathers ashy grey with a single broad black band near the end and the extreme tip white. Beneath, the general colour is pale rufous fawn, with dark spots or streaks, both of which disappear on the thighs and under tail coverts, and the tail is greyish white with indistinct bars.

The female, which scarcely exceeds her consort in size, differs by the top of the head being reddish fawn with dark streaks, the upper parts being banded with bluish black, and the tail rufous with several incomplete black bars. The young males are nearly like the females, the tail turning blue first and the head last.

A further specialisation in the kestrel would involve a similar change of colour in the female, and to this there is an approximation in a dark southern race, in which the rump and part of the tail of the hen-bird tend to blue.

The kestrel ranges over the whole of Europe and Northern Asia, migrating in winter to the north of China, India, and North-Eastern Africa, and occasionally straying into the western and southern parts of the latter continent. It is replaced in the New

World by the so-called American sparrow-hawk (*F sparverius*), in which the centre of the crown of the head of the male is rufous, and the wing coverts are blue with black spots.

Although its chief food consists of field and other mice, the kestrel occasionally kills small birds, and will also eat frogs, beetles, worms, and grubs, while in India it frequently devours lizards. That it will occasionally kill a young partridge or chicken is doubtless true, but such small robberies are far more than counterbalanced by the benefits it confers on the agriculturist by the destruction of hosts of pernicious rodents, and it ought, therefore, to be carefully preserved, instead of ruthlessly shot.

Although occasionally placed in a hollow tree, the nest is more generally situated among rocks or old buildings, while still more frequently a pair of kestrels takes advantage of the deserted nest of some other bird, such as a crow, magpie, or raven.

The eggs, usually four or five, but sometimes as many as six in number, may be either mottled all over with brownish red or orange, or blotched with these colours upon a light ground. They are generally hatched late in April, or early in the following month.

Writing of the American so-called sparrow-hawk, Dr. A. K. Fisher summarises its value to the agriculturist as follows : " The subject of the food of this hawk is one of great interest, and, considered in its economic bearings, is one that should be carefully studied. The sparrow-hawk is almost exclusively insectivorous, except when insect-food is difficult to obtain.

" In localities where grasshoppers and crickets are abundant these hawks congregate, often in moderate sized flocks, and gorge themselves continuously. Rarely do they touch any other form of food until, either by the advancing season or other natural causes, the grasshopper crop is so lessened that their hunger cannot be appeased without undue exertion. Then other kinds of insects and other forms of life contribute to their fare ; and beetles, spiders, mice, shrews, small snakes, lizards, or even birds may be required to bring up the balance.

" In some places in the West and South telegraph-poles pass for miles through treeless plains and savannas. For lack of better perches, the sparrow-hawks often use these poles for resting-places, from which they make short trips to pick up a grasshopper or mouse, which they carry back to their perch. At times, when grasshoppers are abundant, such a line of poles is pretty well occupied by these hawks. In the vicinity of Washington it is the exception not to find grasshoppers or crickets in the stomachs of sparrow-hawks, even when killed during the months of January and February, unless the ground is covered with snow. It is wonderful how the birds can discover the half-concealed, semi-dormant insects, which in colour

KESTRELS

closely resemble the ground or dry grass. Whether they are attracted by a slight movement, or distinguish the form of their prey as it sits motionless, is difficult to prove, but in any case the acuteness of their vision is of a character we are unable to appreciate."

LESSER KESTREL

This kestrel (*F. cenchris*) is an inhabitant of Southern and South-Eastern Europe, migrating in winter to South Africa, and, although scarcely smaller than the typical species, has shorter wings. In the adult male the head, hind part of the neck, rump, upper tail coverts, and tail are bluish grey, the latter having a broad subterminal dark band and a white tip, and the whole of the back is cinnamon rufous without black spots. The throat is yellowish white, and most of the other under parts are cinnamon-coloured with small black spots, becoming larger on the sides of the body, but disappearing on the thighs, which are uniform pale rufous.

Although the cere and limbs resemble those of the typical species in colour, the claws are generally white. The female is very similar to the hen of the latter, although lighter in colour, and with white claws.

Spain, Malta, Southern Italy, and especially Greece, are some of the countries where the lesser kestrel is most common ; but it also ranges into Syria, Turkey, Asia Minor, and Persia, and has been obtained from the steppes of Western Siberia. It may be seen on the Acropolis of Athens, the churches of Madrid, and the Moorish temples of Granada.

In Greece and Spain the lesser kestrel nests late in April or early in May, selecting either buildings, rocks, or hollow trees for its breeding place, and being found often in company with the ordinary kestrel. In Malta it may be seen in flocks, where its prey is chiefly small birds

Both kinds of kestrel were held in high veneration by the ancient Egyptians, their function being supposed to be to investigate, in conjunction with Anubis, the actions of the soul. Their destruction involved the penalty of death, and, writes Dr. Leith Adams, " no trouble was spared in preserving them, so that, beside the sacred birds in captivity, it was customary to place food in the way of wild individuals. The kestrel, therefore, must have enjoyed unbounded freedom and protection ; and it is a remarkable circumstance nowadays that, being one of the most common rapacious birds of Egypt, it is far more familiar than any of the others, allowing man to approach it within a few yards."

PIGMY FALCONS, OR FALCONETS

As there are pigmy parrots and pigmy owls, so there exist diminutive representatives of the falcons, which, although not larger than larks, are as bold and dauntless as their larger relatives. These pigmy falcons range from the Eastern Himalaya, through Tenasserim and Burma, to the Malay Islands, and thence to the Philippines, and are also represented by an outlying species in the Nicobar Islands ; and since they differ from the typical falcons by their oval nostrils, which have neither a central tubercle nor an overhanging flap of skin, they are referred to a distinct genus (*Microhierax*). The beak is short, with a sharp tooth, and a notch on each side often described as a double tooth ; the wings are short, the tail is of no great length, and the third toe is not much longer than the others.

The black-legged falconet (*M. fringillarius*), which inhabits Tenasserim, the Malay Peninsula, Java, Sumatra, and Borneo, measures 6·1 inches in length. The upper parts, quills, and tail feathers are deep bluish black, with the inner webs of the two latter barred with white ; the forehead, together with a stripe running from the eye down the side of the neck, and likewise the front of the cheek, the throat, and breast are white, and the abdomen is tinged with rufous ; the lores and the spaces behind the eye, as well as the sides of the body and outer aspects of the thighs, being glossy black. In the adult the beak and feet are dark, but in young birds the former is yellow at the base.

The white legged falconet (*M. melanoleucus*), of Cachar and Assam, differs by its white abdomen and thighs ; while the Philippine falconet (*M. erythrogenys*) is distinguished from the latter by its black thighs. The smallest of all is the red-legged falconet (*M. cœrulescens*), which measures only 5½ inches, and ranges from Nepal and Sikkim, through Tenasserim and Burma, to Cambodia. It is distinguished from all the others by its white legs, and derives its name from its rufous thighs.

All the falconets are quick and active in their movements, making their way with a rapid and direct flight, during which the wings are constantly flapped. They are generally to be seen hawking insects with swallow-like speed, and, when tired, invariably select a dead branch upon which to rest. Their chief food appears to consist of dragon-flies, beetles, and butterflies, although they undoubtedly at times attack and kill birds which may exceed themselves in size. A black-legged falconet has been seen to swoop at a rock-thrush, and a male has been shot with a living and partially plucked swallow in its talons. All the species nest in hollow trees, making at the bottom of the cavity a pad of the wings of dragon-flies and butterflies, upon which to lay their eggs. The latter are white, but the number in a clutch does not appear to be ascertained. It is said that the Malays train falconets for hawking, throwing them from the hand at the quarry.

BLACK-LEGGED FALCONET

THE MISSISSIPPI FALCON

The three remaining genera of falcons are distinguished from the foregoing by their oval nostrils being provided with an overhanging flap of skin. In this group the oval nostrils have the long axis parallel or oblique to the beak, whereas in the pigmy falcons it is at right angles to the same. Of these genera, the one to which the Mississippi falcon (*Ictinia*) belongs is characterised by the beak having but one notch, and the wings reaching the tip of the tail ; whereas in the other two (*Baza* and *Harpagus*) the beak has two notches, and the wing does not reach the end of the tail.

The Mississippi falcon is one of two American species which represent the genus, and are characterised by the leaden black plumage of the upper parts, and the grey head, neck, and under parts. In the typical species the secondary feathers of the wing are silvery grey, like the head, whereas in the other (*I. plumbea*) they are of the same black hue as the primaries, this species being also distinguished by the presence of three white bars on the tail. The Mississippi falcon, which ranges from the southern United States to Guatemala, is 13½ inches in length, while the other species, which extends from Mexico to Brazil, is a fraction larger.

In its native land, where it is generally known as the Mississippi kite, the typical species is a common bird in many districts, more especially in parts of Texas. Its favourite feeding grounds are said to be cotton-fields, where it may be seen at one moment soaring high in the air, and soon after just skimming above the tops of the plants or flying between the rows. It seldom alights, but may now and then be observed perched on some dead tree, when it suffers itself to be approached within fifteen or twenty yards before taking wing. The food of this species is believed to consist mainly of large insects, probably supplemented with small rodents and reptiles. The nest is built in a tree, generally in a fork, and may be used for two or more seasons in succession. Usually two or three eggs are laid, which differ from those of most members of the family in being uniform bluish white, without spots. In defence of their nest and young, these birds are said to display great courage.

CRESTED FALCONS

The crested falcons (*Baza*), of which there are several species ranging from India through Malaya to North Australia, Africa, and Madagascar, differ, as already mentioned, from the last genus by having two notches on the edge of the beak and by the shorter wings, while they are distinguished from all other members of the subfamily by the crest of elongated feathers at the back of the head. These birds vary from 14 to 17 inches in length, and many of them are remarkable for their handsome colouring.

The Indian representative of the genus is the black crested falcon, or, as it is commonly called, kite (*B. lophotes*), which has the plumage of the upper parts glossy greenish black, and a uniformly black tail. It is a rare bird, frequenting forests, and feeding almost exclusively on insects. In all the other species the tail is brown or grey, with darker bars; some, like the Philippine crested falcon (*B. magnirostris*), having the breast marked with broad transverse bars of white and chestnut; while in the West African cuckoo-falcon (*B. cuculoides*) the brown bands are narrower, less continuous, and confined to the sides of the body beneath the wings. Three Central and South American falcons, constituting the genus *Harpagus*, differ from the crested falcons by the absence of the plume of feathers and the presence of a tubercle in the centre of each nostril.

HONEY-BUZZARDS

All the preceding genera are included in the subfamily *Falconinæ*, but those now claiming attention belong to a second subfamily, the *Aquilinæ*, which includes honey-buzzards, kites, eagles, and so forth. The members of this group differ from the last by the sides of the upper half of the beak being simply festooned, instead of notched, although they resemble them in having the hind aspect of the metatarsus reticulated—that is to say, covered with small and polygonal scales. As regards their insectivorous habits, the Mississippi and crested falcons serve to connect the more typical members of the preceding subfamily with the kites. In the whole group the nostrils are not concealed by plumes.

A rare visitor to the British Isles, the honey-buzzard (*Pernis nellivora*) is a well-known although locally distributed bird on the Continent, and the only European representative of the small genus to which it belongs. Honey-buzzards agree with a considerable number of other genera in having the lower portion of the metatarsus bare, the length of the naked part being, however, less than that of the third toe, exclusive of the claw; and also in the oblique form of the nostrils, which are generally closed by a membrane, so as to render their aperture little more than a slit. They are, however, more specially characterised by the tail being rounded, with the outer feathers inferior in length to the middle pair.

From their immediate allies honey-buzzards are distinguished by the shortness of that portion of the beak in advance of the cere, as compared with the third toe; while the beak itself is stout and the feathers on the lores are short and not produced beyond the hind edge of the nostril. The wings are long and large, and the tail also elongated; the toes being of moderate length, and the claws but slightly curved. The shortness of the feathers on the lores, together with its peculiar gait, which has been compared to the running of a hen, renders the honey-buzzard the most unhawk-like of all the British representatives of the family.

The honey-buzzard is subject to a great amount of variation in the colour and markings of the plumage, more especially in birds of the first and second years. Generally speaking, it may be said, however, that the adult male has an ashy grey head, brown upper parts, with the feathers margined with a lighter tint and showing a dark median streak, and the tail pale brown, with the extreme tip whitish, and marked by three dark transverse bars.

Beneath, the plumage is white, narrowly streaked with brown, such streaks expanding on the sides of the body into spade-shaped markings. There may be some white on the tips of the wing feathers. The eye is straw-coloured, the beak

MISSISSIPPI FALCON AND SWALLOW-TAILED KITES

black, and the foot yellow with black claws.

Young birds are generally brown or yellowish brown, and have the shafts of the feathers distinctly streaked with black, and the under parts more rufous than the upper surface. The ashy brown tail is broadly tipped with buffish white, and crossed by two distinct chocolate bars, one near the end and the other near the middle, between which are a number of imperfect dark bars. The eye is hazel. The length of the adult bird is about 25½ inches, so that it may be compared in size to a kite.

The honey-buzzard ranges over the greater part of Europe, and probably occurs in several parts of Northern Asia, as it has been recorded from Japan and near Pekin. In Sweden it breeds within the Arctic Circle, and it has frequently nested in England. During the winter it migrates to Arabia, Africa, and Madagascar. In India it is replaced by the crested

CRESTED HONEY-BUZZARD

honey-buzzard (*P. ptilorhynchus*)**,** a species ranging through the Malay region, distinguished by the low crest of the adults, and remarkable for its great individual variation, some individuals being light tawny while others are nearly black. A third species (*P. celebensis*) inhabits Celebes.

The honey-buzzard derives its name from its habit of feeding on the grubs of bees and wasps, digging out the combs with its claws, and tearing them to pieces. It will, however, also eat adult insects of various kinds, together with worms, slugs, the eggs of birds, moles, and even grain. It may be taken in traps baited with wasp or bee comb; and in captivity has been known to kill and eat rats, as well as comparatively large birds. The nest is generally placed at a considerable height from the ground in some tall oak, and composed of lichen-clad sticks, lined with wool and the leaves of the oak and beech. It has been stated that in France the honey-buzzard surrounds the nest, after the young are hatched, with a barrier of leafy boughs, which is renewed from time to time as the foliage withers; but whether this is to prevent the young from falling out, or to act as a screen, is not ascertained. The eggs are not more than three in number, and usually have a buffish white ground colour, upon which are dark blotches.

BLACK-WINGED KITE

A much smaller bird than the last, the black-winged kite (*Elanus cœruleus*) is one of the best-known representatives of a small genus widely distributed over both hemispheres. Agreeing with the honey-buzzards in their nearly even or

slightly emarginate tails, the hawks of this genus differ by the more elongated beak, of which the length in advance of the cere is greater (instead of less) than half the length of the third toe, exclusive of the claw. They are further characterised by the extreme shortness of the bare portion on the front of the metatarsus, by the feathered lores, and by the wings reaching to the end of the tail; these characters distinguishing them from certain allied genera which there is not space to notice.

The black-winged kite, which is an inhabitant of South-Eastern Europe, Africa, and India, attains a length of just over 13 inches. Above, it is of a beautiful ash-grey colour, with the forehead and under parts white, and the shoulders and lesser wing coverts deep glossy black; the lores and a narrow streak above the eye being also sable. The eye is full carmine red, the beak black, and the cere, like the feet, yellow. In young birds the upper surface is brownish grey, and the under side yellowish streaked with brown, most of the feathers having light borders, and the iris being yellow. In America this species is replaced by the white-tailed kite (*E. leucurus*), easily distinguished by the feathers of the tail (except the middle pair, which are grey) being pure white; while two other species inhabit Australia, and a fifth the Philippines, Java, Borneo, and Celebes.

Mr. A. O. Hume writes that the black-winged kites hover over grass in the fashion of a kestrel, "but in a clumsier and heavier manner. The wings point upwards, so that they are within 3 to 4 inches of each other, instead of being retained nearly horizontally as in the kestrel, and the legs and tail hang down unlike those of any other bird that I have noticed. Thus hovering, they after a time slowly descend, and when within a few feet of the ground generally drop

HONEY-BUZZARDS

suddenly. They are very tame, bold birds, passing unconcernedly within a few feet of a sportsman when busy hunting over fields or grass, and sitting composedly on the bare end of a bough whilst, gun in hand, one walks up to within a few paces of their perch."

They are frequently to be seen sitting on the telegraph wires alongside the Indian railways; and in Egypt they may be observed (as shown in the illustration) perched on the summits of the long poles used for raising water from the Nile. The nests are usually placed in low trees; and the eggs have a creamy or bluish white ground, sparingly streaked and blotched with pale yellowish brown, and are usually two or three in number. One of the Australian species generally nests in large companies; the nests being placed as near together as possible, and composed of twigs, lined with the cast pellets of the fur of the rodents on which the birds have fed. The black-winged species subsists chiefly on insects, but also devours rats and mice.

The American white-tailed kite does not apparently breed northwards of South California, but extends south to the Argentine. Its habits seem to be very similar to those of the other species; but whereas in North America it usually lays four or five eggs, in Argentina the number reaches eight. Messrs. Sclater and Hudson write that " it is a handsome bird, with large ruby-red irides, and when seen at a distance its snow-white plumage and buoyant flight give it a striking resemblance to a gull. Its wing-power is indeed marvellous. It delights to soar, like the martins, during a high wind, and will spend hours in this sport, rising and falling alternately; and at times, seeming to abandon itself to the fury of the gale, is blown away like thistledown, until, suddenly recovering itself, it shoots back to its original position. Where there are tall poplar trees, these birds amuse themselves by perching on the topmost slender twigs, balancing themselves with outspread wings, each bird on a separate tree, until the tree-tops are swept by the wind from under them, when they often remain poised almost motionless in the air until the twigs return to their feet."

RED AND BLACK KITES

KITES

Although the term kite is commonly applied to many members of the present family, it should properly be restricted to the species of the genus *Milvus*, and belongs, strictly speaking, only to the European, or red, kite (*M. ictinus*), also known in England as the glead. In Britain the kite is one of those species which has

BLACK-WINGED KITE

suffered most severely from incessant persecution, having gradually diminished in numbers from the time of Shakespeare, when these birds were to be seen in numbers on the Thames in London, till the present day, when it is practically extinct in the southern and midland counties, although still lingering in the west and north.

Kites belong to a group of five genera easily distinguished from the foregoing members of the subfamily by their more or less deeply forked tails, in which the outermost feathers are the longest. In the kites the forking of the tail is of moderate depth, and approximately equal in length to the interval between the tips of the primary and secondary quills, while the head is devoid of a crest. The wings are long, reaching nearly to the end of the tail, with the fourth or the third and fourth quills the longest, the beak slightly festooned, and the metatarsus and toes short, with claws of moderate length. There are some half-dozen species, exclusively confined to the Old World, where they range over all the continents.

Kites are the scavengers of the hawk family, feeding chiefly on refuse and garbage, although also consuming insects, reptiles, and such young or feeble birds or mammals as they can capture. Spending most of their time on the wing, they soar gracefully in large, sweeping circles, and form a striking feature in the bird-life of all Eastern cities. Their nests may be built either in trees or buildings, or on rocks.

RED KITE

The typical, or red, kite of Europe (*M. ictinus*), which attains a length of about 24 inches, differs from all its congeners by its rufous tail and the general rufous tinge of the entire plumage. In old males the head and throat are whitish with brown streaks, the upper parts having the feathers dark brown in the middle with rufous edgings, tending to buff on the extreme margins, more especially in the wing coverts. The primary quills and primary coverts are black, with some white at the base of their inner webs, the upper tail coverts rufous, the tail feathers reddish brown, with their inner webs barred with dark brown, and the under parts rufous brown with a dark median streak to each feather. The beak is horn-colour, the cere and eye, together with the legs and feet, yellow, and the claws black.

The kite is distributed over the greater part of Europe, breeding so far north as the south of Scandinavia, and becoming gradually more rare in the eastern districts. In winter it ranges to Lower Egypt, Algeria, and Palestine. The nest is built either in the fork of a tree or, more rarely, in a cleft of rock; and the three or four eggs are laid in April or May. Nothing comes amiss to a kite when building, and, while the main framework of the nest is formed of sticks, these are supplemented by all kinds of rubbish, such as bones, fragments of leather, and rags, the latter forming the lining. When their nest is attacked, the parent birds make a vigorous resistance. As already mentioned, the kite was a favourite quarry in hawking, showing excellent sport by the manner in which it endeavoured to baffle the falcon in its efforts to gain the advantage of position. More rarely the kite itself was trained to fly at smaller birds.

THE KITE

BLACK KITE

The black, or migratory, kite (M. migrans) is a rather smaller bird, distinguished from the last by its dark brown tail, faintly barred with a still deeper tint, and the general dark brown hue of the plumage of the upper parts, with the exception of the head and throat, where the feathers are whitish with dark stripes. It is further characterised by the black beak, and the absence of any distinct patch of white at the base of the primary quills. This kite is distributed over the whole of Africa and Madagascar, whence it migrates to Southern and Western Europe, occasionally reaching Scandinavia, and having been taken in England. This kite appears on the Swiss lakes and rivers about the middle of April, and leaves early in the autumn. Frequently it may be seen fishing in the Lake of Geneva, and often, while one of the pair is engaged in this occupation, its fellow will be soaring high in the air.

As red kites were formerly wont to play the part of scavengers in London, so do black kites at the present day in the narrow lanes of Cairo. "Assisted," writes Dr. Leith Adams, "by its ally, the Egyptian kite (M. ægyptius), which may be distinguished from the other

on wing by the pale colour of its bill, they hover over the refuse-heaps, slaughter-houses, and wherever carrion and offal are collected, now pouncing on their food and bearing it off in their talons, or, with that remorseless activity characteristic of the genus, pursuing pigeons, until the terrified birds, worn out by exhaustion, sink down, and are despatched by the enemy.

Nor is this all; the fisherman has to keep a good look-out when he lands his net, as one or other is sure to be on the look-out for the small fry. They dispute the ownership of a bone with the lean pariah dog, or pick up refuse floating down the river; they hover over the farmer as he ploughs his field, and are the dread of a village from the number of chickens they pilfer. The nest is built in the top of a palm tree, where the Nubians catch them in traps baited with pigeons."

In India and the Himalaya the kite is replaced by the smaller pariah, or govind, kite (M. govinda), the chil of the natives, distinguished by the well-marked patch of white at the base of the primaries. There is, however, in India another and larger species (M. melanotis), measuring about 25 inches in length, against 20 in the smaller species, and also distinguished by some differences in colouring, this larger species ranging eastwards to China, Japan, and Formosa. The pariah kite ranges to elevations of about eight thousand feet in the Himalaya, and abounds in every Indian city and village, where it performs the same useful offices as does the black species in Egypt.

These kites frequently display the most astonishing familiarity and impudence; and, when in camp, I have seen a portion of my dinner snatched from a plate carried by a servant by one of these marauders. So numerous are they that in Calcutta from two hundred to three hundred may be seen together at a time; and when the white ants are swarming, the air is sometimes almost darkened by the hosts of kites, buzzards, and crows which collect to prey upon the flying insects. Their Indian name, chil, is given to them after their cry, which is a kind of long, tremulous squeal. In the plains the breeding time lasts from January to April. The nest is nearly always placed in a tree, and mostly in a fork. The usual number of eggs is two.

BLACK KITE

SWALLOW-TAILED KITES

Distinguished from all its relatives, with the exception of an allied species, by its deeply-forked tail and extremely long wings, the swallow-tailed kite of America (Elanoides furcatus), with its striking piebald plumage, cannot be mistaken for any other member of the family.

This bird may be compared in size to the pariah kite, its total length being 21 inches. As regards colour, the entire head and neck, together with the hind part of the back and rump and the whole of the under surface, are pure white; while nearly all the rest of the upper plumage is black with greyish or purplish reflections in different regions. The beak is dark steely blue, the eye dark reddish brown, and the foot bluish white.

The range of this handsome and dashing bird extends from the southern States of North America to Colombia and Brazil, a few individuals being occasionally blown across the Atlantic to the western shores of Europe. Of its habits, Dr. W. L. Ralph writes as follows: " Excepting perhaps the turkey-vulture, I think this bird is the most graceful of any while on the wing. It has the same easy floating motion, but at times it flies very rapidly and turns very quickly, which is something I have never seen the former bird do. Their motions are very swallow-like, and that, with their forked tails, makes them look like gigantic swallows; and, like the chimney-swifts, they have a habit of travelling together in small companies, usually consisting of three individuals, especially when they first return from the south.

" During the breeding season flocks consisting of from two or three to ten or twelve birds, but oftener of three, may be seen following one another around, frequently uttering their calls, and circling in and out among the tree-tops so fast as to make one dizzy to look at them. Except during this season, one seldom sees one of these birds unless it is flying, and I have often wondered if they did not at times sleep while on the wing. At least I know that they usually, if not always, eat while flying; for I have many times seen one sailing leisurely along, occasionally bending its head to tear a piece from a small snake that is held in its talons, and I have never seen one alight to eat its food, as other birds of prey do. When hunting, they fly quite close to the ground, like marsh-harriers, but at other times they sail above the tree-tops, and sometimes so far above that it takes a good eye to see them. Their food consists almost entirely of reptiles; small snakes seem to be a favourite article of food with them. I have never seen one catch a bird, and believe they do not. This habit of eating snakes has given them the name of snake-hawk among the natives of Florida."

These birds begin to arrive from the south in the latter State about the middle of March, but do not become common till two or three weeks later. There they nest in April, usually building in tall pines, frequently at a height of 90 and sometimes as much as 130 feet from the ground. The nest is a very irregular structure of mossy twigs, and usually contains two eggs, spotted and blotched with rich brown and ferruginous.

The African swallow-tailed kite (*Nauclerus riocouri*) is about two-thirds the size of the above, with relatively shorter wings. It is greyish above and white beneath, and is confined to the western and northeastern parts of the African continent.

VULTURINE SEA-EAGLE

The conspicuous bird known to naturalists as the vulturine sea-eagle (*Gypohierax angolensis*) is the first member of a group of four genera which, while agreeing with the preceding in the shortness of the bare portion of the metatarsus, differ in the absence of a flap of membrane to the nostrils, which have a clean, bony margin. In three of them the aperture of the nostril is oval, with its longer axis placed more or less nearly at right angles to that of the beak, but in *Haliastur* the aperture is circular. In all the tail is rounded or slightly emarginate. It may be well to mention that *Haliastur* is represented by the common bramini, or maroon-backed, kite (*H. indus*), easily recognised by its white head, neck, throat, and breast, and the maroon chestnut of the rest of the plumage.

SWALLOW-TAILED KITE

The vulturine sea-eagle, which is the sole representative of its genus, differs from the other forms with oval nostrils by the naked space above the eye, and is characterised by its particoloured plumage. It has a peculiarly vulture-like appearance, and may be compared in size to a kite, the total length of the male being 23 inches, while the female is $1\frac{1}{2}$ inches longer. The beak and head are elongated and the wings very long and pointed, and the short tail is very markedly rounded.

In the adult the colour of the plumage is pure white, with the exception of the ends of the primary quills, the secondaries, the tail feathers, save their tips, and most of the scapulars, which are black. The cere is grey, the bare skin of the face flesh-coloured, the eye light yellow, and the foot rosy flesh-coloured. The feathers of the hind part of the head are somewhat elongated, so as to form a slight crest. In the young the whole plumage is dark brown, and the eye also brown; the complete change to the adult dress not taking place till the third or fourth year.

This bird is exclusively African, and is met with on the west coast from Senegambia to Angola, and on the opposite side of the continent on Pemba Island, near

Zanzibar. Although so like a vulture in general appearance, in its habits it much more resembles the sea-eagles. One of the commonest birds on the west coast, it is essentially a fish-eater, frequenting the sea-coast and rivers, and but rarely seen in the dry highlands of the interior. Its favourite haunts are the wide mangrove swamps bordering the larger rivers, where it may always be seen in numbers, sometimes associating in pairs, and at other times singly. When seated, it may be easily mistaken for a vulture, but its flight, although slower, is more like that of a sea-eagle.

When fishing, it generally flies close to the surface of the water, returning as soon as it has captured a fish to the shore to devour its prey. In the breeding season these birds proceed higher up the rivers, where the trees are taller, and thus afford better nesting places than the low mangroves. The number of eggs in a nest is usually two.

SEA-EAGLES

The noble birds known as sea-eagles (*Haliaëtus*), which include the largest member of the whole family, differ from the preceding genus by the absence of a naked space above the eye, and are further characterised by the lanceolate feathers of the crown of the head, and by the wings reaching nearly or quite to the end of the tail. The beak is long and powerful, straight for some distance from the base, and then curving regularly downwards in a deep hook. In the leg the metatarsus is feathered for nearly half its length, and the naked portion reticulated down to the toes, while the latter are scutellated above. The strong, curved claws are grooved beneath, that of the first toe being the largest of all.

There are some eight species of sea-eagles distributed over the whole world, with the exception of South America; the habits of all are generally similar. It

WHITE-TAILED SEA-EAGLE

may be mentioned that they are often confounded with the true eagles, from which they may be distinguished at a glance by the naked lower half of the metatarsus and the scutellation of its front surface. The sea-eagles may be divided into three groups, according to whether the tail in the adult is entirely white, black with a white band at the end, or white with terminal band of black.

Although several of the species are more commonly found in the neighbourhood of the coasts, sea-eagles are also met with in the interior of the various continents and islands in the neighbourhood of the larger rivers and lakes. Writing of the white-tailed sea-eagle, Mr. H. L. Seebohm observes that "the haunts of this noble-looking bird are the barren hills of the Hebrides and the adjacent isles, and the wild mountain country of the mainland in the west. On the bold and rocky headlands of this wild, rugged coast, whose hoary peaks are washed by the treacherous waters of the Minch, the sea-eagle finds a congenial home. In Pomerania, especially between Stettin and the Baltic, the sea-eagle is a common resident, building in forests. It builds an enormous nest, sometimes six or eight feet in diameter, near the top of a pine, or on the horizontal branch of an oak or beech, preferring forests near inland seas and large lakes. Instances have been known of its breeding in the same 'horst' for twenty years in succession. Every year some addition is made to the nest, until it becomes some five or six feet high.

"Occasionally a pair of sea-eagles has two 'horsts,' which are used alternately. They are shy birds and leave the nest at the least alarm, but they do not easily forsake their old home. If the eggs are taken early in the season, the birds will frequently lay again in the same nest. They make a very flat nest, and generally line it on the top with moss. The male and female are said to sit alternately, and the female is said to be shyer than the male at the nest. Two is the usual

VULTURINE SEA-EAGLE

number of eggs, but frequently only one is found ; in rare cases as many as three are laid. Eggs may be taken from the first week in March to the middle of April."

The nest may be situated either on rocks, in trees, or on the ground. In some countries the cliffs on which it is built are of comparatively easy access ; but at the present day in the Hebrides, as formerly on the west coast of Ireland, these birds build on ledges of the most stupendous cliffs, where their eyries can only be approached by the aid of ropes lowered from above. Many anecdotes record the boldness of the Irish peasants in thus attacking the strongholds of both golden and sea-eagles. The food of the white-tailed sea-eagle, like that of its allies, consists chiefly of fish and water-fowl ; although these birds at times will not disdain a meal of carrion, while they probably carry off an occasional lamb or kid. It is related that an instance has occurred of a sea-eagle, when attempting to carry off a large salmon, into which it had firmly fixed its talons, being partially dragged under water by its prey ; both bird and fish being ultimately secured by a peasant who had witnessed the scene.

In India Pallas's sea-eagle always builds in trees, its nest being very similar to that of the last species, and the eggs laid from November to January. The nest may be occupied for several years, but the construction of a new one demands immense labour on the part of the birds. "I once," writes Mr. A. O. Hume, "watched a young pair constantly occupied for a full month building a new nest, which they were still working on when I left. Nothing can seem rougher or more ragged than their nest when finished, and yet out of every four sticks and branches that they brought they rejected and threw down at least three. Both birds brought materials, and side by side the pair would work away, throwing down almost as many sticks as they brought ; then apparently they would quarrel over the matter, there would be a great squealing, and one would fly away and sit sulky on some cliff-point near at hand ; after a time the one left on the nest would go off in quest of materials.

Immediately the other would drop softly on to the nest, and be very busy till the absent bird returned, not infrequently with a fish instead of a stick.

"It is a curious fact that, if the female, which is much the larger, brought the fish to the nest, the male set to work on it at once, without so much as 'by your leave' ; while if the male brought it, the female used to eye it, sidle gradually up, and only take slow and modest mouthfuls. When, however, the female begins to sit, the male will bring her fish or fowl, and go off for other food for himself, not attempting to share it with her ; and when not on the nest neither seems to presume with the other's capture without permission."

The eggs, like those of the other species, are uniformly coloured, being in this case pale greyish white ; their usual number is three. Like the white-tailed sea-eagle, this species will often lay again when its nest is robbed, but this is never the case with the American white-headed species. So long as there are merely eggs in the nest, Pallas's sea-eagle never makes any attempt at defending its home, and the same is the case after the young are hatched. In New Zealand, however, a native who had been sent up a tree to visit a nest was fiercely attacked, at first by the female, and then by both birds in concert, so that it was necessary to disable the eagles by shooting, in order to prevent the man being hurled from the tree.

Continuing his account of its habits, Mr. Hume states that Pallas's sea-eagle is never found far away from rivers, lakes, or swamps. "Early in the morning, even in the cold weather, it goes down to the water-side, and has a good bathe. It is amusing to watch this large bird standing up to its belly in water, sitting down, first on one side, then on the other, so as to wash the wings and back, ducking the head in and out, and splashing, spluttering, and fluttering the wings for all the world like a pigeon or sparrow. After its bath, it resorts to the top of some tree, or, along the banks of large rivers, to some craggy point, where it sits for a while sunning itself, generally with its wings half outspread. Thence it flies off heavily to seek a meal. A large fish near the surface attracts its attention, as it flies pretty low over the river ; down it swoops with more activity and rapidity than its habitual demeanour and method of flight would lead one to expect, and strikes for a breakfast, dashing its huge feet and long legs into the water right up to the body."

This action shows how admirably adapted is the conformation of the bird to its mode of life, as heavily feathered legs like these of the true eagles would become heavy and bedraggled with water. The food of these birds is, however, by no means confined to fish ; they may frequently be seen on the larger Indian rivers hawking for ducks, teal, and paddi-birds, and will pursue and carry off such a large animal as a wounded wild goose, of which the weight may be as much as seven pounds. Captain Hutton states that he has watched one of these birds sitting on a dead tree on the river-bank suddenly utter its shrill, clamorous, half croak-like, half scream-like cry, spread out its wings, and sweep across the water in search of winged game on the plains. Rising at first in wide circles, until nearly lost to view, it would gradually descend in similar gyrations, until with a sudden swoop it would dart upon some unfortunate partridge or hare, and bear it off in its talons.

WHTE-HEADED SEA-EAGLE

The American white-headed sea-eagle ranges from the frozen regions of Alaska and the Aleutian Islands to the torrid plains of Mexico, although it is only a summer visitor to the more northern portions of its habitat. The nests appear to be similar to those of the European species, and but rarely contain more than a single pair of eggs. Usually situated in tall pines, at a height varying from twenty to one hundred feet above the ground, they may occasionally be found on the ground itself. These birds subsist more on winged game captured by their own exertions than on fish ; the accusation of their gaining subsistence mainly by robbing the osprey being unfounded. Still, however, like others of their genus, there is no doubt that these birds do at times obtain a meal in this comparatively easy manner ; and in some cases they have to depend entirely on fish for food .

An anonymous writer states that on one occasion he noticed one of these sea-eagles hovering over the sea in a manner very similar to that of the osprey when about to strike a fish. "Suddenly he plunged down and grappled with what I supposed to be a large fish, but was unable to rise with it from the water, and after struggling a while he lay with wings extended and apparently exhausted. After resting a minute or two, he again raised himself out of the water, and I saw he had some large black object in the grasp of one of his talons, which he succeeded in towing along the top of the water toward the shore a short distance, and then letting go his hold. He was then joined by two other eagles, and by taking turns they soon succeeded in getting it to the shore." The booty was a large cormorant, upon which the eagles were about to feast.

It is a remarkable fact that, of the two eggs usually laid by this species, one is always superior in size to the other ; the difference between the two in this respect being sometimes very great. Steller's sea-eagle subsists on young seals, Arctic hares and foxes, and ptarmigan, but it will also eat dead fish and the carcases of mammals.

WHITE-TAILED SEA-EAGLE

In the first group the white-tailed, or grey, sea-eagle (H. albicilla) is noteworthy as being the only species met with in the British Isles. In addition to the character from which it takes its name, it is distinguished by the brown abdomen, the brownish wing coverts, and the ashy brown hue of the head and neck, which are lighter than the back. The female attains a length of 38 inches, the male being

AFRICAN SEA-EAGLES

about 4½ inches less. This species ranges across Europe and Northern Asia from Ireland to Japan, and also occurs in Southern Greenland, while it extends southwards to North-Western India. Its distribution includes the whole of Europe, but it has now become rare in the British Isles, although still breeding in the Hebrides.

STELLER'S AND COREAN SEA-EAGLES

The largest of all eagles are the giant, or Steller's, sea-eagle (H. pelagicus), and the allied Corean sea-eagle (H. branicki), the former attaining a length of 41 inches. Steller's sea-eagle, which is confined to the north-eastern regions of the Old World, inhabiting North-Eastern Siberia, North China, Japan, and Kamchatka, is distinguished by its pure white wing coverts, thighs, and upper and lower tail coverts, and further characterised by the distinctly wedge-shaped tail, which has fourteen feathers in place of the usual twelve. In young birds the wing coverts and thighs are, however, brownish, although in this state the species can be distinguished from the white-tailed sea-eagle by the head and neck being of the same dark hue as the back. The Corean species is a uniform slaty black colour, without the white shoulder patches, thighs, and tail coverts. In correspondence with their giant size, the cry of both these species is much louder and more penetrating than that of other eagles.

WHITE-HEADED SEA-EAGLE

The white-headed sea-eagle, or bald eagle (H. leucocephalus), the national emblem of the United States, differs from the white-tailed species by having the whole of the head and neck pure white ; the rest of the plumage of the upper parts being dark brown, approaching black, while beneath the colour is a lighter brown. The length of the female is 38 inches. This bird ranges over the whole of North America, extending southwards to Florida, California, and Mexico.

PALLAS'S SEA-EAGLE

The species known as Pallas's sea-eagle (H. leucophæus) differs from all the preceding by having the tail of the adult white with a broad band of black at the end ; the remainder of the plumage, except the sides of the face, which are buffish white, being various shades of brown. It is a smaller bird than the foregoing, measuring only 30 inches in length. Typically an inhabitant of the Caspian region, it ranges eastwards to India and Burma.

WHITE-BELLIED SEA-EAGLE

The white-bellied sea-eagle (H. leucogaster), which is still smaller, its length not exceeding 28 inches, differs from all the others by the tail being black with a broad terminal band of white ; and is further characterised by the white head, neck, and under parts, the general tint of the upper surface being grey slightly shaded with brown. This eagle extends from India and Ceylon through the Malay region to Australia.

AFRICAN AND MALAGASY SEA-EAGLES

The handsomest of the whole group is the African sea-eagle (*H. vocifer*), which is smaller than all the northern species, attaining a length of only 25 inches in the female. Resembling the white-headed sea-eagle in its white head, neck, and tail, this species is distinguished by the white area extending on to the interscapular region above and including the breast below, and by the whole of the abdomen, together with the axillaries, being of a deep chestnut hue, while the upper parts are blackish brown, passing into black on the primary quills.

The species is confined to Africa, where it ranges over the whole continent, and is replaced in Madagascar by the Malagasy sea-eagle (*H. vociferoides*), distinguished by the white being confined to the head and neck, the brown under parts, and the chestnut under wing coverts ; the latter character distinguishing it from the larger white-headed sea-eagle, in which these coverts are brown.

Remains of an extinct sea-eagle are to be found in the Miocene deposits of France.

ORIENTAL FISH-EAGLES

The Oriental fish-eagles constitute a genus (*Polioaëtus*) restricted to the Indo-Malay region. The large Oriental fish-eagle (*P. ichthyaëtus*) somewhat exceeds the osprey in size, whereas the smaller *P. plumbeus* is inferior in this respect. The larger species has the upper plumage brown, becoming paler on the middle of the back and darker on the wings, the head and neck ashy grey, and the tail white, with a broad bar of brown at the tip. Its range extends from India to Celebes, and its food consists mostly of fish. The smaller species lacks the white base of the tail. Both kinds haunt rivers rather than the coast, and have loud and plaintive notes. The nest, which is very large, is placed in a tree, and often lined with green leaves, and the two or three eggs are white.

BATELEUR EAGLE

BATELEUR EAGLE

An inhabitant of the whole of Africa lying to the south of the Sahara Desert, the handsomely coloured bird known as the bateleur eagle (*Helotarsus ecaudatus*) differs from the sea-eagles, and indeed from all other members of the family, by the extreme shortness of its tail, which is much inferior in length to the wings. A further point of distinction is to be found in the feathers of the head, which are elongated so as to form a voluminous crest.

As regards colour, this bird is perhaps the most striking of all eagles, presenting bold contrasts of maroon, black, and grey, which give to the entire plumage a most pleasing effect. The head, neck, and under parts are of a deep glossy black, the same hue also obtaining on the scapulars, contrasted with which is the chestnut maroon of the hind part of the neck and the greater portion of the back. The wing coverts are brown with a bronzy sheen, the primary quills blackish, externally shaded with grey, and the secondaries mostly grey with white tips, although the innermost have the sooty hue of the scapulars. The tail, with its inferior coverts, is chestnut brown, like the back ; the under surface of the wings being mainly grey and white. The cere and naked skin in front of the eyes, together with the feet, are deep coral red, the eye brown, and the beak black.

Such are the striking colours of the ordinary form of the bateleur eagle, although individuals have been obtained in which the chestnut maroon of the back is replaced by creamy fulvous. Such birds have been regarded as representing a distinct species, but it is quite likely they will prove to be merely the very old stage of the ordinary bird. The females attain a length of 25 and the males of about 21 inches. The colour of the cere and face fades in captive birds to a pale orange yellow tint, the same change showing itself in captive specimens of the accipitrines known as caracaras. The bateleur eagle is a common bird in many parts of Africa, preferring mountains to plains, and generally frequenting open districts rather than forests.

In Abyssinia, where they are by no means abundant, they have been obtained from considerable elevations in the mountains. Dr. W. T. Blanford describes them " as soaring at a great height, their pointed wings and extremely short tail rendering them no less conspicuous than the contrast between the white under side of the wings and the black body. The flight is superb, more like that of a vulture than of an eagle, as the bird sweeps along with motionless wings, occasionally high up in the air, but more frequently at about one hundred and fifty to two hundred feet above the ground."

Awakening with the first streaks of dawn, the bateleur leaves the tree on which it has roosted during the night in search of food, and after hunting for some hours seeks a resting place in which to pass the hottest portion of the day, issuing forth again to hunt in the evening. These eagles prey upon young antelopes, lambs, and sick sheep, and will also eat carrion, as well as kill and devour the smaller mammals. Their chief food consists, however, of various snakes and lizards, of which they are said to consume a larger amount than the secretary-bird. Snakes of all sizes, whether venomous or harmless, are attacked by the bateleur, and speedily disabled by rapid blows from its powerful beak. The species, like many other animals which feed on serpents, is probably immune to snake-venom.

At such times as the grass jungles are on fire, the bateleur, like the other serpent-eating birds of Central Africa, beats along the line of flame in order to seize the snakes and other reptiles as they creep out, sometimes dashing into the very thick of the smoke to secure its prey. The nests of these birds are usually built in tall trees, and frequently in those whose boughs are thickly beset with thorns. At the proper season each contains from two to four white eggs. The breeding season takes place at the beginning of the hot weather, when snakes are more easily captured than when the grass is long and rank.

BUZZARD-EAGLES AND HARRIER-EAGLES

The remaining members of that section of the subfamily *Aquilinæ* characterised by the partially bare metatarsus have the naked portion longer than in the preceding group, and either equal in length to or longer than the third toe, exclusive of the claw. Of the several genera thus characterised, the buzzard-eagles (*Butastur*), which range from India, China, and Japan through the Malay region to New Guinea, and also occur in North-Eastern Africa, differ from the rest in having the oval nostrils provided with a membrane above ; the others having a clean bony margin to these organs. Omitting three unimportant genera, severally represented by a single species, mention may be made of the harrier-eagles (*Circaëtus*), all characterised by

HARRIER-EAGLE

the nostrils taking the form of transverse ovals, by the feathers of the small crest being of a lance-like shape, and the elongation of the wing. The long tail is nearly even, the metatarsus long and reticulate, the short beak somewhat compressed and deeply hooked at the extremity, and the toes very short.

Most of the few species of this genus are confined to Africa, but the European harrier-eagle (*C. gallicus*) has a much wider distribution, ranging from the countries bordering the Mediterranean to India and the small islands of Timor and Flores, and being sometimes found in Central Europe. These eagles are usually met with in open plains, living much on the wing, and feeding chiefly on snakes and other reptiles ; and in appearance and habits resembling buzzards,

with which they are connected by the above-mentioned buzzard-eagles.

The typical harrier-eagle is one of the smaller members of the group, the females measuring 26 inches, against 32 in the largest African species. It is thus rather larger than a kite. The general colour of the adult is dark brown, with a purplish gloss above, and the head tending to ashy brown, the quills being dusky black. The tail is pale ashy brown, with a white tip and three dusky transverse bars. Beneath, the colour is white, the throat narrowly streaked with brown, and with a black shaft-stripe to each feather ; while the flanks are banded with widely separated dark bars. The eye is orange yellow, the cere whitish, the beak horn-coloured at the tip and grey at the base, and the foot pale greyish brown.

In India this harrier-eagle is spread over all the more open parts of the country, generally avoiding thick jungle and forest. "It may often," writes Dr. Jerdon, "be seen sitting on a low tree, whence it occasionally darts on its quarry ; but it generally circles in the air, taking a long and lofty flight, now and then flying heavily along the ground like a harrier. I have frequently seen it hover in the air like a kestrel, and drop down on its prey, like a stone, afterwards. It is a rather noisy bird, frequently uttering a wild, plaintive scream. I have seen several together occasionally, but it is usually solitary. Its chief food is snakes and lizards, but it will eat anything—rats, weakly birds, crabs, frogs, centipedes, and large insects. I have seen one strike at a wounded hare, and it will occasionally carry off a wounded teal or duck."

This species, sometimes termed the short-toed eagle, nests in Upper India from January to March, nearly always building in trees, and laying one or two eggs of a pale bluish white colour. The nest, which is formed of sticks, and from two to three feet in diameter by from six inches to a foot in depth, may be almost entirely devoid of lining, or so thickly coated with grass or straw that the eggs look as though packed in a basket for travelling. This eagle is comparatively rarely met with in the south of France, where it is known as Jean-le-Blanc ; but is more common in Palestine. Nests have been taken in France in the middle of May.

SERPENT-EAGLES

Although the term serpent-eagle is not infrequently applied to the members of the preceding genus, as a matter of convenience it is far preferable to restrict it to the nearly allied species coming under the generic title of *Spilornis*. These birds are distinguished from harrier-eagles by the feathers of the crest being of greater length, and rounded, instead of lanceolate, at the tip, and also by the shorter wings. The genus is mainly characteristic of India and the Malay region, although also represented in the Philippines, the south of China, and Formosa. In habits these eagles are more arboreal and far less constantly on the wing than harrier-eagles, darting on the snakes and other reptiles which form their food from the boughs of trees. Serpent-eagles derive their scientific name from the white or pale spots which ornament the dark-coloured plumage of all the species save one, and the name of spotted eagles would have been exceeding appropriate had it not been already employed in another sense.

The Indian serpent-eagle (*S. chila*) is by far the largest member of the genus, the females, which measure 30 inches in length, being decidedly handsome birds. The head is black, with conspicuous white bases to the long feathers of the crest; above and below, the general colour is brown, with small spots on the scapulars and wing coverts, and larger ones on the hind part of the lower surface, the chest being uniform. The quills have some dusky markings, and the tail is mottled with white and crossed with three bars of darker brown.

Two other species of the genus share in this general type of colouring, but in another pair the chest is rufous, one of these (*S. suluënsis*) having the abdomen banded instead of spotted with white, while in the sixth (*S. holospilus*), from the Philippines, the entire body is spotted. The Indian serpent-eagle ranges from India to China and Formosa, and in the first-named country is most common in jungly districts, although also found in wooded places. In addition to reptiles, it eats large insects and frogs, catching the latter in tanks. It nests in trees, laying two white eggs marked with a few dark specks.

AFRICAN CRESTED EAGLE

The handsome bird known as the African crested eagle (*Lophoaëtus occipitalis*) is the sole representative of a genus forming the last group of the *Aquilinæ*; the members of which differ from all the preceding forms by the metatarsus being completely feathered throughout its length. The African crested eagle belongs to a group of several genera characterised by the tail being nearly square or slightly rounded; and is distinguished from all the others, with the exception of the true crested eagles, by the length of the interval between the tips of the primaries and secondaries of the wings being inferior to that of the metatarsus. The great size and pendent character of the crest of the present bird at once serve to mark its distinctness from the members of the next genus. The nostril is circular, the beak short, and the

metatarsus of considerable length, with short feathers. In point of size the African crested eagle is somewhat inferior to the red kite, the total length of the female being 21 inches. The general colour of the plumage is chocolate brown, with some of the feathers on the back and wing coverts paler and the head darker, with a black crest. The forehead and legs are whitish, there are a few white spots on the upper tail coverts, and the under wing coverts are also mostly white. The tail has dark bars, the beak is bluish, with a black tip, the cere and feet are yellow, and the claws black.

This eagle is one of the most widely distributed of African accipitrines, ranging all over that continent, from the Cape to the Red Sea, wherever there are wooded districts. It frequents mountains and plains alike, and is even represented in such of the open regions as have patches of mimosa jungle, more especially on the river-banks. In the wooded parts of the Upper Nile it is especially common, and may be seen sitting placidly among the branches of a mimosa, not far removed from the main stem. From this coign of vantage it watches for its prey, swooping down like lightning upon any mouse, rat, ground-squirrel, or dove or other small bird that may chance to come within its range.

In general habits it is very similar to the crested eagles, and, for its size, one of the most powerful and active of the accipitrines. In addition to small mammals and birds, it consumes numbers of lizards and snakes, and also eats fish and frogs, while, when hard pressed, it will resort to carrion. It has been seen perched on a branch in the neighbourhood of a slaughter-house, watching its opportunity to feast on the offal or to seize a bone. Little is known of its breeding habits, although it is said to nest in trees, and lay two nearly round eggs, of a pale ground colour blotched with reddish brown.

AFRICAN CRESTED EAGLE

CRESTED EAGLES

There is a difference of opinion among naturalists as to the best English name for the members of the genus *Spizaëtus*, some terming them hawk-eagles, while by others they are designated crested eagles. These eagles are readily distinguished by the crest (occasionally absent) being very much smaller than in the African crested eagle, and the shorter wings. The beak is short and sharply curved at the tip, with a prominent festoon; the toes are large, and very unequal, and the claws strong and very much curved. The genus, which is represented by a considerable number of species, has a very wide geographical distribution, being spread all over Africa, the Indian and Malay regions, Celebes, Japan, and Formosa, and also found in Central and South America, exclusive of the extreme south.

SOUTH AFRICAN CRESTED EAGLE

The South African *S. bellicosus* is one of the largest members of the genus, the total length of the female being 31 inches. It belongs to a group in which the chest is uniformly coloured, and is distinguished from some of its allies by the barred tail. In the immature bird the general colour of the upper parts is pale brown, with white margins to the feathers of the back, the feathers of the head and neck are white, with a terminal spot of brown, the greater and primary wing coverts and quills ashy brown, tipped with white and barred with darker brown, and the tail feathers are likewise ashy brown, with buffish white tips and crossed with eleven dark brown bars. With the exception of a few dark brown spots on the chest and under wing coverts, the whole of the under parts is uniform buffish white.

In the adult the general colour becomes dark brown above, the head being dark brown, with narrow pale margins to the feathers; the tail has but six bars, the front of the neck and chest are dark brown, and the remainder of the under surface white with some dark spots. All the Oriental species are smaller, some having the inferior portion of the under surface marked with dark barrings.

MARSH CRESTED EAGLE

The following account of the habits of the marsh crested eagle (*S. limnaëtus*), which ranges from India to Java, is given by Captain Feilden, who writes from Pegu, and observes that this eagle "seems to be a very common bird about Thyetmyo; every ravine in the spurs of the Aracan Mountains seems to contain one or more pairs, as well as every wooded stream in the lower ground. Their wild, screaming whistle is almost always to be heard long before the bird is seen, as it sits in some large tree rising above the rest of the jungle, or wheels in circles far overhead; it is one of the wildest and wariest of birds. One that I took from the nest nearly two years ago is still as wild as ever, and constantly ruffles up the feathers of its head till they look almost like the crest of a bloodsucker, leaving the top of the head almost bare. It has also a habit of throwing back the head, apparently looking for a hole in the top of its cage, and bending backwards till it frequently falls over.

"These birds, so far as I know, feed on mynas, rats, and frogs. I have taken a young bird from the nest in the middle of May, and seen several young birds about the end of that month. They build the usual hawk-eagle's nest in the fork of the largest and most inaccessible tree that they can find, invariably overhanging the bed of a stream. Either numbers of these birds build and do not lay, or else they desert their nests on the slightest suspicion of having been discovered. Several pairs of birds belonging to nests in

SOUTH AFRICAN CRESTED EAGLE

more remote parts of the jungle seemed all to have succeeded in rearing one young each. The Burmese state that the birds lay only one egg, which is pure white. While the trees are in full leaf, these eagles shelter themselves in the middle of some thick tree during the heat of the day." A later observer in the same district, Mr. W. Davison, in commenting on this account, states that he found the crested eagles perfectly silent, and accordingly believes that the peculiar cry is uttered only during the breeding season.

CHANGEABLE CRESTED EAGLE

Another Indian species, the changeable crested eagle (*S. caligatus*), known in Garhwal as the peacock-killer, is said to destroy a large number of game-birds. Mr. R. Thompson writes that he once saw one of these eagles "stoop at a peacock which was on the ground, and strike at his head. The peacock dodged, rose, and flew into a patch of tall grass, where he lay concealed. The eagle took himself to a tree close by, whence he quietly watched the movements of the other. After a while the peacock began to move from his place of concealment; the moment he was well out of the grass the eagle darted down and caught him by the neck."

HAWK-EAGLES

Omitting mention of a few comparatively unimportant genera, attention may be directed to those species to which it is convenient to restrict the name of hawk-eagles (*Nisaëtus*). Together with true eagles, hawk-eagles may be distinguished from the foregoing genera with feathered metatarsi by the interval between the tips of the primary and secondary quills being less than the length of the metatarsus; and they are further characterised by the absence of a crest. The hawk-eagles have the metatarsus of considerable length, but of no great thickness; and their wings are, as a rule, proportionately shorter than in the true eagles, while there are generally more large scales on the upper surface of the toes than in the latter.

The most sure way of distinguishing between the two genera is by comparing the length of the fourth toe, measured from the beginning of the metatarsal feathers, and exclusive of the claw, with the circumference of the beak in front of the cere, when it will be found that while in the hawk-eagles the two diameters are equal, in the true eagles the former is less than the latter. The range of the hawk-eagles includes Africa, the north coast of the Mediterranean, India, Ceylon, and Australia.

BONELLI'S HAWK-EAGLE

Among the small number of species constituting this genus, the best known is Bonelli's hawk-eagle (*N. fasciatus*), which is at the same time one of the largest, the female measuring 26 inches in length, and thus being somewhat more than two-thirds the size of the golden eagle. In general colour the adult bird (shown in the lower figure of the illustration) is dark brown above, with some white about the head and in the region of the neck; the quills are deep brown, with white mottlings on their inner webs, and the tail is ashy brown, with a broad terminal band of dark brown, and several incomplete bars of the same tint higher up.

The axillaries are white, streaked with black, and the under parts white with dark shaft-stripes of variable breadth to the feathers, passing on the flanks into arrow-head-like markings. The beak is black, with a lighter base, the eye yellow, the cere dull yellow, and the foot whitish yellow. In young birds, as shown in the upper figure of the engraving, the general colour of the upper parts is brown, and that of the head, neck, and under parts fawn, with distinct black shaft-stripes to all the feathers.

The range of this fine eagle includes the regions lying on both sides of the Mediterranean, whence it extends eastwards through Palestine and Syria to Arabia. In India, where it is termed " mohrangi " (*i.e.*, peacock-killer), it is generally only seen in hilly or jungly districts, although it occasionally resorts to neighbouring cultivated ground. It is common in the Nilgiri Hills of Madras, where its nests are often placed on such precipitous cliffs as to be accessible only with the aid of ropes. Passing much of its time on the wing, and invariably visiting certain spots within its beat at almost the same hour day by day, this eagle may be seen, when in repose, perched either on the summit of some tall tree or a rocky prominence.

Its prey consists of various game-birds, herons, ducks, and other water-fowl, as well as hares and other small mammals; and it is said at times to carry off trained falcons that are employed in hawking. It also occasionally kills peafowl, and is a great marauder in poultry-yards and dove-cots. Dr. Jerdon writes as follows in reference to its pigeon-killing habits: " On the pigeons taking flight, one of the eagles pounced down from a vast height on the flock, but directing its swoop rather under the pigeons than directly at them. Its mate, watching the moment when, alarmed by the first swoop, the pigeons rose in confusion, pounced unerringly on one of them, and carried it off; and the other eagle, having risen again, also made another, and, this time, a fatal swoop."

Nesting in the Nilgiris and Himalaya on rocky cliffs, in the plains of India Bonelli's eagle more generally selects the tall clay banks of the larger rivers on which to build, although instances are known of the nest being placed in trees. In the plains of India the breeding season is in December and January, but is delayed in the Himalaya till April and May. The nest is four to six feet in diameter, and varies in height from a few inches to a couple of feet; its summit being always finished off level, with scarcely any central hollow. The eggs, two in number, are oval in shape, frequently unspotted, and at most but faintly blotched with pale yellowish or reddish brown on a greyish ground.

BONELLI'S HAWK-EAGLES

Bonelli's eagle is a common bird in Spain, and a pair breeds regularly upon the rock of Gibraltar. It is likewise fairly abundant in Palestine.

BOOTED HAWK-EAGLE

The booted, or dwarf, hawk-eagle (*N. pennatus*), which is a far smaller bird than the last, and may be compared in size to a kite, the total length of the female being only 24 inches, may be easily recognised by the conspicuous white patch on the shoulder. In the greater relative length of the wings and the generally brown colour of the eyes it differs from the two more typical members of the genus, and approaches the true eagles, although it has the characteristic long legs of the present group.

This bird is subject to great variation with regard to the colour of the plumage of the under parts; a difference which was long considered to be due to age, and has given rise to much discussion. It has, for instance, been considered that the dark-coloured phase represented on the left of the illustration was the immature dress, while the light individual on the right was an individual in the adult plumage. Dr. Scully, writing from observations made in Gilgit, states, however, that in that district " the dark and light forms are about equally common, the difference in colour not being dependent upon sex "; and adds that he captured a nestling with white under parts, thus effectually disposing of the theory that the dark form was the young.

In the light phase the general colour of the upper parts is brown, with a tinge of purple on the scapulars, and the above-mentioned distinct white patch on the uppermost feathers of that series. The lowest scapular and wing coverts have buffish white borders, and the quills are blackish, with light borders to the secondaries. The head and neck are fawn colour, with streaks of dark brown, the sides of the face being streaked with blackish, and the frontal feathers nearly white.

A slight lengthening of the feathers at the back of the head gives rise to an incipient crest ; and the brown tail is tipped with dull white, and marked with several indistinct darker bars. On the under parts the ground colour is buffish white, with a tinge of fawn on the throat and chest, upon which are a number of dark streaks, disappearing on the abdomen and thighs. The beak is bluish black, with a pale blue base, and the cere and feet are yellow. In the dark phase the plumage differs from that of the adult by the brown colour of the under parts, where the feathers have black shaft-lines.

The booted eagle inhabits all the countries bordering the Mediterranean, extending into Southern Africa and South-Eastern Europe, and also occurring in Gilgit, India, and Ceylon. It is represented in Australia by the nearly allied *N. morphnoides.* In India the species under consideration frequents groves, gardens, and cultivated lands ; and in the neighbourhood of towns and villages inflicts serious loss on the owners of pigeons and poultry. This eagle generally swoops down on its prey—which includes small mammals —while circling in the air, but will occasionally pounce down from a bough. It breeds in Spain and other parts of Southern Europe, as well as in India and Africa ; the nest being apparently always situated in a tree. Nests observed in Spain always contained two eggs ; this seeming to be invariably the number laid by this eagle.

In Spain the booted eagle is one of the most common accipitrines, arriving late in April and remaining till October. "The nests," writes Lord Lilford, "of which we found several, were generally placed on the lowest branches of a tall pine, at the junction of the main trunk, and were built of sticks, but inside invariably contained fresh twigs with the green leaves adhering to them."

The breeding season in Spain lasts from April to June ; and the oval eggs have greyish or dead white grounds, which may or may not be blotched with pale yellowish or reddish brown. The booted eagle is remarkable for its shrill, piercing scream, unlike any cry of any other accipitrine. In Gilgit, where this eagle is found from March till October, it breeds at an elevation of five thousand feet.

TRUE EAGLES

The characters by which the true eagles (*Aquila*) may be distinguished from the hawk-eagles having

already been indicated under the heading of the latter (page 1206), it will suffice to refer to some of the leading features of the present group. The true eagles are all birds of large size, and, with the exception of Steller's sea-eagle, include the largest representatives of the whole family. In all of them the beak is strong and of moderate length, curving gradually from the cere, with a sharp point and nearly straight cutting edges ; while the nostrils may be either oval and oblique or circular.

The wings are large and long, and have the fourth quill rather the longest. The feathered metatarsus is of moderate length ; and its small, reticulated scales extend far on to the toes, which have only a few large plates near the claws ; these features at once serving to distinguish the limb of one of these birds from that of a sea-eagle. The claws are of moderate size and curvature.

Eagles are mostly birds of plain and dark-coloured plumage, with the iris of the eye coloured some tinge of brown. Inferior in courage to falcons, eagles are much superior in this respect to kites and buzzards ; and, while the majority kill their own prey, few will refuse to eat the carcases of such animals as they may find dead, and some feed greedily on carrion.

The range of the genus includes the whole of Europe and Africa and the greater part of Asia, but stops short of the Malay region and does not extend to Australia. In America eagles are found so far south as Mexico.

BOOTED HAWK-EAGLES

GOLDEN EAGLE

From its large size and magnificent appearance, the golden eagle (*Aquila chrysaëtus*) has by almost universal assent been regarded as the "king of birds," although the tendency of modern writers has been rather to detract from the boldness and fierceness of its character, and one naturalist at least has even gone so far as to suggest the accusation of downright cowardice. All, however, who have enjoyed the opportunity of seeing the flight of this splendid bird are in full accord as to its power and majestic character.

The female of the golden eagle usually attains a length of $35\frac{1}{2}$ inches, while the male is some 3 inches less. In the fully adult bird the pointed feathers covering the head and neck are rufous brown, tending to tawny on the back of the neck, but the general colour of the plumage of the upper parts is blackish brown, with light margins to the feathers of the middle of the back and the wing coverts. The primary quills are nearly black, the feathers of the abdomen, thighs, and legs pale brown, and those of the remainder of the under parts blackish brown. The tail is blackish at the tip and browner

THE GOLDEN EAGLE

towards the root, where it is mottled with ashy grey, and is crossed near the middle by one or two greyish bands. The beak is bluish horn-colour, darkening at the tip, the cere yellow, the eye hazel, and the foot yellow, with black claws.

In young birds the whole of the root of the tail is whitish or pure white, becoming gradually mottled with grey and brown towards the middle, and only the terminal third of the feathers is nearly black. The feathers on the back of the neck are also generally less rufous, the general colour of the plumage of the body and wings is darker and more uniform, and the primary quills, except the first three, have much white at their roots. In this state the bird is termed a "ring-tail." There is, however, a great amount of individual variation in the colouring of golden eagles, some old birds, for instance, being almost uniformly dark brown, others golden brown, while in some the upper parts are blackish and the lower parts golden brown. In others, again, the white at the base of the primary quills is retained, and in some cases the quills are banded. Very rarely white individuals have been observed.

In the Old World the range of the golden eagle embraces the whole of Europe and Northern Asia, extending southwards into Northern China and the Himalaya; while a few individuals straggle into peninsular India. The bird is common in Palestine during the winter, is more rarely met with in Arabia, Egypt, and Abyssinia, and breeds in Algeria. It is now definitely settled that the so-called Canadian eagle of North America is identical with the Old World species, its range extending from Alaska to California and Mexico. The young of the American race are peculiarly light-coloured in the region of the head and neck; and many American specimens attain a very large size, even up to 41 inches; but nearly equally large examples have been obtained from Northern India. In the United Kingdom the golden eagle still holds its own to a limited extent in the Scottish Highlands, and probably also breeds in some of the wilder mountainous districts of Ireland.

Generally a rock-haunting and cleft-nesting bird, in many parts of Lapland, Siberia, and the North American prairies the golden eagle frequents more open districts, where it is compelled to nest either in trees or on the steep clay-banks of rivers and streams. Its powerful build and strong, rapid flight render it more than a match for any animal of its size, and its food consequently comprises many of the larger kinds of game, as well as lambs. In Europe these eagles prey largely upon fawns, hares, rabbits, and the various kinds of feathered game, and are consequently formidable enemies to the game-preserver. One has been known to carry off a wounded grouse from in front of the guns of the sportsmen, while another is recorded to have picked up a hare running before hounds.

In pursuing hares and rabbits, two eagles will at times combine their efforts in the chase. An Irish peasant reported that in coursing hares one bird was the active follower, while another remained in reserve at a distance of forty or fifty yards. If the hare, by a sudden turn, freed herself from her most pressing enemy, the second bird instantly took up the chase, and thus prevented the victim from having a moment's respite. That such a sporting bird can deign to feed on carrion seems surprising. Nevertheless, the golden eagle will not only eat such garbage when pressed by hunger, but actually seems to prefer it, and it is owing to this unsavoury taste that these birds are so easily approached and killed.

exclusively confined to that series of feathers; and the tail is ashy grey, marked with indistinct dark bars for the greater part of its extent, but its terminal portion is blackish, with a narrow fulvous border.

The young bird is rather light brown above, with the feathers tipped with buffish fawn, so as to give a spotted appearance to the plumage, and some of the wing coverts have whitish ends; the plumage of the under surface is tawny fulvous, the breast feathers being margined with brown, so as to look as though streaked. The tail is uniform brown, tipped with buffish white. In an intermediate stage the brown edgings of the breast feathers appear to extend to their middles, so that the whole plumage becomes brown, and it is when in this state that the bird is so often mistaken for the golden eagle. At all ages the cere and feet are pale yellow, while the beak is bluish and the eye brownish yellow.

The imperial eagle is mainly a southern bird, occurring in South-Eastern and rarely Central Europe, whence it ranges through Palestine and the adjacent countries to India and China. In Northern Africa it is replaced by Adalbert's eagle (*A. adalberti*), which also occurs in Spain, and differs by the white patch on the wing extending on to the carpal plumes. In the northern part of India the imperial eagle regularly breeds in the Himalaya, but the majority of the specimens seen in the plains of India are winter visitors, although a few remain to nest in the Upper Punjab. In Southern India the species is rare, although it is not uncommon in the high tablelands of the peninsula.

In India, according to Dr. Jerdon, this eagle "prefers the neighbourhood of hills, and the bare open country, or thin and low jungle. It may frequently be seen seated on the ground, or on a stone on the top of a low hill, till an hour after sunrise, when it rises, apparently unwillingly, and takes a cast after game at no great elevation, hunting slowly over the bushy valleys and ravines, and occasionally over cultivated ground. If unsuccessful in its search, it reseats itself, and after an interval again takes wing, and this time soars to a great height, circling slowly in the air, and traversing a large extent of country. It pounces on hares, florikans, rats, lizards, and various other mammals and birds, and in default of these will eat carrion. I have several times seen one captured in a net by a portion of a carcase of a sheep being put down as a bait. When it does condescend to partake of carrion, it allows no other bird to approach till it has satisfied its hunger."

In Palestine this splendid bird is abundant, and may be said, in summer at least, to replace the golden eagle of Europe. "There is a beauty and majesty in its movements," writes Canon Tristram, "and in its great fearlessness of man, when in search of food, which at once attracts one; while the very

distinct white scapulars and the light head show conspicuously when on the wing. Unlike the golden eagle, it was as common at one time of the year as another, though we never took a nest."

This account gives an idea that the imperial eagle is a noble and courageous bird endowed with considerable fierceness. The experience of naturalists in India does not, however, countenance the attribution of these qualities, although it has been humorously suggested that its deficiencies in these respects may be due to the enervating nature of the climate. Mr. A. O. Hume writes that "I have driven the female off hard-set eggs, and plundered the nest before the eyes of the pair, without either flapping a pinion, even to defend what even a little shrike will swoop at once to save. I have seen a couple of crows thrash one of them soundly; and, whether it be that familiarity breeds contempt, I am bound to record that, after having seen many hundreds, and shot, I daresay, a good hundred myself, I look upon the *Königs-adler* as no better than a great hulking kite." Contrary to the opinion of Dr. Jerdon, the same writer adds that in his experience this eagle is generally a foul feeder.

The nest appears to be always situated in a tree, and is of large size; one taken in a pollard-tree on the Danube having a circumference of about fifteen feet, and being lined with wool. The eggs are very variable in size; and have a greyish white ground, usually unspotted, but sometimes marked with pale brown, or more rarely purplish brown. In the Punjab the usual laying time is February and March, but it may be

IMPERIAL EAGLE

prolonged for another month ; the nest referred to above from the Danubian provinces was taken at the end of April.

SPOTTED EAGLE

The spotted eagle (*A. maculata*) of Central Europe, which is selected as an example of species much smaller than the golden eagle, of which it is only about one-third the size, is a bird which has received more than the usual liberal allowance of scientific names. The total length of the adult female is 25 inches, and that of the male only half an inch less. The general colour of the adult is liver-brown on the upper parts, with the head somewhat lighter, and its upper feathers lanceolate. The wing coverts are somewhat paler, with simple whitey brown margins, and the quills blackish, shaded with ashy on the primaries, and browner on the secondaries. The tail feathers are lighter than the quills, with their inner webs bronzy, and the tips inclining to tawny ; the under tail coverts being earthy brown with lighter tips, and the lower surface of the tail uniform brown. The beak is bluish horn colour, the cere yellow, the eye hazel, and the toes yellow with black claws.

In the young bird the general colour is a darker chocolate brown, the tips of the wing coverts, inner secondaries, upper tail coverts, and tail feathers being marked with somewhat crescentic spots of a pale wood-brown ; the cheeks and under surface pale brown, becoming lighter, with a tinge of tawny on the under tail coverts ; some of the chest feathers are rather darker brown, with tawny brown centres, and certain of the under wing coverts have light tips. It is, of course, only in the immature and intermediate stages of plumage that the name "spotted eagle" is strictly applicable to the bird.

The ordinary form of the spotted eagle inhabits Central Europe, ranging into Northern Germany, Pomerania, and Poland, and migrating during the winter into Egypt and other parts of Northern Africa. In Southern and Western Europe it is rare. Eastwards it doubtless extends into Palestine, and it is represented in India by a variety distinguished by the general presence of small white spots on the lesser wing coverts.

There is also a bigger race, or species, known as the larger spotted eagle (*A. clanga*), attaining a length of 26½ inches in the female. This race is characteristic of South-Eastern Europe, being seldom found in Poland, Pomerania, and Germany, but ranging eastwards into Siberia. During their migrations specimens of the spotted eagle are occasionally blown on to the English coasts, and an immature example in an exhausted condition was captured at Colchester in November, 1891. In general appearance the adult of this species is very similar to the golden eagle in miniature. It is

SPOTTED EAGLES

especially abundant in Pomerania, where, as in most parts of Europe, it frequents wooded districts, sometimes building in low blackthorn bushes, or even on the ground itself.

In India this eagle is always found either in the neighbourhood of swamps or where the country has been irrigated ; and on one occasion there was a sudden immigration of a number of these birds into a district where irrigation works had been recently opened. This eagle generally sits in a slouching kite-like fashion across a branch, halfway up a tree ; whereas imperial and tawny eagles generally sit bolt upright at the very top of a tree, and consequently cannot be seen by an observer immediately beneath. The spotted eagle commonly nests in trees.

OTHER SPECIES

Other species of the genus are the tawny eagle (*A. rapax*) of Africa, distinguished by the tawny hue of the immature plumage ; the slightly smaller but closely allied Indian tawny eagle (*A. vindhiana*) ; the small brown Wahlberg's eagle (*A. wahlbergi*) of Africa, distinguished by a slight occipital crest ; and the remarkable South African vulturine eagle (*A. verreauxi*), which differs from all the rest in having the lower part of the back and rump white, the rest of the plumage being black. Remains of extinct eagles, some of which probably belong to *Nisaëtus*, while others may pertain to *Aquila*, occur in the Miocene strata of France. The gigantic *Harpagornis*, from the superficial deposits of New Zealand, was by far the largest representative of the whole family.

WEDGE-TAILED EAGLE

The wedge-tailed eagle (*Uroaëtus audax*) of Australia is a large species generically separated from the true eagles by its regularly graduated, wedge-shaped tail, in which, when closed, the middle pair of feathers is far longer than the outer ones ; whereas in the true eagles the difference in the length of the corresponding feathers is inappreciable.

This fine eagle attains a total length of 38 inches in the male, and has the general colour of the plumage black, with yellow cere and feet. In young birds the general colour is rufous tawny. These birds are found both in the forests and on the open plains of Australia and Tasmania, frequently soaring at a great height in circles, with no apparent movement of the wings. The large nest is invariably placed in the fork of a gum-tree, sometimes at no great height from the ground. Carrion appears to be the chief food of these eagles.

MONKEY-EATING EAGLE

The forests of the Philippines are the home of a very fine eagle (*Pithecophaga jefferyi*), characterised by the great depth and compression of the beak, which is

SPOTTED, TAWNY, MONKEY-EATING, AND HARPY EAGLES

SPOTTED EAGLE

TAWNY EAGLE

MONKEY-EATING EAGLE

HARPY EAGLE

unlike that of any other eagle, and comparable in some degree to that of the great black cockatoo. This bird is very considerably larger than the under-mentioned harpy, and has a much bigger and heavier skull.

The head is crested, and the general colour of the plumage brown; with the head, neck, under parts and the tips of many of the upper feathers buff. The whole metatarsus and foot are covered with reticulated scales, and yellow in colour, while the cere is blue. This eagle lives high up in the forest trees, and, according to native reports, feeds mainly on macaque monkeys (*Macacus cynomolgus*), although in inhabited districts making raids on poultry-yards.

HARPY EAGLES

The accipitrines now to be considered include the harpy eagles, buzzards, and their kin, forming the subfamily *Buteoninæ*. While agreeing with all the fore-

HARPY EAGLE

going types in having the tibia considerably longer than the metatarsus, they differ in that the posterior aspect of the metatarsal segment of the leg is covered with large transverse plates instead of small reticulate scales. The largest members of this subfamily are the magnificent harpy eagles, which, while rivalling the true eagles in size and strength, have the plated metatarsus of the buzzards, and may be easily recognised by their long crests of feathers. They are exclusively American, and mainly confined to South and Central America, although one species ranges into Mexico.

Represented by four well-defined species, the harpies are referred to three genera.

The Guiana harpy eagle (*Morphnus guianensis*) is readily characterised by the length of its tail, which is fully four times as long as the metatarsus. The range of this species includes Amazonia and Guiana as well as Panama. The crowned harpy (*Harpyhaliaëtus coronatus*), which has a more extensive distribution, extending from Northern Patagonia and Chile to Central America, differs by the much shorter tail, of which the length is less than thrice that of the metatarsus. Both these species agree in that the interval between the summit of the nostril and the upper line of the beak is less than the length of the nostril; whereas in the true harpy (*Thrasaëtus harpyia*), ranging from Bolivia and Paraguay to Mexico, the corresponding interval is greater than the length of the nostril.

The largest of the three is the last-named species, of which the total length is 38 inches. The Guiana species occupies a middle position in point of size, measuring 36 inches in length. Like the others, it has the greater portion of the metatarsus naked, and a powerful and strongly-curved beak. In this species the crest is very long and pointed, but varies considerably according to the age of the bird. In the immature stage the head, neck, breast, abdomen, rump, and thighs are white, faintly spotted here and there with yellow; the feathers of the back, shoulders, and wing coverts mottled with reddish grey; the quills blackish brown, with small, reddish grey oblique bars; and the tail similarly coloured, but with the bars horizontal. The adult is much darker, having the head and throat greyish brown, most of the upper parts dark blackish brown shaded and mottled with ashy, the upper tail coverts with white tips and irregular white barrings, the chest dark-coloured, and the remainder of the under parts white. The dark tail is tipped with whitish brown and crossed with three pale bars, above which are some whitish markings.

Little is known of the mode of life of this handsome bird, which occurs both in the forests near the coasts, and the wooded districts of the plains, but more commonly on the banks of the rivers. During its periods of repose this eagle will sit for hours on the summit of some dead tree, uttering at intervals its peculiarly loud and harsh cry. Its prey comprises mammals and birds, and its nest is said to be generally built in a hollow tree. More is known concerning the true harpy eagle, the most powerful bird of prey in North America, which breeds in Southern Mexico, and thence to Brazil and Bolivia.

Known to the Spaniards as the king eagle, and to the Aztecs as the winged wolf, the harpy attacks and kills animals of more than thrice its own size and weight; turkeys, fawns, foxes, badgers, peccaries, sloths, and monkeys alike falling victims to this fell destroyer. In regions which it frequents the harpy may be seen sailing in the early morning high up in the clear sky, or wheeling in circles over the forests; while from

THE BUZZARD

in the wooded parts of the country. It belongs to a large group of the genus in which the tail is marked by more or less complete dark transverse bars, the number of such bars in this species varying from ten to thirteen.

The general colour of the plumage is clear dark brown, becoming paler on the crown of the head and cheeks and much darker on the primary quills; but there is such an extraordinary amount of individual variation in respect of colour that scarcely any two birds can be found precisely alike. The under parts are, however, generally yellowish white, with the feathers more or less streaked with brown; but the flanks and thighs are of a more uniformly brown hue. The under wing coverts are also light-coloured, and the under tail coverts white; while the tail, which is brown above and greyish white below, is barred on both aspects.

Some buzzards are, however, brown all over; while in others the throat and chest are brown, and, as well as the thighs, are as dark as the upper surface, only the remainder of the under parts being light-coloured. The colour of the eyes varies from dark hazel to light brownish yellow; the legs and toes are yellow, and the claws black. White specimens are occasionally met with. The length of the male is about 22 inches, and that of the female about an inch more.

The buzzard is distributed over the greater part of Europe, where it is in many districts comparatively abundant. In Northern Africa and Eastern Europe it is, however, replaced by the nearly-allied desert-buzzard (*B. desertorum*), which also ranges into India; while in Japan and China its place is occupied by *B. plumipes*, distinguished by the greater extent to which the metatarsus is feathered. This species also ranges

March to June the tree-tops resound with the loud cries of its young. The nest may be situated either in a lofty tree or on the ledge of a cliff.

All the three genera above mentioned are characterised by the shortness of the interval between the tips of the primary and secondary quills, which is less than the length of the metatarsus. Three other genera from South and Central America, viz. *Urubitinga*, *Buteogallus*, and *Busarellus*, comprise much smaller buzzard-like birds, agreeing with the harpies in the above-mentioned character, but differing by the absence of crests. The last two genera have only a single species each; but there are several kinds of urubitingas, two of which range northwards into the south of Mexico.

BUZZARDS

"The buzzard," writes Gilbert White, "is a dastardly bird, and beaten not only by the raven, but even by the carrion-crow"; and no better description could be given of the pusillanimous disposition of the birds of the genus *Buteo*. The buzzards are the typical representatives of the subfamily under consideration, and belong to that section in which the interval between the tips of the primary and secondary quills equals or exceeds the length of the metatarsus. They are specially characterised by the squared tail being of considerable length, and extending markedly below the closed wings; and also by the long oval nostrils, devoid of any central tubercle, and the bare metatarsus. The beak is rather small and weak; the wings have the fourth quill the longest, and the first four deeply notched on their inner margins; the naked metatarsus is of moderate length and covered with scales and scutes; and the toes are short, with strong claws.

Buzzards are represented by nearly twenty species, and have an almost world-wide distribution, although unknown in the Indo-Malay region, as well as in Oceania and Australasia. The typical, or European, buzzard (*B. vulgaris*) is one of the species of British hawks which has suffered the least from the persecution of gamekeepers, and may still not infrequently be seen

GUIANAN HARPY EAGLE

through the Himalaya to Gilgit, and occurs occasionally in India. America possesses another closely allied species in Swainson's buzzard (*B. swainsoni*), ranging over the western part of that continent, and wandering in winter to Central and South America ; while there are several other New World kinds, such as the so-called red-shouldered hawk (*B. lineatus*).

In searching for their prey, which consists mainly of small mammals, birds, and reptiles, buzzards fly slowly and sluggishly ; and their cowardly disposition, to which allusion has already been made, is exhibited by their generally selecting young or feeble animals for victims. At times, however, and especially in the breeding season, these birds will soar in circles high in the air, occasionally uttering their shrill and melancholy whistle-like cry. After feeding, they usually take up their stations on trees, from which, if disturbed, they fly in what appears to be a frightened manner. In England, the nest is usually in a tree, but in the more mountainous districts of Scotland preference is given to rocks. The eggs, usually two or three, but occasionally four in number, much resemble those of the red kite.

In America Swainson's buzzard has been observed nesting in harmonious association with other birds, especially Arkansas kingbirds and shrikes ; the nests of these birds being sometimes only a few inches below those of the buzzards. Fossil remains of the buzzard have been found in caverns in Devonshire and Westmoreland.

ROUGH-LEGGED BUZZARDS

Although the rough-legged buzzards (*Archibuteo*), of which there are few species, differ from typical buzzards merely in having the metatarsus feathered right down to the toes, it is convenient to distinguish them by a separate generic name. Their range includes Central and Northern Europe, Northern Asia, and the whole of North America ; the European species sometimes straggling as far as South Africa.

The European rough-legged buzzard (*A. lagopus*) is a bird somewhat larger than the buzzard, and not exhibiting quite so much individual variation in colour as the latter. Ranging over northern and central Europe and Siberia, this buzzard is met with yearly in the British Isles, where it sometimes appears in considerable numbers, more especially in autumn and winter. In the case of such a variable bird it will be unnecessary to give any description of the colouring, beyond stating that the species is particularly characterised by the brown colour of the markings on the flanks and thighs ; and by the ground colour of the head, throat, and chest being white or buffish white, with buff streaks.

In North America this species is replaced by St. John's buzzard (*A. sancti-johannis*), distinguished by its generally darker colour and the larger amount of black on the lower surface. The ferruginous buzzard (*A. ferrugineus*) of south-western North America differs by the white flanks and the chestnut fawn of the flanks. A fourth species (*A. strophiatus*), characterised by its uniformly brown head, neck, and chest, inhabits Nepal and Tibet.

The habits of the rough-legged buzzards are so generally similar to those of the members of the genus *Buteo*, that they require but brief notice. The individuals of the European species visiting Britain prefer, however, open districts, more especially where rabbits are abundant ; those rodents, together with water-fowl, constituting a large proportion of their food. The flight of the rough-legged buzzard is slow but smooth, and, except during the periods of migration, not of long continuance. The nest, which is made rather late in the season, is generally placed in a high tree, and may contain from three to five eggs, which are subject to great variation in form, size, and coloration.

Breeding commonly in the higher parts of Norway and Sweden, the rough-legged buzzard ranges as far polewards as the North Cape, and at times nests in the British Isles. During the breeding season it utters a kind of wailing cry, which has been compared to the mew of a cat. America possesses four other genera of buzzard-like hawks, of which only *Asturina* possesses more than two species ; and a fifth genus (*Urospizias*), with one species, is confined to Australia. It should be added that it has been proposed, on account of the feathered metatarsus, to remove the rough-legged buzzards from association with the typical buzzards, and place them among the eagles ; but this seems to be giving too much importance to a minor character.

SPARROW-HAWKS

With the possible exception of some of the American forms just alluded to, the accipitrines hitherto described

ROUGH-LEGGED BUZZARDS

have the metatarsus considerably shorter than the tibia. These are followed by a group of long-legged hawks characterised by the great elongation of the metatarsus, which is approximately or quite equal in this respect to the tibia. This group, as represented by the sparrow-hawks (*Accipiter*), goshawks, and harriers, constitutes the subfamily *Accipitrinæ*. For its size the European sparrow-hawk is one of the most dashing and rapacious of all the accipitrines, although its depradations are too frequently attributed to the harmless kestrel. In common with its congeners, the sparrow-hawk agrees with the great majority of the subfamily in having the sides of the face completely feathered,

SPARROW-HAWK

and the lores furnished with bristles, while it resembles a smaller number of genera in the absence of reticulated scales on the back of the metatarsus.

Sparrow-hawks may be distinguished from all their allies by the great length of the third toe, which (exclusive of the claw) is more than double the length of the ridge of the beak, measured from the front edge of the cere. The short beak curves regularly from the base, and has a distinct festoon in the upper cutting-edge, while the nostrils are oval. The wings are short, not reaching within a long distance of the end of the tail, and have the fourth and fifth quills nearly equal and longer than the others. The long metatarsus is smooth, and covered with greave-like plates, and the toes are long and slender, with sharp, curved claws. There are more than twenty species of sparrow-hawks distributed over the whole globe, with the exception of Oceania, the west of Australia, and New Guinea. A few are rather larger than the European species, while many are considerably smaller.

EUROPEAN SPARROW-HAWK

The typical sparrow-hawk (*A. nisus*) is still an abundant bird in the wooded districts of England, and the female, the only accipitrine which inflicts much damage upon game preserves. It belongs to a group of the genus characterised by the banded thighs, the absence of a collar round the neck, and the number of bars on the tail not exceeding five. In the adult male the plumage of the upper parts, with the exception of a white spot on the nape of the neck, is dark bluish

grey, the cheeks, chin, and under parts are rufous, barred with bands of dark rufous brown, narrower than the intervening light spaces; and the tail is greyish brown, with from three to five dark bands. The beak is blue, and the iris orange; the legs and toes are yellow, and the claws black. The total length is about 13 inches. The female is some $2\frac{1}{2}$ inches longer than the male, and differs by the general colour of the upper parts (except the white spot on the nape) being brown, with many of the feathers white at the base, and the primaries and tail lighter than the rest; the under parts being greyish white barred with brown.

This species is distributed over the whole of Europe and Northern Asia, and extends during the winter into the north of Africa, India, and China. In certain parts of Germany, Switzerland, and France some individuals are found differing by their superior size and certain peculiarities in colouring. The sparrow-hawk is a frequenter of wooded districts, where it may always be distinguished from the kestrel, when on the wing, by its bold, dashing flight. Its prey includes the smaller mammals and birds; and while young pheasants and partridges frequently fall victims to its swoop, the chickens in a farmyard are by no means secure from its rapaciousness. It is during the breeding season that this hawk displays the greatest boldness and most frequently ventures into the farmyard; such visits being paid as much for the purpose of capturing sparrows and other small birds as for preying on chickens.

The sparrow-hawk breeds from the extreme north of Europe as far south as the Himalaya; and although generally constructing a nest of its own, not infrequently takes possession of that of a crow or some other bird. The eggs, four or five in number, are remarkable for the beauty of their colouring, being generally blotched with large patches of brownish crimson on a pale ground, and often having the dark markings collected on certain parts of the shell, leaving the rest bare.

In Europe the sparrow-hawk used to be extensively employed in hawking, and was flown against blackbirds, thrushes, quails, landrails, partridges, and the like. Quail-hawking with this bird is still largely pursued in Hungary and the Danubian provinces; where it is considered no uncommon feat for a sparrow-hawk to kill from seventy to eighty quail in a day.

In India both this species and the smaller besra hawk (*A. virgatus*)—distinguished by its uniformly coloured thighs—are largely trained. Both these kinds of hawks are commonly flown in India at sand-grouse and the cream-coloured courser.

In North America the sparrow-hawk is represented by two nearly allied species known as the sharp-shinned hawk (*A. fuscus*, or *velox*), and Cooper's hawk (*A. cooperi*), in both of which the rufous bars on the under surface are wider than the intervening spaces. While the former is somewhat smaller than the sparrow-hawk, the latter is as much larger.

Mr. E. H. Forbush writes as follows of the breeding habits of the sharp-shinned hawk: "From April until early June, according to the latitude, the wooing of the hawks begins. Perched in an exposed position, the male issues his shrillest call notes, moving about from place to place until the female responds. The ardent courtship is soon over, and the happy pair fly away in company to select a suitable nesting place.

Nest-building occupies about one week. The nest is usually placed rather high in an evergreen tree, in some sequestered locality. More rarely, it is located in a deciduous tree, in a hollow tree, or on some lofty ledge or cliff. Sometimes an old crow's nest or a squirrel's nest is utilised as a basis upon which to construct the home. In this case the nest is a large, conspicuous structure; but, ordinarily, it is not very noticeable, and in some cases is well concealed by the foliage. It usually consists of a platform of sticks, resting on a whorl of branches and fixed against the trunk of the tree. Dry grasses and strips of bark are usually placed upon this foundation and interwoven to form the nest-lining. Some nests are less skilfully formed and are unlined.

"The eggs vary in number from three to five, and are pale white, greenish or bluish white, very heavily blotched, spotted, and marked with light brown, dark brown, drab, fawn, and lavender. These markings often form a ring about some part of the egg. Both sexes join in incubation, and in the care of the young which, when first hatched, are covered with soft white down.

"The young are confined to the nest for about four weeks. Then they begin to climb and flutter about among the branches; but, if undisturbed, they remain in the vicinity of the nest for several weeks longer, where they are still fed by the parents. The woods now resound with their shrill, squealing cries. Having finally strengthened their wings by exercise among the tree-tops, they attempt longer flights, and soon leave their home for ever."

GOSHAWKS

The European goshawk, or goose-hawk (*Astur palumbarius*), is the type of a large genus differing from the last by the length of the ridge of the beak from in front of the cere exceeding half the length of the third toe without the claw; and further distinguished

SPARROW-HAWKS

by the fourth toe being about equal in length to the second, without the claw; by the overhanging tufts of feathers on the thighs, and the absence of any tubercle in the bony nostrils. The beak is short, with a distinct festoon in its cutting edge, the short wings

THE GOSHAWK

generally have the fourth quill the longest, the metatarsus usually has large scutes in front, and the toes are of only moderate length. Goshawks have an almost cosmopolitan distribution, although they are unknown in part of Oceania and the southern portion of South America. While the more typical forms are equal in size to the largest falcons, the smaller kinds are not larger than sparrow-hawks; and so closely are goshawks and sparrow-hawks thus connected, that some naturalists unite the two genera.

In general appearance the European goshawk is indeed, very like a large sparrow-hawk; having, in the male, the plumage of the upper parts deep bluish grey, darker on the head and neck, with a light band above the eye, while beneath, it is white transversely barred with greyish brown, and the tail bearing four dark bars and a white tip. In the female the upper plumage has a browner tinge, and the young bird is brown above, with five dark bars on the tail. The colour of the beak, cere, and limbs is nearly the same as in the sparrow-hawk. The male attains a length of 19½, and the female of 23 inches. The goshawk has a range nearly the same as that of the sparrow-hawk, although it does not appear to descend from the Himalaya to the plains of India.

In North America it is replaced by the American goshawk (*A. atricapillus*), distinguished by its slightly superior size, and by the plumage of the under parts being merely flecked with ashy grey, instead of barred. Although rare in Britain, the goshawk is common in Germany and other parts of the Continent, breeding as far north as Lapland. Instead of "stooping" to its quarry, after the manner of the falcons, the goshawk flies along after it, and takes by the mode technically known as "raking." It is flown at the larger game-birds, as well as at hares and rabbits; and

THE GOSHAWK

will not infrequently follow its prey for some distance in covert. The nest, which is usually built in a tall tree on the outskirts of a wood or forest, may contain from three to four eggs. These may be either unspotted white, or more or less streaked with olive, or flecked with reddish brown.

WHISTLING HAWKS

Nearly allied to the goshawks is a group (*Melierax*) of African species characterised by the possession of a more uneful voice than hawks. By observers the note of these birds is described as a mellow piping whistle; and, accordingly, it seems better that they should be designated whistling hawks, rather than " chanting goshawks," as they were originally termed, when somewhat exaggerated notions obtained as to the extent of their vocal powers.

These hawks differ from goshawks by the presence of a tubercle in the nostrils, situated near the upper margin, and are distinguished from the allied South American genus *Parabuteo* by the small extent to which the metatarsus is feathered, as well as by the whole of the outer side of that segment of the leg being covered with reticulate scales.

The many-zoned hawk (*M. polyzonus*) is a large and handsomely-coloured bird inhabiting North-Eastern Africa,

and ranging thence across the continent to Senegambia. The males measure $20\frac{1}{2}$ inches, and the females 21 inches in length. Like all the species except one, the general colour of the upper parts is pearly grey, the chest ashy grey, and the abdomen white barred with a number of very fine greyish black bands, so as to present a kind of speckled appearance.

The species is particularly characterised by the absence of bars on the middle tail feathers, and the white upper tail coverts barred with slaty grey. The beak is blackish, with a vermilion base, the eye pale brown, and the legs, feet, and cere vermilion.

A nearly allied species is the South African whistling hawk (*M. canorus*); but the much smaller and widely distributed black whistling hawk (*M. niger*) differs from all the others by its sable plumage, in striking contrast to which stands out the brilliant red of the iris, cere, base of the bill, and feet and legs.

In Abyssinia the many-zoned species is found at considerable elevations above the sea, where it is usually to be seen perched on a tree, although occasionally on the ground. Its food consists of reptiles and insects, and its flight is rather slow, somewhat like that of a buzzard, and seldom prolonged for any great distance.

HARRIER HAWKS

Omitting detailed mention of the tropical American genera *Parabuteo* and *Geranospizias*, and the West African *Urotriorchis* (with a single species), the next on the list are the American harrier-hawks, and the cosmopolitan harriers; both of which are distinguished from all the foregoing types by having an imperfect disc of feathers round the eyes—thus recalling the owls—and also by the hind aspect of the metatarsus being covered with reticulate scales, instead of large plates.

With regard to the harrier hawks (*Micrastur*), of which there are several species, ranging from Southern Mexico over the greater part of South America, it will suffice to state that they are distinguished by having circular nostrils with a bony excrescence, and form an intermediate step between the goshawks and the harriers, having the heavy build of the former, and the facial discs of the latter.

HARRIERS

The harriers (*Circus*), of which there are some eighteen species, are long-winged and slender-built birds, remarkable for the great diversity existing in most cases

MANY-ZONED HAWK

between the plumage of the two sexes, and deriving their name from their harrying propensities. The nostrils differ from those of the harrier-hawks in being oval, and devoid of any bony excrescence, and are partly concealed by the radiating feathers of the lores.

The beak is small, curving regularly from the base, with only a slight festoon in its upper cutting edge. The long wings have the first quill very short, and the third and fourth the longest, and the tail is of considerable length, and rounded. In length the metatarsus is relatively greater than in any other members of the family; the toes are somewhat short, and not very unequal in length, and the claws very sharp and but slightly curved.

Harriers are distributed over the greater part of the globe, occurring in such widely distant countries as New Zealand and Great Britain although absent from several regions, such as Malaya, Persia, and Arabia, where they might reasonably have been expected to occur.

Of the numerous species of the genus, no less than three inhabit the British Islands, where, however, the drainage of the fenlands has reduced their numbers to a very considerable extent, more especially in the case of the marsh-harrier.

In habits all harriers are very similar, although some, like the species last named, prefer low marshy spots, where they may be seen with their heavy, flapping wings slowly skimming over the reeds, while others, like the hen-harrier, also frequent the drier hillsides. They all roost on or near the ground, and, when not hunting, may be seen perched on some low bough, post, or hillock. Harriers are in the habit of hunting their prey to a great extent in the morning and evening, and feed on small birds, mammals, and reptiles; the marsh-haunting species supplementing this diet largely with frogs and fish, while some eat grasshoppers and other large insects. The nest is usually placed on the ground, and, in the European species at least, the eggs (three or four in number) are nearly uniform pale bluish or yellowish green.

In addition to their facial discs and crepuscular habits, harriers show another resemblance to owls in their habit of laying their eggs at intervals, so that both eggs and nestlings may be taken from the same nest. In hunting, harriers frequently beat and quarter their ground almost with the regularity of spaniels.

THE HEN-HARRIER

So different in appearance are the males and females of the hen-harrier (*C. cyaneus*) that they were long regarded as distinct—the female

NAKED-CHEEKED HAWK

being termed the ringtail—and it was not till Colonel Montagu brought up a brood from the nest that their specific unity was established. In the adult male the general colour of the plumage is bluish grey above, with the throat and chest nearly similar; while the rest of the under parts, inclusive of the thighs as well as the upper tail coverts, are pure white. On the upper surface of the tail the two middle pairs of feathers are uniform grey, and the others more or less indistinctly barred.

On the other hand, in the female, or ringtail, the prevailing hue of the upper parts is brown, and the head is surrounded by a distinct ruff of mingled white and brown feathers; many of the feathers, especially the wing coverts, having lighter margins. Below, the ground colour is reddish buff, each feather having a larger or smaller dark brown central mark, and a still darker shaft. The tail is greyish brown, with a white tip, and all the feathers banded with darker brown. In both sexes the legs and toes are yellow, with black claws, but the cere is a more greenish yellow in the female than in the male. The young male resembles the female in colour, but may be distinguished by its relatively shorter wing.

In length the male measures about 21 and the female 22 inches. This harrier is found throughout Europe and Siberia; extending in winter into the north-east of Africa, Northern India, and China. In Britain the hen-harrier seems always to have been the rarest species, but the effects of drainage have not told so severely upon its numbers as on those of the marsh-harrier.

AMERICAN HARRIER

The American harrier (*C. hudsonianus*), commonly known as the marsh-hawk, replaces the hen-harrier in North America, and is distinguished by the more decided grey of the upper parts and throat, as well as by some flecks of reddish brown on the white of the under surface in the male; the naked portion of the metatarsus is also slightly longer.

THE HEN-HARRIER

MONTAGU'S AND PALE-CHESTED
HARRIERS

PALE-CHESTED HARRIER

The pale-chested harrier (*C. macrurus*), is a slightly smaller bird than either of the two last, from both of which it may be at once distinguished by the white upper tail coverts being banded with grey. The uniformly coloured middle tail feathers are distinctive of the males of this group of species. The pale harrier, although unknown in Britain, is pretty generally distributed over Europe so far north as the 60th parallel, and is also found over the great part of Africa, exclusive of the forest regions of the west coast, and eastwards ranges into India, Burma, and China.

MONTAGU'S HARRIER

The harrier (*C. pygargus*) which takes its popular name from the distinguished ornithologist Colonel Montagu, by whom it was first recognised as a distinct species, and of which a male is represented in the upper figure of the illustration, differs from the species referred to above by the white thighs of the male being flecked with reddish brown; but it may be still more readily recognised by the three dark bands crossing the secondaries, one of which is visible when the wings are closed. The middle tail feathers are uniform bluish grey, and the lateral ones white with reddish orange bars; the under parts, behind the chest, being coloured like the latter. The general colour of the female is brown of various shades. Montagu's harrier is lighter and more slenderly built than the hen-harrier, and appears to have been the most common of the British species. Its distribution is almost identical with that of the pale harrier.

MARSH-HARRIER

The largest and most powerful of all the three British species is the marsh-harrier, or moor-buzzard (*C. æruginosus*), in which the female measures 23 inches in length. In this species the two sexes are nearly alike at all ages, the prevailing colour of the plumage of the upper parts being brown. It may be recognised by the nearly uniform rufous thighs and the plain bluish grey tail of the adult; young birds having the tail brown, with some slight rufous mottlings, and lacking the blue grey found on the secondaries of the old birds.

The distribution of the marsh-harrier is likewise very similar to that of the two preceding species; this bird ranging from Britain to Japan, and from Siberia to South Africa and India. The draining of the fens and other of its haunts has rendered it a comparatively rare bird in England at the present time.

BARE-CHEEKED HAWKS

Resembling the whistling hawks in the barred plumage of the under parts, the bare-cheeked hawks of Africa and Madagascar differ from all the other members of the subfamily in having the region of the mouth and the sides of the face completely devoid of feathers.

The African species (*Polyboroides typicus*) measures $27\frac{1}{2}$ inches in the female and 2 inches in the male. Its general colour above is dark grey, this tint extending round the neck to occupy the throat and chest, but the remainder of the under parts is marked with rather broad alternating bands of black and white. The head is crested, and the black tail has a narrow white tip, and a broadish band of white at a distance of about one-third from the end.

This species has a wide range in Africa, but is replaced in Madagascar by *P. radiatus*, distinguished by its silvergrey colour above, and the finer banding of the under parts. These birds prey chiefly upon lizards, snakes, and frogs, and possess the unique peculiarity of being able to move the ankle joint forwards as well as backwards, thus giving an extraordinary range of movement to the lower part of the leg, which is said to be of the greatest advantage in extracting their reptilian prey from the crannies where they lie concealed.

Like the harpy eagles, these hawks often seek for reptiles along the line of jungle fires, and also frequent marshes and swamps in search of frogs. The toes are remarkable for their extreme lateral compression, which is said to be also a feature admirably adapted for capturing the reptiles on which these birds prey. In addition to reptiles, these hawks also kill and eat small birds and mammals, especially such of the latter as, like shrew-mice, frequent moist localities.

CARACARAS

The remaining members of the hawk family are mainly South American, and constitute by themselves the subfamily *Polyborinæ*. These birds, which are commonly designated caracaras, and take their name from the cry of their Brazilian representatives, differ not only in general appearance from more typical hawks, but likewise in their mode of life. In the first place, whereas in all other members of the family the third and fourth toes alone are connected together at their bases by a small web, in the caracaras both the second and fourth toes are so connected with the middle one. They are all long-legged birds, with the metatarsus naked; the beak is generally characterised by its depth and compression, and there is more or less naked skin on the sides of the face.

In their general habits caracaras are chiefly terrestrial, and nest on the ground; and as they run well and rapidly, they recall in these respects the game-birds. Mr. W. H. Hudson remarks that they are " carrion eaters, also killers on their own account, and, like wild dogs, sometimes hunt in packs, which gives them an advantage. They are the unfailing attendants of all flesh-hunters, human or feline, and also furiously pursue and persecute all eagles and true vultures that venture on the pampas." Formerly the caracaras were considered to be allied to the secretary-bird, but their true affinities are nearer to the harriers, and when on the wing the smaller species present a striking resemblance to the latter.

BRAZILIAN CARACARA

The caracaras may be divided into two genera, according to the form of the nostrils. The largest member of the group is the Brazilian caracara, known in the Argentine as the carancha (*Polyborus tharus*), and belonging to the genus with oval nostrils. This fine bird, which ranges over the whole of South America, may be compared in size to a small eagle, attaining a

BRAZILIAN CARACARA

PALE VARIETY OF BRAZILIAN CARACARA

length of fully 26 inches. Its head is crested, and the ground colour of the upper parts deep blackish brown; the feathers of the back and wing coverts being marked with narrow whitish cross-bars. The tail is mostly buffish white, with darker bars; and the sides of the head and under parts are of the same ground colour, marked, except on the head and throat, with narrow black bars. The large beak is pale blue, the cere and naked portion of the face are normally carmine red, and the legs and feet yellow. Under certain conditions the naked portions of the face may, however, assume a pale colour.

In Northern South America, as well as in Central America and Southern North America, together with Cuba and Trinidad, there occurs the rather smaller Audubon's caracara (*P. cheriway*); and a third species (*P. lutosus*) characterises the island of Guadeloupe. Although largely carrion eaters, these birds will attack living prey, the Brazilian species sometimes venturing to encounter the skunk. In North America they generally nest in cabbage-palms.

In the North American species of *Polyborus* the eggs are generally two or three in number, and have a pale ground colour, almost concealed by dark blotchings.

FALKLAND ISLAND CARACARA

The Falkland Island caracara (*Ibycter australis*) may be taken as a well-known example of the second genus, in which the nostrils are circular, and most of the species of considerably smaller dimensions than the last. This bird, which attains a total length of 25 inches, has the plumage of a general black hue, but the nape and neck are marked with streaks of white, and there are also similar white markings on the throat and chest, passing on the abdomen into minute spots. The quills are dark brown, with lighter tips, and the black tail has a broad white band at the end. The feathers on the inner surfaces of the thighs are tawny, the cere and feet yellow, the greater part of the beak yellowish, and the eye brown.

This species is restricted to the Falkland Islands, but is replaced in the Amazon districts and some adjacent parts of South America by the black caracara (*I. ater*), which is a much smaller bird, measuring only 16 inches in length, and characterised by the whole plumage, with the exception of a white band across the base of the tail, being black, with greenish reflections.

THE CHIMACHIMA

Agreeing in size with the black caracara is the very differently coloured bird known as the chimachima (*I. chimachima*). This caracara ranges from Brazil northwards of the tropic through Colombia into Panama. In the adult the prevailing colour may be said to be white; a streak from the eye towards the back of the head, the back, wings, and tail being mainly dark brown, with lighter margins to many of the feathers. The first four primary quills are white with dark markings in the middle of their length, and the remainder yellowish white at their base, with dark brown tips. The tail feathers have a lightish ground, marked with narrow brown bars for the greater part of their length, but near the end show a broad blackish band tipped with white.

The large eye is greyish brown, the beak bluish white at the base, becoming lighter at the tip; the cere and a bare space round the eye orange tinged with red, and the feet pale yellow.

In young birds the top of the head and cheeks are dark brown, the sides and back of the neck brown with yellowish white streaks, the feathers of the back brown, with straw-coloured or fulvous margins, and those of most of the under parts ochery coloured, with brown margins in the region of the chest, whereby a general striped appearance is produced.

THE CHIMANGO

The chimango (*I. chimango*) of the southern portion of South America and Tierra del Fuego differs by having the under parts and under wing coverts brownish ochre-colour in the adult; the feathers of the under surface of the body having dark brown shaft stripes.

Writing of the habits of the caracaras, which he collectively designates carrion hawks, Darwin states that chimangos may often be seen in company with caranchas, although the two are by no means friends, as the following quotation from his pen shows. "When the carancha is quietly seated on the branch of a tree or on the ground, the chimango often continues for a long time flying backwards and forwards, up and down, in a semicircle, trying each time at the bottom of the curve to strike its larger relative. The carancha takes little notice, except by bobbing its head."

Of the Falkland Island species he observes that "these birds in many respects resemble the caranchas. They live on the flesh of dead animals and on marine productions; and on the Ramirez rocks their whole sustenance must depend on the sea. They are

extraordinarily tame and fearless, and haunt the neighbourhood of houses for offal. If a hunting-party kills an animal, a number soon collect and patiently await, standing on the ground on all sides. After eating, their uncovered craws are largely protruded, giving them a disgusting appearance. They readily attack wounded birds; a cormorant in this state having taken to the shore, was immediately seized on

CHIMACHIMA AND FALKLAND ISLAND CARACARAS

by several, and its death hastened by their blows." Darwin adds that, like the caranchas, several of these birds will sometimes wait at the mouth of a rabbit-hole, and together seize on the animal when it comes out.

In addition to being exceedingly mischievous, these chimangos are "quarrelsome and very passionate, tearing up the grass with their bills from rage. They are not truly gregarious, they do not soar, and their flight is heavy and clumsy; on the ground they run extremely fast, very much like pheasants. They are noisy, uttering several harsh cries, one of which is exceedingly like that of the English rook; hence the sealers always call them rooks.

"It is a curious circumstance that, when crying out, they throw their heads upwards and backwards, after the same manner as the carancha. They build in the rocky cliffs of the sea coast, but only on the small adjoining islets, and not on the two main islands; this is a singular precaution in so tame and fearless a bird."

SOME MEMBERS OF THE VULTURE FAMILY

GRIFFON VULTURE

PONDICHERRY VULTURE

KOLBE'S VULTURES

VULTURES

As a matter of convenience it is found advisable to separate the true, or Old World, vultures (*Vulturidæ*) from the hawk family, although it is difficult to draw any well-marked line of distinction between the two groups, which are intimately connected by the lammergeiers. All vultures are, however, birds of large size, and, with the exception of the lammergeiers, characterised by the head and neck being more or less bare, or clothed only with short, stubbly down, true feathers being absent from the crown of the head. The males are as large as or larger than the females.

In all the species the beak is rather long, compressed, and straight for some distance from its base, after which it is sharply bent down, and, although its upper half may be sinuated, it is never toothed. The cere is very large, and the metatarsus, which is generally naked, is comparatively short, stout, and covered with small reticulated scales. The toes have rather long and slightly curved claws, the third toe being always long and the first one short, while the third and fourth toes are joined at their bases by a membrane. As in the preceding family, the nostrils are separated by a median partition, and the feathers furnished with after-shafts. The typical vultures, together with the lammergeiers, are restricted to the warmer regions of the Old World, where they are almost universally distributed, although absent from the Malay Islands, Ceylon, Madagascar, and Australia.

LAMMERGEIERS

The magnificent bird known as the lammergeier, or bearded vulture (*Gypaëtus barbatus*), is the typical representative of a genus in regard to the systematic position of which there has been some difference of opinion among naturalists. It differs from typical vultures in having the head covered with feathers, instead of being naked or downy, and thereby approaches the eagles, among which it is sometimes placed; but its general affinities are decidedly with the vultures.

In addition to having the head fully feathered, the lammergeier is characterised by having the oval nostrils concealed by a number of stiff bristles, and also by the presence of a tuft, or long beard of forwardly directed bristles. The long, compressed beak ascends in front of the cere, and then curves downwards, with its tip much hooked. The wings are long, with the first quill rather longer than the second, and the third the longest, and the tail is also long and distinctly wedge-shaped.

The lammergeier, which ranges from the mountains of Southern Europe and North-Eastern Africa through Asia Minor and Palestine, and thence to the Himalaya, Central Africa, and the North of China, is distinguished by the metatarsus being feathered down to the toes, and the presence of black markings on the cheeks, and commonly attains a length of about 42 inches. On the other hand, the somewhat smaller bare-legged lammergeier (*G. ossifragus*), ranging from the mountainous districts of North-Eastern to those of South Africa, has the lower part of the metatarsus naked, and the sides of the cheeks entirely white. The lammergeier of North-Western Africa has also been separated as a third species, under the name of *G. atlantis*.

THE LAMMERGEIER

In the adult of the typical species the crown of the head and sides of the face are white, with the bristles over the nostrils and a broad cheek stripe, as well as some scattered streaks, black; the rest of the head and nape being whitish, with the lanceolate feathers of the latter more or less tinged with bright tawny. The upper parts are black, tending to brown on the rump, and a tinge of ochre brown on the scapulars, with all the shafts of the back feathers whitish, as are those of the wing coverts, wings, and tail. Beneath, the general colour is rich orange tawny, not infrequently with a black gorget on the chest. The beak is horn colour and the feet leaden grey; while the iris of the eye is pale orange, and the surrounding sclerotic membrane, or "white," a blood-colour, thus producing, with the black pupil, a most remarkable appearance. In the young bird, the head, neck, and throat are blackish brown, and the rest of the body plumage pale brown, with the exception of some creamy white patches on the upper part of the back. The female is somewhat larger than the male, and the expanse of wing often exceeds 9 feet. Indian examples are those which commonly show the black gorget on the chest.

The lammergeier is essentially a mountain bird, and, in spite of numerous stories to the contrary, appears to subsist mainly on animals not slaughtered by itself and carrion, although it may occasionally attack and kill some of the smaller animals; such at least are undoubtedly its habits in the Himalaya. When on the wing, the lammergeier may be easily recognised by its long, pointed wings and tail; and also by its mode of flight, which is even and gliding, with an occasional flap of the wings. When hunting, it skims along the

sides of the mountains, following every undulation of the hillside, and working backwards and forwards in regular "beats," so that scarcely anything escapes its search.

In the Alps the lammergeier is now well-nigh exterminated, the last Swiss specimen having been found poisoned in the winter of 1887. This was a female which had been known to haunt the Bietsch Horn for some twenty-five years previously, its mate having been killed in 1862. It is stated, however, that a single bird was seen in Switzerland in 1888. In the Italian Alps the lammergeier is still met with, while in Spain and the Caucasus it is abundant. In the Himalaya these splendid birds may be seen in numbers during spring in the outer ranges, especially in the neighbourhood of the hill-station of Mari, but in the summer they migrate northwards to Kashmir, Baltistan, Ladak, etc.

Usually a shy bird, in the neighbourhood of Abbotabad lammergeiers became quite accustomed to the shooting on a rifle-range, and would approach close to the men. When driven down by cold and bad weather they will often collect in numbers round the military hill-camps to feed on the offal. Circumstantial stories of attacks by Alpine lammergeiers on children will be found in many works; but those who have examined the weak feet of those birds will form their own opinion as to their credibility. With regard to their alleged depredations on flocks, an anonymous observer writes that "I never heard of the Himalayan lammergeiers attacking anything, and in Kashmir have often watched them passing over flocks of goats, on one occasion close over some female ibex with kids. Also in Dagshai I frequently observed them sail round within a few yards of fowls and tame pigeons, but never saw them attempt a raid on any living thing, always contenting themselves with bones thrown out after the soldiers' dinners, or with offal from the slaughter-houses." This is also the experience of other naturalists in the Himalaya, one of whom mentions that, although these birds never molest fowls and pigeons picketed as lures for hawks, they always come down to a carcase or a heap of bones.

The lammergeier seems, indeed, to be specially partial to bones, which it will sometimes drop from a great height on to rocks in order to smash them; while in Algeria it is stated to do the same with tortoises. In Spain these birds are commonly known by the name of bone-smasher; and there is little doubt that the "ossifrage" of Scripture refers to the lammergeier. All these traits of character strongly confirm the view that the lammergeier is a vulture rather than an eagle; and it has been suggested that its general habits and gait, more especially its manner of walking and holding its tail when feeding on the ground, ally it to the scavenger-vultures.

In the Himalaya the lammergeier breeds from November to February, selecting almost inaccessible ledges for the construction of its nest, at elevations of five thousand feet and upwards. Mr. R. Thompson states that "the nest, a

CINEREOUS VULTURE

huge platform, some four or five feet in diameter, is constructed of small sticks and thick twigs, placed so as to form a footing for the young, and is lined with pieces of cloth, rags, etc." There is usually, both in the Himalaya and the Atlas, a single egg to a nest, although, rarely, a pair may be met with. The eggs are oval, and rather small for the size of the bird, with their external surface dull and chalky, of a buff ground colour, often clouded with darker markings. The young bird has been known to remain in the nest for upwards of four months.

CINEREOUS VULTURE

The typical representative of the true vultures, and the only living member of its genus, is the cinereous, or black, vulture (*Vultur monachus*), which differs from all other members of the family in its circular nostrils. This bird derives its name from the plumage being generally entirely black, with chocolate reflections. The head is covered with thick velvety down, developed to form a conspicuous patch at the occiput, and on the cheeks more silky and produced into tufts. The naked portions of the head and neck are livid flesh-colour, the eyes dark brown, the beak black, and the feet yellowish. In total length the bird is about 42 inches.

This vulture inhabits the countries bordering both sides of the Mediterranean, whence it extends eastwards to India and China. Unlike the griffon-vulture, to be next mentioned, this species is partial to wooded districts; although both kinds frequently meet over the same carcase. It nests generally in trees, although failing these on rocks, and builds a bulky nest of boughs lined with twigs, in which is laid a single large white egg, more or less richly marked with red.

Like its kin, the black vulture is a bird of heavy and ungraceful form and a generally repulsive appearance; its habits, when not engaged in feeding, being sluggish and inert, its attitude slouching, and its disposition cowardly. It also resembles its allies in feeding entirely on dead animals and other refuse; and it is these carrion-eating habits which render vultures so invaluable in tropical countries, where the care bestowed upon sanitary matters appears to vary inversely with the rise of temperature.

Repulsive and hideous-looking as are the members of a group of vultures assembled round the carcase of a large animal, and gorging themselves to satiety upon its contents, their appearance is very different as they are seen wheeling in circles at a great height in the blue sky of a tropical noon; and no spectacle is more interesting than to watch the vultures flocking up from all parts when some of their number have detected a prey, and dropped to earth to feast upon the find. Much discussion has taken place with regard to the manner in which vultures discover their prey, although it is now ascertained that this is mainly due

GROUP OF VULTURES

1. Black, or cinereous, vultures.   2. Scavenger vultures.   3. Griffon-vultures

to their marvellously keen power of sight. On this subject Dr. Jerdon writes that he has "known a small piece of fresh meat—a forequarter of a miserable sheep—exposed in the open bare plain where the eye barely discovered a few floating specks in the air high above, and in less than half an hour there would be a number of vultures feeding on it. It is out of the question that smell can have anything to do with this, and we know from experiments that vultures will discover and descend on a stuffed carcase of an animal, while they will neglect one well hidden, although putrid and offensive.

"I do not mean to assert that their sense of sight is illimitable, and, in the cases in which I have myself experimented, I do not mean to imply that the very distant birds, that looked like specks were those to discover the piece of fresh meat; but ever and anon a bird at a much lower elevation, but still very high above the earth, would sail past, keenly urged by hunger to a closer investigation, and on his espying the morsel, and moving towards it, others at a greater distance, urged by his motions, would descend lower, and on being certified themselves, perhaps on the ground near, would drop down in a series of oblique plunges till they reached the ground also. That vultures have also a strong sense of smell is, however, undeniable; many experiments are recorded to show this; and I have myself frequently seen them flying closely, and apparently in an excited and unusual manner, over a copse or thicket in which a putrefying carcase was placed."

It is only when the birds are flying at a low elevation that they are able to detect such hidden carrion. Not uncommon in the Himalaya at all seasons, the cinereous vulture visits the plains of Northern India during winter, and is in some districts one of the commonest of its tribe at that season. Some individuals are of much lighter colour than the typical form, but there is every gradation in the colour of the plumage from the one to the other type. In Bulgaria the breeding season begins early in March; and the young birds are described as ugly in the extreme, being covered with brownish grey down, and having a pink cere and pale yellow legs and feet.

GRIFFON-VULTURES

The second European representative of the vultures is the griffon-vulture (*Gyps fulvus*), which, together with several other species, constitutes a genus characterised by the somewhat oval and transversely placed nostrils, by the length of the metatarsus being less than that of the third toe, and the presence of fourteen feathers in the tail. The vultures of this genus range over the whole of Africa except the forest districts of the west coast and the interior, the countries bordering the Mediterranean, a considerable portion of Eastern Europe, and thence through Persia to India, and so on to Siam and the Malay Peninsula.

The griffon, or fulvous vulture, is a very variable species, ranging from Spain and North-Eastern Africa to India and Turkestan; the eastern form having a more rufous tinge of plumage. It is specially characterised by each of the feathers of the rump and lower part of the back having a pale line along the shaft, and by the under wing coverts being ashy or tawny rufous.

In the typical form from Eastern Europe the large ruff round the throat is white, and the upper parts of the body ashy fulvous, the rump and lower portion of the back being dark brown, with the above-mentioned fulvous centres to the feathers, while the wing coverts are mostly edged and tipped with creamy white, and the upper tail coverts pale ochery buff. The quills and tail are black, and the under parts pale creamy brown with narrow whitish shaft-stripes to the feathers. The eye is reddish orange, the cere bluish black, the beak pale horn-colour, and the foot leaden grey. The total length of the bird is about 40 inches.

The Himalayan griffon (*G. himalayensis*), ranging from the Himalaya to Turkestan, differs by the white under wing coverts; while the African Rüppell's vulture (*G. rueppelli*) may always be distinguished by the feathers on the lower part of the back and rump being brown, with broad grey or fulvous margins, instead of with light shaft lines, as well as by the yellowish white ruff and the deep orange beak.

The long-beaked griffon (*G. indicus*) is rather smaller than the typical form of the European species, and differs from all the rest by its unusually bare head and thin beak, and is further characterised by the feathers on the lower part of the back and rump being whitish, with faint brownish margins. It is an inhabitant of India and the countries bordering the eastern side of the Bay of Bengal.

Remains of an extinct species of griffon-vulture occur in the Miocene deposits of Malta.

Unlike the black vulture, the European griffon-vulture frequents open and rocky districts. Regarding its flight, Mr. O. Salvin writes that " it is a fine sight to watch the ease with which the griffon sails through the air; the apparently effortless extension of the wings seems amply to sustain its huge body, and no flapping motion is necessary to enable it to mount to a great height. It is only on leaving a rock that a few strokes are requisite to attain the necessary impulse, after which, with primaries bent upward by the force of the air, it performs its stately evolutions by soaring only. In alighting, the bird drops its legs some distance from the rock, and, sailing to within a few yards, it checks its velocity by two or three heavy strokes of the wings."

All griffon-vultures invariably nest on rocks, and in the south of Europe probably lay in February, as young ones are commonly found in most nests early in April. During incubation one bird sits constantly, and if driven off, immediately returns. The nest is an immense structure composed entirely of sticks, and it is common to find from two to six nests placed near together. In the case of the Himalayan species, at any rate, only a single egg is laid in each

nest, the ground colour being greyish white, upon which there may or may not be dark markings. In some cases the Himalayan griffon takes possession of the nest of an eagle before its rightful owners have thought about breeding.

Gifted with the power of undergoing long fasts, the griffon, when it can obtain sufficient food, is a perfect glutton, Canon Tristram mentioning that he has seen one of these birds, which was too gorged to stand, continue its feast while lying on its side. Griffon-vultures, both of the common species and of the kind confined to Africa, are exceedingly abundant in Abyssinia.

The long-beaked vulture, which is found all over India, although it does not enter villages and towns, is remarkable for always building in large societies, which commonly include from ten to thirty pairs of birds. Such breeding places are always situated on ledges of cliffs; and one near Ajmir, described by Mr. A. O. Hume, " was a cliff-face some one hundred feet high by three hundred wide, all broken up into irregular ledges, of which the highest overhung all the rest. In amongst the ledges were a few dwarf banyan trees, whose long bare roots and rootlets hung down, here and there, in dense grey giant skeins. All the ledges but the uppermost, when looked at from below, seemed garnished with heavy white fringes, the white droppings of the birds having run down in close parallel lines in a wonderfully symmetrical fashion over the weather-smoothed edges of the terraces. Seen from a distance, the whole cliff-face seemed mottled with huge patches of whitewash. Bleached bones and dusky quills strewed every little plateau, and nestled in every cranny."

GRIFFON-VULTURES

The young of the long-beaked vultures which were found at the end of March presented the appearance of huge unwieldy masses of yellow down, and were so fat that they could not support themselves on their feet for more than a few moments. According to native reports, they do not leave the breeding place until three or four months old.

WHITE-BACKED VULTURES

India and Africa possess certain vultures agreeing with the long-beaked griffon in having a white patch on the rump and lower part of the back, but differing in the presence of only twelve tail feathers, on which account they are assigned to a separate genus—*Pseudogyps*. The Indian species (*P. bengalensis*) has the rest of the plumage mainly black, while in *P. africanus* it is browner. The former is the most common vulture in India, where it is found in immense numbers,

RÜPPELL'S VULTURE

colour of its plumage is brown, and the inner surface of the thigh is feathered.

In the smaller Pondicherry vulture (*O. calvus*), on the other hand, the inner surface of the thigh is naked, and the plumage black; hence it is often spoken of as the black vulture, although that name more properly belongs to the representative of the genus *Vultur*. Ranging from India through Burma to Siam, but by no means abundant in individuals, the Pondicherry vulture is usually seen alone or in pairs, although occasionally four or five may be observed hunting in company over some rocky hill. Some of the other Indian vultures usually give place when this species arrives on the scene, on which account it is commonly known as the raj-sogno, or king-vulture, among the natives of parts of India.

This vulture is a late breeder, generally laying in March, although some individuals begin so early as the end of January, and others delay till April. It appears to build invariably in trees; tall pipals and banyans being its especial favourites. An

both in the open country and in towns, and it likewise extends to Burma and Malaya. Collecting round the carcase of every dead animal in numbers, these vultures may also at times be seen perched singly on a dead human body floating down the Ganges with their wings widely spread, in order to steady themselves while they enjoy their ghastly meal. They breed both on rocks and in large trees, and, like all other Indian vultures, lay but one egg in a season.

EARED VULTURES

Far less common than the members of the preceding genera are the two species of eared vultures (*Otogyps*), so termed on account of the large naked fleshy lappets hanging down each side of the neck. In addition to these lappets and other fleshy folds about the head, these vultures are distinguished by the completely bare head, and by the length of the middle toe being less than that of the metatarsus. Of the two kinds, the African eared vulture (*O. auricularis*), which ranges from Abyssinia to the Cape, and occasionally visits the south of Europe, is considerably the larger, and is, indeed, only inferior in size to the condor, attaining a length of some 45 inches; the general

PONDICHERRY VULTURES GORGING

1239

anonymous writer mentions that in April, 1887, he came across a nest of this vulture in Sirmur. "Being on the hillside above, I could look right down into the nest; the owner was sitting very close, and it was only when I got quite near, shouted, and threw sticks at it, that it moved; then, standing up, it opened its beak and spread out its wings by way of intimidation, at the same time disclosing to view one large white egg, upon which it had been sitting. The nest, placed in the crown of the tree, was an enormous mass of sticks, with finer ones as a lining; and the large, round white egg was very nearly hatched." A nest which had been in use for several years contained over six hundredweight of material.

ABYSSINIAN VULTURE

Nearly allied is the Abyssinian vulture (*Lophogyps occipitalis*), distinguished by the head being covered with down, which forms a ridge on the occiput, and by the absence of the neck lappets. It is a comparatively small species, with blackish brown plumage; and while probably inhabiting the whole of the east side of Africa, is found on the west only in Senegal.

SCAVENGER-VULTURES

The scavenger-vultures (*Neophron*), of which there are two well-defined species, derive their name from the loathsome nature of the food of their typical representative, which consists chiefly of ordure; and are accordingly the most disgusting of their tribe. They are distinguished from all other vultures by their elongated longitudinal nostrils, and likewise by the slenderness and length of the beak, and are smaller than the other members of the family. The head and neck are partly bare, and the wings long and somewhat pointed, with the third quill the longest.

The white scavenger-vulture, commonly known as the Egyptian vulture (*N. percnopterus*), which has occasionally visited the British Islands, is characterised by the general white hue of the plumage of the adult. The long hackles on the back of the head and neck have, however, a rusty tinge, and the secondary quills are mostly brown, and the primaries black. The typical form, which attains a length of 25 inches, and has the beak of a pale brown horny colour, inhabits the countries bordering both sides of the Mediterranean and Red Seas, whence it extends southwards to the Cape, and eastwards to Persia and North-Western India. In peninsular India it is replaced by a variety or species distinguished by its inferior size and yellow

BROWN SCAVENGER-VULTURE

beak. In young birds the plumage is a dirty brown colour, with the back and rump tawny; and during the intermediate stage the plumage becomes mottled with brown and white.

The Egyptian vulture is commonly seen in pairs or singly, and when on the ground stalks about with a peculiarly high action of the legs. In addition to the food already alluded to, these birds also eat carrion; but their feeble beaks render them unable to tear open the tough hides of large animals, and they have to wait till the carcase is opened by their more powerful kindred. These birds build either on rocks or large buildings, or in trees, frequently in the suburbs of towns.

The nest is large and composed of sticks and rubbish, usually lined with rags; its general shape being that of an irregular platform, with a slight depression in the centre. Mr. A. O. Hume observes that in many parts of India "wayfarers, as they pass particular trees, have a semi-religious custom of tearing a strip off their clothes to hang thereon, and the tree soon becomes loaded with rags and tatters. These are a perfect godsend to the neophrons of the neighbourhood, whom I have more than once watched robbing these local shrines of their trophies by the score. Sometimes the rags of various colours are laid out neatly in the nest, as if an attempt had been made to please the eye; sometimes they are irregularly jumbled up with the materials of the nest." The eggs, which are generally laid in the latter part of March, are commonly two in number. In size, colour, and texture specimens differ much, but they are generally chalky, and vary in colour from pure greyish or reddish white, with a few specks at one end, to a uniform dingy blood-red hue. The brown scavenger-vulture (*N. pileatus*) has the general colour of the plumage chocolate brown, with the quills and tail black; the naked portion of the head and neck being of a purple hue during life. In the typical South African race the total length of the bird is some 26 inches, but in North-Eastern and Western Africa there is a rather smaller race, with a relatively longer and more slender beak. Compared with the Egyptian vulture, Dr. W. T. Blanford observes that the present species is "far more vulturine both in its flight and food. Numbers usually collect around a carcase, which is very rarely, if ever, the case with *N. percnopterus*. The difference is best shown in the fact that both Europeans and Eastern people frequently speak of *N. percnopterus* as a kite, whilst no one could ever consider *N. pileatus* as anything else than a vulture."

THE SECRETARY-BIRD

THE very remarkable African species known as the secretary-bird (*Serpentarius secretarius*) differs so widely from all other accipitrines in external appearance that an ordinary observer might have considerable hesitation in referring it to the same order. Doubts have, indeed, been entertained by some ornithologists as to its right to be included in the Accipitres, but it appears, on the whole, to be allied to the vultures, next to which it is placed, as the representative of a distinct family, *Serpentariidæ*.

Structurally, the secretary-bird differs from all other members of the order by the great elongation of the tibia and metatarsus, which give it somewhat of the appearance of a crane with an eagle's beak; and it is also distinguished from the members of the two foregoing families by having basipterygoid processes on the rostrum of the base of the skull, and by its tufted oil-gland. It resembles both groups, however, in having the two nostrils separated by a median partition, and by the presence of a syrinx, or organ of voice, at the lower part of its windpipe. Its short-toed feet resemble those of the caracaras in having the three front toes joined by short webs at their bases.

In addition to the crest of plumes at the back of the head and its lanky limbs, the secretary-bird is characterised by the great prolongation of the two middle feathers of the tail, which communicate an almost unique appearance. When adult, the bird somewhat exceeds 4 feet in height, while the length of the tail is just under 2 feet. The prevailing hue of the plumage is delicate pearly grey, with the quills and primary coverts black, and the crest feathers either grey tipped with black, or wholly black. The upper tail coverts are white; and of the tail feathers the long middle pair have white tips preceded by a broad black band, but are elsewhere pure grey, while the others are darker grey, with white tips and two blackish bars. On the under parts the breast and under wing coverts are white, with a faint ashy tinge, the thighs and abdomen black, and the under tail coverts white. The eyes are grey, and the leg and foot yellowish.

The existing secretary-bird ranges over the whole of South Africa, and extends along the eastern side of the continent to the Sudan and Abyssinia, while on the west coast it is found in Senegambia. During the Miocene period the genus was represented by a species inhabiting the south of France, distinguished by its relatively shorter and stouter legs.

Living generally in pairs, secretary-birds are far from uncommon in many parts of South Africa, although rare in the Abyssinian highlands. One of their peculiarities is the pace at which they can walk, a wounded individual being described by Dr. Blanford as walking away as fast as he could run after it. From the number of snakes, lizards, locusts, etc., taken from the stomachs of these birds, there can be no doubt that they are in general large consumers of those reptiles and insects, although there may perhaps be some hesitation in accepting all the stories as to the large size of the snakes they habitually kill. Messrs. Nicolls and Eglington throw considerable doubts on the snake-killing propensities of these birds, and state that they have known them in South Africa endeavour to avoid coming into contact with even small snakes.

On the other hand, they are declared by the same writers to be deadly foes to the young of all kinds of game-birds, as well as of hares and antelopes, on which account they advocate their destruction rather than their protection. In a specimen examined by Mr. H. A. Bryden the stomach was found to contain a small tortoise, a mouse, four lizards, and a large quantity of locusts. "There were no snakes," writes the narrator, "or remains of snakes; nor were there any indications that the great bird had been recently feeding on hares or game-birds." Other writers state that in some districts these birds feed largely on tortoises. With regard to its breeding habits, it appears that during June or July the males begin to fight among themselves for the possession of the females; and, so soon as the victor goes off with a consort, the two set about the repair of the nest. The latter is placed in a tall bush or mimosa tree, and is said to be used for several years in succession. It is formed of sticks and clay at the base, while its flat top is covered with vegetable wool, feathers, and other soft substances. In August the hen bird lays from three to four eggs, about the size of those of a goose, and generally either pure white, or white faintly spotted with red. During the time that the hen is sitting, she is regularly fed by the cock, and in the course of about six weeks the young are hatched. For a long period the latter are completely helpless and unable to stand on their long legs, and it appears that they do not leave the nest for five or six months.

THE SECRETARY-BIRD

In spite of spending such a large portion of its time on or near the ground, the secretary-bird can fly well and strongly, although somewhat heavily, soaring high in the air, with motionless, outstretched wings, with the head out in front and the legs extended backwards.

CHARACTERISTIC MEMBERS OF THE CONDOR FAMILY

THE CONDOR

KING-CONDOR

TURKEY-VULTURES

CONDORS

THAT birds so closely resembling in general appearance the true vultures as do the condors (*Cathartidæ*) of the New World should be far less closely related to the former than are the falcons or even the secretary-bird may seem extraordinary, but is nevertheless a fact; and the external resemblance between the members of the two groups must accordingly be attributed to the effects of that parallelism in development to which allusion has already been made in this work. So different, indeed, are these birds from the other families described in this section that they are now regarded as the representatives of a distinct subordinal group. This group—Cathartæ—it is convenient to call condors, although the name condor properly designates only a single species.

Agreeing in general appearance and their bare heads and necks with the vultures of the Old World, the American members of the condor tribe can be distinguished at a glance by the absence of any partition between the two nostrils, so that there is a hole right through the upper part of the beak. They also differ from the *Falconidæ* and *Vulturidæ* by the absence of after-shafts to the feathers; in which respect, as also in the presence of basipterygoid processes on the rostrum of the base of the skull and in the naked oil-gland, they resemble owls. A remarkable peculiarity of the group is the absence of a syrinx, or voice-organ, in the lower part of the windpipe, in consequence of which the only sound that these birds can utter is a kind of hiss. In their length of limb condors agree with the Old World vultures, but the first toe is more elevated. There are, altogether, ten species of these birds, of which the majority are at least partly South American, although the range of the family extends about as far north as the northern boundary of the United States.

TYPICAL CONDORS

Largest of all the birds of prey, the condor of the Andes (*Sarcorhamphus gryphus*) is the type of a genus characterised by the head of the male being furnished with a large, erect fleshy wattle, which forms a median crest immediately behind the beak; and also by the rounded wings, in which the primary and secondary quills are of nearly equal length, exceeding twice the length of the tail. The first toe is very short, and the second and fourth toes are of nearly equal length. The female lacks the head-wattle of the male, but in both sexes the beak is characterised by its comparative shortness and depth.

In the male condor the general colour of the plumage may be described as glossy black with grey on the wings; most of the wing coverts, as well as all the secondaries and the inner primaries, having their external margins ashy white. The large downy ruff round the neck is pure white, and the bare parts of the head, neck, and chest have a wrinkled and mostly dark-coloured skin, developed into a wattle on the throat and another on the chest. Horny brown at the base, the beak becomes ivory white at the tip; while the feet are blackish, and the iris of the eye pale brown. In the smooth-headed and smaller female the iris is red, and there are no wattles on the neck and chest. The length of the male is about 48 inches, the body is of immense size and weight, and the span of the wings probably reaches 9 feet. The lesser condor (*S. æquatorialis*), of Ecuador and Quito, has a uniformly brown plumage, and the whole beak blackish.

The condor is especially characteristic of the Peruvian and Chilian Andes, where it is usually found in the zone lying between nine thousand and sixteen thousand feet; its range extends, however, from Quito to the extreme southern point of the continent, and in Patagonia it frequents the steep cliffs on the coast. It has been often stated that these birds may be seen soaring round the highest peaks of the Andes, whence they suddenly descend to the level of the plains, but this has been

shown to be incorrect. In the neighbourhood of Chimborazo Mr. E. Whymper never observed these birds anywhere near the mountain summits, and accordingly concludes that the upper limit of their ordinary range cannot be more than sixteen thousand feet; while in the same district they do not appear to descend below some nine thousand feet. Since, however, condors in Patagonia are commonly seen at the sea-level, it is probable that there is an upland and a lowland race, and that the same birds do not range from the level of the sea to elevations of sixteen thousand feet.

In regard to their habits when on the wing, Mr. Whymper writes that "on the few occasions upon which we were approached by condors in a menacing manner, we became aware of their presence from their shadows being cast upon us by a nearly vertical sun. They never came near when the sun was concealed, and if they hovered in our neighbourhood they always kept the sun at their backs. This cannot be their invariable habit in a country where the sun is so often invisible, though possibly it is adopted whenever there is a chance, and the motive is obvious. The objects to be attacked are dazzled by the sun's rays, while the assailants are enabled to inspect their brilliantly lighted intended victims at their ease, whose eyes are picked out at the earliest opportunity, and they are thus rendered completely defenceless. The herdsmen on Autisana had lifelong familiarity with the condor, and did not stand in awe of it. They told me that the bird was particularly addicted to old horse and young calf, and might, after feeding, be easily caught with the lasso."

Mr. Darwin writes that the old birds generally live in pairs, but on the inland basaltic cliffs of Santa Cruz there is a spot which used to be haunted by scores of these birds. " On coming suddenly to the brow of the precipice, it was a grand spectacle to see between twenty and thirty of these fine birds start heavily from their resting-place, and wheel away in majestic circles. Having gorged themselves with carrion on the plains below, they retire to their favourite ledges

CONDORS FLOCKING TO A DEAD GUANACO

to digest their food. From these facts the condor must to a certain degree be considered as a gregarious bird. In this part of the country they live altogether on the guanacos which have died a natural death, or, as more commonly happens, have been killed by the pumas. I believe, from what I saw in Patagonia, that they do not on ordinary occasions extend their daily excursions to any great distance from their regular sleeping-places.

"The condors may often be seen at a great height, soaring over a certain spot in the most graceful circles. On some occasions I am sure that they do this only for pleasure, but on others the Chileno countryman tells you that they are watching a dying animal, or the puma devouring its prey. If the condors glide down, and then suddenly all rise together, the Chileno knows

that it is the puma which, watching the carcase, has sprung out to drive away the robbers. Besides feeding on carrion, the condors frequently attack young goats and lambs; and the shepherd dogs are trained, whenever they pass over, to run out, and, looking upwards, to bark violently." From the feeble grasping power of their feet, and especially the small size of the first toe, it is perfectly evident that condors cannot carry off animals of any size, and all the legends of their flying away with children may accordingly be discredited.

Frequently roosting in trees on the lower grounds during a considerable portion of the year, in the breeding season condors retire to the most inaccessible parts of the mountains or sea cliffs. Here, during the summer months of November and December, the female deposits two large white eggs on some rocky ledge, without any attempt at making a nest. The young are clothed with grey down, and remain a long time in the breeding place, where they have been observed as late as May. Owing to their destructive propensities, condors are incessantly persecuted by the natives, and have thus been greatly reduced in numbers in many districts. Mr. Whymper states, however, that so many as a dozen may still be seen at a time in the neighbourhood of Chimborazo. The birds may be either lassoed when gorged, or noosed while roosting in trees; and the Chilenos also capture them by surrounding a carcase with a fence of sticks, in which an opening is left, and then galloping up on horseback when the birds are gorged, and thus enclosing them. As a condor requires a certain space in which to run before being able to rise from level ground, the fence effectually prevents their escape.

To shoot a condor on the wing requires some stratagem, as at a distance of thirty or forty yards a charge of buckshot produces no effect. Mr. J. R. H. MacFarlane relates that he was able to draw the birds within distance by tying up his dog and concealing himself behind a rock close by. " Soon," he writes, " I perceived that the plaintive noises made by my dog had produced an effect; gradually the condors passed and repassed in their majestic flight, curiosity bringing them each time nearer and nearer, till at last I saw the most inquisitive bird passing within five yards of my retreat, when to drop the lock and deliver the contents of both barrels was the work of a second. To see a heavy bird such as a mallard suddenly drop with a thud is generally satisfactory, so my feelings may be understood when my raptorial friend plumped down about two hundred feet below, sliding and rolling down the sand of the precipice, at the foot of which I found him lying as dead as a stone."

KING CONDOR

The brilliantly - coloured king condor (*Gypagus*, or *Gyparchus*, *papa*) is distinguished generically from the typical condor, to which it is much inferior in size, by the second toe being longer than the fourth, and by the whole of the front of the head of the male being covered with wattles, while the female has a single upright wattle over the nostril. During life the naked portions of the head and neck of the male are coloured with shades of orange, purple, and crimson; the plumage of a large portion of the upper parts is cream-colour tending to fawn; the greater wing coverts and quills, together with the lower part of the beak, rump, upper tail coverts, and tail, are black, and nearly all the under parts white with a tinge of cream. Round the neck the feathers are deep grey, the beak is yellowish horn-colour, with a brown base, the foot greyish black, and the eye white. The female is more soberly coloured, having the whole of the upper surface dark.

This species has a more northerly range than the typical condor, extending from Brazil to Mexico, Texas, and Florida, and also occurring in Trinidad. Reaching in the mountains to an elevation of about five thousand feet, this splendid bird has its true home in primeval forest or well-wooded plains, and is utterly unknown in dry open districts or on barren mountains. A comparatively scarce bird, it roosts at night in low trees—frequently in company—and

THE KING-CONDOR

sallies forth at early dawn in search of carrion and other food. Although the female is known to lay two white eggs, there is some uncertainty as to the location of the nest. The naturalist Azara was told by the natives that it was always placed in hollow trees, but this has been doubted by other writers; and Dr. Burmeister states that the nest is built high up on a tree, frequently on the very summit of one that is dead and bare.

BLACK CONDOR

The members of the three remaining genera of condors are readily distinguished from the preceding forms by the absence of an erect wattle on the naked head in both sexes, and further characterised by the wings being pointed and less than twice the length of the tail, with their primary quills considerably longer than the secondaries. The present species (*Catharistes uruba*), often known as the American black vulture, which is the sole representative of its genus, is characterised by the squared extremity of the tail, and by the interval between the tips of the primaries and secondaries being less than the length of the metatarsus. In colour the black condor is nearly uniform black, although the shafts of the primary quills are white on both sides, and those of the tail feathers brown above and white beneath. Both the beak and feet are bluish, and the eyes dark brown. The total length is only about 25 inches.

BLACK CONDOR

Its regular range extends from about the northern frontier of Patagonia to North Carolina and Texas; while irregularly, or casually, the bird is found so far north as New York and South Dakota. In the United States it is commonly known as the carrion-crow. With the exception of the extreme northern portion of its range, the black condor is a resident species in the districts it frequents, and far more abundant near the coast than in the interior, in the United States being more numerous than the turkey-vulture in the former situations, but outnumbered by that bird in the heart of the country.

As the habits of this condor are very similar to those of the turkey-vulture, it will suffice to say that these birds are more or less gregarious, frequently breeding in small companies, and making little or no nest for the reception of their two eggs, which appear to be always placed on the ground, either under the protection of low bushes, logs, or rocks, or in perfectly open situations. They rarely breed north of latitude of 39°, and in the southern United States the eggs are laid early in March. The ground colour of the eggs is pale greyish green, with more or fewer reddish markings. Describing a breeding place of these birds on a small island off South Carolina, Mr. W. Hoxie states that, under a dense growth of yucca, he has "taken nineteen eggs in one afternoon, and seen at the same time five or six pairs of newly hatched young. There is never the slightest attempt at forming a nest, or even excavating a hollow. The eggs are laid far in under the intertwining stems of the yucca, and, in the semi-shadows, are quite hard to be seen. The parent birds have, however, the habit of always following the same path in leaving and approaching their precious charge; and, after a little experience, I learned to distinguish these traces so well that I seldom failed to follow them up and secure the coveted treasure."

guided by scent, the views of his adversary have been very generally accepted.

The turkey-vulture (*Cathartes*, or *Rhinogryphus*, *aura*) is one of several species, distinguished from the black condor by the rounded form of the tail, and by the interval between the tips of the primary and secondary quills exceeding the length of the metatarsus. The present species is one of the smaller representatives of the genus, measuring 30 inches in length, and characterised by its plumage being generally black, with the wings washed with brown, the shafts of the primaries brown on the upper surface, and the red head.

The allied *C. perniger* of Guiana, Amazonia, and Peru has the plumage all black, and the head yellow; *C. falclandicus*, of the Falkland Islands, Patagonia, and Chile, has the wings washed with grey, and the head pink; and *C. urubitinga*, or *yurrovianus*, ranging from Amazonia to Eastern Mexico, differs by its orange head and the white shafts on both sides of the primaries.

The typical turkey-vulture has the widest distribution of any member of the family, ranging over nearly the whole of temperate and tropical America, inclusive of the West Indies. In the southern and middle United States these birds are exceedingly common, and in some of the southern towns and villages, when not molested, may be seen perambulating the streets, or roosting on the housetops, with perfect unconcern of the passers-by. They look their best when aloft, as their flight is exceedingly easy and graceful; while the apparent absence of all effort as they sail in stately manner overhead, in ever-changing circles and without any apparent movement of their well-shaped wings, makes them really attractive objects to watch. Like all their kin, they are, however, essentially scavengers, and when on the ground by no means pleasing creatures. Dr. W. J. Ralph writes that, although carrion-

A GROUP OF TURKEY-VULTURES

TURKEY-VULTURES

The name of the turkey-vulture, or turkey-buzzard, as it is commonly called in North America, will always be associated with that of Charles Waterton, as being the bird which gave rise to the great dispute between that original observer and the American ornithologist Audubon as to whether condors detect their prey by sight or smell. Although the English naturalist stoutly maintained that Audubon's experiments were inconclusive, and that the turkey-vulture was solely

eaters, they prefer fresh meat to that which is tainted, but that being unable to kill game for themselves, while their weak bills are incapable of tearing open the skins of large animals, they have seldom an opportunity of exercising their preference. "When they find a dead animal they will not leave it until all but the bones and other hard parts has been consumed, and if it be a large one, or if it have a tough skin, they will often remain near it for days, roosting by night in the trees near by.

PELICANS

"Pelicans commonly occur in enormous flocks in the neighbourhood of swamps, estuaries, and rivers, and are sometimes so numerous that in India Mr. A. O. Hume writes of having seen miles of them."

I Y

FRIGATE AND TROPIC BIRDS

"The frigate-bird is one of the most swift and active of all pelagic birds, spending much of its time on the wing, often, far away from land. . . . Tropic-birds often follow in the wake of vessels for long distances and display great boldness."

MANDARIN DUCKS

"The splendidly-coloured mandarin duck has one of the scapular feathers expanded into a large fan, of which the colour is mostly chestnut brown, but with a broad purple band on the outer hind border."

NIGHT-HERONS AND WHALE-HEADED STORK

"The night-herons are comparatively small birds, taking their name from their habit of spending the day in sleep and waking up in the evening to
pass the greater part of the night in searching for food."

"After they have eaten—and sometimes they will gorge themselves until the food runs out of their mouths when they move—they will, if they are not too full to fly, roost in the nearest trees until their meal is partly digested, and then begin eating again. Many times I have seen these birds in company with the black vulture floating down a stream on a dead alligator, cow, or other large animal, crowded so closely together that they could hardly keep their balance, and followed by a number on the wing.

"In spite of this close crowding they never seem to fight much when feeding, although one will at times peck and hiss at another; and at times two will tug at a particularly tough fragment until it either breaks or the weaker bird gives up his hold."

The nesting habits of the turkey-vultures are very similar to those of the black condor, although, instead of always laying its eggs on the bare ground, the present species will also nest in caverns and crevices of rocks, or in hollow trees, while it has been known to take possession of a deserted heron's nest in a cactus. Generally, the smell of a nest is unbearable; and when disturbed the parent birds have sometimes the habit of disgorging the contents of their stomach at an intruder, instead of moving. The young, which are covered at first with soft white down, are fed in a similar manner.

The eggs are usually two, but may be three in number; and an instance of four young in one nest is recorded. In colour the eggs are creamy white, thinly blotched with red and chocolate. At times the nests, if such they can be called, are in companies, but at others singly. The only sound uttered is a kind of hissing wheeze, generally heard when the birds are disturbed.

THE CALIFORNIAN CONDOR

Far larger than the other members of the preceding genus is the Californian condor (*Pseudogryphus*, or *Gymnogyps, californianus*), which may even exceed the typical condor in expanse of wing. In this bird there is no distinct ruff of downy feathers round the neck, and the general colour of the plumage is brownish black, although the tips of the greater wing coverts are whitish, forming a line across the closed wing, and there is a broad band of white along the under side of the wing, which renders the bird easily recognised when flying overhead. This condor always had a very restricted distribution, being confined to the Pacific coast region of the United States from Oregon to northern Lower California, and it now appears to be found only in California, where its home is in the almost inaccessible secondary ranges running parallel to the Sierra Nevada.

Never very numerous, the Californian condor has been decimated by the poisoned meat laid out by the stockmen for the destruction of carnivorous mammals, and was at one time supposed to be in imminent danger of extermination, although in some of the most barren and inaccessible mountains it appears to have again begun to hold its own, so that there is a possibility of its increase. Although, from the weakness of their claws and beaks, the powers of offence of these condors are comparatively small in proportion to their size, yet their strength is very great, as is attested by the fact that four are known to have dragged the carcase of a young bear weighing one hundred pounds for a distance of two hundred yards.

The flight of this bird, according to Major Bendire, "is graceful beyond comparison, as it sails majestically overhead in gradually contracting or expanding circles, now gently falling with the wind, and again rising easily against it, without a perceptible motion of its pinions. While on the wing, it looks more than the peer of any of our birds, the golden eagle not excepted." Mr. W. L. Finley has paid several visits to the actual haunts of this bird high up in the San Bernadino Range of Southern California, when that writer and his companion were able to approach the old birds without any manifestations of alarm or fierceness on the part of the latter. These birds, it appears, lay only a single egg in a season, and the young is of remarkably slow development, the black quill feathers not showing until the nestling is more than two months old. It has been ascertained that there are only forty-one eggs of the species in collections, and the number of adult birds in captivity at the date of Mr. Finley's visit was believed to be half a dozen. The huge nest may be placed either on rocks or in trees, one being situated on the limb of a large redwood tree at a height of seventy-five feet from the ground, and close to the stem. The eggs are of a uniform greenish white colour.

Numerous remains of fossil condors, some referable to extinct genera, have recently been discovered in the Tertiary asphalt-deposits near Los Angeles, California.

CALIFORNIAN CONDORS
Photographs by H. T. Bohlam and W. L. Finley

A CONDOR CHICK
This bird was 54 days old and weighed 6 pounds

I z

ORDER VII. STEGANOPODES
CHARACTERISTICS OF THE CORMORANT GROUP

THE members of the group of birds forming the order Steganopodes agree with those last considered in having bridged, or desmognathous, palates, and likewise in the want of a projecting external process at the lower end of the humerus, or upper wing bone. The order, which includes not only cormorants, but also darters, gannets, pelicans, and frigate and tropic birds, is distinguished from all others by the whole four toes being connected together by webs, which generally extend to their extremities ; while the posterior angle of the lower half of the beak is not produced behind its point of attachment to the skull.

These birds are further characterised by the shortness of their legs —this shortness being most marked in the frigate-birds—and also by the plumage of the neck being without gaps, and continuous. Their skulls lack the deep grooves for glands on the frontal region characterising many other aquatic birds ; and its basal rostrum has no basipterygoid processes for the articulation of the pterygoid bones. There is a tufted oil-gland, and the young are helpless, and pass through a downy stage.

As a rule, the body is elongated, the neck of medium length, and the head small ; but the beak may be either long or short. The wings may be long and rounded, or exceedingly elongated and pointed ; and although the tail is variable in form, it is always very different from that of other swimming birds.

Although several members of the group frequent the coast, it is only the representatives of three families that are purely pelagic in their habits, many of the species inhabiting rivers or lakes far removed from the sea. All are carnivorous, subsisting partially or entirely on fish ; but their breeding habits vary considerably, although both parents take their share in incubation.

The eggs, which may be either one, or from two to four in number, are of relatively small size, much elongated, and generally invested with a chalky coating over the uniformly coloured shell. Occasionally, however, they are smooth-shelled, with dark markings upon a light ground.

While some fish by diving into the water from a height, others capture their prey by thrusting their necks down into the water as they swim, while yet others follow the fish of which they are in pursuit beneath the water. Some diversity of view obtains among naturalists as to the number of family groups into which these birds should be divided.

CORMORANTS FEEDING THEIR YOUNG

CLASSIFICATION OF STEGANOPODES MENTIONED IN THIS WORK

CORMORANTS AND DARTERS

CORMORANTS (*Phalacrocorax*), of which there are some forty species, are the typical representatives of the first family (*Phalacrocoracidæ*) of the order, and characterised by the elongated but powerful body, the long neck, which may vary considerably in thickness, moderately long and narrow beak, of which the tip is sharply deflected, and by the linear and concealed nostrils. The face and throat are naked, the legs short and stout, with the first toe articulated to the inner side of the metatarsus, and the claw of the third toe has a serrated inner margin. The wings are of moderate length, with the third quill the longest, and the tail has either twelve or fourteen feathers remarkable for their extreme stiffness.

Cormorants, although far more numerous in the warmer regions of the globe than in northern climates, have an almost cosmopolitan distribution, inhabiting countries as remote from one another as Great Britain and New Zealand. Whereas, however, some seldom leave the neighbourhood of the sea, where they take up their stations on rocky islands, others frequent reedy swamps and marshes, or the banks of rivers and lakes, and rarely, if ever, visit the sea. While the more northern species are migratory, this is not the case with their more southern cousins. Fossil cormorants date in Europe from the lower portion of the Miocene period.

All cormorants are characterised by the dark blackish, bluish, or greenish hue of the plumage of the upper parts, which generally has a more or less marked metallic tinge; and the head may be ornamented with one or two crests of feathers.

The best-known, and at the same time the typical representative of the genus, is the great, or black, cormorant (*P. carbo*), which ranges over the whole of Europe, a large part of Eastern North America, Northern Africa and Egypt, and the greater portion of Asia, and is represented by a closely allied species (*P. punctatus*) in Australia and New Zealand.

The species is characterised by the presence of fourteen tail feathers, and attains a length of about 36 inches. In the adult bird the plumage of the head and part of the neck during spring and summer is black, with a number of hair-like white feathers intermingled, and the feathers of the back of the head elongated into a crest. The back and wing coverts are dark brown, with black margins to the feathers, the quills and tail

black, and the lower portion of the neck and under parts, except for a white patch on the thigh, bluish black. Of the naked portions, the base of the upper half of the beak, together with the dilatable membrane of the lower half of the beak, is yellow, the greater part of the beak is horny, and the legs and toes are black.

In the northern part of its range the black species is accompanied by the smaller green, or crested cormorant, or shag (*P. graculus*), as it is indifferently called, which also ranges still farther to the north. This British species, in addition to its smaller size, may be distinguished by the presence of only twelve feathers in the tail, and the general green hue of the plumage, which lacks the white patch on the thigh. Like the larger species, both sexes have a crest in the breeding season, but this is wanting in winter, and in young birds at all times. This cormorant is essentially a marine species. It is replaced in the Mediterranean by an allied form, *P. desmaresti*, which has brighter-coloured plumage, no crest, and is likewise an inhabitant of salt or brackish water. Among other species may be mentioned the Indo-Malay *P. javanicus*, the African *P. africanus*, and the pied *P. melanoleucus*.

Cormorants are by far the most expert divers of the order to which they belong, and both swim and dive with a speed and power which cannot fail to arouse the admiration of beholders. On

CORMORANTS
NESTING

land their movements are awkward and ungainly, but their flight, although heavy, is strong and comparatively swift. Many of the species feed almost exclusively on fish, and all are the very type of greediness, as after having eaten till they can swallow no more, they will not infrequently still try to catch any prey that may come within their reach. When fishing, cormorants often swim with their heads below water, and they also capture a large number of fish by pouncing down upon them from a perch near the bank, as they appear at the surface of the water.

In general, cormorants are social birds, and frequently associate in vast flocks, as is the case with the African species, which is found in such numbers on the rocks near Cape Town as at times to darken the air when on the wing. Such companies continue together during the breeding season, and may make their nests either in the neighbourhood of swamps, or on ledges of rock.

In Burma vast flocks of the typical species breed on low trees at a height of from fifteen to twenty feet above the water on the margin of a swamp; and there are other similar breeding places in India. In one of the latter instances Mr. Doig writes that "the nests were large platforms of sticks, about two feet in diameter one way and two and a half feet the other; that is, they were more oval than circular. The eggs were laid on a thin bedding of rush and grass, and the greatest number in one nest was seven. Some had only three, others four, five, and six; the latter seeming to be the normal number, although some nests had only four young ones."

That this breeding place was a very ancient one was evident by the circumstance that the nests were built on the top of those of previous years. The eggs, which have a very pale blue shell, much encrusted with chalky matter, become very dirty during the process of incubation. In Kerguelen Island Professor Moseley states that the

CRESTED CORMORANTS

warty cormorant (*P. verrucosus*) breeds in companies on the ledges of the cliffs sloping down to the sea. These cormorants make a neat, compact, round nest, raised about a foot from the ground, and composed of mud, with a lining of grass. The number of eggs on this island was only two or three in a nest.

He also states that the young birds, with their coat of black down, were exceedingly ugly; and that "when there are three in the nest nearly full-fledged they form an absurd sight, since the nest is then not big enough to hold more than one properly, so the greater part of the bodies of the three young project out; and then, to crown the absurdity, the mother comes and sits on the top of these three young as big as herself.'

The young feed themselves by thrusting their heads far down into their parents' throats, and extracting the half-digested fish from their stomachs. Although often roosting on rocks, in some places cormorants spend the night in trees; and on certain parts of the Nile in Egypt they congregate at night by hundreds in the palm-trees fringing its banks.

Young cormorants have the throat and under parts white, and the general colour of the upper surface dull brown, glossed on the head, neck, and back with bluish green. When the under parts change from white to dark, is not definitely known; and in rare instances the white on the under surface appears to persist till the bird is practically adult, as a full-grown white-breasted cormorant was shot off the Scilly Islands in June, 1909.

For some time a discussion has been going on with regard to the food of Australian cormorants and the harm these birds are alleged to inflict on local fisheries. It is emphatically affirmed that, instead of existing exclusively on fish (as is almost always stated to be the case with all cormorants), these birds feed very largely on crabs and shrimps, which themselves are harmful to fisheries on account of their partiality to fish-spawn. Moreover, instead of subsisting very largely on the introduced trout, as has been alleged, the local cormorants are stated to be much fonder of eels, which are of little importance as food-fish.

In China and Japan cormorants have been trained to fish for their masters from time immemorial, and early in the seventeenth century this practice was introduced into Europe as a sport, which was followed alike in Holland, France, and England. In the East the cormorants are taught to fish either from the bank or from a raft, and although young or imperfectly trained birds wear a collar, to which a cord may be attached, to prevent them swallowing their prey, in many cases the fully-trained birds are allowed to fish without any kind of restraint.

Till they receive permission to forage for themselves, they invariably bring all their captures to their owner; and it is said that when the bird has seized a fish too large for it to carry unaided, another immediately comes to its assistance. In captivity cormorants are readily tamed, and exhibit considerable intelligence and attachment. Although generally considered highly unpalatable, their flesh is relished by Arabs and Lapps.

Not only on account of being the largest member of the genus, but as having been exterminated comparatively soon after its discovery, Pallas's cormorant (*P. perspicillatus*) claims passing notice. The plumage both above and below was a deep lustrous green, with a blue gloss on the neck, and purplish reflections on the scapulars. Long, straw-coloured feathers were interspersed on the neck, and the shafts of the tail feathers were white. Pale naked rings round the eyes suggested the specific name. Discovered on Bering Island in 1741, this fine species seems to have become extinct within about a century from that date.

A cormorant from the Galapagos Islands has been referred to a separate genus, under the name of *Nannopterum harrisi*.

DARTERS

The darters, snake-birds, or snake-necks, which are sometimes assigned to a family by themselves, but may be described here as a genus (*Plotus*), form a group of four species readily distinguished from the cormorants by the much elongated body, the extraordinarily long and thick neck, and the small flat and narrow head, terminating in a straight, conical beak with a point as sharp as a dagger, and its edges finely serrated at the tip. The legs are placed very far back on the body, and have long toes; the wings are elongated, but bluntly pointed, with the third quill the longest; and the long tail is rounded, and composed of twelve stiff feathers gradually increasing in width towards their tips. Both the quills and the body feathers are lustrous, and generally show metallic tints, those on the upper parts being more or less elongated.

Of the four species, one (*P. levaillanti*) is African, another (*P. anhinga*) South American, a third, the black-bellied darter (*P. melanogaster*), inhabits India, Burma, and the Malay region, while the fourth is Australian.

In the African species, the prevailing hue of the plumage is black, with a metallic green lustre, the feathers of the back and wing coverts having white shaft-streaks. The neck is rusty, with a blackish brown streak running backwards from the eye, and beneath this a line of white. The eye is generally reddish yellow, the naked areas on the head yellowish green, the beak horn-colour, and the foot greenish grey. In the female, the tints are less bright. The New and Old World species, although externally so alike, differ remarkably in the structure of their internal organs.

Darters frequent the banks of rivers, lakes, and swamps, where they may be found either singly, in pairs, or in immense flocks, and generally select localities where trees are abundant, well-wooded islands being their especial favourites. On the Chobi River Livingstone states that one of these birds may be seen perched on almost every rock and stump, "either sunning itself over the stream, or standing erect with outstretched wings. Occasionally it may be seen fishing, with its body so much submerged that hardly anything but the neck appears above the water. Its time of feeding is by night, and, as the sun declines, it may be seen flying in flocks to the fishing grounds. It is a most difficult bird to catch, even when disabled, in consequence of its expertness in diving; it goes down so adroitly, and comes up again in such unlikely places, that the most skilful boatmen rarely secure them.

Of the black-bellied Indian species, Mr. G. Reid writes that "during the day it is fond of sunning itself on the grassy banks of lakes and on the bare branches of trees on their margins, flying off or darting into the water on the approach of danger. It is capable of moving for considerable distances under water, and usually swims with nothing but its head and neck exposed, though, when danger threatens, everything but its beak disappears, till it considers it has gone far enough to be perfectly safe, when it gradually shows up again."

When swimming with only the head and neck exposed, these birds may easily be mistaken for snakes, but their flight is exceedingly like that of cormorants. Their food consists exclusively of small fishes, which they capture in the water and transfix with their sharp beaks. From observations made on a captive specimen, it appears that when fishing the darter swims beneath the surface of the water with its wings partially expanded, and a peculiar jerky action of the head and neck, suggestive of a man poising a spear before throwing. When within striking distance, the bird, by a vigorous lunge of the neck, impales the fish on the tip of its beak, and immediately afterwards rises to the surface, when it shakes off its prey by a series of jerks of the head and neck. In order to accomplish this bayoneting process, the darter has a peculiar " kink " in the vertebræ of the neck, which can be suddenly straightened out by muscular action, when the head is necessarily shot forwards.

Darters build in trees, the African species generally placing its nest, which is very like that of the tropic-bird, on a bough from four to eight feet above the water. The eggs, which are three to four in number, have light green shells, thickly encrusted with the usual chalky coating. Soon after they are hatched, the young have naked heads, but are elsewhere covered with dirty white down.

BLACK-BELLIED
DARTER

GANNETS—PELICANS—FRIGATE-BIRDS—TROPIC-BIRDS

GANNETS

THE large and somewhat goose-like birds known as gannets and boobies (family *Sulidæ*), of which there are some eleven species, all included in the typical genus *Sula*, are much more stoutly built than darters, with shorter and thicker necks and beaks. The beak itself is strong and conical, with its horny covering composed of several pieces, its cutting edges serrated, and its gape extending behind the level of the eyes ; the nostrils being, as in cormorants, situated at its base are almost invisible. The legs are short, and the claw of the third toe is pectinated like that of cormorants. The wings are of great length, with the first quill the longest ; and the twelve-feathered tail is rather short and wedge-shaped. A naked area occupies the face and throat. The skeleton differs from that of cormorants and darters by the circumstance that the furcula is not united by bone to the summit of the breast-bone.

The European, or white, gannet (*S. bassana*), as the typical and best-known example of the genus, will serve as the chief example of the group. Measuring about 34 inches in total length, the adult gannet has the plumage entirely white, with the exception of that of the head and neck, which is buff, and the black primaries of the wings. The beak is horny white, the naked part of the face bluish black, the eye straw-colour, the front of the leg and foot green, and the remainder nearly black. In young birds the plumage of the upper parts is blackish brown flecked with white, and beneath mingled ashy and buff.

Although occasionally driven inland by stress of weather, the gannet, like its congeners, is a coast-haunting bird, associating on certain cliffs, such as the well-known Bass Rock on the coast of Scotland, in countless swarms. Its range extends over the coasts of the Northern Hemisphere so far north as latitude 70° and so far south as the Tropics ; although the birds only frequent the southern portion of their habitat during winter, and are but seldom seen at any time in the Mediterranean.

In South Africa the place of this species is taken by the Cape gannet (*S. capensis*), distinguished by its nearly black tail ; and the greater number of the representatives of the genus are inhabitants of the Southern Hemisphere.

Although still breeding off the Welsh coast, on Grassholm Island, it is on the Scottish and Irish shores that the gannet is found in greatest numbers ; the Bass Rock being, however, the only station on the eastern coast where these birds resort for breeding. Gannets are also abundant in the Orkneys and Hebrides, and although less numerous on the Norwegian coasts, reappear in vast swarms on the shores of North America.

The gannets on the Bass Rock have been so frequently described that it will be unnecessary to give any account of the wondrous scene. It may be mentioned, however, that the birds usually assemble in March, although laying does not generally begin till May ; and some idea of the vast numbers of these birds may be obtained from the fact that formerly from fifteen hundred to two thousand young have been taken in a season.

The nest, which is generally about six inches in height, is formed of a mass of seaweed and grass placed upon the bare rock ; and in this is laid a single egg, which is at first chalky white, with a faint blue tinge. During incubation the birds become so tame that they will allow themselves to be handled ; and it is somewhat curious that, on the ledges of the Bass Rock, almost all the sitting birds have their heads turned towards the cliff (page 941.)

Gannets feed exclusively on fish, and commit great devastation upon the shoals of herrings and pilchards, in search of which they often wander for long distances. Mr. Couch observes that " the gannet takes its prey in a different manner from any other of our aquatic birds ; for, traversing the air in all directions, as soon as it discovers the fish, it rises at such a height as experience shows best calculated to carry it by a downward motion to the required depth ; and then, partially closing its wings, it falls perpendicularly on the prey,

THE GANNET

and rarely without success, the time between the plunge and immersion being about fifteen seconds."

The serrated third claw of the gannet, like that of the cormorant, appears to be for the purpose of dressing the plumage, and not for aiding in the capture of the prey, which is taken entirely by means of the beak. The number of gannets nesting on Grassholm Island does not exceed 300 pairs, and as these birds do not rear more than two young in a season, there has been, as the result of repeated interference by trespassers and the ravages of herring gulls, no practical increase for the past few years. These birds are only on Grassholm during the nesting season, so that the quantity of fish they destroy is comparatively insignificant, and they ought therefore to be protected, as this is now the only breeding place on the English and Welsh coasts.

On many of the islands of the southern seas gannets, or boobies, of various species, breed in vast numbers and exhibit remarkable tameness, or, rather, absence of fear. Among such breeding-places may be mentioned St. Paul's Rocks, Booby Island, off Fernando Noronha, and Raine Island, off North-Eastern Australia.

The white-bellied gannet (*S. leucogaster*) of St. Paul's Rocks and Raine Island makes a slight nest of green twigs and grass on the ground; while the blue-eyed gannet (*S. cyanops*) merely digs a hole about an inch and a half deep. The latter species is nearly white, with the naked parts of the face blue and the eye bright yellow; but the smaller Australian *S. piscatrix* differs from both the others by its bright red feet. Professor Moseley writes that "on the low cliffs of Booby Island the noddies (terns) and boobies nest on all the available ledges, and sat on their nests quite undisturbed as we rowed past them. It was curious to see the doves nesting together with these two sea-birds on the same ledges and with their nests intermingled."

Remains of extinct gannets are found in the lower portion of the Miocene deposits of France; and the rocks belonging to the middle portion of the same period have yielded bones of a gannet-like bird with wings even longer than those of the albatross, for which the name of *Pelargornis* has been proposed. Nearly allied to the latter is the so-called *Argillornis* from the much older London Clay of England. Still more remarkable is the tooth-billed cormorant (*Odontopteryx*), of the latter formation, which, while apparently allied to the cormorants, differs from all existing birds in having the bony margins of the beak produced into a number of tooth-like processes. It is represented by a much larger species in the Tertiary rocks of Brazil.

PELICANS

Although pelicans (family *Pelecanidæ*) are now unknown in Britain, the occurrence of their bones in the fens of Norfolk and Cambridge indicates that comparatively recently they were at least occasional visitors. The largest representatives of their order, these birds are distinguished from all others by the enormous development of the beak, which is of great length, much flattened, and marked by a number of furrows. To the lower half of the beak is affixed a large dilatable pouch of great capacity; so that the whole beak may be compared to a bag-net, of which the upper half acts as a lid. The extremity of the latter ends in a slightly hooked knob, of which the horny covering is from time to time shed. The body is very massive, the neck long and comparatively slender, the head small, and the legs short with very elongated toes. The wings, in which the third quill is the longest, are large and broad; and the tail, which contains from eighteen to twenty-four feathers, is short, broad, and rounded (page 1247.)

PELICANS

Although thick, the general plumage is remarkable for its harshness and roughness, the feathers of the breast ending in narrow points; and the back of the head is generally furnished with a helmet-like crest. The looseness of the plumage and its constant damp condition render pelicans decidedly dishevelled and disreputable-looking birds. The adults of the two sexes are nearly similar in colour, but the young are very different. In the skeleton the furcula is welded to the upper part of the breast-bone, as in cormorants; but the vertebræ of the back differ from those of the latter in having saddle-shaped, instead of ball-and-socket, surfaces for articulation with one another. All the bones, and likewise the integuments, are penetrated to a most remarkable extent by air-cavities.

Pelicans, of which there are some half-score of kinds, are restricted to the tropical and warmer regions of the globe, where they have a very wide distribution. They are all very similar in general appearance and habits, although the American white pelican (*Pelecanus trachyrhynchus*) differs from the rest in being an expert diver. The typical European pelican (*P. onocrotalus*), as the best known representative of the genus, will serve to illustrate the habits of all. It belongs to a group characterised by the feathers of the forehead extending forwards in a point on to the upper part of the beak.

During the breeding season the back of the head carries a somewhat elongated crest ; the upper half of the beak is reddish at the base and yellowish at the tip, with a line of crimson along the middle, the lower half is pale red, and the pouch and naked space round the eye, as well as the feet, are flesh-coloured. Of the plumage, the primaries and bastard-wing are black, the long feathers on the front of the lower part of the neck yellow, and the remainder white, with a tinge of rose-colour. The tail has eighteen feathers. In birds of the first year the plumage is uniformly greyish brown, the lanceolate feathers of the breast being wanting ; and it is not till some years later that the full plumage is acquired, the depth of the rose-tint being most marked during the breeding season.

This species, which attains a length of about 5 feet, inhabits the more southern parts of Europe and Northern Africa, ranging southwards to Senegambia and Mozambique, and also occurring in North-Western India. While common in Hungary, the Crimea, Egypt, and the Ionian Islands, it only occurs occasionally in France and Algeria. In India there is a rather smaller species (*P. roseus*), distinguished by the presence of a long pendent crest at all seasons ; this bird also ranging over Greece, Egypt, Abyssinia, and Africa.

The other European species is the crested pelican (*P. crispus*), which belongs to the group in which the feathers of the forehead are truncated in front and terminate more or less squarely on the base of the beak. In this species the general plumage is white tinged with grey, the wing black, and the feathers of the crown and back of the head crinkled and elongated into a large crest. The eye is silver-white, the beak greyish yellow above, the pouch blood-red shaded with blue, and the foot black. Its eastern range extends to China and Mongolia. The Philippine species (*P. philippinensis*) extends from India to the Philippines. *P. conspicillatus* is restricted to Australasia, and there are several peculiar American species in addition to the one already mentioned. Fossil pelicans occur commonly in the Miocene deposits of Europe, and also in the Pliocene of Northern India.

Pelicans commonly occur in enormous flocks in the neighbourhood of swamps, estuaries, and rivers (p. 73), and are sometimes so numerous that in India Mr. A. O. Hume writes of having seen *miles* of them. Their food is mainly fish, of which they consume immense quantities, but crayfish have been taken from the stomach of the American species. In fishing they generally select water of sufficient depth to swim in, but not too deep to prevent them touching the bottom when swimming with their heads beneath the surface. In this posture a flock will frequently form a line or horseshoe, each bird stationed about a yard from its neighbour, and fish the water in a most regular and systematic manner from bank to bank. On reaching the opposite bank, the great, clumsy birds either waddle on shore to preen and dress their feathers, and afford time for the digestion of their meal, or take flight to another piece of water.

In general, their periods of feeding and repose are marked out with great regularity. The females attend to the feeding of the young, which is effected by the old birds pressing their beaks against their breasts and raising the lid-like upper half of the former, when the young birds thrust their heads into the pouch and help themselves to the fish. This statement applies to *P. onocrotalus*, but in the case of *P. crispus*, as observed in Albania, the young birds have been seen to thrust their heads into the parental throat much below the opening of the pouch, thus resembling young cormorants. The nests of this species are generally in groups of six or eight, the majority mere flat rings of sticks on the ground, but a few forming large structures of sticks

some two feet in height, very similar to cormorants' nests. It is doubtless the above-mentioned feeding action, coupled with the pinky white colour of the plumage, that gave origin to the old fable of the pelican feeding her offspring from the blood of her own breast.

The eggs, from two to three in number, have thick, bluish white shells, encrusted with chalky matter, and it is not uncommon to find both eggs and half-fledged young in the same nest. In India, at least, the male and female birds not infrequently associate in separate flocks. In spite of their bulk and clumsy form, pelicans display extreme activity when on the wing, flying in long lines with the neck bent back over the body ; and all who have seen flocks of these birds under such circumstances describe it as one of the most imposing and striking scenes that can well be imagined.

FRIGATE-BIRDS

The members of the two remaining families of the Steganopodes—each represented by only a single genus—differ from all the foregoing groups in being completely pelagic in their habits. The frigate, or man-of-war, birds (*Fregatidæ*) are characterised by the slender body, short and thick neck, long and powerful hooked beak, of which both halves are deflected at the end, the extremely short legs, feathered down to the toes, the elongated and sharply pointed wings, and the deep, swallow-like forking of the long tail. The feet differ from those of other members of the order by the webs extending only a short distance up the long and sharply clawed toes ; and these birds are further characterised by the first quill of the wing being the longest, as well as by the tail having twelve feathers. There is a tract devoid of feathers around the eye and on the throat. The bones are more permeated by air-cavities than in any other bird, and there is a large dilatable air-sac beneath the throat.

In the great frigate-bird (*Fregatus aquila*), which inhabits the warmer regions of the Atlantic, Indian, and Pacific Oceans, the plumage of the adult male is brownish black, shot with metallic green and purple on the head, neck, back, breast, and sides, and shaded with grey on the wings. The eye is brown, with the surrounding bare space purplish blue, the beak light blue at the base, white in the middle, and dark horn-colour at the tip, the throat-sac orange red in the breeding season, and the foot carmine red above and orange beneath. The females differ by their duller tints, and the presence of a larger or smaller pure white area on the breast (page 1248.)

The lesser frigate-bird (*F. minor*, or *F. ariel*), which is confined to the Indo-Pacific, differs by its smaller size, the less bronzy sheen of the plumage, and the presence of a white patch on each flank.

The frigate-bird, which has received the title of the son of the sun, is one of the most swift and active of all pelagic birds, spending much of its time on the wing, often far away from land, and subsisting largely on the fish which it compels terns and other birds to disgorge. In regard to their predatory habits, Dr. H. O. Forbes writes that "in the Cocos-Keeling Islands, hiding in the lee of the cocoanut trees, the frigate-birds would sally out on the successful fishers returning in the evening, and perpetrate a vigorous assault on them until they disgorged for their behoof at least a share of their supper, which they caught in mid-air as it fell. The swoop after the falling spoil was so elegant an evolution that I always hoped that the poor noddy would give up as heavy a morsel as possible, in order to necessitate a correspondingly eager dive after it. Refractory gannets were often seized by the

MEMBERS OF THE PELICAN FAMILY

Reading from left to right the species represented are 1, 4, and 5, Brown Pelicans; 2 and 3, Australian Pelicans; 6, Red-backed Pelican

tail by the frigate-birds, and treated to a shake that rarely failed of successful results. Fierce foes as they were in the air, on *terra firma* they roosted near each other like the best of friends."

On the Island of Fernando Noronha the frigate-birds breed on the verge of an inaccessible precipice, the nests being visible on looking down from the top, and each containing a single egg. On the other hand, in the unmolested Raine Island these birds nest on the ground.

The following account of the frigate-birds on Christmas Island, in the Indian Ocean, is given by Dr. C. W. Andrews : "Numbers of these birds could nearly always be seen sailing and circling in the air at all heights ; in calm weather they often soar till scarcely visible. The flight is wonderfully graceful, and it is a pleasure to watch a group moving along the coast in a succession of sweeping circles, rising against the wind, or descending with it. In flight the head is carried close to the body, so that the bird seems to have no neck, and the tip of the beak is about on a level with the anterior angle of the outstretched wings. The feathers are often cleaned during flight, and occasionally the bird shakes itself like a dog that has just left the water, dropping through the air meanwhile.

"The young birds seem to be able to fly perfectly well as soon as they leave the nest, and groups of them could often be seen near the coast stooping to the water, one after the other, to pick up leaves and other floating objects, and then dropping them, apparently practising the method by which their parents obtain their food, which consists of surface fish and cephalopods. I never saw a frigate-bird dive.

"The old birds by no means depend for food on the fish they catch themselves, but systematically rob the gannets, which breed in great numbers on the island. Towards sunset many frigate-birds may be seen sailing along the coast watching for the return of the gannets, full-fed from the fishing grounds. The birds being well aware of what is in store for them, and knowing that if they can reach the shelter of the trees they are safe, approach the island at a great speed, flying as low down as possible. Usually, while they are still at some distance, two or three frigate-birds give chase, and hunt the gannet backwards and forwards, continually trying to get beneath it and cut off its retreat to the trees. The chase may last several minutes, but at length the exhausted bird disgorges some of the fish it had swallowed, and this is immediately caught in mid-air by one of the pursuers. Mr. Ross told me that occasionally two frigate-birds would come into collision and break their wings, but this I never saw.

"The twigs for building the nests are obtained on the same system of robbery, and, although these birds will pick up twigs floating in the sea and lying on the beach, I never saw one attempt to break them off the dead branches as the gannets do. If, when a nest is partly built, the bird in charge of it is killed, dozens of its neighbours come round and steal the material thus conveniently collected for them. The nest consists merely of a few handfuls of twigs placed on the fork of a small branch, and it seems wonderful how the egg remains on it. When the young has been hatched a few days, the nest becomes converted into a hard, nearly flat cake of twigs and excrement. Old nests, and those of gannets, are often utilised.

"About the beginning of January the adult males begin to acquire the remarkable pouch of scarlet skin beneath their throat. This they can inflate till it is nearly as large as the rest of the body, and a dozen or more of these birds sitting in a tree with outstretched drooping wings and this great scarlet bladder under their heads are a most remarkable sight. When a hen bird approaches the tree the males utter a peculiar cry, a sort of ' Wow-wow-wow-wow,' and clatter their beaks like castanets, at the same time shaking the wings

THE GREAT FRIGATE-BIRD

When they take to flight, the air is allowed to escape from the pouch, but occasionally they might be seen flying with it partly inflated.

"The pairing season extended from January till April ; eggs were found in February, and in August there were still many young birds in white down, but by October all had flown. The young continue to get a certain amount of food from their parents even after the latter have begun to build again."

TROPIC-BIRDS

The tropic-birds (family *Phaëthontidæ*), or "boatswains," as they are commonly called by sailors, are represented by about half a dozen species, and are somewhat inferior in size to the common English gull. In general appearance they are not unlike terns, from which they are, however, distinguished at a glance by the greatly elongated middle pair of feathers of the tail.

IMMATURE RED-BEAKED TROPIC-BIRD

distinguished by its yellow beak and the red middle tail feathers. Very distinct is the yellow tropic-bird (*P. fulvus*), of the Indian Ocean, in which the general colour, inclusive of the beak, is orange yellow, with black on some of the wing coverts and primaries. The West Indian species has been named *P. americanus*, while a species from the Indian Ocean is distinguished as *P. indicus*, and another widely spread one as *P. lepturus*. Tropic-birds often follow in the wake of vessels for long distances, and display great boldness. During the breeding season they frequent the Bermuda and Pacific Islands in great numbers, generally breeding in companies and making their nests in the holes in rocks.

I had the good fortune to see a living specimen of the red-beaked tropic-bird, which came on board the R.M.S. Magdalena in the South Atlantic on September 5, 1893, during the night, in an apparently exhausted condition. After a night's rest it recovered, and flew away on being liberated. The pearly lustre of the lovely grebe-like plumage of the head and neck was particularly striking; and the beauty of the two long tail feathers of this child of the ocean excited the admiration of all the beholders.

Dr. Andrews describes the habits of the tropic-birds on Christmas Island as follows:

In addition to this feature, they differ from frigate-birds by the conical and pointed beak, near the base of which are situated the very large nostrils, by the longer and naked metatarsus, the completely webbed toes, and the absence of a bare space round the eye, and of a throat-sac.

The longest-known and most widely distributed species is the red-beaked tropic-bird (*Phaëthon æthereus*), ranging over the tropical regions of the Atlantic and Pacific Oceans. In the adult the body plumage is white, with a reddish tinge, and black shaft-stripes to the feathers; the outer webs of the primaries are white, the hinder secondaries mingled black and white, and the two long tail feathers white. The beak is coral-red, the eye brown, the leg yellow, and the web and toes black. In younger birds the feathers of the back have black bands at the tips; while in a still younger stage the middle tail feathers are not elongated, and the beak is brown.

The white tropic-bird (*P. rubricauda*) of the tropical Indian and Pacific Oceans has the general colour of the plumage white, as in the first species, but is

"The most beautiful of sea-birds is the yellow tropic-bird, which, though much less numerous than the frigate-birds, is still fairly common. The flight of these birds is swift, though, owing to the rapidity of the strokes of the wing, it often seems as if they were labouring. I never saw them sail except for a short distance when wheeling round. On hot days they may be seen in twos and threes, flying rapidly up and down above and among the tree-tops, continually uttering their peculiar crackling cry, and pausing now and then to hover before holes in the trees which seem to offer an eligible position for a nest.

"It can hardly be said, however, that they make a nest, for the single dark brown, mottled egg is merely placed in a slight hollow on the floor of a hole in a tree or in the sea-cliff. Eggs and young were obtained in August and September; the breeding season seems to be less definite than in the case of the other birds."

Remains of a fossil tropic-bird (*Prophaëthon*) have been obtained from the lower Eocene deposits of the Isle of Sheppey.

ORDER VIII. ODONTORMÆ—EXTINCT

From strata in the United States older than the Tertiary period have been obtained remains of birds in which the beak was provided with a full series of teeth. Of these toothed birds there are two very well marked modifications, both from strata corresponding approximately in age with the Chalk and associated formations of Europe, and hence frequently spoken of as Cretaceous birds. In their general organisation these birds approximate closely to the toothless birds of the present day, but differ, not only in the possession of teeth, but also by the circumstance that the two branches of the lower half of the beak remain completely separate in front, instead of having a solid bony union.

Of these toothed birds, the one type is known as *Ichthyornis*, and comprises somewhat gull-like species

characterised by having the numerous series of teeth implanted in distinct sockets, and also by the vertebræ, or joints of the backbone, articulating with one another by means of cup-like surfaces, whereas in the neck —and generally also in the back—of all existing birds, such surfaces are saddle-shaped. Although the skeleton of *Ichthyornis* shows many resemblances to that of the gulls, this being especially the case in the skull, which comes very close to that of the skimmers (*Rhynchops*), the skeleton differs, among other points, by the circumstance that there is no projecting process on the outer side of the lower end of the humerus, or upper wing-bone. In this respect, *Ichthyornis* and its relatives agree with the members of the cormorant group, next which they may be provisionally placed as the representatives of the order Odontormæ.

ORDER IX. ANSERES
CHARACTERISTICS OF THE DUCK TRIBE

Taking the term duck tribe to include ducks, geese, swans, etc., the members of the order Anseres, together with the succeeding orders of flamingoes (Phœnicopteri) and screamers (Palamedæ), comprise birds with bridged (desmognathous) palates, broadly distinguished from those hitherto described by the circumstance that their young are covered with down when hatched, and are able to run within a few hours of their first appearance in the world. The members of these three orders are accordingly the only birds which have bridged palates, and "precocious" young.

In the collective group, the three front toes are either completely webbed, or united by a fold of skin ; and in most cases the beak is either depressed and expanded, or has its extremity so bent down as to be at right angles to its base, while the hind angle of its lower half is produced in a recurved process behind the point of articulation with the skull. Generally the rostrum of the base of the skull has oval basipterygoid facets placed relatively far forwards, and in all cases the oil-gland is tufted. Many members of the group are more or less completely herbivorous.

All the members of the duck tribe are distinguished by the legs being short, and inferior in length to the wings, and by the tibia being usually feathered nearly or quite to the ankle, and scarcely free from the body. The shank, or metatarsus, is characterised by the shortness and backward direction of the trochlea, or pulley, for the second toe, and the tibia distinguished by the marked inflection of its lower extremity. The first toe, although generally small, is always present, and the three front toes, except in one instance, are completely webbed. The relatively short beak is comparatively straight, and more or less depressed and laterally expanded, with peculiar parallel plates on its edges ; while the rostrum of the lower surface of the skull shows well-marked basipterygoid facets for the articulation of the pterygoid bones. In the skeleton of the body the coracoid bone is relatively long and narrow, and loosely articulated to the breast bone. The plumage is characterised by its dense and compact nature, and the facility with which water is thrown off from its surface. In the wings there are always ten primary quills, but the number of tail feathers is liable to variation.

WILD DUCK, OR MALLARD

All the members of the order moult annually in the autumn, and the quills of the wings are generally shed so rapidly as to incapacitate the birds for flight for some days. In ducks, however, the males change their contour-feathers twice in the year, and for a short period assume what is commonly known as the "eclipse plumage." This corresponds with the non-breeding dress of other birds, the breeding plumage being worn for the greater part of the year. All the members of the duck tribe lay uniformly coloured eggs, of which the number in a clutch is large, the eggs being further characterised by their hard and usually very smooth shells.

The general external appearance of the members of the duck tribe is too well known to need special mention. It may be observed, however, that their build is that best adapted for rapid progress through the water, the breast and fore part of the body being broad and rounded, the hind extremity narrow and tapering, and the legs placed relatively far back.

Although it has been attempted to divide the members of the order into several distinct families, the whole of them are so nearly allied that it seems impossible to do more than group the genera of the one family *Anatidæ* under several subfamilies, and even some of these are very difficult of definition. The species of the family, which are between one and two hundred in number, are distributed all over the globe, although more numerous in the higher latitudes of the Northern Hemisphere than elsewhere. All are thoroughly aquatic in their habits ; but while the majority are swimmers, the members of one group are expert divers.

As a rule, they associate in flocks of larger or smaller size, and migrate in numbers to the northern portions of their habitat for the breeding season. They are all birds of strong flight, and when on the wing fly in the well-known chevron-shaped formation, frequently at a great height in the air. Although the majority of the species are more or less omnivorous in their diet, the mergansers subsist exclusively on fish, while the greater part of the food of the geese consists of grass. The group is not a very ancient one, the earliest known forms occurring in the lower beds of the Miocene division of the Tertiary period.

CLASSIFICATION OF ANSERES MENTIONED IN THIS WORK

ORDER
Ducks, Geese, and Swans—Anseres
FAMILY
Ducks, Geese, and Swans—Anatidæ
GENUS 1
Swans—Cygnus
SPECIES
Whistling swan . . . . Cygnus musicus
Bewick's swan . . . . C. bewicki
American swan . . . . C. columbianus
Trumpeter swan . . . . C. buccinator
Mute swan . . . . C. olor
Polish swan . . . . C. immutabilis
Black-necked swan . . . . C. nigricollis
GENUS 2
Black Swan—Chenopsis
SPECIES
Black swan . . . . Chenopsis atrata
GENUS 3
Coscoroba Swan—Coscoroba
SPECIES
Coscoroba . . . . Coscoroba candida
GENUS 4
Anseranas
SPECIES
Half-webbed goose . . Anseranas semipalmatus
GENUS 5
Spur-winged Geese—Plectropterus
SPECIES
Spur-winged goose . . . . Plectropterus gambensis
Rüppell's spur-winged goose . . . . . . P. rueppelli
Black spur-wing . . . . P. niger
Shoan spur-wing . . . . P. shoanus
GENUS 6
Muscovy Duck—Carina
SPECIES
Muscovy duck . . . . Carina moschata
GENUS 7
Comb-Ducks—Sarcidiornis
SPECIES
Indian comb-duck . . Sarcidiornis melanonotus
American comb-duck . . . . S. carunculatus
GENUS 8
Nettopus
SPECIES
Cotton teal . . . . Nettopus coromandelianus
GENUS 9
Æx
SPECIES
Summer-duck . . . . Æx sponsa
Mandarin-duck . . . . Æ. galericulata
GENUS 10
Cereopsis
SPECIES
Cape Barron goose . . . . Cereopsis novæ-hollandiæ
GENUS 11
Typical Geese—Anser
SPECIES
Grey-lag goose . . . . Anser cinereus
White-fronted goose . . . . A. albifrons
North American goose . . . . A. gambeli
Bean-goose . . . . A. segetum
Pink-footed goose . . . . A. brachyrhynchus
GENUS 12
Snow-geese—Chen
SPECIES
Snow-goose . . . . Chen hyperboreus
Ross's goose . . . . C. rossi
Blue-winged goose . . . . C. cœrulescens
GENUS 13
Brent-Geese—Branta
SPECIES
Brent-goose . . . . Branta bernicla
White-bellied goose . . . . B. glaucogaster
American brent-goose . . . . B. nigricans
Bernicle-goose . . . . B. leucopsis
Canada brent-goose . . . . B. canadensis
Hutchins's goose . . . . B. hutchinsi
Red-breasted goose . . . . B. ruficollis
GENUS 14
Clœphaga
SPECIES
Upland goose . . , ... , , . Clœphaga magellanica

Kelp goose . . . . C. antarctica
GENUS 15
Chenonetta
SPECIES
Australian brent-goose . . . . . . Chenonetta jubata
GENUS 16
Nesochen
SPECIES
Sandwich Island goose . . Nesochen sandvicensis
GENUS 17
Knob-winged Geese—Chenalopex
SPECIES
Knob-winged goose . . . . Chenalopex ægyptiaca
South American knob-winged goose . . C. jubata
GENUS 18
Tree-Ducks—Dendrocygna
SPECIES
Tree-duck . . . . Dendrocygna viduata
Indian tree-duck . . . . D. javanica
GENUS 19
Sheldrakes—Tadorna
SPECIES
Sheldrake . . . . Tadorna cornuta
Ruddy sheldrake . . . . T. casarca
GENUS 20
Typical Ducks—Anas
SPECIES
Wild duck . . . . Anas boscas
Spot-bill duck . . . . A. pœcilorhyncha
Dusky duck . . . . A. obscura
GENUS 21
Chaulelasmus
SPECIES
Gadwall . . . . Chaulelasmus
strepera
Coues's gadwall . . . . C. couesi
GENUS 22
Shovellers—Spatula
SPECIES
Shoveller . . . . Spatula clypeata
South American shoveller . . . . S. platalea
Cape shoveller . . . . S. capensis
GENUS 23
Pintail Ducks—Dafila
SPECIES
Pintail . . . . Dafila acuta
Chilian pintail . . . . D. spinicauda
American Bahama duck . . . . D. bahamensis
South African red-billed duck . . . . D. erythro-
rhyncha
GENUS 24
Teal—Nettium
SPECIES
Teal . . . . Nettium crecca
American teal . . . . N. carolinense
GENUS 25
Querquedula
SPECIES
Garganey, or summer teal . . Querquedula circia
American blue-winged teal . . . . Q. discolor
Cinnamon teal . . . . Q. cyanoptera
Asiatic clucking teal . . . . Q. formosa
GENUS 26
Wigeon—Mareca
SPECIES
Wigeon . . . . Mareca penelope
North American wigeon . . . . M. americana
Chilian wigeon . . . . M. sibilatrix
GENUS 27
Red Pochards—Netta
SPECIES
Red-crested pochard . . . . Netta rufina
GENUS 28
Scaup and Pochards—Nyroca
SPECIES
Scaup duck . . . . Nyroca marila
American pochard . . . . N. affinis
Tufted duck . . . . N. fuligula
The pochard . . . . N. ferina

Red-headed pochard . . . . N. americana
Canvas-backed duck . . . . N. vallisneria
White-eyed pochard . . . . N. ferruginea
Australian white-eye . . . . N. australis
GENUS 29
Golden-eyes—Clangula
SPECIES
Golden-eye . . . . Clangula glaucion
Barrow's golden-eye . . . . C. islandica
Buffel-headed duck . . . . C. albeola
GENUS 30
Steamer-Duck—Tachyeres
SPECIES
Steamer-duck . . . . Tachyeres cinereus
GENUS 31
Harlequin-Duck—Histrionicus
SPECIES
Harlequin-duck . . . . Histrionicus torquatus
GENUS 32
Long-tailed Duck—Harelda
SPECIES
Long-tailed duck . . . . Harelda glacialis
GENUS 33
Eider Ducks—Somateria
SPECIES
The eider . . . . Somateria mollissima
American eider . . . . S. borealis
King-eider . . . . S. spectabilis
Steller's eider . . . . S. stelleri
Fischer's eider . . . . S. fischeri
Labrador duck . . . . S. labradoria
GENUS 34
Scoters—Œdemia
SPECIES
The scoter . . . . Œdemia nigra
American scoter . . . . Œ. americana
Velvet-scoter . . . . Œ. fusca
American surf-scoter . . . . Œ. perspicillata
GENUS 35
Stiff-tailed Ducks—Erismatura
SPECIES
White-faced duck . . . . Erismatura leucocephala
North American duck . . . . E. rubida
Ferruginous duck . . . . E. ferruginea
Australian stiff-tailed duck . . . . E. australis
GENUS 36
Musk-Duck—Biziura
SPECIES
Musk-duck . . . . Biziura lobata
GENUS 37
White-backed Duck—Thalassornis
SPECIES
White-backed duck . . . . Thalassornis leuconotus
GENUS 38
Mergansers—Merganser
SPECIES
Auckland merganser . . . . . . Merganser australis
Brazilian merganser . . . . M. brasiliensis
Goosander . . . . M. castor
Red-breasted merganser . . . . M. serrator
Hooded merganser . . . . M. cucullatus
GENUS 39
Smew—Mergus
SPECIES
Smew . . . . Mergus albellus
GENUS 40
Merganetta
GENUS 41
Hymenolæmus
SPECIES
New Zealand merganser . . . . Hymenolæmus
malacorhynchus
GENUS 42
Salvadorina
SPECIES
Papuan merganser . . Salvadorina waiginiensis

THE UPPER TWO PICTURES SHOW THE BIRDS NESTING; THE LOWER ONE A MALE ON A NORFOLK BROAD

SWANS, GEESE, AND DUCKS

SWANS

So indissolubly was the attribute of whiteness connected among the ancients with the swans that the idea of a black swan, as expressed in the well-known line, *rara avis in terris, nigroque simillima cygno* (a rare bird in the world, and most like to a black swan), was considered a mere flight of the poetic imagination. Nevertheless, not only does a black swan exist, but a second species is remarkable for having a black head and neck and a white body.

The swans, which form the subfamily *Cygninæ*, are typically characterised by their exceedingly long necks, the naked lores, the simple first toe, and the metatarsus reticulated and shorter than the third toe with the claw. All these birds are of large size, and have the flexible and slender neck as long as, or longer than, the body; while the beak exceeds the head in length, and has its edges parallel, and the terminal nail small. The tail feathers vary from twenty to twenty-four in number, and, with the exception of the black Australian swan, the plumage is entirely or mainly white in the adult state. The two sexes are nearly alike, and there is but a single moult.

Swans, of which there are comparatively few species, are distributed over the greater part of the world except Africa south of the Sahara, North Australia, and the northern districts of South America. The gracefulness of their form, and especially the beautiful curving of the neck, are proverbial; and they are all birds of powerful flight, more aquatic in their habits than geese, but also walking well on land. Frequenting lakes and other inland waters in summer, they often seek the sea in winter; but while some prefer open waters, others, like Bewick's swan, rather favour marshes and narrow rivers. Their food consists of the seeds, stems, and roots of flags and other water plants, supplemented by insects and molluscs.

All the white swans are migratory, and during their migrations fly both by night and day. Like geese, they are more or less gregarious, especially during winter; and they also resemble those birds in pairing apparently for life. Their large untidy nests are placed on the ground, often among tussocks of coarse grass, and contain from three to eight dull whitish eggs. As a rule, the young birds have feathered lores, and a greyish brown plumage. The call note is loud and trumpet-like.

WHISTLING SWAN

At least two species of swans are winter visitors to the British Islands, while a third occurs in a domesti-

WHISTLING SWAN

cated state, although probably a few wild individuals also arrive. The first of these is the whooper, or whistling, swan (*Cygnus musicus*), which belongs to a group of species common to the northern half of both the Old and New Worlds, and characterised by the comparatively short and rounded tail. The whooper is specially distinguished by the lores and the basal portion of the beak to below the nostrils being yellow and the remainder of the nostrils black. In length this species reaches 60 inches.

The whooper is essentially an Arctic species, breeding chiefly within the Arctic Circle either on the islands in the deltas of the great rivers, or on the lakes of the Siberian tundras. Iceland and the northern parts of Scandinavia are also favourite nesting places of this species, which appears to breed in pairs and not in small flocks. Apparently during its winter migration this species does not, except in unusually severe winters, go so far south as some of its allies, although at times it reaches the Mediterranean Islands, Egypt, Algeria, and Palestine. Eastwards, it visits the Caspian, Persia, Turkestan, China, and Japan, but it is unknown in India proper. The nesting season begins in the latter half of May, the usual period of incubation being about six weeks; but the young birds are unable to fly before the end of August. In diet these swans are mainly vegetarians.

BEWICK'S SWAN

Bewick's swan (*C. bewicki*), which is a considerably smaller bird than the last, may be distinguished by the yellow of the beak not extending below the nostrils; the total length being about 50 inches. The general distribution of this species is very similar to that of the whooper, although this swan is only an accidental visitor to Norway, and does not breed in Iceland. Indeed, it is only within the last forty years that its nest and eggs were first obtained, and even now very little is known of its breeding habits, since this swan is even a more northerly bird than the whooper. Its note is less loud and harsh than that of the latter, being in fact somewhat musical in sound. In winter these swans congregate in enormous flocks, which may be numbered by hundreds, or even thousands, and they are at all times exceedingly wary and difficult to approach.

In both the whooper and Bewick's swan the windpipe is bent upon itself, and received into a cavity in the front of the breast bone, from which it again emerges to enter the chest; but the nature of the folding is different in the two species, and serves to distinguish them.

TRUMPETER SWAN

North America possesses two representatives of this group of swans, namely, the typical American swan (*C. columbianus*), and the trumpeter swan (*C. buccinator*), each of which has the windpipe folded. Both these species have black beaks, but in the former the number of tail feathers is usually twenty, the beak is not longer than the head, and the naked skin of the lores generally shows a yellow spot; while in the latter there are twenty-four tail feathers, the beak is longer than the head, and there is no yellow on the lores. The trumpeter somewhat exceeds the whooper in size, whereas the other species is somewhat smaller.

In defence of wounded companions the American swan is stated to display great affection, a number having been known to collect round a disabled bird and aid its escape by pushing it forward in the water and supporting its broken wing. In southerly migration these swans collect in flocks of twenty or thirty, flying only when the wind is favourable, and then ascending to a great height in the air. The flock flies in the form of an elongated wedge, the rate of progress being estimated at upwards of a hundred miles an hour.

BEWICK'S SWAN

In Britain the species appears to be represented only by domesticated birds. While swimming, the mute swan is the most graceful of all its kin, being the one in which alone the neck is bent in true "swan-like" form. Deriving its name from the absence of any cry in the domesticated breed, the species in a wild state trumpets like the whooper. The nesting time—during which the male displays extreme pugnacity—takes place in May; the nests being generally built in association, and the number of eggs in each varying from five to eight. The pale green colour of the eggs is a distinctive character.

The largest swannery in England is the one at Abbotsbury, near Weymouth, belonging to the Earl of Ilchester, where in 1880 there were upwards of fourteen hundred birds. This swannery, which dates from very ancient times, is situated on the estuary known as the Fleet, of which the upper portion is brackish while the lower parts are completely salt. In the breeding season the nests cover a large area near the shore, and while some of the young birds remain to increase the numbers in the swannery, others wander out into the Fleet and become nearly wild. The severe winter of 1880-81 reduced the number of swans to about eight hundred, an average which has been since maintained.

MUTE SWAN

The mute swan (*C. olor*) of the Old World indicates a second group of the genus, characterised by the relatively long and wedge-shaped tail, the presence of a large fleshy knob, or tubercle, at the base of the beak, and the absence of a fold of the windpipe entering the breast-bone. In addition to these features, the mute swan may be recognised by the colouring of the beak, in which the base, together with the lores and tubercle, is black, while the terminal portion is orange red; the colouring being therefore just the reverse of that met with in the whooper. In size the mute swan agrees with the latter. The tubercle of the beak attains its greatest development in old males.

BLACK SWAN

The range of the species includes Europe and some portions of Asia, the breeding area embracing South Sweden, parts of Germany, Russia, Transylvania, Turkestan, etc., while during winter these birds enter Northern Africa, Egypt, and North-Western India.

POLISH SWAN

A considerable amount of discussion has taken place as to whether the so-called Polish swan (*C. immutabilis*), distinguished by the smaller size of the tubercle on the beak, the black edges to the gape, and the slaty legs, as well by the plumage of the cygnets being often white from birth, is entitled to rank as a distinct species. It seems, however, that the distinctive features of the adult are due to immaturity, and that the white plumage of the cygnets is merely an effect of domestication, so that this bird is not entitled to rank as a distinct species.

BLACK-NECKED SWAN

The handsome black-necked swan (*C. nigricollis*) from Chile, Argentina, and other southern districts of South America, is easily distinguished from all the preceding by the black head and neck; the rest of the plumage being white, and the lores and base of the beak red. It agrees with the mute swan in having the tail long and wedge-shaped, but differs in the scalloped margin of the web of the toes. Remains of the whooper and Bewick's swan in the superficial deposits of the Thames Valley indicate that those birds were contemporaries of the mammoth. From the Mioceen of Malta have been obtained bones of the extinct Falconer's swan (*Cygnus falconeri*), a bird of larger size than any existing species, from which it differed by its extremely short and goose-like toes.

BLACK SWAN

The black swan (*Chenopsis atrata*) differs from all its relatives, not only in the predominant hue of the adult plumage being blackish, but also by the young having feathered lores, and likewise by the extreme shortness of the tail, and the crispness of the scapular and inner secondary feathers, and is therefore referred to a genus by itself. The naked parts of the head and the skin at the base of the beak are red, and the feathers of the pinion white, but otherwise the bird is black. Inferior in size to the whooper, this elegant swan is far less shy than the majority of its kindred; and when flying overhead at night utters a decidedly musical call-note.

In Victoria the "Old Bushman" writes that after the young birds can fly, black swans were common "on all the large swamps and lagoons; sometimes in good-sized flocks, but generally in small companies, which I took to be old birds and birds of the year. Early in summer they retire to their breeding haunts, and we saw very little of them again till the swamps and water-holes filled. They appear to breed in August and September. The nest is a large heap of rushes, and the female lays five to seven dirty white eggs, not so large as those of the mute swan."

The islands in Westernport Bay are favourite nesting sites of this species. Being a bird of heavy flight, the black swan always endeavours to save itself, if possible, by swimming rather than by taking wing.

COSCOROBA SWAN

A small South American species, known as the coscoroba (*Coscoroba candida*), has, on account of

BLACK AND WHITE GOOSE

SPUR-WINGED GOOSE

its feathered lores and somewhat goose-like habits, been transferred by some naturalists from the swans to the geese, although all its characters are essentially those of the former; the feathered lores of the adult being only one step in advance of the condition obtaining in the black swan. This bird, which is a native of the southern districts of South America, is about the size of a goose, with the plumage white, except for black tips to the primary quills, and the pink beak and feet.

PIED GOOSE

An altogether peculiar type is the pied, or half-webbed, goose (*Anseranas semipalmatus*) of Australia, in which the front toes are only webbed at the base, and the hind one is very long and not raised above the level of the former, and furnished with a large claw. The lores are naked, and the metatarsus is reticulate and longer than the third toe. This remarkable bird, which is about the size of the brent-goose, constitutes a distinct subfamily (*Anseraninæ*) by itself, and has a dull black and white plumage, and a hooked beak, with a large, warty comb-like prominence on the front of the head. The claws are long and sharp, and the whole foot is adapted for perching.

In accordance with this structure, these birds sit for hours on the branches of the Australian tea-tree, and but seldom enter the water. Their cry is loud and hoarse, but quite unlike that of an ordinary goose; and the windpipe is folded on itself, although on the side of, instead of within, the breast bone, as in the swans.

SPUR-WINGED GEESE

A third subfamily, the *Plectropterinæ*, is typified by the African spur-winged geese, of which there are four species. These birds take their name from the long spur on each wing, which is sharply pointed and attached to the outer side of the wrist joint. The lores are naked, and the metatarsus is covered in front with large plates; and the beak is of considerable length and of nearly equal width throughout, terminating in a nail-like knob, and having at its base a large protuberance. In the adult the front of the head is bare and warty, and the cheeks and part of the neck are also naked. The leg is of considerable length, with the lower part of the tibia bare, the metatarsus wide and compressed, and the first toe relatively long, simple, and elevated, the front webs being somewhat deeply incised.

In *Plectropterus gambensis* the plumage of all the upper parts and the sides of the breast is black, tinged with coppery green ; the wings are mottled with white, the abdomen white with patches of black behind the thighs, the naked parts of the face reddish, and the beak and legs reddish and orange yellow. In size the bird nearly equals the English wild goose. The Gambian spur-winged goose inhabits tropical Africa, ranging from Senegambia southwards to the Transvaal, but is replaced in Abyssinia and the adjacent regions by Rüppell's spur-winged goose (*P. rueppelli*), in South-East Africa by *P. niger*, and in Shoa by *P. shoanus*.

In the Sudan these birds are generally found in small parties, which for a considerable part of the year frequent the banks of rivers, although during the moulting time, when unable to fly, they seek the retirement and shelter of the reedy marshes and swamps, and in the breeding season the flocks divide up into pairs. Farther south they frequent the reedy margins of Lake Ngami and the Chobi and Zambezi rivers, where they breed in immense numbers. When, however, the smaller watercourses and pools are filled with water, these birds desert the impenetrable swamps, to wander in pairs over the country.

The broods usually number from eight to twelve, the old birds remaining with their progeny for the remainder of the season following the nesting. They do not feed in the daytime, when they may be observed in the open water, or standing motionless on some dry bank, rocky prominence, or island. When on the wing, they continuously utter a low, hissing noise, and shortly after sundown, just before darkness sets in, leave their day resorts and fly to the feeding ground, which is generally a meadow or swamp overgrown with grass, when they spend the night in search of leeches and other water-animals. The nest is a huge structure of reeds and flags, generally built among the reeds, but occasionally in a low bush ; and to the northward the number of eggs is said to be much less than that above-mentioned. During the night they generally fly low; and, in accordance with the length of their legs, walk less awkwardly than geese. Shy and wary, as well as endowed with great vitality, these birds are difficult to kill, and the flesh of the old ones is extremely rank and tough. They are easily tamed, and thrive in confinement, although their disposition is pugnacious.

MUSCOVY DUCK

In the same subfamily as the spur-winged geese is included the well-known but mis-called Muscovy duck (*Carina moschata*), whose proper title is the musk-duck, although that name is commonly applied to another species. These birds are familiar as ornamental water-fowl in England (page 1284), although they are natives of Central and South America, where their range extends from Mexico to Argentina. They are relatively large birds, with the head crested and the lores and forehead of the males covered with warty carunculations. The general colour of the upper parts is glossy green, passing into purple on the back, with the wing coverts white. The head, neck, and under parts are, however, brownish black ; the beak is black and white : the feet are black ; and the warty

parts of the head of the drake red. Muscovy ducks inhabit swamps in forests, where they roost and breed in trees, and feed on maize, mandioc-roots, and marsh vegetation.

COMB-DUCKS

To the same subfamily belong the so-called comb-ducks, of which there is one Indian and African species (*Sarcidiornis melanonotus*) and the tropical American *S. carunculatus*; both these being large and somewhat goose-like birds, with short and high beaks, character-ised by the presence of a blunt spur on the wing, a fleshy protuberance at the base of the beak of the male, and the glossy blackish plumage of the back; the wings being brightly marked like those of ducks. Although the two sexes are very similar, the males are much larger than the females. The Indian species measures from 30 to 34 inches in length. In habits it approaches the tree-ducks, frequently perching on trees, and generally nesting in holes in their trunks.

COTTON-TEAL

The Indian cotton-teal (*Netiopus coromandelianus*) is a member of a genus with one African and two Australian representatives. In form they somewhat resemble miniature comb-ducks, although lacking the comb and spur, and also differing by the more sombre coloration of the female. The beak, moreover, is still shorter and higher at the base, and the tail differs from that of all the typical ducks in having only twelve feathers. The Indian species, which associates in large flocks, measures 13 or 14 inches in length. These pigmy geese, as they have been called, inhabit small lakes, and are notable for their diving powers. They utter cackling cries, and generally nest in trees or ruined buildings, but sometimes, it is reported, in grass.

SUMMER AND MANDARIN DUCKS

According to the scheme of classification adopted in the British Museum, the summer, or wood, duck

MUSCOVY DUCK

(*Æx. sponsa*) of North America, and the mandarin-duck (*Æx. galericulata*) are placed next the cotton-teal, although it is by no means certain that their proper place is not with the typical ducks.

The brilliantly-coloured and elegantly-marked plumage, and the long, silky pendent crest of the males, serve at once to distinguish these birds from all other members of the family; but they are further characterised by the beak being much shorter than the head, with its base elevated and produced upwards and backwards in an angle nearly to each eye, while

CAPE BARRON GOOSE

its tip is depressed and covered with an unusually large nail. The inner secondaries are broad and rounded, and the tail feathers are not pointed.

The two species agree in the general plan of their gorgeous colouring, but are distinguished by a difference in the arrangement of the feathering at the base of the beak; and also by the circumstance that whereas in the mandarin-duck the tail feathers are short and exceeded in length by the under tail coverts, in the American species the long and very broad tail feathers extend far beyond the coverts. Full description of the coloration of those beautiful birds would occupy too much space (page 1249).

The summer-duck derives its name from being found in most parts of the United States at that season, while it takes its second title from its habit of frequenting woods, among the trees of which it flies with the facility of a pigeon. The beauty of its plumage, its graceful carriage when swimming, and the gentleness of its disposition, make it a universal favourite in America, where it is frequently induced to nest in gardens.

Going about in pairs or small parties, the summer-duck generally lays its eggs in hollow trees, but may take possession of the deserted nests of other birds. In diet it is a somewhat miscellaneous feeder, its food in autumn being largely composed of acorns. The range of this bird extends from the fur-countries throughout temperate North America. The splendidly coloured mandarin-duck has one of the scapular feathers expanded into a large fan, of which the colour is mostly chestnut brown, but with a broad purple band on the outer hind border.

Of late years the American species has decreased very rapidly in numbers. "Its tree-loving habit,"

writes Mr. W. Dutcher, " is one of the causes of decrease The increase of population in the country, and the consequent clearing of the land for agricultural purposes, the ruthless destruction of the forests, and the draining of swamp-lands, have lessened the number of breeding sites. This applies particularly to the eastern and middle-western section of the country. In many localities where the wood-duck was known to breed until within a few years, it is not now found, owing to the fact that every tree suitable for nesting has been cut down. This cause of decrease is largely due to the habits of the species, and in some degree to the unwise practice of deforestation, which, unhappily, is so common in these days."

CAPE BARRON GOOSE

The large species commonly known as the Cape Barron goose (*Cereopsis novæ-hollandiæ*), a native of South Australia and Tasmania, is the sole existing representative of a subfamily (*Cereopsinæ*) characterised by the extreme shortness of the beak, which is covered at the base with a waxy skin, and has its extremity bent down and truncated so as to approximate in appearance to that of a fowl. The body is very stoutly built and massive, the neck short and thick, the head small, the leg long, and the foot with short toes, powerful nails, and deeply incised webs. The wings are broad, with strong quills; the tail is rounded, and the body-plumage soft.

The colour of the plumage is a clear ashy grey, with brown reflections, passing into lighter grey on the crown of the head, and marked on the head with blackish brown spots near the tips of the feathers; the under tail coverts and the tips of some of the wing feathers being also blackish brown. The eye is scarlet, the beak black, with its waxy covering greenish yellow, and the leg and foot blackish.

In habits the Cape Barron goose is much more of a land than a water bird, its gait being very unlike that of an ordinary goose, and its rate of swimming slow. The flight is, moreover, heavy. Essentially diurnal in

CAPE BARRON GOOSE

their habits, these birds are nowhere common, and are rapidly diminishing in number, having been even exterminated in some of the smaller Australian islands. During a long sojourn in Victoria, the " Old Bushman " states that he only saw these birds on two occasions—

" once in a small flock, and once when two pitched with the tame geese at Mordialloc (as they are fond of doing), and which were caught alive. They soon became tame, and used to stalk about the paddock ; but they were very pugnacious with the other geese. Their call note was a deep, trumpet-like sound."

The nest, although no great work of art, is better

GREY LAG GOOSE

built than that of most members of the family, being smoothly rounded inside, and decorated with feathers and down. In size the eggs are relatively small, while in form they are rounded, and in colour yellowish white. The period of incubation varies from thirty to thirty-eight days, according to the weather, and the young are able to run immediately after breaking the egg.

Till within a comparatively recent date New Zealand was inhabited by a nearly allied but larger goose (*Cnemiornis calcitrans*), which, like so many of the large birds of those islands, had totally lost the power of flight, the wings being very small, and the keel of the breast-bone wanting. In all probability these birds were exterminated by the Maori. As in the Cape Barron goose, the coracoid bone of this extinct species is much wider and shorter than that of other members of the family.

TYPICAL GEESE

The typical geese (genus *Anser*), together with several allied genera, constitute a subfamily, *Anserinæ*, distinguished by the following characteristics, and including some forty species, with, collectively, an almost world-wide distribution. In size the geese occupy a middle position in the family, none being very large. The neck is of moderate length, being always shorter than the body ; the lores are feathered ; the beak is not longer than the head, and tapers to the extremity, which is covered by a large nail-like knob ; while the metatarsus is rather long, exceeding the third toe in length, and covered on all sides with reticulate scales. The number of tail feathers may be either fourteen or sixteen ; and although the two

sexes are usually very much alike, there is great specific variation in colour. Only a single autumnal moult of the plumage takes place, and all these birds are essentially vegetable-feeders, many of them grazing in the well-known manner of the domesticated breeds.

They are all birds of strong, though somewhat heavy, flight ; and although some are confined to the Southern Hemisphere, the majority seek the remote regions of the north in which to breed, ranging in winter over the warmer parts of the same hemisphere. As compared with swans, their more elevated bodies and relatively longer legs—in which the tibia is feathered nearly to the ankle—are indicative of more terrestrial habits. In the members of the genus *Anser* there is but little, if any, black in the plumage of the head and neck ; the beak and feet are light-coloured, and usually reddish in the adult, and the tail has sixteen feathers.

The genus, as now restricted, is represented by some eleven species, ranging over the cold and temperate regions of the globe, but becoming almost cosmopolitan in the winter. Of these the typical member is the grey lag goose (*A. cinereus*), which is probably the parent form of the domesticated breeds, and is the only species breeding in the British Isles. It is characterised by the white or whitish nail on the beak ; by the remainder of the beak, together with the feet, being usually flesh-coloured, although liable to vary from creamy white to purplish red ; and the slaty grey wing coverts and rump. In length, the male measures about 35, and the female 30 inches. Breeding at the present day in the British Isles only in the north of Scotland and Ireland, the grey lag goose ranges all over Europe and North and Central Asia so far east as Amurland, while in winter it spreads over Southern China and Upper India.

The white-fronted goose (*A. albifrons*), of which there is a larger and a smaller phase, is another British species, although only a winter visitor, and also found in India during the cold season. It is a much smaller bird than the preceding, the length of the larger phase

WHITE-FRONTED GOOSE

only reaching 27 inches, while in the smaller it varies from 24 to 20 inches. The beak is generally orange yellow, with a white nail, the feet being likewise of the former hue ; while the forehead is characterised by the presence of a variable amount of white feathers at the base of the beak, and the plumage of the breast is much mottled in the adult with brownish black. In the Old World the distribution of this species is very similar to that of the last, but it is also found during winter in North-Eastern Africa ; and it also occurs in Greenland, and is represented in the rest of North America by a variety (*A. gambeli*). The smaller form is often termed the dwarf goose.

Agreeing nearly in size with the grey lag goose, the bean-goose (*A. segetum*) —another well-known British species— may be readily distinguished by the black nail of the beak, the middle portion of the beak being orange yellow, and its base black ; while the legs and feet are also orange yellow or orange. This species also ranges over the greater part of the northern half of the Old World, occurring during the winter in Britain, on the shores of the Mediterranean, in India, and Japan. It is, however, essentially a northern bird, only breeding in Scandinavia to the north of latitude 64°, and in Siberia on the tundras by lakes and pools beyond or near the limits of forest.

The pink-footed goose (*A. brachyrhynchus*) is a closely-allied smaller species, or race, measuring only 28 inches in length, and characterised by the middle portion of the beak being generally pinkish, although sometimes orange yellow ; and the feet usually flesh-coloured. Breeding in Spitzbergen, probably Iceland, and perhaps Novaya Zemlya, this small goose visits the British Isles in great numbers during the winter, while it occurs rarely in Northern India.

Geese for the greater part of the year frequent marshes, lakes, moors, or open plains, where there is water ; but during the winter not infrequently seek the sea-coast. Their harsh "gaggling" notes are among the most discordant of sounds ; and although they associate in flocks during the winter, and frequently also breed in company, each male has only a single consort. The nest is of large size, with the numerous eggs of a creamy white colour ; and both sexes take part in the work of incubation. In undisturbed districts they feed during the day, but when frequently fired at their feeding hours are mostly nocturnal. Shoots of young grass and corn form their favourite food ; but the under mentioned snow-goose, however, subsists largely on berries in summer (page 1274).

Writing of the grey lag goose in India, Mr. A. O. Hume observes that, when not feeding, these birds "spend their time dozing or dawdling about on the margin of some lake or the bank of some river, always by preference choosing some island in these for their noontide siesta. Unless disturbed, they very rarely take to the water. Although they rise rather awkwardly and slowly, with violent and rather noisy flappings of the wings, they fly very strongly and easily when once off, and I do not know a more beautiful sight than the sudden and rapid descent of a large flock from high in the air to some sandbank. The flock comes along in sober state, circles round decorously once or twice, and then suddenly down they

come with incredible rapidity, twisting and turning with an ease and grace for which no one could at other times have given them credit."

When passing from one piece of water to another, these geese frequently fly in an irregular mass, but, when journeying long distances, the flock generally ascends to a great height, and flies either in a line or a

PINK-FOOTED GEESE

chevron. During winter in India these geese are commonly seen in flocks of from thirty to a hundred, but at times a thousand or more may be collected together. The grey lag does not go so far north to breed as the bean-goose, and its northward, and sometimes also its southward, migration is consequently earlier. The nest of the grey lag goose is built of grass and flags, without lining, and is usually placed either at the base of a tussock of coarse grass or among heather, the general number of eggs being six.

Shy and wild as is the grey lag goose in many districts, on the larger Indian rivers it may be easily approached within range, with the aid of a boat protected in front by a screen, behind which the sportsman lies concealed. In this manner a flock standing on a sandbank may be approached within a hundred yards without causing much disturbance. "As you approach nearer," writes Mr. Hume, "all begin to walk slowly away, and, as a rule, if you persist in coming within twenty yards, and coming on quicker than they can walk, they rise and fly ; or if you stand up in the boat, or make any sudden noise, they will equally take to wing, but if you drift quietly down on them, they will let you come within twenty or thirty yards without quitting the bank." With the first shot they rise with a deafening clamour, generally circling round the boat, and often affording the chance of a second shot.   R. LYDEKKER

DOMESTICATED GEESE

It is evident that the goose was domesticated at a very early period of the world's history. References are made to it in Sanscrit writings, and tablets found in some of the ancient Egyptian monuments show that it was kept in a tame state on the banks of the Nile four thousand years ago.

The progenitor of the European races is the grey lag (*A. cinereus*), which is common over the entire continent. So far as is known, the other species, such as the bean, the white-fronted, and the pink-footed, have no ancestral influence upon our breeds. At one period, when the major part of Europe was open land, with a great amount of fen or marsh, the grey lag was very common, but with increasing populations and enclosures many districts know it no longer. It is still, however, found in the North of Scotland, in Scandinavia, and Finland at one season ; and on the shores of the Mediterranean Sea, both north and south, at another. From time to time crosses have taken place between the grey lag and domesticated geese, the progeny proving fertile, which may be accepted as proof of their affinity.

The method of bringing the goose into the service of man was undoubtedly the same as with other species of poultry—that is, by securing young birds from the wild parents' nests and rearing them in captivity. The provision of an abundant supply of food would tend to eliminate the desire for greater liberty, and reconcile them to the new conditions. So simple a plan would recommend itself to people in all countries, whether civilised or semi-civilised. When the first specimens were secured in this way, and had grown to maturity, they would be the progenitors of others. At first it is more than likely that some time elapsed before they had fully adapted themselves to the new conditions, but with patience on the part of breeders that could ultimately be accomplished.

It is essential to bear in mind that geese would not, except, perhaps, at first, be kept in confinement, but on open lands, so that they had a considerable measure of liberty. They were, however, tempted to return home at night by the provision of good quarters, where protection was afforded, and an abundant supply of food. It is evident that in Egypt the value of the goose for food was appreciated, as on tablets in one of the old tombs the process of cramming by hand is shown. At that time the goose was regarded as a sacred bird, possibly in order that the priests might have an abundant supply. And in Italy, during the Empire, geese were bred largely for the sake of their flesh and livers.

In most countries, goose-breeding has been largely followed at one period or another, especially where there are open lands, by the sides of rivers and streams, and on commons. That is the case now over large areas of Europe. In Western Germany and Eastern Prussia, in many parts of Southern Germany, Austria, Hungary, and the Balkan States, and in Southern Russia, this is an important branch of livestock-breeding. Such was the case in the United Kingdom, but, excepting in Ireland, upon somewhat different lines.

So long as each village had its common land, goose-breeding was extensively followed, more especially by cottagers and small occupiers, who were thus able to rear a few every year either for home consumption or sale. But with the enclosure of such open spaces and advancement of cultivation a great change has come about, and fewer are kept every year. The same is true elsewhere. In France, with the exception of two or three departments where the conditions are favourable, geese have not increased in number. In the Netherlands, Denmark, Northern Italy, and parts of Germany—in fact, wherever the soil is brought more under cultivation—geese steadily decrease in number.

Geese require abundance of range, and to be profitable must find the greater part of their food. The price realised does not allow a sufficient margin to pay for a supplied diet. They are essentially grass eaters, and consequently marsh or fen lands, not of much value for other purposes, are found to yield the best results. At one time geese were largely kept for the production of quills for writing, but with the introduction of the steel pen the demand for these has greatly decreased. The down, however, commands the highest price of all poultry feathers, and in Eastern and Southern Europe makes an important addition to the returns secured by breeders.

Correlative with the reduction in the supply of geese in the United Kingdom has been an even greater falling off in the consumption of these birds, owing to a change in taste. The flesh is very full in flavour and luscious. At one time there was a large sale of geese at Christmas among our industrial population, but changes in habits of life and increased means have led to preference for the turkey.

As might be anticipated from the migratory nature of the goose, and its natural distribution over a wide extent of country, variations are less marked than where one country is the habitat, and it is removed to another set of conditions. Hence, although there are marked differences to be met with, these are by no means extreme. In one respect all show the results of domestication, by a considerable increase in size of body. The grey lag weighs 7 to 9 pounds, whereas some of the larger domesticated breeds scale as high as 28 pounds. It is interesting to note that those specially kept in the northern latitudes have attained the greatest weight, whereas in the case of those within the warmer areas, although there is a marked advance in size, yet it is to a much less degree.

In addition, the domestic goose carries proportionately a greater amount of flesh, and she lays more eggs than the wild bird ; but as goose eggs are not marketable for table purposes, there is no incentive to stimulation of production at other than the regular breeding season. The former of these changes may be partly due to selection and breeding, but only to a limited extent. All animals and birds brought from the warm to the temperate or cold zones tend to increase of egg production. A further change is seen in that some of the races have lost much of the setting instinct, and are unreliable for hatching and rearing.

EMBDEN GEESE

BREEDS

As all respective breeds are valued in accordance with their flesh qualities, classification is simple, and we give brief particulars as to their individual characteristics.

In Southern Europe the Roman goose is widely distributed ; in Western Europe the Embden and Toulouse are found about equally ; in Northern Europe the Pomeranian is largely met with.

BREED	COLOUR OF PLUMAGE	SIZE
Roman	White, black and white ..	Medium
Embden	White	Large
Toulouse	Grey	Large
Saddleback, or Pomeranian	Parti (grey and white) ..	Large
Danubian..	White	Medium
Canadian	Grey and brown	Medium
Russian	White, grey	Large
Egyptian	Mixed brown and yellow ..	Small
Chinese	White, brown	Medium
African	Grey..	Large

ROMAN—This race of geese is of great antiquity in Italy. Medium in size of body, which is long, and weighs 8 to 10 pounds ; low in leg ; good in meat qualities.

EMBDEN—Found extensively in Northern Europe, the Embden is white in colour of plumage ; rather long in leg ; broad in body but flat in front ; abundant and fine in flesh qualities. This goose is rapid in growth, and in consequence is used for killing at Michaelmas.

TOULOUSE — These geese are grey in plumage and very large in size, being much fuller in front than the Embden, giving the appearance of great length of body together with massiveness. The neck is long and the head large. This breed makes large Christmas geese of fine quality, weighing 20 pounds and upwards, as it lends itself to fattening

SADDLEBACK—This is a parti-coloured goose, with dark back, wings, and tail, otherwise resembling the Embden.

CANADIAN — The Canadian is a small goose, grey and brown in colour of plumage ; not often seen.

TOULOUSE GEESE

RUSSIAN GEESE—These are of three kinds, of which the Arsamas and Tula are the more important. They are white and grey respectively, and were formerly used for fighting. They are very large and muscular, with short heads and beaks.

EGYPTIAN—A rich-coloured goose of small size, kept chiefly for ornamental purposes. The colour of the plumage is yellow, brown, and chestnut.

CHINESE AND AFRICAN—These geese are very similar, except that the last-named is much the larger. All have a prominent protuberance, or knob, on the forehead.

From what has already been stated, it is evident that the opportunities for goose-breeding are strictly limited for the great majority of farmers, and, except in the case of those who live near common or open lands, it would be inadvisable for small occupiers or poultry-keepers to attempt this industry. Farmers may breed a few for home consumption, but on pasture or arable farms, where the land is good in quality, to keep and breed large numbers of geese would occupy ground which might be more profitably cultivated. On poorer land, such as hill or sheep-farms, where sufficient growth is to be obtained by the birds being able to roam over a wide area, success may be achieved.

In either case there would be no profit if all the food required had to be supplied, as the chance of making the business pay is to produce as cheaply as possible, except in the case of green geese marketed in the spring and early summer, for with them is a larger margin between cost and price obtained.

Geese are gregarious, and can be kept together in considerable numbers without quarrelling among the males, who are very devoted to their mates during the hatching period, looking after and protecting them. They can be kept on almost any land in ordinary seasons, but extremes of wet or drought are not beneficial for them. In the former case, marsh or fen land becomes too moist, and in the latter excessive dryness not only deprives the birds of the food they would otherwise obtain, but also, in some districts, causes lung troubles.

The ideal place for breeding and young stock is where the ground is undulating or even hilly, but with watercourses in the valleys or gullies ; and, in fact, good sheep pasturage is excellent for geese. Here, however, they cannot be fed off, and for this purpose they should be removed to the lower lying and richer ground. Whilst hardy in every sense, it is desirable that they shall be well housed at night, with a perfectly dry floor. It is better if part of the house is open in front, and buildings in the form common for sheep-folds or pig-pens may be copied with advantage, even to the open forecourt.

REARING GOSLINGS

When the period of laying approaches, say, about the beginning of March—except for green geese, which are hatched from November onwards, and to secure eggs for which some measure of forcing is essential—it is desirable to provide large, roomy nests in a quiet place, removing the eggs as laid. Some of these may be placed under large, well-feathered hens, giving from five or seven to each, but as soon as the goose begins to sit she may be given thirteen or fifteen, in accordance with her size, and left alone to manage the business in accordance with her own instinct.

Artificial methods of hatching and rearing have been tried, but these are not recommended, as the result is seldom satisfactory. Moreover, they are unnecessary, for the number of eggs produced by geese is small as compared with hens and ducks. The period of hatching is thirty days, and when the process is completed by the youngsters making their appearance, they should be left in the nest for at least forty-eight hours, during which time food need not be supplied to them, but care must be taken to provide an abundant supply of good grain and water for the parent goose during the entire time and immediately after hatching.

For the first eight or ten weeks of the gosling's life, there should be supplied twice a day food in the form of any good mixture of steeped grain or meal mixed with water. For this purpose oats, wheat, barley, and some maize are all excellent, and variety is better than sameness. In the morning the quantity need not be large, as it is desirable that they obtain as much natural food as possible, not only to keep down the cost, but also because it is better for them. The second meal in the afternoon should be a full one, as much as they will eat. This will provide for the night, and also have the effect of bringing them home.

Where the flocks are large, it is customary to send them out in charge of a boy as soon as they are deserted by the mother, and his work during the summer is to drive them to the feeding ground and bring them back in the evening. In a favourable season and place they need no food during this second stage, but if feed is deficient they must be given extra food, or sold to those who are more favourably situated.

Large quantities of geese are brought from Ireland and the Continent about harvest time, and sold to farmers, who feed them off on the stubbles or roots, which brings them into good condition for killing. For Christmas they are fattened in pens. EDWARD BROWN

SNOW-GEESE

The typical snow-goose (*Chen hyperboreus*), of which there is a large and small race, belongs to a second group of the subfamily characterised by the very stout and slightly convex beak, and by the head and neck, or the whole plumage of the adult, with the exception of the primaries, being entirely white. The snow-goose is one of those in which the primaries are black, and the rest of the plumage white; the smaller variety measuring 23 inches in length. Distributed over the whole of North America, this essentially northern species probably has a circumpolar distribution, and nests on the barren Arctic tundras, although but little is known of its habits.

Ross's goose (*C.* [*Exanthemops*] *rossi*), of north-western North America, is a smaller form, with numerous caruncles at the base of its shorter beak, while the American blue-winged goose (*C. cœrulescens*) has a large portion of the plumage of the body greyish brown, with bluish grey wing coverts and rump.

BRENT-GEESE

Although nearly allied to the snow-geese, the brent-geese (*Branta*) of the Northern Hemisphere are distinguished from the typical geese by their darker plumage, in which the head and neck are chiefly black, and the beak and feet entirely black, at all ages. All these birds are characterised by their short, subconical beaks, of which the length is considerably less than

LESSER SNOW-GEESE

BLUE SNOW-GOOSE

HUTCHINS' BRENT-GOOSE

that of the head, both halves having their inner edges nearly straight, and their plates nearly or completely concealed, while the nail at the tip is ovate, and the nostrils oval and nearly central. The long wings are also more pointed than in typical geese, and the tail is short and rounded.

Of the more typical representatives of the genus, mention may be made first of the brent-goose (*B. bernicla*), characterised by the head and neck being black, with the exception of a white patch on each side of the latter. The length is about 22 inches, and in the typical form the upper part of the breast is black, while the lower part of the latter and the abdomen are slaty grey. There is, however, a species or race (*B. glaucogaster*) in which the under parts below the breast are nearly white.

The brent-goose inhabits all Arctic Europe and part of Asia, wintering in the British Isles, North Germany, France, Belgium, and so on, and occasionally ranging to the Mediterranean and the valley of the Nile. It breeds in Spitzbergen, Novaya Zemlya, and the islands of Arctic Siberia, and thence to the extreme north ; while in America it nests in Greenland, and ranges southwards on the east side of that continent so far as New York, or even Texas. In Western Arctic America it is replaced by the American brent-goose (*B. nigricans*), distinguished by the white of the middle of the neck forming an almost complete collar ; the winter range of this species extending along the Pacific seaboard so far as Lower California.

The bernicle-goose (*B. leucopsis*)—anciently supposed by some extraordinary confusion of ideas to have been produced from the well-known ship-barnacles—is a larger species, measuring upwards of 25 inches in length, and easily recognised by the greater part of the front of the head being white, although the lores and the feathers at the base on the upper half of the beak are black. The plumage of the upper parts is largely lavender-grey, but the scapulars, wing

coverts, and many of the wing feathers are tipped with a bluish black crescent, edged with white at the end, while the primaries and tail feathers are almost black, the breast and abdomen being greyish white, and the under tail coverts pure white.

This species is an inhabitant of the coasts of Northern Europe, ranging in winter to the British Isles, and occasionally found so far south as Spain and Italy. How far eastwards it extends in Northern Asia is at present unknown, and there is no definite information as to its breeding, although it probably nests in Novaya Zemlya, Spitzbergen, and the regions still further north. It probably also breeds in Greenland, being occasionally found on the Atlantic coasts of North America.

A fourth very distinct representative of the genus is the Canada brent-goose (*B. canadensis*), easily recognised by its black head and neck, with a large triangular patch of white on each cheek, usually joined by a band beneath the throat, but sometimes separated by a narrow black line. Occasionally there is also a white collar encircling the lower part of the neck. As regards the rest of the plumage, the tail, rump, and primaries are brownish black, the upper tail coverts and region of the vent white, and the remainder greyish brown, lighter below than above, with the tips of the feathers paler. This goose, which is variable in size and colouring, inhabits North America, as far south as Mexico. *B. hutchinsi* is an allied Arctic species.

Very different from all the above is the handsome bird known as the red-breasted goose (*B. ruficollis*), which may be recognised by the black forehead, white lores, and the rich chestnut of the neck and upper part of the breast bordered above with white. The ear coverts have also an angular patch of chestnut bordered with white ; the upper parts are blackish brown, the top of the head, part of the sides of the face, the back of the neck, the throat, the primaries, tail feathers, and lower breast black, and the upper and lower tail coverts and the abdomen white. In length this bird measures from 21 to 22 inches. Its native home is the tundras of Siberia, whence it wanders occasionally during the winter to Scandinavia, Northern Germany, Holland, the British Isles, and other parts of Europe.

From being such exclusively Arctic birds, our knowledge of the habits of the more typical brent-geese is not so intimate as would be desirable. In Europe during the winter they generally frequent the neighbourhood of the coasts, although at times penetrating some distance inland. Usually collecting at this season in considerable flocks, these birds always indicate their near presence by the constant gaggling kept up as they feed, or by the hoarse *cronk* of their call-note. The food of the bernicle-goose consists chiefly of grasses and bents growing on the sand-hills ; while the brent-goose eats seaweeds and other water-plants, as well as crustaceans and other small aquatic creatures. On the other hand, the Canada goose subsists largely on berries and corn.

During its migrations the latter species assembles in flocks, which unite together to form a vast column, with each section under an appointed leader. At such times they generally fly throughout the night, although occasionally resting in the daytime. When about to alight, pioneers descend from the flock to select a favourable and safe feeding ground ; and during the whole time that it is on the ground, the flock is guarded by sentinels. The watchfulness of these guardians renders a flock of Canada geese almost impossible to approach by stalking ; and the plan adopted in many parts of the United States is to dig pits in a stubble field, in which the sportsmen take up their position surrounded by a number of decoys. The geese are then shot during their morning and evening flights from lake to lake, when they are attracted within easy range by the decoys.

In Magdalen Islands the Canada goose makes its nest in marshy plains, occasionally laying so many as nine eggs in a clutch. The brent-goose, on the other hand, breeds on the sides of slopes on the bare space left between the line of snow and the sea-ice ; the four eggs being deposited on a bed of grass, moss, and saxifrage, overlain with down. Occasionally the nest of another bird is adopted by some of the members of this genus. All the brent-geese are readily tamed, and breed in confinement, several of the species crossing with one another.

UPLAND AND KELP-GEESE

The representatives of the brent-geese in the Southern Hemisphere differ more or less markedly from their northern cousins, and are accordingly separated as *Cloëphaga*. Together with certain other allied genera, they are now regarded as forming a separate subfamily, the *Chenonettinæ*, although the undermentioned Sandwich Island goose is included in the *Anserinæ*. Several of these birds lack the black heads and necks of the northern species ; and in some, such as the upland goose (*Cl. magellanica*), ranging from the Falkland Islands to Chile, and the kelp-goose (*Cl. antarctica*) of the Falkland Islands and Patagonia, the male has a pure white head, while that of the female is chestnut brown. In other cases the difference between the two sexes is less marked, although the male still has a lighter head and neck.

Other species are the small Australian brent-goose (*Chenonetta jubata*), which is of the size of a duck, and characterised by the extreme shortness of its beak and its blackish head and neck, and the Sandwich Island goose (*Nesochen sandvicensis*), each of which is now referred to a genus by itself. The upland goose, which, like some other members of the genus, has a small spur on its wing, visits Patagonia in great numbers during

RED-BREASTED GEESE

UPLAND GOOSE

the winter, and inflicts much damage on the growing crops of young corn and clover.

KNOB-WINGED GEESE

These geese, of which there are two species, namely, the Egyptian goose (*Chenalopex*, or *Alopochen*, *ægyptiaca*) and the knob-winged goose (*C. jubata*) of South America, are now included in the subfamily *Anatinæ*, typified by the ducks, of which the distinctive characters are given later (p. 1278). The Egyptian species is characterised by the beak being equal in length to the head, and of rather slender form, with the tip bent suddenly down so as almost to conceal the lower mandible, and the nostrils placed near its base. The wings are rather long and broad, and are each armed with a small bare knob, while the tail has fourteen rounded feathers. The legs are relatively long, with the metatarsus exceeding the length of the third toe ; and the first toe is well developed. The windpipe of the male differs from that of ordinary geese in being dilated at the lower end.

In colour the Egyptian goose has the sides of the head and front of the neck mottled yellowish white ; a patch round the eye, the hind part of the neck, and a collar round the lower part of the latter are chestnut brown ; on the upper parts the general hue is mingled grey and black, and that of the under parts yellowish brown, marked with black and white, and becoming lighter on the hind part of the breast and abdomen, the breast having a patch of chestnut brown. The carpal portion of the wing and wing coverts are white, with black tips to the smaller coverts ; the secondaries are tinged with reddish bay, and edged with chestnut, and the primaries and tail feathers brilliant black. The eye is yellow, the beak horn-colour above, with the tip pink, the nail, margin, and base dark brown, and the lower half cherry-red ; the legs and feet being pink.

This handsomely coloured bird, which is the vulpanser of Herodotus, was domesticated by the ancient Egyptians, and, although not sacred, was the emblem of Seb, the father of Osiris. It now occurs in the Nile valley southwards of Cairo, ranging thence over the greater part of tropical Africa, and being the common wild goose of Cape Colony.

Going about either singly or in pairs, the Egyptian goose frequents both rapidly running streams and pools and lakes ; and its nest may be situated either on dry land or among long swampy grass in the Zambezi district. Further north these birds have, however, been known to rear their young on ledges of steep cliffs. The goslings leave their parents so soon as they are strong enough to fly. When on the wing, a loud, harsh, grating noise, which has been compared to the bark of a dog, is continually uttered.

This goose has been more or less completely acclimatised in England, where it may not infrequently be seen on ornamental waters, and in confinement has bred with several other members of the family—among them the spur-winged goose. The flesh is superior in quality to that of the latter species. The windpipe of the male is peculiar in having a large bony capsule on the left side of its lower extremity.

TREE-DUCKS OR WHISTLING-TEAL

There being no representatives of the group in Britain, the idea of ducks habitually perching in trees may seem to many persons somewhat unnatural, yet this is the normal habit of the tree-ducks, or, as they are generally called in India, whistling-teal (*Dendrocygna*). Although approaching the more typical ducks in the form of the beak, which is somewhat depressed at the end, the members of this genus may be distinguished from the former by the front of the metatarsus being covered with small reticulate, or mosaic-like scales, in which respect they resemble geese.

The lores are feathered, the legs rather long, with the lower portion of the tibia bare, the wings short and rounded, and the abbreviated tail almost concealed by the coverts. The sexes are nearly alike ; and although in some species there is a bright patch, or speculum, on the wing, in colouring these birds approach the Egyptian goose and ruddy sheldrake, to both of which they may be allied. In their voice, as well as in the plumage undergoing but one moult, and likewise in the vegetable nature of their food, these birds again approach geese, and differ from ducks.

Tree-ducks are distributed throughout the tropical and subtropical regions of the world ; and it is highly remarkable that one species (*D. viduata*) is common to South America, tropical Africa, and Madagascar.

AUSTRALIAN BRENT-GOOSE

The general colour of the plumage of these birds is some shade of brown or chestnut, with the back, wings, and tail variously marked with darker brown and slaty; but in one of the American species the abdomen is black, while in a second the under parts are dirty white. The Indian *D. javanica*, which measures about 20 inches in length, frequents well-wooded, well-watered, and well-drained districts throughout India; being found during the breeding season in pairs, but in the cold weather and spring associating in flocks, which may number from twenty to two thousand head.

Migratory in their habits, these birds, writes Mr. A. O. Hume, are very tame and familiar, "frequenting village ponds, and living on the trees surrounding such, even on trees growing inside the enclosures of cottages. They are rather dull birds, slow on the wing and easily shot, and they have a habit of circling round and round the gunner when one of their number has been shot that often proves fatal to the greater portion of the flock, when it unfortunately falls under the tender mercies of butchers. When absolutely required for food, a pair or so may be shot, but they are indifferent eating, and fly so poorly that they really afford no sport."

These birds derive their name of whistling-teal from their double hissing whistle-like note, which is always uttered when the birds are alarmed or about to fly, and is often repeated during flight, although but seldom heard when they are feeding or at rest. The nest may be situated either in a hollow tree or between the fork of a large branch, or on the ground, and if built by the birds themselves is unlined; a deserted crow's nest is, however, often taken advantage of. The number of eggs is generally from ten to twelve. When the nest is in a tree, the young are carried down by the parent birds to the water. Mr. Hume has observed the ducklings carried in the claws of their parents, but it has been stated that they are sometimes borne on their backs.

SHELDRAKES

The handsome birds known as sheldrakes (*Tadorna*)—meaning shield-drakes—which are near relations of the tree-ducks, may be regarded as more typical members of the *Anatinæ* than either knob-winged geese or tree-ducks, so that the characteristics of the subfamily may be conveniently given in this place.

Exclusive of the two aberrant genera, the members of this group are relatively short-necked birds of smaller size than the typical geese, from which they differ in having the front of the metatarsus covered with large

I, EGYPTIAN GOOSE; 2 AND 3, TREE-DUCKS

plates, and the length of that segment shorter than the third toe; while they are further characterised by having only a small membrane attached to the first toe. The beak is variable, and the number of tail feathers ranges from fourteen to eighteen. In the males the lower end of the windpipe is dilated, as it is in the spur-winged and Egyptian goose, the comb-ducks, and others. None of these birds is in the habit of diving for food.

Sheldrakes resemble tree-ducks in that the plumage of the two sexes is nearly alike; but in the more typical ducks there is usually great difference between the two, the males having a very beautiful colouring, with a bright metallic patch, or speculum, on the wing. The sheldrakes further agree with the tree-ducks in having but a single annual moult; whereas, in many of the ducks the males moult their contour feathers once in the early summer and again in autumn, so as to wear the non-breeding, or "eclipse," plumage for a very brief period. The subfamily comprises a very large number of species arranged under many genera, and having an almost world-wide distribution, although most widely spread during the winter of the Northern Hemisphere. Space admits of reference only to some of the more important genera. In addition to the similarity in the colouring of the sexes and their single moult, the sheldrakes are characterised by the presence of a conspicuous white patch on the front of the wing, by the relative length of the metatarsus (above which a portion of the tibia is bare), and also by the prevalence of chestnut, black, and white—often in strongly contrasting masses—in the plumage. The beak is about equal in length to the head, and higher than broad at the base (near which are situated the nostrils), with the nail bent down and hooked. In the long and powerful wings the second quill is the longest. Sheldrakes form a group of six species breeding in the temperate regions of Europe, Asia, Africa, and Australia, and visiting India and the adjacent countries in winter, but quite unknown in the New World.

The handsomest and, in Europe, the best known representative of the genus is the typical sheldrake, or burrow-duck (*T. cornuta*), which is sufficiently characterised by the head and neck being dark glossy green, below which is a broad collar of white, followed by a band of rich chestnut extending across the back and breast, the remainder of the plumage being mainly black and white, with the speculum of the wing marked by green and chestnut on the secondaries. The beak is red, and the legs and toes are flesh pink. The usual length is about 25 inches.

This sheldrake is essentially an inhabitant of the temperate regions of the northern half of the Old World, being a resident throughout the year in the British Isles, and scarcely ever penetrating within either the Arctic Circle or the Tropics. From Britain its range extends to Japan, where it is a winter visitor; and the limits of its migration include Persia, North-Western India, and North Africa; while it breeds not only in Europe, but in Southern Siberia, Mongolia, Turkestan, and the neighbouring countries. Essentially a coast bird in Europe, in India the sheldrake is more commonly found on inland waters, though it haunts the shores of Sind.

On the coasts of Europe these birds prefer sandy districts, especially with numerous rabbit-burrows, in which they breed, and hence derive their name of burrow-duck. The nest is always situated deep down in a burrow of some sort, and frequently in one describing part of a circle, so that it may be situated so much as ten or twelve feet from the entrance. It is composed of bents of grass, lined with fine soft down. In the Frisian Islands the natives construct burrows for these birds to nest in, and make a regular harvest of the eggs; the number laid by a single bird, if some are from time to time removed, reaching as many as thirty. The note of the sheldrake is a shrill whistle, and its food usually consists of seaweed and various small marine animals. Its conspicuous white and dark plumage renders the sheldrake easy of detection among the ducks, but, in India at least, it is extremely shy and difficult to approach.

RUDDY SHELDRAKE

A very different-looking bird to the last is the ruddy sheldrake, or Bramini duck (*T. casarca*), which, while only a rare visitor to the British Isles and North-Western Europe generally, breeds in Spain, the valley of the Danube, and Southern Russia in great numbers, and thence extends through Persia, Turkestan, and Southern Siberia to Amurland and Japan; while in winter it visits India, Burma, and China in swarms. Although the species is largely migratory in Asia and non-migratory in Europe, its occurrence during the winter in North Africa indicates that some individuals make a periodical move even in the western portion of its habitat.

The greater part of the plumage of the Bramini duck is a full orange-brown, but in summer the male has a black ring round the neck; and at all times the point of the wing and wing coverts are pale buffy white, the primaries, rump, and tail feathers blackish leaden grey, and the secondaries rather lighter, with a brilliant bronzy green speculum formed by their outer webs, except at the tips. The beak and legs are leaden and blackish. In size this bird corresponds closely with the ordinary sheldrake. Some of the favourite breeding places of the Bramini are the great lakes of the

Tibetan highlands, such as the Pangkong and Tsomorari, on the former of which I have seen these birds in vast numbers. In such regions they build in clefts or cavities of rocks, but in other districts the nests are more commonly placed in burrows and other holes, while in Mongolia they have even been known to be situated in the fireplaces of deserted villages.

Visiting the country during winter in myriads, Braminies at that season are to be met with on every piece of water in India; and, as Mr. A. O. Hume observes, no object is more familiar in river scenery "than a pair of these ducks standing or squatting side by side on the banks, or on some chur (island); no sounds are more perpetually heard as one floats lazily down with the stream than their loud warning notes, repeated more earnestly as one draws nearer and nearer, and followed by the sharp patter of their wings as they rise on the approach of the boat. Very wary they are, and yet not at all afraid of men, so long as they keep just out of gunshot."

Uneatable, except when skinned, and then by no means a *bonne bouche*, the Bramini duck is most cordially detested by the Indian sportsman, as its harsh cry and noisy flight put up all other water-fowl in the neighbourhood while still beyond shooting range.

WILD DUCK

The handsome wild duck, or mallard (*Anas boscas*), is the typical representative not only of the true ducks of the genus to which it belongs, but likewise of all the fresh-water non-diving ducks of the present subfamily; the general characters of which have already been mentioned under the head of the sheldrakes. The typical ducks are characterised by having the broad and depressed beak about equal in length to the head, with its sides either parallel or partially dilated, and both upper and lower halves provided with well-marked transverse plates on their inner edges; the oval nostrils being situated in advance of its base.

The legs are shorter than in the sheldrakes, and placed nearly under the centre of the body, with the metatarsus somewhat rounded in front. The wings are rather long and pointed, and the tail, which may be either pointed or wedge-shaped, is comparatively short. Of the typical ducks there are numerous species, with a cosmopolitan distribution; and while in the wild duck the plumage of the two sexes is very distinct, this is not the case in some species, such as the Indian spot-bill duck (*A. pœcilorhyncha*).

Such a familiar species as the British wild duck—the ancestral stock of most domesticated breeds—might seem to require little or no description, but the omission of such a notice would entail confusion later. It is a little difficult to know by what name to allude to the species, as the word mallard means the male, and it is, therefore, strictly speaking, incorrect to use

THE SHELDRAKE

such a term as either a mallard drake or a duck mallard. The species is characterised by the male being more brightly coloured than the female, except for a short period at the close of the breeding season; and by the brilliancy of the wing speculum in both sexes at all times. In winter the adult male has the four middle tail feathers curled upwards; the head and neck are brilliant velvety green, and separated by a white collar from the rich chestnut of the breast; while the wing speculum is a brilliant metallic violet, bounded in front by a black and then a white bar, and behind by two similar bands. The beak is yellowish green, and the legs and feet orange red. In length the bird measures about 22 inches (page 1300).

On the other hand, the female at all times and the male at the end of the breeding season have the wings coloured as above, and the whole of the rest of the plumage variegated with dusky and ochre, the former appearing in the centre of the feathers and on the upper parts, and the latter on the edges of the feathers and lower parts. Such characters suffice shortly to distinguish this handsome species from its allies. As regards its distribution, the mallard may be said to inhabit the whole of the Northern Hemisphere, although its chief range is restricted to the zone lying between the Arctic Circle and the Tropic.

The following account of the habits of the mallard in North America and of its utility to agriculturists is given by Mr. E. H. Fornish: "Like all freshwater ducks the mallard is largely a vegetarian, but it prefers soft, succulent vegetable matter when such is to be found, and probably cannot thrive without a considerable ration of animal food as well, of which all our wild ducks are fond. This bird becomes of considerable economic value to the farmer at times because of the nature of its food. It sometimes attacks sprouting or ripened grain, but like most freshwater fowl it is undoubtedly of service in destroying such insects as the locusts and army-worms, which sometimes become serious pests.

"Mallards and other wild ducks are of much service to the rice-planters of the south, for they feed largely on the crayfish which injure the dikes and levees, and on the volunteer or red rice which they glean in the fields after the harvest, and which, if left to grow, produces the red rice so deleterious to the crop. The mallard is of great value to the country as a means of food-supply alone. Undoubtedly the annual sum received for mallards in the markets of the United States would run into very large figures."

Limits of space preclude any detailed account of the habits of the various species of ducks, but the following excellent account, referring to the mallard, may be quoted from Macgillivray, who writes that "marshy places, the margins of lakes, pools, and rivers, as well as brooks, rills, and ditches, are its principal places of resort at all seasons. It walks with ease, even runs with considerable speed, swims,

WILD DUCK ON NEST

and on occasion dives, although not in search of food. Seeds of grasses and other plants, fleshy and fibrous roots, worms, molluscs, insects, small reptiles, and fishes are the objects of its search. In shallow water it reaches the bottom with its bill, keeping the hind part of the body erect by a continued motion of the feet. On the water it sits rather lightly, with the tail considerably inclined upwards; when searching under the surface, it keeps the tail flat on the water; and when puddling at the bottom with its hind part up, it directs the head backward.

"The male emits a rather low and soft cry between a croak and a murmur, and the female a louder and clearer jabber. Both on being alarmed, and especially on flying off, quack; but the quack of the female is much the louder. When feeding they are silent, but when satiated they often amuse themselves with various jabberings, swim about, approach each other, move their heads backward and forward, 'duck' in the water, throwing it up over their backs, shoot along its surface, half-flying, half-running, and, in short, are quite playful when in good humour. On being surprised or alarmed, whether on shore or on water, they spring up at once with a bound, rise obliquely to a considerable height, and fly off with great speed, their hard-quilled wings whistling against the air. When in full flight, their velocity is very great, being probably a hundred miles in the hour. Like other ducks, they impel themselves by quickly repeated flaps, without sailings or undulations."

With regard to the foregoing statement as to the speed of the mallard's flight, it is probable that there is considerable exaggeration, since a recent writer records a case where a couple of wild ducks started off at full speed in front of a train which had disturbed them, and, although the train was running at the rate of only thirty-seven miles per hour, the birds were overtaken. Like most of its kindred, the wild duck usually builds its nest in a depression of the ground near the margin of water, although at times some distance from the latter. The nest is lined with dry grass, leaves, or down; the smooth eggs being of a dull greenish grey colour. The under-mentioned gadwall, however, lays creamy yellow eggs, varying in number from nine to thirteen.

Instances are on record of wild ducks nesting in trees at considerable heights above the ground, from which the young were doubtless carried down in the same manner as those of the tree-ducks. Essentially a winter migrant when breeding in high northern latitudes, the mallard appears at that season in immense numbers in certain districts of the British Isles as well as in the plains of India. These birds are, however, rarely seen in large flocks, usually associating in parties of from three to ten, and later on in pairs. In common with other water-fowl, hosts of these ducks are taken in decoys or shot from punts with swivel-guns.

DOMESTICATED DUCKS

DUSKY DUCK

The dusky duck (*A. obscura*), of eastern North America, may be taken as an example of a second group of the genus in which the sexes are alike at all seasons, and there is no white at the base of the wing. In this bird the prevailing colour of the plumage is dusky, with the feathers bordered with dull ochre, the head and neck being deep dull buff streaked with dusky, and the wing speculum usually deep violet.

R. LYDEKKER

DOMESTICATED DUCKS

It is generally supposed that our present races of ducks all had the mallard, or wild species, as their common progenitor, and that they have been domesticated either by hatching the eggs of the wild birds, rearing them under domestication, or by capturing wild stock and keeping them under artificial conditions.

The wild duck is very widely distributed, being found from Eastern Asia to North America, which favours the argument that the ducks of to-day have descended in the way indicated. The effects of domestication are noticeable with all classes of stock, there being a change not only in colour and size, but also in fecundity and disposition, but when compared with other birds, sports in breeds of wild birds, hence the origin of this variety is easily explained. The premier breed in this country is that known to-day as the Aylesbury, or, as it was termed, the White English. The modern name is due to the fact that this breed has been kept for many years in the Vale of Aylesbury in Buckinghamshire, where the conditions as to climate and soil are exceptionally suited for this class of water-fowl.

In appearance the Aylesbury is boat-shaped—that is, the body line is level with the ground, the legs being placed almost in the centre of the body. The plumage is white, without a trace of yellow; the beak is fine, and of a delicate flesh colour; the head and bill are long and perfectly straight, and the legs are a light orange. In weight the drake should be 9 to 10 pounds, and the duck 8 to 9 pounds, but stock birds, if they possess large frames, are better if they weigh a pound less.

For the production of market ducklings, the Aylesbury stand foremost among all domestic races, for they are rapid in growth and mature early. Ducklings of this breed can be killed at eight weeks old, weighing from 4 to 5½ pounds. As the demand for ducklings on the English markets is from February to May, it is essential to have birds that mature early, and the quickness of growth noticed with the Aylesbury makes it the best

A GROUP OF AYLESBURY DUCKS

it is remarkable to note how comparatively few characteristics have been changed in some breeds.

One other point may be mentioned as evidence in favour of the descent of the domesticated duck from the wild species, namely, that the wild birds breed freely with the tame, and, moreover, the progeny are fertile. On the other hand, the only argument against this is that wild ducks are monogamous, and the tame are polygamous, which is, however, insufficient to weigh against the mass of evidence on the other side.

BREEDS

There is a very large number of varieties of domesticated ducks, differing greatly in size, shape, and colour of plumage, but many of these are purely ornamental, and do not come to any great extent under present consideration. Belonging to what may be termed the economic class are the following: Aylesbury, Rouen, Pekin, Indian Runner, Cayuga, Huttegem, Blue Swedish, and Muscovy. A short description of the external characteristics and economic qualities of these will suffice.

AYLESBURY—White ducks occasionally appear as breed for this trade. As egg-layers they are very good, not, of course, quite so prolific as some of the other breeds, but flocks have been known to produce an average of 150 eggs in the course of twelve months.

ROUEN—The Rouen duck resembles its wild progenitor more closely than any other breed, and there is practically no doubt that this variety is the result of direct breeding from the mallard. The Rouen is a large, massive bird, very long and wide in frame. The plumage is brilliant in the male during the breeding season, but afterwards it changes to that of the female, as in the case of the mallard. The head and neck are a rich green, below which is a clear white band; the breast is a deep claret, the flanks, stern, and abdomen are a blue French grey, the flanks and sides being marked with black; the back and rump are a rich green black, the flight feathers are slaty black, with a brown tinge, and across are broad purple bands, outside which are narrow bands of black, and then an outer bar of white. The ground body colour of the female is a golden chestnut or brown, each feather pencilled with rich black; the wing bar is the same as in the male. The bill is green yellow, with a black tip; the legs and feet are brick red.

For flesh qualities the Rouen is the finest of all the races, in that the meat is abundant and very fine in quality. It has been mentioned that the largest demand is for early ducklings, and for this trade the Rouen is of little use, for it matures slowly, but for the autumn trade it is undoubtedly the best. Very few Rouens, however, are kept, for the expense of feeding them until they are five to six months old is so great that little profit remains. The males weigh from 9 to 11 pounds, and the females 8 to 10 pounds.

PEKIN—The Pekin duck is a native of China, and was imported direct into England and America. The body is of medium length, but broad, the legs being placed further back than in the case of the Aylesbury, giving an upright carriage. In colour the Pekin is white, but with a canary tinge running throughout the plumage. The bill is bright orange in colour, and the legs and feet a dark orange. As an egg-layer, this breed stands above the larger races of ducks. It is very hardy and an excellent forager. The adults attain a good size and carry a considerable amount of flesh, but the ducklings are thin until they are eleven to twelve weeks old. The egg-laying capacity has been increased at the expense of the meat qualities. In weight, the males run 7½ to 9 pounds, and the females 6 to 7½ pounds.

INDIAN RUNNERS — Indian Runners have only been known in this country about sixty-five years, The first were a trio brought from India to Whitehaven. A second consignment was obtained a few years later, and in all probability the present birds are descended principally from these. The body is long and fine, and carried erect. In colour the head is greyish fawn in the duck, and bronze green in the drake, with narrow bands of white dividing the base of the bill from the head. The neck, wing flights, and fluff are white, the remainder of the body fawn or sometimes grey. The bill is green in adults, yellow in ducklings; the legs and feet a bright deep orange red. The males weigh 4 to 4½ pounds, and the females 3½ to 4 pounds.

The chief economic quality of these birds lies in their fecundity. It is no uncommon thing for them to lay nearly 200 eggs per annum, and, moreover, they continue in profit until they are five, six, and even seven years old. The eggs are smaller, however, than is usual with ducks, but this is an advantage to the vendor, as they can thus be mixed with hens' eggs.

CAYUGA—Coming from America in the first instance, the Cayuga duck is frequently called the black American. Its origin is obscure, but evidence appears to indicate that it is descended from a black sport of the Rouen. This breed has never received the attention that it undoubtedly deserves in view of its economic qualities. In appearance the body is very long and wide, and carries a large amount of meat. The colour of the plumage is a deep metallic black with great brilliancy on the wings; the bill is slaty black, the legs and feet a dull orange brown, lighter between the toes.

This breed is only a fair layer, for this quality has not been specially developed. They are very meaty, however, the flesh having a fine flavour and being almost white in colour. A cross between the Cayuga and the Pekin produces hardy, quick-growing ducklings. The English standard weight for males is 6 to 7 pounds, and for females 5 to 6 pounds, but in America they are required to be one pound heavier.

HUTTEGEM — The Huttegem race is bred largely in East Flanders, where hundreds of thousands are reared annually. This breed is of medium size, long, but rather narrow in body. In colour of plumage there are two varieties, namely, blue and dark fawn or tawny. The Huttegem is an early layer, a grand forager, and extremely hardy. It grows rapidly, and at five to six weeks is ready for fattening.

BLUE SWEDISH—The Blue Swedish has been kept for many years in Germany—in fact, it is supposed to have been introduced as far back as 1835 from Pommern, which formerly was part of the kingdom of Sweden. The body is long, broad and deep, and follows the Rouen in shape. The greater part of the body is a dark steel-blue grey, with the outer edges of the feathers marked with black. The bill is olive green in the male and brown in the female; the legs orange red. The weights are for drakes 6½ to 8 pounds, and for ducks 5½ to 7 pounds. Although good layers, the special characteristic of this race is its fine table qualities. The meat is abundant and well flavoured. It is a rapid grower, and fattens well.

MUSCOVY—The last breed of the economic races to be mentioned is the Muscovy. It is found in South America in a wild state, hence it differs from other domesticated ducks in this respect. In body it is very long, broad, and deep, and boat-shaped. There are a number of varieties, including pied black, deep black, and blue dun. The bill, legs, and feet are orange

ROUEN DUCKS

PEKIN DUCKS

yellow. The males often reach 12 pounds in weight, but the females never more than 8 pounds. The Muscovy ducks are poor layers, but being quick in growth and carrying an abundance of flesh of fine flavour when young, they make good table birds.

ORNAMENTAL VARIETIES

There are a large number of ornamental ducks, but, generally speaking, these are more commonly kept on the Continent than in this country. Some of these are among the most beautiful in plumage to be found in the feathered world. At the largest shows there is usually only one class for the ornamental varieties, namely, for the call duck. Of this breed there are two varieties, the grey and the white.

To mention the names of a few of the principal breeds, there are the black East India ducks, known also as the Buenos Aires and Labrador; the Mandarin, a native of China; the Carolina, from the United States and the West India Islands; the teals, found in Europe and another variety in Japan; the sheldrakes, common in Britain and in New Zealand; the pintails; whistling ducks, including the widow and red-billed whistler ducks. These are all more or less easy to breed under domestication, but they cannot be given their liberty, excepting, perhaps, in the case of the whistling ducks, which can be kept, on account of their tameness, in grass runs if given water on which to swim.

INDIAN RUNNER DUCKS

MANAGEMENT

The first point to be considered in the management of ducks is the selection of stock. For early ducklings there is nothing better than the Aylesbury or the Pekin; the Aylesbury is sometimes found to be a trifle more hardy. It is essential to obtain good birds of pure breed, and they should be large and well grown specimens. For securing spring ducklings the eggs must be gathered from birds hatched in February or March, mated with drakes one year older. If, however, the progeny are to be reared for stock purposes the ducks should be two years old, as it is a very great mistake to rear from immature stock. The birds chosen to produce spring ducklings require to be mated in October, and in this way early eggs are obtained.

A duck-house does not require to be as lofty as a fowl-house, for the former birds roost on the ground. A pen of ducks, that is ten ducks and three drakes, can be accommodated in a house built in the following proportions: 6 feet long, 4½ feet wide, 4½ feet high in front, and 3½ feet high at the back. Such houses must be well ventilated, and it is a good plan to make the top of the front to the depth of about a foot of wire netting instead of solid boarding.

Wherever possible, ducks should be given their liberty, for they will not only gather a large amount of their food, but they will enrich the soil. If kept in confinement the breeding pens should be given access to water, as this helps materially in increasing the fertility of the eggs. To prevent the birds laying away, a small run of wire netting should be placed round the house; confinement to this until 11 a.m. will ensure the greater number of the eggs being laid in the house.

The food supplied should be of a feeding nature and not fattening. The staple meals used are barley meal and toppings, mixed with butchers' offal or tallow greaves. Trough-feeding is necessary, and all remains should be cleared away after each meal. Two feeds a day will be found sufficient.

REARING DUCKLINGS

In the majority of the great duck-rearing districts in England and on the Continent hens are used exclusively for hatching, but in some instances incubators are employed. The latter are coming into use more and more each year, for they have been proved satisfactory, and certainly they reduce the labour and expense very considerably, seeing that hatching is carried out during the colder months of the year. The arrangements for hatching ducks' eggs are practically the same as for hens' eggs, with the exception that better results are obtained if the former eggs are sprinkled with warm water two or three times a week during the process.

Ducklings require very little brooding, and therefore artificial

CAYUGA DUCKS

means are seldom employed. From fifteen to eighteen can be placed under each hen in a roomy coop, and after the first few days can be given their liberty, if they are intended to be reared to maturity; otherwise it is advisable to keep the hens with their broods under shelter. The feeding during the first five weeks is the same whether stock or fattening ducklings are being reared. Feeding should be carried out every two hours during the first week, and for this nothing is better than hard boiled eggs, chopped fine and mixed with breadcrumbs moistened with hot water. Biscuit meal may be used in place of the breadcrumbs with equal results.

After one week, and until five weeks old, the food is changed, the number of meals being dropped to five a day, and barleymeal, bran, toppings, oatmeal, and maizemeal are all suitable for the purpose; oatmeal however, is rather too expensive a diet to give. Meat in one form or another is essential to good growth, and for this nothing is better than tallow scrap cake. Birds destined for stock should be given access to water, as this encourages a good growth, and after they are five weeks old four feeds a day will be sufficient during the next six weeks, and then three meals should be given.

When raising market ducklings the object during the first five weeks is to build up the frame, afterwards fattening foods being employed with a view to increase of flesh. For this nothing is better than cooked rice mixed with fat and tallow scrap cake, although barley-meal, oatmeal, and toppings can all be used in addition. During this latter period feeding three times a day is ample. Birds undergoing the fattening process should not be allowed to swim, as this tends to decrease the quantity and quality of the flesh, but a couple of days before they are ready for killing they should be given the opportunity of swimming, which will cleanse the feathers and thus enhance their value. Green food and grit are two very important items, and they should be fed regularly from the beginning.

After starving for twenty-four hours, the ducklings should be killed by dislocation of the neck, and if fastened up by the legs with the head in a downward position, the flesh will be whitened owing to the blood flowing away from the body. Plucking is carried out two or three minutes after killing, and all feathers are taken out except on the wings and an inch or two down the neck. When thoroughly cool they should be graded according to size, and packed in shallow baskets.

Reference has been made to the demand for spring ducklings, and the value of the trade is illustrated by the following table of prices obtained in Smithfield market: January, 6s. to 10s. per couple; February, 6s. 6d. to 11s.; March, 9s. to 18s.; April, 7s. to 12s.; May, 6s. to 8s.; June, 5s. to 7s. Considering that these birds are only some eight weeks old when marketed, the profit from this branch of poultry-keeping will be readily realised. WILLIAM BROWN

THE GADWALL

This British duck (*Chaulelasmus strepera*) is a well-characterised species, now generally separated from the mallard as a distinct genus. Structurally it is distinguished by the narrower and shorter beak, in which the edges are not quite parallel, the transverse plates visible externally, and the upper border not convex in front; while the species is further characterised by the dull colouring of the wing bar, which is simple black and white—mainly the latter. The gadwall is a very widely spread species, occurring in Europe, Asia, Africa, and North America; and is represented on Fanning Island, in the South Pacific, by the somewhat smaller Coues' gadwall (*C. couesi*).

SHOVELLERS

The enormous size and ungainly form of the flat beak serve at once to differentiate the large duck known as the shoveller, together with its few immediate relatives, from all its allies. In these birds the beak is considerably longer than the head, compressed at the base, and very broad at the tip, where the upper half overhangs the lower, behind which the transverse plates are distinctly exposed. The wings are pointed, with the first and second quills the longest, and the short and graduated tail includes fourteen feathers. The legs are very short.

The shoveller (*Spatula clypeata*), which in the British Isles is mainly a winter visitor, is spread over the entire Northern Hemisphere. In the male the head and neck are dark metallic green, the breast and lower part of the neck white, the abdomen and sides chestnut, the wing bar green with a white border in front, the back and inner scapulars dusky brown, and the outer scapulars white; the beak being lead colour, and the legs and feet reddish orange, with black nails. The female lacks the brilliant colour of the drake, having most of the feathers mottled with two shades of brown, the back and scapulars being nearly

DOMESTICATED MUSCOVY DUCKS

uniform dusky, and the beak brown, with its lower half orange. In length the male reaches about 20 inches. The genus is represented by a second species (*S. platalea*) in South America, by a third (*S. capensis*) in Africa, and by two others in Australia, although one of the latter is sometimes assigned to a genus by itself.

Nesting in large numbers near or within the Arctic Circle, and more sparingly in lower latitudes, the shoveller begins to arrive during September in the British Isles, where it sojourns till the following April or May. In the New World it breeds from Alaska to Texas, and winters so far south as Guatemala; while it spreads in numbers over the plains of India during the cold season.

Writing of its habits in India, Mr. A. O. Hume remarks that the shoveller is very tame, and in some districts may be met with "on every trumpery little village pond, half surrounded by huts, the resort of the washerwomen, and of the entire population for the purposes of ablution, and of the village herds, driven thither twice a day for water. Filthy is quite an inadequate expression for many of these reeking sinks of pollution, but foul or fair the shoveller is equally at home in them, and may be seen at all hours feeding along the edge, now just in and now just out of the water, making no epicurean selection, but feeding on pretty well every organic substance that comes to hand, nice or nasty."

In Great Britain, on the other hand, it is a shy and wary bird, frequenting lakes, ponds, and sluggish rivers. The nest, usually situated on dry ground beneath a tussock of grass, is made of dry grass; and the eggs, which are covered up with down plucked by the female from her own breast, vary in number from eight to fourteen, and are greenish buff in colour.

PINTAIL DUCKS

The elongation of the middle pair of tail feathers in the male gives to the almost cosmopolitan pintail duck (*Dafila acuta*) its distinctive title, and at the same time affords one of the most striking characteristics of the small genus of which this bird is the typical representative. In both sexes of the pintail the neck is unusually long and slender; while the beak is about equal in length to the head, with its edges nearly parallel, although expanding slightly towards the tip, and with the transverse plates very little exposed.

The wings are long and pointed, with the first and second quills the longest; and the tail is likewise sharply pointed in both sexes, the male not only having its two middle feathers elongated and pointed, but also showing an equally marked lengthening of the lanceolate scapular feathers. The legs are rather short, and the webs of the feet slightly excavated in front.

The pintail resembles the mallard in the circumstance that during the summer the male assumes a plumage resembling that of the female. At other times the former sex has the head and upper part of the neck dark brown; most of the upper parts grey, formed by undulating lines of greyish and blackish; the front of the neck, breast, and a considerable portion of the under parts, white; the wing-bar dark green, the long

THE SHOVELLER

tail feathers black, and the beak and feet lead-colour or brownish. The female is nearly brown throughout, the feathers of the upper parts being mottled with two shades, while those on the under surface are nearly uniform; the tail feathers showing white markings on a brown ground. The length of the male pintail varies from 24 to 28 inches.

Found throughout the circumpolar regions, the pintail is a migratory species, ranging in winter so far south as Panama and Cuba in the New World, and in the Old World to the Mediterranean, Persia, Ceylon, China, Borneo, and Japan. Its main breeding area in the Old World lies to the north of latitude 60°, but it descends below this limit in Northern Germany and Russia, and still more so in Siberia. A silent bird during the day, the pintail utters a low, quacking sound at night. It generally frequents shallow waters, where it feeds upon both vegetable and animal food; and in winter commonly associates in flocks, which in India may include from twenty to two hundred, or occasionally thousands of individuals, and are at times composed exclusively of male birds.

The flight of the pintail is rapid in the extreme; and this, together with its shy and wary habits, makes it one of the most difficult ducks to shoot, although the excellence of its flesh renders it of especial value to the sportsman. When once flushed, pintail almost invariably fly clean away, and cannot be driven backwards and forwards from one piece of water to another like so many other ducks. From the closeness of its breast plumage, it is especially necessary in the case of the pintail to allow the bird to pass before firing.

In the Southern Hemisphere there are several allied ducks, such as the Chilian pintail (*D. spinicauda*) of lower South America, the South American Bahama duck (*D. bahamensis*), and the red-billed duck (*D. erythrorhyncha*) of South Africa, the two last of which are referred by some naturalists to the distinct genus *Pœcilonetta*. They differ from the true pintail in the slight elongation of the middle tail feathers of the male, and the uniformly dull and much spotted colouring of the two sexes.

TEAL

The group of beautiful little ducks known as teal (*Nettium*), while presenting a great general resemblance to pintails, are distinguished, in addition to their small size, by their much shorter necks, and the short and rounded tail of sixteen feathers, the scapulars of the male being also less pointed and elongated. The beak is about equal in length to the head, with its edges nearly parallel, and the lamellæ very slightly exposed. In the foot the first toe is very short, and the fourth much shorter than the third.

The typical teal (*N. crecca*) is the best known representative of a group of the genus in which the nape of the neck in the male is ornamented with a small mane-like crest. In length this species measures only 14½ inches ; and in the ordinary plumage the male is characterised by the very fine linear markings of the back, the bright green band, bordered with buff, on the side of the head, the rest of the head chestnut, the wing-bar black, green, and purple, tipped with white, and the breast white, spotted with black.

The female has the upper plumage for the most part of two shades of brown, and the wing-bar mainly black, with but little green. This species is distributed over Europe and Asia generally, breeding in the British Isles, and visiting India and North Africa in winter ; while it occasionally occurs in eastern North America. On the latter continent its place is taken by the American green-winged teal (*N. carolinense*), distinguished by the presence of a broad white crescent on each side of the breast.

Teal breed either among reeds and sedge on the margin of lakes and swamps, or on boggy moors ; the nest being a large structure composed of water-plants, lined with feathers or down, and the number of eggs in a clutch varying from eight to ten in Britain, and from ten to fifteen in Lapland. When unmolested, teal feed both by night and day, but when much shot at they become mainly nocturnal feeders. In India, where they arrive by thousands in the cold season, teal frequent large sheets of water in the daytime, and resort to rice-fields and shallow marshes in the evening.

Nearly as swift on the wing as pintail, teal, writes Mr. A. O. Hume, " turn and twist in the air with a rapidity second only to the cotton-teal, and they have a habit after being flushed of dropping suddenly again. They swim easily, but not very rapidly, and they cannot dive to much purpose, so that a wounded bird, unless there are weeds near, under which it can lie with only the bill above water, has, as a rule, but a poor chance of escape. On the land, if the ground be fairly smooth, they walk with tolerable ease ; but it is rare to see them, as one often sees the wigeon, well out on the dry sward, walking for pleasure.

Their chief food is of a vegetable nature, but they also consume water-insects and molluscs. The common teal is usually seen in India in moderate-sized parties, but occasionally in large flocks, although never in the countless thousands in which the garganey sometimes congregates in that country. In March, however, they associate in pairs, and then afford very pretty shooting when lying on the water beneath the steep banks of the larger rivers. The teal is the easiest of all ducks to net and snare ; immense numbers being captured during the cold weather in India, and kept alive through the summer in specially constructed " tealeries."

GARGANEY

The garganey, or summer teal (*Querquedula circia*), is a larger bird representing a second genus, in which the head is crestless, the beak broader and expanded at the tip, and the wing coverts bluish. The garganeys are, in fact, more nearly related to the shoveller than to the typical teal. In the male, of which the length is from 15 to 16 inches, the plumage of the back is not vermiculated ; the upper part of the head is dark brown, beneath which is a white stripe running above the eye and thence down the side of the neck ; the wing coverts are pale bluish grey ; the wing-bar dull green bordered with white ; the front of the neck and breast brown ; and the middle of the abdomen white. The garganey is a migratory species widely distributed over Europe and Asia, occasionally visiting the British Isles in spring, and wintering in the Mediterranean countries, India, China, Japan, etc.

The American blue-winged teal (*Q. discolor*) differs by the distinctly blue wing coverts, the presence of a white crescent between the beak and the eye, and by the under tail coverts being black, instead of white spotted with brown, in the male. The cinnamon-teal (*Q. cyanoptera*) of Western America differs from the latter by the chestnut, instead of lead coloured, head and neck of the male ; and there are several other species, in some of which, such as the Asiatic clucking teal (*Q. formosa*), the scapulars are elongated.

Photo, J. Atkinson

PINTAIL

WIGEON

The last genus of the subfamily *Anatinæ* represented in the British Isles is that which includes the typical wigeon (*Mareca penelope*), the North American wigeon (*M. americana*), and the Chilian wigeon (*M. sibilatrix*) of South America. These birds have the beak considerably shorter than the head, and very like that of the gadwall, but with the transverse plates scarcely exposed, and slightly concave above. The rather long and pointed wings have the first and second quills the longest ; the tail is short and pointed, the wing-bar mainly black, and there is a white patch on the lesser wing coverts. In the legs, a small portion of the tibia is bare, and the first toe has a small membranous lobe.

The male wigeon, which measures from 18 to 20 inches in length, may be recognised by its chestnut head and neck, minutely spotted with green (except on the forehead and top, where it is whitish), by the black-and-white fine curvilinear markings of the back and flanks, the white on the wing coverts, and by the wing bar being formed by one green band bordered by two equally wide black ones. The female is a more soberly coloured bird, lacking the bright head colours of the male, and the wing bar greyish brown. In the late summer the plumage of the male, although always the brighter, approximates to that of his partner.

The slightly larger American wigeon has the head and neck of the male whitish, slightly speckled with black, and with a metallic green patch on each side of the head, which may extend some distance down the neck ; while the female has a black wing bar. In the Chilian wigeon the wing bar is velvety black in both sexes. The common wigeon is a migratory species having a distribution very similar to that of the teal, breeding occasionally in the northern parts of the British Isles, as well as in France, Germany, and the Danube Valley, but more generally in the belt lying between the Arctic Circle and the 60th parallel.

At all times gregarious, these birds are even social in the breeding season; and while in the British Isles principally frequenting estuaries and the neighbourhood of the coast, in India they are spread over all the inland waters. Their habit of walking on land near the margin of water has been already mentioned under the head of the teal; and it may be added that they differ from those birds in the facility with which they dive when wounded. They breed in well-watered districts where the ground is partly swampy and partly covered with low scrub; the nest being placed near water beneath tussocks of grass, or at some distance off under the shelter of a bush. May or June is the usual nesting time; and the number of eggs in a clutch is usually from six to ten, although occasionally more. In their partiality for grazing wigeon resemble geese.

POCHARDS AND SCAUP-DUCKS

The pochards and their near allies the scaup-ducks, which may be included in two genera, *Netta* and *Nyroca*, although divided by some naturalists into three generic groups, are the first representatives of a subfamily, *Nyrocainæ*, distinguished structurally from the *Anatinæ* by having a distinct pendent lobe or membrane attached to the first toe; while in habits they differ by their practice of diving in search of food, and their extreme expertness on the water. As a rule, the sexes are different in colour; and the males undergo a partial second moult in summer. Of some forty species of diving-ducks, as the whole group may be collectively designated, the majority are confined to the Northern Hemisphere and

WIGEON   *Photograph, J. Atkinson*

South America, although there are three Australian species and another in Africa.

The pochards (pronounced pockards) and their relatives are characterised by the beak being not longer than the head, and having its base somewhat elevated, and its broad tip depressed; while the tail feathers are short, moderately stiff, rounded at the tips, and more than half-concealed by the coverts. The wings are rather short and pointed, and the metatarsus is characterised by its lateral compression.

The red-crested pochard (*Netta rufina*) differs from the other members of the group by the head of the male being rufous and furnished with a full, soft, rounded, and bushy crest; the beak being vermilion, the front of the neck and breast rich dark brown, and the wing bar white. The female is devoid of a crest, and has the head and neck yellowish white speckled with black, and no white speculum. This species, which is the sole representative of its genus, inhabits Southern and

Eastern Europe (occasionally ranging northwards to the British Isles), Northern Africa, and India.

On the other hand, the widely-distributed scaup-duck (*Nyroca marila*), of Europe, Asia, and the whole of North America, may be taken as the typical representative of a second genus, in the first group of which the males have no crest, but the head and neck of a uniform black colour; the beak being about equal in length to the second toe, with its nail differing from that of the red-crested pochard by being small and narrow, in place of large and broad. In the male scaup the head, neck, and breast are purplish black, the back and scapulars white with fine black curvilinear markings, and the wing-bar and under parts white. America is the home of a closely-allied species known as *N. affinis*, or *N. mariloides*.

Very distinct is the tufted duck (*N. fuligula*), which has a circumpolar distribution, and reaches India, the Mediterranean, and Central America in winter. It is specially characterised by the tuft of feathers crowning the head in both sexes, the black head and neck of the drake, and the uniformly coloured back of both sexes.

A third group of the genus (*Aythya*) is represented by the common pochard (*N. ferina*) of Europe and Northern Asia, and the red-headed pochard (*N. americana*) and canvas-backed duck (*N. [Aristonetta] vallisneria*) of North America, as well as other forms. In all these the beak is rather longer than the inner toe, and the head and neck of the adult males are red.

Nearly allied are the white-eyed pochard (*N. ferruginea*) of Europe and Asia, and the Australian white-eye (*N. australis*), which take their name from the white ring formed by the iris of the eye. In the adult male of the European species the head, neck, and upper breast are chestnut brown, the wing speculum white, and the beak leaden blue; while in the female the head and neck are pale chestnut.

During its sojourn in the British Isles, from October to March or April, the typical pochard is generally met with on the coast, although in other districts, and especially India, it is an inland bird at the same season. A bad walker, this duck is essentially a diver and swimmer, associating in India in immense flocks on open sheets of water of medium depth. These birds feed chiefly by night, but in undisturbed districts may be seen diving at all hours of the day in search of the stems and roots of water-plants which constitute their chief food.

The same habits characterise the American canvas-back, which is met with in countless numbers on the Chesapeake, where it dives for vallisneria grass, locally known as celery. Both these ducks are most excellent table birds; and while in India the pochard is taken by hundreds in nets placed in the water, the canvas-back is usually shot in America, one device being to attract the birds within range by going out at night in a boat furnished with a powerful lamp and reflector in the bows.

Such pochards as remain to breed in the British Isles usually nest in May and the first half of June ; the nest being constructed of rushes, grass, or flags, sometimes placed among the rank vegetation near the margin of the water, but at other times being a floating structure. The greenish grey eggs vary from eight to twelve or even fourteen in number. Writing of the red-crested pochard, Mr. A. O. Hume observes that he has " watched flocks of them, scores of times, diving for an hour at a time, with a pertinacity and energy unsurpassed by any other wild-fowl. Examine closely their favourite haunts, and you will find these to be almost invariably just those waters in which they must dive for their food." The haunts are usually deep broads where the beds of water-weed are several feet below the surface.

GOLDEN-EYES

The handsomely-coloured ducks known as golden-eye and buffel-head, together with Barrow's golden-eye (*Clangula islandica*) of North America, constitute a genus characterised by the beak being much shorter than the head, and high and broad at the base, but depressed at the tip, where it is covered by a rather small and bent-down nail. The nostrils are situated near the middle of the beak, in which the transverse plates are concealed by the overlapping of the upper half. The wings are pointed and rather short, with the first quill the longest ; and the tail of sixteen feathers is rounded and of medium length. In the male the colouring is black and white, but it is brown and white in the female.

The golden-eye (*C. glaucion*) takes its name from the golden yellow hue of the iris of the eye, and the male

TUFTED DUCK

may be recognised by the metallic green of the head and upper neck, the white patch at the base of the beak below the eye, and by the scapular region being striped with white. This species, which measures from 16 to 19 inches in length, inhabits Northern Europe and Asia, migrating south in winter ; and is represented by a variety in North America. It always builds in holes in trees at a considerable height above the ground.

Of the American species, Barrow's golden-eye may be distinguished by the white patch behind the beak extending to a point above the level of the eye ; while in the smaller buffel-headed duck (*C. albeola*), which has occasionally straggled across the Atlantic, the white patch on the head of the male is placed behind the eye and extends right across the occiput.

STEAMER-DUCK

Related to the golden-eye is the steamer-duck, or logger-head (*Tachyeres cinereus*), of Chile, Patagonia, and the Falkland Islands, in which the plumage is grey, with the head lighter, the throat rufous, the secondaries and under parts white, and the beak and feet orange yellow. The narrow middle tail feathers are curled up, and the wings very short. Never strong on the wing, these ducks apparently lose the power of flight when adult. They derive their name from the splashing they make in the water ; and their note is like that of a bull-frog.

HARLEQUIN-DUCK

The well-known harlequin-duck (*Histrionicus torquatus*), of the northern latitudes of both hemispheres, alone represents an allied genus, distinguished by the larger size of the nail on the beak, the presence of only fourteen feathers in the tail, and by the near equality in the length of the first and second quills of the wing.

The male is characterised by the general leaden hue of its plumage, relieved by white markings on the head and white collars on the lower part of the neck and breast, as well as by the purple wing-bar, while the female is greyish brown, with white patches on the head. In summer an inland species associating in pairs, in winter the harlequin-duck collects in flocks to frequent sheltered bays and inlets on rocky coasts.

LONG-TAILED DUCK

Easily recognised by the great elongation of the two middle tail feathers of the male, the long-tailed duck (*Harelda glacialis*), which is, like the last, the sole member of its genus, occupies in respect of this feature a position among the diving series analogous to that held by the pintail in the non-diving group. In both sexes the beak is very short and tapering, with a large decurved nail at the tip, and the nostrils situated near the base. The wings are rather short and pointed ; the scapular feathers of the male are lengthened ; and the tail, which has fourteen feathers, is short and graduated in the female.

In the male, of which the length is from 22 to 26 inches, the prevailing colour of the head and neck in the ordinary dress is white, with an oval brown patch on the sides of the latter ; the breast, middle of the back, rump, and middle tail feathers are black, the feathers and under parts pure white. The female is a more sombrely coloured bird, with the sides of the head white and those of the neck brown.

As its Latin name implies, the long-tailed duck is an essentially Arctic species, ranging to the most northerly known lands of both hemispheres, and not generally migrating very far south in winter, although it has been known to reach Northern Italy. Occasionally occurring as a winter visitor in Britain, it regularly frequents at that season the Caspian, Northern China, Japan, and the northern United States.

This duck, which appears in numbers on the Kara Sea, and breeds in Novaya Zemlya, Northern Russia, and all through North Siberia, is mainly marine in its habits, feeding on molluscs, crustaceans, and small fishes, in search of which it dives with remarkable expertness. During the breeding season it resorts, however, to freshwaters, on the margins of which its nests are constructed among low bushes. The note of the male is loud, but almost indescribable in words; and when flying the members of this sex present an exceedingly graceful appearance, moving with very rapid strokes of the wings, with the long tail feathers floating behind.

EIDER-DUCKS

Well known on account of the beautifully soft down collected from their nests, the eider-ducks (*Somateria*) are best characterised by the elongated scapular feathers and the presence of emerald or pale green markings on the heads of the males, these two characters serving to distinguish them from other diving ducks. Both sexes may be recognised by the beak being shorter than the head, and swollen and elevated at the base, with small and lateral nostrils, but more especially by the feathers of the forehead extending downwards nearly to the nostrils between its divided upper portion. Generally, the prevailing colours of the plumage of males are black and white. Eiders are now represented by six well-defined species, confined to the northern regions of the Old World, two of which occur in the British Isles, although one of these merely as a very occasional visitor.

The typical eider (*S. mollissima*), which is mainly confined to the Eastern Hemisphere, and is the only resident British species, may be recognised by the upper part of the back and scapulars of the male being white in the breeding plumage, while the top of the head and under parts are black, the female being pale rufous brown, with darker markings. Young males are at first like the females; but in the first year, as shown in the upper figures of the illustration on page 1290, the wing coverts and secondaries become white, and in the third year the full plumage is assumed. In summer, with the second moult, old males become almost black. In north-eastern North America it is represented by a local race, *S. m. dresseri*. Two allied American species have been named *S. borealis* and *S. v-nigra*.

A much handsomer bird is the king-eider (*S. [Erionetta] spectabilis*), which is circumpolar and a rare visitor to Britain. In both sexes the feathering on the forehead is continued on the beak as far as the hind border of the eye, but that on the cheeks stops short at the gape. The most conspicuous feature of the drake is the orange red beak, with a distinct swelling at the root. The drake in breeding plumage has the upper part of the back white, but the elongated scapulars black.

On the other hand, in the handsome Steller's eider (*S. [Heniconetta] stelleri*), which is a still more exclusively Arctic bird, the adult male in nuptial plumage has the whole back black, the long scapulars white on their inner, and bluish black on their outer webs, and a bluish black collar on the neck.

The sixth species is Fischer's eider (*S. [Arctonetta] fischeri*) of Bering Sea and Alaska.

All the species of eider-duck, as well as the red-breasted merganser, have a summer moulting plumage

analogous to that assumed by the mallard after the breeding season. As in the last-named species, this plumage lasts only during the time when the birds are unable to fly, owing to the shedding of their flight feathers, and its dull colour is doubtless for the purpose of rendering them as inconspicuous as possible during this period. The feathers of this temporary dress,

AN EIDER DRAKE

like those of the first plumage of all birds, are very inferior in structure as compared with those of the ordinary plumage. The moulting plumage of the king-eider was long considered the ordinary dress of immature birds.

All the eiders are exclusively dwellers on rocky coasts, where they subsist mainly on molluscs and crustaceans; and while birds of slow and heavy, although powerful, flight, and at the same time clumsy walkers on land, in the sea, which is their true home, they are most expert divers and swimmers. Iceland and the Farne Islands are well-known breeding resorts of the typical eider, and the following account of a colony on a small island near the former is given by Mr. C. W. Sheppard, who states that on landing, "the ducks and their nests were everywhere. Great brown ducks sat upon their nests in masses, and at every step started from under our feet. It was with difficulty we avoided treading on some of the nests. On the coast of the opposite shore was a wall built of large stones, just above the high-water level, about 3 feet in height, and of considerable thickness. At the bottom, on both sides of it, alternate stones had been left out, so as to form a series of square apartments for the ducks to nest in. Almost every compartment was occupied, and as we walked along the shore a long line of ducks flew out, one after the other. The surface of the water also was perfectly white with drakes, who welcomed their brown wives with loud and clamorous cooing.

"The house itself was a marvel. The earthen walls that surrounded it, and the window embrasures were occupied by ducks. On the ground the house was fringed with ducks. On the turf slopes of its roof we could see ducks, and a duck sat on the door-scraper. The grassy banks had been cut into square patches, about 18 inches having been removed, and each hollow had been filled with ducks. A windmill was infested, and so were all the outhouses, mounds, rocks, and crevices. The ducks were everywhere. Many were so tame that we could stroke them on their nests; and the good lady told us that there was scarcely a duck on the island that would not allow her to take its eggs without flight or fear."

In all cases the eiders build on the ground, and their not very numerous eggs are of some shade of green. In Labrador, where the numbers of these valuable birds have been greatly reduced by "eggers," Mr. A. S. Packard, writing of his experiences many years ago, observes that in the middle of June "all the eiders were busy in making their nests and in laying their eggs. The old or completed nests contained a great mass of down, and were twelve to fifteen inches in outside diameter, the downy mass in which the eggs sank being five or six inches high, the newer nests were without down; and there were about five eggs to a nest. Most of the nests which we saw were built on low land near pools, and not far from the sea water, in a dense thicket of dwarf spruce trees."

EIDER-DUCKS AND NEST

The species referred to in this account is the Eastern American eider (*S. m. dresseri*), which differs from the typical race of the European species by the greater convexity of the beak, and greater development of the elongated scapulars. The nest is formed of seaweed, lined with down from the body of the female bird; the lining being gradually added during the month occupied by incubation, till at length it reaches such an amount as to completely conceal the eggs.

The product of down yielded by a single nest is about one-sixth of a pound; the local value of the commodity varying from twelve to fifteen shillings per pound. Although such thoroughly gregarious birds at all seasons, it is somewhat remarkable that the males of none of the eiders take any share in the work of incubation.

The pied Labrador duck (*S. labradoria*) is a species which may be included among the eiders, although frequently referred to a distinct genus, *Camptolæmus*. A handsome bird, formerly abundant on the coast of Labrador and the mouth of the St. Lawrence, it appears to have become extinct since 1852.

SCOTERS

The black marine ducks known as scoters derive their scientific title, *Œdemia*, from the swollen beak, which is deep, large, and strong, with the tip much depressed, and entirely covered by the large, flat nail; the oval and lateral nostrils being placed near the middle of the beak. The wings are pointed and rather short, and the graduated tail is likewise short and pointed. Placed relatively far back on the body, the legs are noticeable for the shortness of the metatarsus; while the large feet are characterised by the second toe being fully as long as the third. In the males the colour is black, with or without white on the head or wing; but in the females the prevailing hue is dusky greyish brown. The scoters, of which there are five species, although confined to the Northern Hemisphere, are far less exclusively Arctic birds than the eiders.

The typical scoter (*Œ. nigra*), which inhabits a large portion of Europe and Northern Asia, is characterised by the entire plumage of the male being black. In Japan and North America it is replaced by the American scoter (*Œ. americana*), in which the whole of the protuberance at the base of the beak is orange yellow, instead of mainly blackish blue. The velvet scoter (*Œ. fusca*), which is also a winter visitor to the British Isles, although far less common than the preceding, differs in that the male has a small white patch behind the eye, and a white bar on the wing. Widely spread along the more northern coasts of Europe and Asia, this scoter is represented by a race (*Œ. f. deglandi*) in North America.

As another well-marked member of the genus, mention may be made of the North American surf-scoter (*Œ. perspicillata*), of which stragglers occasionally reach Great Britain. The male may be recognised in its breeding plumage by the presence of one broad patch of white on the forehead and another on the nape of the neck.

All the scoters are regular migrants, and marine and gregarious in their habits; the typical species assembling in such countless numbers on the British coasts in winter as on some occasions to cause the water to appear literally black. Scoters generally arrive from their summer quarters in September and October, and return in the following April or May. During the breeding season the flocks of adults break up into pairs;

FERRUGINOUS DUCK

although this is not the case with the immature birds, which do not breed during their first spring, but remain congregated throughout the summer. In the case of both the typical and the surf scoter flocks of these immature birds frequent the British Isles during summer instead of going northwards.

All are late breeders, the nesting of the typical species not beginning in Iceland till the middle of June, while in Arctic Russia it is deferred for a fortnight or so later. Islands in the rivers and lakes of the Arctic tundras, where the ground is covered with dwarf birch and willow, form the favourite breeding grounds of the scoters; and the eggs, which are usually from five to nine in number, are deposited in a mere hole in the ground, those of the typical species being greyish buff in colour, with a dull exterior. Although rather awkward walkers, all the scoters fly with rapidity, and are fully equal to their allies in swimming and diving. Their food in winter consists of various small aquatic invertebrates, and in summer of water plants. Their flesh is so coarse as to be almost uneatable.

Remains of extinct scoters, which have been referred to the genus *Nyroca* (*Fuligula*) used in a wide sense. occur in the Lower Miocene strata of France, which have also yielded others belonging to typical ducks, and described as *Anas*.

STIFF-TAILED DUCKS

A separate subfamily, *Erismaturinæ*, with only three or four genera, is typified by the members of the genus *Erismatura*, known as stiff-tailed ducks, all of which are lacustrine rather than marine in their habits; many being characteristic of the Southern Hemisphere. While agreeing with the preceding genera in their broad and depressed beaks, these ducks are distinguished by the feathers of the tail being very narrow and very rigid, with the inferior surface grooved. Moreover, the tail coverts are so short as scarcely to overlap the base of the tail, which is rather long and graduated, and may contain as many

as twenty-four feathers. All are said to be expert divers, and in flight and habits some more resemble a grebe than a duck.

Southern Europe, Northern Africa, and parts of Asia are the home of the white-faced duck (*E. leucocephala*) distinguished by the breadth and size of the nail at the end of the beak. In other species, such as *E. rubida* of North America and the ferruginous duck (*E. ferruginea*) of South America, as well as in the Australian *E. australis*, the nail is very small and narrow.

MUSK-DUCK

Very different from all these is the great musk-duck (*Biziura lobata*) of Australia, alone representing a separate genus, characterised by the marked superiority in the size of the male over the female, and the presence of a large lobe of skin depending from the chin of the former sex, females having only a rudiment of the lobe. The general colour of the plumage is brown with buff mottlings; but the beak and its appendage are greenish black, and the feet dusky. These ducks, which dive well, feed on mussels, worms, and leeches, roost in trees, and resort to the sea as well as lakes. Their cry is compared to the dropping of water.

WHITE-BEAKED DUCK

The white-beaked duck (*Thalassornis leuconotus*) of Southern and Eastern Africa represents another genus, with an outlying species, or race, in Madagascar. The plumage is chiefly mingled black and yellow, with the rump white, the wings, tail, and feet brownish, and the beak bluish grey.

MERGANSERS

Under the general designation of mergansers may be included a subfamily group, *Merginæ*, of diving and

THE GOOSANDER

fish-eating birds, which differ from the other members of the family in the extreme narrowness of their beaks, although resembling the diving ducks in the structure of their feet. The beak, which may be either longer or shorter than the head, is, in addition to its narrowness, straight and slender, furnished on its edges with saw-like plates and terminating in a conspicuous hooked nail; the longitudinally elliptical nostrils being lateral and placed near the middle of its length. The wings are of moderate length, with the first and second quills the longest, and the relatively short legs are placed somewhat backwardly on the body.

Of the eight or nine species of mergansers, the majority are inhabitants of the northern portions of both hemispheres, migrating southwards in winter, but one species, *Merganser australis*, is from the Aucklands; and another, *M. brasiliensis*, inhabits Brazil. The four European species are met with in the British Isles, although two are but casual visitants, and only one is a regular breeder.

The goosander (*Merganser castor*), which occasionally breeds in the northern parts of Britain, belongs to a group characterised by the beak being longer than the head, and having long recurved serrations; while the metatarsus is rather long, and a depressed and pointed crest is present in both sexes. A handsomely-coloured bird, the adult male goosander in its breeding plumage is characterised by its vermilion beak and the shining, greenish black head and upper part of the neck, as well as by the lower portion of the neck and under parts being whitish, with a rosy tinge on the breast.

HOODED MERGANSER

The upper part of the back and the scapulars are black, as are the primaries; the lower portion of the back, tail coverts, and tail feathers are ashy grey, and the point of the wing and wing coverts white. In the female the head and upper part of the neck are pale chestnut, and the upper parts and wings, except the white secondaries, mainly grey. In length the male varies from 25 to 28 inches. The goosander ranges over the northern portions of the Old World, migrating in winter to the northern shores of the Mediterranean, India, and Japan, and being replaced in North America by a race or allied species.

Nearly allied is the red-breasted merganser (*M. serrator*), which has a circumpolar distribution, and breeds regularly in Scotland and Ireland. It is a rather smaller bird than the goosander, the male having the head and upper part of the neck greenish black, the middle of the neck (except a dark streak behind) white, the lower portion of the neck and upper part of the breast buff streaked with black, the white feathers on the sides of the breast bordered with black, and those on the flanks marked with fine wavy blackish grey lines.

Very different from either of the above is the hooded merganser (*M. [Lophodytes] cucullatus*), distinguished by the black beak being shorter than the head, with smaller serrations, by the shorter metatarsus and longer wing, and more especially by the full semicircular, erect, and compressed crest of hair-like feathers. In the male the head and upper part of the neck are black, with the exception of the hind portion of the crest, which is white edged with black, and the white breast is marked on each side by two black crescentic bands. Mainly North American, where it ranges from Alaska to Mexico, this merganser is a casual visitor to Europe.

Still more different is the beautiful smew (*Mergus albellus*), in which the beak is much shorter and deeper, with small and inconspicuous serrations, and the crest much smaller than in the preceding species; while the tail has frequently sixteen, in place of the usual eighteen feathers. The male smew, which varies from 17 to 18 inches in length, has a greenish black patch on the occiput, extending in a point on each side of the head, and another between the eye and the beak, but the rest of the head, neck, and under parts mostly white, the plumage of the upper parts being pied with black, brown, grey, and white. Females have the head and back of the neck mainly reddish brown, with an inconspicuous crest. The smew is an inhabitant of the more Arctic regions of the Old World in the breeding season, rarely visiting the British Isles in winter, but to the eastward migrating so far south as the north of Africa, Northern India, and Japan.

Although in Europe mergansers very generally frequent the coast, those species which visit India are more commonly observed on inland waters. All are strong, albeit somewhat heavy, fliers, and most expert swimmers and divers, but on land their movements are awkward and ungainly. Their food consists entirely of fish, molluscs, and crustaceans, most of which are procured by diving, and in consequence of this diet their flesh is unpalatable in the extreme. When fishing in flocks, as is often the habit of the goosander, the whole party may frequently be seen to dive simultaneously, although not uncommonly a few remain above water as if to act as sentinels.

While the red-breasted merganser nests on the ground among bushes, heather, or long grass, the goosander nearly always, if not invariably, selects a hollow tree, or, failing that, a cleft in a rock, as a breeding place, sometimes taking advantage of the nest of a crow or other bird. The creamy white eggs of the latter species are from eight to twelve in number; and the young, so soon as hatched, are carried down one by one from the nest to the water in the beak of their parent. When floating at ease, the goosander sits as high in the water as a duck, but when swimming settles down as deep as a cormorant, while, when pursued, nothing more than the head and neck appears.

On the larger Indian rivers, writes Mr. A. O. Hume, "they will float down with the stream for a couple of miles, and if not hungry, they rise and fly back again; but more commonly they fish their way back, diving incessantly the whole way, and, despite their activity, taking a long time to make their way back from where they started from. When gorged, they often sit on some rock in the middle of the water, sitting very upright and cormorant-like, often half-opening their wings to the sun. In the interior, where you find them in smaller streams, they are rarely in parties of more than three or four—most generally at that time in pairs—and then they are either flying up-stream or floating down, twisting round and round in the rapids, or fishing vigorously in some deep pool near the foot of a waterfall or rapid." Although generally silent, mergansers utter at times, especially when on the wing, a harsh, unmusical kurr.

Certainly beautiful coloured birds from the mountains of Chile, Peru, and Ecuador, constitute the genus *Merganetta*, which, with *Hymenolœmus malacorhynchus* of New Zealand and the Papuan *Salvadorina waigiuensis*, has been referred to a separate sub-family, *Merganettinæ*.   R. LYDEKKER

ORDER X. PHŒNICOPTERI
FLAMINGOES

WITH an apparently intuitive perception of its zoological relationship, the Persians apply the name of kaj-i-surkh (red goose) to the flamingo, and have thus forestalled the naturalist, by whom these birds were formerly associated with the storks and herons. The members of the order mentioned in this work are the following :

FAMILY
Phœnicopteridæ

GENUS
Phœnicopterus

SPECIES

European flamingo	Phœnicopterus roseus
American flamingo	P. ruber
	P. chilensis
	P. andinus
	P. jamesi
	P. minor

Possessing in common with ducks and screamers the features mentioned on page 1262, flamingoes (family *Phœnicopteridæ*), if there were only the existing forms to deal with, might be readily distinguished by the peculiar form of the beak ; but it happens that there are certain nearly allied extinct birds in which the beak appears to have been of more normal shape, and it is therefore necessary to rely largely on other features in defining the order.

All the members of the group are readily characterised by the great length of the legs, in which the tibia may not be very much longer than the metatarsus, while the first toe is rudimentary, or even wanting. The lower end of the tibia differs widely from that of the duck tribe in that its lower end is not bent inwards ; and the corresponding extremity of the metatarsus is very similar to that of the storks, having the pulley, or trochlea, for the second toe markedly shorter than either of the others, and much bent back, whereas in the storks and herons these three trochleæ are of nearly equal length.

In the existing species the basipterygoid facets on the rostrum of the skull are rudimentary ; and in all cases the coracoid is characterised by its shortness and breadth, and its firm articulation with the breast bone. In their long legs and neck, and the absence of unfeathered areas on the latter, as well as in many features of their internal anatomy, flamingoes resemble storks ; and as their extinct allies were, perhaps, still more stork-like, the family may be regarded as in a great degree intermediate between storks and ducks, but showing strong signs of an ancestral connection with the former.

Existing flamingoes of which there are six species, constitute the genus *Phœnicopterus*, and are readily characterised by the beak of the adult being sharply bent down at an angle in front of the nostrils ; with the upper half broad and flattened, and the lower one deep and channelled.

While some species have a small first toe, in others this is completely wanting, and in all nearly the whole length of the tibia is devoid of feathers. The neck is of great length and slenderness, and the wing of moderate size, with the first quill slightly the longest, and the tail is short and even.

Flamingoes, although unknown in Australia, are distributed over the warmer regions of the greater part of both hemispheres, a few individuals occasionally wandering so far north as the British Isles and Northern Germany. With the exception of two species inhabiting the Chilian Andes, these birds frequent open country in the neighbourhood of large rivers, where the water may be either fresh, brackish, or salt. In a fossil state flamingoes occur in the lower Miocene rocks of France.

All the members of the genus are characterised by the general red hue of the plumage—either rosy white or full scarlet—with black on the wings (page 55). In the adult of the European flamingo (*P. roseus*) the whole of the plumage is rosy white, with the exception of the quills of the wings, which are black, and the light scarlet wing coverts. The eyes and the naked skin round them are yellow ; the beak is rosy red at the base and black at the tip, and the legs and feet are pinkish red. Young birds, on the other hand, lack nearly all the rose colour, and their secondary quills are barred with black, and all the naked parts leaden in colour. A full-grown bird may vary from 5 feet to as much as 6 feet 5 inches in length.

The European flamingo visits the salt-marshes and lagoons at the mouth of the Rhone and other districts in the south of France during the breeding season, where it may at times be met with in thousands. It is also abundant in similar localities in Spain ; and its range extends southwards to the Cape, and eastwards to Lake Baikal, India, Ceylon, etc.

THE FLAMINGO

Flocks of flamingoes, as they may be seen by the lakes of North-Western India, form one of the most wonderful sights in the world. On the lakes of Sind, the flocks comprise tens of thousands of individuals, which may be seen either massed upon the water, looking like huge rosy islands, or floating above it like a cloud at sunset. Still more wonderful, writes Mr. A. O. Hume, is it " to see one of these enormous flocks rise suddenly when alarmed ; as you approach

A GROUP OF FLAMINGOES

and India, which in general appearance much resembles the European species

Although essentially waders, flamingoes, when in deep water, can swim well and powerfully, carrying the neck nearly straight and inclined somewhat forwards, and moving in a series of jerks. In flight the neck and legs are stretched straight out in front and behind; the flock progressing in the same formation as geese, and uttering "gaggling" cries almost indistinguishable from those of the latter. Although flamingoes consume large quantities of molluscs, especially those of the genus *Cerithium*, it appears that, in some districts at any rate, their food consists largely of various water plants, which are pulled up from beneath the surface. When feeding on molluscs, flamingoes turn their heads the wrong way up, in which position the bent beak forms a most efficient spoon-like instrument for scooping up the shell-fish. In young flamingoes, whose food is of a different nature, the beak is nearly straight.

The nests at the mouth of the Guadalquivir are in the form of round, basin-shaped elevations of mud placed in close continuity on the mud-flats (p. 78). They vary from 2 to 6 inches in height, but the majority are very shallow, and present somewhat the appearance of a number of plates spread over the plain. Other single nests are, however, situated in the water, and are in consequence much taller. The eggs, two in number, have a chalky external coating, beneath which is a greenish blue shell.

During incubation the birds have their long red legs doubled under their bodies, the knees projecting backwards beyond the tail, and their graceful necks neatly coiled away among their back-feathers, in the same fashion as that of a sitting swan, with their heads resting on their breasts.

The period of incubation lasts a month; and the young take to the water almost immediately after hatching, swimming to a much greater extent than their parents. When conditions are not favourable, nests like the above cannot be formed, and the eggs are dropped anywhere; while, in some seasons, from persecution or want of water, the birds do not breed at all.

During the Miocene period there existed in Europe numerous flamingo-like birds which cannot be referred to the existing genus, even if they belong to the same family. The best-known of these, which have been named *Palælodus*, were smaller birds than modern flamingoes, from which they were distinguished by their relatively shorter and stouter legs and longer toes, while it is probable that the beak was straight. *Scaniornis*, of the Chalk of Sweden, is believed to be an allied type of bird.   R. LYDEKKER.

them, so long as they remain on the water at rest, they look simply like a mass of faintly rosy snow. A rifle is fired, and then the exposure of the upper and under coverts of the wing turns the mass into a gigantic, brilliantly r sy scarf, waving too and fro in mighty folds, as it floats away."

A much more gorgeously-coloured bird than the European species is the tropical American *P. ruber*, ranging as far south as Para and the Galapagos Islands, in which the general colour of the plumage is light vermilion, with brighter wing coverts, the base of the beak being yellow and the legs red. To the south of Central Peru, in Uruguay, and perhaps in Brazil this species is replaced by *P. chilensis*, distinguished by the legs being grey with red joints, while the black of the beak extends upwards above the bend.

In all the foregoing species a hind toe is present, but this is lacking in two other South American species, namely *P. (Phænicoparrus) andinus*, the largest member of the family, of the Chilian and Bolivian Andes and Argentina, and *P. (P.) jamesi*, of Southern Peru and Chile, in both of which the beak is yellow at the base and red in the middle, while the legs are yellow in the former and red in the latter. Lastly, there is *P. (Phæniconaias) minor*, of Africa, Madagascar,

ORDER XI. PALAMEDEÆ
SCREAMERS

IN the skeleton of any ordinary bird some of the anterior ribs are provided with backwardly directed projections, known as uncinate processes. In the peculiar South American birds known as screamers these processes are, however, wanting, and since they are present in all other birds and many reptiles, it will be evident that screamers form a very specialised group, although in some other respects they are of a somewhat generalised type.

The following existing species alone represent the order :

FAMILY
Screamers—Palamedeidæ
GENUS 1
Horned Screamer—Palamedea
SPECIES
Horned screamer.........Palamedea cornuta
GENUS 2
Chauna
SPECIES
Chajá ....Chauna chavaria
Derbian screamer ....C. derbiana

Although these strange birds exhibit certain resemblances in their internal anatomy to storks and cranes, it is now considered that their nearest affinities are with the ducks and flamingoes. Agreeing with those two groups in the features mentioned on page 1262, screamers are readily distinguished from both **by** their short, hen-like beaks and medium-sized legs, of which the toes are not completely webbed, but furnished with long claws, the elongation being most pronounced in the case of the claw of the first toe.

Internally, in addition to the absence of uncinate processes, screamers are characterised by the presence of distinct basipterygoid processes on the rostrum, or rod-like bar, on the under surface of the skull, by the number of vertebræ in the neck being more than eighteen (which is not the case in the two allied orders), and likewise by the absence of any bare spinal tract in the plumage of the upper parts ; while the hind half of the beak, although recurved, is not produced much backwards.

Another peculiarity is to be found in the circumstance that the skin when touched is yielding and crackling, owing to the presence of a layer of air-cells, which communicates to it a bubbly appearance. In colour and texture the eggs resemble those of geese.

Screamers are birds of the size of swans, but of totally different appearance, having a hen-like beak, with a waxy growth at the base, medium-sized neck, very inflated crop, a pair of powerful spurs on the front of each wing, and the long-toed legs bare to a considerable distance above the ankle joint. Although the second and third toes are free, the third and fourth are connected at the base by a web. The long and powerful wings have the third quill the longest, the rounded tail has twelve feathers, and the contour feathers are soft and on the neck narrow. Both sexes are alike in plumage.

The screamers (family *Palamedeidæ*) are divided into two genera, of which the first is represented by the horned screamer (*Palamedea cornuta*) of Guiana and Amazonia, characterised by the presence of a slender, horn-like process, 5 or 6 inches, arising from the middle of the head, and curving upwards and forwards. Of the two spurs on the wing, the foremost is by far the longer and more powerful. In colour the soft feathers on the top of the head are whitish grey, with blackish

HORNED SCREAMERS

tips ; those of the cheeks, throat, upper neck, wings, and tail are dark brown ; the inner secondaries and greater wing coverts having a greenish metallic sheen, and the smaller wing coverts yellowish roots ; while the feathers of the lower portion of the neck and the upper part of the breast are silver grey, broadly banded with black, and those of the abdomen pure white. The eye is orange, the beak blackish brown with a whitish tip, the horn whitish grey, and the foot ashy grey.

The members of the second genus have no horn on the head, and include the crested screamer, or chajá (*Chauna chavaria*), of Argentina, and the Derbian screamer (*C. derbiana*) of Colombia. In the former the general colour of the plumage is slaty blue, with a black ring round the neck, while the naked skin round the eyes and the legs are red. In the case of the Argentine species, these birds only utter their powerful scream of alarm occasionally ; while during the night, or when soaring high in the air, they give vent to somewhat melodious notes, audible when they are too high up to be visible.

"At certain times," writes Mr. W. H. Hudson, " in districts favourable to them, the chajás often assemble in immense flocks, thousands of individuals being sometimes seen congregated together ; and in these gatherings the birds often all sing in concert. They invariably—though without rising—sing at intervals throughout the night, ' counting the hours,' as the Gauchos say, the first song being about nine o'clock, the second at midnight, and the third just before dawn, but the hours vary in different districts.

"Although living for a considerable part of the year in large flocks, screamers pair for life, and during the breeding season are only to be seen in couples. The chajá (pronounced chahá), or Argentine species, breed among the rushes of lagoons, and during a visit to Argentina in 1893 I had the opportunity of observing the habits of a pair which were nesting in a small *laguna* a couple of miles or so from the house. The laguna in question contained large growths of reeds and flags, forming masses intersected by open channels, and at the time of my visit (the latter part of October) growing to a considerable height above the water. Like other similar spots in this part of Argentina, it was tenanted by large flocks of ducks and coots, while black-necked swans, small parties of the lovely red South-American flamingo, and a few storks were generally also to be seen.

"On my first visit to the laguna, for the purpose of duck-shooting, I was surprised to see a pair of large grey birds, with short beaks, and looking somewhat like huge geese, swimming about unconcernedly among the other denizens of the lagoon, since I had no idea that this was the habit of chajás. On approaching the birds, I was, however, soon convinced that they were really chajás. They allowed me to approach within easy gunshot, when they rose heavily and flapped slowly to the bank, where they alighted. That they had a nest among the reeds in the middle of the luguna I felt assured, but the depth of water prevented my wading to the spot. I had, however, reason to believe that the young were already hatched and swimming about among the reeds.

"As soon as I reached the shore, the chajás once more returned to the water, and again began swimming about among the ducks. During several subsequent visits to the same spot, I nearly always saw the birds swimming far out in the water ; and, indeed, it was only once or twice that I observed them on land. It is therefore evident that during the nesting season chajás are thoroughly aquatic in their habits."

GROUP GASTORNITHES

As they may possibly have some connection with the duck tribe, it may be convenient to mention here certain giant extinct flightless birds from the Lower Eocene strata of France, England, and the United States, which constitute the family *Gastornithidæ*. All have a bony bridge at the lower end of the tibia, and in the European *Gastornis* the component bones of the skull remained separate throughout life. Possibly there may have been a large tooth on each side of the upper jaw, while the long union of the two branches of the lower half of the beak was short. In North America the group is represented by the allied genus *Diatryma*.

R. LYDEKKER

CRESTED SCREAMER

ORDER XII.   HERODIONES

CHARACTERISTICS OF THE HERON TRIBE

WITH the exception of the extreme north, herons—of which there are some seventy species—are met with in all parts of the globe, and at almost all habitable elevations. They are, however, most numerous in tropical and subtropical regions, where they form the predominating element in the bird-life of swamps and marshes. A few seem to prefer the sea-coast, others more generally frequent rivers, but the majority confine themselves to lakes and marshes. Some, again, are to be met with in the open country, while others are partial to thickets or woods. Their gait is slow and measured, and their flight of considerable strength, but uniform, and

GREAT AMERICAN EGRETS

accompanied by continual flapping of the wings. Many of the herons habitually associate in large flocks, and all build in companies ; their large nests containing from three to six un-spotted whitish or bluish green eggs. Essentially waders, most members of the family are able to swim to a certain extent, and, like the other members of the order, all of them are carnivorous ; fish forming the greater portion of their diet, although many of the smaller species are large eaters of insects, and all devour animals of any kind that they are able to capture. The following table sets out the species dealt with in the subsequent pages.

CLASSIFICATION OF HERODIONES MENTIONED IN THIS WORK

HERONS

The European heron (*Ardea cinerea*) is the type of a genus and family (*Ardeidæ*); the latter characterised by the long, straight, subconical beak, in which the nostrils are pierced in a groove at the base, and partially concealed by a membrane. The long and slender legs are naked for some distance above the ankle-joint; the front of the metatarsus is covered with large scales; and the toes, of which the third and fourth are partially joined by a web, are of moderate length, the third being much shorter than the metatarsus. The wings are moderate, with the second quill the longest, and the short tail has twelve feathers of nearly equal length.

Formerly strictly preserved in Britain for the royal sport of hawking, the heron is in most parts left to look after itself, although several of its breeding places are still well protected. Its distinguishing features are the crest of long blackish feathers depending from the back of the head; the white forehead and cheeks; the grey hue of the plumage of the upper parts, tail, and wings; the black primaries; and the long white feathers covering the chest, above which the front of the neck is white marked with elongated bluish grey spots, the under parts being greyish white with black streaks. The beak is yellow, the lore yellowish green, the eye yellow, and the legs and toes greenish yellow, with the claws brown. In total length the heron measures about 3 feet. The female is less brightly coloured, and has shorter plumes than the male.

The heron ranges over the greater part of Europe, although not found in the extreme north, but in the south it is mostly a winter visitor only, although it breeds on the Lower Danube. Eastwards it ranges through Asia to China and Japan, and is common in many parts of India and Ceylon, and it has been recorded from Australia. It also ranges over Africa to the Cape, although it is doubtful if it breeds in the south of that continent.

Nearly allied to the preceding is the more slender-necked purple heron (*A. purpurea*), in which the crown and back of the head, together with the plumes, are purplish black, the cheeks and sides of the neck fawn with bluish black streaks, the back and wing coverts slaty grey, the long feathers on the back chestnut, the tail grey, the chin pale, the neck reddish buff, the point of the shoulder and under wing coverts chestnut, and the under parts maroon-red anteriorly, and a mixture of maroon, grey, and black posteriorly. The beak and eye are yellow, as is the tibia, but the greater portion of the metatarsus and feet is brown, the claws being black.

A rare straggler to Great Britain, the purple heron is common in Holland and Spain, and ranges over the greater part of Europe to the southward of Central Germany. To the eastward it ranges from the Mediterranean to the Indo-Malay region, the north of China, and the Philippines, in such districts as are suitable to its habits, but only breeds in the warmer regions. Common and resident in Egypt, it appears to be mainly a winter visitor to most other parts of Africa, although a permanent inhabitant of certain marshy districts.

HERONS ON THE NEST

The last member of this group of the genus that will be noticed is the goliath heron (*A. goliath*), of which the total length is about half as much again as that of the grey species. In this splendid bird the crest takes the form of a number of moderately long pointed feathers. The head and crest, the point of the shoulder, and the under parts, with the exception of the white throat, are reddish chestnut brown, the sides and back of the neck bright bluish grey; the upper parts more ashy grey, and the long loose plumes on the front of the neck externally white and internally black, frequently with reddish shaft-stripes. The eye is yellow, the lore green, the upper half of the beak black, the lower greenish yellow at the tip and many-coloured at the base, while the legs and feet are black (page 19).

This heron is widely distributed over Africa; and in 1845–46 numerous specimens were obtained in the market at Calcutta, since which date there seems to be no definite record of its occurrence in India, although it may have been seen in Ceylon.

Water of every kind, from the sea-marge to the mountain-stream, forms the favourite haunt and hunting ground of herons; and there the grey species may be seen standing alone and silent, knee-deep in the flood, watching patiently for a passing fish, with its head drawn back and ready to strike with unerring aim at a moment's notice.

INDIAN ADJUTANT STORKS

"Adjutants generally congregate in vast flocks, although in the neighbourhood of towns solitary birds may often be observed, either stalking about alone or standing with outspread wings to dry their plumage, or perched on one leg while asleep on some building or tree."

2 C

WILD DUCKS, OR MALLARDS

"Like most of its kindred, the wild duck usually builds its nest in a depression of the ground near the margin of water, although at times some distance from the latter. The nest is lined with dry grass, leaves, or down; the smooth eggs being of a dull greenish grey colour."

FLORICAN AND MACQUEEN'S BUSTARD

"Essentially terrestrial and chiefly inhabitants of open plains and steppes, bustards are admirably adapted for running and walking, although they are likewise powerful and rapid in flight. Their mottled plumage of brown, black, and grey harmonises with the coloration of their surroundings."

EAST AFRICAN BALEARIC CRANE

"Terrestrial in their habits—it is said never perching on trees—all cranes build on the ground; their huge nests being placed in swamps, and the two, or occasionally three, eggs having a greenish ground more or less spotted with reddish."

Although the chief food of these birds consists of fish, all kinds of water-animals not too large for their capacities are captured easily, among them being frogs, snakes, water-rats, young water-fowl, crustaceans, insects and worms.

The usual time for fishing is early in the morning and late in the evening, but on moonlight nights the business is continued till a later hour. In spite of its extreme voraciousness, the heron is not considered a wholly unwelcome visitor to trout-streams, on account of the number of water-rats and coarse fish it destroys. Mostly solitary during the winter, the heron assembles in the early spring for nesting in large numbers; the "heronry" being generally situated in tall trees, and occupied for generation after generation.

Heronries have been so often described that it will be unnecessary to repeat the details here, although it may be observed that the nest, which is of large size, and relatively flat and wide, is formed of sticks and lined with twigs, fibres, and grass, and that the three or four eggs are bluish green in colour. While the hen is sitting, the male bird takes his stand during the hours of rest on a branch hard by, where he may at times be seen maintaining his position in the face of a gale. Both parents take a part in feeding the young, and after the first brood is able to take care of itself a second clutch of eggs is laid.

One of the English counties most famous for its heronries was Lincolnshire, and more especially its south-eastern portion, which included those of Leake (near Boston), Spalding, Donington, and Cressy Hall, all of which are now extinct. The Leake heronry occupied a very large tree, which was literally covered with nests, until it was felled about the year 1830; while the Cressy heronry, which was described by Pennant in 1769, contained some eighty nests. At the present day only five heronries in the county are known, the largest of which is reported to contain twenty pairs of birds.

In English heronries the nests are commonly built in oaks, elms, or wych-elms, but in Kashmir the magnificent chunars or plane trees are the favourite breeding resorts of these birds. Occasionally the nests are built on rocky cliffs overgrown with ivy or low shrubs. The alarm-cry of the heron is the well-known hoarse "crank, crank," but in the breeding season the note is more prolonged.

In Sind, where the grey heron is very numerous, it is employed by the natives as a decoy-bird for other water-fowl. "About every fisherman's village," writes Mr. A. O. Hume, "hundreds may be seen perched about on the boats, on stacks of brushwood thrown into the water, and on poles, perfectly motionless, and more like stuffed than living birds. The eyelids of all are sewn up; they dare not move, poor things, and, wherever they are placed for the day, there they remain immovable. Generally they are lightly tethered by one leg, but I saw several, perhaps old prisoners, in no way tied." Occasionally a bird gets loose and flies skywards in the usual circling manner, and in such cases they are never known to return, but wander forth to perish miserably from hunger.

The purple heron is a more nocturnal bird than the grey species, approximating in its habits to the bittern. The goliath heron does not appear to breed in companies. A nest seen by Major E. A. Butler in Natal "was situated in the centre of an open valley, and placed on the top of a patch of green sedge beaten down by the wind and rain, and forming, as it were, a sort of small island, being raised about two feet above the level of the water. It consisted of a dense mass of dry sedge and reeds lined with dark-coloured sedge and a species of aquatic creeper, being about two feet in diameter and very flat on the surface, and exposed to view from all sides. The male bird was sitting, and as we approached he raised himself off the nest and walked slowly away in an erect attitude for a few yards before taking flight." The three eggs, although larger, were similar to those of the common species.

GOLIATH HERONS IN BREEDING PLUMAGE

WHITE HERONS AND EGRETS

Very different in appearance to the representatives of the typical genus is the great white heron (*Herodias alba*), which, together with the numerous smaller birds known as egrets, is characterised by its more slender body and limbs, the extremely long neck, less robust beak, the white plumage, and the beautiful elongated plume-like feathers of the back. On account of these differences most naturalists now refer these birds to a distinct genus from the typical *Ardea*.

The great white heron is a few inches longer than the grey species, and has the whole plumage of a glistening silvery white; the feathers at the back of the head are but slightly elongated, although those on the lower part of the front of the neck attain a considerable length; while the long filament-like feathers of the back are developed only during the breeding season. In the latter period the beak is black, although yellow in the autumn, the lore green, and the eye yellow, while the limbs are nearly black.

An exceedingly rare straggler to Western Europe and

the British Isles, this splendid heron is more common in Spain and the south of France, but it is abundant in Sicily and along the south-eastern borders of the Mediterranean. Eastwards it extends through Asia Minor, Turkestan, and the warmer parts of Asia to Manchuria and Japan; being migratory in the more northern districts, but resident in India, Burma, etc., where its size is somewhat smaller. It also occurs during winter in North Africa, but in Australia and New Zealand is replaced by a closely allied bird (*H. flavirostris*), in which the beak is stated to be yellow at all seasons.

This species feeds on small fish, reptiles, molluscs, and insects. As a rule silent, it leaves its feeding ground early in the evening to seek a roosting place among tall trees; and in Ceylon and India breeds in company with spoonbills, grey herons, and other waders in similar situations. The nest is remarkably flat, with scarcely any hollow for the reception of the three or four greenish eggs.

Writing of the New Zealand species, Sir W. L. Buller observes that " it is very interesting to watch this stately bird stalking about in its haunts, or fishing in the shallow water, its snow-white plumage rendering it a very conspicuous object. I have always found it very shy and difficult to approach, the slightest sound exciting its suspicion and making it take wing. It flies high and in wide circles, the wings forming slow and regular flappings, the head being drawn in upon the shoulders, and the legs trailing behind."

In New Zealand the white heron breeds in several places near the sea in company with the white-throated cormorant; upwards of twenty-five nests having been counted in one of these haunts. When this species breeds in association with the grey heron, it usually occupies the middle region of the trees, of which the tops are occupied by the herons, while the lower boughs may be tenanted by night-herons.

THE LITTLE EGRET

The little egret (*H. garzetta*), which is one of the rarest stragglers to Britain, may be taken as a well-known example of a group of small white herons collectively known as egrets. The male, which measures about 25 inches in length, during spring and summer has the whole plumage pure white, with a crest of two long, narrow feathers, some elongated plumes on the lower part of the front of the neck, and the filament-like feathers of the back greatly developed. The beak is black, the lore lavender, the eye varying from yellow to pale lavender and the leg mostly black, although yellowish interiorly. The winter dress lacks the crest and the plumes on the back.

In Southern and South-Eastern Europe this egret is a common species, and it ranges thence through Asia Minor and Persia to India, China, and Japan, while it occurs locally throughout Africa, and has been obtained from Northern Australia. The little egret nests in

bushes and trees in the neighbourhood of swamps, in company with the other waders; the nest being a platform-like structure of sticks intermingled with a few reeds, upon which are laid from three to six bluish green eggs. The bird differs from the white heron in being generally very noisy.

Both this and the preceding species occur in great numbers on the inland waters of Sind; and both, like the grey heron, are kept in confinement by the fishermen. Mr. A. O. Hume states that a single boat of about twenty feet in length will contain " a man and his wife, an old man, some relatives, six children, six or eight herons (grey and white), a couple of cormorants, a kid, a dog, and otter-spears, nets, lines, hooks, and the like, of all descriptions." The breeding plumes of this and the other species of egrets are known in the feather trade as " ospreys," although their proper title is aigrettes.

BUFF-BACKED HERON

Among other species, brief reference may be made to the beautiful buff-backed heron (*Bubulcus russatus*), which is so common along the banks of the Nile, where it is often pointed out to tourists as the sacred ibis. During the breeding season this bird has the plumage of the head, neck, and breast rufous buff, and some long plumes on the back also of the same tint; the remainder being white, with a tinge of creamy on the wing coverts. The beak is reddish at the base and yellow at the tip, the eye and lore are golden pink,

GREAT WHITE HERON

and the limbs yellowish red. This bird always displays great partiality for cultivated grounds, feeding not only upon frogs and locusts, but likewise on worms and larvæ turned up by the plough, as well as on ticks from the backs of cattle—from which habit it is frequently termed the cattle-egret. The only other member of the genus is the Indian cattle-egret (*B. coromandus*).

SQUACCO HERON

The squacco heron (*Ardeola ralloides*), typifying an Old World genus of five species, is a still smaller species than the last, measuring only 19 inches in length, and is of special interest as forming a connecting link between the preceding groups and the herons. Its distinctive features are the great length of the beak, and the presence of a mane-like crest extending from the back of the head all down the neck. In the full plumage the feathers on the top of the head are yellowish brown, with dark streaks; those of the crest are white, with black borders; the sides of the head and neck are reddish buff, the interscapulars and long hair-like feathers of the back pale reddish brown, and the remainder of the plumage white.

The beak is blue at the base and black at the tip, the lore green, and the legs yellowish green, with black claws. Essentially a South European and African bird, the squacco ranges in summer over the more northern parts of the Continent, and has been taken on a considerable number of occasions in the British Isles.

NIGHT-HERONS

The night-herons, of which the European species (*Nycticorax griseus*) is the best known, are comparatively small birds, taking their name from the habit of spending the day in sleep and waking up in the evening to pass the greater part of the night in searching for food. They are distinguished by the relatively short beak being very thick at the base and slightly bent down at the tip, the moderately long and stout legs, in which a portion of the tibia is naked and the metatarsus longer than the third toe, and the very broad wings; and also by the plumage, with the exception of some three thread-like plumes from the back of the head, being smoother and more compact than in the true herons. The large plates on the front of the metatarsus are six-sided, and the tail has twelve feathers.

In the adult of the typical species the crown of the head, the nape, upper part of the back, and shoulders are blackish green, the remainder of the upper parts and the sides of the neck ashy grey, the under parts pale straw-colour, and the head-plumes (which in old birds may be increased above the ordinary three) pure white. The eye is a fine purple red, the beak black with a yellow base, the lore green, and the foot greenish yellow (page 1250). In young birds the head-plumes are absent, the general colour of the upper plumage is brown with longitudinal rusty yellow and yellowish white flecks, while the under parts have a whitish, and the neck a yellow ground with brown markings, both the eye and beak being brown. In total length the night-heron measures about 23 inches.

The night-herons have an almost world-wide distribution, being found in regions so remote from one another as Great Britain and New Zealand; and the common European species has likewise a very wide range. In Northern Europe the latter is a comparatively rare visitor, and is said to be becoming less numerous in the north of Germany and Holland, where it breeds; but it is abundant in Spain, Italy, and the Danubian provinces. Thence it extends eastwards through Palestine to India, Burma, China, and Japan, as well

as the Malay Islands; while it ranges throughout Africa, and is represented in North America by a rather larger race, which in South America passes into a darker variety.

The home of the night-heron is generally in thickly wooded districts, and by preference in the near neighbourhood of swamps; although not infrequently

THE LITTLE EGRET

these birds inhabit groves at considerable distances from water, whence they make long nocturnal flights to their fishing-grounds. Except during the breeding season, they seldom, unless disturbed, rouse themselves from their slumbers in the daytime; but when the young are hatched the parents are compelled to go abroad in search of food during the daylight hours.

Perching with its neck resting on its shoulders, the night-heron, when disturbed from its slumbers, flies but a short distance, and again settles. When on the wing, the head is drawn between the shoulders, and the legs stretched out behind; the flight being slow and flapping, and the course of the bird indicated in the darkness by the utterance from time to time of a characteristic croak.

In Europe the breeding season lasts from May to July; the nests being generally placed in bushes or low trees near swamps, but at other times in groves which may be also tenanted by other members of the order, though rarely among reeds. Large numbers of birds associate in these breeding-places, and when the young are hatched the noise made by the birds as darkness comes on is deafening. The nests in some places are made of rice-straw, and are remarkable for their size and solid structure; and the pale greenish blue eggs vary from three to five in number. The food of these birds comprises aquatic insects, worms molluscs frogs, and small fish.

LITTLE BITTERN

Omitting mention of certain comparatively unimportant genera, brief reference may be made to the little bittern (*Ardetta minuta*) as the representative of a small genus in some respects connecting the night-herons with the true bitterns. These birds are much smaller than night-herons, measuring only 13 inches in length. While agreeing with the foregoing genera in having the second quill of the wing the longest (although but slightly so), and the third toe shorter than the metatarsus they differ in having only ten

THE NIGHT-HERON

a decidedly striking bird ; and its mottled plumage of buff, brown, and black is adapted to harmonise with the dead stalks of the reeds and flags among which it habitually skulks.

As regards colouring, the crown of the head is black with a tinge of bronzy green, the elongated feathers at the back of the head and nape being barred with black and buff ; the remainder of the body plumage is characterised by having a buffish ground variously marked with reddish brown and blackish brown flecks, bars, and streaks, with a dark stripe from behind the angle of the beak and another down the front of the throat. The primaries are mingled greyish black and chestnut, and the tail feathers reddish brown with black markings. The beak is greenish yellow, tending to horn-colour at the tip, the lore green, the eye yellow, and the leg and foot green with pale horn-coloured claws. In length a male bittern may vary from 28 to 30 inches.

The American bittern (*B. lentiginosus*), which is an accidental visitor to Britain, differs from the typical species, not only by its inferior size and more slender limbs, but likewise by the uniformly lead-brown hue of the primary quills of the wings.

The bittern, like so many members of the present family, has a wide geographical distribution, extending all over Europe as far north as latitude 60°, and even to 64° on the Yenisei, in Asia, and ranging eastwards through Central Asia to China and Japan. It also occurs in Persia and Northern and Central India, as well as in Burma ; and likewise ranges over the whole of Africa, in localities suited to its habits. The American species is found over the greater part of North and Central America, but is replaced in Guiana and Brazil by *B. pennatus*. Another species, *B. capensis*, inhabits South Africa, while a fifth kind, *B. pœciloptilus*, is a native of Australia, New Caledonia, and New Zealand.

The bittern is essentially a bird of the swamps, among the reeds and bulrushes of which it either skulks in a rail-like manner, or stands erect, when it presents a strange resemblance to a pointed stump.

short feathers in the tail, in the tibia being feathered nearly to the ankle, and in the greater length of the toes. The legs are rather short, and the straight, slender, pointed beak is slightly longer than the head.

In the male the plumage of the crown of the head, nape, back, and shoulders, as well as the primaries and tail feathers, is shining greenish black ; and the wing coverts and under parts are tawny buff, marked on the breast and flanks with black. The beak, lore, and eye are yellow, and the legs and feet greenish yellow.

The smallest member of the heron tribe found in Great Britain, where it is an occasional visitor, the little bittern ranges over Southern Europe to Northern Africa, and extends eastwards to Kashmir and North-Western India. Migrating to South Africa, it is represented there by a distinct resident species ; while in the rest of Africa its place is taken by a smaller bird.

BITTERNS

Before the drainage of the fens and the general advance of cultivation, the " boom " of the bittern was a familiar sound in many parts of England, but the bird is now only a somewhat rare visitor, although a nest was taken so recently as the year 1868. The bittern (*Botaurus stellaris*) is the typical representative of a genus easily characterised by the great length of the toes, of which the third is as long as the metatarsus, by the first three quills being of nearly equal length and the longest in the wing, and by the short tail comprising ten soft feathers. The strong beak is rather longer than the head, somewhat higher than broad, with the extremity of its upper half slightly curved downwards, the longitudinal slit-like nostrils being partially covered by a bare membrane.

The legs are of medium length, feathered nearly down to the ankle, and with large shield-like plates on the front of the metatarsus ; while the toes are of very unequal length, with the first unusually elongated. Owing to the equality in length of the first three quills, the somewhat elongated wings are rounded at their extremities. There is but little difference between the plumage of the young and mature birds. Although inferior in size to the heron, from which it differs markedly in its much shorter and thicker neck, larger and plumeless head, and shorter beak, the bittern is

THE LITTLE BITTERN

THE BITTERN

animals. In its stomach may be found molluscs, cray-fish, frogs, lizards, small snakes, and fishes, as well as insects. Such prey is captured with great address, by spearing, as the bird walks or wades stealthily along ; the thrust of the bill being marvellously quick and skilful." It may be added that in America as well as in the Old World bitterns are to a certain extent migratory.

BOAT-BILLED HERON

The last member of the family to which it will be necessary to allude is the remarkable boat-billed heron (*Canchroma cochlearia*) of South America, which, while agreeing with the other representatives of the group in essential characters, differs by the broad head, terminating in the wide and boat-like beak from which this bird derives its name. The boat-bill is about the size of a night-heron, and resembles the more typical members of the family in the pendent plumes at the back of the head, and the presence of twelve comparatively stiff feathers in the tail. The broad beak is rounded off in front, where it is somewhat bent down ; the legs are rather short and feathered to the ankle, with toes of moderate length, the wings strong and large, with the fourth quill the longest, and the tail feathers short and truncated.

The crest is large and formed by the feathers of the back of the head and nape, but there are no elongated plumes on the back, and the front of the throat is naked. In colour the forehead, throat, fore part of the neck, and cheeks are white, the lower part of the neck and breast yellowish white, the back clear grey, the hind region of the upper part of the neck and the under parts rusty reddish brown, passing into black on the sides, and the wing and tail feathers whitish grey. The eye is mostly brown, the beak brown with a yellow border to the lower half, and the leg yellowish.

The savaku, as the bird is called by the natives of South America, frequents the thick woods bordering the Brazilian rivers, where it may be seen either solitary or in pairs during the breeding season. These birds are more numerous in the interior than near the coast, and may be observed either in the low bushes on the banks or perched on boughs high above the river. Their food consists of various aquatic creatures, especially worms ; but from the conformation of the beak, which is probably used for grovelling in the mud, it is doubtful if these birds can catch fish.

When disturbed in the day among a bed of reeds, it generally rises within easy shot, and after flapping lazily along for a short distance, once more takes to covert. While on the wing, it utters a resounding cry, replaced during the breeding season by the hollow " boom," from which the bird derives its name ; and in its evening flights the bittern is said to soar in circles to vast heights. The breeding season in Europe begins in March and April ; and the nest, which is formed of a mass of reeds and flags, is placed either in a thick covert or on the marge of a swamp. The four eggs are olive brown in colour, but may be tinged with green when fresh laid.

Instead of " booming," the American species during the breeding season utters a cry which has been compared to the sound produced by hitting a stake with a mallet. Writing of the American bird, Dr. Coues observes that " when the bittern is disturbed at his meditation, he gives a vigorous spring, croaks at the moment in a manner highly suggestive of his displeasure, and flies off as fast as he can, though in rather a loose, lumbering way. For some distance he flaps heavily with dangling legs and outstretched neck ; but when settled on his course he proceeds more smoothly, with regular, measured wing beats, the head drawn in closely, and the legs stretched out behind together like a rudder. The food of this bird consists of various kinds of small aquatic

THE BOAT-BILLED HERON

THE WHALE-HEADED STORK

THE extraordinary gigantic bird known as the whale-headed, or shoe-billed stork (*Balæniceps rex*), which is peculiar to certain parts of Africa, forms the single representative of a distinct family (*Balænicipitidæ*), whose nearest relationship appears to be with the herons, of which family it may be a highly modified offshoot. While agreeing with the herons in the presence of powder-down patches on the rump, and the absence of bare tracts on the sides of the neck, as well as in several internal features, the whale-head is distinguished by the absence of a comb-like edge to the claw of the third toe, and like-wise by the V-shaped furcula having no process jutting forth into the angle.

Apart from these structural features, the large size of these birds and their extraordinary beaks render them perfectly distinguishable at a glance from all their allies. The broad and depressed beak, unlike that of the boat-billed heron, is concave in profile, with a strong ridge down the middle of the upper half, the tip produced into a bold hook, and the cutting edges highly curved, the minute nostrils being situated at its base and not placed in a groove. The lower half of the beak is covered with a soft, leathery skin for the greater part of its length, although horny at the tip. The legs are very long, and naked for a considerable distance above the ankle, and the elongated toes are not webbed.

The long and broad wings have the third and fourth quills the longest, the tail is of moderate length, with twelve feathers, and there is a short bushy crest at the back of the head. The prevailing ground-colour of the plumage is clear ashy grey, the larger body feathers being bordered with lighter grey, and the wing and tail feathers greyish black. The eye is yellow, the beak horn colour, and the leg black. In size this bird comes between the white and the marabou stork, although nearer to the latter than the former.

Known to the Arabs as *abu markub* (father-of-a-shoe), this giant bird is restricted to the White Nile and its affluents, and, although everywhere rare, is most numerous in the districts of Kitsh and Nuer in Northern Equatoria, where it may be found either singly, in pairs, or in small companies. It always frequents regions the most remote from human habitations, where it may be seen standing—sometimes breast-deep—in the water by the side of some tall papyrus stem, and frequently resting on one leg only (page 1250).

Very seldom is this bird seen away from the neighbourhood of tall reeds, although it sometimes takes its station on a white-ant hill on the bank, and occasionally resorts to open reaches of the river. When first disturbed by a boat, it will fly off slowly above the reeds with a great noise, and again settle ; but if roused a second time it rises high into the air, and will not again return to its haunt until the danger is past.

WHALE-HEADED STORKS

The flight is not unlike that of the marabou stork, but the heavy beak is generally kept resting on the crop. The only sound it utters is a loud snapping of the beak, in which respect it resembles the storks. Its principal food is fish, in order to capture which the bird often stands breast-deep in the stream with its enormous beak lowered to the surface of the water; while at other times several individuals combine to drive the fish towards the shallows by marching in a semi-circle through the water, and making a great flapping of their wings. It has been asserted that these storks kill and eat snakes ; but it is probable that the statement has arisen from their devouring the bichir known as the bichir (*Polypterus*), which the natives sometimes term a water-snake. That dead carcases and carrion are also consumed appears to be well ascertained.

The breeding season takes place during the rains ; the nest being situated on some slight elevation among the reeds, especially one surrounded on all sides by water. Here these giant birds collect a vast quantity of stalks and water-plants, often solidified with mud, so as to form an accumulation of about a yard in height. The eggs, which are small in proportion to the size of the bird, have thick white shells, overlain with a chalky coating : they are bluish when first laid, but become brownish as incubation progresses. Young taken from the nest thrive well on a fish diet, and are easily tamed.

THE HAMMER-HEAD

From a structural point of view, the small brown African bird known as the hammer-head, or umbre (*Scopus umbretta*), is even more remarkable than the preceding, since it combines many features common to the herons and storks, and may accordingly be regarded as nearly allied to the common ancestral stock from which those two groups have originated; it forms the family *Scopidæ*. It differs from the herons in the absence of powder-down patches on the rump, and of a comb-like cap to the claw of the third toe, as well as in having the angle of the furcula without any median projection; but it resembles that group in having the rings of the lower branches of the wind-pipe incomplete behind, and closed with membrane.

In some other parts of its internal anatomy it agrees with the herons on the one hand and the storks on the other; but it differs from all herons except the boat-billed species in the shortness of its triangular tongue, and thereby resembles the whale-head and the storks, while it is peculiar in having large bare tracts on the sides of the neck. The hammer-head measures about 25 inches in total length, and has a somewhat cylindrical body, a short and thick neck, a very large head, and a beak rather longer than the head, much compressed, straight, and bent down at the tip. The legs and toes are of medium length, the latter connected at their bases by a web; the wing is broad and rounded, with its third quill the longest; the tail is moderately long and has twelve feathers, and the contour feathers are thick and long, those on the back and sides of the head being developed into a broad and bushy crest.

The colour is uniform umber-brown, generally brighter on the under surface; the quills of the wings being shining and darker than the back, while those of the tail have a broad, purplish brown band at the tip, and smaller bars near the root. The eye is brown, the beak black, and the leg blackish brown or black

THE HAMMER-HEAD

Nowhere abundant, the hammer-head is spread all over Africa, as well as Madagascar and the south of Arabia, and, although generally inhabiting the plains, in Abyssinia ascends to an elevation of some nine thousand feet in the mountains. It frequents the neighbourhood of water in wooded districts, and appears to be generally found singly or in pairs. Resembling in many of its general habits the ibises, the hammer-head when passing from lake to lake flies strongly, and ascends high into the air, and is reported to utter a kind of croaking cry.

The most interesting feature connected with this singular bird is, however, its nest, which is a huge dome-like structure of sticks, so firmly built that it will bear the weight of a man, and frequently from a yard and a half to two yards or more in diameter. Generally placed in a fork of a tree near the ground, although sometimes in a rocky cleft, the nest has a single entrance situated on its most concealed side. Internally it contains three chambers, with entrances so small that the bird can only enter by creeping.

The sleeping chamber occupies the highest portion of the nest, in order to be safe from floods, and in this, on a bed of water-plants, are laid the white eggs, which are from three to five in number, and are incubated by each parent in turn. The middle chamber serves for the young when they are too big for the inner one, while the first is used as a look-out station.

In Angola the nests of other birds are said to be taken by the hammer-head. The chief food of these birds appears to consist generally of fish, but in some districts, at least, river-mussels, frogs, lizards, small snakes, and worms and insects constitute a portion of the diet. Although the two members of a pair do not always remain together, they appear to be associated for life; and at times the two birds, or occasionally three, will go through a peculiar kind of dance-like performance. As a rule, these birds do not leave their hiding-places till evening,

HAMMER-HEAD WITH CREST RAISED

SOME MEMBERS OF THE STORK FAMILY

INDIAN ADJUTANT

AFRICAN MARABOU

MAGUARI STORK

AMERICAN JABIRUS

STORKS

Storks (family *Ciconiidæ*) may be distinguished externally from herons by the absence of a comb-like structure on the inner edge of the claw of the third toe, by the metatarsus being covered with small reticulate scales, the absence of powder-down patches on the sides of the rump, and by the feathering on the under surface of the lower half of the beak not extending in advance of the line of the nostrils. In the skeleton, the furcula, which is generally U-shaped, is characterised by the absence of any median projection into its angle.

All storks have short, triangular tongues, whereas herons (except the boat-bill) have long ones; and, with the exception of two genera, they are characterised by the rings of the bronchial tubes being complete. There are certain other anatomical features, into the consideration of which it will be unnecessary to enter.

As supplemental characters, it may be mentioned that in all the members of the family the body is plump; the beak is in the form of a long, compressed cone, with a sharp point, but may be either turned up at the extremity or gaping in the middle; the leg is long, strong, and naked for a considerable distance above the ankle; the toes are short, and the three front ones connected by a short basal web; the wings large; and the short and rounded tail consists of twelve feathers. The contour feathers of the head and neck may be either narrow and elongated, or short and rounded; although in some cases they may become woolly or hairy, or in old age may have horny lance-like tips. The two sexes may be distinguished by a difference in size, while the colours of the young are duller than those of the old birds. The members of the family, about twenty in number, have a world-wide distribution; those inhabiting the northern regions of the globe being migratory. They are all diurnal in their habits, and the only sound they utter is produced by a sharp snapping of the beak. Extinct genera carry the family back to the early part of the Miocene period.

TYPICAL STORKS

The typical storks are characterised by their perfectly straight sharp beaks, in the horny covering of which the nostrils are perforated, by the webs of the front toes extending to their first joints, and by the third, fourth, and fifth quills being of nearly equal length. By far the best known species is the white stork (*Ciconia alba*), in which the whole of the plumage, with the exception of the black greater wing coverts and quills, is pure white, the beak being red, the lore, or bare space

round the eye, black, the eye brown, and the leg red, with brown claws. The whole length varies from 42 to 44 inches.

With the exception of the extreme north, the stork ranges over the whole of Europe, although not breeding everywhere, and being merely a very irregular visitor to the British Isles. Eastwards its range extends through Turkey and Persia to Central Asia and a great part of India, while in winter the bird visits Northern Africa in large numbers, and also passes down that continent to the Transvaal and Cape Colony. In France, where it is much persecuted, it is now only a passing visitor, but it breeds in large numbers in Holland, Germany, Poland, and, indeed, over the greater part of Central and Eastern Europe, where it enjoys protection on the part of the inhabitants.

THE WHITE STORK

The stork has become thoroughly accustomed to human habitations and the presence of man, by whom it is esteemed, not only on account of its value as a scavenger, but likewise from its well-known fidelity to its young, which has become proverbial. In Palestine, where they only exceptionally breed, storks make their appearance at the latter part of March on their northern journey, while in Holland and Denmark they generally arrive about the middle of April. They arrive and depart in immense flocks; and on their arrival spread themselves over the country in search of food, which comprises small mammals, birds, reptiles, frogs, insects, and the like.

In most parts of Europe the stork generally builds on chimneys and roofs, where boxes or other receptacles for the nest are frequently placed for its accommodation; and as it returns year after year to the same spot the nest, which is originally a shallow structure of sticks, gradually attains a height of several feet. In the absence of buildings, trees or rocks are, however, adopted for nesting. The eggs, usually from three to five in number, are pure white. During the breeding season the birds keep up a constant clapping noise with their beaks, and this noise not infrequently betrays their whereabouts when soaring at such a height as to be quite invisible to the naked eye.

As an instance of the constancy displayed by the males and females of this species, it is stated that for three years a female which remained during the winter in Europe was visited annually by her mate, when both nested as usual. In the fourth year, however, the male bird also remained with his partner during the winter, and this continued for three years. Eventually both birds were shot, when it was discovered that the female had been prevented from migrating by an old wound. On the other hand, there are well authenticated instances of tame storks having been mobbed and killed by their fellows, and the same fate is stated to have overtaken a female stork whose eggs had been replaced by those of a hen, which in due course were hatched into chickens.

The second European representative of the genus is the black stork (*C. nigra*), which is likewise an occasional visitor to England. In this bird the plumage of the head, neck, and upper parts is brownish black, with a variable metallic lustre, the under parts, from the lower breast, being white, and the wings and tail lacking the lustre of the contour feathers. The eye is reddish brown, the beak blood-red, and the leg carmine.

The black stork, which is a rather smaller bird than its white cousin, inhabits Central and Southern Europe, occasionally ranging northwards, and is found all over Africa, while eastwards it extends to China, and in winter to India. It is a far rarer bird than the white species, and, unlike the latter, shuns human habitations as widely as possible, frequenting the most secluded swamps on the banks of lakes and rivers, and nesting in tall forest trees. The nest, which is lined with moss, generally has a diameter of some four feet, the four greyish white eggs being deposited in a shallow cavity in the centre.

Writing of the habits of a captive individual of this species, Colonel Montague observes that " the stork does not gorge an eel instantly, like the cormorant ; on the contrary, it retires to the margin of the pool and then disables its prey by shaking and beating it with its bill, before it ventures to swallow it. I never observed this bird attempt to swim, but it will wade up to its belly, and occasionally thrust the whole head and neck under water after its prey."

There are a few other Old World representatives of the typical genus, which is, however, unknown in North America. The Maguari stork of South America (*Euxenura maguari*), the tropical African and Indian white-necked stork (*Dissura episcopus*), and the Bornean *D. stormi* represent distinct genera, of which the latter differs from *Ciconia* by having the forehead and sides of the head nude, and the tail deeply forked, with its lower coverts so stiffened as to resemble true rectrices.

WHITE-BELLIED STORK

Although externally not unlike the black stork in general appearance, the white-bellied stork (*Abdimia spheno- rhyncha*) of Africa is made the type of a distinct genus, as it differs from more typical storks in having the rings of the bronchial tubes incomplete behind and closed with membrane, thus indicating that it is a generalised type retaining evidence of the original kinship of the family with the herons.

Considerably smaller than the black stork, this species has the head and neck black, with a purple lustre ; the back, wings, and tail black tinged with green, and the bend of the shoulder and under parts

WHITE-BELLIED STORKS

white. The eye is brown, the naked space around the eye blue, and that on the throat red, the beak greenish with a red tip, and the leg brownish grey, except at the ankle-joint, where it is red.

From Dongola in the Sudan nearly to South Africa this stork is found in vast numbers, although it frequents villages only during the breeding season. Even then it nests but seldom on houses, preferring trees in the neighbourhood, and in the south generally selecting mimosas. Not infrequently it breeds in large companies, as many as thirty nests having been observed in a single tree. The eggs are rather smaller than those of the white stork, but vary considerably in form and dimensions.

The simbil, as this bird is called in the Sudan, receives from the natives of that district much the same venera- tion and protection as are accorded in Holland to its white cousin, with which it closely agrees in its general mode of life.

JABIRU AND SADDLE-BEAKED STORKS

Three very large species, severally known as the jabiru (*Mycteria america*) of tropical America, the saddle-beaked stork (*Ephippiorhynchus senegalensis*) of tropical Africa, and the black-necked stork (*Xenorhynchus asiaticus*), ranging from India to Australia and New Guinea, are the sole representatives of their respective genera. They are all birds of large size, easily recognised by the greatly-elongated beak being nearly straight along its upper border, but curving upwards inferiorly towards the tip, and its cutting edges presenting a similar curvature, while at its base it often has a saddle- like waxy growth. The leg is much elongated, with the toes very short ; the wing long and rounded, with the third quill the longest ; and the short tail sharply truncated. In the two Old World species the upper rings of the bronchial tubes are incomplete behind, as in the white-bellied stork, but in the American genus they are com- plete, like those of the true storks, although narrower at the back than in front.

In the American jabiru the head and neck are bare and black, and the remainder white ; but in the saddle - beaked species the feathered head and neck, the wing coverts, the shoulders, and the tail are black, with a metallic lustre, while the rest of the plumage, in- clusive of the quills, is dazzling white. In the latter species the eye is yellow, and the beak red at the base, then black for a short distance, and blood-red in its anterior half, while the fleshy saddle on the upper part of its base is variously coloured. The legs are mostly greyish brown, but the toes carmine red. In length the male measures upwards of 59 inches.

The saddle-beaked stork is one of the handsomest of all the storks when in its native wilds, being especially beautiful during flight, when the white quills of the wings stand out in marked contrast to their black coverts. It is found on both the White and Blue Nile to the southward of the 14th parallel of north latitude, and thence through the Sudan, but also occurs on both the east and west coasts. Living in pairs, it frequents sand-banks on the rivers, as well as the margins of lakes and swamps ; but it is so shy, and at the same time generally so rare, that very little is known of its habits.

The black-necked species, in which the beak is straight, with a slight upward inclination at the tip, has the head and neck black, glossed with bluish green, and with a coppery tinge on the occiput, the scapulars, some of the wing-coverts, and tail black, shot with metallic green, and the rest of the plumage white.

MARABOU OR ADJUTANT STORKS

The largest, and at the same time by far the ugliest of the storks, are the adjutants, or marabous, of the Oriental region and Africa, which apparently derive their military title from their measured walk. Two of these ungainly birds are distinguished by the presence of a large, naked, pendulous, and dilatable pouch on the front of the throat, which may measure as much as 16 inches, and has no connection with the gullet, although probably communicating with the respiratory organs.

All are characterised by the large body, thick and naked neck, by the head being either bare or thinly clad with down, and by the enormous size of the beak, which is very thick, four-sided, and somewhat wedge-shaped, with a sharp point. The legs are of great length. The whole plumage is rough and untidy-looking ; the large and rounded wings have the fourth quill the longest ; and the moderately long tail is characterised by the great development of its under coverts, which are black for most part of the year, but white in the breeding dress, when they form the well-known marabou or comercolly feathers.

In the African species (*Leptoptilus crumeniferus*), known to the Arabs as abu-scin (father of the leather bottle, or father of the beak), the head is reddish flesh-coloured, sprinkled over with short, hair-like feathers. The plumage of the back is dark metallic green, while that of the neck and under parts is pure white, the quills of the wing and tail being black and lustreless, and the greater wing coverts having their outer webs bordered with white. The eye is brown, the beak dirty whitish yellow, and the leg black, generally with a superficial coating of white. The total length of the male is about 63 inches.

In India and the Burmese countries the genus is represented by the great Indian adjutant (*L. dubius*), of which there is a larger and a smaller race ; while the Javan adjutant (*L. javanicus*) is a smaller Indo-Malay species, distinguished by the absence of the pouch in the throat. Remains of extinct adjutants occur in the Pliocene rocks of the north of India, and probably in the Miocene deposits of France.

To India the adjutants are summer visitors, arriving towards the close of the hot weather, about the end of April or May, and remaining through the rainy season till October. The large species is, however, a somewhat local bird, being most common in Bengal and the north-eastern districts, and well-

AFRICAN MARABOUS

known to all residents in Calcutta, where these birds were formerly in the habit of perching in numbers on the parapets of Government House during the rains. As a rule, they breed in Burma and the Malay countries, a favourite nesting place being some lofty scarped limestone rocks called the Nidong Hills on the Attaran River, to the south-east of Moulmein ; a few nests have, however, been observed in India.

On account of their value as scavengers, these birds are protected by law in Calcutta and some other Indian cities, nothing seeming to come amiss to them in the way of food, from the carcase of a large animal to a dead cat, or from small birds to frogs and fish. Adjutants generally congregate in vast flocks, although in the neighbourhood of towns solitary birds may often be observed, either stalking about alone or standing with outspread wings to dry their plumage, or perched on one leg while asleep on some building or tree (p. 1299).

Their flight, although heavy and flapping, is vigorous and powerful, and they frequently soar at immense heights in the air, from which they descend to join the vultures at their feasts. Writing of the arrival of one of these birds at such a carnival, Sir S. Baker observes that " a pair of long, ungainly legs, hanging down beneath the enormous wings, now touch the ground, and abu-scin has arrived, and he stalks proudly towards the crowds, pecking his way with his long bill through the struggling vultures, and swallowing the lion's share of the repast."

In the Nidong hills the adjutants nest in vast numbers during November and December, and in January the parents may be seen feeding the young birds on the topmost pinnacles of their almost inaccessible rocks. The nest is a large mass of sticks and twigs, devoid of lining, and with scarcely any depression in the centre ; the number of eggs varying from two to four, and these being large, chalky-white ovals. Occasionally, it is stated, the nests are placed in trees; the young birds are thickly covered with fluffy white down.

SHELL-STORKS

The shell-storks, or shell-ibises, as they are often called, of which there is one African (*Anastomus lamelligerus*) and one Indian species (*A. oscitans*), are much smaller birds than any of the preceding, from all of which they are at once distinguished by the two halves of the compressed and serrated beak being in the adult in contact at their two extremities, but gaping widely in the middle. On account of the second and third quills being the longest, the large wings are pointed, and the tail is short.

Although the Indian species has a normal plumage, that of the African kind is remarkable in that the shafts of all the feathers of the throat, under parts, and thighs are prolonged into small, horny processes at their extremities. In colour the whole plumage is blackish, with green and purple reflections ; the eye is red, the beak yellowish, and the leg black. Young birds lack the horny plates at the tips of the feathers.

In length the African species measures about 26 inches. The latter species is widely distributed over Central and Southern Africa, and is also met with in Mozambique. Like its Indian congener, it feeds almost exclusively on molluscs, especially *Ampullariæ*, and, according to Livingstone, breeds among reeds, although it has been stated to nest in trees. In Barotsiland the breeding places are occupied year after year by vast numbers of these birds, and the natives make a regular harvest of the young.

With regard to the peculiar gaping of the beak, Professor V. Ball writes that " this was at one time supposed to be due to attrition of the edges caused by the nature of the food upon which the bird is generally believed to subsist. Dr. Jerdon, however, stated that the bill of a young bird which he examined exhibited the same gaping. This I did not find to be the case with any of the large members which I saw. The bills were very much smaller than in the adult birds, were conical in shape, and the edges were in distinct apposition, or slightly overlapping, throughout. The change does not appear to me to be due to any loss of material

WEST AFRICAN WOOD-STORKS

of the bill by attrition, but to a structural bowing or arching of the mandibles."

WOOD-STORKS

Although agreeing with the other members of the present family in the general form of the beak, the wood-storks, or wood-ibises (*Tantalus* and *Pseudotantalus*) form a kind of connecting link between typical storks and ibises. In these birds the neck is of medium length, the head large, the beak thick, long, rounded, tapering, and curving downwards at the tip; the foot long-toed, with large webs, the wing long and broad, with the second quill the longest, and the tail short and truncated. Unlike storks, the plumage of the adult differs considerably from that of the young. The furcula is V-shaped.

The American wood-stork (*Tantalus loculator*), the sole representative of its genus, is characterised by the whole head and upper part of the neck being bare. On the other hand, the African *Pseudotantalus ibis*, the Indian *P. leucocephalus*, and the Malay *P. cinereus* have only the forehead naked ; while the beak, legs, and tail are much longer.

In the African wood-stork the general colour of the plumage is white, with a tinge of rose on the back ; the scapulars and wing coverts being marked with small purplish streaks below their white tips. The tail feathers and quills are shining greenish black, the eyes yellowish white, the beak waxy yellow, and the leg and foot red. In size the bird is somewhat inferior to the white stork. Young birds have the neck and upper parts ashy grey, and the rest of the plumage yellowish grey. The species is restricted to tropical Africa and Madagascar.

The American wood-stork is a common bird in many parts of the United States, where it associates in large flocks, and feeds entirely on fish and aquatic reptiles, of which it consumes enormous quantities. To procure their food, these birds walk in numbers through shallow, muddy lakes. Audubon writes that " as soon as they have discovered a place abounding in fish, they dance as it were, all through it, until the water becomes thick with the mud stirred from the bottom by their feet. The fishes, on rising to the surface, are instantly struck by the beak of the ibises, and on being deprived of life they turn over, and so remain. In the course of ten or fifteen minutes, hundreds of fishes, young alligators, and water-snakes cover the surface, and the birds greedily swallow them until they are completely gorged."

In the adult bird the head and upper part of the neck are bare and of a livid blue colour, tinged with yellow on the forehead, the legs blue, tinged with yellow on the webs, and the feathers white,

IBISES AND SPOONBILLS

IBISES

THE last group of the order comprises the medium-sized birds known as ibises and spoonbills, represented by some thirty species distributed all over the globe, and now referred to two distinct families, although, except as regards the form of the beak, they are closely allied. All these birds are distinguished from storks by the beak being soft for the greater part of its length, although hard at the tip, and marked by a deep groove extending from the slit-like nostril on each side of the base of its upper half to the very tip, which is truncated and bent down. The limbs are stout and of moderate length, with the front toes connected by a short basal web, the wings are generally pointed, the tail is short and truncated, and the plumage soft.

As regards their skeleton, the lower half of the beak has its hind angle produced into a recurved process behind its articulation with the skull, instead of being truncated as in storks; the skull has a pair of small vacuities on the occipital surface; and the nasal apertures are in the form of extremely long slits (schizorhinal), in place of being ovals. Finally, the furcula resembles that of storks.

All these birds associate in large companies, and differ from the typical members of the preceding family in their habit of probing about with their beaks in water in search of food, till they come in contact with some object, which is then seized. They nest in trees, and lay white eggs.

Ibises, of which there are several genera, form a family (*Ibididæ*) characterised by the slender and nearly cylindrical beak, which tapers gradually towards the tip, and is more or less arched from its base. In all of them the head is more or less bald, although occasionally only the lores are naked; and they generally have plume-like scapular feathers on the hind part of the back.

SACRED IBIS

The sacred ibis of Africa (*Ibis æthiopica*) is the type of a genus characterised by the very long and moderately stout beak; the long wing, in which the second quill is slightly longer than the third; the short twelve-feathered tail; and the general white hue of the plumage. The African species attains a length of about 29 inches, and has the naked head and neck black, the plumose feathers of the back and the tips of the quills greenish black, and the rest of the plumage white, tinged here and there with buff.

The sacred ibis is represented by the closely allied black-headed ibis (*I. melanocephala*) in India; while in Madagascar there is Bernier's ibis (*I. bernieri*), distinguished by the much smaller extent of the naked black portion of the neck; and a third species (*I.*

molucca) inhabits Australia, New Guinea, and Ceram. The Japanese ibis (*Nipponia nippon*), which differs by having only the face bare of feathers, inhabits both Japan and China.

Ibises nest in company, and there is a well-known colony of the Australian species in a swamp in the Casterton district, Victoria. The species breeding in the swamp are the straw-necked and the white ibises (*Carphibis spinicollis* and *Ibis molucca*).

The firing of a shot reveals the enormous numbers of birds frequenting the rookery. In a moment there is a wild commotion, and the air seems whistling with the sounds of hundreds and thousands of wings, and then in one mighty cloud the whole assembly takes flight, making the sky look black and white; the effect being heightened by the long bills, out-stretched necks, and general peculiar appearance of the birds.

Although so common in the country of the Pharaohs during its times of greatness, the sacred ibis is now unknown in Egypt; and doubts have been expressed as to whether it was ever indigenous there.

This species now breeds on the Upper Nile, in Nubia and the Sudan, as it does in Abyssinia, and it extends through the continent to the Cape, where it is, however, of rare occurrence. It is essentially a water-loving species, and, like its Indian cousin, may be met with in small or moderate-sized flocks on the margins of rivers or lakes or in the flooded rice-fields, where it wanders in search of the molluscs, insects, crustaceans, and worms which constitute its chief food. The flesh has a fishy taste, which renders it quite uneatable to Europeans.

SACRED IBIS

WARTY-HEADED IBIS

Among the numerous other genera of the family, reference may first be made to the warty-headed, or black, ibis (*Geronticus papillosus*) of India, and the bald-headed ibis (*G. calvus*) of South Africa, as well-known representatives of an Old World genus distinguished from the true ibises by the longer and more slender beak, the shorter toes, and the bald part of the head being confined to the crown, as well as by the dark hue of the plumage. The Indian species has a triangular patch of red warts on the top of the head; the general colour of the upper plumage being dark brown, passing into black, with the wings and tail steel-blue, the quills dusky black, and the under parts blackish brown.

An exceedingly common bird in India, where it is generally known as the curlew, this ibis is usually found in the open country away from water, where it feeds largely on insects. It builds on high trees, laying from two to four eggs.

GLOSSY IBIS

The glossy ibis (*Plegadis falcinellus*), which is an occasional visitor to the British Isles, represents a genus differing from the last by the still greater length of the beak, and having the elongated metatarsus covered in front with large plates instead of hexagonal scales, and the toes relatively long. In the wings the

STRAW-NECKED IBIS

second and third quills are the longest, and the face alone is naked. This ibis is a dark-coloured bird, the prevailing tints of the plumage being various shades of reddish brown, with purplish reflections. It is remarkable for its wide distribution, ranging over the greater part of Europe and Asia, and also occurring in North America, and rarely in the north of Africa, as well as in Australia. The genus also contains other species, and has an almost cosmopolitan distribution. In Eastern Europe and India, this bird is found breeding in colonies comprising thousands of individuals; the nests being generally placed in low bushes.

SCARLET IBIS

On account of its brilliant colouring brief reference must be made to the beautiful scarlet ibis (*Eudocimus ruber*), ranging from northern South America to Central America and the West Indies, the only other member of the same genus being the white ibis (*E. alba*), which is South American. While agreeing with the preceding in having the front of the metatarsus covered with large scales, these species differ in that the whole front of the head is naked in the adult. Both have the tips of the wings blackish, the rest of the plumage being scarlet in the one, and white in the other.

SPOONBILLS

While the glossy ibis appears never to have been anything more than a casual visitor to England, there is good evidence to show that the beautiful white bird known as the spoonbill (*Platalea leucorodia*), nested in Suffolk and Sussex some three centuries ago, although it is nowadays only a more or less casual visitor to the coast of East Anglia. The genus to which the spoonbill pertains typifies a family (*Plataleidæ*) distinguished from the ibises by the beak being very broad and depressed, widening out at the tip into a spatulate expansion, and, except at the extremity, almost straight. Like storks, spoonbills have no true organ of voice, but they differ from the members of the former group in having the lower end of the windpipe folded in a figure of eight. Their tongues are short like those of storks, but blunted at the end.

Spoonbills, of which there are several species, have a cosmopolitan distribution, although not found in Malaya and Oceania. In the European species, which attains a length of about 32 inches, the whole plumage of the adult, inclusive of the crest at the back of the head, is white, with the exception of a band of buff feathers on the front of the lower part of the neck, and a streak of the same tint up each side of the neck. The roots of some of the feathers of the back also display a rosy tinge. With the exception of the extremity of its rounded portion, where it is yellow, the beak is black, as are also the legs and feet, but the eye is bright red, and a patch of naked skin on the throat is yellow. Young birds have no crests, and have the shafts and tips of the primary quills are black.

The spoonbill ranges over the greater part of Europe except the extreme north, and eastwards it extends across Southern Siberia to Amurland, the north of China, and Japan, its southern range including India and Eastern Africa. Japan has also a smaller species, known as the lesser spoonbill (*P. minor*), while of the two remaining species of the type genus, *P. regia* ranges from Australia to the Moluccas, and *P. alba* inhabits tropical Africa and Madagascar.

The spoonbill frequents either marshes, lakes, or sandbanks in rivers. It feeds in shallow water, in which it dabbles with its broad beak in search of insects, crustaceans, molluscs, frogs, and small fish.

In Holland the nests, which are situated on the mud among reeds, and raised to a height of from twelve to eighteen inches, are composed of reeds and mud, and taper from base to summit, upon which is a slight depression for the eggs. The eggs—usually four in number—are laid at intervals of several days and incubated at once. In colour they are dull white, with reddish brown streaks and spots. In India and Ceylon spoonbills nest in tall trees.

An Australian spoonbill has been referred to a genus by itself, under the name of *Platibis flavipes*. In

SPOONBILLS

America the family is represented by the rosy spoonbill (*Ajaca rosea*), which is rose-pink, with neck, back, and breast white, tail pinkish buff, and wing and tail coverts carmine; the bare head being yellowish green, the lores and throat orange, and the feet crimson. R. LYDEKKER

ORDER XIII. ALECTORIDES
CHARACTERISTICS OF THE BUSTARD AND CRANE TRIBE

THE group with which we have now to deal is taken to include the bustards, cranes, and certain other families, and is one of those ill-defined assemblages of birds which afford illimitable difference of opinion as to the relations of their constituents. For instance, some naturalists remove the bustards from the group to place them with the rails, while others would associate them with the Limicolæ. Others, again, regard the rails (inclusive of the bustards) and the cranes as the representatives of two main subdivisions of the Alectorides. Moreover, the relation of the thicknees to the bustards is by no means universally accepted, some naturalists placing the former group among the Limicolæ, while one ornithologist includes them in the Gaviæ (page 1355).

GROUP OF BUSTARDS

Members of the present group, with the exception of the kagu, agree with game-birds and rails (described later) in having slit (schizognathous) palates, and their young covered with down, and active almost immediately after birth, as well as in the absence of a projecting (ectepicondylar) process on the outer side of the lower end of the humerus, or upper bone of the wing. They are further characterised by the truncation of the hind end of the lower half of the beak; and by this feature, as well as by the absence of any perfora-

tion of the extremity of the breast-bone by the bases of the coracoids, they are distinguished from game-birds.

From the rail tribe they may be distinguished by the circumstance that when their nostrils are oval (holo rhinal) the number of toes is reduced to three, or if four toes are present, either the breast-bone has no notch or the oil-gland is naked; while from pigeons and sand-grouse they are separated by the upper end of the humerus being of normal form. The condition in which the young are born also contributes a point of distinction between the Alectorides and the former of the two groups last mentioned.

The Alectorides may thus be approximately defined as including those schizognathous birds with active young in which the humerus has no process at the lower end, and the angle of the lower half of the beak is truncated; the nostrils being either schizorhinal or holorhinal, but, when the latter, either the number of the toes is reduced to three, or the sternum is entire, or the oil-gland naked; the upper end of the humerus being always of normal form.

The sun-bittern forms, however, an exception in that the young are helpless. The members of this group either have the toes free, or but partially connected by webs.

CLASSIFICATION OF ALECTORIDES MENTIONED IN THIS WORK

ORDER
Bustards and Crane Tribe—Alectorides

FAMILY 1
Bustards and Floricans—Otidiæ
GENUS 1
Typical Bustards—Otis
SPECIES
The bustard .... Otis tarda
Little bustard .... O. tetrax
GENUS 2
Long-beaked Bustards—Eupodotis
SPECIES
Indian bustard .... Eupodotis edwardsi
Australian bustard .... E. australis
Arabian bustard .... E. arabs
Kori bustard .... E. kori
GENUS 3
Hubara Bustards—Hubara
SPECIES
Hubara.................. Hubara undulata
Macqueen's bustard .... H. macqueeni
GENUS 4
Floricans—Sypheotis
SPECIES
Bengal florican .... Sypheotis bengalensis
Lesser florican .... S. aurita

FAMILY 2
Thicknees—Œdicnemidæ
GENUS
Œdicnemus
SPECIES
Thicknee .... Œdicnemus scolopax

FAMILY 3
Seriemas—Cariamidæ
GENUS 1
Cariama
SPECIES
Brazilian seriema .... Cariama cristata
GENUS 2
Chunga
SPECIES
Burmeister's seriema .... Chunga burmeisteri
FAMILY 4
Trumpeters—Psophiidæ
GENUS
Trumpeters—Psophia
SPECIES
Trumpeter............... Psophia crepitans
FAMILY 5
Cranes—Gruidæ
GENUS 1
Typical Cranes—Grus
SPECIES
Crane .... Grus communis
Canadian brown crane .... G. canadensis
Sarus crane .... G. antigone
Malay crane .... G. sharpei
Australian crane .... G. australasiana
White crane .... G. leucogeranus
Whooping crane .... G. americana
Great wattled crane .... G. carunculata
Japanese crane .... G. leucauchen
Stanley crane .... G. paradisea
GENUS 2
Anthropoides
SPECIES
Demoiselle crane .... Anthropoides virgo

GENUS 3
Crowned Cranes—Balearica
SPECIES
Balearic crane............Balearica pavonina
Cape crowned crane .... B. chrysopelargus
East African crowned crane .... B. gibbericeps
FAMILY 6
Courlans—Aramidæ
GENUS
Courlans—Aramus
SPECIES
Brazilian courlan .... Aramus scolopaceus
Florida courlan....................A. pictus
FAMILY 7
Kagu—Rhinochœtidæ
GENUS
Rhinochœtus
SPECIES
Kagu .... Rhinochœtus jubatus
FAMILY 8
Mesitidæ
GENUS
Mesites
SPECIES
Mesites .... Mesites variegatus
FAMILY 9
Sun-bitterns—Eurypygidæ
GENUS
Sun-bitterns—Eurypyga
SPECIES
The sun-bittern .... Eurypyga helias
Greater sun-bittern............... E. major

BUSTARDS AND FLORICANS

THE stoutly-built birds known as bustards and floricans (family *Otididæ*) have the nasal openings in the skull of an oval shape (holorhinal) and only three toes to each foot, while they are further characterised by the absence of bare tracts in the plumage of the sides of the neck, and of an oil-gland. In their skeleton the breast bone has two notches in its hind border; and the furcula is U-shaped. Externally they are characterised by the relatively short beak, in which the oval nostrils are placed near the base, the stout and moderately long legs, in which the metatarsus is shorter than the tibia, the long wings, and the short tail; the number of primary quills being ten, and that of the tail feathers twelve. They undergo a complete moult in autumn, and often a partial one in spring; and the plumage of the two sexes may be nearly similar or considerably different.

Bustards are confined to the Old World, where they are represented by between thirty and forty species, of which a considerable proportion are natives of Africa south of the Sahara. Essentially terrestrial and chiefly inhabitants of open plains and steppes, these birds are admirably adapted for running and walking, although they are likewise powerful and rapid in flight. Their mottled plumage of brown, black, and grey harmonises with the coloration of their surroundings. In some species the food is chiefly vegetable, although supplemented by insects and reptiles, but in others it consists mostly of animal matter.

TYPICAL BUSTARDS

The bustard (*Otis tarda*), which formerly inhabited many of the wilder open districts of Great Britain in large flocks, is the type of a genus which may be taken to include two or three species, and is characterised by the shortness of the beak and the absence of a crest on the head. The legs are relatively short, with a small portion of the tibia bare, and the metatarsus (as in the other genera) reticulated all round, while the wings are somewhat rounded, with the third quill the longest.

The male of the bustard stands between 3 and 4 feet in height, and has a total length of 45 inches, whereas the female measures about 9 inches less. The cock has a tuft of white, bristle-like hairs, passing backwards and downwards from each side of the chin, and partially covering a narrow patch of bare skin. In the same sex the colour of the head is grey, the upper parts are chestnut-buff, with black barrings, the primary quills blackish brown, but the rest of the wings white; the breast is marked with bands of chestnut and grey, the abdomen is white, and the tail feathers are reddish, barred with black and tipped with white. The female, as a rule, lacks the moustache and the bands on the breast. Like many other members of the family, the adult male has an air-pouch opening beneath the tongue, and running some distance down the front of the neck, which is most developed during the breeding season, but at other times probably becomes so contracted as to be almost unnoticeable.

Always unknown in Ireland, and having disappeared at an earlier epoch from Scotland, the bustard was probably exterminated as a resident English specie· in or about the year 1838; and it is now known only as a rare and casual visitor to the southern counties. Eastwards its range extends across Central and Southern Europe, through Palestine, Turkestan, and Southern Siberia to Manchuria; while it is a winter visitor to China and Japan, and occasionally straggles into Asia Minor, North Persia, and North-Western India. It also inhabits North-Western Africa, where it has now become rare; it is very scarce in France and Greece, and for years it has ceased to exist in Scandinavia. The Manchurian bustard has been separated as *O. dybowskii*, but scarcely seems to be more than a local race of the European species.

Haunting the great steppes and plains—whether barren or under corn-cultivation—of Europe and Asia, the bustard is a shy and wary bird, associating during the winter in large flocks, but apparently breaking up into pairs in the breeding season, although even then several such pairs may frequent the same neighbourhood, and the immature individuals still remain in companies. Its food consists mainly of grain and the young shoots of cereals and other plants, but it will also consume insects, as well as small reptiles and mammals. Drinking appears to be quite unnecessary to these birds and their kin. Generally silent, the female when alarmed gives vent to a kind of hiss, as does her partner; but the male has also a call-note which has been compared to the syllable "prunt."

The breeding season begins in May, towards the latter part of which the two, or occasionally three, eggs are laid in a hollow in the ground, which may be situated either in the open plain, or in a corn-field, and may or may not have a scanty lining of dry grass. In colour the eggs vary from pale buff to some shade of greenish or brownish olive, speckled with reddish brown or grey. During the breeding season the males, which sometimes desert their consorts, are apt to be very pugnacious, instances having been known where they have actually attacked human beings.

Mr. A. C. Nicholson observes that "bustards when flushed generally fly two miles or more, sometimes at least a hundred yards high. They never try to run; one that I had winged making the most awkward attempt possible to get away from me, and, though a young bird, showing much more disposition to fight than to get away by running. They fly with a regular flap of the wings, and much faster than they appear to go. I cannot imagine greyhounds being able to catch bustards, though there seems to be a good authority for believing they did." A full-grown male bustard will weigh from 26 to 30 pounds, or even rather more.

In the breeding season the cocks make a remarkable nuptial display, when the whole plumage is

LITTLE BUSTARD IN BREEDING PLUMAGE

GREAT BUSTARDS
The upper bird on the left is a male, the lower a female; on the right is a male in courting attitude

ruffed, and the white under feathers displayed, so that the head and neck are almost buried in a mass of billowy plumage.

LITTLE BUSTARD

Much inferior in size to its larger relative, the little bustard (*O. tetrax*) differs by the absence of the moustache in the male, and displays a greater diversity between the plumage of the two sexes, as well as a seasonal variation in that of the male. In the summer dress the latter sex has the general colour of the upper plumage buffish brown, marked with fine, wavy, black lines, and two black and two white gorgets on the lower part of the neck and breast. On the other hand, the female (which is equal in size to her partner) at all seasons, and the male in winter, have the head and upper parts streaked and blotched with black, and no black gorgets on the breast. In length these birds measure only about 17 inches.

The little bustard, which is only a rare and generally a winter visitor to Great Britain, is widely spread in suitable localities over Europe and Central Asia, ranging in winter to the trans-Indus districts of India and to Northern Africa. From Africa these birds migrate to their northern breeding haunts in vast flocks during April, returning in still greater numbers in October, when it is said that in crossing the plains to the south of the Caucasus they reach to millions.

Although in many of their habits resembling the larger species, their flight is very different, and they often rise to a great height, and flutter and twist about in the air. At other times, however, they fly rapidly and straight; and when on the wing always call continually. Wary in the cool of the morning and evening, during the heat of the day they lie close in the mustard-fields, which are their favourite haunts in the Punjab. "They rise suddenly," writes Mr. A. O. Hume, "with a great pat-pat of the wings; and, though quite invisible till they rise, startle one with the great breadth of pure white they suddenly reveal, the whole of the secondaries and much of the primaries being white."

An extinct bustard belonging to this or one of the allied genera has been described from the middle Miocene rocks of Bavaria, and serves to indicate the comparative antiquity of the group.

LONG-BEAKED BUSTARDS

Africa is the home of two or three large species of bustards belonging to a genus (*Eupodotis*) distinguished from the preceding by the greater length of the beak and legs, of which there is one outlying representative in India (*E. edwardsi*), and another (*E. australis*) in Australia. The wings are large and long; there is a crest at the back of the head, the feathers of the throat and fore part of the neck are elongated, and the plumage of the two sexes is nearly similar, although the females lack the neck-pouches found in the males, and are much inferior in size to their consorts. The general type of colouring conforms to that obtaining in the members of the preceding genus.

The great Indian bustard frequents open, bare or grassy plains, and in the rainy season collects in small flocks, while in the cold weather it may be observed in wheat-fields, to which it resorts for the purpose of feeding on the grasshoppers which form its favourite food. Failing insect-food, it will, however, take to fruits and seeds. When flushed, it generally flies for a long distance at a low elevation before settling again. This species is certainly polygamous, and during the breeding season the males, like those of many other members of the family, are in the habit of making a display before the females for the purpose of attraction.

Describing this display, Mr. Hume remarks that, "first the male begins to strut about, holding his head up as high as if he wanted to lift himself off his legs;

then, after a few turns, he puffs out the upper part of the throat just under the jaws, then draws it in again, then puffs it again, and so on, two, three, or four times, and then suddenly out goes the whole throat down to the breast, and that part of it next the latter swells more and more; his tail, already cocked, begins to turn right back, and the lower throat-bag gets bigger and bigger and longer and longer, till it looks to be within six inches of the ground. All the feathers of the throat stand out, and, looked at in front, he seems to have a huge bag covered with feathers hanging down between his legs, which wobbles about as he struts here and there, with wings partly un-closed, and occasional sharp snappings of his bill. From time to time he utters a sort of deep moan, and stands quite still, and then off he struts again close up to the female, and then away from her."

ARABIAN BUSTARD

In addition to insects, these birds consume large numbers of rats, mice, and reptiles, and this coarse feeding renders their flesh unpalatable. Difficult to approach within gunshot range by stalking, bustards may frequently be bagged by driving. In length the cock of this species measures from 45 to 50 inches, and the general weight is from 17 to 22 pounds.

Of the African representatives of the genus, the Arabian bustard (*E. arabs*) of Northern Africa and Arabia has the eye pale brown, with dark radiating streaks, the beak dusky above and dirty white below, and the legs yellowish. A still finer bird is the South African kori bustard (*E. kori*)—the *ghaum-pauw* of the Boers —which attains a size and weight considerably exceeding that of its Indian cousin. This bird derives its Dutch name from its habit of feeding on the gum of a species of mimosa, although it is likewise very partial to grasshoppers; and it differs from many of its allies in being voiceless. Messrs. Eglington and Nicholls write that, when feeding on the open plains, the kori is a very "difficult bird to approach sufficiently near for the range of a shot-gun; and the best plan to adopt under such circumstances, if on horseback, is to ride slowly round at a distance of a couple of hundred yards from the bird and gradually narrow the circle. If this tactic is adopted it will, like most others of the bustard tribe, often lie down as if to escape notice, and thus a shot may be obtained, although not without the expenditure of time and trouble." It seems

probable that the Indian bustard lays only a single egg; the two eggs not infrequently found on the ground at a distance of a yard or so apart apparently belonging to different birds.

HUBARA BUSTARDS

Omitting mention of a number of African bustards which have been referred to no less than six different genera, attention may be directed to the hubara (*Hubara undulata*) of the Mediterranean countries and the nearly allied Macqueen's bustard (*H. macqueeni*) of Western Asia, which represent a genus characterised by the rather short legs, the lengthened and basally depressed beak, and the presence of a ruff on the neck and a crest on the head; the latter appendages being larger in the male than the female. Breeding in Turkestan and South-Western Siberia, as well as in Afghanistan and Northern Persia, Macqueen's bustard ranges during the winter into North-Western India and Southern Persia, whence a few individuals straggle to Eastern and Central Europe (page 1301).

In India this species usually makes its appearance in September, departing again with the beginning of the hot season at the end of March or beginning of April. During its sojourn in that country it may be met with in pairs, or even solitary, although far more generally in small flocks; its favourite haunts being barren plains dotted here and there with small patches of covert. It is a silent bird, and chiefly a vegetable-feeder, although its African cousin is said to be insectivorous. Preferring running to flying, Macqueen's bustard, when on an open plain, has a habit of squatting close to the ground beneath a protecting bush or stone, and is at such times invisible even to a practised eye. Directly, however, it reaches taller covert, it raises itself to its full height, in order to have a good view of its pursuers. In districts where camels are commonly employed, these birds are easily approached by a gunner mounted on one of those animals.

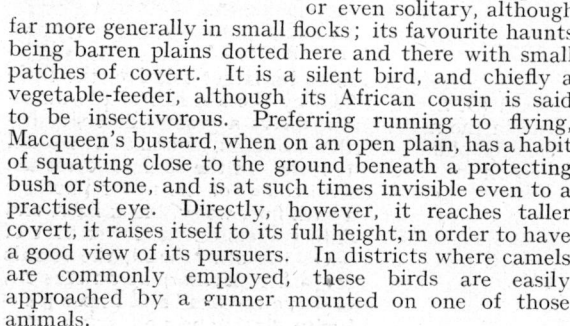

FLORICANS

Nearly allied to the bustards are the Indian birds known as floricans, of which there are two species— namely, the Bengal florican (*Sypheotis bengalensis*), and the lesser florican (*S. aurita*). They are characterised by the moderately long, arched, and somewhat broad beak; by the long legs, in which a considerable portion of the tibia is bare; and by the males (which are smaller than the females) undergoing a second moult in spring, after which the plumage becomes mostly black, with more or less white on the wings, while either a head-crest or ear-tuft is developed, and the plumes of the breast may become much lengthened.

The hens and young males are coloured much after the ordinary bustard type, and the former undergo no spring moult. In the case of the lesser florican, the male of which has an ear-tuft in place of a crest, the winter plumage of both sexes is alike ; but in the larger species the black breeding dress of the male, which is acquired by a moult, may be retained throughout the greater part of the winter (page 1301).

Florican are exclusively Indian birds, spending the whole of their time in that country, although the smaller species makes seasonal migrations from one district to another. The dark and conspicuous breeding plumage of the male would of itself be sufficient to indicate a difference in the habits of these birds from those of other bustards. Mr. Brian Hodgson, writing many years ago, stated that although the Bengal species dwells exclusively upon plains, it never frequents " nude or cultivated plains. Shelter of nature's furnishing is indispensable to it, and it solely inhabits wide-spreading plains, sufficiently elevated to be free from inundation, and sufficiently moist to yield a pretty copious crop of grasses ; but grasses not so thick nor so high as to impede the movements or vision of a well-sized bird that is ever afoot and always on the look-out. In spite of the exquisite flavour for which these birds are so famed, florican are by no means fastidious in their food, scarcely anything, from lizards and snakes to young shoots and grass, coming amiss. They are, however, generally more herbivorous than carnivorous, although when the country is overrun with locusts they feed almost entirely upon those noisome insects."

Shy and wary in disposition, the florican, except on the rare occasions when it is in thick covert, is a difficult bird to approach within range, more especially as it is a strong flyer, and will carry a heavy charge of shot without harm. Unlike a heron, a florican flies with its head stretched out in front, and its legs tucked away beneath the body. Except in the breeding season, when they utter a kind of cluck, florican are silent birds ; and they are almost peculiar in that the two sexes, even during the pairing time, live apart from one another in small companies. During the latter season, the troops of males and females come into the same neighbourhood ;

GREAT BUSTARD

and when a male wishes to attract a temporary partner, he does so by going through an elaborate series of performances somewhat similar to the well-known pantomimic display of the cock turkey, although more prolonged and energetic ; the bird at times rising perpendicularly in the air, and humming in a peculiar deep tone. The female lays two eggs in an apology for a nest at the foot of a tussock in some thick grass jungle ; one egg being generally more richly coloured than the other. In winter floricans become very fat.   R. LYDEKKER

SHOOTING THE BUSTARDS
BY MAJOR F. G. ALEXANDER

Several years ago Mr. A. O. Hume, of the Bengal Civil Service, the eminent ornithologist, asked me to study the habits and movements of the three-toed bustard family. He wished to learn the habits of the great bustard, and particularly requested me to forward its eggs to him. He also solicited information in regard to the lesser florican, and hoped I would obtain eggs of that very interesting bird. I sent him a dozen eggs of the bustard and over twenty eggs of the florican, and made observations on those birds and the hubara, which does not breed in India.

The bustard, when in flight, never ceases to flap its wings, and this peculiarity has often helped me to distinguish it at a distance from other large birds. I believe the great northern diver, too, when flying, never ceases to work its pinions, but although I have shot one fine specimen, I have never seen the latter in flight.

I have killed a large number of bustards, and the two places where I found them plentiful were Sholapore and the country between the Beema river and Seroor (Deccan). There are two methods of killing *Eupodotis edwardsi*, namely, by stalking and driving, the former necessitating the use of a small-bore rifle, either ·360 or ·220. The latter plan is to have the birds driven towards spaces they usually fly over. Once, near Seroor, in company with a professional phansipardy (native snarer), I saw during the monsoon twelve bustards assembled together on the open plain.

Near at hand were some very high jowaree crops, five hundred yards in width and about seven hundred yards in length. The crops comprised a series of fields adjoining one another. My native friend advised me to take up my position in the heart of the cultivation, for he appeared to know instinctively the course of flight the birds when disturbed would take. I had a breech-loading gun, loaded with swan-shot, and the whole covey passed over and adjacent to my position. The birds flew very low, about seventy-five feet from the earth, and I was able to secure three fine specimens. The bustard rarely flies high. The average weight of the cock bustards I have shot was about 20 pounds.

I preferred stalking. The bustard will generally allow a sportsman to approach within one hundred yards and its body offers a fair mark at that distance. I have seen peafowl hunted by Bheels on foot with bows and arrows. The birds become exhausted after a couple of flights, and fall an easy prey to the arrow, and I think that on the open Deccan plains, a horseman could similarly ride a bustard into a state of final collapse. They fly slowly, and a good horse would not be obliged to overwork itself to follow the bird at a racing pace.

The phansipardy catches the bustard with horse-hair nooses. A stretch of continuous nooses, sometimes two hundred yards in length, is pegged down near the bustard's habitual feeding place, and three or four men skilfully drive the bird in the desired direction. The men never approach too near, lest they cause the bird to fly. I have frequently watched the performance.

Wounded bustards should be approached with caution. Like the heron, bittern, and other long-necked birds, they will, if possible, dart with their sharp beaks at the human eye. Bustard skins are much appreciated by anglers, certain feathers being valuable for the manufacture of flies.

The eggs I found were all on bare ground, and I never found more than one egg in the usual shallow earth depression. In colour the eggs varied greatly. Some were sky blue, others varied shades of olive green, similar in colour to those of the nightingale.

Anglo-Indians never see the hubara in its best plumage. It breeds in North Afghanistan, and Colonel H. Heath, once of the 11th Bengal Lancers, found some eggs in that locality. I have watched the birds in September descending the Moola Pass, and I have killed a lot of them in Kutch Bhuj and Sind. The birds I have found in Sind fed mostly on mustard-fields, eighteen miles north of Jacobabad. It is almost impossible to approach them on foot, but I have always engaged a camel for the sport, and I made a point of selecting a camel low in stature. In the winter months of October and November I have started for a day's hubara-shooting, and frequently returned with a dozen birds and more.

Sind camel-drivers quickly detect the crouching hubara, for no one would believe unless he had seen it how wonderfully the hubara can lie on a flat sand and be practically invisible to ordinary sight. When the driver spots a hubara, he points the bird out to the sportsman sitting behind him. Having done so, the driver moves the camel round and round the hubara in decreasing circles until the bird is within shooting distance. Some sportsmen prefer to fire from the camel's back, but I always dropped off the camel on the reverse side to the bird, and had my shot from *terra firma*. Hence arises the advantage of a short-statured camel. The birds are excellent eating, but in the cold weather they should be hung as long as possible.

In Kutch Bhuj they frequent thicker bushed resorts, and one can stalk them far more easily on foot than in Sind. The eyes of all the bustard tribe are abnormally brilliant, especially as regards the irises. The pupils are very small. Of all the game birds I have examined, the eyes of the bustard tribe are the most beautiful and intense in expression.

The florican is the most beautiful game bird to be found on the plains of India. It is a mysterious bird, and the male, unlike the bustard and the hubara, changes its plumage in the breeding season. The male

bird, during the non-breeding season, can hardly be distinguished from the female. Both of them in the non-breeding season have virtually the same plumage. At Sholapore I killed a specimen in every month of the year, which I think only one other sportsman has ever done. I killed it in its varying plumage from brown to black, and many specimens were half brown and half black. I am alluding, of course, to the cock bird.

At Mhow, Neemuch, and Agra, where I have shot the bird, it is rarely found except in the breeding season, and where the birds go in the non-breeding season and hide themselves has always been an enigma to naturalists and sportsmen. I believe one or two have been shot between Mhow and Neemuch during the non-breeding season, but it would appear that, like the corn-crake, the florican is a runner, and very secretive except when matrimonially inclined. When courting, the lesser florican springs about three or four feet in the air with its wings outspread, and utters a croak like that of a frog. You may then be sure that its mate is close at hand.

I have been very fortunate with florican, and when Mr. Hume asked me for florican eggs, which are very hard to find, I adopted a method of my own, whereby I not only found the eggs, but killed more birds than would have been killed by the ordinary practice of engaging beaters to make the birds rise.

The florican resides in long grass, sometimes interspersed with bushes, and as a rule I took out

BENGAL FLORICAN

two natives with me. Those men held a rope about thirty yards in length, which was garnished with cattle-bells tied on at intervals of a yard. Everyone has seen the brass bells which ornament the necks of cattle and sheep, and those bells moved every florican within the area they passed over. When I saw a hen florican rise, I immediately went to the spot and very often found its eggs. The natives with the rope were a yard in advance of me, and I followed the centre of the rope.

A florican on eggs will allow an ordinary beater to pass within a yard of its nest, and the bird will not move. Sportsmen have returned from a florican shoot, beating in the ordinary way, and have killed three or four birds. I have covered the same ground on the following day with my rope and bells, and bagged sixteen birds. The flesh of the florican is delicious, but it is not advisable to eat the bird when Spanish flies are in the air. The florican is fond of the Spanish fly, and the medicinal properties of the fly are transferred to the flesh of the bird.

When I was at Futtehpore Sikri in 1892, I was out after blackbuck. The natives there knew nothing of the florican, but one day, whilst in a grass jungle, I heard the well-known croak of the florican, and thereafter I killed a lot of them. They were apparently the lesser florican, and unknown to the local shikaris.

Another of the Indian bustards is what Indian sportsmen call the "goggle-eyed," or "stone plover." They run at a tremendous pace, and, when they do fly, their wings strike the air with irregular flaps. The birds are not worth pursuing for food, although they belong to an illustrious family.　　　F. G. ALEXANDER

THICKNEES

Although placed by many naturalists with the plovers in the order Limicolæ, the genus of birds typically represented by the European thicknee, or stone-curlew (*Œdicnemus scolopax*) agrees with the bustards in the holorhinal skull, and the absence of a process at the lower end of the humerus, as well as in the three-toed feet, and may accordingly be regarded as nearly allied to the latter.

Externally thicknees (family *Œdicnemidæ*) differ from bustards by the presence of a tufted oil-gland, by the form and position of the nostrils, by the feet being webbed to the second joint, and by the second, in place of the third, quill of the wing being the longest. Internally they differ by the vertebræ of the back articulating by cup-and-ball, instead of saddle-shaped, surfaces, and thereby resemble plovers. Both groups have two notches on the hind border of the breast-bone, and in both the metatarsus is reticulated all round. In the thicknees the beak is of moderate length, stout, and nearly straight, with a slight depression at the base, and the ridge of the upper half prominent; the long nostrils, which do not open in a groove, being placed near the middle of its length. The wings are of moderate length, the tail is graduated and formed of twelve feathers. and the legs are rather long, with a small part of the tibia bare. In all the species the eye is large, and the plumage mottled and striated with shades of buff and brown.

The European species, which measures from 16 to 17 inches in length, is especially characterised by the conspicuous streaking of the breast, the presence of a dark bar across the lesser wing coverts, and the white tips to the greater wing coverts. A common summer visitor to the heathy and other open districts of England, as well as to many parts of North-Western Europe, the ordinary thicknee is a permanent resident on the shores of the Mediterranean and in North

THE THICKNEE

America, as well as in Palestine and Persia; while in summer it also visits Turkestan and Western Siberia, and in winter migrates to India. India also possesses a resident variety distinguished by its shorter wing; while the genus is represented by six species in Africa, by three in South America, and one in Australia; the last being, however, sometimes referred to a genus apart.

The thicknees are largely nocturnal in their habits, and frequent much the same kind of country as bustards, where they feed chiefly on worms, slugs, and insects, although they will also devour field-mice and reptiles. Their cry, although harsh, is loud and clear, and uttered with the greatest frequency on moonlight nights. A rapid runner, the European thicknee is likewise a bird of strong flight, frequently flying at some considerable height above the ground. The two blotched or streaked eggs are laid in England upon bare stony ground, with which their colouring harmonises so exactly as to render them practically invisible; but in India, where the number is occasionally three, the hollow is lined with a little grass.

Both sexes take part in incubation; and if a sitting bird be disturbed, it will immediately run off, leaving the eggs to be protected by their resemblance to the surroundings. After running a short distance, the bird itself will generally lie down and skulk, with its outstretched neck closely applied to the ground, and in this position is most likely to be mistaken for a large stone, unless its large eye should happen to attract the spectator's attention. Young thicknees squat down in the same manner; and, being smaller, are still less conspicuous.

SOUTH AMERICAN THICKNEE

SERIEMAS AND TRUMPETERS

SERIEMAS

THE remarkable birds known as seriemas (family *Cariamidæ*), of which there are two species, assigned to as many genera, and confined to South America, are some of those puzzling forms which render systematic ornithology so difficult and unsatisfactory. Various views have obtained as to the relationship of these birds, some naturalists believing them to be allied to the secretary-bird. On this view they were at one time placed among the birds of prey, but as they possess the slit (schizognathous) palate, which is the older type, it is clear that if they have relation to the secretary-bird, the latter must be transferred here, as being a more specialised form.

Many naturalists are, however, now of opinion that the nearest allies of the seriemas are rails, bustards,

The Brazilian seriema (*Cariama cristata*), from South-Eastern Brazil, is a long-legged and rather long-necked bird, of somewhat larger size than a bittern, with a peculiarly upright carriage. The head is large, and the beak comparatively short, broad, and depressed, with its tip bent down somewhat after the fashion of that of a vulture. In the leg the tibia is bare for some distance, the metatarsus is covered in front with large shield-like plates, and the short toes are provided with strong curved claws, which also recall those of a bird of prey. A tuft of bristly feathers arises from the base of the beak, there is a short crest on the neck, and the feathers of the breast are lanceolate. The wing is short, although hard and powerful, with the fourth and fifth quills the longest, and the secondaries greatly elongated; the tail of ten feathers being long and graduated. The internal anatomy comes nearest to

BRAZILIAN SERIEMA

and cranes, although there is still much divergence of view as to their exact position; and the plan of placing them between the bustards and cranes, in near association with the trumpeters, must be regarded as a more or less provisional measure; the inclusion of these two families in the Alectorides seriously interfering with any attempt to define that group. In any case, a linear arrangement of the members of this and the allied orders cannot possibly express their true relationships.

While agreeing with bustards in their holorhinal skulls, and the absence of tracts bare of plumage on the sides of the neck, the seriemas differ by the presence of four toes, and by the breast-bone having but one notch, as well as by the presence of a naked oil-gland; the latter being almost the only character by which the group can be differentiated from the rails, in which the oil-gland is tufted.

that of the cranes, with some approach to the rails. In general colour the plumage is grey, each feather being marked with zigzag darker lines on the upper parts; the elongated feathers of the head and neck are blackish brown, the wing quills brown, with white bands on the inner webs, the middle pair of tail feathers uniform greyish brown, and the other eight blackish brown with white tips and roots. The iris of the eye is sulphur-yellow, the naked ring round the eye bluish, the beak coral-red, and the leg reddish brown in front, and redder on the sides. The female is more yellowish grey in colour, with a shorter crest on the neck. Burmeister's seriema (*Chunga burmeisteri*), from Argentina, now generally considered to represent a distinct genus, is smaller and browner, with scarcely any tuft at the base of the beak.

The most remarkable feature about the Brazilian seriema is its resemblance, both as regards form, carriage, and the colour of the plumage, to the secretary-bird, with which, as already mentioned, it has been associated by some naturalists. If it be right to place the bird in its present serial position, and to associate the secretary-bird with the accipitrines, it is almost impossible to account for this resemblance in any satisfactory way; the circumstance that the two birds are inhabitants of widely-separated continents, putting mimicry out of the question.

Seriemas inhabit open districts in the interior of Brazil, where the ground is either clad with grass, or dotted over with low vegetation; and are generally found in pairs, or, during the breeding season, in family parties of three or four. The colour of the plumage harmonises well with that of the soil of the grassless districts.

Mainly diurnal in its habits, the sericma often reveals its presence by its peculiar cry, which has been compared to the bark of a dog, and is most generally uttered in the early morning. In spite of being so essentially cursorial, at night these birds roost on boughs of trees. Their food consists chiefly of snakes, lizards, and the like, on which account these birds are strictly protected by the Brazilians. Young rats, mice, and worms also form a portion of the diet. During the pairing time, which takes place in February, the male attracts the females by a display analagous to that noticed under the head of the bustards. The nest of twigs is built in a low or moderately tall tree, and at the proper season contains a pair of pale-coloured eggs sparingly blotched with rusty red. The down-clad young remain, it is said, a few days in the nest before they are carried down by their parents. Seriemas have laid in the London Zoological Gardens, and in two instances a young bird has been hatched, but in both the offspring has been devoured by its parent.

GIANT SERIEMA

Certain very remarkable birds from the Miocene Tertiary deposits of Patagonia constituting the family *Phororhachidæ*, and typified by *Phororhachis longissima*, may be provisionally regarded as flightless relatives of the seriema. Although in one species the tibia measures 30 inches in length, the legs of these extraordinary birds bear no proportion to the immense skull, as large as that of a horse, and characterised by the great depth and narrowness of the upper half of the beak, which terminates in a strong hook. In the base of this beak are pierced the nasal apertures, and there is a complete partition between the eye sockets of opposite sides. The furcula is slender, the metatarsus much elongated, and the first toe present.

THE TRUMPETER

Although the wings were small, they appear to have been well developed; and it is probable that the tail was of considerable length.

TRUMPETERS

The trumpeters (family *Psophiidæ*), although less aberrant than the seriemas, form another South American family of somewhat doubtful affinity, which may be best placed here, as apparently connecting the seriemas with the cranes. While agreeing with the two preceding families in having oval (holorhinal) nasal apertures in the skull, they differ from both in that the breast-bone has no notch, while there are long tracts devoid of plumage on the sides of the neck, and the number of toes is four.

In appearance, these birds, of which there are several species, may be likened to large, long-legged blackish guinea-fowls, the head and beak being strikingly fowl-like. In all of them the body is stout, the neck of moderate length, the head of medium size, the beak short and swollen, with its base convex, and its tip bent down and compressed; the leg is long, with much of the tibia bare; and the toes (of which the third and fourth are connected by a basal membrane), are furnished with sharply-pointed claws. The short wings have the fourth quill the longest, the tail is abbreviated, and the plumage is generally elongated above, but becomes downy beneath.

In the typical trumpeter, or agami (*Psophia crepitans*), the general hue of the plumage is black, with purple and greenish reflections in certain parts, and steel-blue on the lower part of the neck and breast. The eye is reddish brown, the bare skin round the eye, as well as the leg, flesh-coloured, and the beak greyish white. Trumpeters are forest-haunting birds, living in troops, which may number as many as a hundred or two hundred head; and take their name from the peculiarly clear and trumpet-like cry, which is uttered with widely opened beak, and lasts for fully a minute. To produce this deep-toned cry, the windpipe is specially modified, being elongated so as to extend under the skin of the abdomen.

These birds are poor flyers, nesting on the ground beneath the foot of trees, where they lay ten or more bright green eggs, and subsisting on fruits, corn, and insects. By the natives of Brazil they are tamed and domesticated for the purpose of protecting ordinary poultry, and in this state exhibit remarkable attachment and affection towards their owners.

DEMOISELLE CRANE

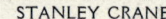

STANLEY CRANE

MANCHURIAN CRANE

SAND-HILL CRANE

CRANES

For a long period associated with herons and storks, to which they present a marked outward similarity, cranes (family *Gruidæ*) differ widely from those birds in the structure of the palate, and the condition of their new-born young, as well as in many features of the anatomy of their skeleton and soft parts. Externally they are characterised by their elongated legs and neck, generally long beak, the long wing, with ten primary quills, the plumed and elongated inner secondaries, the short twelve-feathered tail, and the elevation of the small first toe above the level of the other three.

In their skeleton they differ from all the preceding families of this order in that the nasal apertures of the skull are in the form of long slits (schizorhinal); but they agree with the trumpeters in the absence of any notch in the breast-bone, and also in the presence of a very large aperture on the inner face of the lower end of the coracoid bone. The metatarsus resembles that of the ducks and flamingoes in that the trochlea, or pulley, for the outer toe is much shorter than the one for the second—a feature which at once distinguishes this bone from the corresponding one of a heron or stork, in which the three trochleæ are sub-equal; and they differ from bustards in the V-shaped furcula. In the presence of bare tracts some distance up the neck, cranes approximate to trumpeters and rails; and they are further characterised by the oil-gland being tufted. Their plumage undergoes a double annual moult. In the colouring of their plumage cranes present a curious parallelism to herons and storks, some being mainly grey, while in others white predominates.

Cranes are represented by about nineteen species, of which the greater number are confined to the Old World; there being none in South America. Geologically they are a somewhat ancient group, as remains referred to the existing genus have been obtained from strata of Upper Eocene age. This harmonises with the view that cranes form the ancestral stock from which originated the rails, the Limicolæ, and most of the other birds treated in this section. It will, however, scarcely support the opinion that herons are likewise descended from cranes, seeing that a member of the former group existed in the London Clay, belonging to the lower part of the Eocene period; and it is scarcely likely that the metatarsal bone of a heron could have been derived from that of a crane.

TYPICAL CRANES

Although the members of the family have been arranged under several genera, it seem preferable to include the majority in the typical genus *Grus*. In the ordinary cranes the long and straight beak is of moderate length, compressed and pointed, with the nostrils placed in a groove near the middle, and partially closed behind by membrane; the wings have the third quill the longest; a large part of the tibia is bare; the front of the metatarsus is covered with plates, and the toes are short, with blunt nails. Generally there is a naked region about the eye and the base of the beak, and occasionally the entire head may be devoid of feathers. They are birds of large size, with the plumage either grey or white; and the elongation of the inner secondaries into a kind of false tail gives them a peculiarly graceful appearance.

Inhabiting extensive plains and swamps, and endowed with a powerful and long-sustained flight, most cranes are in the habit of performing migrations of great length. The windpipe being lengthened and arranged in coils within a cavity in the breast-bone enables them to utter, when alarmed or on the wing, a loud trumpet-like call, which is often audible at a distance of a couple of miles.

Terrestrial in their habits—it is said never perching on trees—all cranes build on the ground; their huge nests being placed in swamps, and the two, or occasionally three, eggs having a greenish ground more or less spotted with reddish.

The European crane (*G. communis*), which some three centuries ago nested in the British Isles, where it is now only a rare visitor, is the typical representative of the genus, and characterised by the moderate length of the beak, which is high and sloping at the base and straight in its terminal half, by the naked forehead, cheeks, and crown, and the general grey hue of the plumage. The naked part of the crown is reddish, the sides of the face and neck are white, and the elongated secondaries black. Young birds are nearly uniformly coloured. In length, full-grown specimens of this species measure from 43 to 48 inches.

The crane is widely distributed over Europe and Central and Northern Asia, visiting India, Persia, South China, and

THE CRANE

Northern Africa in winter, and passing through Japan on its migrations. Its breeding range extends from the Arctic Circle in Western Siberia to Italy and the Danube Valley. In North America this species is represented by the brown crane (*G. canadensis*). Cranes usually reach their breeding grounds in Central Europe from the south at the end of March or April, and a month later they arrive in the Arctic regions.

At all times gregarious, they migrate in vast flocks, which fly during the day at a great height in the air in a V or W shaped formation, each bird having its long legs stretched out behind. Writing of the flight of the American species, Dr. Newberry observes that, under the orders of an experienced leader, " each bird keeps his place in the ranks; the advancing column now rides higher over some suspected spot, now falls along an open sandy reach, swaying meanwhile to the right or left. As it passes on, the individual birds are blended in the hazy distance, till, just before lost to view, the line becomes like an immense serpent gliding mysteriously through the air. When about to alight, fearful lest the shadows of the woods harbour unseen dangers, the cranes pass by the leafy intricacies where the ibises and other less suspicious birds feed, and choose a spot for the advantages it may offer of uninterrupted vision. By nature one of the most wary and discreet of birds, his experience has taught the crane to value this gift and put it to the best use. His vigilance is rarely relaxed, even when he is feeding, where less thoughtful birds would feel perfectly secure."

This wariness renders the crane an exceedingly difficult bird to shoot, although the flocks frequenting the sandbanks of the Indian rivers may be readily approached in a boat, to the passing of which they are indifferent. Cranes feed regularly in the early morning, and also at other times in the day, and at night ; the vast quantity of grain a flock will consume renders their visits by no means welcome to the cultivator. In sleeping, they invariably stand upon one leg, with the head and neck thrust in among the plumage of the back. In the bogs of Lapland cranes breed in vast numbers ; the nest being made of small twigs intertwined with long, sedgy grass, with a diameter of about 2 feet, and a depth of several inches.

SARUS CRANE

The sarus crane (*G. antigone*) of India, which attains

A GROUP OF DEMOISELLE CRANES

a length of 52 inches, together with the nearly allied Malay crane (*G. sharpei*) and the Australian crane (*G. australasiana*), represent a second group of the genus (*Antigone*) characterised by the longer beak, and by the head and neck being bare and covered for 3 or 4 inches with numerous crimson warts, from which grow a few scanty black hairs, most developed round the nape. Below this the neck is whitish grey, passing gradually into the blue-grey of the rest of the plumage, except the quills and inner webs of the tail feathers, which are dusky slaty. In old birds, however, the elongated feathers become nearly white.

The sarus is confined to India, where it is always found in the neighbourhood of water, and is less gregarious than the European species, being generally seen in pairs. It is also far less of a grain-eating bird ; and, except when driven by drought, it does not migrate. It is likewise tame and confiding, and so attached are the members of a pair that on two occasions the survivor has been known to pine away and die on the death of its mate ; it is therefore recommended that, if sportsmen must kill these beautiful birds, they should always shoot the pair.

WHITE CRANES

Far more beautiful than either of the foregoing is the lovely white crane (*G. leucogeranus*), inhabiting a vast area in Central and Northern Asia, and migrating in winter to India, and probably other Oriental countries. It is characterised by having the head and neck only partially bare, and the whole plumage, with the exception of the black quills, white, the legs and naked skin of the face being red. North America also possesses a white representative of the genus in the whooping crane (*G. americana*). Mr. A. O. Hume observes that the Asiatic species "is the lily of birds ; and, stand in what position it may, the entire outline of its form presents a series of the most graceful and harmonious curves." This crane is found only where there are large sheets of shallow water, in which grow abundance of the rushes and other aquatic plants forming its chief nutriment.

To show how deceptive is the appearance of cranes when seen from a distance, Dr. E. Coues relates that once, while prongbuck-shooting on the prairie, his companion and himself saw what they "took to be an antelope standing quietly feeding, with his broad, white stern towards us, and only about five hundred yards off. We attempted for at least fifteen minutes to 'flag' the creature up to us, waving a handkerchief on a ramrod in the most approved style. This proving unavailing, my friend proceeded to stalk the game, and crawled on his belly for

AUSTRALIAN CRANES

CROWNED CRANE

about half the distance before the 'antelope' unfolded his broad, black-tipped wings and flapped off, revealing at length a whooping crane."

GREAT WATTLED CRANE

Among the other members of the genus the great wattled crane (G. *carunculata*) of South Africa takes its name from the presence of two feathered flaps of skin depending from the chin; the general colour of the upper plumage being slaty grey, with the neck white and the remainder black. This crane goes about in pairs, which haunt one locality for years.

JAPANESE CRANE

The tan-cho, or Japanese crane (G. *leucauchen*), which ranges to Siberia, Corea, and China, is grey, with the hind part of the crown, nape, throat, and inner secondaries white, and the rest of the wing-quills and tail black, with the base part of the crown and cheeks red.

STANLEY CRANE

A very distinct species is the large Stanley crane (G. *paradisea*)—often referred to the distinct genus *Tetrapteryx*—of South Africa, in which the whole plumage is leaden blue, with the exception of the white crown of the head and the black extremities of the drooping secondaries. This species, although widely distributed, is nowhere abundant, and is always found in pairs. It inhabits the open plains, at a great distance from water, and is mainly carnivorous. In confinement it becomes extremely tame, although in the wild state it is very shy.

DEMOISELLE CRANE

Allied to the last is the elegant demoiselle crane (*Anthropoides virgo*), which breeds in Northern Africa, Spain, Southern Russia, and a large area of Central and Eastern Asia, but in winter visits Central Africa and India. It is distinguished from all the foregoing, except the Stanley crane, by its shorter beak, longer legs, and shorter neck, as well as by its inferior size, and the long lanceolate feathers of the neck and breast. In length this bird is only about 30 inches; and in colour the head, neck, and long breast-plumes are black; a tuft of loose white feathers extends outwards and

backwards from the eye. The general hue is purplish grey, with the quills black.

In India, where it arrives late in October, this crane associates in flocks comprising from fifty to one hundred individuals, and frequents rivers rather than marshes. Being mainly a vegetable-feeder, it is very destructive to grain. The eggs are olive green speckled with rufous; and, while the female is sitting, the male keeps constant guard. Although somewhat apt to wound its assailant with its sharp inner claw, this crane affords good sport with a falcon.

CROWNED CRANES

The three species of African crowned cranes, genus *Balearica*, take their name from the narrow fan-shaped crest of twisted bristle-like feathers radiating from an elongated centre on the top of the head, by which they can be immediately recognised. They are further characterised by the stout body, moderately long neck, large head, and the moderate length of the beak, which is regularly conical, as well as by the broad wings, in which the fourth quill is the longest, and by the long legs and powerful claws. The cheeks are naked, and the feathers of the lower part of the neck hackle-shaped. Of the three species, the Balearic crane (B. *pavonina*) is mainly a North and West African form, the Cape crowned crane (B. *regulorum*, or *chrysopelargus*) is from the southern districts, and B. *gibbericeps* is East African.

In the southern species, or Kafir crane, the general colour of the plumage is leaden grey, the crown shows rings of white and yellow, with black tips to its component bristles, the bare parts of the face are red, the top of the head and chin is black, as is the tail, and the outer feathers of the wings are white and the inner red, both being overhung by some loose yellow plumes. In the Balearic crane, on the other hand, while the front part of the naked area on the side of the face is red, the hind portion is glistening white (p. 1302). The habits of both appear to be very similar to those of several of the typical cranes; these birds associating either in pairs or small companies, and frequenting the neighbourhood of water. On the west coast the Balearic crane is domesticated by the natives.

COURLANS

AGREEING in its osteology and feathering very closely with the cranes, the Brazilian courlan, or limpkin (*Aramus scolopaceus*), of tropical South America is generally regarded as indicating a distinct family (*Aramidæ*), although by some naturalists it is placed with the rails, from which it is at once distinguished by the slit-like nasal apertures of the skull. This bird,

THE KAGU

which measures 25 inches in length, is not unlike a large rail in general appearance, having a somewhat slender, straight beak, double the length of the head, and characterised by its extreme lateral compression. At the base of the beak the slit-like nostrils are situated in a groove extending along half its length. The legs and feet are long and slender; the lower half of the tibia being bare, and the compressed metatarsus covered with large scutes. The wings are broad and rounded.

In colour the Brazilian courlan is chocolate-brown, with purple and bronze reflections on the upper parts, and some longitudinal white flecks on the head and sides of the neck. In the West Indies, Florida, and Central America its place is taken by the Florida courlan (*A. pictus*, or *giganteus*), distinguished by the white markings extending over the back, wing coverts, and lower parts. Courlan frequent swampy districts, and are remarkably rail-like in their habits, flying with the same slow, flapping flight, and, when flushed, soon dropping again. Among reeds, where they make regular paths, their movements are extremely rapid.

KAGU

A remarkable grey-coloured bird from New Caledonia, known as the kagu (*Rhinochætus jubatus*), forms the type of a distinct family (*Rhinochætidæ*) nearly allied to the cranes, from which it is probably a specialised offshoot. Somewhat larger than a night-heron, the kagu is easily recognised by its moderately long beak, general grey colour, and the elongated pendent crest arising from the back of the head. While agreeing with the cranes in the form of the nasal apertures in the skull and the absence of a notch in the breast-bone, the kagu differs by the presence of a powder-down patch on each side of the rump, and the naked oil-gland; and it is unique among the group in having a bridged (desmognathous) palate. The plumage of the under parts is reddish brown, as is the tip of the tail, the primary quills are barred with black, white, and rufous, and the beak, legs, and feet orange. The kagu is, to some extent at least, a nocturnal bird, feeding upon worms, molluscs, and insects; but of its breeding habits nothing is at present known, although its eggs are reddish buff, with brown and grey markings. It is remarkable for the strange antics it performs; these being exhibited to a certain extent even in captivity, and recalling those of the cranes. The cry is a kind of guttural and rattling scream.

MESITES

Naturalists differ as to the position to be assigned to a remarkable bird from Madagascar, known scientifically as *Mesites* (or *Mesœnas*) *variegatus*, some of them placing it next the kagu, while by others it is considered to form a family, *Mesitidæ*, intermediate between ordinary game-birds and tinamus. It differs from the kagu, and resembles the other members of the present group in having a slit (schizognathous) palate, and also in that the nostrils are perforated instead of completely separated. It is further distinguished from the kagu by the presence of a notch on each side of the lower border of the breast-bone, and the more complex powder-down patches. The structure of the palate clearly shows that it is a less specialised bird than the kagu. It may be mentioned that in the possession of powder-down patches these birds approach the herons, and it is in part owing to this feature that a relationship between the two groups has been suggested. The beak is rather long, and the general colour of the plumage is cinnamon above with black and tawny markings, and white below with black spots and reddish flanks; the female being, however, mainly rufous below

THE MESITES

SUN-BITTERNS

THE last of these aberrant crane-like birds, the so-called sun-bittern (family *Eurypygidæ*) of South America, is structurally characterised by having a notch on each side of the breast-bone, a naked oil-gland, and powder-down patches, but shows no bare tracts on the sides of the neck. It is unique among the group in having helpless young. The sun-bittern frequents the wooded banks of rivers, and is especially common on the Orinoco. Frequently solitary, although occasionally seen in pairs, the sun-bittern derives its name from its habit of basking in sunny spots, where it delights to spread out its plumage. Its food consists of flies and other insects, which are sought on the ground and low herbage; the bird at such times being in constant motion, with its head darting here and there, and seldom taking to flight. In capturing insects it suddenly darts out its head with lightning-like rapidity, and scarcely ever fails in its aim. The nest is usually placed in a tree, at a distance of a few feet from the ground; the eggs being two in number, and of a greyish colour, with blotches and specks of reddish.

THE SUN-BITTERN

GREATER SUN-BITTERN

A second species, *E. major*, is a native of Central America, Ecuador, and Colombia, and also possesses remarkably handsome and variegated plumage; the range of the typical species extending from Venezuela to Bolivia and Central Brazil. Like the kagu, these birds apparently indicate a very ancient type, and show resemblance to the night-herons, although they are eessentially members of the crane group. The nestlings, though covered with down, have to be fed by the parent birds for some time before they are able to leave the nest and shift for themselves.

R. LYDEKKER

bittern (*Eurypyga helias*) is a comparatively small bird, measuring only 16 inches in length, with a long pointed beak, and a somewhat thin and elongated neck, and a peculiar transversely striped coloration of white, brown, and black.

The head and neck are black, with a brown streak above the eye, and another running backwards from the angle of the beak to the neck, the chin and throat are white, the feathers of the back and scapular region black striped with rusty red, the bastard wing and wing coverts black and white; the feathers of the neck barred with brown and black, those of the under parts yellowish or brownish white, the quills clear grey, mottled with white and black, and barred with brown, and the tail feathers are similarly coloured, but distinguished by the broad bands of black passing posteriorly into brown. The eye is red, the beak waxy yellow, and the leg straw-coloured.

This bird, which has been not inaptly compared to a large, broad-winged butterfly when in flight, always

GREATER SUN-BITTERN WITH PLUMAGE DISPLAYED

ORDER XIV. LIMICOLÆ
CHARACTERISTICS OF THE PLOVER-LIKE BIRDS

THE plovers and gulls, together with certain allied forms, are all closely connected, but may be conveniently divided into two orders, Limicolæ and Gaviæ, of which the second is represented by the gulls and terns. Both groups have cleft (schizognathous) palates and the young are covered with down and active at birth. They differ, however, from all the preceding groups of birds in that the upper wing-bone, or humerus, is furnished with a projecting (ectepicondylar) process on the outer side of its lower extremity; and they are also characterised by the vertebræ of the back having their articular surfaces of a more or less cup-and-ball type, instead of saddle-shaped. In all of them, except the black-backed courser, the nasal apertures in the skull are slit-like (schizorhinal), in all the oil gland is tufted, and on the upper part of the back the spinal tract of feathers is forked. The group includes considerably over three hundred species.

The plovers, snipe, sandpipers, coursers, and their allies, are long-legged, and frequently long-billed, birds, characterised by the hind angle of the lower half of the beak being produced backwards and recurved, by the very general presence of basipterygoid processes on the inferior rod, or rostrum, of the skull, and by the feet being but seldom completely webbed, as well as by the absence of a certain feature connected with the bones of the wing which is characteristic of the gulls, and will be alluded to under that heading. As a rule, the breast-bone has two notches on its hind border; and in some cases the third toe is serrated, while the third and fourth toes may be connected for some distance by a web, or all three front toes may have lobe-like expansions, or even a web. In all cases the first toe is small, and it may be elevated above the plane of the others, or even wanting. The wings are relatively long and pointed, with ten primary quills, and the tail is short, with the number of feathers variable.

In most cases these birds undergo an autumnal and a spring moult; the young birds in their first plumage, more or less closely resembling the adults in their summer dress. In their first autumn the young begin to change into the second plumage, differing very little from the winter dress of the adults; the change taking place, however, not by a moult, but by an actual alteration in the colour of the feathers themselves, although a few battered feathers may be replaced. In the succeeding spring these immature birds assume the bright summer plumage of the adults, although they differ from the

latter in having brighter wing coverts; these feathers being only changed by the adults in the autumn, and thus permanently presenting the full hues of the winter dress.

In habits all the members of the order are more or less migratory, and from this cause the winter distribution of the group is well-nigh cosmopolitan. Considerable diversity of view obtains as to the classification of the typical Limicolæ. By some naturalists they are divided into the three family groups of plovers, sandpipers and snipes, and pratincoles; the thicknees—here classed with the bustards—being added as a fourth. An equally marked diversity of view obtains as to the number of genera into which these birds should be divided. The following table sets forth the classification that has been adopted for the species mentioned in this work.

WOODCOCK IN FLIGHT

CLASSIFICATION OF LIMICOLÆ MENTIONED IN THIS WORK

ORDER
Plover-like Birds—Limicolæ

FAMILY 1
Pratincoles and Coursers—Glareolidæ

GENUS 1
Pratincoles—Glareola
SPECIES

The pratincole .... Glareola pratincola
Nordmann's pratincole .... G. melanoptera
Indian pratincole .... G. orientalis
White-naped pratincole .... G. nuchalis
Büttikofer's pratincole .... G. megapoda

GENUS 2
Coursers—Cursorius
SPECIES

Cream-coloured courser .... Cursorius gallicus
Lesser courser .... C. somalensis
Jerdon's courser .... C. bitorquatus
Lichtenstein's courser ...... C. senegalensis

GENUS 3
Pluvianus
SPECIES

Black-backed courser ...... Pluvianus ægyptius

FAMILY 2
Plover Family—Charadriidæ

GENUS 1
Ringed Plovers and Dotterels—Ægialitis
SPECIES

Ringed plover .... Ægialitis hiaticula
Short-webbed ringed plover .. Æ. semipalmata
Little ringed plover .... Æ. dubia
Hodgson's ringed plover .... Æ. placida
Kill-deer plover .... Æ. vocifera
Kentish plover .... Æ. alexandrina
Mongolian sand plover .... Æ. mongolica
Sand plover .... Æ. asiatica
Dotterel .... Æ. morinella
Eastern dotterel .... Æ. veredus
Falkland Island dotterel .... Æ. modestus

GENUS 2
Pluvianellus
SPECIES

Magellanic plover ...... Pluvianellus sociabilis

GENUS 3
Anarhynchus
SPECIES

The wrybill .... Anarhynchus frontalis

GENUS 4
Golden Plovers—Charadrius
SPECIES

Golden plover .... Charadrius pluvialis
Eastern golden plover .... C. fulvus

GENUS 5
Grey Plover—Squatarola
SPECIES

Grey plover .... Squatarola helvetica

GENUS 6
Lapwings—Vanellus
SPECIES

The lapwing .... Vanellus vulgaris
Cayenne lapwing .... V. cayennensis

GENUS 7
Three-toed Lapwings—Hoplopterus
SPECIES

Spur-winged lapwing .... Hoplopterus armatus

GENUS 8
Wattled Lapwings—Sarcogrammus
SPECIES

Red-wattled lapwing .... Sarcogrammus indicus
White-collared lapwing .... S. atrinuchalis

GENUS 9
Three-toed Wattled Lapwings—Sarciophorus
SPECIES

Yellow-wattled lapwing .. Sarciophorus bilobus

GENUS 10
Lobivanellus

GENUS 11
Stilts—Himantopus
SPECIES

Black-winged stilt ...... Himantopus candidus

Australian stilt .... H. leucocephalus
Chilian stilt .... H. brasiliensis

GENUS 12
Avocets—Recurvirostra
SPECIES

Avocet .... Recurvirostra avocetta
Peruvian avocet .... R. andina
North American avocet .... R. americana

GENUS 13
Banded Avocet—Cladorhynchus
SPECIES

Banded avocet ...... Cladorhynchus pectoralis

GENUS 14
Oyster-catchers—Hæmatopus
SPECIES

The oyster-catcher .... Hæmatopus ostralegus
Japanese oyster-catcher .... H. osculans
American oyster-catcher .... H. palleatus
Australian oyster-catcher .... H. unicolor
Black oyster-catcher .... H. niger

GENUS 15
Ibidorhynchus
SPECIES

Ibisbill .... Ibidorhynchus struthersi

GENUS 16
Curlews and Whimbrels—Numenius
SPECIES

The curlew .... Numenius arquata
The whimbrel .... N. phœopus
Eskimo whimbrel .... N. borealis
Lesser wimbrel .... N. minutus
American whimbrel .... N. hudsonianus

GENUS 17
Phalaropes—Phalaropus
SPECIES

Grey phalarope .... Phalaropus fulicarius
Red-necked phalarope .... P. hyperboreus
Wilson's phalarope .... P. wilsoni

GENUS 18
Sandpipers and Redshanks—Totanus
SPECIES

Sandpiper .... Totanus hypoleucus
Green sandpiper .... T. ochropus
Redshank .... T. calidris
Greenshank .... T. glottis
Wood-sandpiper .... T. glareola
Spotted sandpiper .... T. fuscus

GENUS 19
Ruffs—Pavoncella
SPECIES

The ruff .... Pavoncella pugnax

GENUS 20
Godwits—Limosa
SPECIES

Bar-tailed godwit .... Limosa lapponica
American bar-tailed godwit .... L. fedoa
Black-tailed godwit .... L. belgica
American black-tailed godwit .... L. hudsonica

GENUS 21
Snipe-billed Sandpipers—Macrorhamphus
SPECIES

Red-breasted godwit .. Macrorhamphus griseus
Taczanowski's sandpiper ...... M. taczanowskii

GENUS 22
Micropalama
SPECIES

Stilt-sandpiper ...... Micropalama himantopus

GENUS 23
Ereunetes
SPECIES

Short-webbed sandpiper .... Ereunetes pusillus

GENUS 24
Turnstones—Strepsilas
SPECIES

The turnstone .... Strepsilas interpres
Black turnstone .... S. melanocephalus

GENUS 25
Knot and Dunlin—Tringa
SPECIES

Knot .... Tringa canutus

Dunlin .... T. alpina
Broad-billed sandpiper ...... T. platyrhyncha
Stint........................ T. minuta
Purple sandpiper .... T. maritima
Curlew sandpiper............. T. subarquata

GENUS 26
Sanderling—Calidris
SPECIES

Sanderling................ Calidris arenaria

GENUS 27
Eurhinorhynchus
SPECIES

Spoon-billed sandpiper ...... Eurhinorhynchus pygmæus

GENUS 28
Painted Snipe—Rostratula
SPECIES

Indian painted snipe .... Rostratula capensis
Australian painted snipe.......... R. australis
South American painted snipe .. R. semicollaris

GENUS 29
Phegornis
SPECIES

Short-winged sandpiper.... Phegornis mitchelli

GENUS 30
Æchmorhynchus
SPECIES

Sharp-billed sandpiper ...... Æchmorhynchus cancellatus

GENUS 31
Prosobonia
SPECIES

White-winged sandpiper......... Prosobonia leucoptera

GENUS 32
Woodcock—Scolopax
SPECIES

The woodcock .... Scolopax rusticula
Moluccan woodcock .... S. rochusseni
Horsfield's woodcock .... S. saturata
American woodcock .... S. minor

GENUS 33
Snipe—Gallinago
SPECIES

Solitary snipe .... Gallinago solitaria
Wood-snipe .... G. nemoricola
Pintail snipe .... G. stenura
Auckland snipe .... G. aucklandica
Great snipe ....G. major
Swinhoe's snipe .... G. megala
The snipe .... G. cœlestis
Wilson's snipe ....G. wilsoni
Jack-snipe................... G. gallinula

FAMILY 3
Jacanas and Water-pheasants—Parridæ

GENUS 1
Jacanas—Parra
SPECIES

Brazilian jacana .... Parra nigra

GENUS 2
Water-pheasant—Hydrophasianus
SPECIES

Water-pheasant .... Hydrophasianus chirurgus

FAMILY 4
Sheath-bills—Chionididæ

GENUS 1
Sheath-bills—Chionis
SPECIES

Magellan sheath-bill .... Chionis alba
Kerguelen sheath-bill .... C. minor
Crozet sheath-bill............. C. crosettensis

GENUS 2
Seed-snipe—Thinocorys

GENUS 3
Attagis
SPECIES

Peruvian seed-snipe .... Attagis gayi
Falkland seed-snipe .... A. malouinus
Chimborazo seed-snipe...... A. chimborasensis

1333

PRATINCOLES AND COURSERS

THE birds of this group (family *Glareolidæ*] differ from all the other members of the order in the want of basipterygoid processes on the rostrum of the under surface of the skull, and are further characterised by having their oval nostrils opening on the surface of the beak without being sunk in a groove. In both these characters they resemble the thicknees, to which the black-backed courser presents a further approximation in the oval (holorhinal) nasal apertures of the skull.

Externally, these birds may be distinguished from thicknees and bustards by the presence of four toes in the pratincoles, and by the metatarsus of the coursers being covered with large shield-like plates instead of reticulated scales. The absence of basipterygoid processes in these birds cannot justify their affiliation to the gulls, but it may be a question whether the pratincoles are rightly included in the same family as the coursers.

PRATINCOLES

The forked tail and somewhat swallow-like appearance and habits of the pratincoles (*Glareola*) render it, at first sight, somewhat difficult to believe that these birds are near relatives of the plovers, but closer observation will show that their comparatively long legs are adapted for runing in the usual plover-like manner, and that it is only when on the wing hawking for flies that a superficial resemblance is presented to swallows. Moreover, in certain members of the genus, the forking of the tail is well-nigh obsolete. As a group, these birds, of which there are about half a score species, are characterised by the presence of the first toe, and by the tail being more or less forked. The third toe is united to the fourth by a short membrane, and the first quill of the wings is the longest.

These birds have been regarded as specially modified allies of the coursers, retaining the first toe of the

EUROPEAN PRATINCOLES

ancestral stock. Many of them show resemblances to the latter in their black under wing coverts, white upper tail coverts, and the serration of the claw of the third toe. The group is confined to the Old World, where it is represented in Europe, Asia, Africa, and Australia, but the majority of the species are tropical.

Like coursers, pratincoles feed almost exclusively on insects, although they differ from their allies in capturing their prey while on the wing. They frequent sandy plains or marshes, and the banks of rivers and lakes, as well as lagoons. At all times of the year they associate in flocks, although each male selects a single partner.

The European pratincole (*G. pratincola*), which is the typical representative of the group, is a small bird measuring from 9 to 10 inches in length, and inhabiting the warmer parts of Europe, Asia, and Africa; an occasional straggler reaching the British Isles. In colour most of the upper parts are clove-brown, the primaries nearly black, the upper tail coverts white, the feathers of the deeply forked tail white at the base, and elsewhere brownish black, the chin white, the throat pale buff, bordered by a black line ascending to the eye, the breast brownish buff, the under parts and thighs buffish white, and the under wing coverts and axillaries chestnut. The especial characteristics of the species are the great length of the outer tail feathers and the chestnut axillaries.

Nordmann's pratincole (*G. melanoptera*), which inhabits a large area of Central and Northern Asia in summer, migrating in winter to South Africa, may be distinguished by its black axillaries; while the Indian pratincole (*G. orientalis*), ranging from India to Northern Australia, differs from the European species by the slight forking of its tail. The white-naped pratincole (*G. nuchalis*) and Büttikofer's pratincole (*G. megapoda, or G. marchei*) may be cited as examples of an African group of the genus, in which the nape has a light-coloured collar, and the forking of the tail is very slight.

Of the typical species Mr. H. L. Seebohm writes that, although it sometimes frequents cultivated lands, "its favourite haunts are on the sandy tracts either near the sea or on the table-lands of the interior. The pratincole spends a considerable portion of its time in the air, hawking for insects like a gigantic swallow, skimming along with graceful motion, wheeling and darting about, chasing its prey in all directions. Upon the ground it is equally at ease, and runs to and fro with surprising swiftness in spite of its short legs. Sometimes it even wades in the little pools with which its haunts often abound; frequently it flies at a considerable height, occasionally very low, just skimming along above the ground."

Beetles and grasshoppers appear to constitute its favourite food. These birds do not make any nest, but lay their two or three eggs on the bare ground, in most cases without even taking the trouble of scratching a hollow for their reception. The eggs, which are generally laid in May, are nearly oval, and extremely fragile; their ground-colour varying from yellow to slaty grey, upon which are numerous streaks and blotches of dark blackish brown. Like many other members of the order, pratincoles endeavour to draw intruders away from their nests by simulating lameness or some other injury. An early migrant, this species usually reaches its breeding grounds in Spain, France, the valley of the Danube, Asia Minor, or Northern Africa during April.

COURSERS

Although agreeing with lapwings in the presence of large shield-like plates covering their legs, the handsome birds known as coursers resemble pratincoles in the absence of grooves in the beak for the nostrils, and likewise in the characters of the base of the skull, although they differ in the absence of the first toe, in the short and nearly even tail, and in their habit of taking their food while on the ground. They may be included in the *Glareolidæ*, of which they form a separate subfamily, the *Cursoriinæ*.

The typical genus *Cursorius*, inclusive of *Rhinoptilus*, comprises about a dozen well-defined species, which are mainly restricted to the warmer parts of the Old World, exclusive of Australia; but the African black-backed courser represents a genus (*Pluvianus*) by itself, distinguished from all other members of the order by the oval (holo-rhinal) nasal apertures of the skull.

The best known and typical representative of the group is the cream-coloured courser (*C. gallicus*), which inhabits the desert areas stretching from Northern and North-Eastern Africa, through Arabia, Persia, Baluchistan, and Afghanistan, to the Punjab, Sind, and Rajputana, and occasionally wanders into Britain and other parts of Europe. A somewhat aberrant member of the group as regards colouring, this species is characterised by the general pale, wood-brown hue tinged with reddish buff of the upper parts.

The head is buff on the top, and grey tipped with black behind, a white, and below it a black streak runs above the eye, the primaries and under wing coverts are nearly black, the secondaries dark brown with buff outer webs and white tips, the tail feathers marked with a black spot near the end, the under parts buffish white, and the legs cream-colour. The nearly black axillaries and under wing coverts, coupled with the buff outer webs of the secondaries, will, however, serve to distinguish it from all its allies; the lesser courser (*C. somalensis*), of Somaliland, being smaller, with greyish buff axillaries. In length the cream-coloured courser varies from 9 to 10 inches.

Essentially a desert bird, the cream-coloured courser harmonises so closely in colouring with its sombre surroundings as to be almost invisible at a short distance. In such districts, Mr. Seebohm states that " it lives on the arid sand plains or on the bare elevated plateaus, where scarce a tuft of scanty herbage or a bush is to be found. It loves to frequent the bases of sand-hills, and is sometimes seen in the miserable desert pastures or amongst the sand-dunes on the outskirts of the oases. In these dismal, uninteresting regions the courser trips about in pairs, or less frequently in little parties. If it is not exactly a shy bird, it appears to be a very wary one, and runs quickly off to conceal itself as the traveller approaches. It prefers to run like lightning over the sand rather than to take wing, every now and then pausing for a moment to look warily around to see if it is still pursued.

"When alarmed, it often runs off and conceals itself either by squatting close to the sand, or hiding under a stone or tuft of herbage, where its sand-coloured plumage effectually conceals it from view. It generally runs a little distance before taking wing and seldom seems to fly very high. If a flock be observed, they are usually seen scattered up and down the sandy tract, not feeding close together. When danger threatens, each looks out for itself, taking refuge in the nearest available covert, or crouching flat down on the sand."

The food of this bird consists of insects and their larvæ, more especially the swarms of grasshoppers frequenting its haunts. It is reported to lay its two or three eggs generally in a hollow of the ground, which may be a natural one or excavated by the bird itself; but in the Punjab it may nest among stubble or beneath tussocks of grass. The eggs have an ochery buff ground-colour, blotched and speckled with buffish brown, and marbled with greyish veinings which appear to underlie the darker colours.

The black-backed courser (*Pluvianus ægyptius*)

BLACK-BACKED COURSER

differs, as already mentioned, in the character of the nasal region of the skull from its allies, and is on this account referred to a distinct genus. Externally, it may be recognised at a glance by its uniformly black back and scapulars, the black also extending as a band on each side of the breast, running forwards as a streak below the eye to the beak, and crowning the summit of the head.

The black-backed courser resembles Jerdon's courser (*Cursorius [Rhinoptilus] bitorquatus*) of India in having white bands across some of the primary quills, and also in the absence of serrations on the claw of the third toe; but in the relative shortness of the metatarsus it approaches Lichtenstein's courser (*C. senegalensis*) of tropical Africa, in which the serrations of the claw of the third toe may also be sometimes wanting. An accidental visitor to Spain, Algeria, and Palestine, the black-backed courser inhabits the Nile Valley, from Cairo to Khartum, and thence ranges across Central Africa to the Gabun and Angola

This courser, often termed the black-headed plover, is very common on the banks of the Nile, where several pairs may often be seen on a single sandbank, and brings itself under notice by the loud chattering cry it utters every time it takes wing. The most remarkable peculiarity in its habits is its custom of burying its eggs in moist sand, where they undergo incubation, the trait having been verified during the Sudan expedition, when Captain Verner on two occasions had the good fortune to come across a clutch of three eggs thus buried, in the second instance having seen the bird at work. In another case it was noticed that one of the birds damped the sand round the eggs by first wetting its breast at the water's edge, and then running to squat down for a couple of minutes. The action of the sun on the damp sand gives rise to a bleaching process in the eggs, which in their regularly oval contour resemble those of the cream-coloured courser.

THE PLOVER FAMILY

THE rest of the more typical members of the order Limicolæ may be included in the family *Charadriidæ* of which the essential feature is that the rostrum on the base of the skull is furnished with basipterygoid processes. This family may be subdivided into three subfamilies, of which the first is represented by the plovers, dotterels, and lapwings. While agreeing with pratincoles and coursers in having the third and fourth toes connected by a web at the base, these short-billed birds of the subfamily *Chara-driinæ* differ in that the nostrils are situated in a groove extending considerably in advance of the basal fourth of the beak.

Plovers as a whole inhabit almost every description of country, from bare mountain tops to cultivated lands, open moors and commons, and the seashore. During the breeding season they are more or less sociable, and in the winter often congregate in large flocks. They run and walk with ease, and their flight is powerful, moderately quick, and sustained. Their usual note is a loud and shrill whistle, often considerably modulated during the pairing season into a musical trill, uttered as the birds take short flights in the air, after the manner of pipits. All feed on insects, worms, molluscs, and the like, and they nest either in depressions on the ground, or on shingle or sand ; while their eggs, like those of lapwings, are generally four in number and of the well-known pear shape, with a ground-colour of some shade of buff, upon which are brownish black blotches and streaks and underlying markings of grey.

RINGED PLOVERS

The members of the genus *Ægialitis* and the next genus may be distinguished from all other representatives of the subfamily by the peculiar shape of the beak, coupled with the circumstance that in the sharply pointed wings the first quill is the longest ; the beak, after tapering regularly for about half its length, swelling out suddenly above and below near the tip. In this character these birds resemble lapwings, from which they are distinguished not only by a difference in the relative lengths of the quills of the wings, but likewise by the circumstance that the two middle tail feathers are of a uniform brown colour for more then two-thirds their length, without any white at their base, and also by the scales on the metatarsus being of the reticulated type.

The ringed plovers derive their name from the dark ring or gorget round the neck of the majority of the species, a white ring being also generally present above the dark one ; but in one species this only forms a collar on the back of the neck, and in another both are wanting. Obviously, therefore, this dark ring —which is black in the breeding dress of the males— will not serve to characterise the genus ; and the more typical members of the group may be best defined by the absence of the first toe, the dark transverse band near the end of the tail feathers, and the white abdomen

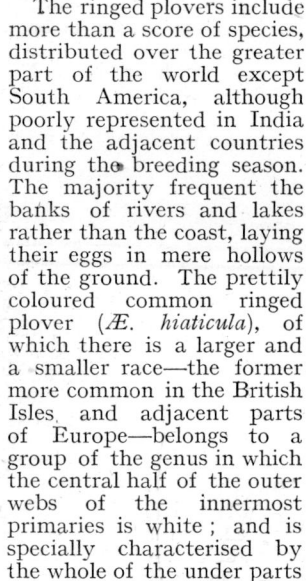

LITTLE RINGED PLOVER

and axillaries ; the two latter features serving to distinguish them from the three-toed dotterels, which also have a dark band across the tail. The beak is always much shorter than the head, and generally pale-coloured at the base, and the legs and feet are invariably of a light tint. Moreover, while the middle pair of tail feathers have only very small white tips, in the other feathers of this region the size of this white tip gradually increases to the outermost pair.

The ringed plovers include more than a score of species, distributed over the greater part of the world except South America, although poorly represented in India and the adjacent countries during the breeding season. The majority frequent the banks of rivers and lakes rather than the coast, laying their eggs in mere hollows of the ground. The prettily coloured common ringed plover (*Æ. hiaticula*), of which there is a larger and a smaller race—the former more common in the British Isles and adjacent parts of Europe—belongs to a group of the genus in which the central half of the outer webs of the innermost primaries is white ; and is specially characterised by the whole of the under parts being white, with the exception of the lores and a single broad band across the breast, both of which are black in adult males, and also by the web between the third and fourth toes extending only to their first joints. In length it varies from 8 to 7 inches.

The larger race is the only one definitely known to breed in Britain, while the smaller one nests in Greenland, Iceland, and Novaya Zemlya, as well as in Western Siberia, Turkestan, and Northern Africa ; in summer it visits the greater part of Europe northward of the Alps, and in winter spreads over the basin of the Mediterranean and Africa. In North America it is represented by the short-webbed ringed plover (*Æ. semipalmata*), differing by the web between the third and fourth toes extending to their second joints, and likewise by the presence of a shorter web between the second and third toes.

The little ringed plover (*Æ. dubia*), which is an occasional visitor to Britain, and breeds over the greater part of Europe and Asia north of the Himalaya, wintering in India and Africa, may be taken as an example of the second group of smaller species characterised by the dark outer webs of the inner primaries. It is specially distinguished by the scapulars being coloured like the back, and by the outer tail feathers being less than a quarter of an inch shorter than the central pair, the latter feature distinguishing it from Hodgson's ringed plover (*Æ. placida*) of India. In length this species is 6½ inches, but a resident Indian variety is smaller. Another well-known representative of the first group is the American kill-deer plover (*Æ. vocifera*), which measures from 9 to 10 inches in length, and is characterised by the chestnut-buff colour of the lower part of the back, rump, and upper tail coverts.

In England the breeding season of the common ringed plover begins in March, and the flocks which have collected during the winter begin to break up into pairs ; the eggs are not, however, laid till April, May, or June, and have been found so late as August. When their breeding grounds are visited, the birds exhibit but little anxiety, as their protective coloration renders the eggs very difficult of detection.

SAND-PLOVERS

The Kentish plover (*Æ. alexandrina*) and the sand-plovers such as *Æ. mongolica* and *Æ. asiatica*, while agreeing with the ringed plovers in the absence of the first toe and the white abdomen, are distinguished by the lack of a distinct dark band near the end of the tail feathers, and also by the white bases of the outer webs of the innermost primary quills ; the latter feature forming a white wing-patch somewhat similar to that occurring in the common ringed plover and its allies, although smaller.

There are numerous species of sand-plovers— some of which are often separated as *Ochthodromus* —distributed over the greater part of the world except the Arctic regions, but more numerous in the Southern than the Northern Hemisphere. The Kentish plover, which breeds on the shores of Kent and Sussex, as well as on the coasts of the seas and salt lakes of a great portion of Europe and Asia, visiting India and Africa in winter, may be recognised by the white collar round the neck, the dark patch on each side of the breast, the presence of a white area on the central portion of the shaft of the third primary quill, and the black legs ; the length varying from 6 to 7 inches. Beyond the circumstance that they are all shore-birds, mainly frequenting open stretches of sand, upon which the eggs are laid, there is nothing calling for notice in the habits of sand-plovers.

DOTTERELS

As already mentioned, the sand-plovers are frequently separated from the ringed plovers as *Ochthodromus*, while the dotterel is regarded as representing a third genus (*Eudromias*). The chief ground for thus splitting up the group is that the typical sand-plovers and dotterels differ from the ringed plovers in having a breeding dress distinct from the winter plumage ; but since there is a complete passage from species with a distinct nuptial garb to others which have none through species like the Kentish plover, with little change in this respect, it is preferable to include the whole assemblage in the typical genus. Structurally ringed plovers and dotterels do not differ from the typical plovers, all having only three toes ; and the distinction is therefore one of plumage, and that this is not very great is indicated by the dark under parts of the dotterel in breeding plumage.

The dotterel (*Æ. morinella*), which attains a length of 9 inches, and, as just mentioned, resembles the typical plovers in having the abdomen of the adult in the breeding plumage black, may be recognised by this feature, coupled with the rich chestnut hue of the lower part of the breast at the same season, the grey axillaries, and the circumstance that the beak is shorter than the third toe without the claw ; the two latter features serving to distinguish this prettily-marked bird at all seasons.

Although both sexes of the dotterel are very much alike, the female is somewhat the larger and handsomer of the two, being coloured more brightly, and having more black on the abdomen ; but in both there is the same white crescent, narrowly bordered with black, on the breast.

The dotterel chiefly breeds on the northern tundras, beyond the limits of forest, of Europe and Asia, although a few nest in the northern parts of Britain ; while it winters in Palestine, Egypt, and North Africa, some individuals remaining on the northern border of the Mediterranean. An allied species is the eastern dotterel (*Æ. veredus*), which breeds in Mongolia, and winters in the countries from Java to Australia ; this species being distinguished by its shorter third toe, and the white abdomen in the summer dress.

" The dotterel," observes Mr. Seebohm, " is essentially a bird of the fallows, and where there is no cultivated land it picks out the dry, bare places on which to feed. It avoids the swamps, and is seldom or never seen on the banks of rivers or lakes. The seashore has no attractions for the dotterel, nor does it seem to care for pasture ; but it loves to trip amongst clods of earth, and seeks its food on the bare mountain-sides. There it is very tame, and is easier to approach than any other species of plover with which I am acquainted." From this tameness the bird derives its title, the name " dotterel " signifying a foolish or dull person.

Dotterels migrate in even greater numbers than the typical plovers, and from the circumstance that out of the tens of thousands that pass in spring from Africa to the Arctic tundras scarcely any are seen to alight in the intervening countries, it is surmised that this tremendous journey is accomplished in the course of a single night. Dotterels formerly bred in the neighbourhood of Carlisle. The nest is merely a slight hollow in the ground, or among moss or grass, in which three eggs are deposited.

THE WRYBILL

The male dotterel takes by far the larger share in the work of incubation and rearing the young ; this being not infrequently the case in those rare instances where the female is superior in size and brilliancy of coloration to her lord and master. The reason for such a total change in the relations of the two sexes remains, however, a complete mystery.

The Falkland Island dotterel (*Æ. [Zonibyx] modestus*), which ranges from Chile and Argentina to Tierra del Fuego, is peculiar in having four toes. Another South American species is the rare Magellanic plover (*Pluvianellus sociabilis*), representing a distinct genus whose proper serial position is somewhat doubtful ; its general colour is grey above, and white beneath.

WRYBILL

The curious New Zealand wrybill (*Anaˑhynchus frontalis*) must likewise be allowed to rank as a genus by itself, on account of the marked lateral curvature of the beak. It is a three-toed species, grey above and white below, with a dark gorget on the throat. The flexure of the beak enables the bird to pick up insects sheltering by stones with perfect ease.

GOLDEN PLOVERS

The more typical plovers are, as already mentioned, closely allied to the dotterel and its relatives, which they resemble in inhabiting open plains, mountains, and the Siberian tundras, as well as the shores of seas and lakes, and in this respect agree with their cousins, the lapwings. In constructing slight nests for the reception of their four eggs, they likewise differ from the ringed plovers, and resemble dotterels.

The handsome and well-known bird termed the golden plover (*Charadrius pluvialis*) is the typical representative, not only of the plovers, but likewise of the entire genus and family. Plovers, in which the first toe may be absent or present, are collectively characterised by the barred tails of the adults, the black under parts in the breeding dress, and the minute reticulation of the scales of the metatarsus.

The golden plover, which attains a length of from 10 to 11 inches, represents a genus of two species characterised by having three toes, all the tail feathers barred, and the axillaries white. In the breeding dress of the adult male the upper parts are nearly black, spotted with yellow, the forehead, a stripe above the eye, the sides of the neck, the axillaries, thighs, flanks, and under tail coverts white, with some dusky mottling ; and the lores, chin, throat, breast, and abdomen black. The beak and legs are nearly black, and the eyes dark hazel. In the female the white parts have more dusky mottlings, and the dark under areas are browner, with some white feathers.

Breeding locally in Britain and some other districts of North-Western Europe, this species has its chief nesting haunts on the fjelds of Norway and the Russian and Siberian tundras ; but in winter it frequents the shores of the Mediterranean, whence it wanders so far south as the Cape. To the east of the Yenesei it is replaced by the eastern golden plover (*C. fulvus*), distinguished by its greyish brown axillaries ; this species wintering in India, Australia, and the intermediate regions, and being replaced in America by a short-toed local race (*C. f. dominicus*), whose breeding grounds are in the northern half of that continent, but which wanders in winter to South America.

The golden plover, whose habits may be taken as typical of those of the group, is a bird of powerful and sustained flight, flying when in flocks in a more or less wedge-shaped formation, and wheeling in the air, especially before pitching on the ground, in a peculiarly graceful manner. On the ground it is also equally active, running and walking with speed, and often wading breast-deep in the shallows. Frequenting in summer open moors, heaths, and tundras, in winter it resorts to low-lying marshes, meadows near the sea, and flat coasts ; and its Asiatic ally is at that time frequently to be seen on the marshy lakes (*jhils*) of India.

To a certain extent gregarious, even in the breeding season, the golden plover collects in immense flocks in autumn preparatory to its migration, and during the latter period moves in companies which may be numbered by thousands. Towards the end of October and beginning of November these birds fly over from Continental Europe in almost one incessant stream. the flocks succeeding one another so quickly as to form a nearly unbroken throng. This plover feeds largely by night, but the nature of its food naturally varies somewhat with its seasonal change of habit, in summer consisting largely of insects, and in winter mainly of various small aquatic animals.

In Great Britain the breeding season begins about the middle of May, the nest being formed of dry herbage, with scraps of heath and moss, and situated either in a hole in the ground, on a tuft of herbage, under the shelter of a bunch of cotton-grass, or, more rarely, among short grass or heath. The eggs are very like those of the lapwing, from which they may be distinguished by their superior size, the absence of olive in the markings, and their brighter colour. The parent birds are adepts in the art of inveigling away the intruder from the neighbourhood of their eggs or young, the latter scattering themselves in all directions at the first alarm, to seek protection by skulking among the surrounding herbage.

GREY PLOVER

The second British representative of the group is the grey plover (*Squatarola helvetica*), a rather larger bird, easily distinguished by the presence of a small first toe, on which account it is regarded as representing a genus by itself, and the black axillaries ; its breeding range comprises the circumpolar tundras beyond the forest regions, its winter range including Southern Europe, Africa, India, Japan, Australia, Brazil, and Peru. It resembles the golden plover in undergoing a marked seasonal change of plumage.

LAPWINGS

Closely allied to the plovers are the birds commonly known as lapwings, or green plovers (*Vanellus*), which differ from the typical plovers in having at least the

LAPWINGS

basal third of the middle pair of tail feathers white ; by the wings, which may or may not be armed with a spur, being blunt, with the first and second quills shorter than the third or fourth, which are of nearly equal length ; and by the front of the metatarsus being covered with large shield-like plates instead of small reticulated scales. The head is often provided with a crest.

The first toe may or may not be present, and the presence or absence of this affords grounds for dividing the group into two sections, which are considered worthy of generic distinction, the four-toed types being termed *Vanellus*, while those with but three toes are designated *Hoplopterus*. About fourteen species of lapwings are generally recognised, these being distributed over the temperate and tropical portions of Europe, Asia, Africa, and South America.

These birds derive their common English name from their slow and flapping flight, which is at the same time graceful, and often very erratic. In general habits they closely resemble plovers, but most of them are gregarious at all seasons, and in summer their favourite haunts are open downs, moors, fallows, or marshy commons, although some kinds seek the neighbourhood of the coast in winter. Partially nocturnal, their food comprises insects, worms, and molluscs, and their well-known cries are loud and frequently melancholy in tone. Their nesting habits and eggs are similar to those of the plovers.

The European lapwing (*Vanellus vulgaris*) is the typical representative of its genus, and such a familiar bird as to need little in the way of description. Belonging to a group in which there is no spur on the wing, this species is specially distinguished by the combination of a metallic lustre on the green plumage of the upper parts and the absence of white on the wing coverts, while it is also the only member of the two genera in which both the upper and under tail coverts are chestnut-buff. The crest is of great length.

This handsome bird has the widest geographical range of any of the lapwings, extending from Britain to Japan, and also occurring on the two sides of the American Continent in Alaska and Greenland, while in winter it migrates so far south as Northern Africa, Persia, and India. Resident throughout the year in the British Isles, to the Arctic regions of Scandinavia and the tundras of Siberia it is but a summer visitor. Not only is this bird the most widely distributed member of the genus, but the species is probably the one most numerous in individuals, as is attested by the enormous number of its eggs which reach the English market, where they form by far the greater proportion of those sold as plovers' eggs.

When associated in their enormous winter flocks, lapwings are among the most difficult of birds to approach, more especially from their constant habit of changing their ground. When the breeding place is approached, the old bird, writes Mr. Seebohm, " glides steadily off the nest, runs a little distance, then rises in the air, to flutter restlessly above the intruder's head, uttering its harsh, wailing cries. So closely do the eggs resemble surrounding objects in colour that it is no easy task to find them ; but the old birds very often betray their whereabouts by hovering above them ; at these times the birds are easily approached, often coming within a few feet. When the young are hatched, they soon follow their parents in search of food. If menaced by danger, the old birds quit their offspring at once, fly into the air, or reel and tumble along the ground as if wounded, while the nestlings scurry off in different directions and hide themselves among the herbage."

CAYENNE LAPWING

As an American species of this genus reference may be made to the Cayenne lapwing (*V. cayennensis*) and

EGYPTIAN SPUR-WINGED LAPWINGS

its variety the Patagonian lapwing, in which the crest is very small. These birds, which are known in Argentina by the name of teru-teru, generally live in pairs, and have a curious habit of indulging frequently in a kind of dance or march. Mr. W. H. Hudson writes that anyone watching a pair of these birds will see an individual from another pair rise and fly to them. Advancing to receive their visitor, the pair place themselves behind it ; " then all three, keeping step, begin uttering a rapid, resonant drumming note, in time with their movements, the notes of the pair behind being emitted in a stream, like a drum-roll, while the leader utters loud single notes at regular intervals. The march ceases ; the leader elevates his wings and stands erect and motionless, still uttering loud notes, while the other two, with puffed-out plumage and standing exactly abreast, stoop forward and downward until the tips of their beaks touch the ground, and, sinking their rhythmical voices to a murmur, remain for some time in this posture. The performance is then over, and the visitor goes back to his own ground and mate, to receive a visitor himself later on."

On the pampas these lapwings are a perfect nuisance, dashing up during the breeding season almost into the face of the traveller, and then suddenly wheeling off with a sudden swoop, at the same time giving vent to their harsh and monotonous cry of " teru-teru." This extreme boldness and perfect fearlessness of man are, however, characteristic of most of the birds of the Argentine pampas.

THREE-TOED LAPWINGS

Of the three-toed lapwings, among which are some species with a wing-spur and others without the same, while the presence of a crest is likewise inconstant, the best known example is the Egyptian spur-winged lapwing (*Hoplopterus armatus*, or *spinosus*). This bird, which breeds in the valley of the Nile, in Senegambia, and probably also in the intervening districts of Central Africa, migrates in the spring to Palestine and some parts of South-Eastern Europe. It has large spurs, and may be distinguished from its allies by the greater wing coverts being white, and the lesser ones brown ; while it is also unique in having, when adult, the crown of the head, forehead, nape, chin, throat, breast, flanks, and legs black. It is extremely common in Egypt and Nubia, where it frequents the banks of lakes, rivers, and canals, as well as marshes and swamps.

The chief interest connected with this species is that it appears to be the bird alluded to by Herodotus as being in the habit of entering the open mouths of crocodiles for the purpose of feeding. For a long time it was considered that the black-backed courser was the bird in question; also that the whole story was a myth. Dr. Leith Adams gave, however, good reasons for regarding the zic-zac (as this bird is called by the natives) as being really the one mentioned, and later observations confirm the original story. Early in 1876 Mr. J. M. Cook noticed several birds called by all the natives the " crocodile-bird " in the neighbourhood of some large crocodiles on a large sandbank on the Nile. Concealing himself in a pit he

RED-WATTLED LAPWING

watched one of these birds deliberately go up to a crocodile, apparently asleep, which opened its jaws. The bird hopped in, and the crocodile closed its jaws, opening them again a couple of minutes later for the bird to come out and run down to the water to drink, or possibly vomit. The same bird was seen to go through the same performance three times. The so-called crocodile-bird was subsequently identified with the present species.

WATTLED LAPWINGS

That cordially-hated Indian bird, the " did-he-do-it " (so called from its cry, which alarms all worthier game in its neighbourhood), or red-wattled lapwing (Sarcogrammus indicus), may be taken to represent a large group of species inhabiting the warmer parts of the Old World, all of which are distinguished from the members of the two preceding genera by the presence of a fleshy lobe or wattle between the eye and the beak. Like the other lapwings they may be divided into groups according to the number of the toes ; two of the four-toed species constituting the genus Sarcogrammus, while two of those in which the first toe is absent are separated as Sarciophorus; the Indian yellow-wattled lapwing (S. bilobus) being a familiar example of the latter group.

The red-wattled species, frequently termed the bronze-winged mottled lapwing, which may be distinguished by the broad white band at the end of the tail, ranges from Southern Persia and Baluchistan all over India and Ceylon, where it is one of the commonest of birds, but in Gilgit, and probably Kashmir, occurs only as a summer visitor. To the east of the Bay of Bengal it is replaced by a species (Sarcogrammus atrinuchalis) differing by having a white collar on the back of the neck behind the black of the head and the forepart of the neck, while the white

stripe through the eye stops short at the ear coverts instead of being continued down the sides of the neck. The genus Lobivanellus is restricted to Africa and Australia.

STILTS

The beautiful long-legged birds known as stilts and avocets are the first representatives of the second sub-family (Hæmatopinæ) of the group under consideration, the members of which are characterised by the nostrils being situated in the basal fourth of the elongated beak, by at least the third and fourth toes being united at their bases by a membrane, by the metatarsus being reticulated on all sides, by the pied or grey colouring of the plumage, and the absence of a distinct breeding dress. The latter character distinguishes them from the under-mentioned Totaninæ, and from most of the Charadriinæ.

The stilts, or stilt-plovers (Himan opus), derive their title from the extreme elongation of their slender legs, which recall those of the jacanas and parras, and are specially distinguished by the length of the metatarsus, which is equal to or greater than that of the long, slender, and nearly straight beak, by the absence of the first toe, the slight webbing of the front toes, and the black plumage of the upper parts. The wings of these birds are long and pointed, with the first quill the longest ; the tail is rounded, a large portion of the tibia is bare, and the beak is slightly curved upwards at the point, with the nostrils at the sides of its base slit-like in form. The genus includes six or seven species, distributed over Southern Europe and Asia, Africa, Australasia, and a considerable part of America, although wanting in the northern regions of that continent.

A single species, the black-winged stilt (H. candidus), which is an occasional visitor to Britain, inhabits Southern Europe, and may be distinguished from its allies by having in the adult condition the whole of the head and neck white, although immature examples have some black on the crown of the head and back of the neck. In the adult male, which measures from 13 to 14 inches in length, the upper parts and wings are black, glossed with green on the back, the upper tail coverts and tail pearly grey, and the rest of the plumage pure white ; the beak being black, and the eyes, legs, and feet crimson. Resident in India, this bird visits Burma in the winter, and straggles so far east as New Zealand, while in summer it resorts to Southern Europe, and is found at all seasons in many parts of Africa.

One of its nearest allies is the Australian stilt (H. leucocephalus), in which the back of the neck is black, with a white collar separating it from the dark area of the back. Of the South American species, the Chilian stilt (H. brasiliensis), which winters in Brazil, has the black of the neck extending forwards beneath the eye.

Stilts are essentially marsh-birds, although they always keep to open water, in which they may be seen standing up to their knees on the look-out for insects, molluscs, tadpoles, and so forth ; their most favourite resorts being lagoons where the water is brackish.

They are generally found in small parties, and whether on land, in the water, or in the air, are remarkable for their graceful appearance. They walk with a deliberate step, which may be quickened into a run ; and they fly straight but slowly, with the neck outstretched and the long legs extended beyond the tail.

Ordinarily silent and far from shy, in the breeding season these birds utter a cry resembling the syllables " kit, kot, kit," and are most assiduous in endeavouring to lure intruders away from the vicinity of their nests. In India stilts breed in enormous numbers, laying most of their eggs in June, although in Spain they are at least a month earlier ; one of the favourite haunts being some salt-works near Delhi, where the brine is distributed in shallow pools over acres of ground. The nest varies according to the nature of the locality, being more bulky in moist situations, and sometimes even floating on the water. The four eggs are pear-shaped, and of a buffish brown ground-colour, upon which are blackish brown streaks and blotches, with underlying markings of grey.

AVOCETS

Although they are closely connected with the stilts by two aberrant species, the still more graceful avocets are separated as a genus (*Recurvirostra*), of which the one distinctive character applicable to all the members is the more fully webbed feet. In the more typical forms, however, such as the European avocet (*R. avocetta*), the beak is strongly curved upwards at the extremity, the webbed feet are furnished with a small first toe, and the plumage of the upper parts is pied. The connection with the stilts is formed in one way by the Peruvian avocet (*R. andina*), in which the plumage of the upper parts is black; and in another by the banded avocet of Southern Australia, which is sometimes assigned to a genus by itself under the name of *Cladorhynchus*, *pectoralis* (or *leucocephalus*), while by other naturalists it is included in *Himantopus*, and by yet others in *Recurvirostra*. In this bird the plumage is pied, the beak straight, and the first toe wanting. Apart from this doubtful bird, the avocets include four species, having much the same distribution as the stilts, with the exception that none breeds in India or the adjacent countries.

The European avocet, which was formerly a frequent visitor to the fenny districts of England, is characterised in the adult dress by the black upper surface of the head and hind part of the neck, and the white innermost secondaries ; the young birds in their first plumage have the dark parts of the plumage brown, and the secondaries barred with white. The total length of the bird is 18 inches. Owing to drainage, the European breeding places of the avocet are now restricted to certain islands off Denmark and Holland, the marshes of Southern Spain, the delta of the Rhone, and the lagoons of the Black Sea ; but to the eastwards

it nests in Palestine, Persia, Turkestan, the south-west of Siberia, and also in Africa. In winter these birds resort to India, China, and more rarely Japan, and they reach their European breeding places in April and May, and depart in September. The North American avocet (*R. americana*), ranging from the Great Slave Lake to Texas, differs at all seasons by its white secondaries, and in the breeding season by the pale chestnut hue of the head and neck.

The habits of avocets are so similar to those of stilts that one account will serve for both ; and this notice of the group may be concluded with the following description of the appearance of a colony of these birds on the Arkansas. "The avocets," writes Dr. Coues, " walked leisurely about, up to the belly in water, with graceful, deliberate steps, each of which was accompanied by a swaying of the head and neck. When approached too closely, they rose lightly from the water, uttering their peculiar cries, flapped leisurely to a little distance, and again alighted to pursue their peaceful search for food, forgetting, or at least not heeding, their recent alarm. As they rose from the water their singular long legs were allowed to dangle for a few moments, but were afterwards stretched stiffly backwards, as a counterpoise to their long necks ; and, thus balanced, their light bodies were supported with the greatest ease by their ample wings. When about to re-alight, they sailed without flapping for a little distance, just clearing the water, their legs again hanging loosely ; as they touched the ground, their long wings were held almost upright for an instant, then deliberately folded, and settled in place with a few slight motions."

BLACK-WINGED STILT

OYSTER-CATCHERS

Much more stoutly built and with shorter and thicker neck and legs than the stilts, the oyster-catchers, or sea-pies (*Hæmatopus*), may be diagnosed by the metatarsus being inferior in length to the nearly straight and rather thick beak. The long and pointed wings extend, when closed, to about the extremity of the squared tail ; the beak is somewhat compressed and truncate at the tip, with considerable specific variation in outline ; only a small portion of the tibia is bare, the reticulated metatarsus is short and stout, and the first toe wanting.

The European oyster-catcher (*H. ostralegus*), which is a resident in the British Isles, is the typical representative of the genus, and while four other species resemble it in their pied plumage, the remaining two are black. The distribution of the genus is almost world-wide. Agreeing with all the other Old World forms in its dull crimson red legs, the European species is specially characterised by the lower part of the back, rump, and upper tail coverts being white, and the white pattern on the primaries well marked on the outer webs of the fourth and fifth quills of that series. In this species the beak and region round the eye are orange, but all the upper parts are black, with the exception of the lower portion of the back, rump, and upper tail coverts, the basal portion of the tail feathers, and a band across the wing comprising the greater wing coverts and some of the secondaries,

THE AVOCET

which are white. The primaries are also more or less marked with white; and, with the exception of the chin, throat, breast, and a few of the wing coverts, all the under parts are white. In length this bird varies from 16 to 17 inches.

Migratory in many districts, this species inhabits the whole of Europe, and a considerable portion of the eastern half of Asia, as well as Northern Africa, ranging to the Arctic Circle, and visiting Western India in winter. In Japan, Northern China, Amurland, etc., it is replaced by the Japanese oyster-catcher (*H. osculans*), distinguished by its longer beak, and the white on the primaries not appearing till the sixth quill; but in the New World its place is taken by the American oyster-catcher (*H. palleatus*), in which (as in all the New World species) the legs are pale flesh-coloured, while the upper parts below the neck are black, with the exception of the greater wing coverts and tail coverts, which are brown instead of black. The black species are the Australian black oyster-catcher (*H. unicolor*), represented by a variety in Africa; and the American black oyster-catcher (*H. niger*), characterised by the great compression of its large beak, which in the South American race tends to curve upwards at the tip.

Mainly coast-birds, although frequently ascending rivers for a long distance inland, oyster-catchers derive their name from the habit of feeding largely on bivalve molluscs, the shells of which their compressed beaks are admirably adapted for prising open. The same efficient instrument serves for detaching limpets from their hold on rocks, and extracts marine worms and other creatures from their burrows in the sand.

It was long a puzzle how the oyster-catcher opened the shells of the mussels which form its main diet; but it appears that the great majority of the molluscs are opened from the dorsal border, when the valves are gaping, by the bird thrusting its beak into the aperture and then using it as a lever, at the same time severing the adductor muscles. If one of the valves be fractured in the process, the lever action becomes unnecessary. About 9 per cent. of the mussels are opened on the ventral border, where the aperture for the byssus renders them as vulnerable when the valves are closed as when open. Mussels presenting this aspect are carefully searched for by the birds. Finally, about 13 per cent. of the mussels are attacked at the posterior extremity of the shell.

THE IBISBILL

The fourth and last generic group of the *Hæmatopinæ* is represented by the Central Asian ibisbill (*Ibidorhynchus struthersi*), a remarkable bird distinguished by the beak being curved down in the manner of that of an ibis. The beak and feet are red, the front of the head is black, and the general tone of the remainder of the plumage olive.

CURLEWS AND WHIMBRELS

Although evidently related to the preceding genera, the curlews belong to the third subfamily, *Totaninæ*, of the plover tribe, in which, at least for the lower portion of its front half, the metatarsus is covered with large plates; and they are defined by this feature, coupled with the circumstance that the long beak is so arched that the chord drawn from the base to the tip will pass below the inferior border of its lower half. The curlews have moderately long and slender necks, with the beak generally longer than the metatarsus, although this is not the case with the Eskimo whimbrel (*Numenius borealis*) and the lesser whimbrel (*N. minutus*). In the legs a large portion of the tibia is devoid of feathers, and there is a small first toe. As a rule, only the lower portion of the front of the metatarsus is covered with large plates, but in the least whimbrel this segment of the leg is thus protected on all sides.

The wings are moderate and pointed, with the first quill the longest, and the tail is squared. The plumage is coloured with various shades of brown and buff, producing a mottled appearance, recalling that of the thicknees, and evidently adapted for protective resemblance. With the exception of the two species above mentioned, all the curlews have pale bars on the inner webs of their primary quills; and, like the other members of the subfamily, they have a special breeding dress. Curlews are represented by nine species, two of which have well-marked local varieties, and during the breeding season are confined to North America, Europe, Northern Africa, and Asia north of the Himalaya, although in winter they have a cosmopolitan range.

The typical European curlew (*N. arquata*) is a large bird, measuring from 21 to 26 inches in length, which may be diagnosed by its metatarsus exceeding 3 inches in length, and by the lower region of the back and rump being much paler in colour than the remainder of the upper parts. In the breeding plumage of the adult male the general hue of the upper parts is pale brown, shading into white on the wing coverts, each feather having a dark brown centre; the under parts are white, tinged on the neck and breast with pale brown, where the feathers are also streaked with dark brown. The rump is white, the upper tail coverts are white or whitish, streaked or barred with brown, the quills dark brown with white bars, and the tail feathers white or whitish with dark brown bars. The beak is dark brown, and the legs and feet are slaty grey.

This species is resident in the British Islands, whence it extends as far east as the Caspian, beyond which the typical form is replaced by a paler variety, ranging into Eastern Siberia and Amurland. The breeding range extends from the confines of the Arctic Circle to Holland; and while the migratory individuals of the European form pass the winter in Africa, the eastern race is met with at that season in India.

The whimbrel (*N. phæopus*), which is a smaller bird than the curlew, measuring only 16 to 18 inches, with a relatively shorter beak, may be distinguished, in common with some other species, by the crown of the head being of a uniform pale brown colour, with a lighter median longitudinal streak; its distinctive specific characteristic being that the lower portion of the back is much lighter than the rest of the upper parts. Although a more northern species than the curlew, not breeding in the British Islands south of the Orkneys and Shetlands, the distribution of the whimbrel is very similar, the common form being replaced in Eastern Asia by a variety which winters in India and Australia.

The nearly allied American whimbrel (*N. hudsonianus*), whose winter range extends to Patagonia, differs by the chestnut axillaries and under wing coverts, and the similarity in the colour of all the upper parts. The still smaller Eskimo whimbrel (*N. borealis*), which breeds in Arctic America, and occasionally straggles during migration to Great Britain, differs by the absence of barring on the primary quills; while the least whimbrel (*N. minutus*), which breeds in Eastern Siberia and winters in Malaya and Australia, may be distinguished from the latter by the metatarsus being covered with plates both in front and behind.

All the members of the genus are of very similar habits, frequenting moors, inland marshes, and uplands

OYSTER-CATCHER IN FLIGHT

shot range. Whenever alarmed, they utter their well-known piercing cry as they rise in the air; and these weird notes, especially when a flock of birds join in the chorus, may be heard at great distances across the moors.

Gregarious in winter, the birds break up into pairs in the spring; and in the breeding season lay, in a slight nest on the ground, four somewhat pear-shaped eggs, of which the ground-colour is olive green, marked with spots of brown and grey. In summer the food of the European species consists of insects, larvæ, and worms, sometimes supplemented by berries; but in winter it is largely composed of small marine crustaceans and molluscs. Although generally so shy and wary, in the breeding season curlews are far bolder, and when the young are hatched, both parent birds will often fly anxiously round and round the head of any intruder on their domain.

Geologically these birds are known to date from the period of the middle Miocene, remains of small species having been obtained from strata of that age in France; and it is not improbable that they date from the still older upper Eocene beds of the Paris basin.

PHALAROPES

The three species of phalaropes (*Phalaropus*), two of which are met with in Britain, are readily distinguished from other members of the family by the sides of the three front toes being provided with lobe-like expansions, somewhat similar to those of the coots, and likewise by the marked lateral compression of the metatarsus, which is covered with large plates on both aspects. The beak is of medium length, straight, somewhat depressed and relatively weak, with the oval nostrils at its base surrounded by an elevated rim. The first toe, although small, is present, and a small portion of the tibia bare. In the elongated and pointed wings the first quill exceeds all the others in length, and the short tail is of a somewhat rounded form. The plumage, like that of the avocets, is remarkable for its softness.

During the breeding season these birds are confined to the northern regions of Europe, Asia, and America, two being inhabitants of the circumpolar regions, while the third pertains to the Western Hemisphere. They are all more aquatic in their habits than any other members of the family, and chiefly frequent deeply

THE CURLEW

during summer, and seeking the coasts more while on migration and in winter. Even more wary than oyster-catchers, curlews take wing at the least alarm, and rarely allow themselves to be approached within gun-

indented coasts, although also found on the shores of inland lakes. In general appearance they approach the sandpipers, but have shorter legs, and the females are more brightly coloured than the males. Practically they are sandpipers specially adapted for marsh-life by their lobulated toes.

The grey phalarope (*P. fulicarius*), which is but an irregular visitor to the British Isles, attains a length of 8 inches, and is remarkable for the difference in the colour of the winter and summer plumage of the under parts. The species may be recognised at all seasons by the comparative shortness and width of the beak, and by the middle tail feathers exceeding the outermost in width by half an inch. In the breeding plumage the whole of the under parts is rich chestnut, and the back and rump are black ; but in winter most of the under parts, as well as a patch before the point of the wings, are pearly grey, and the under parts pure white. Breeding in the circumpolar regions locally, but nowhere in continental Europe, this species occasionally visits North Africa in winter, and has been recorded from New Zealand and Chile.

The slightly smaller red-necked phalarope (*P. hyperboreus*), which has likewise a circumpolar distribution, and breeds in the Shetlands, Orkneys, Outer Hebrides, and the west of Ireland, may be recognised by the tapering and pointed beak, which (like that of the preceding species) does not exceed an inch in length, and also by the smaller difference between the lengths of the central and outer tail feathers. The chief breeding haunts are beyond the limits of forest ; but in winter this species spreads over Europe, Northern India, the Malay region, China, New Guinea, Mexico, and Central America. Finally, Wilson's phalarope (*P. wilsoni*), which breeds on the great lakes of North America, and migrates in winter so far south as Patagonia, differs from both the others in the great length of its slender, tapering bill, which exceeds an inch.

RED-NECKED PHALAROPE

SANDPIPERS AND REDSHANK

The typical sandpipers and their near relatives the redshank and greenshank are characterised by the nearly straight beak, and by the feathers of the forehead extending in advance of the angle of the gape. In length the beak is moderate, and it has its tip hard, and the nostrils slit-like and lateral. The first toe is always present, the metatarsus (except in the Pacific species, where they are absent from the greater portion of the back) is covered with large plates both before and behind, and some portion of the tibia is bare. In the long and pointed wings the first quill is the longest, but there is considerable variation in the form and number of the tail feathers, which in the great majority of species are barred.

The genus *Totanus* comprises about a score of species, of which a large number are represented in the British Isles, and throughout the breeding season are distributed over the boreal and temperate regions of the Northern Hemisphere, but in winter become collectively cosmopolitan. Frequenting moors, marshes, and tundras during the breeding season, these familiar and pretty little birds resort to the seacoasts in winter throughout many portions of their range, and are in the habit of performing migrations of enormous length. Their food consists of insects, crustaceans, and molluscs, supplemented by fish ; and their shrill, piping notes are among the most familiar sounds of the seashore. More or less gregarious and social in their habits, especially in winter, all are monogamous ; and their scanty nests are usually placed on the ground, and contain, at the proper season, four pear-shaped spotted eggs. Among the better-known British forms are the common sandpiper (*Totanus hypoleucus*), the green sandpiper (*T. ochropus*), the redshank (*T. calidris*), the greenshank (*T. glottis*), the wood-sandpiper (*T. glareola*), and the spotted sandpiper (*T. fuscus*).

THE RUFF

Of much greater interest than any of the above is the well-known ruff (*Pavoncella*, or *Machetes*, *pugnax*), a species characterised by the periodical assumption by the males of a large ruff round the neck, which is scarcely ever exactly similar in any two individuals ; the general plumage of that sex being likewise very variable at the same season. The immature males and females (reeves) resemble ordinary sandpipers, but may always be recognised by their white axillaries, coupled with the absence of any white on the quills and central upper tail coverts. In length the male measures about 12 inches and the female some 2 inches less.

Formerly common in the English marshes, the ruff is now mainly a passing visitor to Britain. Its breeding haunts range from the most northern lands of Europe and Asia so far south as the valley of the Danube and the Kirghiz Steppes, while in winter it wanders as far as the Cape, Northern India, Burma, and even more remote regions. Next to the extraordinary variation in the character of the plumage, the most interesting features about the ruff are the extreme pugnacity displayed by the cocks, and the circumstance that these birds differ from all their kin in being polygamous—the females largely exceeding the males in number.

During the pairing season the cocks congregate at certain spots known as "hills," and there display their pugnacious propensities, although little serious harm results to the combatants. The nest, which is roughly lined with dead grass and sedge, is usually placed on a tussock in the middle of a swamp. Years ago enormous numbers of ruffs and reeves were netted in the Lincolnshire marshes during the breeding season.

GODWITS

Nearly allied to the two preceding groups are the birds known as godwits (*Limosa*), distinguished by the feathers of the forehead not extending in advance of the angle of the gape, the extremity of the long beak being hard and but little expanded. A large portion of the tibia is devoid of feathers, and the claw of the third toe is comb-like. Were it not that there is a difference in the conformation of the upper part of the breast-bone in the two groups, the godwits could scarcely be separated generically from the typical sandpipers.

These birds are represented by four or five species, which breed in the Temperate and Arctic portions of the Northern Hemisphere, but migrate far to the south in winter, and two of which frequent the British Isles. Of the latter, the bar-tailed godwit, (*L. lapponica*), which measures 15 or 16 inches in length, has in summer the upper tail coverts and tail white with dark brown barrings, but is especially characterised by the lower part of the back, rump, axillaries, and under wing coverts being white with obscure brown markings. Breeding locally on the Arctic tundras of Europe and Western Asia, the ordinary form is replaced by a variety eastwards of the Yenisei ; while in North America it is represented by the American bar-tailed godwit (*L. fedoa*), in which the axillaries and under wing coverts are chestnut.

Rarer in Britain than the bar-tailed species, the black-tailed godwit (*L. belgica*) may be recognised by the tail feathers being black with white bases, and the white axillaries. This Old World form is represented in Eastern Asia by a variety, while in the New World its place is taken by the American black-tailed godwit (*L. hudsonica*), distinguished by its dark brown axillaries and under wing coverts.

All the godwits migrate far south in winter, the two Old World kinds then reaching Africa and India, and their eastern varieties visiting Australia. Although frequently breeding far inland, the godwits are essentially shore-birds in winter, and for such a habitat acquire in autumn a mud-coloured livery.

SNIPE-BILLED SANDPIPERS

Here may be noticed certain species forming a link between the godwits and their allies on the one hand, and the snipe on the other. All are characterised by having the frontal feathers arranged as in the former, but the extremity of the beak soft, expanded, and roughened as in the latter. The species most nearly allied to the true godwits are the Canadian red-breasted

THE RUFF IN BREEDING PLUMAGE

BLACK-TAILED GODWIT

godwit (*Macrorhamphus griseus*), and Taczanowski's sandpiper (*M. taczanowskii*) ; the former of which is common to the northern parts of both hemispheres, and descends in winter to South America, while the latter is a Siberian bird, migrating in the cold season to India and Borneo.

The stilt-sand-piper (*Micropalama himantopus*), which breeds in eastern North America and the West Indies, represents by itself a genus characterised by the great length of the legs. Finally there is the short-webbed sandpiper (*Ereunetes pusillus*), of the northern parts of both hemispheres, which takes its name from its partially webbed feet, and has a broad, shovel-shaped beak.

TURNSTONES

The pied and partially rufous European bird well named the turnstone is the typical representative of a genus of which the two members resemble plovers in that the nostrils extend beyond the basal fourth of the beak, the beak itself being short, thick at the base, tapering, somewhat conical, and without any swelling near the tip, whereby it differs from those of the preceding members of the subfamily ; while the metatarsus is covered with large plates in front, and reticulated behind. In the elongated wings the first quill is the longest, and the short and nearly even tail includes twelve feathers. The tibia is bare for a short distance, and the first toe is present. The turnstones breed in the Arctic regions and migrate south in winter.

The typical turnstone (*Strepsilas*, or *Arenaria*, *interpres*), which is a circumpolar species visiting the British coasts in autumn and spring, and occasionally tarrying there for the winter, may be recognised by its pure white chin and throat ; the general colouring of the summer plumage being mottled black, white, and chestnut, and the total length of the bird 9½ inches. The black turnstone (*S. melanocephalus*) of Western North America, in addition to its broader wings, differs by the white lower part of the back, and the absence of a pure white throat and neck. Both sexes lose their chestnut feathers, and likewise the white markings on the head, in winter. The turnstone, which in winter occurs so far away

from its northern home as South America and New Zealand, takes its name from its habit of overturning pebbles with its beak to obtain the various marine creatures that lurk beneath their shelter. In such tasks the breast as well as the beak is occasionally brought into requisition. Except during migration, the turnstone is essentially a littoral bird, and in Britain is generally seen in pairs or small parties, frequently in association with other waders. Although generally running along the shore, and taking short flights when disturbed, it is not destitute of the power of swimming, and its cry is a clear loud whistle.

KNOT, STINT, AND SANDERLING

Several well-known small British shore-birds, such as the knot (*Tringa canutus*), the dunlin (*T. alpina*), the broad-billed sand-piper (*T. platyrhyncha*), the stint (*T. minuta*), the purple sand-piper (*T. maritima*), the curlew sand-piper (*T. subarquata*), and the sanderling (*Calidris arenaria*), constitute a large group, of which the last-named species forms a genus by itself on account of the absence of the first toe, which is present in the remainder. These birds differ from the godwits and ruffs in that the toes are cleft to the base, without any sign of webs, and by the soft and flexible character of the beak, which is narrow, slightly compressed, and rugose towards the tip, where it may be slightly bent down, and is always shorter than the combined length of the metatarsus and third toe. The first primary quill of the wing largely exceeds the fourth in length, and the tail is uniformly coloured.

In addition to the sanderling, the group, which is split up by many naturalists into several genera, comprises a considerable number of species, and is confined in the breeding season to the higher latitudes of the Northern Hemisphere, although in winter becoming cosmopolitan. Of the numerous species visiting the British Isles, only the dunlin breeds there, and that but sparingly. Among these, the curlew sand-piper demands notice on account of its curved beak; while still more remarkable is the broadly expanded tip of the beak of the spoon-billed sand-piper (*Eurynorhynchus pygmæus*), a species probably breeding to the northward of Bering Strait, and representing a genus by itself.

The sanderling, easily recognised by the absence of the first toe, the black legs, and broad beak, breeds near the coasts of many portions of the Arctic Ocean, although not on the Norwegian and Russian portions, and has been taken so far south as Java.

PAINTED SNIPE

The beautiful birds commonly known as painted snipe may be taken as the first representatives of the last subfamily (*Scolopacinæ*) of the plover tribe.

The more typical members of this subfamily, such as snipe and woodcock, have the toes free, as in the knot and dunlin group, but are characterised by a very distinct style of plumage, which does not show a seasonal change, and also by the large eyes, situated far back in the head, and the backward position of the orifice of the ear-hole, usually just below the hind-border of the eye-socket

The long and slender beak is soft and highly sensitive, and the metatarsus is short, not exceeding the middle

KNOT SAND-PIPER

toe and claw in length. The members of the group are more or less nocturnal in their habits.

The painted snipe, of which there are three species, are abnormal members of the group, characterised by the plumage of the two sexes being unlike, and by the downward curvature of the tip of the beak.

The best known representative of the genus is the Indian painted snipe (*Rostratula capensis*)—so familiar to snipe-shooters in Bengal—which is distributed all over Africa south of the Sahara, Madagascar, Arabia, India, Ceylon, Burma, and the Malay region, and thence to the Philippines, China, and Southern Japan. This is one of the two largest species, and specially characterised by the large number of buff eye-like spots on the primary quills of the wings. The adult female is somewhat the larger and more brightly coloured bird, and may always be recognised by the olive green wing coverts, in which each feather is crossed by nearly a dozen narrow dark bars. In the adult female the neck is deep chestnut, shading into black on the breast; and the outermost of the inner secondaries are white, forming a conspicuous stripe.

The adult male, on the other hand, has only two dark bars on each feather of the wing coverts, with a buff patch between them. In both sexes the quills of the wings are olive grey, with narrow dark bars, and a series of five or more buff eye-like spots on the outer webs, and the inner webs with similar spots alternating with white bars. The olive grey tail has four or five rows of these same buff spots on both webs of the feathers, all of which are tipped with buff. The plumage of the upper parts is more or less olivaceous, with the feathers marked by fine zigzag lines; but the chin and lower part of the breast are white, the white area of the latter passing on to the shoulder to form a stripe on the scapular region. In addition to the pale stripe down the middle of the head, there is likewise a light area round each eye.

The Australian species (*R. australis*) may be distinguished by having two instead of four buff spots on the outer web of the eighth primary quill; while the female is peculiar in possessing a much convoluted windpipe. The South American painted snipe (*R. semicollaris*), wandering in summer so far south as Patagonia and wintering in Peru and Brazil, is a much smaller bird than either of the others, with conspicuous large round white spots on the black wing coverts.

Differing from true snipe in their shorter beaks, and low, flapping flight, painted snipe haunt the same marshy districts as the latter; and although they afford but poor sport, the beauty of one of these birds as it falls on the ground with outstretched wings and tail displaying the spots is unrivalled. Although resident throughout the year in India, the Indian species has to change its quarters a good deal in the drier districts of that country, and is only a migrant to the North-West. When breeding, these birds are always found in pairs; and, so far as my own experience goes, this is generally the case in lower Bengal all through the colder months, but at certain times of the year they are more frequently met with in small parties. The number of eggs is four; and both parent birds are always in the neighbourhood of the nest. The young birds, when first hatched, have the beak quite short.

Nearly allied to the painted snipe is the short-winged sand-piper (*Phegornis mitchelli*) of Chile and Peru, distinguished by the feature from which it takes its name, and likewise by the absence of the first toe. It is brown above, and white with narrow and closely approximated dusky bars below. From the knot and its allies this sand-piper differs by the slight inequality in the length of the first four primary quills

THE STINT

of the wing. The same feature occurs in two so-called sand-pipers inhabiting the Southern Hemisphere, namely, the sharp-billed sand-piper (*Æchmorhynchus cancellatus*), of Christmas Island and other islands in Oceania, and the white-winged sand-piper (*Prosobonia leucoptera*), of Tahiti and Oceania. Several other generic types must be passed over without mention.

WOODCOCK

The extreme length of the slender beak, which is more than twice that of the metatarsus, serves at once to distinguish woodcock and snipe from their relatives. The long and straight beak is swollen at the sides, and soft and rugose at the tip, with the laterally placed and basal nostrils covered with a membrane. The long wings are generally pointed, and the rounded tail comprises a variable number of feathers. Although in all the species the metatarsus is covered both in front and behind with large shield-like plates, the tibia may be either feathered to its base, or partially naked; but a small first toe, elevated above the level of the others, is always present. There is little difference between the summer and winter dress; and the peculiar mottled russet or ashy tone of the plumage is admirably adapted for concealing the birds in their native haunts.

All these birds are more or less nocturnal in their habits; and all are endowed with the power of strong, rapid, and long-sustained flight, frequently accompanied by those peculiar zigzag dartings when frightened, which renders snipe-shooting in many countries so difficult to the inexperienced. The long and sensitive beak is adapted for probing in soft mud in search of the insects, larvæ, and worms on which these birds chiefly subsist. Although each male invariably pairs with a single female in all the species, some may be gregarious at certain seasons, while others are always solitary. All frequent either marshes or woodland swamps; and they make slight nests on the ground in which are deposited four pear-shaped and spotted eggs. In the young the beak is comparatively short. The group comprises more than a score of species, some of which have a world-wide distribution; four of the species occurring in the British Isles, where, however, only two breed.

Contrasted with the typical snipe, the woodcock differs so markedly in several features that, in spite of the existence of more or less completely intermediate types, it may be taken to typify a genus by itself. Among the differences, it may be noticed that whereas in the typical snipe a considerable portion of the tibia is bare, in the woodcock it is completely feathered; there are fourteen tail feathers in the former and twelve in the latter. In the snipe the primaries are long and the secondaries short, but the reverse is the case with its cousin; the black markings on the head of the snipe are longitudinal, and begin at the beak, while in the woodcock they are transverse and confined to the back of the head; the under surfaces of the tail feathers of the woodcock have silvery white tips, which are wanting in the snipe; the snipe has uniformly-coloured primary quills, while those of the woodcock are barred; lastly, the eggs of the woodcock have a much paler ground-colour than those of the snipe.

Measuring from 13 to 14 inches in length, the European woodcock (*Scolopax rusticula*) may be distinguished from its allies by the transverse markings on the head, and the silvery tips to the under surfaces of the tail feathers, coupled with the barred breast, and the bar on both webs of the primaries; and it will thus be unnecessary to describe the bird in detail, although reference must be made to its large, brown, beady eye.

Breeding so far north as the Arctic Circle in forest districts, and so far south as the Alps, Caucasus, and Himalaya, at considerable elevations, as well as in the mountains of Japan, the common woodcock ranges over the greater part of Europe and Asia, visiting India and the adjacent regions in winter. Although the individuals breeding in the extreme north are migratory, those whose nesting-haunts are more to the south are probably resident.

The smaller North American woodcock (*S. minor*) differs by the remarkable narrowness of the first three primary quills, and the nearly uniform colour

WOODCOCK AND CHICKS

of all the primaries and under parts, and is sometimes referred to a genus by itself. The Moluccan woodcock (*S.* [*Neoscolopax*] *rochusseni*) has a uniform breast and barred primaries; while in the medium-sized Horsfield's woodcock (*S. saturata*) of Java and New Guinea, only the outer webs of the primaries are barred.

Essentially nocturnal and solitary in its habits, the woodcock passes the day skulking among the thick shade of woods, from which it issues forth at evening to search for food in the marshes or along the banks of streams. Worms, of which it will consume a prodigious quantity, form its chief nutriment; and it appears that it ascertains their position by plunging its beak deep down into the mud and remaining motionless for a few seconds. If any subterranean movement is then detected, the beak is once more plunged in the direction indicated, and the hapless worm extracted. When flushed during daylight, the woodcock rises with a "whirr" of its wings, and occasionally uttering a snipe-like cry. It always flies much less rapidly than a snipe, and does not dart so much; while after a long journey its flight is so slow and flapping that in the Himalaya I have kicked up these birds from beneath my feet without at first realising what they were.

During the pairing season male woodcocks forsake for a time their usual skulking habits, and fly slowly up and down in the open at morn and eve in a peculiar manner, at the same time uttering a characteristic cry. The term "rôding" is applied to this nuptial flight; and if two cocks thus engaged should chance to meet a fight immediately ensues. Breeding very early in the season, the woodcock nests in a mere depression of the ground, which it lines abundantly with dry grass and leaves; the four eggs being generally laid in April. The nest is usually situated among dead fern, with the colours of which the plumage of the old birds harmonises. The young are at times carried to a safer spot by their parent, who takes them one by one between her thighs, and partially supports them by the beak.

THE SNIPE

SNIPE

A small number of species of snipe are characterised by possessing dark and pale longitudinal head-markings, and more than sixteen tail feathers; the tibia being occasionally feathered to the ankle joint, while the inner webs of the primaries are either plain, or have the bars confined to their terminal portions. Of these, the solitary snipe (*Gallinago solitaria*), which breeds in Turkestan and the Himalaya, visiting India in winter, and represented by a variety in Eastern Siberia and Japan, may be distinguished by the white streaks on the outer borders of the scapulars; the usual number of tail feathers being apparently eighteen. It inhabits bare, treeless districts.

Another member is the wood-snipe (*G. nemoricola*), of the Himalaya, India, and Burma, which has the habits of a woodcock, and may be recognised by the shortest secondary quills projecting more than half an inch beyond the longest of the primary coverts—a character indicating limited flying powers; while the tibia is usually feathered to the joint. The small pintail snipe (*G. stenura*), which breeds so far north as the Arctic Circle from the Yenisei to the Pacific, and winters in India, China, Burma, Malaya, and so on, is characterised by its twenty-six tail feathers, of which the eight outermost on each side are very narrow, although gradually increasing in width.

In this place may be mentioned a small group from the Southern Hemisphere, of which the Auckland Island snipe (*G. aucklandica*) is a well-known representative. They are mostly South American, and differ from both the aberrant and the typical snipe either by having not more than sixteen tail feathers, or by the tibia being feathered almost or completely to the joint.

The more typical snipe, while agreeing with the Old World species mentioned above in the longitudinal black markings on the head, differ by the absence of a median pale streak on the crown, and are further characterised by the number of tail feathers never exceeding sixteen, by a considerable portion of the tibia being bare, and by the total absence of bars on the inner webs of the primary quills.

Of these, the great snipe (*G. major*), which has sixteen tail feathers, and measures from $10\frac{1}{2}$ to $11\frac{1}{2}$ inches in length, is characterised by the greater portion of the four outer tail feathers on each side being white, and by the broad white tips to the median tail coverts. A rare straggler during (chiefly autumnal) migration to the British Isles, the great snipe breeds in Northern and some parts of South-Eastern Europe, and so far eastwards as the valley of the Yenisei, while in winter the majority sojourn in South Africa. Eastwards of the Yenisei its place is taken by Swinhoe's snipe (*G. megala*), which belongs to the preceding group, having twenty tail feathers.

The best-known member of the whole group is the typical snipe (*G. cœlestis*), some of the leading features of which have been already mentioned. This species, which attains a length of $10\frac{1}{2}$ inches, is characterised by possessing fourteen tail feathers, by the breast being marked with longitudinal dark streaks, and the axillaries white, more or less marked with grey. The breeding range of the snipe comprises all Northern and Central Europe so far as the Arctic Ocean, and southwards to the Alps and Southern Russia, while eastwards it extends through Siberia and Turkestan to South-Eastern Mongolia. In winter the birds from the northern portion of this extensive area spread themselves over the countries on both sides of the Mediterranean, Persia, India, Ceylon, Burma, China, and the Philippines.

In North America this species is replaced by the species or race known as Wilson's snipe (*G. wilsoni*, or *delicata*), in the typical form of which the beak is shorter, and the tail feathers sixteen in number, while the axillaries are barred with brown, and the breast is marked with transverse bars. The breeding area of Wilson's snipe extends from the Arctic Circle to the Northern United States; but in winter the species ranges to central and northern South America. The last species of which mention can be made is the jack-snipe (*G. gallinula*), a common winter visitor to Britain, characterised by its small size (length, $7\frac{1}{2}$ inches), its twelve tail feathers, the purple gloss on the feathers of the upper parts, and the metallic green of the inner webs of the scapulars. On account of having four, in place of the usual two, notches on the hind border of the breast-bone, this species is sometimes generically separated from its relatives under the name of *Limnocryptes*.

Undergoing but slight seasonal variation in plumage, snipe are to be found at all times of the year among the protection afforded by the sedge, grass, or other vegetation of marshy places, from which they rise suddenly when flushed, with the well-known cry, but without much whirring of the wings, and dart off with lightning-like rapidity. Of the flight of Wilson's snipe, Dr. G. B. Grinnell observes that "most birds when they rise from the ground appear to have some definite idea of the direction in which they wish to go, and having started in a particular line of flight, keep to it, unless turned by some alarming apparition before them. Not so with the snipe, however; he springs from the ground uttering his curious squeaking cry, darts a few yards one way, changes his mind, and turns almost at right angles to his original course; then he appears to think he has made a mistake, and now alters his direction, and so twists off, 'angling' across the meadow until he is out of gunshot. He then either rises high in the air and swings about for awhile, looking for a desirable spot to alight, or else settles down into a straight, swift course, which he keeps up until his flight is over, or he has come to a spot which is to his liking, when he throws himself to the earth, and with a peculiar toss of his wings checks his progress, and alights."

These birds do not generally indulge in such vagaries, but fly straight away. I have, however, occasionally seen the common species dart, although the pintail does so but very rarely. Unless flushed, snipe are rarely seen on the wing during the day; and their chief feeding time, like their migration, is by night. In Europe snipe are essentially solitary birds, but this can scarcely be said to be the case in India, where a "whisp" of from six to a dozen may often be seen flying together over a marsh; and these birds may often be flushed in crowds from one spot, where they must have been feeding in close proximity. They are never found away from covert, although on rare occasions the common species has been observed perching on a tree; and they never settle where the water is deep enough to wet the feathers of the breast.

At ordinary seasons a very silent bird, when breeding, the common snipe utters a peculiar two-syllabled note, compared to "tyik-tyuk," of which the utterance is accompanied by a nodding of the head. Moreover, the males at the same season indulge in the peculiar performance known as "drumming," during which they may be seen flying diagonally upwards or round and round in large circles, and then suddenly swooping down with vibrating half-closed wings and outspread tail; the "drumming," which has been compared to the bleating of a goat, being only produced during the descent.

In Britain newly laid eggs of the common snipe may be found from the middle of April till the middle of May; the nest being a hollow, lined with dried grass, usually placed in the midlde of a tussock of rushes or coarse grass in a swamp, or under the protecting shelter of the same. The four eggs are somewhat variable in hue, the ground-colour being some shade of buff or olive, upon which are large blotches of rich, dark brown, with large underlying markings of lighter brown and grey. The main duty of incubation is performed by the hen-bird; and but a single brood is produced during the year. In the Arctic regions the eggs, like those of the jack-snipe, are not laid till June.

JACANAS AND WATER-PHEASANTS

Mainly from the circumstance that many of them have a naked shield on the forehead, like that of coots and moor-hens, the members of the present small family, *Parridæ*, were formerly classed with the rails, although their true position appears to be here. From the *Charadriidæ* they are distinguished by the presence of unossified vacuities in the occipital surface of the skull, while they differ from all other birds in the extraordinary elongation of their toes. They are handsomely-coloured birds, black or black and white being the predominating tints; but the young are less brilliant than the adults. The group is confined to South America, Africa south of the Tropic of Cancer, the Indian region, Australia, and Papua.

The jacanas (*Parra*), of which there are about ten species, have a distribution co-extensive with that of the family; the species shown in the illustration, *P. nigra*, being an inhabitant of Brazil. They are long-legged, slenderly-built birds, with short tails, spurs on the wings, and the aforesaid shield on the head. Insectivorous in their diet, they frequent lakes and quiet rivers, where their long toes enable them to walk over the leaves of the giant water-lilies. The nest is a rude structure, built near the edge of the water; and

THE BRAZILIAN JACANA

the eggs, which vary from four to six in number, and have a bluish green ground with liver-coloured spots, often rest on the bare soil. Some naturalists split up the group into five genera, terming the Indian species *Metopidius indicus*, instead of *Parra indica*. Nor is this all, for in some books the name *Parra* is replaced by *Jacana* for the three typical South American species; a change which, if adopted, would involve the substitution of *Jacanidæ* for *Parridæ* as the family name.

The largest member of the family is the beautiful water-pheasant (*Hydrophasianus chirurgus*) of India and Ceylon, which is the sole representative of its genus, and easily recognised by the elongation of the two middle tail feathers, and the pied plumage. These birds, which are abundant on the lakes of Kashmir, as well as those of India, usually assume their breeding plumage in May or June; and utter a peculiar mewing, or wailing sound, which can be heard for a considerable distance. The nest may be either a floating structure of grass and herbage, or fixed among the growing stalks of rice, and in July or August receives a clutch of from four to seven bronzy brown or green eggs.

SHEATH-BILLS AND SEED-SNIPE

IN this place brief mention may be made of certain birds which appear to connect to some extent the members of the preceding families with the gulls. These comprise the sheath-bills (*Chionididæ*), represented by one species (*Chionis alba*) in the Falkland Islands and Straits of Magellan; a second (*C. minor*) in Kerguelen Island; and a third (*C. crosettensis*) in the Crozet group; and the seed-snipe (family *Thinocorythidæ*) with the two genera *Thinocorys* and *Attagis* of temperate South America.

All these birds differ from the *Charadriidæ*, and resemble the coursers and gulls in the absence of basipterygoid processes on the rostrum of the skull, and also of a pair of vacuities on the occipital face of the latter; the sheath-bills having more or less slit-like (schizorhinal) nasal apertures in the skull, while those of the seed-snipe approximate to the oval (holorhinal) type.

The sheath-bills in Kerguelen Island, writes Professor Moseley, "are present everywhere on the coast, and from their extreme tameness and inquisitive habits, are always attracting one's attention. A pair or two of them always forms part of any view on the coast. The birds are pure white, about the size of a very large pigeon, but with the appearance rather of a fowl. They have light pink-coloured legs, with partial webbing at the toes, small spurs on the inner sides of the wings, and a black bill, with a most curious lamina of horny matter projecting over the nostrils. Round the eye is a tumid, pink ring, bare of feathers; about the head are wattle-like warts. The

LESSER SHEATH-BILLS

birds nest under fallen rocks along the cliffs, often in places where the nest is difficult of access. The nest is made of grass and bents, and the eggs are usually two in number, of the shape of those of the plovers, and of a somewhat similar colouring, spotted dark red and brown." When first hatched, the young are black. The adult birds utter a harsh note, and feed chiefly on seaweed and molluscs; their fearlessness being such that they will often allow themselves to be knocked on the head with a stick.

The seed-snipe, or quail-snipe, are small, short-billed birds with the general appearance and habits of quail, living in dry inland districts, where they subsist on plants, roots, and insects.

The species shown in the illustration (*Attagis gayi*) is a native of Peru and Chile; a second species, *A. malouinus*, inhabits the Falkland Islands, while a third kind, *A. chimborasensis*, is found on Chimborazo and other high mountains in Ecuador. In both genera the beak is rather short and compressed, with the aperture of the nostrils in most cases closed by a horny membrane covered with short feathers. Generally these birds are met with in pairs or small coveys of five or six, which frequent the same spots for long periods. Although they inhabit desert regions, the nest is placed near a lake; the number of eggs in a clutch being either four or five. The ground

GAY'S SEED-SNIPE.

colour is creamy buff, upon which are chocolate and other markings.

R. LYDEKKER.

END OF SECOND VOLUME